Representati

	I B	II B	III A	IV A	V A	VI A	VII A	2 He 4.0026
			5 B 10.811	6 C 12.01115	7 N 14.0067	8 O 15.9994	9 F 18.9984	10 Ne 20.183
			13 Al 26.9815	14 Si 28.086	15 P 30.9738	16 S 32.064	17 Cl 35.453	18 Ar 39.948
28 Ni 58.71	29 Cu 63.54	30 Zn 65.37	31 Ga 69.72	32 Ge 72.59	33 As 74.9216	34 Se 78.96	35 Br 79.909	36 Kr 83.80
46 Pd 106.4	47 Ag 107.870	48 Cd 112.40	49 In 114.82	50 Sn 118.69	51 Sb 121.75	52 Te 127.60	53 I 126.9044	54 Xe 131.30
78 Pt 195.09	79 Au 196.967	80 Hg 200.59	81 Tl 204.37	82 Pb 207.19	83 Bi 208.980	84 Po (210)	85 At (210)	86 Rn (222)

Transition Elements

63 Eu 151.96	64 Gd 157.25	65 Tb 158.924	66 Dy 162.50	67 Ho 164.930	68 Er 167.26	69 Tm 168.934	70 Yb 173.04
95 Am (243)	96 Cm (247)	97 Bk (247)	98 Cf (251)	99 Es (254)	100 Fm (257)	101 Md (256)	102 No (256)

numbers of most stable isotopes.

Daniel B. Murphy, Ph.D., The Pennsylvania State University, is Associate Professor of Chemistry at Herbert H. Lehman College of The City University of New York, formerly a part of Hunter College. He has also taught at the University of Scranton, The Pennsylvania State University, and Fordham University.

Viateur Rousseau, Ph.D., New York University, is Professor and Chairman of the Department of Chemistry at Iona College and Adjunct Professor of Chemistry at Fordham University. He has also taught at New York University and the College of Mount St. Vincent.

William F. Kieffer, who acted as Editorial Consultant during the preparation of the manuscript, is Professor of Chemistry at the College of Wooster. He is well known as a teacher and as the long-time editor of the *Journal of Chemical Education.*

FOUNDATIONS OF COLLEGE CHEMISTRY

DANIEL B. MURPHY
HERBERT H. LEHMAN COLLEGE OF
THE CITY UNIVERSITY OF NEW YORK

VIATEUR ROUSSEAU
IONA COLLEGE

Editorial Consultant
WILLIAM F. KIEFFER
COLLEGE OF WOOSTER

THE RONALD PRESS COMPANY • NEW YORK

2MP

Library of Congress Catalog Card Number: 74–75640
PRINTED IN THE UNITED STATES OF AMERICA

To Lorraine and Noreen
our wives
for their unfailing patience, devotion
and encouragement

PREFACE

In writing an introductory textbook to be used by classes composed of students of mixed background, ability, and goals, it is of utmost importance to present the subject in such a way as to interest and challenge the better prepared and strongly motivated students without discouraging or overwhelming the others. The key to this, we believe, lies in organizing the material so that there is an orderly, logical progression from observation to theory, and from the simple to the complex. By proceeding in this manner, we feel that we have been able to write a modern text that will provide a solid foundation of fundamental facts and theories on which the chemistry student can build.

The topic order reflects the way in which chemistry has developed, not along a straight line from its beginning to the present, but rather as a complex tapestry woven of many strands, each with an influence—sometimes a very subtle one—on all the others. After a basic introduction to atomic theory and properties of gases, we take up kinetic-molecular theory and proceed through the application of the gas laws and a consideration of atomic weight to the propounding of the periodic law. At this point, a new thread is woven in with the first chapter on electrochemistry (electrolytes), which leads naturally to the concept of the electron and the problem of bonding. This also provides a logical place to introduce the principles of oxidation and reduction and to illustrate the manipulation of redox equations. After covering atomic theory, we return to the periodic law, the relationship between chemical properties and atomic structure, and the nature of chemical bonding. The foregoing principles are then applied in the discussion of the nature of real gases, liquids, solids, and solutions. The historical figures in the development of chemical principles and the process of discovery are woven into the discussions.

Thermodynamic principles are frequently applied, especially in the chapters on equilibrium and electrochemistry. The concepts of Gibbs free energy, entropy, and reversible and irreversible work are developed intuitively, using simple mathematics, thus preparing the student for the more rigorous approach which he will encounter later in the course in physical chemistry. "Pure" thermodynamics lacks reality for the beginning student, who is usually not accustomed to thinking in abstract terms.

Solutions, ionic equilibria, and electrochemistry are discussed in considerable detail. This is "real chemistry" for the beginning student, and illustrates the direct application of theory to practice in the laboratory. With the current trend toward making the laboratory more quantitative and increasingly analytical, this material assumes greater importance in the introductory course. At the same time, we have tried to organize these chapters in such a way that the instructor may stop at almost any point once he believes that the needs of his students have been met.

We have provided for only a few chapters that could be described as strictly descriptive chemistry. This is not meant to imply that we consider the properties of individual elements and their compounds to be unimportant. On the contrary. A chemist, after all, works with chemicals, and he must know them as familiar friends. It is our belief that descriptive chemistry should permeate the entire subject, and that topics should be illustrated wherever possible with the properties of real compounds. A general description of the elements and their properties is presented together with the periodic law early in the book. The last few chapters discuss that part of descriptive chemistry which could not be covered adequately elsewhere. In these chapters, the properties of elements and compounds are presented in such a way as to emphasize trends, similarities, and comparisons among them. In this way the material is more readily retained, and is made more meaningful and useful to the student.

Special emphasis has been placed on group IVA. The elements of that group occupy a unique position, their properties ranging from those of the nonmetal carbon through amphoteric tin to metallic lead. Much of the comparative chemistry of the metals and nonmetals can therefore be summarized in a discussion of these elements. The organic chemistry of carbon is presented in somewhat more than customary detail in a separate chapter. The transition elements are discussed together as a unit. Trends among their properties are emphasized, and these trends are related where possible to the arrangement of electrons in the atoms. The discussion of metal complexes is up to date, and especially thorough for an introductory text. The importance of antibonding orbitals is emphasized here, as it is elsewhere in the book, for example in the discussions of metallic bonding and of bonding in the oxygen molecule.

Numerous solved illustrative examples appear throughout the text. With the student in mind, each has been chosen to illustrate the point immediately under discussion in as straightforward a fashion as possible, and the solution is presented in step-by-step detail in every case. Questions and problems at the ends of chapters provide ample opportunities for drill and review.

A selected list of reading references is given at the end of each chapter. These have been chosen for their interest, pertinence, and readability. The student with a serious interest in chemistry should start early to build his own personal reference library.

We particularly wish to thank Professor William F. Kieffer, of the College of Wooster, who, as Editorial Consultant, read both the initial draft and the final manuscript in their entirety, and who provided us with detailed, point-by-point criticisms and suggestions for improvement.

The help and encouragement of our friends and colleagues were invaluable during our writing of this book. We especially wish to express our appreciation to our associates at Herbert H. Lehman College, Iona College, Hunter College, and Fordham University, who read portions of the manuscript and who offered many helpful suggestions and criticisms. Special thanks are due Professor Louis Campisi, of Iona College, particularly for his help with the material on transition metals and metal complexes; Professor Frederick P. Young and Miss Alice E. Vrbsky, of the Geology Department of Lehman College, for providing crystal specimens for Chapter 9; and Mr. James Sondberg, of the Lehman College Chemistry Department, whose photographs were used in drawing several of the illustrations. We also wish to thank the Board of Higher Education of the City of New York, and the administration of Hunter College of The City University of New York, of which Lehman College was formerly a part, for providing one of us with a sabbatical leave in order to prepare the final manuscript of the text.

Chemistry is a fascinating subject. If we have been able, in these pages, to convey some of our love for chemistry and to make it easier for others to appreciate its fascination, we will have been well rewarded.

Daniel B. Murphy
Viateur Rousseau

New York, New York
New Rochelle, New York
March, 1969

CONTENTS

Appendixes

FOUNDATIONS OF
COLLEGE CHEMISTRY

The chymists are a strange class of
mortals, impelled by an almost insane impulse
to seek their pleasure among smoke and vapour,
soot and flame, poisons and poverty, yet among
all these evils I seem to live so sweetly,
that may I die if I would change places
with the Persian King.

—J. J. Becher, 1669

1 INTRODUCTION

After three centuries, there are still few chemists who would prefer to be King of Persia, not merely because the evils have been alleviated, or because the Shah's position is any less attractive, but because chemistry continues to be a subject of endless fascination. Its fascination is that of the unknown. Like an explorer, a chemist never knows what he will find around the next bend in the river, or over the next hill. Every explorer has his share of disappointments and long, dull stretches when it seems that no progress at all is being made. But the chemist considers this a small price to pay for the thrill of discovery. Gazing for the first time on crystals of a compound no one has ever seen before may not be as grand as being the first to sight an unknown shore, but it happens more often, and the joy is never dulled by repetition.

A chemist is a scientist. The word science comes from the Latin *scio*, "I know," and a scientist is simply a person with an insatiable desire to know and understand his environment. Children are born scientists. Driven by curiosity, they examine everything, touch everything, taste everything, ask endless questions. To whatever degree we have retained our childhood curiosity about things, to that extent all of us are scientists as well.

The Scientific Approach 1.1

Laws, *hypotheses*, and *theories* are the basis of science, and these in turn are grounded in *observation* and *experiment*. Repeated observation may show us that, under the same circumstances, a certain event will always take place. Before long, our curiosity will lead us to ask the question, "Why?". We then attempt an answer by offering an explanation, or hypothesis. Human nature being what it is, our hypothesis will soon be challenged with the demand, "Prove it!" We must then subject our hypothesis to experiment to see if it correctly predicts the results which we observe.

There is nothing mysterious about the scientific approach to things. In fact, we have been putting it into practice all of our lives. If a little boy finds that every time he takes out his crayons his mother tells him not to scribble on the wall, he has discovered a law governing his environment. He proposes a hypothesis when he reasons that he mustn't scribble because he will be spanked if he does. When he goes ahead and applies his crayons to the wall, he is subjecting his hypothesis to experiment. Later, as proof of his hypothesis is applied to the seat of his trousers, he can console himself with the thought that at least his approach to the problem was scientific.

A ***scientific law*** *is a concise statement of observed fact* and as such exists independently of any explanation which may be offered for it. As greater knowledge is acquired, such laws are expressed in increasingly precise language, and, if possible, in mathematical form. At the same time, the hypotheses offered to explain the laws are tested by experiment. The hypotheses that fail the test are (or should be) discarded. Those which survive and remain consistent with new discoveries may be raised to the dignity of ***theories.*** Theories, in turn, often lead to the discovery of new laws, and thus the cycle is completed.

When written in this way, the scientific approach sounds cut and dried, but, as we shall see, scientists are human, and chance, accident, intuition, and luck play an important part in scientific discovery. A scientist doesn't often wake up in the morning telling himself, "Today I shall discover a new law." The approach from law through hypothesis to theory is seldom consciously applied, and many years may pass and many persons be involved in progressing from law to theory. *But basic to every scientific investigation is careful observation and thorough experimentation, and implicit in every experiment, however simple, is the testing of a hypothesis,* even though the hypothesis may be little more than a hunch.

1.2 The Alchemists

To quote "The Walrus and the Carpenter," the world is made of many things: of shoes, and ships, and sealing wax, of cabbages, and kings. Not only are the things of the world infinite in variety, but they also seem to undergo constant change. Ice melts, wood burns, iron rusts. The value ascribed to gold in early times came more from its immutability or resistance to change than from its scarcity. The philosophers of ancient Greece offered several hypotheses to explain the variety of things in nature and the numerous transformations which they underwent. Among these hypotheses was that of Aristotle, who proposed that all substances were composed of a universal "prime matter" whose "substantial form" was modified according to the relative contributions of the four fundamental principles of heat, cold, dryness, and moistness. Combining these principles in pairs generated the four "elements": earth (cold, dry), air (hot, moist), fire (hot, dry), and

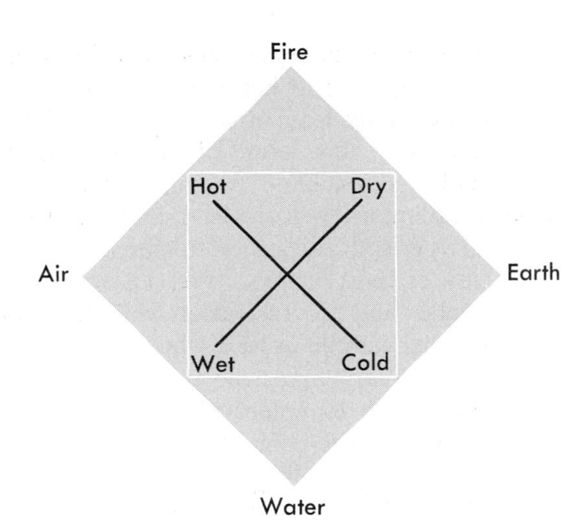

Fig. 1.1 Relationships among the four principles and the four elements of Aristotle.

water (cold, moist) (Fig. 1.1). All other substances were formed by combining these elements in different proportions. Thus, liquid water was converted to air (steam) by adding fire. The ratio of water to earth was greater in liquid mercury than it was in solid silver, and gold contained more fire.

Until relatively recent times, actually to work with one's hands was considered to be beneath the dignity of a scholar. Practical work in chemistry and other fields was carried out by artisans who, while perhaps very competent, had virtually no interest in theory and philosophical speculation. The hypotheses of the early philosophers therefore remained unchallenged by experiment, and for centuries they were considered adequate to explain the behavior of the physical universe. With the collapse of the Roman empire came a decline in scholarship as the western world divided itself into constantly warring petty kingdoms and principalities. During this turmoil, the ancient writings disappeared from view. Later, as Europe again became more settled, there was time once more for scholarly pursuits. The works of the ancients were rediscovered in the monasteries where they had been preserved. To the new scholars, it seemed that in these works, and especially in those of Aristotle, were to be found the answers to all of the riddles of nature.

The new philosophers differed from the old in being willing to experiment. The intent of their experiments was not, however, to test the validity of Aristotle's ideas. Rather, it was taken for granted that these hypotheses were true, and the purpose of experiment was to apply them to the solution of practical problems. Among these problems was that of changing corruptible base metals to more perfect gold. Understandably, the alchemists, who were the forerunners of today's chemists, believed it possible to change base metals into gold through chemical manipulation. Assuming the truth of the concept of prime matter and substantial form, they were naturally led to the conclusion that if a base metal could be colored yellow by melting it with copper, then its conversion to gold had been partly effected.

Experiment sometimes seemed to confirm the alchemists' beliefs. Occasionally, intense heating of some mixture containing lead or other base metal would leave a small residue of genuine gold in the crucible. To the alchemist, this seemed to be proof that transmutation of other metals to gold was possible. We know now that the gold had been present all along as an impurity in the lead, and that the fire had simply oxidized and driven off the lead and other substances, or caused them to be absorbed by the clay of the crucible. We can appreciate the alchemist's dreams of quick wealth, and his frustration when the experiment could not be repeated with another sample of lead which did not happen to contain any gold.

For many years, the alchemists experimented with mixtures and potions, attempting to unlock the secrets of nature, to discover the philosopher's stone with the power to change lead into gold, and the elixir of life, which would cure all ills. Later, as their efforts continued to lead up one blind alley and down another, the alchemists wrote ever more obscurely, desperately hoping in this way to retain their scholarly status by inspiring awe among the uninitiated. Their writings took on the trappings of magic, and alchemy sank into a morass of mysticism, ignorance, and outright fakery.

1.3 Elements and Compounds

About three hundred years ago, the more sincere alchemists and learned men had come to realize that their efforts to uncover the secrets of the universe, based as they were on the assumed truth of Aristotle's concept of the four elements, were as fruitless as the quest for the legendary Holy Grail. They began to design their experiments not to fit a preconceived idea, but simply to ask questions of nature. They abandoned mysticism and secrecy and began to record their observations carefully, completely, and in plain language. Most important, they began to keep track of the quantities of substances which were used and produced in their experiments. Chemistry progressed very little during the centuries that it remained a purely qualitative study. By contrast, its development has been at an explosive rate since it first became a quantitative science in the seventeenth century.

Out of the work of the first real chemists there gradually developed a new picture of an element as one of a limited number of substances out of which all other substances are made. All other substances can be resolved into these elements, but they themselves cannot be decomposed by any ordinary means at the chemist's disposal. The elements are thus analogous to the letters of the alphabet from which an infinite number of words may be made by joining different letters in proper arrangements. *A substance composed of more than one element combined in definite, fixed relative proportions by weight is a* ***compound***. Compounds may be compared to words, which to make sense must contain the proper number and kinds of letters arranged in the correct order.

With the development of new techniques of investigation, substances once thought to be elements have been found to be compounds, and substances believed to be compounds have turned out to be elements. Nevertheless, the definition of an ***element*** as *a uniform or homogeneous substance* *which cannot be further decomposed by ordinary chemical means* has sufficed for many years despite the vagueness of the term "ordinary chemical means." As we progress in our study of chemistry, we shall see how this definition has been modified to cope with developments in experimental methods.

Matter, Mass, and Weight 1.4

Chemistry is concerned with the properties and transformations of matter. For our purposes, we may define ***matter*** as *that which possesses mass and occupies space.* Mass is related to weight, but it is not the same thing. The mass of an object is determined by its relative inertia, or resistance to change in motion, and it remains the same under all conditions. When a given mass is accelerated, the force exerted is equal to the product of the mass times the acceleration:

$$f = m \times a$$

If the acceleration happens to be that due to gravity, we call this force the weight. Thus, a 180-lb astronaut subjected to 5*G* at takeoff weighs 900 lb; in orbit he weighs nothing. On the moon, where gravity is one-sixth that on the earth, he weighs only 30 lb. Yet throughout all this, the quantity of astronaut, that is, his mass, remains the same.

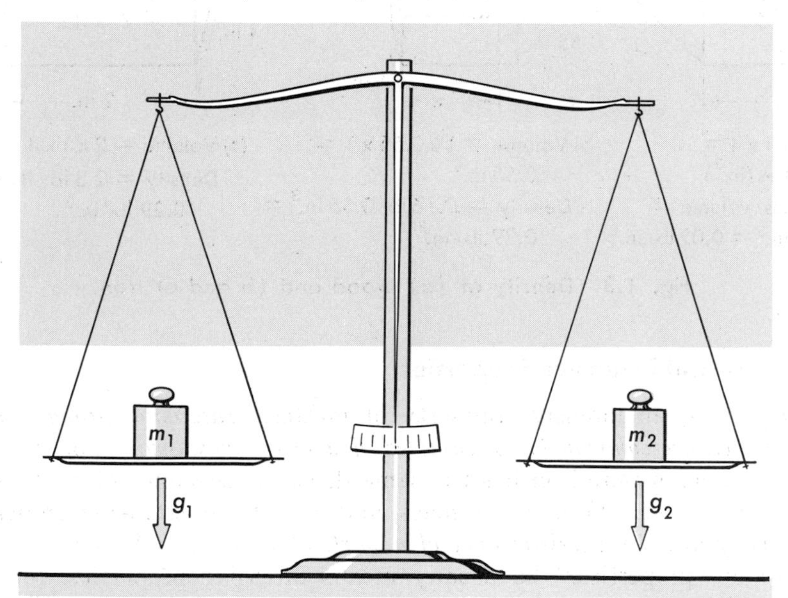

Fig. 1.2 The balance: $m_1g_1 = w_1 = w_2 = m_2g_2$. If $g_1 = g_2$, $m_1 = m_2$.

Clearly then, the mass is of greater significance to the scientist than the weight. Mass, in the sense of relative inertia, is rather difficult to measure directly, but by using a balance, one can compare the weights of two objects while they are subjected to the same gravitational pull. Under this condition, two objects with the same weight must possess the same mass (Fig. 1.2). Despite the important distinction between mass and weight, through custom and usage the term weight is often used when the correct term is mass. Usually this causes no serious confusion provided the true meaning of the word is understood.

1.5 Density

The mass of an object and the space it occupies are related by the density. Everyone knows that a block of wood weighs less than a block of iron of the same size. We say that iron is more dense than wood, or that it has a greater density. ***Density*** is defined as *mass per unit volume:*

$$d = \frac{m}{V}$$

Together with such attributes as color and solubility, density is one of the characteristic ***physical properties*** of a substance (Fig. 1.3).

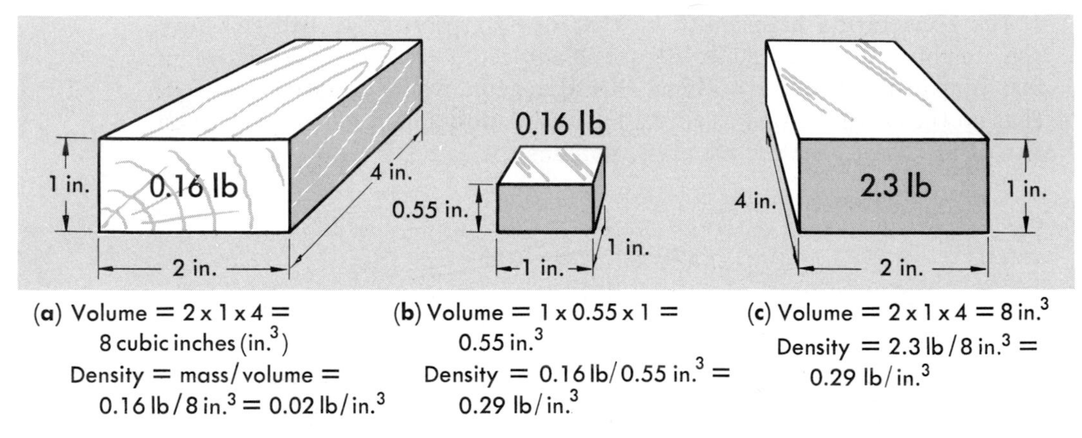

(a) Volume = 2 x 1 x 4 = 8 cubic inches (in.^{3})
Density = mass/volume = 0.16 lb/8 in.^{3} = 0.02 lb/in.^{3}

(b) Volume = 1 x 0.55 x 1 = 0.55 in.^{3}
Density = 0.16 lb/0.55 in.^{3} = 0.29 lb/in.^{3}

(c) Volume = 2 x 1 x 4 = 8 in.^{3}
Density = 2.3 lb/8 in.^{3} = 0.29 lb/in.^{3}

Fig. 1.3 Density of (a) wood and (b and c) iron.

1.6 Intensive and Extensive Properties

Density is an intensive property of matter. ***Intensive properties*** *are those which are common to all samples of a given substance.* For instance, every sample of pure iron has the same density, the same color, the same tendency to rust. Size, shape, mass, and weight are ***extensive properties,*** since they are *characteristic only of a particular sample.* When a chemist speaks of "properties," he usually means intensive properties, for it is these which are inherent in the nature of a substance.

1.7 Energy

To overcome the inertia of an object and set it in motion requires the application of a certain amount of force. The product of the force applied times the distance through which the object is moved is the work done:

$$w = f \times d$$

Energy is defined as the *capacity to do work.* ***Kinetic energy*** (from the Greek *kinein,* to move; the word cinema has same origin) is that energy which an object possesses by virtue of its ***motion.*** A bowling ball has the capacity to knock down the pins simply because it is moving. The amount of kinetic energy which an object has depends upon the mass of the object and how fast it is moving. A bullet fired from a rifle at 2500 ft/sec will do a lot more damage than the same bullet tossed by hand. A cannonball fired at the same speed will do more harm than the bullet. Kinetic energy is equal to one-half the product of the mass times the square of the speed:

$$\text{K.E.} = \tfrac{1}{2}mv^2$$

Energy may also be stored in an object as ***potential energy,*** which is the energy a body possesses by virtue of its ***position.*** A rock atop a mountain has potential energy. It is not doing work, but it has the capacity to do work by rolling down the mountainside. As it rolls, its potential energy is converted to kinetic energy, which can be used to perform work, such as knocking down some trees.

The total energy of a system is equal to the sum of its kinetic energy and potential energy. Both kinetic and potential energy may be present in various forms. Mechanical energy, electrical energy, chemical energy, light, heat, and sound are all forms of energy. One form of energy can be changed into another—the mechanical energy of a falling rock is changed into heat and sound when the rock hits the ground—but *the total amount of all forms of energy in the system remains the same.* This important principle is known as the ***law of conservation of energy.***

Conservation of Mass 1.8

Closely associated with the law of conservation of energy is that of conservation of mass. According to the ***law of conservation of mass,*** *the total mass of the products of any chemical reaction is exactly equal to the total mass of the original reactants.* Most of chemical theory and practice is based on the assumption that these two laws are completely valid. It is true that over the past sixty years, the equivalence of mass and energy has been demonstrated. Matter can be destroyed, but that destruction must be accompanied by the creation of an equivalent amount of energy. The equivalence of mass and energy is expressed by the familiar Einstein equation,

$$E = mc^2$$

where E is the quantity of energy created by the destruction of an amount of mass m, and c represents the speed of light. A simple calculation will show that the energy released by the destruction of even the smallest mass detectable on a good analytical balance (about 0.0000007 oz) would be about as much as would be released by the explosion of 14,000 gal of gasoline—more than enough to reduce the apparatus, the laboratory, and the chemist to small pieces. Therefore, even if all of the energy of a chemical reaction came from the destruction of matter—something which is most definitely not true—the amount of matter destroyed could at most be only a completely negligible fraction of the total mass involved. For that reason alone, we are justified in assuming that in ordinary chemical reactions the laws of conservation of mass and of energy hold with absolute rigor to the limit of practical measurement.

1.9 The Metric System

Measurements of mass, length, and volume necessarily have an arbitrary character. When a sack of sugar is described as weighing ten pounds, it means simply that it weighs ten times as much as a certain object stored in a vault at the Bureau of Standards or elsewhere, whose mass has been defined by law as representing one pound. The inch was originally taken as the length of three barleycorns laid end to end, and of course it could vary according to which barleycorns were chosen.* The definition of a foot is equally arbitrary, and the fact that there are twelve inches to the foot is as much fortuitous as intentional.

Even today, systems of weights and measures in common use vary from one country to another, and most of them suffer from the same drawback as our own familiar English system—their various units bear no simple relation to one another. Thus we have twelve inches in a foot, three feet in a yard, five and one-half yards in a rod, and 320 rods in a mile.

Toward the end of the eighteenth century the situation was one of complete chaos. Systems and units varied not only from one country to another but from city to city, and even within a city, according to the trade guild or corporation. The opportunities for error, fraud, misunderstanding, and dispute were unlimited. Sovereigns attempted from time to time to impose order and unity, issuing royal decrees which for the most part were greeted by indifference or outright hostility. Those accustomed to their local measures saw no reason to change; those merchants and nobles who profited from the confusion did not want to lose their advantage. Conditions in France were at least as bad as, and probably worse than, anywhere in Europe. Talleyrand described the unimaginable disorder of the French measures as "ghastly." It took the combined influence of a revolution whose objective was the obliteration of all traces of the monarchy, and of the French scientists who most recognized the necessity of precise measurement, to introduce order and uniformity for the first time. Which was more effective in bringing about reform—the revolution or the scientists—is difficult to say, but the result of their often stormy collaboration was the creation of the metric system, now universally used in scientific work.

The French scientists, notable among them the chemist Antoine-Laurent Lavoisier, who earlier had demonstrated the elementary nature of oxygen and its function in combustion, realized the advantage of a system based on a natural, invariant standard which could not be lost or mislaid. They chose as the basis of their system the ***meter,*** which they defined as one ten-millionth of the distance from the North Pole to the equator at the

* As late as the War of 1812, the United States Navy, when ordering cannons and cannonballs from two different manufacturers, enclosed an envelope with three barleycorns with each order to avoid the possible embarrassment of cannonballs too big for the guns.

longitude of Paris.* The members of the French Academy of course did not actually hike through the snow drifts and jungles with a ruler, but instead surveyed a base line across France and into Spain, from Dunkerque to Barcelona, with the greatest accuracy possible. The size of the earth was then determined in terms of the base line by astronomical observation, permitting definition of the meter. Considering that much of this work was carried out during the Reign of Terror, a time when everyone was under suspicion, and many, including Lavoisier, died on the guillotine, one must credit the academicians with admirable sangfroid.

The meter, which is 39.37 inches long, is divided into one hundred equal parts, or ***centimeters*** (cm), each of which is further divided into ten ***millimeters*** (mm). A cube 10 cm on an edge, thus containing 1000 cubic centimeters (cc or cm^3), is called a ***liter*** (l).† A liter is slightly larger than a quart. The mass of one liter of water at the temperature at which its density is greatest (slightly above freezing) was defined as the ***kilogram*** (kg), which then became the standard of mass. In this way, both weights and measures in the metric system are related ultimately to the same universal standard, the meter. The kilogram is divided into one thousand ***grams*** (g), and each of these in turn into one thousand ***milligrams*** (0.001 g = 1 mg).

Heat and Temperature 1.10

Almost every process or reaction is accompanied by a change in the energy of the reactants. This energy is usually in the form of heat, and the reactants become hotter or colder. The *relative hotness* of something is described in terms of its temperature. We say that something hot has a high temperature, while something cold has a low temperature. When one object is described as being hotter than another, it means simply that *heat will flow from the hotter to the cooler object until their temperatures are equal.*

The relationship between heat and temperature is somewhat similar to that between mass and density. Just as two different-size objects with the same density will have different masses, so two bodies at the same temperature may contain different amounts of heat. The furnace and the kitchen stove may be at the same temperature, but there is certainly more heat in the furnace. ***Heat** measures the quantity of energy;* ***temperature** describes its intensity.* As we shall see, heat is a measure of the total kinetic energy possessed by the molecules of an object; temperature is a measure of the average kinetic energy possessed by the individual molecules.

Temperature is usually measured with the aid of a thermometer. This is a device based on the observation that most substances expand upon heating. The ordinary chemical thermometer consists of a thin-walled glass bulb filled with mercury and attached to a narrow glass tube, or

* For the most precise work, the meter has more recently been redefined as 1,650,763.73 times the wavelength of the orange-red line in the spectrum of krypton-86 in a vacuum at −210°C, but this has had no effect on its length, which was originally determined as described above.

† Because of a slight error, the standard liter does not contain exactly 1000 cc (1 l = 1000.028 cc). The thousandth part of a liter is therefore referred to as a ***milliliter*** (ml) and is the usual volume unit. For most purposes the cubic centimeter and milliliter are equivalent.

capillary. If the thermometer bulb is heated, say by being immersed in a beaker of hot water, heat will flow from the hot water to the cooler thermometer, raising its temperature and causing the mercury to expand into the capillary. The higher the temperature, the farther the mercury will rise in the capillary. The relative temperatures of two objects can be compared by placing the thermometer in contact with each object in turn and measuring the height to which the mercury level rises in each instance. A scale engraved on the thermometer stem simplifies the measurement.

The scale of temperature is as arbitrary as the system of weights and measures, and several such scales have been devised and used. The most familiar of these are the ***Fahrenheit scale,*** still in common use in the English-speaking world, and the ***centigrade scale,*** or ***Celsius scale,*** used universally in scientific work. On a Celsius thermometer, the height to which the mercury rises when the bulb is immersed in melting ice is assigned a value of zero degrees Celsius (0°C). The bulb is then placed in boiling water and the new position of the mercury level is marked 100°C. The distance between the two marks is divided into 100 equal parts, or Celsius degrees. On the Fahrenheit scale, the melting and boiling temperatures of water are assigned values of 32°F and 212°F, respectively,* and there are 180 Fahrenheit degrees between the two temperatures. A Celsius degree is therefore $\frac{180}{100} = \frac{9}{5}$ as large as a Fahrenheit degree.

Heat is also measured in terms of an arbitrary unit, the calorie (abbreviated cal). One ***calorie*** is defined as *the quantity of heat required to raise the temperature of one gram of water from 14.5°C to 15.5°C.* This is a rather small amount of heat, and it is often more convenient to use the ***kilocalorie,*** which is equal to 1000 calories. The large calorie, or Calorie (abbreviated Cal), of calorie charts and diet tables is actually the kilocalorie.

Different substances have different capacities for heat. For example, it takes about 30 times as much heat to raise the temperature of a given mass of water 1°C as it takes to raise the temperature of an equal mass of mercury by the same amount. The heat capacity is often expressed in terms of the ***specific heat,*** which is defined as *the quantity of heat in calories required to raise the temperature of 1 g of a substance 1°C.* By this definition, the specific heat of water at 15°C is 1 cal/g × °C; that of mercury at the same temperature is 0.033 cal/g × °C.

The heat capacity of a substance varies somewhat with temperature, but within a limited temperature range this variation is usually small enough to be neglected in all but the most precise work. A change in physical state, however, is usually accompanied by a pronounced change in heat capacity. For example, the specific heat of liquid water between 0° and 100°C is nearly constant at 1.00 cal/g × °C, but for ice at 0° and steam at 100° the respective values are 0.505 and 0.482 cal/g × °C.

* Gabriel Fahrenheit believed, incorrectly, that the coldest temperature likely in the wintertime would be no less than the temperature of a mixture of sal ammoniac (ammonium chloride) and ice, and accordingly he called this temperature zero. It has been suggested that the curious assignment of 212° for the boiling point of water resulted from the choice of 100° as corresponding to body temperature. If this is true, one must conclude that Fahrenheit was running a slight fever at the time.

Reading Suggestions 1.11

There are several good histories of chemistry. One of the best, *A Short History of Chemistry*, by J. R. Partington, is available in paperback (Harper Torchbook #TB 522, Harper & Row, New York, 1960). More comprehensive, although less detailed in its discussion of alchemy and its beginnings in Greek philosophy, is *The Development of Modern Chemistry*, by Aaron J. Ihde (Harper & Row, New York, 1964). *The Evolution of Chemistry*, by Eduard Farber (The Ronald Press Company, New York, 1969), includes an interesting, brief description of medieval chemical technology in Chapter 6. *Through Alchemy to Chemistry*, by John Read (Harper Torchbook #TB 561), is an especially readable and entertaining account of chemistry's ancestry and early youth.

The origin of the metric system and the establishment of international standards of weights and measures is described by Henri Moreau in the *Journal of Chemical Education*, vol. 30, pp. 3–20 (1953). The *Journal of Chemical Education*, usually abbreviated *J. Chem. Ed.*, is a treasure trove of chemical information, and we shall find many occasions to cite articles from its pages.

Questions and Problems

1.1 Classify each of the following statements as being a law, a theory, or a hypothesis:

The sun rises in the East.
Music from a juke box is produced by a band of midgets inside the box.
All matter is composed of atoms.
$2 + 2 = 5$.
Gravity is caused by the curvature of space.
Black cats bring bad luck.
Fish bite better when the moon is full.
The gravitational pull of the moon and sun causes the tides.
When the sun and moon are on the same side of the earth, the result is a flood tide.
$E = mc^2$.

Can you make a clear distinction in every case?

1.2 When a diamond is heated by itself in a vacuum, it is converted completely into graphite. Does this prove that diamond is a compound?

1.3 When the substance calcite is heated, it produces a gas and a residue of lime. The residue always weighs exactly 0.56 times as much as the original calcite. From these observations, can you say whether calcite is an element or a compound? Do you have enough information to decide if lime is an element or a compound? Can you say anything about the gas?

1.4 Which weighs more, a pound of lead or a pound of feathers? Which has the greater mass? Which has the greater density?

1.5 A student is performing an experiment which calls for 20.0 g of concentrated sulfuric acid. If the density of the acid is 1.84 g/ml, what volume of the acid should the student take?

1.6 The density of water is 1.00 g/cm^3. If a cubic foot of water weighs 28.3 kg, how many centimeters are there in an inch?

1.7 A liter of water weighs 2 lb $3\frac{1}{4}$ oz. From this, calculate the number of grams in a pound.

1.8 A 5.00-cm³ sample of mercury weighs 68.0 g. Calculate the density of the metal.

1.9 Which possesses the greater kinetic energy: a 2900-lb automobile traveling at 25 mph, or a 1-oz bullet traveling at 2500 ft/sec?

1.10 Derive equations for the conversion of Fahrenheit temperatures to Celsius, and vice versa. *Ans.* $°F = \frac{9}{5}C + 32$, $°C = \frac{5}{9}(F - 32)$

1.11 At what temperature do the Fahrenheit and Celsius temperature scales coincide?

1.12 A cube of gold 5.00 cm on an edge weighs 2.415 kg. Calculate the density of gold.

1.13 The specific heat of copper is approximately 0.09 cal/g-°C. The amount of heat required to raise the temperature of 50.0 g of copper from 25° to 100°C would be sufficient to raise the temperature of water from 25°C to what temperature? (The specific heat of water is 1.00 cal/g-°C.)

1.14 The density of copper is 8.92 g/cm³; that of aluminum is 2.70 g/cm³. How many grams of copper will occupy the same volume as 45.0 g of aluminum?

1.15 Normal body temperature is 98.6°F. What temperature does this correspond to on the Celsius scale?

1.16 An iron strip is 2.45 m long, 12.2 cm wide, and 8.42 mm thick. If the density of iron is 7.86 g/cm³, how much does the strip weigh?

1.17 A stone dropped into a graduated cylinder containing 20.0 ml of water raised the water level in the cylinder to 28.3 ml. If the stone weighs 22.4 g, what is its density?

1.18 Atmospheric pressure can support a column of mercury 76.0 cm high. (a) Calculate the pressure of the atmosphere in g/cm². The acceleration due to gravity is 980 cm/sec². (b) Calculate the pressure of the atmosphere in dynes/cm² (1 dyne = 1 g-cm/sec²).

1.19 About 13,000 (1.3×10^4) calories are produced when 1.0 g of natural gas is burned. If a gram of natural gas could be converted completely into energy, how many calories would be released? (1 cal = 4.186×10^7 ergs; 1 erg = 1 dyne-cm; the speed of light is 3.0×10^{10} cm/sec.)

1.20 On the now-obsolete Reaumur scale of temperature, the freezing and boiling points of water are 0°R and 80°R, respectively. If tin melts at 449.5°F, what is its melting point in degrees Reaumur?

1.21 Dunkerque (latitude 51.124°N) and Barcelona (latitude 41.403°N) lie along the same meridian exactly 671.2 miles apart. Using this information, calculate the length of the meter in inches.

> **Whether the ultimate particles of a body . . . are all alike . . . is a matter of some importance.**
>
> **—John Dalton, 1808**

2 QUANTITATIVE MEASUREMENTS

As we saw in the last chapter, the real development of chemistry as a science started in the seventeenth century, when chemists first began to measure the quantities of substances which took part in chemical reactions. When they did so, they gradually came to realize that *the elements do not react haphazardly with one another, but always combine in the same relative mass proportions.*

Law of Constant Composition 2.1

The French physician Jean Rey observed as early as 1630 that when one heats a sample of tin in air—forming what we now know to be tin oxide—its mass increases up to a point, after which there is no further change. For example, we find that if we heat 10.0 g of tin we obtain 12.7 g of the oxide; 29.7 g of tin yields 37.7 g of oxide. The mass ratio of tin to oxygen, that is, the number of grams of tin per gram of oxygen in the oxide, may be calculated in each case as follows:

	I	II
Weight of oxide	12.7 g	37.7 g
Weight of tin in oxide	10.0 g	29.7 g
Weight of oxygen in oxide	2.7 g	8.0 g
Ratio: grams of tin to grams of oxygen	3.7	3.7

Whatever quantity of tin is used, and however the oxide is produced, the ratio of the mass of tin to that of oxygen in the oxide is always found to be 3.7. The oxide, in other words, has a *definite composition* of 3.7 parts of tin to 1 part of oxygen.

This constancy of composition is not restricted to the oxide of tin but is characteristic of all compounds, and it distinguishes a compound from a mixture. The composition of a mixture may vary widely, but that of a true compound is fixed. Zinc and sulfur, for example, may be mixed in any proportions, but zinc sulfide, the product of their chemical combination, always contains the elements in the proportion of 2.04 g of zinc for every 1.00 g of sulfur. If 4.00 g of sulfur is heated with 10.00 g of zinc, 1.84 g of zinc will be found to remain unchanged after reaction. On the other hand, if 4.00 g of zinc is heated with 10.00 g of sulfur, only 1.96 g of sulfur will combine with the zinc. The zinc sulfide produced each time, however, will have the elements present in the same proportions: 2.04 g of zinc for every 1.00 g of sulfur. *Any given sample of a pure compound, regardless of its source or how it is prepared, always contains the same elements united in the same definite relative proportions by mass.*

2.2 Equivalent Weights

Burning 1.0 g of hydrogen in the air produces 9.0 g of water. The difference, 8.0 g, is the amount of oxygen which combined with the hydrogen. The same quantity of hydrogen, 1.0 g, reacts with 35.5 g of chlorine to form the compound hydrogen chloride. One might say then that the masses 8.0 g of oxygen and 35.5 g of chlorine are in a sense *equivalent* to one another, inasmuch as they both react with the same mass, 1.0 g, of hydrogen.

Let us see whether this equivalence between 8.0 g of oxygen and 35.5 g of chlorine holds with other elements. Here, for a few elements, are the masses of each which are found experimentally to combine with 8.0 g of oxygen to form the corresponding oxides:

20.0 g of calcium	combines with	8.0 g of oxygen.
23.0 g of sodium	combines with	8.0 g of oxygen.
7.0 g of silicon	combines with	8.0 g of oxygen.
103.6 g of lead	combines with	8.0 g of oxygen.

Now if we analyze the chlorides of each of these elements we obtain the following results:

20.0 g of calcium	combines with	35.5 g of chlorine.
23.0 g of sodium	combines with	35.5 g of chlorine.
7.0 g of silicon	combines with	35.5 g of chlorine.
103.6 g of lead	combines with	35.5 g of chlorine.

Just as with hydrogen, we find that the amount of each element which reacts with 8.0 g of oxygen is also the amount which combines with a fixed weight of chlorine. As before, 8.0 g of oxygen and 35.5 g of chlorine are seen to be equivalent to one another. Similarly, 1.0 g of hydrogen is equivalent to 23.0 g of sodium or 7.0 g of silicon with respect to its reaction with oxygen or chlorine. Such quantitative relationships are found among all of the elements. Whenever elements combine to form compounds, they do so in quantities proportional to their equivalent weights. By definition, *the* ***equivalent weight*** *of an element is that weight which will combine with or displace 8.0 g* of oxygen or the equivalent weight of any other element.* The determination of equivalent weights is illustrated in the following examples.†

Example 2.1

When 10.00 g of tin metal is heated in the air, 12.69 g of the oxide is produced. Calculate the equivalent weight of the tin.

Solution: The difference between the mass of the oxide and the mass of the tin, 12.69 − 10.00 = 2.69 g, is the mass of oxygen that combined with 10.00 g of tin. The equivalent weight of tin is the mass of the metal that combines with 8.00 g of oxygen. Therefore,

$$\text{Equivalent weight of tin} = \frac{(10.00\ \text{g})(8.00\ \text{g})}{(2.69\ \text{g})} = 29.7\ \text{g}$$

Example 2.2

A 0.346-g sample of zinc metal dissolves in a solution of a tin salt, displacing 0.314 g of tin metal. Calculate the equivalent weight of zinc.

Solution: The equivalent weight of tin was found in Example 2.1 to be 29.7 g. Since 0.346 g of zinc displaces 0.314 g of tin, the equivalent weight of zinc, that is, the mass of zinc that will displace 29.7 g of tin, can be calculated as follows:

$$\text{Equivalent weight of zinc} = \frac{(0.346\ \text{g})(29.7\ \text{g})}{(0.314\ \text{g})} = 32.7\ \text{g}$$

Example 2.3

Phosphorus forms two oxides. Oxide I contains 56.34% phosphorus; oxide II contains 43.65% phosphorus. Calculate the equivalent weight of phosphorus in each oxide.

Solution: Oxide I contains 56.34 g of phosphorus in every 100.00 g of the oxide. The remainder, 100.00 − 56.34 = 43.66 g, is oxygen. The equivalent weight of phosphorus in oxide I is therefore:

$$\text{Oxide I:} \qquad \frac{(56.34\ \text{g})(8.00\ \text{g})}{(43.66\ \text{g})} = 10.32\ \text{g}$$

Similarly, in oxide II, the equivalent weight of phosphorus is:

$$\text{Oxide II:} \qquad \frac{(43.65\ \text{g})(8.00\ \text{g})}{(56.35\ \text{g})} = 6.20\ \text{g}$$

An element that forms more than one oxide will have more than one equivalent weight, as we have just seen to be the case with phosphorus.

* More precisely, 7.9997 g. Any mass of any element could have been chosen as the basis of equivalent weights, and in fact several others have been used in the past. Oxygen was chosen simply for convenience. It forms compounds, in most cases by direct combination, with nearly all of the other elements. An equivalent weight of 8.0 g for oxygen makes that of hydrogen approximately unity and also results in no element having an equivalent weight of less than one.

† For a discussion of significant figures, see Appendix A.

These equivalent weights, however, will invariably be found to possess a least common multiple (LCM), which is a number that is evenly divisible by each of them. Thus 30.96, which is evenly divisible by both 10.32 (30.96/10.32 = 3) and 6.20 (30.96/6.20 = 5) is the least common multiple of the two equivalent weights of phosphorus. Examples of some other elements that have more than one equivalent weight are given in Table 2.1.

TABLE 2.1 Equivalent Weights of Some Elements

Element	Equivalent Weight(s), g	LCM
Carbon	6.00, 3.00	6.00
Chlorine	35.45	—
Copper	63.54, 31.77	63.54
Manganese	27.47, 18.31, 13.74, 9.16, 7.85	54.94
Sulfur	16.03, 8.02, 5.34	16.03
Tin	59.34, 29.67	59.34
Zinc	32.68	—

2.3 Dalton's Atomic Theory

In an effort to explain the law of constant composition and the existence of equivalent weights, John Dalton proposed an atomic theory of matter. According to Dalton, the elements are made up of extremely small particles which he called ***atoms,*** from the Greek *atomos*, meaning indivisible. These atoms retain their identity throughout all chemical and physical changes. Dalton considered all atoms of the same element to be identical in every respect, and most important, to have the same mass. Atoms of different elements he assumed to have different characteristic masses. Formation of a chemical compound, according to this theory, involves the union of whole atoms in a simple, fixed, numerical ratio. The idea that matter is composed of atoms was not original with Dalton. Since earliest times philosophers had speculated upon whether or not matter could be infinitely subdivided into smaller and smaller parts. The concept of the atom as the ultimate, indivisible particle of matter can be traced back at least to Leucippus (about 450 B.C.) and Democritus (460–370 B.C.) and has been in and out of fashion many times over the intervening centuries to the present. Dalton's contribution lay in placing the concept in a modern framework and in attributing definite and invariant properties to the atoms of different elements.

2.4 Atomic Weight

Dalton's theory offers a simple explanation of the law of constant composition. If definite numbers of atoms of different elements combine to form a compound, and if these atoms have characteristic masses, then they must necessarily combine in definite mass proportions. For instance, the compound hydrogen chloride always contains 35.5 g of chlorine for every 1.0 g of hydrogen. Assuming, for lack of evidence to the contrary, that the simplest physical unit, or ***molecule,**** of hydrogen chloride consists of one atom of hydrogen combined with one atom of chlorine, then this mass ratio would be expected, *provided that the relative mass of a chlorine atom is 35.5 times that of a hydrogen atom.* The mass of one atom of an element relative to some arbitrarily chosen unit taken as a standard is referred to as that element's ***atomic weight.*** If an ***atomic mass unit*** (amu) is chosen so as to make the atomic weight of hydrogen 1.0 amu, then the atomic weight of chlorine becomes 35.5 amu.

In arriving at an atomic weight of 35.5 amu for chlorine, the assumption was made that every molecule of hydrogen chloride contains one atom of each element. There may just as well be two atoms of chlorine to every one of hydrogen in the compound, in which case the atomic weight of chlorine is only half as much: 17.8 amu. We are confronted by a dilemma: it is a simple matter to determine the relative masses of the atoms in a molecule of a compound provided that the numbers of atoms of each kind present in the molecule are known, but there seems to be no way to find out how many atoms are present in the molecule without first knowing their relative masses.

Elements combine with one another in quantities proportional to their equivalent weights simply because the equivalent weights are in proportion to the relative weights of the atoms. The atomic weight is therefore numerically related to the equivalent weight, although it is not necessarily equal to it. For example, if we assume that the atomic weight of hydrogen is 1 amu, then if there is one atom of hydrogen and one of oxygen in a water molecule, the atomic weight of oxygen is 8, equal to its equivalent weight. On the other hand, if there are two atoms of hydrogen to one of oxygen, the atomic weight of oxygen must be $2 \times 8 = 16$, if the mass ratio is to remain 1:8.

It would appear, then, that the atomic weight of an element is numerically equal to some whole number multiple of the equivalent weight. This would account for the fact that when an element exhibits several equivalent weights, all of them have a least common multiple.

Let us pursue this idea a little further. Five different experimentally determined equivalent weights were listed for manganese in Table 2.1. These had the numerical values: 27.47, 18.31, 13.74, 9.16, and 7.85. The atomic weight should therefore be at least 27.47 amu. But 27.47 cannot be

* Dalton did not distinguish clearly between atoms and molecules. He used the term *atom* for two concepts: the smallest unit of an element which can undergo chemical change, and the smallest particle of a compound into which it can be divided without losing its chemical identity. The term ***molecule*** was first applied to the latter concept by Amadeo Avogadro in 1811.

the correct value because it is not evenly divisible by all of the other equivalent weights:

$$
\begin{aligned}
27.47 \div 27.47 &= 1 \\
27.47 \div 18.31 &= 1.5 \\
27.47 \div 13.74 &= 2 \\
27.47 \div 9.16 &= 3 \\
27.47 \div 7.85 &= 3.5
\end{aligned}
$$

Doubling 27.47 gives 54.94, which is evenly divisible by all of the equivalent weight values:

$$
\begin{aligned}
54.94 \div 27.47 &= 2 \\
54.94 \div 18.31 &= 3 \\
54.94 \div 13.74 &= 4 \\
54.94 \div 9.16 &= 6 \\
54.94 \div 7.85 &= 7
\end{aligned}
$$

The atomic weight of manganese is then no less than 54.94 amu, although it could still be 109.88 or some other whole-number multiple of 54.94.

2.5 Valence

For oxygen we saw that the number by which the equivalent weight must be multiplied in order to give the correct atomic weight depends upon the number of hydrogen atoms which combine with an atom of oxygen; that is, it depends upon the *combining capacity* of oxygen toward hydrogen. The combining capacity of an element is expressed in terms of its ***valence.*** The relationship among the equivalent weight, the atomic weight, and the valence is

$$\text{Atomic weight} = \text{Equivalent weight} \times \text{Valence}$$

If an element is found to have more than one equivalent weight, it means that it must have more than one valence. Thus phosphorus, for which two equivalent weights were calculated in Example 2.3, must exhibit a different valence in each of its two oxides. Manganese, with five equivalent weights, must have five different valences. If the atomic weight of manganese is 54.94, these valences are 2, 3, 4, 6, and 7. *The valence of an element is determined by the number of other atoms with which an atom of that element can combine. Since atoms react as whole entities, valence can have only whole-number (integral) values.*

2.6 Dulong and Petit's Law

The equivalent weight of an element can be very accurately determined by chemical analysis of one of its compounds. When the valence is known, the atomic weight of the element can then be calculated. At the time when not even the approximate atomic weights were known, however, there was no way of determining the valences. Nevertheless, through good luck and some educated guesses, the proper multiples were applied in a number of cases, and by 1819 the correct atomic weights had been assigned to a dozen or more elements. In that year two French chemists, P. L. Dulong and A. T. Petit, published a table showing that the product of the atomic weight multiplied by the specific heat (Sec. 1.10) of each of those elements was approximately constant. Using the present value for the atomic mass unit, this constant is about 6 amu-cal/g-°C:

$$\text{Atomic weight} \times \text{Specific heat} = 6 \text{ amu-cal/g-}^\circ\text{C}$$

This relationship affords a means of determining the approximate atomic weight of an element, and from that is obtained the appropriate factor by which to multiply the equivalent weight in order to find the exact atomic weight.

Example 2.4

It takes 97.0 cal to raise the temperature of 10.0 g of tin from 0° to 18°C. Using the value for the equivalent weight of tin calculated in Example 2.1, determine the exact atomic weight of tin and its valence in the oxide.

Solution:

$$\text{Specific heat} = \frac{(97.0 \text{ cal})}{(18^\circ\text{C})(10.0 \text{ g})} = 0.054 \text{ cal/g-}^\circ\text{C}$$

$$\text{Approximate atomic weight} = \frac{6 \text{ amu-cal/g-}^\circ\text{C}}{0.054 \text{ cal/g-}^\circ\text{C}} \approx 111 \text{ amu}$$

$$\text{Valence} = \frac{111 \text{ amu}}{29.7 \text{ amu}} \approx 4$$

$$\text{Exact atomic weight} = 4 \times 29.7 \text{ amu} = 119 \text{ amu}$$

The application of Dulong and Petit's law made it possible to determine the correct atomic weights of a large number of elements. Unfortunately, many of the lighter elements, among them carbon, oxygen, and nitrogen, do not obey the law, and their atomic weights as a result remained in dispute until after 1860. Since that time, the application of other methods for determining atomic weights (discussed in Chapters 3, 4, and 6), together with refinement of experimental techniques, has permitted the assignment of correct atomic weights to all of the known elements. It is important to remember that the atomic weights of the elements are their relative weights based upon an arbitrary standard, and that therefore their numerical values depend upon the standard chosen. For many years the atomic mass unit was defined by assigning a value of 16.0000 amu to the atomic weight of oxygen. Beginning in 1913 it became evident that Dalton's original assumption that all of the atoms of a given element have exactly the same mass is not entirely correct. Most elements, including oxygen, exist as mixtures of ***isotopes,*** which we shall define for the present as *atoms of the same element which have essentially identical chemical properties but different masses.* An atomic weight as ordinarily determined is therefore the average value for the mixture of isotopes. Fortunately for the chemist, the relative proportions of atoms of different mass in the naturally occurring isotopic mixture of a given element are, with only a few exceptions, always the same. As a result, although the individual atoms may not all have the same mass, the *average* atomic weight is fixed.

The discovery of isotopes led the physicists to define a new scale of atomic weights based upon a value of exactly 16 amu for the isotope of oxygen present in largest amount in the natural mixture.* On this scale, the average atomic weight of ordinary oxygen became 16.0044 amu. For most purposes, the difference between the two scales was too small to worry about, but it had to be taken into account in the most precise work. Chemists continued to use the older atomic weights, but the existence of two scales was awkward and a nuisance, especially for those working on the border line between physics and chemistry. The need was recognized for a single scale acceptable to both physicists and chemists, and in 1961 the mass of the pure carbon-12 isotope was chosen by international agreement as the new standard for atomic weights, being assigned a value of exactly 12 amu. This resulted in a value of 15.9994 amu for the atomic weight of ordinary oxygen, and the atomic weights of all of the other elements were likewise recalculated. A table of the latest atomic weight values, based on carbon-12, is printed inside the back cover of this book.

2.7 Moles

Once we establish that one atom of A weighs twice as much as one atom of B, we know that 10, 50, or in fact any number of atoms of A must weigh twice as much as 10, 50, or the same number of atoms of B. This makes it a simple matter to count out equal numbers of atoms of different elements. All that is necessary is to see that the masses taken of each element are in the same ratio as the respective atomic weights. The most obvious way to do this is to weigh out a number of grams of each element equal to its atomic weight. For example, the atomic weight of sulfur is 32.064 amu, and that of oxygen is 15.9994 amu. If we were to weigh out 32.064 g of sulfur and 15.9994 g of oxygen, then we would know that we had the same number of atoms of each element. The number of atoms in 32.064 g of sulfur or 15.9994 g of oxygen is known as ***Avogadro's number.*** For the present, it does not matter what the actual numerical value of Avogadro's number is. What is important is that *a mass in grams of any element which is numerically equal to the atomic weight of that element contains Avogadro's number of atoms*. Or, turning the statement about, *the mass in grams of Avogadro's number of atoms of any element is numerically equal to the atomic weight of that element.* Methods for evaluating Avogadro's number will be discussed in later chapters (e.g., in Secs. 6.3 and 6.6).

We are now able to define a standard of *number*, just as we have defined standards of mass and volume. This standard is the mole. *A* ***mole*** *is a quantity containing Avogadro's number of units* (atoms, molecules, or whatever) *under consideration.* Thus, 32.064 g of sulfur and 15.9994 g of oxygen are each one mole of atoms.

Quantities are generally more meaningful to a chemist if expressed in moles rather than in grams because they then represent relative numbers of atoms, molecules, or other units. A chemist, wishing to prepare a

* Natural atmospheric oxygen is a mixture of 99.759% oxygen-16, 0.037% oxygen-17, and 0.204% oxygen-18.

compound in which he knows there are two atoms of sodium for every atom of sulfur, knows that he needs two moles of sodium atoms for every mole of sulfur atoms that he has. If it were not for the fact that his balance can only be calibrated in mass units and not directly in moles, the actual masses of the sodium and sulfur would not matter. The following examples will illustrate how the mole concept is applied to chemical calculation.

Example 2.5

How many moles of sulfur are there in 10.0 g of the element?

Solution: The atomic weight of sulfur is 32.1 amu; therefore one mole of sulfur weighs 32.1 g.

$$\text{Moles of sulfur} = \frac{10.0 \text{ g}}{32.1 \text{ g/mole}} = 0.312 \text{ mole}$$

Example 2.6

How many moles of sodium are needed to react completely with the sulfur in the previous example?

Solution: Two sodium atoms combine with each sulfur atom; therefore $2 \times 0.312 = 0.624$ mole of sodium is needed to react with 0.312 mole of sulfur.

Example 2.7

How many grams of sodium react with 10.0 g of sulfur?

Solution: In the preceding example it was shown that 0.624 mole of sodium reacts with $\frac{10.0 \text{ g}}{32.1 \text{ g/mole}} = 0.312$ mole of sulfur. The moles of sodium are readily translated into grams by multiplying the number of moles by the mass of one mole of sodium:

$$\text{Grams of sodium} = (0.624 \text{ mole})(23.0 \text{ g/mole}) = 14.4 \text{ g}$$

At this point it might be interesting to go back and take a second look at Dulong and Petit's law and see if perhaps there is any reason other than coincidence for the curious relationship between atomic weight and specific heat. We can substitute the mass per mole for the atomic weight of the element without changing the numerical value of Dulong and Petit's constant. Its dimensions, however, become cal/mole-°C:

$$(\text{g/mole})(\text{cal/g-°C}) = \text{cal/mole-°C}$$

Thus the heat capacity *per mole* is the same for all of those elements which obey Dulong and Petit's law, indicating that the quantity of heat required to raise the temperature of a given number of atoms by a certain amount is the same for each of those elements. In other words, each atom, regardless of its mass or nature, has the same capacity for absorbing heat.*

* This relationship holds only for the element in the solid state, in which all of the heat energy absorbed goes to increase the vibratory motion of the atoms in the crystal.

CHEMISTRY — Plate CXXXII

Chemical Characters or Symbols

Fire	Regulus of Antimony	c. Caustic vol. Alkali	A Powder
Air	Arsenic	Potash	Ashes
Water	Regulus of Arsenic	Acids	B A Bath
Earth	K; Cobalt	Vinegar	B.M.; M.B.; Water bath
f. Fixable Air	N. Nickel	Vitriolic Acid	A.B. Sand bath
m. Mephitic Air	S.M. Metallic Substances	Nitrous Acid	V.B. Vapor bath
Clay	C. Calx	Marine Acid	An Hour
Gypsum	Orpiment	F; Æ; Aquafortis	A Day
c. Calcareous Earth	Cinnabar	R; Æ; Aqua Regia	A Night
CV; Quicklime	L.C. Lapis Calaminaris	Vol. Sulphureous Acid	A Month
Vitrifiable or Siliceous Earths	Tutty	Phosphoric Acid	aaa; Amalgam
Fluors or Fusible Earths	Vitriol	V Wine	To Distill
X Talk	Sea Salt	Spirit of Wine	To Sublime
M. Magnesia	Sal Gem	R Rectified	To Precipitate
A; Earth of Alum	Nitre	Æ Ether	A Retort
Sand	Borax	Lime Water	XX. An Alembic
Gold	S S Sedative Salt	Urine	A Crucible
Silver	Sal Ammoniac	Oil	S.S.S. Stratum Super Stratum
Copper	Allum	E. Essential Oil	C.C. Cornu Cervi Hartshorn
Tin	Tartar	Fixed Oil	A Bottle
Lead	Alkali	Sulphur	gr.i. A Grain
Mercury	Fixed Alkali	Hepar of Sulphur	℈i. A Scruple
Iron	Volatile Alkali	Phosphorus	ʒi. A Dram
Zinc	m. Mild fixed Alkali	Phlogiston	℥i. An Ounce
B; W? Bismuth	c. Caustic fixed Alkali	Soap	℔i A Pound
Antimony	m. Mild vol. Alkali	Verdigrise	dwt.i. A Pennyweight
		Glass	
		Caput Mortuum	

Scot Philad.

Fig. 2.1 Alchemical symbols (reproduced from the First American Edition, Encyclopaedia Britannica, Thomas Dobson, Philadelphia, 1798).

The alchemists used an elaborate set of symbols to represent various substances, chemical processes, and even apparatus (Fig. 2.1). A few were probably convenient as abbreviations, and those for zinc and nickel resemble today's symbols. With the majority of them, though, it would appear to have been simpler to write out the words than draw the symbol, and their main purpose seems to have been to bewilder and impress the layman. As chemistry became more respectable, the alchemical symbols fell into disrepute. Only one of them is still used by chemists today. That is the symbol for fire (Δ), which now represents heat or elevated temperature.

John Dalton used circular symbols to represent atoms and to illustrate how atoms combined to form molecules (Fig. 2.2). Dalton's symbols are time-consuming to draw, and it is difficult to remember which one stands for what element. So far as is known, Dalton is the only one ever to have used them.

The symbols used today are derived from the names (often the Latin names) of the elements. They were first introduced by J. J. Berzelius in 1813, and their simplicity and utility led to their being adopted universally. Each of these symbols has more than one meaning, and therein lies its

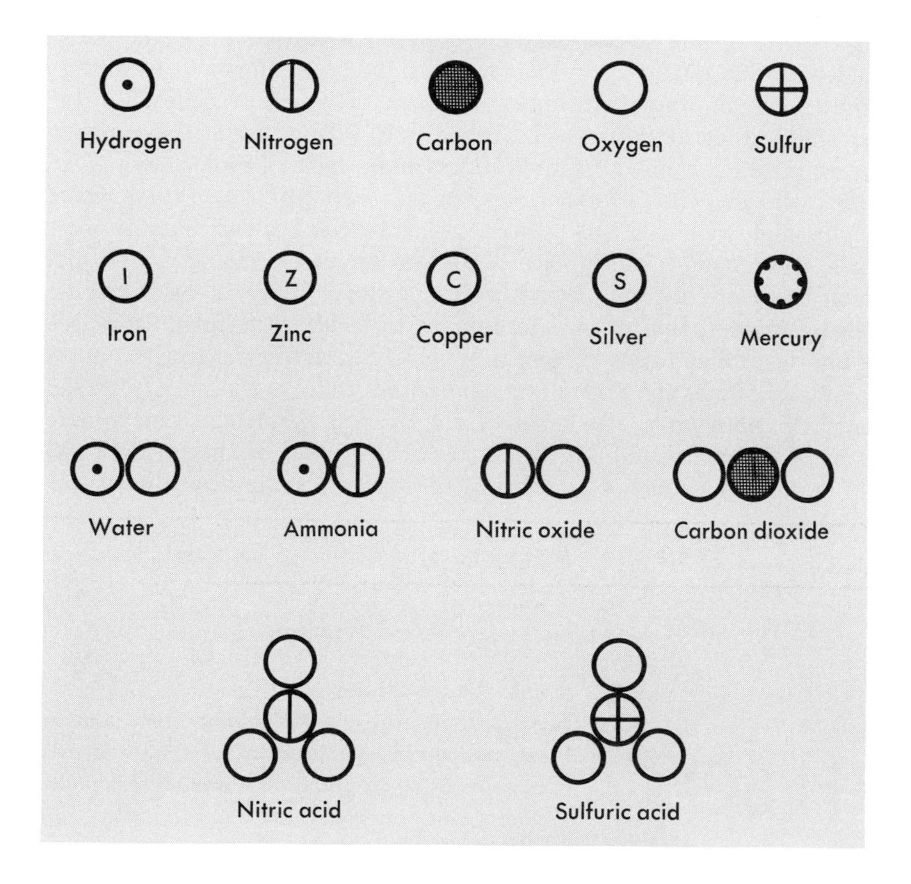

Fig. 2.2 John Dalton's atomic symbols.

usefulness. It is not just an abbreviation for the name of an element, but, like one of Dalton's symbols, it can be used to represent a single atom. We will use symbols in this way later on in drawing the structures of molecules. In addition, its symbol can stand for one mole of an element, as well as for the corresponding mass of one mole (Table 2.2).

TABLE 2.2 Meanings of a Chemical Symbol

The Symbol	Represents
Na	1. The element sodium (Latin: *natrium*). 2. One atom of sodium. 3. One mole (Avogadro's number of atoms) of sodium. 4. 22.9898 g of sodium.

2.9 Chemical Formulas

A compound is represented by a ***chemical formula*** in which symbols are combined to express the number and kinds of atoms which make up a molecule of the compound. Thus, one molecule of sulfuric acid contains two hydrogen, one sulfur, and four oxygen atoms. While this could be written **HHSOOOO**, it is customary to simplify the formula by using subscripts, each of which multiplies the symbol which precedes it. In this way the formula of sulfuric acid becomes H_2SO_4. Just as a symbol represents a mole of atoms, a formula represents a mole of molecules. *The sum of the atomic weights of all of the atoms in the molecular formula is the* ***molecular weight*** (mol. wt.), and this mass in grams is equal to the mass of one mole of the compound. In the case of those compounds (ionic compounds, of which there are a great many) which, as we will see in Sec. 8.5, do not actually exist in the form of individual molecules, the formula represents simply the atomic ratios. Here it is more precise to refer to the sum of the atomic weights as the ***formula weight*** rather than as the molecular weight. For such compounds, the mass of the mole is defined as the number of grams of the compound which is numerically equal to the formula weight. The various meanings of a chemical formula are summarized in Table 2.3.

TABLE 2.3 Meanings of a Chemical Formula

The Formula	Represents
H_2SO_4	1. A molecule of sulfuric acid. 2. Two hydrogen atoms, one sulfur atom, and four oxygen atoms combined to form sulfuric acid. 3. Two moles of hydrogen atoms, one mole of sulfur atoms, and four moles of oxygen atoms combined to form one mole of sulfuric acid. 4. 98.08 g of sulfuric acid.

Radicals 2.10

Frequently, a group of atoms will remain together as a unit throughout many chemical reactions, behaving almost as though it were an element, and bestowing characteristic properties on any compound in which it is present. Such groups of atoms are called ***radicals.*** In writing formulas of compounds, radicals are generally treated as units. To indicate the presence of more than one radical of the same kind in a molecule, the radical is enclosed in parentheses with a subscript outside. Thus, for example, aluminum nitrate is written $Al(NO_3)_3$ rather than AlN_3O_9. The latter formula, while giving the correct proportions of the elements, fails to emphasize the presence of nitrate radicals (NO_3).

Percentage Composition 2.11

Each symbol in the formula of a compound represents, among other things (Table 2.2), the mass of one mole of atoms of the element. The formula represents the mass of one mole of the compound. From this information, the percentage composition, by mass, of the compound can be calculated as shown in the following examples.

Example 2.8

Calculate the percentage composition of copper(II) sulfate, $CuSO_4$.*

Solution: The formula means that there is one mole of copper, one of sulfur, and four of oxygen atoms in one mole of copper(II) sulfate. Translating these molar quantities into the respective masses gives 63.54 g Cu, 32.06 g S, and $4 \times 16.00 = 64.00$ g O in $63.54 + 32.06 + 64.00 = 159.60$ g $CuSO_4$. The percentage of each element in the compound is then:

$$\%Cu = \frac{63.54\text{ g}}{159.60\text{ g}} \times 100 = 39.81\%$$

$$\%S = \frac{32.06\text{ g}}{159.60\text{ g}} \times 100 = 20.09\%$$

$$\%O = \frac{64.00\text{ g}}{159.60\text{ g}} \times 100 = 40.10\%$$

Example 2.9

Assuming that both chemicals sell for the same price per pound, which would be the more economical source of nitrogen, NH_4Cl or $(NH_4)_2SO_4$?

Solution:

$$\%N \text{ in } NH_4Cl = \frac{14.01}{53.50} \times 100 = 26.19\%$$

$$\%N \text{ in } (NH_4)_2SO_4 = \frac{28.02}{132.16} \times 100 = 21.20\%$$

Other factors being equal, NH_4Cl, with the greater percentage of nitrogen, should be the more economical source of that element.

* The naming of inorganic compounds is discussed in Appendix B.

2.12 Percentage Composition by Analysis

Where the formula of a compound is not known, its percentage composition must be determined by analysis. The following example illustrates how this can be done:

Example 2.10

Grape sugar, or *glucose*, contains only carbon, hydrogen, and oxygen. Combustion of a sample of 0.1802 g of glucose yields 0.2641 g of CO_2 and 0.1081 g of H_2O. Calculate the percentage of each element in the compound.

Solution: For each mole (12.01 + 32.06 = 44.07 g) of CO_2 produced, there must have been one mole (12.01 g) of C in the original compound. Likewise, each mole (18.02 g) of H_2O formed represents two moles (2.02 g) of H initially present. Thus:

$$\frac{0.2641 \text{ g } CO_2}{0.1802 \text{ g glucose}} \times \frac{12.01 \text{ g C/mole}}{44.07 \text{ g } CO_2\text{/mole}} \times 100 = 39.94\% \text{ carbon}$$

$$\frac{0.1081 \text{ g } H_2O}{0.1802 \text{ g glucose}} \times \frac{2(1.01 \text{ g H/mole})}{18.02 \text{ g } H_2O\text{/mole}} \times 100 = 6.72\% \text{ hydrogen}$$

Since oxygen is the only other element in the compound, the difference between 100% and the sum of the percentages of carbon and hydrogen must be the percentage of oxygen:

$$100.00 - (39.94 + 6.72) = 53.34\% \text{ oxygen}$$

2.13 Simplest Formula

With the percentage composition known, it becomes possible to calculate the simplest formula which correctly expresses the mole ratios of the elements in the compound.

Example 2.11

From the percentage composition obtained in Example 2.10, calculate the simplest formula of glucose.

Solution: The percentage composition tells us that in every 100.00 g of glucose there are

$$\frac{39.94 \text{ g}}{12.01 \text{ g/mole}} = 3.33 \text{ moles carbon}$$

$$\frac{6.72 \text{ g}}{1.01 \text{ g/mole}} = 6.65 \text{ moles hydrogen}$$

$$\frac{53.34 \text{ g}}{16.00 \text{ g/mole}} = 3.33 \text{ moles oxygen}$$

The atomic ratios of the elements in the compound are therefore 3.33:6.65:3.33, or, to the nearest whole number, 1:2:1. The simplest formula expressing this ratio is CH_2O.

The *simplest formula* merely *expresses the mole ratios of the elements in the compound.* The ***molecular formula,*** which *represents the actual compound,* may be the same as the simplest formula or may be any whole number multiple of it containing the same elements in the same relative proportions. In order to calculate the molecular formula from the simplest formula, the molecular weight of the compound must be known. For example, the molecular weight of glucose is 180.18 g/mole. This is six times what one would calculate from the simplest formula, showing that the molecular formula of glucose must be $6(CH_2O)$, or $C_6H_{12}O_6$. Experimental methods of determining molecular weights are discussed in later chapters (Secs. 3.7, 10.10, and 10.12).

The relative proportions, by mass, of the elements in a compound need not necessarily be expressed in percentages in order to calculate the simplest formula. The following example will illustrate this:

Example 2.12

When 5.00 g of phosphorus is burned in air, 11.44 g of the oxide is produced. Calculate the simplest formula of the oxide.

Solution:

$$\frac{5.00 \text{ g}}{30.97 \text{ g/mole}} = 0.162 \text{ mole phosphorus in oxide}$$

$$\frac{(11.44 \text{ g} - 5.00 \text{ g})}{16.00 \text{ g/mole}} = 0.402 \text{ mole oxygen in oxide}$$

$$\text{Atomic ratio, oxygen/phosphorus} = \frac{0.402 \text{ mole}}{0.162 \text{ mole}} = \frac{2.48}{1}$$

Since an atom cannot be cut in half, the atomic ratio cannot in fact be 2.48:1. Rounding this off to 2:1 is not warranted, because experimental error alone cannot account for the weight of half an atom. If the experimental work were that bad, the analysis would be worthless. The ratio obtained above must therefore be doubled, giving a whole-number ratio of 5:2. The simplest formula of the oxide is then P_2O_5.

Chemical Equations 2.14

When hydrogen is burned in air, it is found that two molecules of hydrogen combine with one molecule of oxygen to yield two molecules of water. Using the appropriate symbols and formulas, this statement may be expressed as follows:

$$2\ H_2 + O_2 \rightarrow 2\ H_2O^*$$

This is an example of a chemical equation. ***A chemical equation** is a condensed way of expressing what occurs in a chemical reaction:* what substances have reacted, what has been produced, and in what relative proportions the reactants have taken part in the reaction. A chemical equation represents an actual chemical reaction; hence the reactants and products, and their formulas, must be known before an equation can be written. This can only be known with certainty from experiment.

* The reason for writing hydrogen as H_2 and oxygen as O_2 rather than as H and O will be made clear in the next chapter.

When zinc metal is dissolved in hydrochloric acid, examination of the products shows them to be zinc chloride ($ZnCl_2$) and hydrogen gas. This could be indicated as follows:

$$Zn + HCl \rightarrow ZnCl_2 + H_2$$

This, however, is not a true chemical equation. Conservation of mass demands that the products of any real chemical reaction must contain the same number and kind of atoms as the reactants, but in the expression above there is one more hydrogen atom and one more chlorine atom in the products than in the reactants. The numbers of chlorine and hydrogen atoms may be equalized by doubling the number of **HCl** molecules as follows:

$$Zn + 2\ HCl \rightarrow ZnCl_2 + H_2$$

The equation is now said to be *balanced.* The first 2 in the equation is called a ***coefficient,*** and it multiplies the entire formula which follows it. Balancing any chemical equation is a matter of adjusting the coefficients until the numbers of atoms of various kinds are the same on both sides of the arrow. Since a chemical equation must agree with the experimental facts, *it is never permissible to change any formulas in order to achieve a balance.* For example, the "equation"

$$KClO_3 \rightarrow KCl + O_3$$

for the decomposition of potassium chlorate is balanced, but not correct, since oxygen is evolved in the reaction in the form of O_2 molecules, not as O_3. Likewise,

$$KClO_3 \rightarrow KClO + O_2$$

although balanced, is also incorrect. **KCl**, not **KClO**, is produced in the reaction. The correctly balanced equation, truly representing the facts, is thus

$$2\ KClO_3 \rightarrow 2\ KCl + 3\ O_2$$

2.15 Calculations from Chemical Equations

The balanced equation

$$H_2SO_4 + 2\ NaOH \rightarrow Na_2SO_4 + 2\ H_2O$$

tells us that one mole of sulfuric acid reacts with two moles of sodium hydroxide (**NaOH**) to yield one mole of sodium sulfate (Na_2SO_4) and two moles of water. In other words, from $2(23.0 + 16.0 + 1.0) = 80.0$ g of **NaOH** we can obtain $(2 \times 23.0) + 32.1 + (4 \times 16.0) = 142.1$ g of Na_2SO_4 by reaction with H_2SO_4. From any other amount of **NaOH**, the yield of Na_2SO_4 will be in proportion to the number of moles taken.

Example 2.13

How many grams of sodium sulfate can be prepared from 25.0 g of sodium hydroxide according to the following equation?

$$H_2SO_4 + 2\ NaOH \rightarrow Na_2SO_4 + 2\ H_2O$$

Solution: The equation shows that for every mole of sodium hydroxide that reacts, half as many moles of sodium sulfate are produced. One mole of $NaOH$ weighs 40.0 g, therefore 25.0 g of $NaOH$ is 25.0/40.0 = 0.625 mole. This much $NaOH$ will produce 0.625/2 = 0.313 mole of Na_2SO_4. One mole of Na_2SO_4 weighs 142.1 g. Therefore 0.313 mole × 142.1 g/mole = 44.5 g of Na_2SO_4 will be formed from 25.0 g of $NaOH$. Summarizing,

$$\frac{25.0\text{ g NaOH}}{2(40.0\text{ g NaOH/mole})} \times 142.1\text{ g Na}_2\text{SO}_4\text{/mole} = 44.5\text{ g Na}_2\text{SO}_4$$

Example 2.14

What weight of 90.0% pure sulfuric acid will be needed to react completely with 25.0 g of $NaOH$ as in Example 2.13?

Solution: The weight of 100% pure sulfuric acid needed is

$$\frac{(25.0\text{ g NaOH})(98.0\text{ g H}_2\text{SO}_4\text{/mole})}{2(40.0\text{ g NaOH/mole})} = 30.6\text{ g H}_2\text{SO}_4$$

But the sulfuric acid to be used contains only 90.0% H_2SO_4, so a larger amount is necessary:

$$\frac{30.6\text{ g H}_2\text{SO}_4}{0.900\text{ g H}_2\text{SO}_4\text{/g acid}} = 34.0\text{ g } 90.0\%\text{ acid needed}$$

Example 2.15

How much silver chloride will be formed by mixing a solution of 100.0 g of silver nitrate with a solution of 50.0 g of sodium chloride?

$$AgNO_3 + NaCl \rightarrow AgCl + NaNO_3$$

Solution: For complete reaction, one mole of $AgNO_3$ will react with one mole of $NaCl$ to give one mole of $AgCl$. Since we have 100.0 g/170.0 g/mole = 0.588 mole of $AgNO_3$ and 50.0 g/58.5 g/mole = 0.855 mole of $NaCl$, the $NaCl$ is present in excess over the amount necessary to react completely with all of the $AgNO_3$ present. We can therefore obtain no more than 0.588 mole, or 84.3 g (143.4 g/mole × 0.588 mole) of $AgCl$. The excess $NaCl$ will simply remain unreacted.

Example 2.16

How many pounds of 70.0% nitric acid can be prepared from 200 lb of Chile saltpeter which contains 85.0% $NaNO_3$?

$$2\ NaNO_3 + H_2SO_4 \rightarrow Na_2SO_4 + 2\ HNO_3$$

Solution: Provided that the masses taken of each compound are in the same ratio as the respective molecular or formula weights, the same number of fundamental units of each will be present. This is true no matter what units of mass are used. This allows us to define the ***pound-mole:*** *the number of pounds of a compound which is numerically equal to its molecular or formula weight.* The method of calculation using pound-moles is the same as in the previous examples. In this case, from the equation we see that one mole of nitric acid is formed from every mole of sodium nitrate that reacts. In 200 lb of Chile saltpeter there are $200 \times 0.85 = 170$ lb of pure $NaNO_3$. Hence:

$$\frac{(170 \text{ lb } NaNO_3)(63.0 \text{ lb } HNO_3/\text{lb-mole})}{(85.0 \text{ lb } NaNO_3/\text{lb-mole})(0.700 \text{ lb } HNO_3/\text{lb acid})} = 180 \text{ lb } 70\% \; HNO_3 \text{ produced}$$

2.16 Writing Formulas and Naming Compounds

Every compound has a definite composition and hence has a single, unique formula corresponding to this composition. Provided that the valences of the elements and radicals which go to make up a compound are known, the simplest formula can usually be written by following a few basic rules. Most of the compounds you will encounter in this book consist of two principal parts: a metal, or more metallic part, and a nonmetal, or less metallic part. In writing a formula, one writes the symbol of the more metallic element, or radical, first, followed by the less metallic. The sum of the valences of the metallic atoms or radicals must be equal to that of the nonmetallic in a stable compound. One of the simplest ways to find the correct subscripts so that the valences balance is to use the valence of the nonmetal as the subscript of the metal, and vice versa, as in the following examples:

$$Na^{1}_{2}(SO^{2}_{4})_{(1)} \qquad Al^{3}_{2}O^{2}_{3} \qquad Al^{3}_{3}P^{3}_{3} = AlP \qquad Al^{3}_{2}(SO_4)^{2}_{3}$$

Sometimes, in our concern for the more exciting aspects of chemistry, we tend to neglect mundane things such as writing formulas and naming compounds. This is a mistake, because formulas and names are a major part of a chemist's basic vocabulary. Therefore, unless you want to be seriously handicapped in your study of chemistry, you must see to it that the symbols, names, and valences of the more common elements and radicals grow so familiar to you that writing them becomes almost automatic. As a minimum, you should know those given in Table 2.4. Practice writing the formulas of compounds using the elements and radicals of Table 2.4 until you can do it as easily as reciting the multiplication tables. This may not be exciting work, but it must be done. The system of chemical nomenclature is more fully discussed in Appendices B and C.

TABLE 2.4 Valences and Names of Common Elements and Radicals

A. Metallic elements and radicals

Valence = 1			
NH_4	Ammonium	Li	Lithium
Cu	Copper(I)	K	Potassium
H	Hydrogen	Ag	Silver
Hg	Mercury(I)	Na	Sodium
Valence = 2			
Ba	Barium	Pb	Lead(II)
Cd	Cadmium	Mg	Magnesium
Ca	Calcium	Mn	Manganese
Cr	Chromium(II)	Hg	Mercury(II)
Co	Cobalt(II)	Sr	Strontium
Cu	Copper(II)	Sn	Tin(II)
Fe	Iron(II)	Zn	Zinc
Valence = 3			
Al	Aluminum	Co	Cobalt(III)
Cr	Chromium(III)	Fe	Iron(III)
Valence = 4			
C	Carbon	Si	Silicon
Pb	Lead(IV)	Sn	Tin(IV)
Valence = 5			
V	Vanadium(V)		

B. Nonmetallic elements and radicals

Valence = 1			
$C_2H_3O_2$	Acetate	ClO	Hypochlorite
Br	Bromine, or Bromide	I	Iodine, or Iodide
ClO_3	Chlorate	NO_3	Nitrate
Cl	Chlorine, or Chloride	NO_2	Nitrite
F	Fluorine, or Fluoride	ClO_4	Perchlorate
OH	Hydroxide	MnO_4	Permanganate
Valence = 2			
CO_3	Carbonate	SO_4	Sulfate
CrO_4	Chromate	SO_3	Sulfite
Cr_2O_7	Dichromate	S	Sulfur, or Sulfide
O	Oxygen, or Oxide	S_2O_3	Thiosulfate
SiO_3	Silicate		
Valence = 3			
N	Nitrogen, or Nitride	P	Phosphorus, or Phosphide
PO_4	Phosphate		

2.17 Reading Suggestions

A chronology of the development of the atomic theory from 550 B.C. to A.D. 1958 is given in Chapter 4 of *Essay on Atomism* by Lancelot Law Whyte (Harper Torchbook #TB 565, Harper & Row, New York, 1963). Those of a philosophical turn of mind will find this little book thought-provoking. John Dalton's original paper, *A New System of Chemical Philosophy*, in which he outlined his atomic theory for the first time, is reprinted in part in *Readings in the Literature of Science*, edited by William C. and Margaret Dampier (Harper Torchbook #TB 512, Harper & Row, New York, 1959, pp. 93–99). An autobiographical sketch in Dalton's own hand is reproduced in a paper by D. I. Duveen and H. S. Klickstein, *J. Chem. Ed.* **32,** 333 (1955). Dulong and Petit's Law is discussed by R. K. Fitzgerel and F. H. Verhoek in *J. Chem. Ed.* **37,** 545 (1960). For a brief discussion of the mole and the new unified atomic weight scale, see E. A. Guggenheim, *J. Chem. Ed.* **38,** 86 (1961). William F. Kieffer has written a very useful and readable paperback, *The Mole Concept in Chemistry*, one volume in the series of *Selected Topics in Chemistry* (Reinhold, New York, 1962). The first 40 pages of Professor Kieffer's book are especially pertinent to the work of this chapter.

Questions and Problems

2.1 Define these terms:

equivalent weight	molecule	radical
atomic weight	valence	simplest formula
atom	mole	molecular formula

2.2 Write the formulas for the following compounds:

lead(II) chromate	copper(II) acetate
aluminum oxide	chromium(III) oxide
sodium silicate	silicon fluoride
magnesium perchlorate	silver sulfate
manganese phosphate	ammonium dichromate
sulfuric acid	nitric acid
sodium hydroxide	calcium hydroxide
sodium bromide	lithium carbonate
copper(I) sulfide	barium sulfate
iron(III) sulfate	iron(II) sulfate

2.3 Name the following compounds:

$K_2Cr_2O_7$	$Cd(NO_3)_2$	$Ca(ClO)_2$
Mg_3N_2	$Ba(OH)_2$	$Pb(C_2H_3O_2)_4$
$Sr_3(PO_4)_2$	$KMnO_4$	Na_2SO_3
$CaCO_3$	$ZnSO_4$	KNO_2
$AgC_2H_3O_2$	$SrCl_2$	$(NH_4)_2S$

2.4 Analysis of a number of different samples of titanium oxide gave the following results:

	I	II	III	IV	V
Weight of sample, g	1.03	0.916	2.61	1.76	3.21
Weight of titanium in sample, g	0.62	0.549	1.57	1.06	1.92

Show that these results are in agreement with the law of constant composition.

2.5 Balance the following equations:

(a) $CaCl_2 + Fe_2(SO_4)_3 \rightarrow CaSO_4 + FeCl_3$

(b) $KClO_3 \rightarrow KCl + KClO_4$

(c) $Ca_3(PO_4)_2 + H_2SO_4 \rightarrow H_3PO_4 + CaSO_4$

(d) $C_{12}H_{22}O_{11} + O_2 \rightarrow CO_2 + H_2O$

(e) $Al_2(SO_4)_3 + Ba(NO_3)_2 \rightarrow Al(NO_3)_3 + BaSO_4$

(f) $(NH_4)_2SO_4 + Ca(OH)_2 \rightarrow NH_3 + H_2O + CaSO_4$

(g) $BaCl_2 + (NH_4)_2CO_3 \rightarrow BaCO_3 + NH_4Cl$

(h) $Al_2(SO_3)_3 + HCl \rightarrow AlCl_3 + H_2O + SO_2$

(i) $CuO + H_3PO_4 \rightarrow Cu_3(PO_4)_2 + H_2O$

(j) $Na_2O_2 + H_2O \rightarrow NaOH + O_2$

2.6 Using the data given in problem 2.4, calculate the equivalent weight of titanium in the oxide.

2.7 A 0.8643-g sample of magnesium yields 3.385 g of the chloride. Calculate the equivalent weight of magnesium.

2.8 Nitrogen forms a series of oxides which contain 25.9%, 30.4%, 36.9%, 46.7%, and 63.7% nitrogen, respectively. What is the equivalent weight of nitrogen in each of the oxides?

2.9 A 5.00-g sample of an element releases 10.7 cal of heat in cooling from 60° to 40°C. Oxidation of 0.328 g of the metal produces 0.469 g of the oxide. Calculate the *exact* atomic weight of the metal and its valence in the oxide.

2.10 How many moles of H_2SO_4 are present in 1.00 liter of 65.0% sulfuric acid if the density of the acid is 1.55 g/ml?

2.11 How many grams of sulfur are present in 3.65 moles of Na_2SO_4?

2.12 Calculate the percentage compositions of each of the following compounds:

(a) $Pb_3(PO_4)_2$

(b) $C_{12}H_{22}O_{11}$

(c) $NH_4Al(SO_4)_2 \cdot 12\,H_2O$

(d) $K_4Fe(CN)_6$

(e) $XePtF_6$

2.13 Which of these compounds contains the largest percentage by weight of chlorine: $KClO_3$, $NaClO_2$, Cl_2O_7, $BrCl$, or $HgCl_2$?

2.14 In the Kjeldahl method of nitrogen analysis, the nitrogen in a compound is converted to ammonia (NH_3) and determined as such. If 2.96 g of a protein yields 0.46 g of ammonia, calculate the percentage of nitrogen in the protein.

2.15 When 1.2319 g of Epsom salt (the hydrate of magnesium sulfate) is heated, water is driven off, and the anhydrous residue weighs 0.6019 g. What is the percentage of water in the hydrate?

2.16 When 3.46 g of the hydrate of sodium carbonate is heated to drive off the water of hydration, the anhydrous residue weighs 2.18 g. What is the formula of the hydrate?

2.17 Iron forms three oxides which contain 77.8%, 70.0%, and 72.5% Fe, respectively. Calculate the simplest formulas of the three oxides.

2.18 How many grams of hydrogen could be obtained by the action of zinc on 500 ml of 35.0% hydrochloric acid, which has a density of 1.20 g/ml? Equation:

$$Zn + 2\,HCl \rightarrow ZnCl_2 + H_2$$

2.19 When 2.00 g of copper powder was heated with sulfur, 2.51 g of the sulfide was formed. What is the simplest formula of the sulfide?

2.20 How many moles are represented by each of the following?
(a) 1.30 kg of Fe_2O_3
(b) 0.012 g of carbon
(c) 6.93 g of $KAl(SO_4)_2 \cdot 12\ H_2O$
(d) 30 mg of Na_3PO_4
(e) 216.3 g of NH_4NO_3

2.21 Calculate the molecular weight or formula weight of each of the following compounds:
(a) H_2SO_4
(b) $K_2Cr_2O_7$
(c) $Ca(H_2PO_4)_2 \cdot H_2O$
(d) $NaMg(UO_2)_3(C_2H_3O_2)_9 \cdot 9\ H_2O$
(e) $Co(NH_3)_6Cl_3$

2.22 Calculate the molecular formulas of the compounds which have the following percentage compositions:
(a) 92.3% C; 7.7% H; mol. wt. 78 amu
(b) 22.6% C; 6.6% H; 70.7% As; mol. wt. 106 amu
(c) 15.1% K; 10.5% Al; 24.8% S; 49.5% O; mol. wt. 258.1 amu
(d) 11.1% N; 3.18% H; 41.3% Cr; 44.5% O; mol. wt. 252 amu
(e) 25.5% Al; 29.3% P; 45.3% O; mol. wt. 106 amu

2.23 How many grams of silver chloride will be formed if 25.0 g of calcium chloride is added to an aqueous solution containing 50.0 g of silver nitrate? Equation:

$$2\ AgNO_3 + CaCl_2 \rightarrow 2\ AgCl + Ca(NO_3)_2$$

2.24 Chloropicrin, CCl_3NO_2, can be made cheaply for use as an insecticide by a process which utilizes the reaction

$$CH_3NO_2 + 3\ Cl_2 \rightarrow CCl_3NO_2 + 3\ HCl$$

How much nitromethane (CH_3NO_2) is needed to prepare 50.0 kg of chloropicrin?

2.25 How many tons of aluminum chloride can be prepared according to the equation

$$Al_2O_3 + 6\ HCl \rightarrow 2\ AlCl_3 + 3\ H_2O$$

starting with 48.0 tons of bauxite ore containing 85.7% Al_2O_3 by weight?

2.26 How many tons of liquid oxygen will be needed to burn 18.6 tons of ethanol in a rocket engine according to the following equation?

$$C_2H_5OH + 3\ O_2 \rightarrow 2\ CO_2 + 3\ H_2O$$

2.27 When 12.3 g of a metal at a temperature of 99.3°C was added to a calorimeter containing 100.0 g of water at 18.6°C, the final temperature of the mixture was found to be 23.7°C. (a) Calculate the approximate atomic weight of the metal. (b) If the chloride of the metal contains 24.7% Cl, what is the valence of the metal, and what is its exact atomic weight?

2.28 Organic compounds are analyzed for chlorine by converting that element to silver chloride, which may be weighed. When 0.2849 g of DDT is analyzed, 0.5762 g of AgCl is produced. What is the percentage of Cl in the insecticide? *Ans.* 50.01%

2.29 Combustion of 0.1246 g of DDT affords 0.2165 g CO_2 and 0.0285 g H_2O. Calculate the percentage of carbon and hydrogen in DDT.

Ans. 47.42% C; 2.54% H

2.30 The molecular weight of DDT is found to be approximately 360 g/mole. From this, and the results obtained in problems 2.28 and 2.29, determine the molecular formula of the compound. *Ans.* $C_{14}H_9Cl_5$

2.31 Complete reduction of 0.2836 g of tungsten oxide yields 0.2249 g of the metal. The specific heat of tungsten is 0.034 cal/g-°C. From this information, determine the formula of the oxide. The symbol for tungsten is W.

2.32 In 1819, Dulong and Petit published the following table of specific heats:

Element	Specific Heat (cal/g)	Element	Specific Heat (cal/g)
Bi	0.0288	Te	0.0912
Pb	0.0293	Cu	0.0949
Au	0.0298	Ni	0.1035
Pt	0.0314	Fe	0.1100
Sn	0.0514	Co	0.1498
Ag	0.0557	S	0.1880
Zn	0.0927		

From these data, and the atomic weights of the elements given in the table printed inside the back cover of the text, calculate an average value for Dulong and Petit's constant. Two of the specific heat values given by Dulong and Petit are incorrect. Which are they?

. . . Turn thy mind the more unto these bodies
Which are here witnessed tumbling in the light:
Namely, because such tumblings are a sign
That motions also of the primal stuff
Secret and viewless lurk beneath, behind.

Lo, all their shifting movement is of old
From the primeval atoms . . .

—Lucretius, *Of the Nature of Things*, 58 B.C.*

3

THE GASEOUS STATE

The term "gas" was coined by Johann Baptista van Helmont (1579–1644), who is supposed to have derived it from the Greek word *chaos*. If this supposition is correct, the term is an apt one, for the molecules of a gas are indeed in a state of constant, chaotic motion. This was recognized long ago by Lucretius, who saw in the jiggling of dust motes in the air a reflection of similar motion on the part of the air molecules. Nineteen centuries elapsed before this idea became incorporated into what is now known as the kinetic molecular theory of matter.

Gas Pressure 3.1

A liquid will rise in a tube against the pull of gravity if suction is applied to the top of the tube. A medicine dropper, a soda straw, and an old-fashioned hand pump all operate on this principle. According to Aristotle, "Nature abhors a vacuum," and thus the liquid is obliged to rise and fill the evacuated space. This "explanation" sufficed for a long time until Galileo pointed out what well-diggers undoubtedly already knew: nature's

* From the translation by William Ellery Leonard, a Dutton Everyman Paperback, E. P. Dutton & Co., Inc., New York, 1957. By permission of the publishers.

abhorrence does not extend much beyond 30 ft, which is about as high as suction can raise a column of water. We realize now that a liquid is not *pulled* up a tube by suction, but rather is *pushed* up by the pressure of the atmosphere. Although we are not usually conscious of it, the atmosphere presses down on all surfaces with considerable force. This force amounts to a pressure of about 14.7 lb/in.^{2} at sea level. If the air is removed from a tube dipping below the surface of a liquid, atmospheric pressure outside the tube is no longer balanced by any corresponding pressure inside, and the liquid is forced upwards (Fig. 3.1). The column of liquid will rise only until its weight per unit area, or pressure* at the base of the column

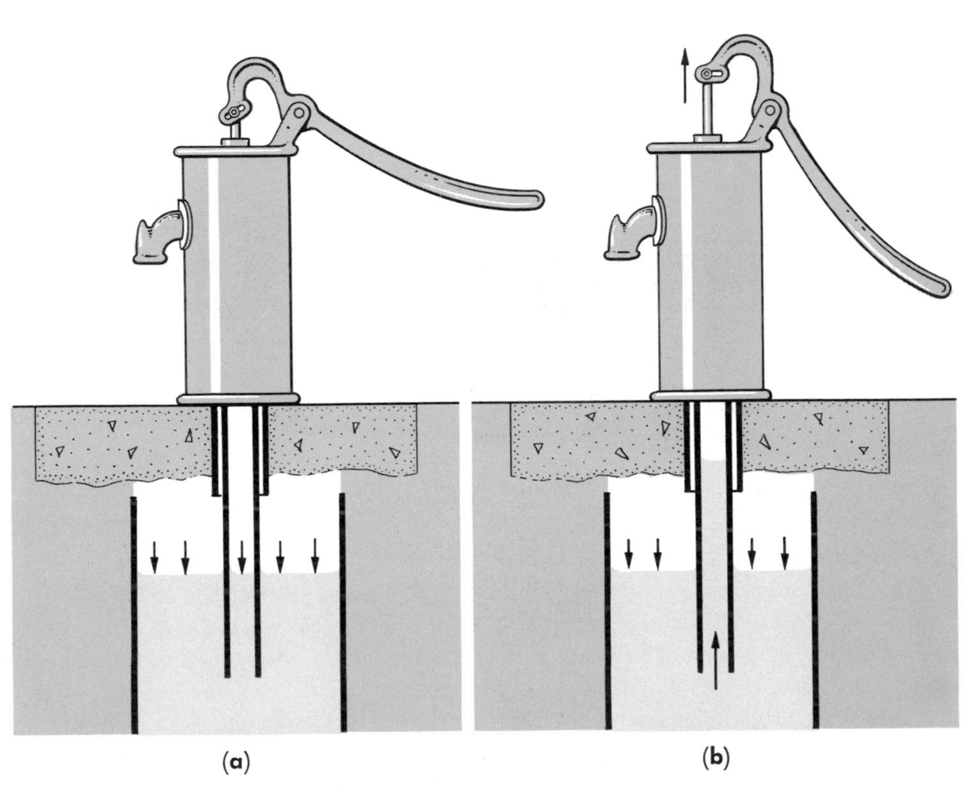

Fig. 3.1 Hand pump. (a) With the pipe filled with air, the atmosphere presses equally on all surfaces of the water. (b) When air is removed from the pipe, the water rises under the pressure of the atmosphere.

is equal to that of the atmosphere. The greater the density of the liquid, the smaller the height to which it will rise. For example, the atmosphere at sea level will support a column of water (d = 1.0 g/ml) a little over 10 m in height, but a column of mercury (d = 13.6 g/ml) only 10/13.6 = 0.76 m tall.

* Recall (Sec. 1.4) that the weight of an object is the product of its mass times gravitational acceleration and is therefore a force. Pressure, by definition, is the force per unit area.

Atmospheric pressure is measured by means of a ***barometer.*** The mercury barometer (Fig. 3.2) devised in 1644 by Evangelista Torricelli, a student of Galileo, consists of a glass tube, filled with mercury and inverted,

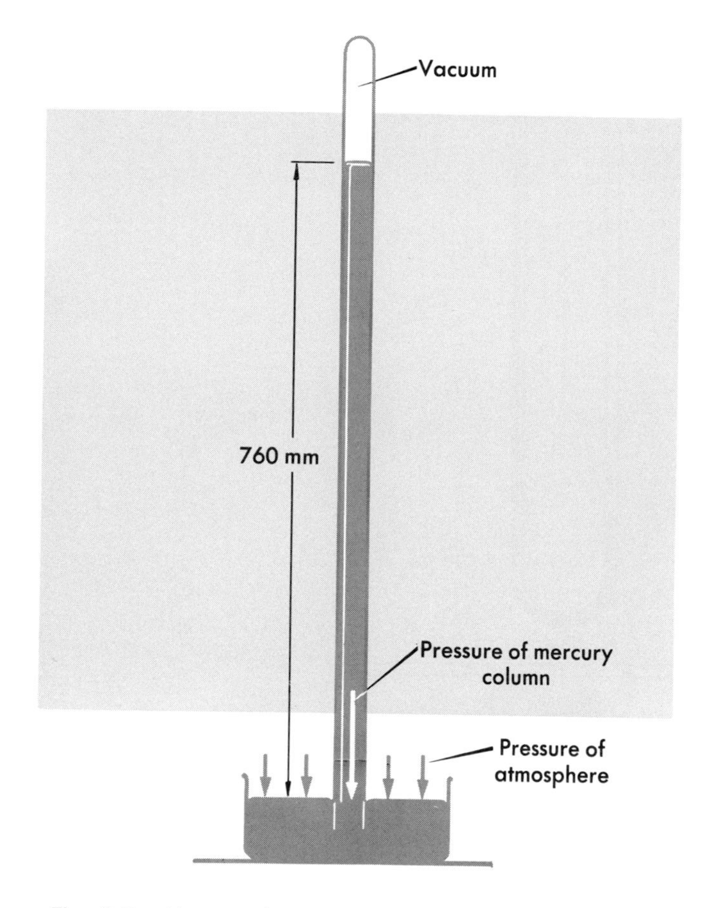

Fig. 3.2 Mercury barometer at a pressure of 1 atm.

with its open end dipping into a dish of mercury. Changes in atmospheric pressure cause the liquid level in the tube to rise and fall so that the pressure exerted by the column of mercury is always equal to the pressure of the atmosphere on the surface of the mercury in the dish. Pressure is commonly expressed either in torricellis or in atmospheres. *One* ***torricelli,*** (abbreviated ***torr***) is defined as *the pressure exerted by a column of mercury 1 mm in height, at 0°C and standard gravity. A pressure of 760 torr is equivalent to one standard* ***atmosphere*** (abbreviated ***atm***).

It is a characteristic of all gases that they exert pressure. An enclosed sample of a gas exerts this pressure equally in all directions against the inner surface of its container. Gas pressure may be measured with a ***manometer,*** which in its simplest form is a mercury barometer modified for attachment to the apparatus (Fig. 3.3). Also characteristic of a gas, and distinguishing

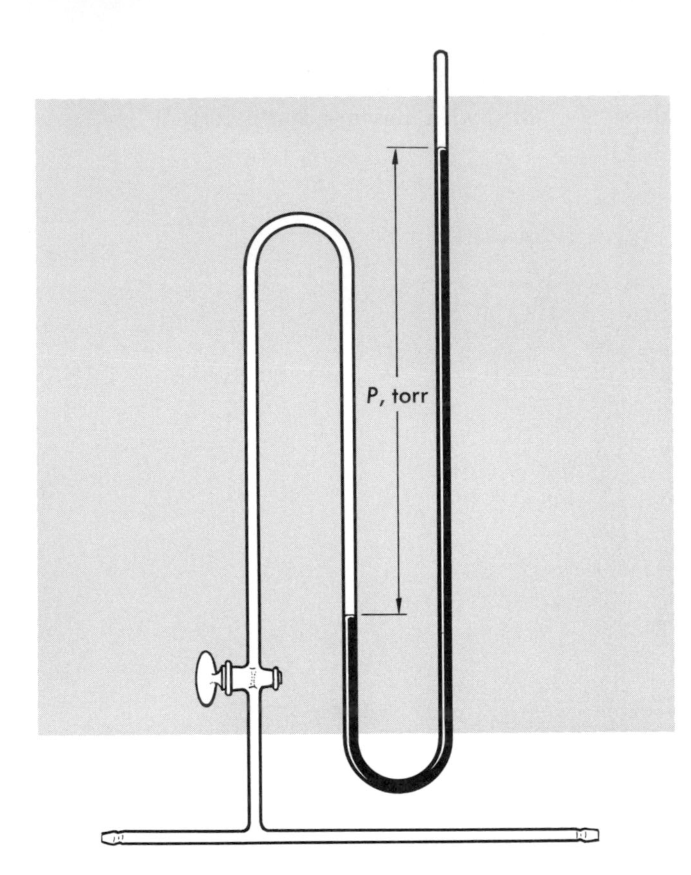

Fig. 3.3 Mercury manometer.

it from a solid or liquid, is its tendency to fill completely any container in which it is confined. There may be a half-filled bottle of milk in the refrigerator, but a half-filled bottle of oxygen gas is an impossibility. As oxygen is removed from the bottle, the remaining gas expands of its own accord in order to occupy the entire volume. A gas may also be compressed, or forced into a smaller space. As anyone knows who has ever pumped up a tire by hand, compressing a gas requires work to overcome the pressure of the gas and its natural tendency to expand.

3.2 Boyle's Law

Compressing a gas into a smaller volume causes its pressure to rise. Conversely, expansion of the gas is accompanied by a decrease in pressure. The relationship between the pressure and volume of a gas was first determined quantitatively in 1660 by Robert Boyle, who found that, provided the temperature remains unchanged, the volume of a given mass of gas is inversely proportional to the pressure exerted upon it. Doubling the pressure on the gas, for example, will reduce its volume to one-half what it was originally.

The proportionality between the pressure and volume of a gas may be expressed as follows:

$$V \propto \frac{1}{P}$$

Introducing a proportionality constant, k,* converts this expression into an equation:

$$V = \frac{k}{P}$$

or

$$PV = k$$

Boyle's law can therefore be expressed as follows: *For a given sample of gas at constant temperature, the product of the pressure of the gas and its volume will always have the same value.* The actual value of k will, of course, be different for each sample of gas taken. If either the pressure or the volume of a gas sample is changed, the other factor must change in proportion so that

$$P_1V_1 = P_2V_2 = P_3V_3 = P_nV_n = k$$

The apparatus shown in Fig. 3.4 can be used to demonstrate Boyle's law. With the mercury level the same in both the closed and open legs of the U-tube, the pressure on the gas sample is equal to that of the atmosphere. When mercury is added, raising the level in the open tube, the pressure on the gas is increased by an amount equal to the pressure of the added column of mercury. This added pressure causes a proportionate decrease in the volume of the gas, and the product PV remains constant. Removing mercury causes the level in the open tube to fall below that in the closed part of the apparatus. The pressure of the atmosphere on the surface of the mercury in the open tube is now balanced by the additional height of mercury in the closed tube as well as by the gas pressure. The pressure on the gas sample is therefore less than atmospheric. The gas expands, and PV has the same value as before.

The practical application of Boyle's law is illustrated by the following examples:

Example 3.1

A tank of helium contains 150 liters of gas at a pressure of 110 atm. What volume would the gas occupy at 1.00 atm, assuming the temperature remains unchanged?

Solution: Let P_1 and V_1 represent the initial pressure and volume, 110 atm and 150 liters, respectively. P_2 is then the final pressure, 1.00 atm, and V_2 the final volume. Then

$$P_1V_1 = k = P_2V_2$$

$$V_2 = \frac{P_1V_1}{P_2} = \frac{110 \text{ atm} \times 150 \text{ liters}}{1.00 \text{ atm}}$$

$$V_2 = 1.65 \times 10^4 \text{ liters}$$

* To illustrate what is meant by a proportionality constant, consider a family's milk bill, which is proportional to the number of quarts of milk consumed:

Size of bill $\propto$ number of quarts consumed.

The exact amount of the bill is equal to the number of quarts multiplied by the price per quart. If we represent the price of a quart of milk by k, then

Size of bill = k (number of quarts consumed).

The price per quart, k, is the *proportionality constant* in this equation.

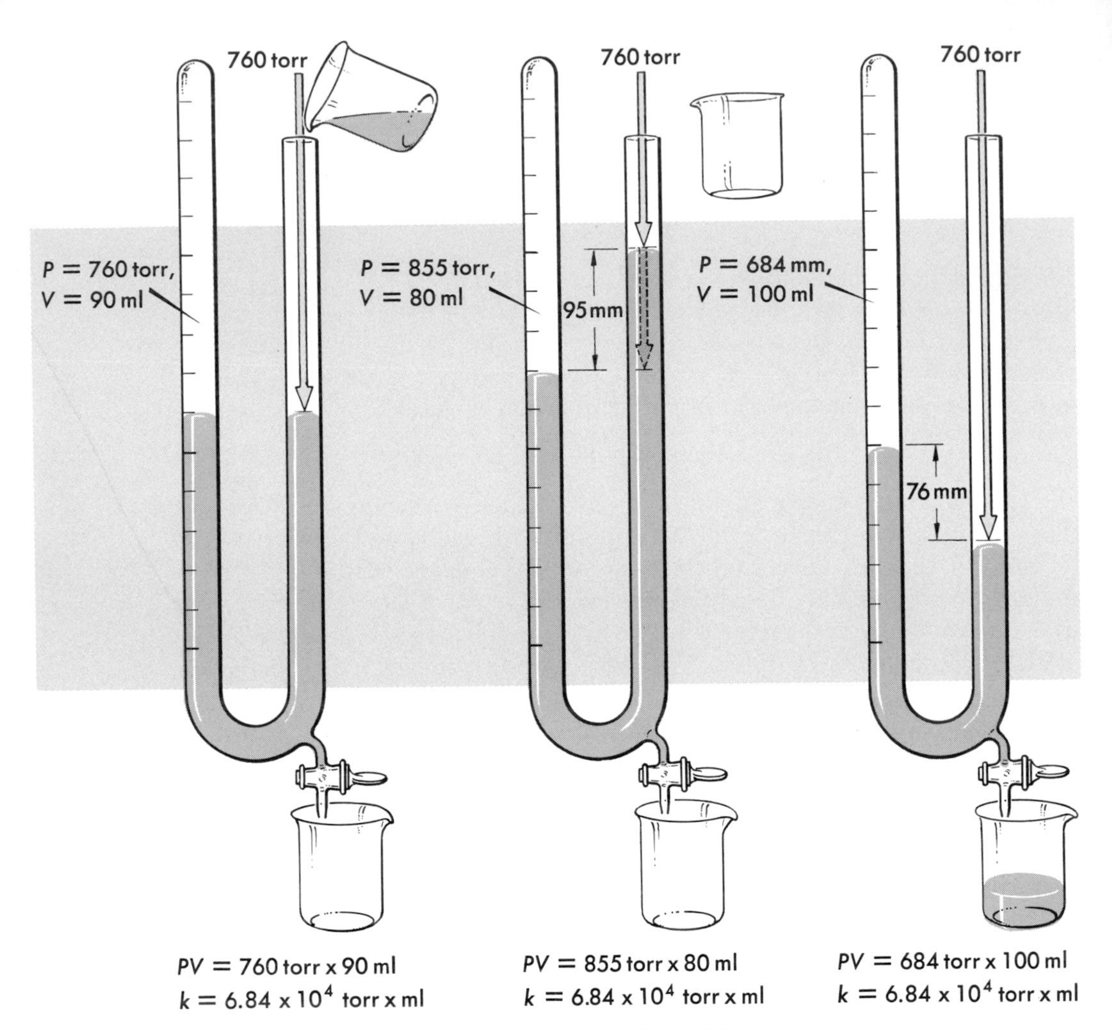

Fig. 3.4 Demonstration of Boyle's law.

Example 3.2

If it takes 5 liters of gas to inflate a toy balloon to a pressure of 2.00 atm, how many balloons can be inflated using the tank of helium from Example 3.1?

Solution: The final pressure P_2 in this case is 2.00 atm. At that pressure, the total volume of the helium will be

$$V_2 = \frac{110 \text{ atm} \times 150 \text{ liters}}{2.00 \text{ atm}}$$

$$V_2 = 8250 \text{ liters}$$

During the process of filling the balloons, the tank cannot be totally evacuated, nor can its pressure fall below that of the gas in the inflated balloon. When the last balloon is filled, therefore, 150 liters of gas must still remain in the tank under a pressure of at least 2 atm. The total volume of helium at 2 atm pressure available for filling balloons is then

$$8250 - 150 = 8100 \text{ liters}$$

Since each balloon requires 5 liters of helium at 2 atm, the total number of balloons that can be inflated to that pressure is

$$\frac{8100 \text{ liters}}{5 \text{ liters/balloon}} = 1620 \text{ balloons}$$

Charles' Law and Gay-Lussac's Law 3.3

Changes in the temperature of a gas are accompanied by changes in the pressure, volume, or both. The laws of Charles and Gay-Lussac, formulated in 1787 and 1802, respectively, relate the volume and pressure of a gas to its temperature. Nearly all substances characteristically expand when heated and contract when cooled. Gases are no exception. Jacques Alexander César Charles observed that if the pressure of a quantity of gas were main-

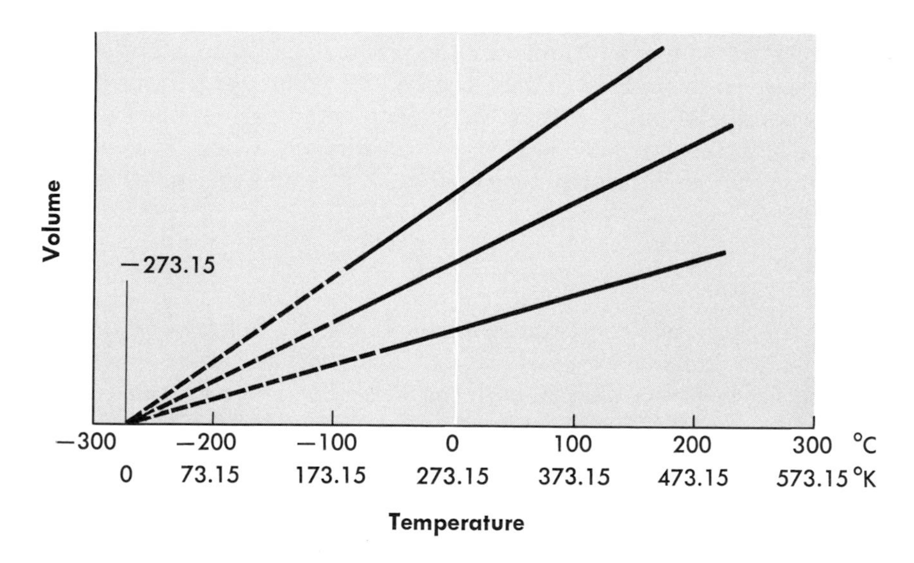

Fig. 3.5 Volume of a gas as a function of temperature. Data are plotted for three different samples of gas.

tained constant and its temperature varied, the change in the volume of the gas was related directly to the change in temperature. A plot of gas volume as a function of temperature at constant pressure is a straight line. Data for three different samples of gas are plotted in Fig. 3.5. The volume in each case is seen to vary linearly with temperature, decreasing regularly as the temperature is lowered. The results are the same whether the samples taken are of the same gas or of different gases, and these results do not depend on the pressure, provided that the pressure remains unchanged throughout the entire range of temperatures.* Extrapolation of the lines shows that they all intersect at −273.15°C, at which temperature each of the gas samples should have a volume of zero. At that temperature, in other words, the gas should vanish completely! There is no need to worry about such an absurd eventuality, which would contradict the law of conservation of mass, because all real gases liquefy before that temperature is reached, and a liquid is under no obligation to obey the laws pertaining to gases. Nevertheless, −273.15°C does appear to be an ***absolute zero,*** or *minimum of temperature* below which one cannot go.

From analytical geometry you will recall that the equation for a straight line is

$$y = mx + b$$

where m is the slope of the line and b the intercept on the y-axis when $x = 0$. In Fig. 3.5 the volume is plotted on the y-axis, temperature on the x-axis, giving

$$V = mt + b$$

The volume of a given sample of gas at constant pressure is therefore directly proportional to the temperature, with the proportionality constant equal to m. If t is given in degrees Celsius, then b, the volume at 0°C, is different for every sample of gas and must be experimentally determined in every case. If, however, we take −273.15°C as zero on a new, *absolute scale* (*Kelvin scale*) of temperatures, then at 0°K, $b = 0$, and the equation above becomes

$$V = mT$$

Charles' law may now be expressed as follows: *At constant pressure, the volume of a gas is directly proportional to its absolute, or Kelvin, temperature.* The same size degree is used on both the Celsius and Kelvin scales, so that 0°C becomes 273.15°K, and in general, °K = °C + 273.15. Provided that the volume of a gas sample is known at one temperature, the volume it would occupy under the same pressure at a different temperature can be calculated from the relationship,

$$\frac{V_1}{T_1} = \frac{V_2}{T_2} = \frac{V_3}{T_3} = \frac{V_n}{T_n} = m$$

Example 3.3

A sample of gas occupies a volume of 500 ml at 30.0°C. What will its volume be at 100°C, assuming no change in pressure?

Solution: Since the gas is being heated, its volume will increase in proportion to the change in its absolute temperature. Its initial temperature T_1 is equal to (30.0 + 273) = 303°K; its final temperature T_2 is (100 + 273) = 373°K. Therefore,

* At very high pressures the plot may deviate appreciably from a straight line. This is discussed more fully in Sec. 9.1.

applying the Charles' law relationships,

$$\frac{V_1}{T_1} = m = \frac{V_2}{T_2}$$

$$V_2 = \frac{V_1T_2}{T_1} = \frac{(500 \text{ ml})(373°\text{K})}{(303°\text{K})}$$

$$V_2 = 615 \text{ ml}$$

Joseph Louis Gay-Lussac found that if a gas is confined in a fixed volume, its pressure varies directly with the temperature, that is, *at constant volume, the pressure of a gas is directly proportional to its absolute, or Kelvin, temperature.* Gay-Lussac's law may be expressed mathematically as follows:

$$\frac{P_1}{T_1} = \frac{P_2}{T_2} = \frac{P_3}{T_3} = \frac{P_n}{T_n} = k$$

Example 3.4

A tank containing 5.00 liters of nitrogen at 75.0 atm pressure and 28.0°C is left standing in the sunlight, and its temperature rises to 50.0°C. What is the final pressure of the gas in the tank?

Solution: Because the gas is in a closed container, its volume is fixed. As the gas is heated, then, according to Gay-Lussac's law, its pressure will rise in proportion to the rise in its absolute temperature. The initial temperature T_1 is 273 + 28.0 = 301°K; the final temperature T_2 is 273 + 50.0 = 323°K.

$$\frac{P_1}{T_1} = k = \frac{P_2}{T_2}$$

$$P_2 = \frac{P_1T_2}{T_1} = \frac{(75.0 \text{ atm})(323°\text{K})}{(301°\text{K})}$$

$$P_2 = 80.5 \text{ atm}$$

Combined Gas Law Equation 3.4

The pressure, volume, and temperature of a given sample of gas are dependent variables. A change in any one of the three will affect either or both of the remaining ones, and once any two are specified, the value of the third is automatically fixed. We will therefore find it convenient to derive an expression combining Boyle's, Charles', and Gay-Lussac's laws into a single equation showing the relationship among these variables. This equation can then be used to calculate the new volume occupied by a given quantity of gas after a simultaneous change in both pressure and temperature.

Assume that we have a sample of gas whose pressure, volume, and Kelvin temperature are P_1, V_1, and T_1, respectively. If the temperature is kept constant while the pressure is changed from P_1 to P_2, the new volume V_x can be calculated from Boyle's law as follows:

$$P_1V_1 = P_2V_x$$

$$V_x = \frac{P_1V_1}{P_2}$$

If the temperature is now changed from the initial value T_1 to the final temperature T_2, keeping the pressure of the gas at P_2, then by Charles' law,

$$\frac{V_x}{T_1} = \frac{V_2}{T_2}$$

and

$$V_x = \frac{V_2 T_1}{T_2}$$

where V_2 is the volume at P_2 and T_2. Equating the two values for V_x obtained above gives

$$\frac{P_1 V_1}{P_2} = \frac{V_2 T_1}{T_2}$$

and this, by rearrangement of terms, collecting all initial conditions on one side of the equation and all final conditions on the other, gives the combined gas law equation:

$$\frac{P_1 V_1}{T_1} = \frac{P_2 V_2}{T_2}$$

Example 3.5

A gas occupies a volume of 2.75 liters at 87.0°C and 150 torr. What volume will the same sample of gas occupy at 25.0°C and 745 torr?

Solution:

$$\frac{(150 \text{ torr})(2.75 \text{ liters})}{(87.0 + 273)°\text{K}} = \frac{(745 \text{ torr})(V_2)}{(25.0 + 273)°\text{K}}$$

$$V_2 = \frac{(150 \text{ torr})(2.75 \text{ liters})(298°\text{K})}{(745 \text{ torr})(360°\text{K})}$$

$$V_2 = 0.458 \text{ liters}$$

3.5 Dalton's Law of Partial Pressures

So long as no chemical reactions take place among them, all gases mix perfectly with one another in any proportions, and a mixture of gases obeys Boyle's, Charles', and Gay-Lussac's laws in the same manner as a pure gas. Each gas in a mixture of gases behaves independently of the others and exerts the same pressure that it would if it were entirely alone in the same total volume. *The pressure which the gas would exert if it occupied the volume by itself* is the ***partial pressure*** of the gas. *The total pressure of a mixture of gases is equal to the sum of the partial pressures of each of the gases in the mixture.* This law, formulated by Dalton in 1802, can be written as follows:

$$P_{\text{total}} = p_1 + p_2 + p_3 + \cdots p_n,$$

where p_1, p_2, p_3, . . . and p_n represent the partial pressures of the various gases in the mixture.

Suppose that we have two glass vessels separated by a stopcock (Fig. 3.6). One vessel has a volume of 5 liters and contains nitrogen at a pressure of

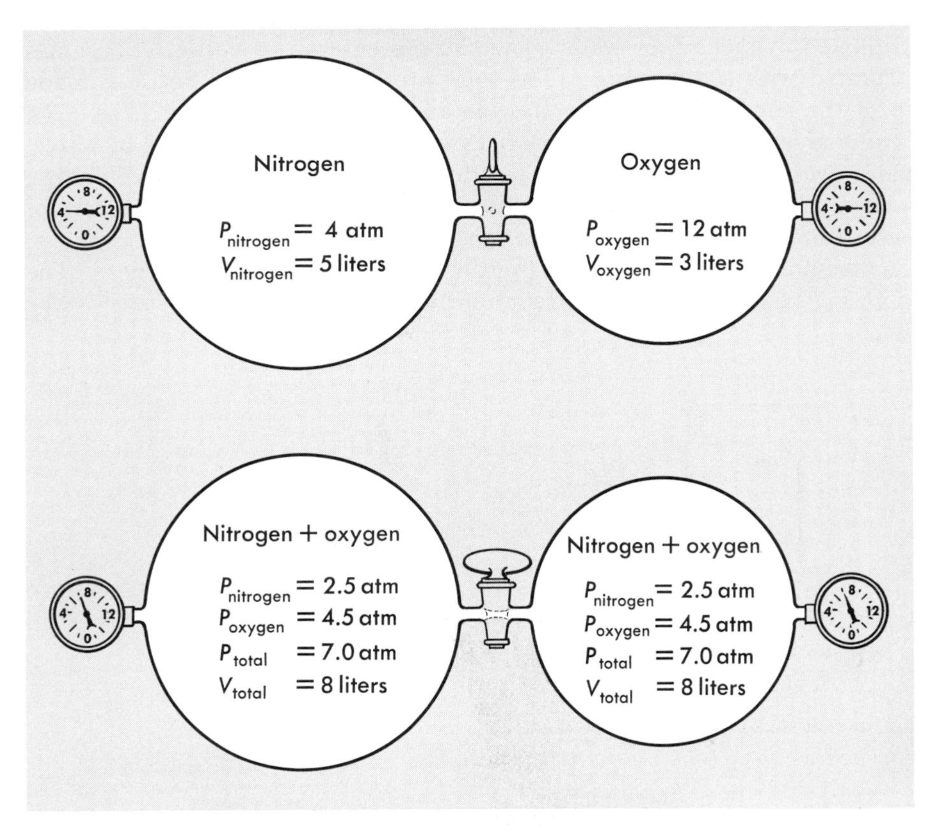

Fig. 3.6 Dalton's law of partial pressures.

4 atm. The other holds 3 liters of oxygen at 12 atm pressure. When the stopcock is opened and the two vessels are connected, the final pressure is found to be 7 atm. Opening the stopcock allows each gas to expand from its initial volume to fill the total volume of 8 liters. The final pressure may be calculated from Boyle's and Dalton's laws as follows:

Partial pressure of nitrogen after mixing:

$$\begin{aligned}(p_{N_2\,\mathrm{final}})(V_{N_2\,\mathrm{final}}) &= (p_{N_2\,\mathrm{initial}})(V_{N_2\,\mathrm{initial}})\\(p_{N_2\,\mathrm{final}})(8\ \mathrm{liters}) &= (4\ \mathrm{atm})(5\ \mathrm{liters})\\(p_{N_2\,\mathrm{final}}) &= 2.5\ \mathrm{atm}\end{aligned}$$

Partial pressure of oxygen after mixing:

$$\begin{aligned}(p_{O_2\,\mathrm{final}})(V_{O_2\,\mathrm{final}}) &= (p_{O_2\,\mathrm{initial}})(V_{O_2\,\mathrm{initial}})\\(p_{O_2\,\mathrm{final}})(8\ \mathrm{liters}) &= (12\ \mathrm{atm})(3\ \mathrm{liters})\\(p_{O_2\,\mathrm{final}}) &= 4.5\ \mathrm{atm}\end{aligned}$$

Total pressure of gas mixture:

$$\begin{aligned}P_{\mathrm{total}} &= p_{N_2\,\mathrm{final}} + p_{O_2\,\mathrm{final}}\\P_{\mathrm{total}} &= 2.5\ \mathrm{atm} + 4.5\ \mathrm{atm} = 7\ \mathrm{atm}\end{aligned}$$

Gases prepared in the laboratory are frequently collected in a bottle or graduated cylinder over water. As the gas enters the bottle, it becomes saturated with water vapor. The total pressure inside the bottle is made up of the partial pressures of the gas and of the water vapor (Fig. 3.7). At any given temperature the partial pressure, or ***vapor pressure*** of water, has a definite value which may be found by consulting published tables, such as that given in the Appendix. Subtracting the vapor pressure of water from the total pressure gives the partial pressure of the gas, that is, the pressure which the gas would exert if it were alone in the container. The following example illustrates this application of Dalton's law.

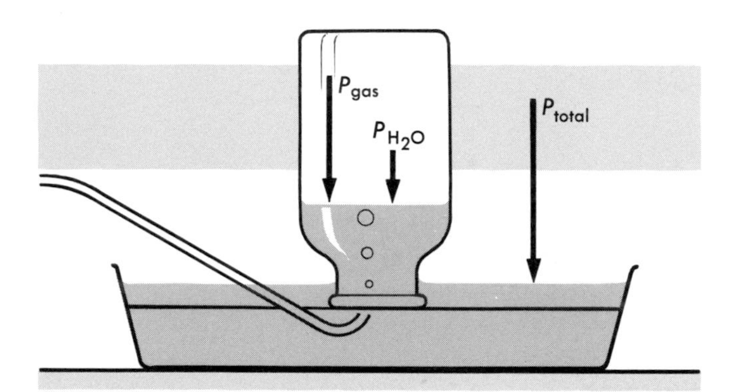

Fig. 3.7 Collecting a gas over water.

Example 3.6

A chemistry student collected 1500 ml of oxygen over water at 27.0°C and 758.0 torr pressure. What volume would the oxygen alone occupy at 0°C and 760.0 torr pressure?

Solution: The total pressure of the gas in the collecting bottle equals the sum of the partial pressures of the oxygen and the water vapor. The partial pressure of the water vapor in this case is equal to its vapor pressure. The vapor pressure of water at 27.0°C is found from the table in the Appendix to be 26.5 torr.

$$\begin{aligned} P_{\text{total}} &= p_{\text{oxygen}} + p_{\text{water}} \\ 758.0 \text{ torr} &= p_{\text{oxygen}} + 26.5 \text{ torr} \\ p_{\text{oxygen}} &= 758.0 \text{ torr} - 26.5 \text{ torr} \\ p_{\text{oxygen}} &= 731.5 \text{ torr} \end{aligned}$$

Now that the partial pressure of the oxygen is known, its volume at 0°C and 760.0 torr can be calculated using the combined gas law:

$$\frac{(731.5 \text{ torr})(1500 \text{ ml})}{(273 + 27)°\text{K}} = \frac{(760 \text{ torr})(V)}{(273 + 0)°\text{K}}$$

$$V = 1315 \text{ ml}$$

Where the partial pressure of a gas saturated with vapor is known or can be calculated, it is possible to determine the vapor pressure, as in the following example.

Example 3.7

Two hundred milliliters of dry air, measured at 740 torr pressure and 25.0°C, is bubbled through ethyl alcohol in a gas-washing bottle, becoming saturated with alcohol vapor in the process. The volume of the gas leaving the wash bottle, measured at the same temperature and pressure, is 217 ml. Calculate the vapor pressure of ethyl alcohol at 25.0°C.

Solution: The total pressure of air and alcohol vapor is equal to the sum of the two partial pressures. Since the temperature is unchanged, the partial pressure of air in the mixture is given by Boyle's law:

$$(740 \text{ torr})(200 \text{ ml}) = (p_{\text{air}})(217 \text{ ml})$$
$$p_{\text{air}} = 682 \text{ torr}$$

The partial pressure of ethyl alcohol in the mixture is then

$$740 \text{ torr} - 682 \text{ torr} = 58 \text{ torr}$$

The vapor pressure of alcohol at 25°C is therefore 58 torr.

The Law of Combining Volumes and Avogadro's Principle 3.6

Joseph Louis Gay-Lussac observed in the course of his study of the behavior of gases that, provided all measurements are made under the same conditions of pressure and temperature, *in any chemical reaction involving gases, the relative volumes of all gases used or produced in the reaction can be expressed as a ratio of whole numbers.* Thus, 200 ml of hydrogen gas reacts with 100 ml of oxygen gas producing 200 ml of water vapor, a ratio of 2:1:2. Equal volumes of hydrogen chloride and ammonia combine to form solid ammonium chloride. One gram of carbon reacts with 1.87 liters of carbon dioxide to yield 3.74 liters of carbon monoxide, both gases being measured at 0°C and 1 atm.

Since atoms are indivisible in ordinary chemical reactions, they must combine in whole number ratios. That is, one atom of one element may combine with one, two, or three, but not with $1\frac{1}{2}$ or $6\frac{7}{8}$ atoms of another. This being the case, one would expect the volume relationships observed by Gay-Lussac provided that *equal volumes of all gases under the same conditions contain the same number of molecules.*

This hypothesis, first proposed by Amadeo Avogadro in 1811, has several important, and at first unexpected, consequences. Gay-Lussac had observed that two volumes of hydrogen combine with one volume of oxygen to form two volumes of water vapor. The smallest possible volume of any gas is that containing one molecule of the gas. Since each water molecule must contain at least one atom of oxygen, in two volumes of water vapor, each containing one molecule, there must be at least two atoms of oxygen. For these to come from one volume of oxygen, each oxygen molecule must consist of at least two atoms. Reasoning in the same fashion we can conclude that since one volume of hydrogen and one volume of chlorine gas give two volumes of hydrogen chloride gas, hydrogen and chlorine molecules must also contain at least two atoms apiece. If hydrogen and oxygen molecules are diatomic, that is, if their formulas are H_2 and O_2

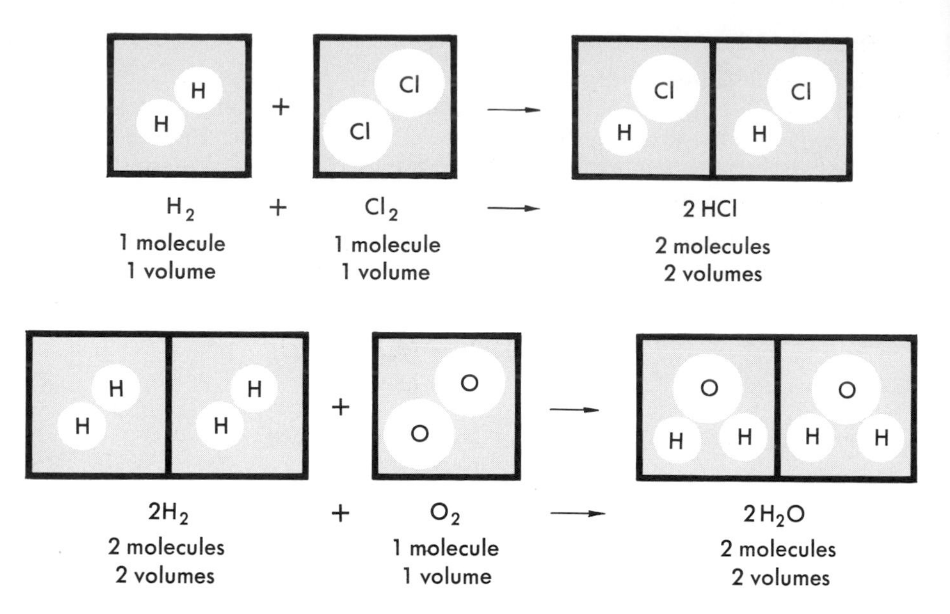

Fig. 3.8 Combining volumes.

respectively, then the water molecule must be H_2O (Fig. 3.8). Oxygen, with an equivalent weight of 8, must then have an atomic weight of 16.

At this point, although we know that the molecules of these gases must each contain at least two atoms, we lack any proof that they are in fact diatomic. The same combining volumes will be obtained if the number of atoms per molecule is 4, 6, 8, or any even number. Thus, if hydrogen should be H_4 and oxygen O_6, then the equation for the formation of water would be

$$\underset{\text{2 volumes}}{2\,H_4} + \underset{\text{1 volume}}{O_6} \rightarrow \underset{\text{2 volumes}}{2\,H_4O_3}$$

giving the observed volume ratio.

Among the gaseous elements, nitrogen and fluorine, as well as hydrogen, oxygen, and chlorine, exist in the form of diatomic molecules. Proof of this came with the determination of the correct atomic and molecular weights of these elements, something which the application of Avogadro's principle made possible, as we shall see in the next section. Bromine (liquid at room temperature) and iodine (solid) are also diatomic, but molecules of the noble gases (**He**, **Ne**, **Ar**, **Kr**, **Xe**, and **Rn**) consist of single atoms.

3.7 Molar Volume and Molecular Weight Determination

Turin, where Avogadro was professor of mathematical physics, was outside the mainstream of scientific activity in 1811, and it remained for one of his countrymen, Stanislao Cannizzaro, to point out the full significance of Avogadro's principle some 49 years after it had first been expressed.

It was pointed out in Chapter 2 (Sec. 2.7) that a mole of one substance must contain the same number of molecules as a mole of any other. If the substance is gaseous, this number of molecules will occupy a definite volume which should be the same for any gas under the same conditions of temperature and pressure. This means that at a given temperature and pressure, the volume is directly proportional to the number of moles of gas present. By calculating all volumes at a chosen set of standard conditions, one can compare relative molar quantities of various gases directly on the basis of their volumes. ***Standard conditions,*** often abbreviated STP for Standard Temperature and Pressure, are defined as

$$273°\text{K } (0°\text{C}) \text{ and } 1 \text{ atm pressure } (760 \text{ torr})$$

At standard conditions, one mole of a gas is found to occupy a volume of about 22.4 liters or 22,400 ml. Hence, if the volume occupied by a given mass of gas is known, the molecular weight of the gas may be readily calculated. The following example will show how this might be done.

Example 3.8

A 0.375 g sample of benzene vapor occupies a volume of 149 ml, measured at 95.0°C and 740 torr. Calculate the molecular weight of benzene.

Solution: The first step is to calculate the volume which would be occupied by 0.375 g of benzene at standard conditions:

$$\frac{(740 \text{ torr})(149 \text{ ml})}{(273 + 95.0)°\text{K}} = \frac{(760 \text{ torr})(V)}{273°\text{K}}$$

$$V = \frac{(149 \text{ ml})(740 \text{ torr})(273°\text{K})}{(760 \text{ torr})(368°\text{K})}$$

$$V = 108 \text{ ml}$$

One mole of benzene would occupy a volume of 22,400 ml at STP. Our 0.375 g sample is therefore 108/22,400 mole, and the molecular weight of benzene is

$$\frac{(0.375 \text{ g})(22{,}400 \text{ ml/mole})}{(108 \text{ ml})} = 77.8 \text{ g/mole}$$

Molecular weights obtained in this way, although usually within a few percent of the exact value, are nevertheless approximate, because real gases and vapors do not obey Boyle's and Charles' laws with absolute exactitude. This will be discussed more fully in Chapter 9.

Determination of Atomic Weights—Cannizzaro's Method 3.8

If one takes a large number of compounds of a given element, it is reasonable to expect that at least one of those compounds will contain just one atom of that element per molecule. If the compounds are volatile, their molecular weights can be determined in the same way that we determined the molecular weight of benzene in Example 3.8. The percentage of the element in question that is present in each of the compounds is obtained by chemical analysis. The product obtained by multiplying this percentage by the molecular weight in each case equals the number of grams of the element in one mole of the compound. This can never be less than the mass of Avogadro's number, one mole, of atoms of the element, since there must be at least one such atom in each molecule of the compound. In addition, because each molecule must contain a whole number of atoms of the element, the mass of that element in one mole of each of its compounds must always be some whole-number multiple of the mass of one mole of its atoms. The determination of the atomic weight of carbon will serve to illustrate this line of reasoning.

TABLE 3.1 Atomic Weight of Carbon

Carbon Compound	Mass of 22.4 liters at STP	% Carbon in Compound	Mass of Carbon in 1 Mole of Compound
Oxide I	28.1 g	42.8	12.0 g
Oxide II	44.2 g	27.1	12.1 g
Benzene	77.8 g	92.3	71.8 g
Ethylene	27.9 g	85.5	23.9 g
Ethyl alcohol	46.4 g	52.3	24.2 g
Chloroform	120.2 g	10.0	12.0 g

An examination of the experimental data given in Table 3.1 will show that the smallest mass of carbon in one mole of any of the compounds analyzed is about 12 g, and the masses of carbon in the other compounds are integral multiples of 12. It is reasonably safe to assume, then, that the mass of one mole of carbon atoms is approximately 12 g, and the atomic weight of carbon is about 12 amu. The experimentally determined equivalent weight of carbon is 6.0056 g in oxide I and 3.0028 g in oxide II. The valence (Sec. 2.5) of carbon in the two oxides is therefore $(12\ g/6.0056\ g) = 2$, and $(12\ g/3.0028\ g) = 4$, respectively. This leads to the formulas **CO** for oxide I, and **CO_2** for oxide II. Multiplying each equivalent weight by the appropriate valence gives the exact mass of one mole of carbon atoms: $6.0056\ g \times 2 = 12.0112\ g$; $3.0028\ g \times 4 = 12.0112\ g$. The exact atomic weight of carbon therefore is 12.0112 amu.

The great value of Cannizzaro's method lay in the fact that it made it possible for the first time to determine the correct atomic weights of just those elements, such as carbon, which do not obey the law of Dulong and Petit. Fortunately, these same elements all form large numbers of volatile compounds. The availability, after 1860, of the correct atomic weights of these elements was directly responsible, a few years later, for the discovery of the periodic law, which is the subject of the next chapter. Knowledge of the correct atomic weight and valence of carbon cleared up most of the confusion regarding molecular formulas of carbon compounds, which up to then had retarded the growth of organic chemistry.

At this point one may retain some mental reservations about the validity of Cannizzaro's method, based as it is on the unproved assumption that the molecules of at least one of the compounds being analyzed contain only one atom each of the element whose atomic weight is to be determined. The more compounds are examined, however, the safer this assumption becomes. Subsequent determinations of the atomic weights of these elements using the mass spectrograph (Sec. 6.5) have confirmed the values obtained by using Cannizzaro's method.

The Universal Gas Constant 3.9

The combined gas-law equation (Sec. 3.4) may be expressed as follows:

$$\frac{PV}{T} = \text{constant}$$

Introducing the molar volume at standard conditions into this expression allows us to evaluate the constant for one mole of any gas:

$$\frac{(1.00 \text{ atm})(22.4 \text{ liters/mole})}{273°\text{K}} = 0.0820 \text{ liter-atm/°K-mole}$$

This constant, for which the symbol R is used, is known as the ***universal gas constant***. We can now write, for one mole of any gas,

$$PV = RT$$

and for n moles of gas,

$$PV = nRT$$

For n we may substitute g/M, where g represents the mass of the gas sample and M its molecular weight, and the expression becomes

$$PV = \left(\frac{\text{g}}{M}\right) RT$$

This form of the combined gas law equation is especially convenient for calculating the volume which will be occupied by a given mass of gas under a given set of conditions, as well as for determining the molecular weight of a gas given its density at specified conditions. The following examples illustrate these applications. The data used in Example 3.10 are the same as in Example 3.8, and you should make it a point to compare the two methods of approaching the same solution.

Example 3.9

Calculate the volume which will be occupied by 7.00 g of nitrogen gas (N_2) at 30.0°C and 850 torr pressure.

Solution: In order to use the value for R obtained above, the pressure must first be converted from torricellis to atmospheres by dividing by 760 torr/atm. Then,

$$PV = \left(\frac{\text{g}}{M}\right) RT$$

$$\frac{(850 \text{ torr})(V)}{760 \text{ torr/atm}} = \frac{(7.00 \text{ g})(0.0820 \text{ liter-atm/°K-mole})(303°\text{K})}{28.0 \text{ g/mole}}$$

$$V = 5.55 \text{ liters}$$

Example 3.10

A 0.375 g sample of benzene vapor occupies a volume of 149 ml measured at 95.0°C and 740 torr. Calculate the molecular weight of benzene.

Solution: Again, we must be careful to have the pressure and volume expressed in the same units as the gas constant, atmospheres and liters, respectively.

$$PV = \left(\frac{g}{M}\right) RT$$

$$\frac{(740 \text{ torr})(0.149 \text{ liters})}{(760 \text{ torrs/atm})} = \frac{(0.375 \text{ g})(0.0820 \text{ liter-atm/°K-mole})(368\text{°K})}{M}$$

$$M = 78.0 \text{ g/mole}$$

The discrepancy of 0.2 g/mole between this answer and that obtained in Example 3.8 corresponds to the uncertainty of ± 1 digit in the third significant figure.

3.10 Gaseous Diffusion and Effusion—Graham's Law

If a tank of chlorine gas standing in a corner of the laboratory begins to leak, the odor of the gas soon is noticed on the other side of the room. We say that the gas has *diffused* through the atmosphere of the laboratory. All gases possess this property of ***diffusion,*** of mixing uniformly without external agitation, and all have the ability to travel from place to place as though self-propelled, which indeed they are, as we shall see.

Different gases diffuse at different rates; lighter ones, like hydrogen and helium, diffuse more rapidly than oxygen and nitrogen, for example. In 1833, Thomas Graham observed that the rate of diffusion of a gas is inversely proportional to the square root of its density. ***Effusion,*** or the passage of a gas through a pin-hole or other very small aperture, also takes place at a rate inversely proportional to the square root of the density of the gas:

$$\text{Rate of diffusion or effusion} \propto \frac{1}{\sqrt{d}}$$

From Avogadro's principle the density, or mass of a given volume of a gas is proportional to its molecular weight, so that Graham's law may also be formulated as follows:

$$\text{Rate of diffusion or effusion} = \frac{(\text{constant})}{\sqrt{M}}$$

or,

$$(\text{rate})(\sqrt{M}) = (\text{constant})$$

For two gases A and B under the same conditions of pressure and temperature,

$$(\text{rate}_A)(\sqrt{M_A}) = (\text{rate}_B)(\sqrt{M_B}),$$

and

$$\frac{\text{rate}_A}{\text{rate}_B} = \frac{\sqrt{M_B}}{\sqrt{M_A}}$$

From this relationship, one may determine the relative rates of diffusion of two gases whose molecular weights are known, or, if one knows the relative rates of diffusion of two gases, and the molecular weight of one, the molecular weight of the other may be calculated, as in the following examples.

Example 3.11

Simultaneously, a cotton plug wet with concentrated hydrochloric acid and one wet with concentrated ammonia solution are placed at opposite ends of a 100-cm glass tube (Fig. 3.9). Gaseous HCl and NH_3 diffuse along the tube in opposite directions, and where they meet they react, forming a deposit of solid NH_4Cl. At what point along the tube will the NH_4Cl be deposited?

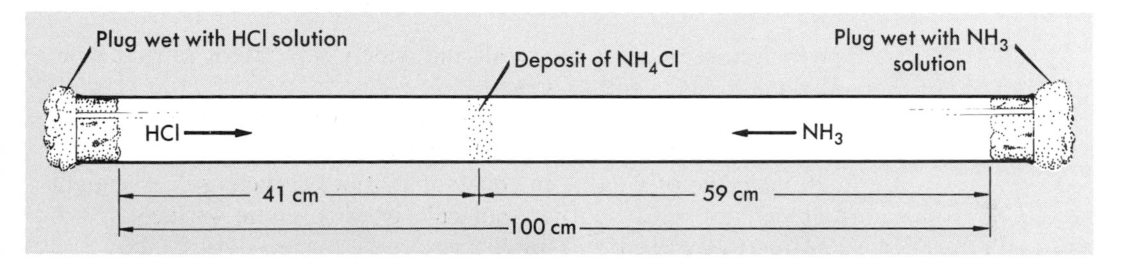

Fig. 3.9 Relative rates of diffusion.

Solution: The relative rates of diffusion of the two gases can be calculated from their molecular weights as follows:

$$\frac{\text{rate}_{NH_3}}{\text{rate}_{HCl}} = \frac{\sqrt{M_{HCl}}}{\sqrt{M_{NH_3}}} = \frac{\sqrt{36.5 \text{ amu}}}{\sqrt{17.0 \text{ amu}}} = \frac{1.44}{1}$$

From this it is seen that the ammonia diffuses along the tube at a rate 1.44 times as fast as the hydrogen chloride gas. Let x equal the distance traveled by the HCl when it encounters the NH_3; then in the same length of time the NH_3 will have traveled the distance $1.44x$. The total length of the tube is 100 cm; therefore,

$$x + 1.44x = 2.44x = 100 \text{ cm}$$
$$x = 41 \text{ cm}$$

Ammonium chloride will thus be deposited at a point in the tube 41 cm from the cotton plug wet with hydrochloric acid.

Example 3.12

It requires 28.0 sec for 10 ml of oxygen gas to pass through a certain capillary tube. At the same temperature and pressure it takes 37.6 sec for butane gas to pass through the same tube. From these data, calculate the molecular weight of butane.

Solution: The rate of effusion of a gas may be expressed in terms of the volume of the gas which effuses in a given length of time. In this instance, therefore,

$$\frac{\text{rate}_{O_2}}{\text{rate}_{\text{butane}}} = \frac{\dfrac{10 \text{ ml}}{28.0 \text{ sec}}}{\dfrac{10 \text{ ml}}{37.6 \text{ sec}}} = \frac{\sqrt{M_{\text{butane}}}}{\sqrt{32 \text{ g/mole}}}$$

and

$$\left(\frac{37.6}{28.0}\right)^2 = \frac{M_{\text{butane}}}{32 \text{ g/mole}}$$

$$M_{\text{butane}} = 57.5 \text{ g/mole}$$

3.11 Kinetic Molecular Theory

Now that the laws describing the behavior of gases have been determined experimentally, the next task is to devise a reasonable theory to account for these laws. Most satisfactory in this regard is the ***kinetic molecular theory,*** the basic assumptions of which are enumerated below.

1. The molecules of a gas are small and widely separated, so that most of the volume of a gas is empty space.
2. There are no attractive or repulsive forces between the molecules of a gas, which behave quite independently of one another.
3. Each molecule of a gas is in constant motion, traveling in a straight line until it collides with another molecule or with some surface. Such collisions are perfectly elastic.
4. The pressure of a gas arises from the sum of the collisions of the molecules with the walls of the container.
5. Although individual gas molecules may possess different amounts of kinetic energy, the average kinetic energy of all of the molecules is proportional to the absolute temperature and is the same for all gases at the same temperature.

The real test of any theory lies in how well it is in agreement with experiment. In the case of the kinetic molecular theory, the agreement is very good indeed.

1. *Most of the volume of a gas is empty space.* One of the most striking characteristics of a gas—its compressibility—follows naturally from this assumption. Compressing a gas becomes merely a matter of pushing the molecules closer together. On this point at least, there is no conflict between theory and fact.

2. *Gas molecules act independently of one another.* According to Dalton's law, when gases are mixed, each exerts pressure as though it alone were occupying the entire volume, and the total pressure is the sum of the partial pressures of all of the gases in the mixture. If the molecules act independently, that is, if they have no influence upon one another, such additivity of properties is a natural consequence, although this alone does not prove the theoretical assumption to be correct.

3. *The molecules of a gas are in constant motion, traveling in straight lines.* Both the expansibility of a gas, which causes it to fill completely any volume into which it is placed, and its diffusibility, are difficult to account for unless one attributes this property of straight-line motion to the molecules. *Collisions of gas molecules with a surface or with one another are perfectly elastic.* An elastic collision is one in which the sum of the kinetic energies of the objects colliding remains unchanged, even though the kinetic

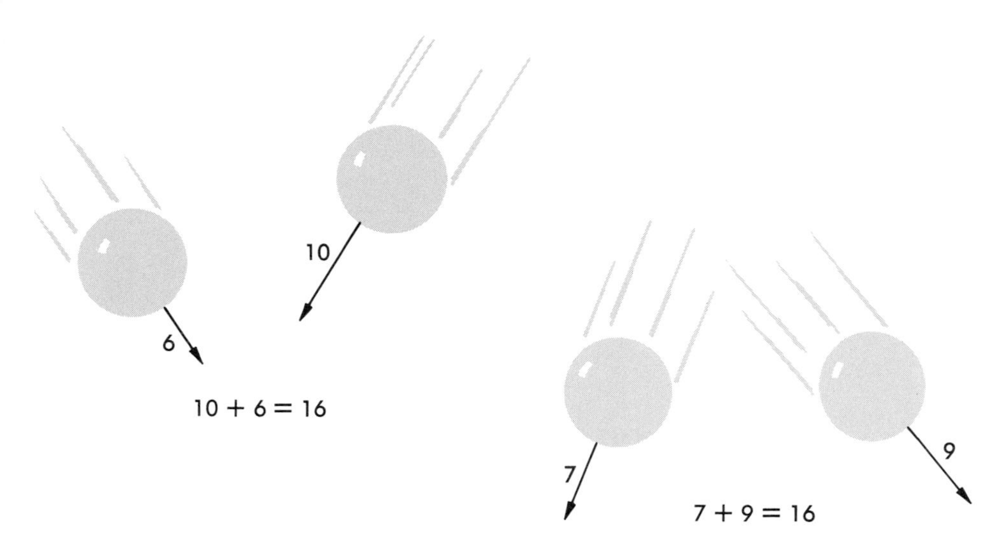

Fig. 3.10 Elastic collision. The lengths of the arrows are drawn in proportion to the relative kinetic energies.

energy of each of the objects considered separately may undergo a change. For example (Fig. 3.10), if two molecules should collide, for the collision to be an elastic one, any kinetic energy which may be lost by one of the molecules must be transferred without loss to the other so that the total kinetic energy of the two molecules, taken together, remains unchanged. Collisions of a rubber ball with the floor are not completely elastic, and after a time a bouncing ball comes to rest. One is forced to conclude that the collisions of gas molecules are perfectly elastic, since otherwise the molecules, like so many rubber balls, would eventually settle to the bottom of their container.

4. *The pressure of a gas arises from the collisions of gas molecules with the walls of the container.* This assumption of the theory is consistent with Boyle's law. Reducing the volume occupied by a gas shortens the distance which the molecules must travel before reaching a wall. As a result, collisions with the walls of the container will be more frequent (Fig. 3.11). Halving the volume of a gas doubles the collision frequency, and hence doubles the pressure. Conversely, an increase in the volume causes a proportional decrease in the pressure.

5. *The average kinetic energy of a gas is proportional to the absolute temperature.* Charles' law states that the pressure of a gas is directly proportional to the absolute temperature. This is exactly what would be expected if an increase in temperature were to cause an increase in the kinetic energy of the gas molecules. The kinetic energy of an object is related to its speed through the expression

$$\text{K.E.} = \tfrac{1}{2}mv^2,$$

where m is the mass of the object, and v is its speed. From this it can be seen that increasing the kinetic energy of a gas causes its molecules to

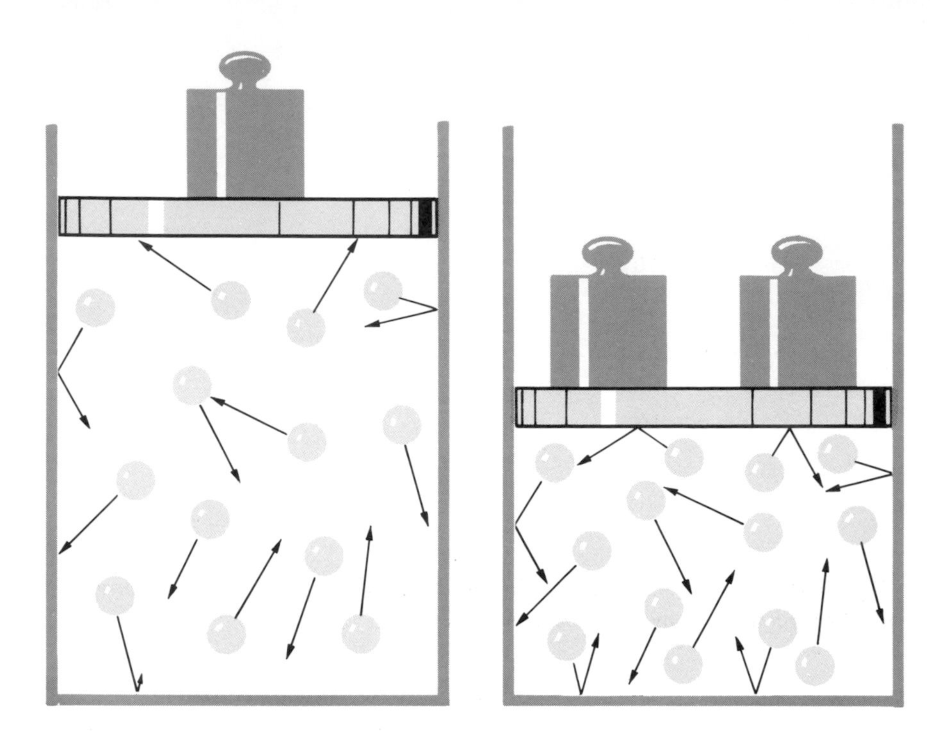

Fig. 3.11 Boyle's law. The number of collisions of gas molecules with the walls of the container, and hence the pressure, is doubled when the gas is forced into one-half its original volume.

move faster. As a result of their greater speed, they will strike the walls of the container more frequently, and because of their greater kinetic energy, the collisions will occur with greater force. The result will be an increase in the pressure of the gas. *The average kinetic energy is the same for all gases at the same temperature.* When two different gases at the same temperature are mixed, there is no change in temperature, and the resulting pressure is equal to the sum of the partial pressures of the two gases. Mixing could not have caused any change in the average kinetic energy of either gas, for otherwise a change in their partial pressures would have been observed. For the kinetic energies of the gases to remain unchanged after mixing, they must have been the same beforehand. Temperature is, in fact, a measure of the average kinetic energy of the molecules. Therefore, *two substances whose molecules possess the same average kinetic energy have the same temperature.*

3.12 Derivation of the Gas Laws from Kinetic Molecular Theory

Kinetic molecular theory has now been shown to be consistent in a qualitative way with the observed behavior of gases. The final demonstration of its validity will come if the properties of gases can be predicted quantitatively from the theory.

According to the theory, the pressure of a gas depends upon three things: the volume; the average kinetic energy of the molecules, which is proportional to the temperature; and the total number of molecules. The theory therefore predicts that *if the volumes of two gas samples at the same temperature are equal, then if they are to have the same pressure, they must each contain the same number of molecules.* Thus the assumptions of the theory lead directly to Avogadro's principle.

The average kinetic energy of its molecules determines the temperature of a gas, but this does not mean that all of the gas molecules have the *same* kinetic energy. Molecular collisions are perfectly elastic and the *total* kinetic energy of the molecules is the same before and after collision. Collision may, however, lead to a *redistribution* of kinetic energy. One molecule, traveling with a certain speed proportional to its kinetic energy, may strike another, give up some of its energy and be moving slower after the collision than it was originally. In turn, the other molecule, having gained the energy lost by the first, will be moving faster after the collision. Because of this constant redistribution of energy, at any one instant some of the molecules will be moving very slowly—perhaps even standing still—some will be moving very rapidly, but most of them will have speeds (and kinetic energies) somewhere near the average. Raising the temperature, that is, adding kinetic energy, will cause an increase in the most probable speed of the molecules, but again at the higher temperature some molecules will be moving much faster, and some much slower than the others. The distribution of molecular speeds at two temperatures is shown in Fig. 3.12.

The average kinetic energy of the molecules of a gas is equal to $\frac{1}{2}m\bar{v}^2$ where $\bar{v}$ is the ***root-mean-square speed,*** that is, the square root of the sum of the squares of the speeds of all of the molecules. Using the root-mean-

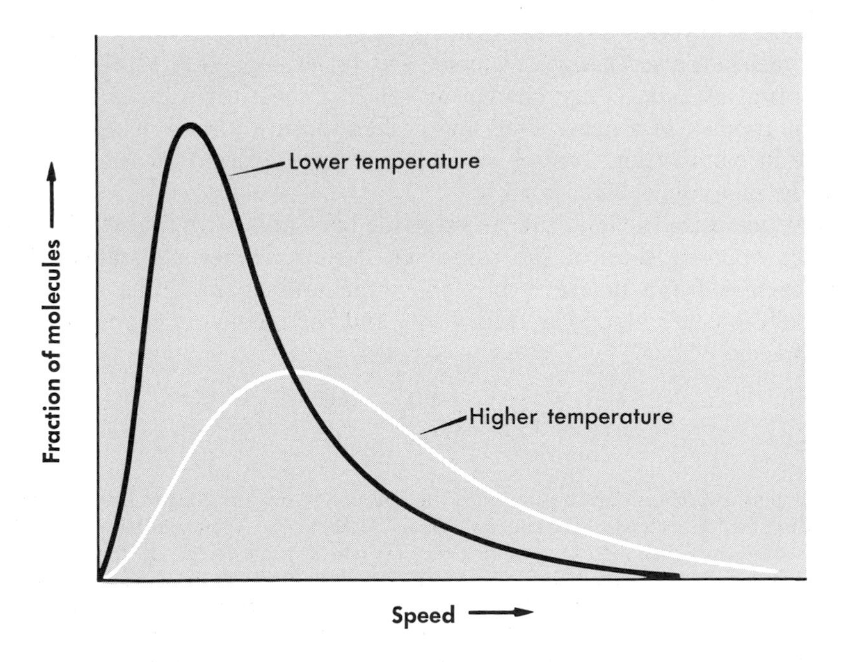

Fig. 3.12 Distribution of molecular speeds at two temperatures.

square speed rather than the average speed allows for the unsymmetrical distribution of molecular speeds which results from the fact that there is a lower limit to how fast a molecule can go (when it's standing still it can't move any slower), but no upper limit (Fig. 3.12).

Since their average kinetic energies are equal, for two gases, A and B, at the same temperature,

$$\tfrac{1}{2}m_A\bar{v}_A^2 = \tfrac{1}{2}m_B\bar{v}_B^2$$

$$\frac{\bar{v}_A^2}{\bar{v}_B^2} = \frac{m_B}{m_A}$$

and

$$\frac{\bar{v}_A}{\bar{v}_B} = \sqrt{\frac{m_B}{m_A}}$$

A gas will diffuse at a rate proportional to the root-mean-square speed of its molecules; therefore, substituting the rate of diffusion for $\bar{v}$, and the molecular weight M for m, the mass of one molecule, we obtain the relationship

$$\frac{\text{rate}_A}{\text{rate}_B} = \sqrt{\frac{M_B}{M_A}}$$

This is Graham's law (introduced in Sec. 3.10), and it is verified by experiment.

Now let us consider a gas confined in a cubic container L cm on a side. Each molecule of the gas possesses momentum equal to the product of its mass m and its velocity $\mathbf{v}$. Each time a molecule hits a wall of the container, it reverses direction, and its velocity changes from $+\mathbf{v}$ to $-\mathbf{v}$.* Its momentum also changes from $m(+\mathbf{v})$ to $m(-\mathbf{v})$ for a total change in momentum of $2m\mathbf{v}$. Any change in velocity constitutes an acceleration, and the product of a mass times an acceleration is a force. Therefore, the change in momentum, $2m\mathbf{v}$, is equal to the force exerted on the wall each time the molecule collides with it.

If we visualize the molecule as traveling back and forth in a straight line between opposite sides of the container, it must travel a distance $2L$ cm after each collision before it hits the same wall again. The number of such collisions per second is thus $\mathbf{v}/2L$, and the change in momentum per second is

$$(2m\mathbf{v})\left(\frac{\mathbf{v}}{2L}\right) = \frac{m\mathbf{v}^2}{L}$$

* The plus and minus signs here refer to the direction of motion along a given coordinate and are not used in their usual arithmetical sense. Although the terms velocity and speed are often used synonymously, strictly speaking they are not the same thing. In the strict sense, as we are using the term here, velocity is a ***vector quantity,*** which means that *it possesses both magnitude and direction.* Saying that an automobile is going 50 mph describes its ***speed.*** Saying that it is going *east* at 50 mph describes its ***velocity.*** If the driver makes a U-turn and heads west at 50 mph, his speed is unchanged, but his velocity *in an easterly direction* has changed from +50 mph to −50 mph.

The molecules of the gas are moving in all directions, but at any given moment, one-third of the total mass of the molecules may be considered as having a root-mean-square velocity $\bar{\mathbf{v}}$ along any one axis of the container. Therefore, for one mole of gas, containing N molecules, the total rate of change in momentum of the molecules colliding with one wall of the container is a force equal to

$$\left(\frac{N}{3}\right)\left(\frac{m\bar{\mathbf{v}}^2}{L}\right)$$

The pressure exerted on the wall is equal to the force per unit area:

$$\text{pressure} = \frac{Nm\bar{\mathbf{v}}^2}{3L(L^2)}$$

or

$$P = \frac{1}{3}\left(\frac{Nm\bar{\mathbf{v}}^2}{L^3}\right)$$

Since L^3 = volume,

$$PV = \tfrac{1}{3}Nm\bar{\mathbf{v}}^2$$

The absolute temperature is proportional to the average kinetic energy so that

$$T = (\mathbf{k})(\tfrac{1}{2}m\bar{\mathbf{v}}^2)$$

and

$$m\bar{v}^2 = \frac{2T}{\mathbf{k}}$$

Substituting this value for $m\bar{v}^2$ in the preceding equation gives

$$PV = \frac{2}{3\mathbf{k}}NT$$

For n moles of gas this becomes

$$PV = nRT$$

where

$$R = \frac{2N}{3\mathbf{k}}$$

This is the same expression of the combined gas law equation as that derived earlier (Sec. 3.9) from Boyle's and Charles' laws and Avogadro's principle.

Reading Suggestions 3.13

Gay-Lussac's original paper on the combination of gaseous substances is reprinted in part on pages 100–105 of *Readings in the Literature of Science*, William C. and Margaret Dampier, eds. (Harper Torchbook #TB 512, Harper & Row, New York, 1949). Immediately following, on pp. 106–111 of this same book, is

Avogadro's paper from the *Journal de Physique* (1811), in which he proposes that equal volumes of all gases under the same conditions contain the same number of molecules and deduces from this principle that the molecules of certain gases must be polyatomic. At the Karlsruhe Congress of 1860 Cannizzaro showed how the application of Avogadro's principle could solve the problem of determining correct atomic weights. This congress and its far-reaching effects are described by A. J. Ihde in *J. Chem. Ed.* **38,** 83 (1961). The behavior of gases and the kinetic theory of matter are presented in delightful fashion in the first chapter of Max Born's book *The Restless Universe* (available as a paperback from Dover Publications, Inc., New York, 1951). A chemistry student will find this book to be a most enjoyable and painless introduction to modern physics. It features unique "motion picture" diagrams in the margins which give the illusion of movement when the pages are flipped.

Questions and Problems

3.1 A sample of a gas has a volume of one liter at 25°C and 1 atm pressure. Predict how its volume will change under each of the following conditions:

(a) The pressure is doubled and the temperature is kept constant.
(b) The Kelvin temperature is doubled and the pressure is kept constant.
(c) The Celsius temperature is doubled and the pressure is kept constant.
(d) The Kelvin temperature is doubled and the pressure is reduced to 0.5 atm.

3.2 Briefly outline the kinetic molecular theory, showing how it serves to account for gaseous diffusion, the nonsettling of gases, and the laws of Boyle, Charles, and Dalton.

3.3 What is meant by the statement that collisions between gas molecules are perfectly elastic? What would happen if this statement were not true?

3.4 Given two equal-size containers, one filled with hydrogen and the other with neon at the same temperature and pressure. Compare or contrast the two containers with respect to the following:

(a) The number of molecules in each container.
(b) The number of atoms in each container.
(c) The average kinetic energy of the molecules in each container.
(d) The relative speeds of the molecules in each container.
(e) The mass of gas in each container.
(f) The density of gas in each container.

3.5 Express each of the following gas pressures in torr:

(a) 2.80 atm
(b) 54.2 atm
(c) 3.61×10^{-3} atm
(d) 34.2 g/cm^2
(e) 6.20 cm Hg

3.6 Express each of the following gas pressures in atmospheres:

(a) 1720 lb/in.^{2}
(b) 85.1 cm Hg
(c) 204 torr
(d) 32 cm H_2O
(e) 1560 g/cm^2

3.7 A sample of oxygen occupies a volume of exactly 500 ml at 25°C and 774 torr pressure. Assuming that the temperature of the gas remains the same, what volume will it occupy at these pressures: (a) 850 torr, (b) 1 atm, (c) 0.5 atm.

3.8 An automobile tire is inflated to a gauge pressure of 28 $lb/in.^2$ at 59°F. After the tire is driven at high speed for a while, the temperature inside the tire rises to 104°F. Calculate the tire pressure at that temperature, assuming that the volume of the tire does not change. (Note: to convert from gauge pressure to absolute pressure, add the pressure of the atmosphere: 14.7 $lb/in.^2$ in this case.)

3.9 A reaction vessel is filled with gas at 20°C and 50 atm pressure. If the vessel can withstand a maximum internal pressure of 75 atm, what is the highest temperature to which it can safely be heated?

3.10 If it takes 4 liters of gas to inflate a toy balloon at 25°C to a pressure of 2 atm, how many balloons can be inflated from a tank containing 20 liters of helium at 100 atm pressure and the same temperature?

3.11 A tank of nitrogen contains 5 ft^3 of gas at a pressure of 1600 $lb/in.^2$ What volume would the gas occupy at the same temperature and at a pressure of 14.7 $lb/in.^2$?

3.12 A pressure of 1 atm will support a column of mercury 76.0 cm high. The density of mercury is about 13.2 times the density of seawater. Using this information, calculate the depth to which a skin diver can descend if he can safely withstand a pressure of 5.0 atm.

3.13 In 1960 the bathyscaphe Trieste reached a depth of 35,800 ft (10,900 m). What pressure was the bathyscaphe subjected to at that depth? (Density of seawater, 1.03 g/ml.)

3.14 A 500-ml sample of gas in a sealed container at 700 torr pressure and 25°C is heated to 100°C. What is the final pressure of the gas?

3.15 A sample of gas occupies 500 ml at 17°C and 770 torr pressure. What would the volume of the gas be at standard conditions?

3.16 A scuba diver exhales 900 ml of air at a depth of 27 fathoms (1 m = 0.55 fathom) where the pressure is 5.0 atm and the temperature 17°C. What would be the volume of the air at the surface, where the temperature is 30°C and the pressure 750 torr?

3.17 A gaseous mixture is prepared by taking 100 ml of xenon, 400 ml of fluorine, and 500 ml of nitrogen, each measured at 27°C and 1.0 atm pressure, and placing them in a container at −100°C and 2.0 atm total pressure. Calculate the partial pressure of each gas in the final mixture. What is the volume of the container?

3.18 The volume of a sample of oxygen, measured over water at 28.0°C and 758.0 torr, is 2470 ml. Calculate the volume of the oxygen at standard conditions.

3.19 What volume of oxygen gas, measured at standard conditions, will be produced by the decomposition of 12.8 g of potassium chlorate according to the equation

$$2\ KClO_3 \rightarrow 2\ KCl + 3\ O_2?$$

3.20 If it takes 10 sec for 15 ml of oxygen to effuse through a pinhole, how long will it take for 15 ml of hydrogen to effuse through the same pinhole?

3.21 How fast must a 16-lb bowling ball be moving for it to possess the same kinetic energy as a 5-oz baseball traveling at 40 mph?

3.22 The average speed of a hydrogen molecule at 0°C is 1.84×10^5 cm/sec. What is the average speed of a molecule of CO_2 at the same temperature?

3.23 A chemist collects a small sample of gas over water in a graduated eudiometer tube (see sketch) and records the following data:

Volume of gas in eudiometer tube: 16.2 cm^3
Atmospheric pressure: 741.2 torr
Water temperature: 30.0°C
Difference in water levels inside and outside tube: 28.1 cm

Using this information, calculate the volume which the dry gas alone would occupy at standard conditions.

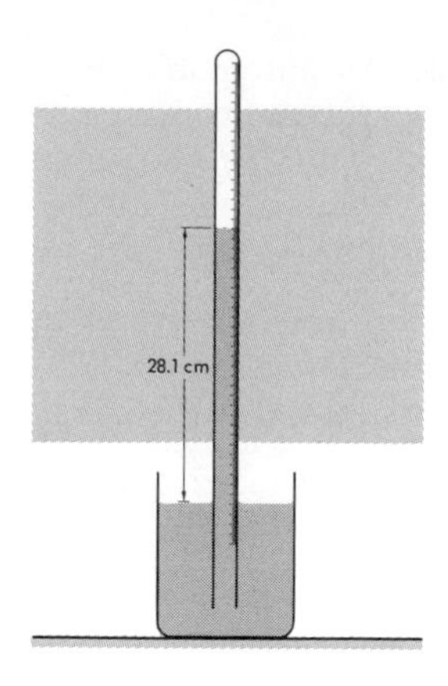

3.24 Samples of each of five volatile compounds of element X were vaporized, and their volumes in the vapor state were measured. Each sample was then condensed and weighed. Finally, each compound was analyzed to determine the percentage of X which it contained. The following data were obtained:

Compound	Sample Weight	Sample Volume	*T*, °C	*P*, torr	%X in Sample
A	1.38 g	306 ml	99.8	759	76.5
B	4.18 g	644 ml	99.9	720	83.8
C	0.78 g	155 ml	90.0	740	91.4
D	1.34 g	336 ml	151.0	800	80.0
E	1.02 g	256 ml	25.0	731	70.4

Use this information to calculate the probable atomic weight of element X.

3.25 Exactly 200 ml of dry helium was bubbled through benzene at 25°C and 760 torr, becoming saturated with benzene vapor in the process. The volume of the gas leaving the bubbler was 223 ml, measured at the same temperature and pressure. Calculate the vapor pressure of benzene at 25°C, and the mass of benzene (mol. wt. = 78 amu) evaporated, in grams.

3.26 Simultaneously, 0.121 g of hydrogen gas and 1.60 g of oxygen gas are injected into an empty box which has a volume of 246 ml and is kept at 273°C. What is the final pressure in the box? Suppose that a spark is passed through the box so that the hydrogen and oxygen can react to form water vapor according to the equation

$$2\ H_2(g) + O_2(g) \rightarrow 2\ H_2O(g)$$

What will be the final pressure in the box if the volume and temperature are kept the same?

3.27 The compound ethylzilch, upon analysis, is found to contain 38.8% carbon, 8.1% hydrogen, and 53.0% zilchium (**Zm**). At 120°C and 1 atm pressure, 250 ml of ethylzilch vapor weighs 0.96 g. The specific heat of metallic zilchium is 0.093 cal/g and the metal forms an oxide containing 19.7% oxygen. What is the molecular formula of ethylzilch?

3.28 Analysis of a certain compound shows it to contain 24.3% carbon, 4.1% hydrogen, and 71.8% chlorine. A 0.87-g sample of the compound, when vaporized in a Victor Meyer apparatus, displaced 21.8 ml of air, measured over water at 22°C and 762 torr. Calculate the molecular formula of the compound. Note: in the Victor Meyer apparatus, the volume of air displaced is equal to the volume which the vapor would occupy under the same conditions of temperature and pressure.

3.29 The combustion apparatus used to determine the mass of a carbon film as described in problem 3.33 is shown in the accompanying sketch. The combustion chamber is shown at A; tube B has a uniform inside diameter of exactly 0.1765 in.; tube C is open to the atmosphere; D is a scale graduated in inches, with the zero mark at the top of the scale. The mercury level in tubes B and C may be adjusted by raising and lowering the leveling bulb E. The system may be opened to the atmosphere by opening the stopcock F. From the experimental data given below, calculate the volume of the combustion apparatus to the zero mark on the scale.

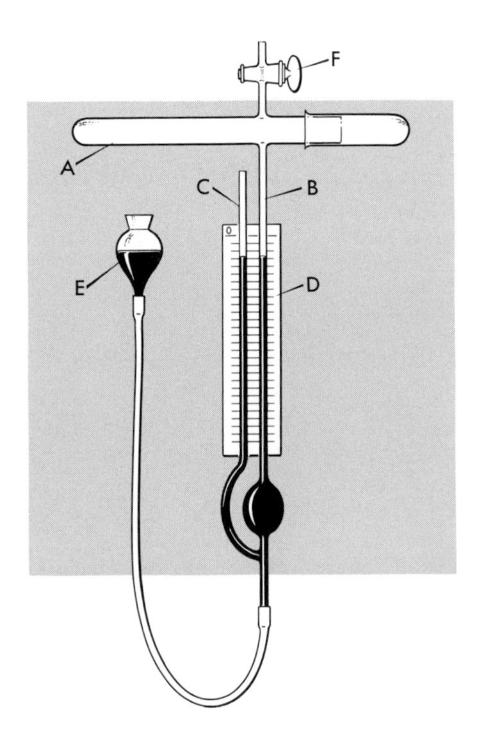

Determination No.		I	II
Mercury level, inches, stopcock open	tube B	0.00	21.00
	tube C	0.00	21.00
Mercury level, inches, stopcock closed	tube B	19.50	2.51
	tube C	21.02	1.00
Atmospheric pressure, inches Hg		28.74	28.74
Temperature, °C		25.8	25.8

Ans. Average of two determinations: 8.56 in.^{3}, or 140.3 cm^3

3.30 It takes 93.0 cal to raise the temperature of 1 kg of a metal 1°C. When treated with acid, 5.12 g of this metal displaced 1935 ml of hydrogen gas measured over water at 750 torr and 18°C. From this information, calculate the exact atomic weight of the metal.

3.31 The radius of a helium atom is approximately 0.9 Å. (a) What fraction of the total gas volume is represented by the volume of the atoms in a sample of helium at standard conditions? (b) What is the average distance between helium atoms at standard conditions? (c) If the pressure of the gas is raised to 500 atm, what fraction of the new total volume will be occupied by the helium atoms? (d) What will be the average distance between helium atoms at 500 atm?

3.32 The uranium isotopes **U-238** and **U-235** are separated by taking advantage of the difference in the rates of effusion of their hexafluorides through a porous partition. Which gas effuses faster, $^{238}UF_6$ or $^{235}UF_6$? How much faster?

3.33 Several years ago, one of the authors of this book found it necessary to determine the mass of a thin film of carbon deposited on a porcelain tube. Since the film could not be weighed directly, its mass was calculated from the increase in gas volume when the film was oxidized in an atmosphere of carbon dioxide:

The following experimental data were obtained:

	Before Combustion	After Combustion
Volume of gas in apparatus, cm^3	142.36	144.89
Atmospheric pressure, torr	728.0	734.0
Temperature, °C	24.7	23.0

From these data, calculate the mass of the carbon film. *Ans.* 2.04×10^{-3} g

Refrain from illusions,
insist on work, and not on words.
Patiently search divine and
scientific truth.

—Mme. Mendeleev's last words to
her son Dmitri, 1850

4

THE PERIODIC LAW

Man has always searched for an underlying order in the operation of the universe, and his instinctive faith that such order exists has driven him to seek and to discover the physical laws which govern his environment. The chemists of a century ago had accumulated a large body of knowledge concerning the behavior of the elements and their compounds. Lacking was any satisfactory system to organize this ever-increasing collection of apparently unrelated facts into a manageable whole. Recognizing the need of such organization if hopeless confusion were to be avoided, and certain that a hidden order existed in this mass of information, chemists had made numerous attempts to classify the elements according to their properties. Indications appeared that the properties of the elements were in some way related to their atomic weights. With atomic weights and valences uncertain, early attempts at classification met with indifferent success. Once Cannizzaro showed the way to the determination of correct atomic weights, progress was rapid, culminating in 1869 in the discovery of the *periodic law*, which stands as a lasting monument to the effort and faith of many men.

Early Attempts at Classification 4.1

(a) Döbereiner's Triads. The first significant attempt to classify elements according to their behavior was made by Johann Wolfgang Döbereiner in the period between 1817 and 1829. Döbereiner pointed out the existence of "triads," or groups of three elements possessing similar chemical properties. The elements of each triad exhibit a nearly constant difference in their atomic weights, so that the atomic weight of the middle element is very nearly the arithmetic mean of the other two. Not only that, but such properties as the density, melting point, solubility of salts, and chemical reactivity of the middle element in most cases are intermediate between those of the other two. Several of Döbereiner's triads are shown in Table 4.1.

TABLE 4.1 Döbereiner's Triads

Element	Atomic Weight (amu)	Difference in Atomic Weight	Density g/ml	Melting Point °C
Lithium	6.9		0.534	179
		16.1		
Sodium	23.0		0.97	97.5
		16.1		
Potassium	39.1		0.86	62
Sulfur	32.1		2.07	95.5
		46.9		
Selenium	79.0		4.81	217
		48.6		
Tellurium	127.6		6.25	452
Chlorine	35.5		1.56[a]	−101
		44.4		
Bromine	79.9		3.12[a]	−7.2
		47.0		
Iodine	126.9		4.93[b]	113.5
Calcium	40.1		1.55	842
		47.5		
Strontium	87.6		2.54	769
		49.7		
Barium	137.3		3.5	725

[a] Liquid. [b] Solid.

(b) The Telluric Helix of de Chancourtois. Although attempts at more extensive correlations of the properties of the elements were made subsequent to Döbereiner's observations, further real progress had to await clarification of the distinction between atomic and equivalent weight, the discovery of a sufficiently large number of elements, and the determination of reasonably accurate atomic weights. By 1860, after Cannizzaro had been instrumental in having Avogadro's principle generally accepted, sufficient progress had been made in those areas so that efforts directed toward the creation of a rational system for classifying the elements could become fruitful.

In 1862, A. E. Béguyer de Chancourtois, professor of geology at the École des Mines in Paris, conceived the idea of plotting the elements in order of their atomic weights along a helix traced at a 45-degree angle around the vertical axis of a cylinder. The surface of the cylinder was divided around its circumference into 16 sections, each corresponding to one unit of atomic weight. Oxygen thus came at the end of the first complete turn of the helix; sulfur, with an atomic weight of 32, at the end of the second turn. The helix is shown in flattened-out form in Fig. 4.1.

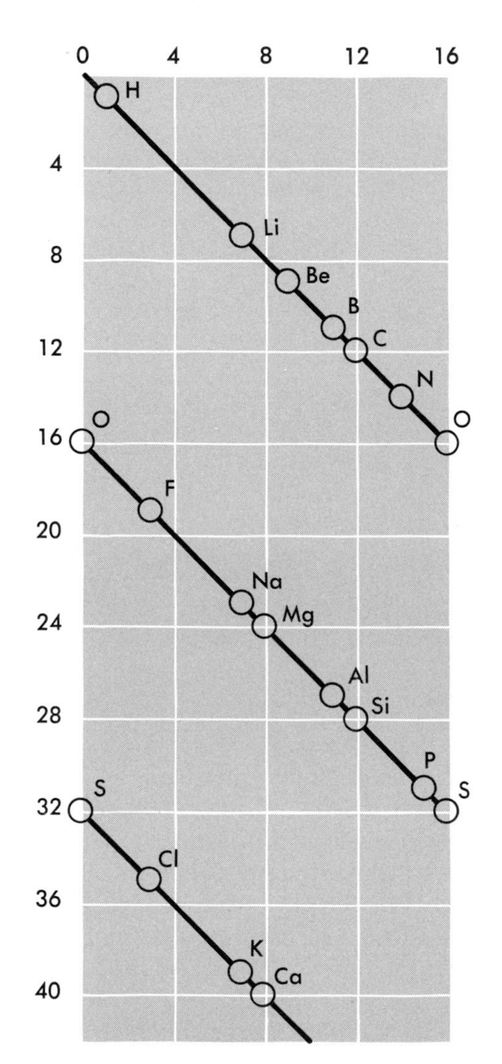

Fig. 4.1 The telluric helix of de Chancourtois.

De Chancourtois assumed that all atomic weights were whole numbers, any fractional values being the result of experimental error. In this he was following the hypothesis that William Prout had proposed in 1815, namely, that hydrogen is the primary substance of which all other elements are composed, and consequently all atomic weights are exact multiples of that of hydrogen.* De Chancourtois pointed out the often striking similarity between elements on the same vertical line, that is, between those whose atomic weights differed by 16 units or multiples of 16 units. The ***telluric helix*** (from the Latin *telluris*, of the earth) was a step in the right direction, but the concept was incomplete, and gained no support.

(c) The Law of Octaves. The English chemist John Newlands made the next important contribution to the classification of the elements. He arranged the then known elements in the order of increasing atomic weights, assigning to them the respective ordinal numbers first, second, third, and so on. When the elements were listed in this manner, similar properties were found to recur at intervals of seven elements. Drawing a rather inappropriate analogy to the musical scale, Newlands referred to this recurrence of properties as the "law of octaves." He drew up a table with the elements arranged in columns of seven, in the order of their atomic weights, with the horizontal rows forming families of related elements (Fig. 4.2). The law of octaves holds up well for the first 17 elements, but

Family	Octave 1	Octave 2	Octave 3	Octave 4	Octave 5	Octave 6	Octave 7	Octave 8
1	H 1	F 8	Cl 15	Co & Ni 22	Br 29	Pd 36	I 42	Pt & Ir 50
2	Li 2	Na 9	K 16	Cu 23	Rb 30	Ag 37	Cs 44	Os 51
3	Be 3	Mg 10	Ca 17	Zn 24	Sr 31	Cd 38	Ba & V 45	Hg 52
4	B 4	Al 11	Cr 19	Y 25	Ce & La 33	U 40	Ta 46	Tl 53
5	C 5	Si 12	Ti 18	In 26	Zr 32	Sn 39	W 47	Pb 54
6	N 6	P 13	Mn 20	As 27	Di & Mo 34	Sb 41	Nb 48	Bi 55
7	O 7	S 14	Fe 21	Se 28	Ro & Ru 35	Te 43	Au 49	Th 56

Fig. 4.2 Newlands' table of octaves (1866).

beyond calcium fails rather badly. Many of the supposed family relationships are strained, and in order to preserve the idea of octaves, Newlands was forced in several instances to assign the same ordinal number to two elements. When he presented his classification of the elements before the Chemical Society of London in 1866, it was severly criticized, and Newlands was even asked facetiously if he had ever tried to arrange the elements in alphabetical order. The paper was rejected as unsuitable for publication in the Society's *Journal*.

Despite the poor reception which his law of octaves received, Newlands was the first to recognize clearly the periodic recurrence of properties among the elements when they are arranged in the order of increasing

* Prout's hypothesis enjoyed some popularity until improvements in analytical techniques led to confirmation of many nonintegral atomic weight values. It then faded from the scene, to be revived in a new form after the discovery of isotopes (Sec. 6.5).

atomic weights. Newlands went on to attain considerable success as an industrial chemist and consultant, but he may well have achieved his greatest satisfaction when, in 1887, the Royal Society belatedly awarded him its Davy medal in recognition of his contribution.

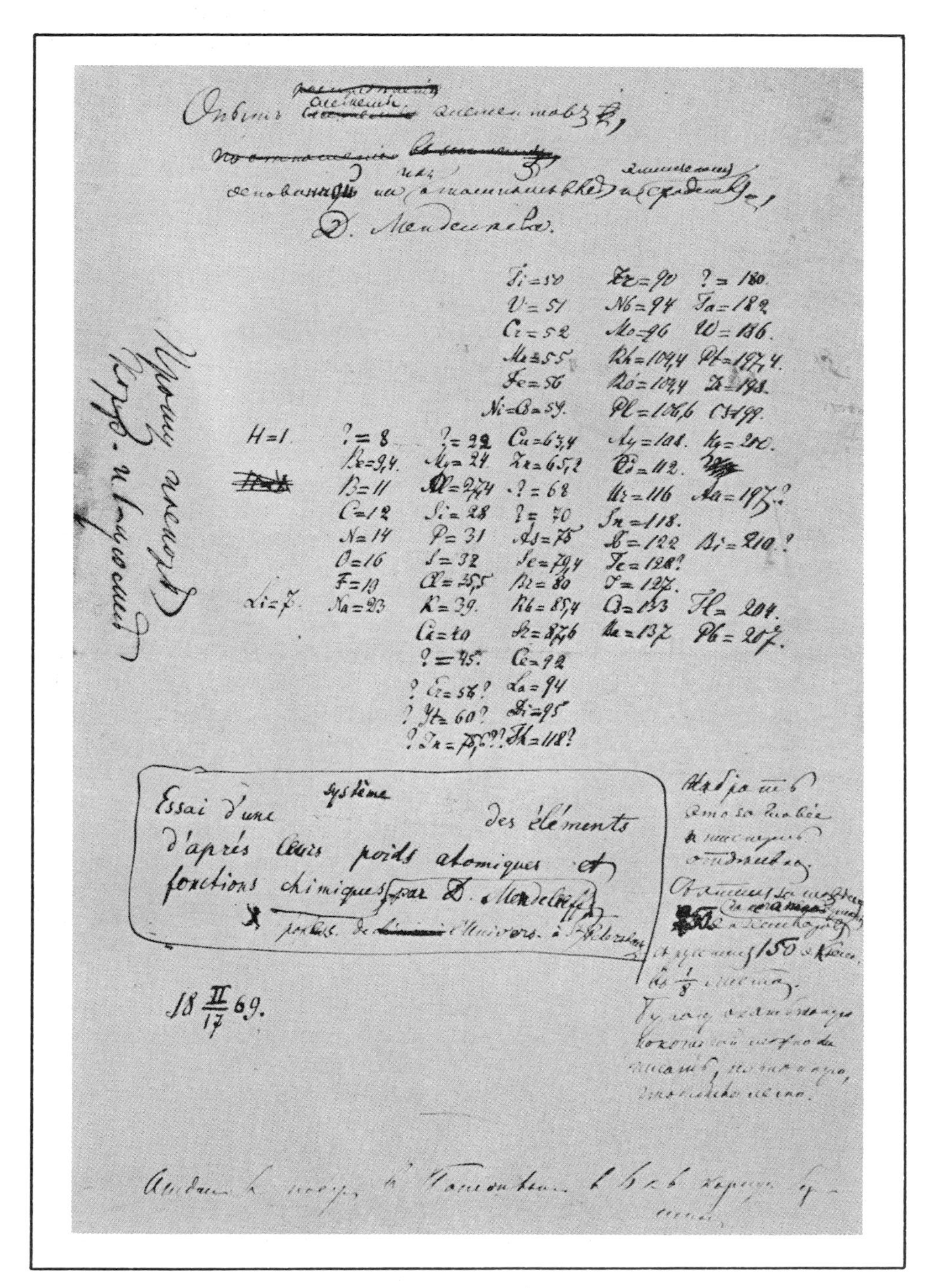

Fig. 4.3 Periodic table in Mendeleev's handwriting, dated February 17 (old style), 1869. (From the *J. Chem. Educ.*, Dec. 1960. Used by permission.)

4.2 The Periodic Law

Despite earlier tentative gropings, most of the credit for the development of the periodic classification of the elements must go to the Russian chemist Dmitri Ivanovich Mendeleev and the German physicist Julius Lothar Meyer. These two men independently, and at nearly the same time, devised extensive and elaborate classifications based upon a broad range of physical and chemical properties. Mendeleev's work was based primarily on the chemical behavior of the elements, while Meyer was more concerned with their physical properties, yet both arrived at nearly identical results which they formulated as the ***periodic law:*** *the properties of the elements are periodic functions of their atomic weights.*

According to one account, Mendeleev had been examining the properties of the known elements in the course of preparing a textbook for his students at the University of St. Petersburg (now Leningrad). To simplify his task, he made a set of cards on each of which he wrote the properties of a single element. As he arranged and rearranged these cards, the periodic recurrence of similar properties when the elements were placed in the order of increasing atomic weights became apparent to him. He then prepared a table listing the elements in vertical columns, with similar elements in horizontal rows, and presented it to the Russian Chemical Society early in 1869. This first table of Mendeleev is reproduced in Fig. 4.3. The resemblance between it and Newlands' table is evident. Unlike Newlands, Mendeleev was unhampered by any belief in a preconceived "law," and his table is relatively free of serious anomalies.

In December of the same year (1869), Meyer prepared a very similar, and in some respects more satisfactory, periodic table (Fig. 4.4). In this table for the first time such elements as zinc, cadmium, mercury, copper, silver, and gold were placed in separate subfamilies rather than being placed in the same families with elements to which they bore only slight resemblance. Meyer also presented the curve which resulted when he plotted the "atomic volume" (the atomic weight divided by the density of the element in the solid state) against the atomic weight. This curve, in which the periodic trend is strikingly evident, is reproduced in Fig. 4.5. The atomic volume is seen to pass through a repeating cycle of maxima and minima, with elements having similar properties appearing at similar positions along the curve. For example, the peaks on the curve are occupied in order by lithium, sodium, potassium, rubidium, and cesium. The first three constitute one of Döbereiner's triads, and this entire group of active metals, all of which exhibit a valence of 1 and form very similar compounds, had long been recognized as a family of closely related elements. They are generally known as the ***alkali metals.*** Nonmetals are found to the left of each peak, metals to the right and in the valleys between peaks.

In 1871 Mendeleev published a more elaborate periodic table in which the families of related elements appear as vertical groups (Fig. 4.6). At the head of each group, representative formulas are given characteristic of the compounds formed with oxygen, hydrogen, or chlorine by the members of that group. This table is essentially the "short" form of the periodic

I	II	III	IV	V	VI	VII	VIII	IX
	B 11	Al 23.7		—		? In 113.4		Tl 202.7
			—		—		—	
	C 12	Si 28		—		Sn 117.8		Pb 206.4
			Ti 48		Zr 89.7		—	
	N 14	P 30.9		As 74.9		Sb 122.1		Bi 207.5
			V 51.2		Nb 93.7		Ta 182.2	
	O 16	S 32		Se 78		Te 128?		
			Cr 52.4		Mo 95.6		W 183.5	
	F 19	Cl 35.4		Br 79.75		I 126.5		
			Mn 54.8		Ru 103.5		Os 198.6?	
			Fe 55.9		Rh 104.1		Iv 196.7	
		Co =	Ni 58.6		Pd 106.2		Pt 196.7	
Li 7.0	Na 22.9	K 39		Rb 85.2		Cs 132.7		
			Cu 63.3		Ag 107.7		Au 192.2	
?Be 9.3	Mg 23.9	Ca 39.9		Sr 87		Ba 136.8		
			Zn 64.9		Cd 111.6		Hg 199.3	

Fig. 4.4 Meyer's periodic table (1869).

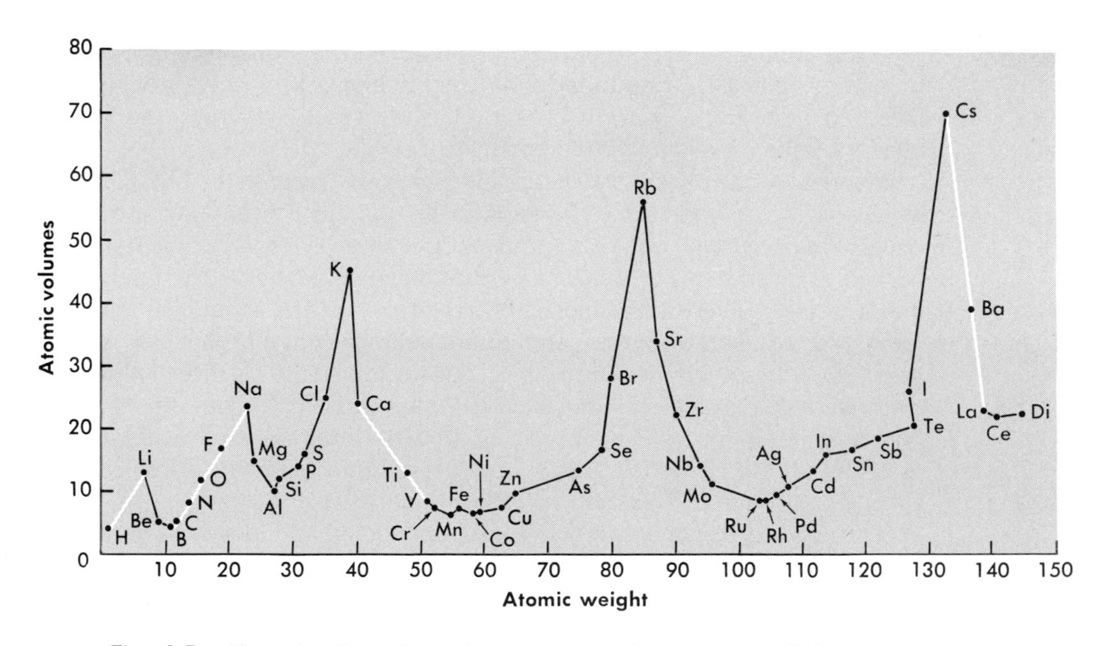

Fig. 4.5 Meyer's plot of atomic volume against atomic weight.

Period	Group I R_2O RCl	Group II RO RCl_2	Group III R_2O_3 RCl	Group IV RO_2 RCl_4	Group V R_2O_5 RH_3	Group VI RO_3 RH_2	Group VII R_2O_7 RH	Group VIII RO_4
1	H = 1							
2	Li = 7	Be = 9.4	B = 11	C = 12	N = 14	O = 16	F = 19	
3	Na = 23	Mg = 24	Al = 27.3	Si = 28	P = 31	S = 32	Cl = 35.5	
4	K = 39	Ca = 40	— = 44	Ti = 48	V = 51	Cr = 52	Mn = 55	Fe = 56, Co = 59 Ni = 59, Cu = 63
5	(Cu = 63)	Zn = 65	— = 68	— = 72	As = 75	Sc = 78	Br = 80	
6	Rb = 85	Sr = 87	?Yt = 88	Zr = 90	Nb = 94	Mo = 96	— = 100	Ru = 104, Rh = 104 Pd = 106, Ag = 108
7	(Ag = 108)	Cd = 112	In = 113	Sn = 118	Sb = 122	Te = 125	I = 127	
8	Cs = 133	Ba = 137	?Di = 138	?Ce = 140	—	—	—	— — — —
9	(—)	—	—	—	—	—	—	
10	—	—	?Er = 178	?La = 180	Ta = 182	W = 184	—	Os = 195, Ir = 197 Pt = 198, Au = 199
11	(Au = 199)	Hg = 200	Tl = 204	Pb = 207	Bi = 208	—	—	
12	—	—	—	Th = 231	—	U = 240	—	— — — —

Fig. 4.6 Mendeleev's periodic table (1871).

table used today, the main difference being the omission of the noble gases helium, neon, argon, krypton, xenon, and radon, which were unknown at that time.

In preparing their tables, Mendeleev and Meyer demonstrated their genius and daring. To avoid incongruous placement of the elements, both men left empty spaces so as not to destroy the rationale of ordered arrangement based upon periodic recurrence of properties. For example, the next known element following calcium in the sequence of increasing atomic weight was titanium. However, placing titanium immediately after calcium in the table would cause it to appear in the same group with aluminum. Its properties indicated titanium to be quadrivalent, and suggested that it belonged more appropriately in the following group, leaving a gap to be filled by some as yet undiscovered element.

Mendeleev went still further. He not only predicted that elements would be discovered to fill the gaps in his table, he even predicted with remarkable accuracy what the properties of three of these elements would be, being guided in his predictions by the known properties of their neighbors in the table. These three elements were those which should fill the gaps lying directly below boron, aluminum, and silicon. Mendeleev named them eka-boron, eka-aluminum, and eka-silicon. Within fifteen years, all three were discovered and shown to have the predicted properties: gallium (eka-aluminum) in 1875 by Lecoq de Boisbaudran, scandium (eka-boron) in 1879 by Lars Frederick Nilson, and germanium (eka-silicon) in 1886 by Clemens Alexander Winkler.

The close correspondence between the predicted and observed properties of germanium is shown in Table 4.2. In this instance the properties of the unknown element were deduced by Mendeleev from a consideration of the properties of zinc, arsenic, silicon, and tin, its neighboring elements in the table.

TABLE 4.2 Predicted and Observed Properties of Germanium

Property	Eka-Silicon Predicted, 1871	Germanium Observed, 1886
Atomic weight	72	72.32
Atomic volume	13 cm^3	13.22 cm^3
Specific gravity	5.5	5.47
Specific heat	0.073 cal/g $\times$ °C	0.076 cal/g $\times$ °C
Valence	4	4
Color	Dark gray	Grayish white
Reaction with water	Will decompose steam with difficulty	Does not decompose water
Reaction with acids and alkalis	Slight with acids; more pronounced with alkalis	Not attacked by HCl or dilute aqueous NaOH; reacts vigorously with molten NaOH
Formula of oxide	EsO_2	GeO_2
Specific gravity of oxide	4.7	4.703
Specific gravity of tetrachloride	1.9 at 0°C	1.887 at 18°C
Boiling point of tetrachloride	Below 100°C	86°C
Boiling point of tetraethyl derivative	160°C	160°C

Mendeleev was well aware of the existence of several anomalies in the periodic table. For example, if properties are a function of atomic weight, how is it possible for iron and cobalt to have the same atomic weight and yet have different chemical and physical properties? Again, why should it be necessary to sacrifice the atomic weight order for iodine (1869 value of atomic weight: 127) and tellurium (1869 atomic weight: 128) in order to avoid an incongrous placement of these two elements in the table? The presence of such anomalies must mean either that the atomic weights are in error, or that they are not the fundamental basis of the periodic law. Mendeleev believed the atomic weights, especially that of tellurium, to be in error, but this was later shown not to be the case.

With the discovery of the noble gases by Ramsay, beginning in 1894, and the addition of an entire new group to the periodic table, it was found that the atomic weight order must also be reversed for potassium (atomic weight 39.1) and argon (atomic weight 39.9) in order to place each of these elements in its proper family group. Gradually it became more apparent that the properties of the elements are not strictly a function of their atomic weights, but rather of some more fundamental factor. It remained for H. G. J. Moseley in 1913 to discover the nature of that factor (Sec. 6.10) and to relate it to the atomic number of the element. The atomic number of an element, which until 1913 had simply indicated its position in the periodic table, is in reality of greater significance than the atomic weight, and the periodic law is more correctly stated as follows: *The properties of the elements are periodic functions of their atomic numbers.*

4.3 The Modern Periodic Table

The preferred form of the modern periodic table is shown in Fig. 4.7. It differs from Mendeleev's table of 1871 in that the subgroups have been separated so as to give 18 vertical columns or family groups. All of the gaps in the earlier table have been filled, and the noble gases, group 0, as well as a number of man-made elements beyond uranium (the transuranium elements) have been added. Of the seven horizontal periods, the first contains 2 elements, the second and third 8 elements, and the fourth and fifth each contain 18 elements. The sixth period consists of 32 elements, including 14 ***lanthanides,*** which are placed below the main body of the table in order to keep the table from being spread out too much on the page. The seventh period begins like the sixth and should contain 32 elements, but it is incomplete. This period includes 14 ***actinides,*** which are chemically analogous to the lanthanides and are placed below them at the bottom of the table.

The elements in the "A" subgroups exhibit the most regular progression in chemical properties and are often referred to as the ***representative elements.*** In the fourth, fifth, and sixth periods, the representative groups IIA and IIIA are separated by ten columns of ***transition elements.*** Properties among the transition elements vary in a less pronounced and more irregular fashion than among the representative elements. In much the same way, the lanthanides and actinides, which are also known as ***inner transition elements,*** separate groups IIA and IIIB in periods six and seven.

4.4 Generalizations Based on Periodicity

Combining power, or valence, is among those properties of the elements which undergo a periodic variation with increasing atomic number. The most common valence of a representative element is usually the same as that which it exhibits toward hydrogen. This valence increases to a maximum of four, and then decreases as one proceeds from one element to the next across a period from group IA through VIIA to group 0. The maximum valence, not often exhibited toward elements other than oxygen, and then not necessarily by every member of the group, is in all cases equal to the group number (Table 4.3). Valences among the transition and inner

TABLE 4.3 Valences of the Representative Elements

	Group Number							
	IA	IIA	IIIA	IVA	VA	VIA	VIIA	0
Valence toward H	1	2	3	4	3	2	1	0
Maximum valence	1	2	3	4	5	6	7	0[a]

[a] Xenon, and possibly krypton and radon, form a few compounds with oxygen and fluorine in which they exhibit a maximum apparent valence of 8 (see Sec. 8.7).

	Representative Elements		Transition Elements										Representative Elements					
PERIOD	I A	II A	III B	VI B	V B	VI B	VII B	VIII	VIII	VIII	I B	II B	III A	IV A	V A	VI A	VII A	0
1	1 H 1.00797																	2 He 4.0026
2	3 Li 6.939	4 Be 9.0122											5 B 10.811	6 C 12.01115	7 N 14.0067	8 O 15.9994	9 F 18.9984	10 Ne 20.183
3	11 Na 22.9898	12 Mg 24.312											13 Al 26.9815	14 Si 28.086	15 P 30.9738	16 S 32.064	17 Cl 35.453	18 Ar 39.948
4	19 K 39.102	20 Ca 40.08	21 Sc 44.956	22 Ti 47.90	23 V 50.942	24 Cr 51.996	25 Mn 54.9380	26 Fe 55.847	27 Co 58.9332	28 Ni 58.71	29 Cu 63.54	30 Zn 65.37	31 Ga 69.72	32 Ge 72.59	33 As 74.9216	34 Se 78.96	35 Br 79.909	36 Kr 83.80
5	37 Rb 85.47	38 Sr 87.62	39 Y 88.905	40 Zr 91.22	41 Nb 92.906	42 Mo 95.94	43 Tc (97)	44 Ru 101.07	45 Rh 102.905	46 Pd 106.4	47 Ag 107.870	48 Cd 112.40	49 In 114.82	50 Sn 118.69	51 Sb 121.75	52 Te 127.60	53 I 126.9044	54 Xe 131.30
6	55 Cs 132.905	56 Ba 137.34	* 71 Lu 174.97	72 Hf 178.49	73 Ta 180.948	74 W 183.85	75 Re 186.2	76 Os 190.2	77 Ir 192.2	78 Pt 195.09	79 Au 196.967	80 Hg 200.59	81 Tl 204.37	82 Pb 207.19	83 Bi 208.980	84 Po (209)	85 At (210)	86 Rn (222)
7	87 Fr (223)	88 Ra (226)	† 103 Lr (257)	104 (260)														

Inner Transition Elements

*Lanthanides	57 La 138.91	58 Ce 140.12	59 Pr 140.907	60 Nd 144.24	61 Pm (145)	62 Sm 150.35	63 Eu 151.96	64 Gd 157.25	65 Tb 158.924	66 Dy 162.50	67 Ho 164.930	68 Er 167.26	69 Tm 168.934	70 Yb 173.04
†Actinides	89 Ac (227)	90 Th 232.038	91 Pa (231)	92 U 238.03	93 Np (237)	94 Pu (244)	95 Am (243)	96 Cm (247)	97 Bk (247)	98 Cf (251)	99 Es (254)	100 Fm (253)	101 Md (256)	102 No (253)

Note: Atomic weights based on ${}^{12}_{6}C = 12$. Numbers in parentheses are mass numbers of most stable isotopes.

Fig. 4.7 Modern periodic table.

transition elements are much more variable, although again their maximum valences are usually equal to their group numbers.

The elements may be broadly classified according to their physical and chemical properties as metals, nonmetals, and metalloids, also called semimetals. Generally speaking, metals exhibit high reflectivity, or luster, can be bent and drawn into wire without shattering, and conduct heat and electricity well, and their oxides dissolve in acids to form salts. To the extent that an element possesses these properties to a greater or lesser degree, it is described as being more or less metallic. By these criteria, copper is a typical metal. It is shiny, ductile, a good electrical and thermal conductor, and its oxide reacts with sulfuric acid to form the salt, copper(II) sulfate:

$$CuO + H_2SO_4 \rightarrow CuSO_4 + H_2O$$

Nonmetals are insulators: extremely poor conductors of electricity. Their crystals are brittle and shatter easily, and many of the nonmetals are gases at ordinary temperatures. Oxides of nonmetals typically dissolve in alkali (base), forming salts. Sulfur, for example, is a nonmetal. It does not conduct electricity, its crystals are readily ground into powder, and its oxides, SO_2 and SO_3, form salts with bases such as sodium hydroxide:

$$SO_2 + 2\ NaOH \rightarrow Na_2SO_3 + H_2O$$

$$SO_3 + 2\ NaOH \rightarrow Na_2SO_4 + H_2O$$

The semimetals are intermediate in properties between the metals and the nonmetals. Some, such as aluminum, are lustrous, and their electrical conductivity is typically metallic, decreasing as the temperature is raised. Others, such as germanium and arsenic, are less metallic in appearance and are ***semiconductors,*** that is, they possess a small electrical conductivity which increases with increasing temperature. Chemically, most are *amphoteric* to some degree, which means that their oxides form salts with both acids and bases:

$$As_2O_3 + 6\ NaOH \rightarrow 2\ Na_3AsO_3 + 3\ H_2O$$

$$As_2O_3 + 6\ HCl \rightarrow 2\ AsCl_3 + 3\ H_2O$$

Proceeding from left to right in any given period, one finds a general trend toward decreasing metallic character from one element to the next. At the same time, within any given group of representative elements, there is a progressive increase in metallic nature as one proceeds from top to bottom. As a result of these two trends, the most typical nonmetals are found in the upper right-hand corner of the periodic table, while the most typical metals are in the lower left (Fig. 4.8).* Furthermore, the dividing line between the metallic and nonmetallic regions of the table is not vertical, but diagonal. This is shown as a stepwise line on the periodic table in Fig. 4.7.

* The noble gases are not usually considered in these trends. All of them are nonmetals, but their reactivity is very small, and they form few compounds.

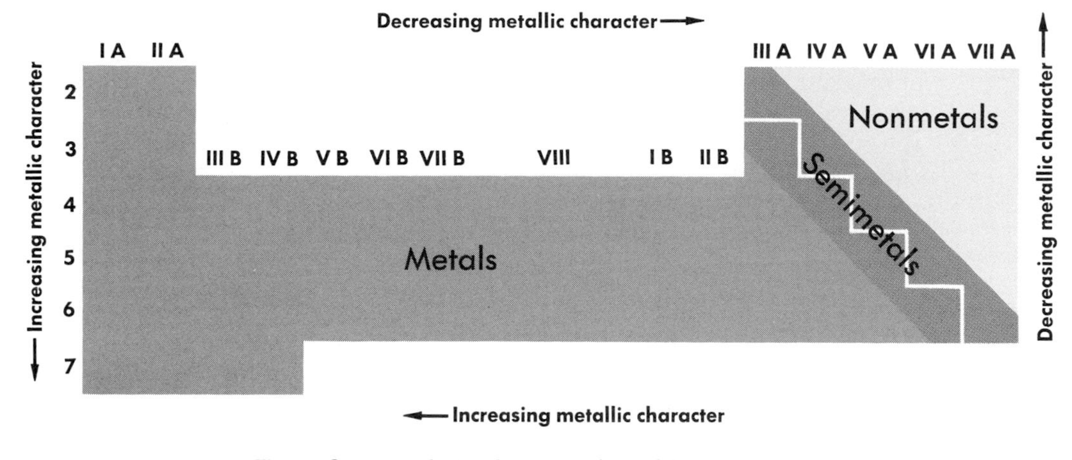

Fig. 4.8 Trends in the periodic table.

Examination of Figs. 4.7 and 4.8 shows that the great majority of the elements—about 80%, in fact—are metals. At the extreme left, in group IA, are found the ***alkali metals,*** generally considered the most metallic of the elements. The alkali metals are soft, low melting, ductile, and very reactive elements, possessing a very high degree of electrical conductivity. The ***alkaline earth metals*** of group IIA exhibit properties somewhat similar to those of the alkali metals, but each group IIA metal in any given period is less reactive, more brittle, and higher melting than the alkali metal which precedes it. The large middle region of the periodic table that lies between groups IIA and IIIA is taken up by the transition and inner transition elements, all of which are metals. The transition elements are so called because they represent a transition between the more reactive metals to their left, and the nonmetals to their right.

To the right, and above the diagonal dividing line, are the nonmetals. If the position of the group 0 elements is excluded, the most reactive nonmetals are found in the upper right-hand portion of the table. Hydrogen is generally placed in group IA because it shares some of the chemical properties of the alkali metals, but it does not properly belong to any one group of elements. Hydrogen is unique in being the only element in its period other than the noble gas helium, and it may be thought of as forming a group of its own.

The distinction between metals and nonmetals for those elements that fall adjacent to the dividing line between the two regions is not always sharp, and it is along this line that the semimetals, or metalloids, are found. Boron, silicon, germanium, arsenic, and tellurium are typical semimetals. Some of the elements located near these semimetals exist in several structural modifications called ***allotropic forms,*** which possess very different physical properties, particularly with respect to their electrical conductivity. For example, above 13°C, tin is normally silvery-white and a metallic conductor. Below that temperature, it exists in a brittle gray allotropic form in which it behaves as a semiconductor. Other examples are the nonmetallic white and red forms of phosphorus which can be converted into a black semimetallic allotrope by heating them under high pressure (Sec. 18.19).

In general, there is not so great a difference in properties between the top and bottom members of a given group as there is between the elements at opposite ends of a period. The most pronounced difference in properties within a group is usually found between the first two elements, that is, those in the second and third periods, respectively. Thus, beryllium in its chemical and physical properties differs more from magnesium than does magnesium from the other members of group IIA. Similarly, there is a greater difference between carbon and silicon than there is between silicon and germanium. Although the different members of a transition group usually show a distinct family resemblance, their properties often vary from one member to the next in an irregular and unpredictable fashion. Proceeding down the periodic table to higher period numbers, the changes in properties within a period become more gradual, and this is especially true with the transition and inner transition elements.

At this point a word of caution should be interjected. All of the properties of all of the elements in each group or each period do not necessarily vary in a simple, direct manner with increasing atomic number, although a general, overall trend will be observed. For example, although the atomic radii of the group IIA elements given in Fig. 4.9 increase regularly from

II A					
Be	Mg	Ca	Sr	Ba	Ra
4	12		38	56	88
0.89	1.37		1.91	1.98	2.28
1.86	1.75		2.6	3.61	5.0
1350	651		800	850	960
1500	1110		1150	1150	1140

Element	K	Ca	Sc	Ti	V	Cr	Mn	Fe	Co	Ni	Cu	Zn	Ga	Ge	As	Se	Br	
Atomic number	19	20	21	22	23	24	25	26	27	28	29	30	31	32	33	34	35	
Atomic radius, Å	2.02	1.74		1.324	1.224	1.172	1.168	1.165	1.157	1.149	1.17	1.25	1.245	1.223	1.21	1.17	1.142	4th
Density, g/cc	0.86	1.55	2.5	4.5	6.1	7.14	7.44	7.9	8.7	8.9	8.92	7.14	5.9	5.36	5.73	4.79	3.119	period
Melting point, °C	62.7	810	1200	1690	1900	1550	1245	1535	1490	1450	1083	420	29.75	960	615	217.4	−7.0	
Boiling point, °C	776	1170	2400	3535	>3000	2482	2097				2325	907	1983	2700	814	688	58	

Fig. 4.9 Properties of the group II A metals and the fourth period elements.

beryllium to radium, no such regularity is exhibited by the densities, melting points, and boiling points of these elements. The corresponding properties of the fourth period elements are also shown in this figure, and again, deviations from the general trends are observed, especially among the transition metals of the period.

Usefulness of the Periodic System 4.5

The periodic system is the framework upon which much of the structure of modern chemistry has been built. By bringing together elements with similar properties, the periodic classification makes it possible to generalize about the chemistry of the elements in terms of group properties. With a knowledge of group properties, one is able to make a reasonable prediction of the properties of a particular member of the group. The periodic chart is therefore an indispensable memory aid, reducing to manageable proportions the amount of specific information which a chemist must know.

Since the time of Mendeleev, the periodic system has been a constant stimulus for research. We have already seen how, in the past, elements whose existence had been unsuspected were deliberately searched for and found because the periodic system predicted their discovery.

Discovery of the periodic law awaited the determination of correct values for the majority of atomic weights, and discovery of the law led in turn to the correction of the few atomic weight values which remained uncertain. Indium, for example, had been assumed to be divalent. Since its equivalent weight was 38.3, this would make its atomic weight 76.6, placing it between arsenic and selenium in the periodic table. These two elements logically belonged in groups VA and VIA, leaving no place for indium. Tripling the equivalent weight of indium, making its atomic weight 114.9, caused it to fall into a blank space in group IIIA, between cadmium and tin. Mendeleev, by comparing the properties of indium with those of cadmium, tin, aluminum, and thallium, was able to show that this blank space was indeed where indium belonged.

The juxtaposition of certain elements in the periodic table can suggest relationships between them which otherwise might remain unsuspected. Many elements have found new applications based upon behavior predicted from their position in the periodic system. Finally, the present theory of atomic structure, developed in subsequent chapters, owes much of its early development and ready acceptance to the fact that it predicts a periodicity of structural features within the atoms exactly paralleling the observed periodicity in chemical and physical properties. This will be discussed further in Chapter 7.

Reading Suggestions 4.6

The prehistory of the periodic system prior to the time of Mendeleev and Meyer is described in an article by J. W. van Spronsen in *J. Chem. Ed.* **36,** 565 (1959). A biography by W. Prandtl of Johann Wolfgang Döbereiner, who was chemical advisor to the great analytical chemist, poet, and philosopher Johann Wolfgang von Goethe, appears in *J. Chem. Ed.* **27,** 176 (1950). For a brief biography of Lothar Meyer, and a description of his derivation of the periodic law independently of Mendeleev, see R. Winderlich, *J. Chem. Ed.* **27,** 365 (1950). A portion of the lecture on the periodic law delivered by Mendeleev before the Chemical Society of London in 1889 will be found on pp. 112–117 of the Dampiers' book *Readings in the Literature of Science* to which we have had occasion to refer in the previous chapters. The Mendeleev Archives and Museum at Leningrad University, and its collection of hand-written manuscripts and other memorabilia of the great Russian chemist, is described by V. A. Krotikov, *J. Chem. Ed.* **37,** 625 (1960). Figure 4.3 is reproduced from this article. Chapter 9 of *The Development of Modern Chemistry,* by Aaron J. Ihde (Harper & Row, New York, 1964), presents a concise but comprehensive history of the development of the periodic system.

Questions

4.1 State the periodic law.

4.2 Compare and contrast (a) group and period, (b) representative element and transition element, (c) inner transition element and transition element, (d) metal and metalloid, (e) metalloid and nonmetal.

4.3 How did the discovery of the periodic law lead to the discovery of elements?

4.4 Why did Mendeleev reverse the order of atomic weights in placing tellurium and iodine in the periodic table?

4.5 How was the atomic weight 72 which appears in Mendeleev's periodic table of 1871 (Fig. 4.6) for a then unknown element arrived at?

4.6 Briefly explain how Moseley's work contributed to the evolution of the periodic law.

4.7 How does one account for the fact that the positions of argon and potassium, cobalt and nickel, tellurium and iodine, and thorium and protactinium appear in the order that is the reverse of that expected from an arrangement based on increasing atomic weight?

4.8 Omitting argon, write the formulas for a chloride of each of the elements with atomic numbers 11 through 20. Repeat for an oxide of each element.

4.9 From their positions in the periodic table, predict which will be more metallic: (a) beryllium or boron, (b) beryllium or calcium, (c) calcium or potassium, (d) arsenic or germanium, (e) arsenic or bismuth.

4.10 To which would you predict cerium to be more closely similar, scandium or titanium?

4.11 By extrapolating from the appropriate data for the other alkali metals (available in a chemical handbook or a reference work in inorganic chemistry), predict the following properties of francium: melting point, boiling point (1 atm), density of solid, valence(s), and water solubility of the chloride.

4.12 Look up the properties of the other halogens and use them to predict the following properties of astatine: melting point, boiling point (1 atm), density in the gaseous, liquid, and solid states, valence(s) toward oxygen and toward hydrogen, solubility of $NaAt$ in water at 25° and 100°C.

4.13 Look up the physical and chemical properties of manganese, rhenium, molybdenum, and ruthenium, and use them to predict as many of the properties as you can of technetium. In similar manner, predict the properties of lawrencium from those of scandium, yttrium, and lutetium.

The chemical power of a current of electricity is in direct proportion to the absolute quantity of electricity which passes . . . .

——Michael Faraday, 1834

5 ELECTROLYSIS; OXIDATION-REDUCTION

Around the same time that Dalton proposed his atomic theory, a number of chemists, notably Sir Humphry Davy at the Royal Institution, were studying the chemical effects of the newly discovered electrical current. Just a few years earlier Alessandro Volta had found that an electric current was produced when two dissimilar metal disks—zinc and silver, for example—were placed on either side of a moist conductor, such as a piece of blotting paper soaked in brine, and then connected with a piece of wire. On this principle, he had constructed the first practical source of electric current, the "voltaic pile" (Fig. 5.1), consisting of alternating pairs of zinc and silver disks separated by pieces of brine-soaked felt.

It was soon discovered that aqueous solutions of many substances, particularly acids, bases, and salts, were capable of conducting electricity. Not only that, but electrical conduction by these substances—later called ***electrolytes*** by Michael Faraday—was accompanied by chemical change. The relationship between electricity and chemical change led Berzelius to conclude that all molecules were held together by electrical forces. Faraday found that the amount of chemical change was proportional to the quantity of electricity which flowed, and, when equal amounts of current flowed, to the equivalent weights of the reactants. In 1887, nearly 90 years after the first electrochemical experiments were performed, Svante Arrhenius pro-

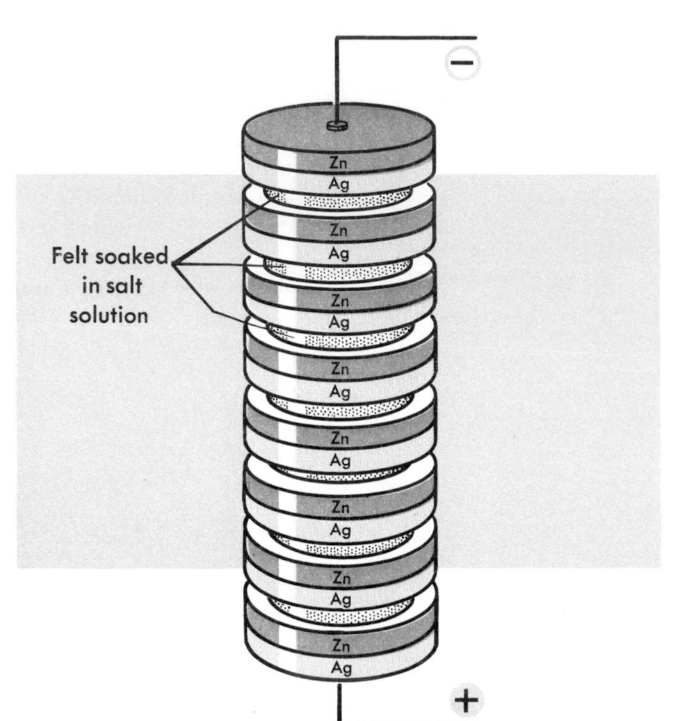

Fig. 5.1 Voltaic pile.

posed a theory of the nature of electrolytes in solution which, with some modifications, remains valid today. Largely out of the study of electrolytes there evolved the concept of ***oxidation state,*** an artificial but very useful device for classifying an element's state of chemical combination.

5.1 Electrolysis

Substances are classified as electrolytes or nonelectrolytes according to whether or not their aqueous solutions will conduct an electric current. Most acids, bases, and salts are electrolytes, while most organic compounds (Chapter 17) are nonelectrolytes. Certain insoluble substances, metal oxides in particular, and most bases and salts conduct electricity when melted, but unlike metals, electrolytes are not appreciably conducting in the solid state.

When two pieces of platinum or other unreactive metal are connected to opposite poles of a battery and then immersed in a solution of an electrolyte, a current flows through the solution, and a chemical reaction takes place at each of the electrodes (Fig. 5.2). Usually, either hydrogen is evolved or some metal is deposited at the electrode, called the ***cathode,*** which is connected to the negative pole of the battery. A nonmetal is generally liberated at the ***anode***. This process is known as ***electrolysis.*** If the molten electrolyte conducts electricity, electrolysis will take place in the absence of a solvent, but the products may be different from those obtained when the electrolyte is in solution. Products from the electrolysis of some typical electrolytes are listed in Table 5.1.

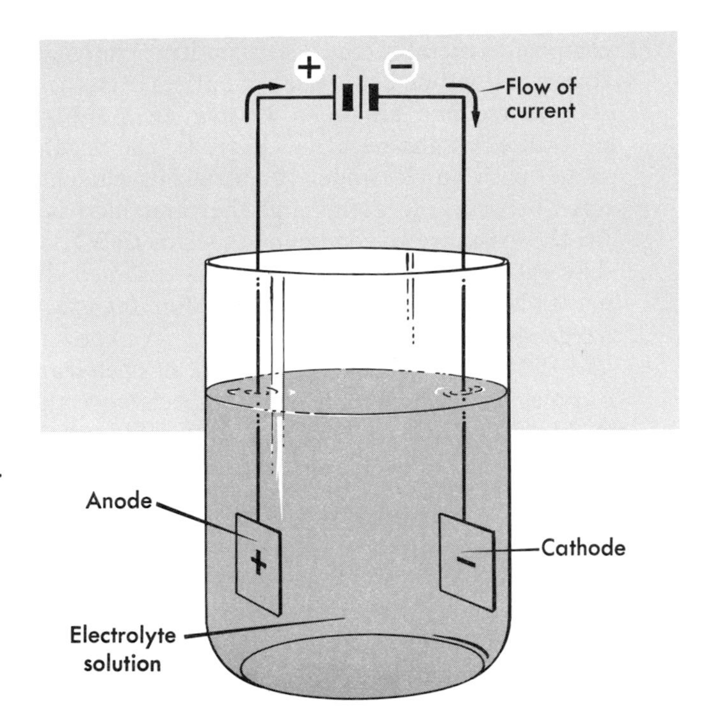

Fig. 5.2 Electrolytic cell.

TABLE 5.1 Some Typical Electrolysis Products

	Produced at Cathode	Produced at Anode
Aqueous Solutions		
Sulfuric acid (H_2SO_4)	H_2	O_2
Acetic acid ($HC_2H_3O_2$)	H_2	O_2
Sodium hydroxide (NaOH)	H_2	O_2
Potassium hydroxide (KOH)	H_2	O_2
Copper(II) sulfate ($CuSO_4$)	Cu	O_2
Copper(II) chloride ($CuCl_2$)	Cu	Cl_2
Sodium chloride (NaCl)	H_2	Cl_2
Silver nitrate ($AgNO_3$)	Ag	O_2
Pure Liquids		
100% sulfuric acid	Does not conduct electricity	
100% acetic acid	Does not conduct electricity	
Molten sodium hydroxide	Na	O_2
Molten potassium hydroxide	K	O_2
Molten sodium chloride	Na	Cl_2

Berzelius concluded that since chemical compounds can be decomposed by electricity, the binding forces between the atoms must be electrical in nature. He reasoned that metals, because they are deposited at the negative electrode, are *electropositive*, while nonmetals, which are liberated at the positive electrode, are *electronegative*. According to this theory, in their compounds metal atoms bear a positive charge, nonmetal atoms a negative charge. Bonding between atoms arises from the attraction of these opposite charges for one another. During electrolysis, the positive charges are neutralized at the negative electrode; the negative charges are neutralized at the positive electrode. Neutralizing the charges destroys the bonding force between the atoms and the compound is decomposed. To account for the existence of compounds such as $CuSO_4$ which contain three or more different kinds of atoms, Berzelius assumed different degrees of electronegativity among the elements, sulfur for example being positive toward oxygen but negative toward copper. We know now that Berzelius' concept and the modern view of the nature of chemical bonding are in essentially complete agreement only with respect to certain simple salts and oxides such as $NaCl$, CaF_2, KBr, and BaO. His idea that the elements possess different relative electronegativities continues to be useful, however (Sec. 8.4).

5.2 Faraday's Laws

About 1834 Michael Faraday observed that *the amount of electrolysis which takes place is in exact proportion to the quantity of electricity which is used.* For example, if current flowing at a certain rate liberates 1 ml of hydrogen gas at the cathode in 5 min, then that same flow of current will liberate 2 ml of hydrogen in 10 min, 3 ml in 15 min, and so forth. *The quantity of electricity is measured in coulombs. One* **coulomb** *is defined as the quantity of electricity which will deposit 0.0011180 g of silver from a solution of silver nitrate. The rate at which electricity flows in a circuit is measured in* ***amperes.*** A current of *1 ampere (1 amp)* corresponds to the transfer of electricity at a rate of *1 coulomb per second.*

Example 5.1

A current of electricity flowing at a steady rate deposited 0.7526 g of silver from a solution of silver nitrate in 10.00 min. Calculate the amperage of the current.

Solution: The amperage is equal to the number of coulombs flowing in the circuit in 1 sec. The total number of coulombs which passed through the circuit is obtained by dividing the mass of silver deposited by that amount (0.001118 g) which would be deposited by 1 coulomb of electricity. Dividing the number of coulombs by the time in seconds that it took for that amount of electricity to flow in the circuit gives the current in coulombs per second, or amperes:

$$\text{Amperes} = \frac{\text{coulombs}}{\text{seconds}} = \frac{(0.7526 \text{ g Ag})}{(0.001118 \text{ g Ag/coulomb})(10.00 \text{ min})(60.00 \text{ sec/min})}$$

$$= 1.122 \text{ amp}$$

Example 5.2

If the current used in Example 5.1 flowed for 20.00 min, how much silver would it deposit in that amount of time?

Solution: If the current continues to flow at the same rate, twice as many coulombs will pass in 20.00 min as in 10.00 min. The amount of silver deposited will therefore be exactly twice as much, as $2 \times 0.7526 = 1.505$ g.

Example 5.3

How many grams of silver will be deposited in 10.00 min by a current having twice the amperage of that used in Example 5.1?

Solution: Doubling the amperage doubles the number of coulombs passing in a given length of time. A 2.244-amp current therefore will deposit twice as much silver in 10.00 min ($2 \times 0.7526 = 1.505$ g in this case) as a current of 1.122 amp.

Faraday also discovered that *the mass of any substance formed by the passage of a given amount of electricity is directly proportional to the equivalent weight of that substance.*

This law is easily demonstrated by connecting two electrolytic cells in series, so that whatever electrical current passes through the first cell must also pass through the second (Fig. 5.3). If, for example, the first cell

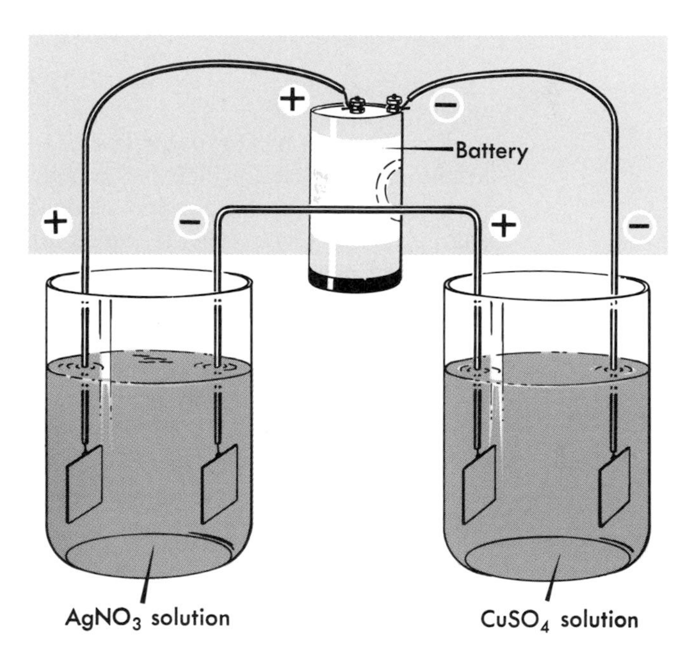

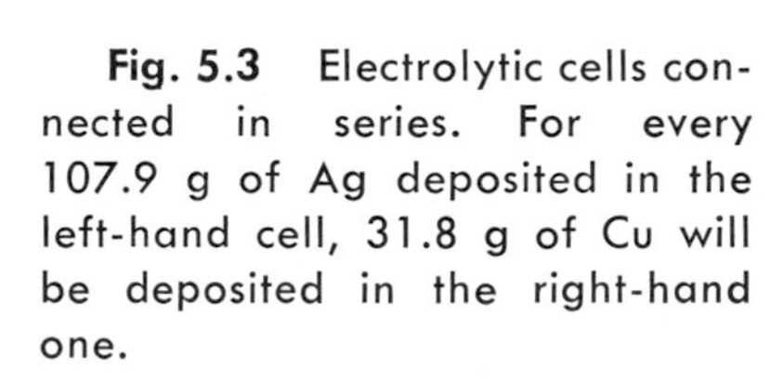

Fig. 5.3 Electrolytic cells connected in series. For every 107.9 g of Ag deposited in the left-hand cell, 31.8 g of Cu will be deposited in the right-hand one.

contains silver nitrate solution and the second cell copper(II) sulfate solution, then no matter how long the current flows and no matter what its amperage, the masses of silver and copper deposited in the two cells will always be in the same ratio as their respective equivalent weights, that is, 107.9:31.8. To liberate one equivalent weight of any element during electrolysis requires the same quantity of electricity: 96,493 coulombs. This quantity of electricity, 96,493 coulombs, is called the ***faraday*** ($\mathfrak{F}$).

Example 5.4

How many grams of chromium will be deposited by electrolysis of a solution of chromium(III) sulfate ($Cr_2(SO_4)_3$) for 30 min using a current of 5 amp?

Solution: One equivalent weight of chromium will be deposited for each faraday of current which flows in the circuit. The equivalent weight of chromium in chromium(III) sulfate is 52.0/3 = 17.3 g. The number of faradays is equal to the total number of coulombs divided by the number of coulombs in a faraday. To three significant figures, 1 $\mathfrak{F}$ = 96,500 coulombs. Thus:

$$\text{Grams Cr deposited} = \frac{(5 \text{ coulombs/sec})(60 \text{ sec/min})(30 \text{ min})(17.3 \text{ g deposited}/\mathfrak{F})}{96{,}500 \text{ coulombs}/\mathfrak{F}}$$

$$= 1.62 \text{ g deposited}$$

Example 5.5

How much oxygen is liberated at the anode during the deposition of 1.62 g of chromium as in Example 5.4?

Solution: For every equivalent weight of chromium deposited at the cathode, one equivalent weight of oxygen must be formed at the anode. The equivalent weight of oxygen is 8.00 g. Therefore,

$$\text{Grams } O_2 \text{ liberated} = \frac{1.62 \text{ g Cr}}{17.3 \text{ g Cr/eq wt}} \times (8.00 \text{ g } O_2\text{/eq wt})$$

$$= 0.750 \text{ g } O_2$$

Reasoning from Faraday's laws, G. J. Stoney suggested the existence of atoms of electricity, which he named ***electrons***. Every electron bears an identical negative charge, and neutralization of each positive or negative charge during electrolysis requires the gain or loss of one electron. The number of electrons which will neutralize the total charge on one mole of singly charged atoms will neutralize the charge on one-half mole of doubly charged atoms. This number of electrons is the faraday. *A **faraday** is thus the charge on a mole of electrons.* One, two, or three faradays of electricity must flow in order to liberate one mole of an element according to whether each atom gains or loses one, two, or three electrons during electrolysis. In electrolysis reactions, the equivalent weight of an element is equal to its atomic weight divided by the number of electrons which it gains or loses, e.g.,

$$Ag^+ + e^- \rightarrow Ag^0 \qquad \text{(eq wt = at wt)}$$
$$Cu^{++} + 2\ e^- \rightarrow Cu^0 \qquad \text{(eq wt = at wt/2)}$$
$$Cr^{+++} + 3\ e^- \rightarrow Cr^0 \qquad \text{(eq wt = at wt/3)}$$
$$Cl^- \rightarrow \tfrac{1}{2}\ Cl_2 + e^- \qquad \text{(eq wt = at wt)}$$
$$O^{--} \rightarrow \tfrac{1}{2}\ O_2 + 2\ e^- \qquad \text{(eq wt = at wt/2)}$$

5.3 Ionization

In order to account for the conductivity of electrolytes, electrolysis, and certain properties of electrolyte solutions which will be discussed in Chapter 10, Svante Arrhenius advanced a theory of electrolytic dissociation and submitted it to the faculty of the University of Uppsala, Sweden, as part of his doctoral thesis. According to Arrhenius, when an electrolyte is dissolved in water, its molecules dissociate immediately and more or less completely into oppositely charged fragments, or ***ions***. Since the conductivity of an electrolyte, measured in terms of its equivalent conductance (Sec. 10.14), was known to increase with dilution (Fig. 5.4), Arrhenius

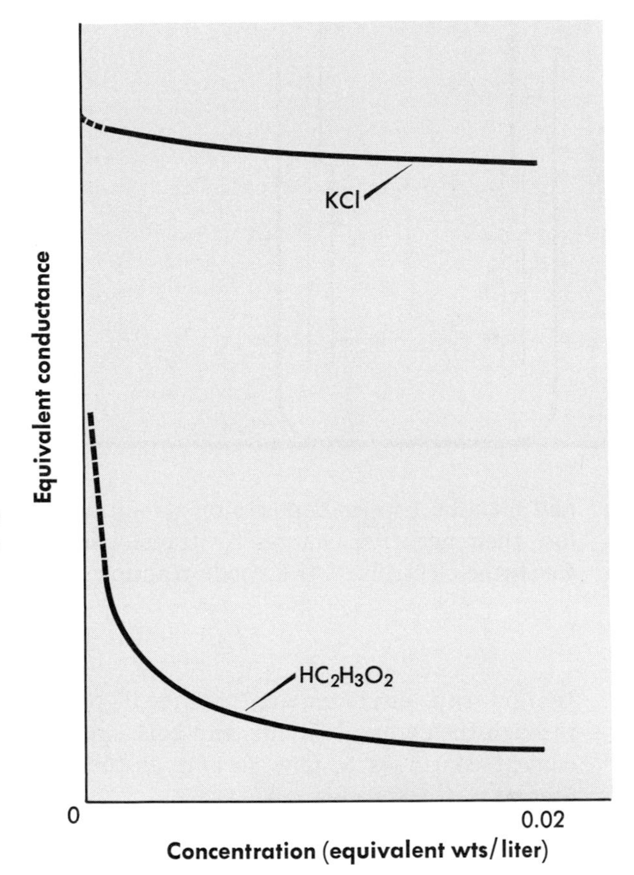

Fig. 5.4 Variation in equivalent conductance with concentration.

assumed that increasing dilution favored dissociation of the electrolyte, complete dissociation being attained only at infinite dilution. Thus, in 100% pure sulfuric or acetic acids, the molecules are undissociated, and the pure liquids do not conduct electricity (Table 5.1). Adding water causes some of the molecules to dissociate into ions (*ionize*), and the solutions are electrically conducting.*

The conduction of electricity by an electrolyte may be pictured in the following way (Fig. 5.5). When electrodes are placed into the electrolyte solution and connected to a battery, the positive ions, or ***cations,*** migrate toward the negatively charged *cathode*. Here each cation picks up one or more electrons. If the electrolyte is copper(II) chloride ($CuCl_2$), for example, the reaction at the cathode is

$$Cu^{++} + 2\ e^- \rightarrow Cu^0$$

* Today, when the existence of ions is pretty much taken for granted, it is sometimes hard to realize what a revolutionary idea electrolytic dissociation was in 1887. Like many bold concepts, it was greeted by a notable lack of enthusiasm, and the thesis was accepted, with reservations, because the candidate otherwise showed promise. Arrhenius later became the first director of the Nobel Institute for Physical Chemistry.

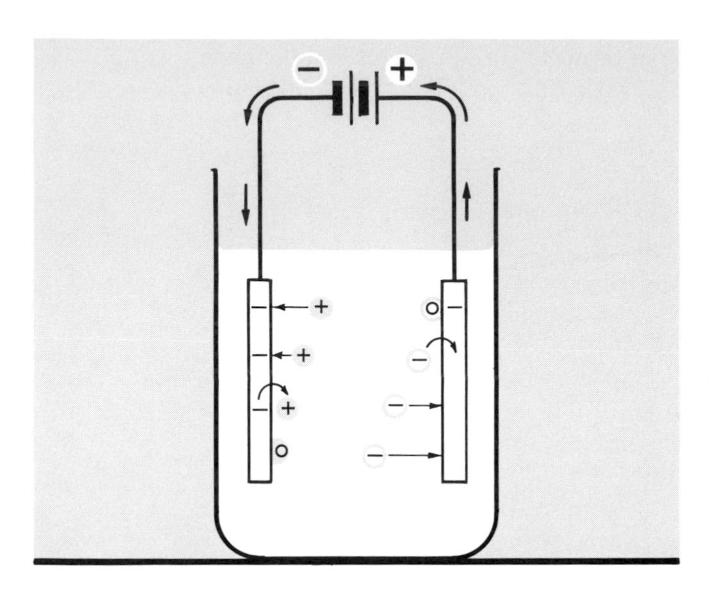

Fig. 5.5 Electrolytic conductivity.

and metallic copper deposits on its surface. The negative ions or ***anions*** lose their negative charges by transferring electrons to the *anode*. With $CuCl_2$ the electrolyte, the anode reaction is

$$2\,Cl^- \rightarrow Cl_2 + 2\,e^-$$

In this way, electrons are "pumped" out of the solution at the anode, through the external circuit, and back into the solution at the cathode, and current continues to flow as long as there are positive and negative ions present in the solution.

It takes energy to remove an electron from an anion or add an electron to a cation. Apparently in some cases it takes less energy to decompose the solvent than it does to neutralize the charges on the ions. For example, sodium is not deposited at the cathode during the electrolysis of an aqueous solution of $NaCl$. Instead, the solvent, water, picks up an electron, and dissociates into hydrogen gas and a hydroxide ion:

$$H_2O + e^- \rightarrow \tfrac{1}{2}\,H_2 + OH^-$$

At the anode, electrons are lost more readily by the chloride ions than by either the water molecules or the hydroxide ions formed in the cathode reaction:

$$Cl^- \rightarrow \tfrac{1}{2}\,Cl_2 + e^-$$

Consequently, during electrolysis of $NaCl$ solution, hydrogen is evolved at the cathode and chlorine at the anode,* and the solution changes from one of sodium chloride to one of sodium hydroxide.

* If the salt solution is very dilute, in addition to chlorine appreciable amounts of oxygen may also be liberated at the anode. The reaction for the formation of oxygen at the anode is

$$H_2O \rightarrow \tfrac{1}{2}\,O_2 + 2\,H^+ + 2\,e^-$$

Similarly, it is more difficult to remove electrons from sulfate ions than from water molecules. During the electrolysis of $CuSO_4$ solution, for example, the electrode reactions are

At the cathode: $Cu^{++} + 2\,e^- \rightarrow Cu^0$
At the anode: $H_2O \rightarrow 2\,H^+ + \frac{1}{2}\,O_2 + 2\,e^-$

The SO_4^{--} ions are unaffected. Eventually, after all of the copper ions have been discharged from the solution, what is left is a solution of sulfuric acid.

Arrhenius' theory of partial ionization increasing with increasing dilution accounts for the behavior of so-called "weak electrolytes" (Sec. 10.16), substances whose solutions conduct electricity, but rather poorly. It does not, however, account for the conductivity of molten salts. Salts such as **NaCl** appear to be composed not of neutral molecules, but entirely of ions, even in the solid state. The solid is nonconducting because the ions are fixed in position and cannot migrate toward the electrodes. Melting the crystal frees them to move and current can flow. In concentrated solution, inter-ionic attraction (Sec. 10.18) causes the ions to form aggregates, reducing the apparent degree of ionization. Added solvent makes it less likely that the ions will come in contact with one another. Fewer aggregates are formed, and those are of smaller size, resulting in an increase in the apparent degree of ionization (Fig. 5.6).

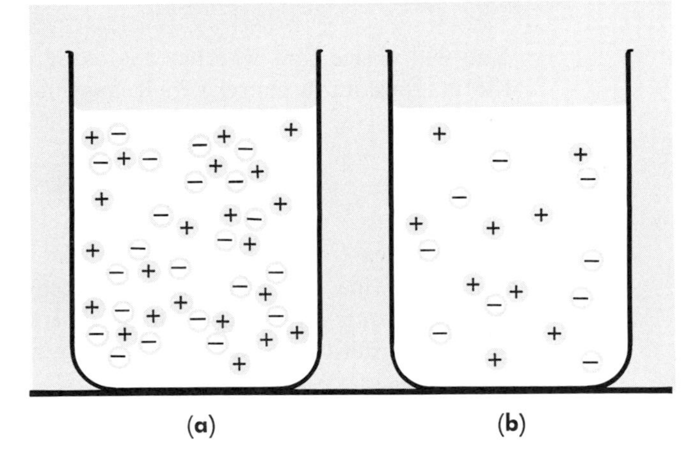

Fig. 5.6 Inter-ionic attraction. (a) Concentrated solution and (b) dilute solution.

Oxidation and Reduction 5.4

A reaction between any substance and oxygen is called ***oxidation.*** Each of the following reactions, therefore, is an oxidation:

$$Mg + \frac{1}{2}\,O_2 \rightarrow MgO$$

$$C + O_2 \rightarrow CO_2$$

$$S + O_2 \rightarrow SO_2$$

$$SO_2 + \frac{1}{2}\,O_2 \rightarrow SO_3$$

Most metallic oxides, such as MgO, have been shown to be ***ionic compounds*** (Sec. 8.5). Their crystals are composed of positive and negative ions, held together by the natural attraction which exists between opposite electrical charges. When magnesium reacts with oxygen, for example, each magnesium atom loses a pair of electrons, transferring them to an oxygen atom. The magnesium becomes a positively charged Mg^{++} ion. The oxygen atoms acquire negative charges, and become oxide ions, O^{--}. The process may be written in two steps as follows:

$$Mg^0 \rightarrow Mg^{++} + 2\ e^-$$
$$\tfrac{1}{2}\ O_2 + 2\ e^- \rightarrow O^{--}$$

In the process of being oxidized, the magnesium has lost electrons. The oxygen, which we can call the ***oxidizing agent,*** has gained electrons.

Magnesium will also burn in chlorine, forming magnesium chloride:

$$Mg + Cl_2 \rightarrow MgCl_2$$

Like the oxide, magnesium chloride is ionic, and this reaction involves electron transfer from magnesium to chlorine:

$$Mg^0 \rightarrow Mg^{++} + 2\ e^-$$
$$Cl_2 + 2\ e^- \rightarrow 2\ Cl^-$$

You will notice that whether the oxide or the chloride is formed, as far as the magnesium is concerned, it has undergone the same reaction in both cases:

$$Mg^0 \rightarrow Mg^{++} + 2\ e^-$$

Since the reaction is the same as it was with oxygen, it is still called oxidation, only this time the oxidizing agent is chlorine. *Any reaction which involves the loss of electrons is described as an* ***oxidation.*** Thus each of the following reactions, however it may be brought about, is an oxidation:

$$Na^0 \rightarrow Na^+ + e^-$$
$$Zn^0 \rightarrow Zn^{++} + 2\ e^-$$
$$Cu^0 \rightarrow Cu^+ + e^-$$
$$Cu^+ \rightarrow Cu^{++} + e^-$$

The opposite of oxidation is ***reduction.*** An important part of metallurgy, for example, consists in the reduction of metallic oxides to the free metals:

$$Fe_2O_3 + 3\ C \rightarrow 2\ Fe + 3\ CO$$
$$Cu_2O + 2\ C \rightarrow 2\ Cu + 2\ CO$$
$$WO_3 + 3\ H_2 \rightarrow W + 3\ H_2O$$

The agents which effect reduction, carbon and hydrogen in the above cases, *are called* **reducing agents.** *Reduction involves the gain of electrons by the substance being reduced:*

$$Fe^{+++} + 3\ e^- \rightarrow Fe^0$$
$$Cu^+ + e^- \rightarrow Cu^0$$

No oxidation can occur unless accompanied by reduction, nor can reduction take place without oxidation. Electrons cannot lie around loose, so no substance can be oxidized—lose electrons—unless some other substance is available to accept those electrons and become reduced in the process. Conversely, if something is to be reduced, the electrons which it needs must come from somewhere, and the agency which supplies the electrons is therefore oxidized. It also follows from this that *the number of electrons lost in the oxidation step must equal the number of electrons gained in the reduction step.*

Oxidation Number 5.5

Consider the reactions:

$$C + O_2 \rightarrow CO_2$$
$$S + O_2 \rightarrow SO_2$$
$$SO_2 + \tfrac{1}{2}\ O_2 \rightarrow SO_3$$

Each of these reactions is obviously an oxidation, yet the products are not ionic compounds. Bonding in nonmetallic oxides is of a different type (covalent bonding, Sec. 8.1), and the atoms in these compounds are not charged in the sense that ions are. Nevertheless, it is often useful to treat these compounds as though the bonds in them were ionic, and assign *oxidation numbers* to the elements according to a set of arbitrary rules. Oxidation and reduction are then described in terms of changes in oxidation state.

The ***oxidation state*** of an element or radical is described by its oxidation number, which is assigned according to the following rules:

1. Atoms of an uncombined element have an oxidation number of zero, even if the element exists in the form of polyatomic molecules. Thus all of the following elements are in the zero oxidation state, with oxidation number 0: Zn, Cu, Na, H_2, O_2, P_4, Cl_2, S_8.
2. The oxidation number of an ion is equal to the charge on the ion. Thus, sodium is in the +1 oxidation state in $NaCl$ and Na_2CO_3; copper is in the +2 oxidation state in $CuSO_4$; and chlorine is in the −1 oxidation state in KCl.
3. Atoms joined by non-ionic bonds are assigned oxidation numbers by imagining each of the bonds to be ionic, with the positive charge residing on the more metallic (more electropositive) atom, and the negative charge on the less metallic (more electronegative) atom. The relative metallic natures of two elements can usually be estimated from their position in the periodic table (Sec. 4.4 and Fig. 4.8). The total charge placed on an

atom by the application of this rule is the oxidation number of the element. For example, in SO_2 there are four bonds between sulfur and oxygen:

$$O{=}S{=}O$$

If the bonds are assumed to be ionic, since oxygen is more electronegative than sulfur, this becomes

$$O^{--} \quad S^{++++} \quad O^{--}$$

The oxidation number of sulfur in SO_2 is therefore $+4$; that of oxygen is -2.

4. Where atoms of the same element are joined by a non-ionic bond, that bond is not included in calculating the oxidation number of the element. Thus in hydrogen peroxide,

$$H{-}O{-}O{-}H$$

the oxidation number of the oxygen is -1.

5. The sum of the oxidation numbers of all of the atoms in a neutral compound must be zero; the sum of the oxidation numbers of all of the atoms in a complex ion must equal the charge on the ion.

Determining the oxidation state of an element in a complex compound is often greatly simplified by remembering that, with rare exceptions (e.g., rule 4 above), the oxidation states of hydrogen and oxygen in their compounds are nearly always $+1$ and -2 respectively, and then applying rule 5. For example, in H_2SO_4, each hydrogen has an oxidation number of $+1$, each oxygen atom an oxidation number of -2. Then,

$$\begin{array}{lcr} \text{2 hydrogen atoms @ } +1 \text{ each} & = & +2 \\ \text{4 oxygen atoms @ } -2 \text{ each} & = & \underline{-8} \\ & & -6 \end{array}$$

For the sum of the oxidation numbers of all of the atoms in the compound to equal zero, the oxidation number of sulfur in sulfuric acid must be $+6$.

Similarly, the oxidation number of manganese in $KMnO_4$ may be calculated as follows: In a compound, the oxidation number of a metal is always positive and usually numerically equal to its valence. The oxidation number of potassium in $KMnO_4$ is therefore $+1$, that of oxygen again is -2. Then,

$$\begin{array}{lcr} \text{1 potassium atom @ } +1 & = & +1 \\ \text{4 oxygen atoms @ } -2 \text{ each} & = & \underline{-8} \\ & & -7 \\ \text{1 manganese atom} & = & \underline{+7} \\ & & 0 \end{array}$$

Therefore, manganese is in the $+7$ oxidation state in $KMnO_4$.

At this point it is well to make a distinction between valence and oxidation state. Valence measures the combining capacity of an atom in terms of the number of bonds (ionic or otherwise) which it may form with other atoms. Valence is a pure number, and as such has no sign, either positive or negative. It is therefore not strictly correct to speak of "positive valence" or "negative valence," even though these expressions are often heard. The oxidation number expresses an arbitrarily defined state of an element in a particular compound. Unless it is zero, the oxidation number is always positive or negative. Any element capable of forming compounds has at least one valence in the sense of having the capacity to form bonds. A sample of that element may or may not exercise its valence according to whether or not it combines with a sample of another element to form a compound. On the other hand, the oxidation state of a free element is always zero, while its oxidation state when it is part of a compound is assigned by following a set of arbitrary rules. The distinction between valence and oxidation state is shown for the element carbon in Table 5.2.

TABLE 5.2 Valence and Oxidation State of Carbon in Several Compounds

Compound	Valences of Carbon	Valence Exercised in Compound	Oxidation State in Compound
Element (C)	2, 4	4*	0
Methane (CH_4)	2, 4	4	−4
Methanol (H_3COH)	2, 4	4	−2
Formaldehyde (H_2CO)	2, 4	4	0
Formic acid ($HCHO_2$)	2, 4	4	+2
Carbon monoxide (CO)	2, 4	2	+2
Carbon dioxide (CO_2)	2, 4	4	+4

* Bonding in solid carbon is discussed in Sec. 18.1.

Redox Equations 5.6

Oxidation and reduction may now be defined more generally in terms of changes in oxidation state. *A substance is oxidized if its oxidation state becomes more positive (or less negative).* Likewise, *a substance is reduced if its oxidation state becomes more negative (or less positive).* Thus in the reaction

$$Na_2SO_3 + I_2 + H_2O \rightarrow Na_2SO_4 + 2\ HI$$

sulfur is *oxidized* from the +4 state in Na_2SO_3 to the +6 state in Na_2SO_4. At the same time, iodine is *reduced* from the zero state in I_2 to the −1 state in HI. Sodium sulfite, Na_2SO_3, is acting as the ***reducing agent;*** iodine, I_2, is the ***oxidizing agent.*** *A reaction* such as this *in which elements undergo changes in their oxidation states is called an* ***oxidation-reduction,*** or ***redox reaction.*** The equation for a redox reaction, as you might expect, is known as a ***redox equation.***

5.7 Balancing Redox Equations

Redox equations more often than not are quite difficult to balance by inspection. There are, however, several systematic ways to go about balancing these equations. Each method accomplishes the same result, but in a somewhat different way. Basic to each method is being able to recognize the oxidizing agent and the reducing agent in the reaction. The method of *oxidation number change* involves balancing the increase in the oxidation number of the element being oxidized against the decrease in the oxidation number of the element which is reduced by adjusting the number of moles of each appearing in the equation. The *ion-electron method* works on the principle of equalizing the number of electrons lost by the reducing agent and gained by the oxidizing agent.

(a) Oxidation Number Change. The reaction between iron(III) chloride and tin(II) chloride will serve as our first example. The unbalanced expression for this reaction is

$$FeCl_3 + SnCl_2 \rightarrow FeCl_2 + SnCl_4$$

While this particular redox equation is easily balanced by inspection, we will apply the oxidation number change method for purposes of illustration. The first step is to identify the elements which undergo a change in oxidation state in the course of the reaction. In this instance, the oxidation number of the iron changes from +3 to +2; that of the tin changes from +2 to +4. The iron is being reduced, the tin oxidized:

$$Fe\ (+3) \rightarrow Fe\ (+2) \qquad \text{(reduction)}$$
$$Sn\ (+2) \rightarrow Sn\ (+4) \qquad \text{(oxidation)}$$

The iron is seen to undergo a change of −1 in its oxidation state, while the oxidation state of the tin changes by +2. This means that two iron atoms can be reduced by one tin atom:

	Total Change in Oxidation Number
$2\ Fe\ (+3) \rightarrow 2\ Fe\ (+2)$	−2
$Sn\ (+2) \rightarrow Sn\ (+4)$	+2
	0

Placing the coefficients of these two "half-reactions" in front of the corresponding compounds gives the balanced equation

$$2\ FeCl_3 + SnCl_2 \rightarrow 2\ FeCl_2 + SnCl_4$$

Now let us try something a little more difficult. The typical oxidation of an iron(II) salt by a permanganate is shown by the following unbalanced expression:

$$FeSO_4 + KMnO_4 + H_2SO_4 \rightarrow Fe_2(SO_4)_3 + MnSO_4 + K_2SO_4 + H_2O$$

Here, iron is being oxidized from the +2 to the +3 state; manganese is being reduced from the +7 to the +2 state. Since two iron atoms appear on the right side of the unbalanced expression, there must necessarily be an equal number on the left, making the unbalanced "half-reactions"

	Change in Oxidation Number
$2\ Fe\ (+2) \rightarrow 2\ Fe\ (+3)$	$2(+1) = +2$
$Mn\ (+7) \rightarrow Mn\ (+2)$	-5

In order to make the total increase in oxidation number equal the total decrease, the expression representing the oxidation of iron must be multiplied by 5, and that for the reduction of manganese multiplied by 2:

	Total Change in Oxidation Number
$5[2\ Fe\ (+2) \rightarrow 2\ Fe\ (+3)]$	$5(+2) = +10$
$2[Mn\ (+7) \rightarrow Mn\ (+2)]$	$2(-5) = -10$
$10\ Fe\ (+2) + 2\ Mn\ (+7) \rightarrow 10\ Fe\ (+3) + 2\ Mn\ (+2)$	0

Placing these coefficients with the corresponding compounds gives us the expression

$$10\ FeSO_4 + 2\ KMnO_4 + H_2SO_4 \rightarrow 5\ Fe_2(SO_4)_3 + 2\ MnSO_4 + K_2SO_4 + H_2O$$

At this point the equation is still not balanced, but now that the proper coefficients are known for the compounds that take part in the oxidation and reduction steps, final balancing is readily done by inspection. Eight molecules of H_2SO_4 are needed to give 18 sulfate radicals on each side of the equation. To take care of the 16 hydrogens from the sulfuric acid, we need 8 water molecules on the right. This also takes care of the 8 oxygen atoms from the two molecules of $KMnO_4$, and the equation is now balanced:

$$10\ FeSO_4 + 2\ KMnO_4 + 8\ H_2SO_4 \rightarrow 5\ Fe_2(SO_4)_3 + 2\ MnSO_4 + K_2SO_4 + 8\ H_2O$$

Finally, let us balance one last equation by this method, this time condensing the various steps somewhat.

Unbalanced expression:

$$NaCrO_2 + NaClO + H_2O \rightarrow Na_2CrO_4 + Cl_2 + NaOH$$

Unbalanced half-reactions:

	Change in Oxidation Number
Oxidation: $Cr\ (+3) \rightarrow Cr\ (+6)$	$+3$
Reduction: $2\ Cl\ (+1) \rightarrow Cl_2\ (0)$	-2

Balanced half-reactions:

	Total Change in Oxidation Number
$2[Cr\ (+3) \rightarrow Cr\ (+6)]$	$2(+3) = +6$
$3[2\ Cl\ (+1) \rightarrow Cl_2\ (0)]$	$3(-2) = -6$

Partially balanced expression:

$$2\ NaCrO_2 + 6\ NaClO + H_2O \rightarrow 2\ Na_2CrO_4 + 3\ Cl_2 + NaOH$$

Fully balanced equation:

$$2\ NaCrO_2 + 6\ NaClO + 2\ H_2O \rightarrow 2\ Na_2CrO_4 + 3\ Cl_2 + 4\ NaOH$$

(b) Ion-Electron Method. Again let us balance the equation for the oxidation of an iron(II) salt by a permanganate, this time applying the ion-electron method. As before, the unbalanced expression for this reaction may be written

$$FeSO_4 + KMnO_4 + H_2SO_4 \rightarrow Fe_2(SO_4)_3 + MnSO_4 + K_2SO_4 + H_2O$$

As the first step in balancing an equation by this method, we write in the ionized form all compounds we know to be ionic. Usually all acids, bases, and salts can be assumed to be ionic. In this case this gives us

$$Fe^{++} + SO_4^{--} + K^+ + MnO_4^- + 2\ H^+ + SO_4^{--} \rightarrow$$
$$2\ Fe^{+++} + 3\ SO_4^{--} + Mn^{++} + 2\ K^+ + SO_4^{--} + H_2O$$

Those ions which appear unchanged on both sides of the equation, so-called "spectator ions," take no actual part in the redox reaction and can therefore be omitted, leaving us with

$$Fe^{++} + MnO_4^- + 2\ H^+ \rightarrow 2\ Fe^{+++} + Mn^{++} + H_2O$$

The coefficients in front of the H^+ and Fe^{+++} at this point will probably be changed before we are finished, so it is best to omit them also. Now we are down to the net ionic expression for the redox reaction:

$$Fe^{++} + MnO_4^- + H^+ \rightarrow Fe^{+++} + Mn^{++} + H_2O$$

which we can proceed to balance. At this point the half-reactions are

$$Fe^{++} \rightarrow Fe^{+++} \quad \text{(oxidation)}$$
$$MnO_4^- \rightarrow Mn^{++} \quad \text{(reduction)}$$

The half-reaction for the reduction is not balanced, there being 4 oxygen atoms on the left, and none on the right. We can take care of the 4 oxygens by adding 4 water molecules to the right side. The hydrogens we get by adding **8** H^+ ions to the left side. We can feel confident about doing this because both H^+ ions and H_2O molecules appear above in the net ionic expression. The expression for the reduction half-reaction is now:

$$MnO_4^- + 8\ H^+ \rightarrow Mn^{++} + 4\ H_2O$$

We now add up the charges on all of the ions on each side of the half-reaction:

$$\underbrace{\underset{(-1)}{MnO_4^-} + \underset{(+8)}{8\ H^+}}_{(+7)} \rightarrow \underbrace{\underset{(+2)}{Mn^{++}} + \underset{(0)}{4\ H_2O}}_{(+2)}$$

To go from a total charge of +7 to a total charge of +2 requires the addition of 5 electrons:

$$5\ e^- + MnO_4^- + 8\ H^+ \rightarrow Mn^{++} + 4\ H_2O$$

Oxidation of Fe^{++} to Fe^{+++} involves the loss of 1 electron per atom of iron. Five Fe^{++} ions are therefore needed to reduce **1** MnO_4^-:

$$5\ Fe^{++} \rightarrow 5\ Fe^{+++} + 5\ e^-$$
$$5\ e^- + MnO_4^- + 8\ H^+ \rightarrow Mn^{++} + 4\ H_2O$$

Adding the two electrically balanced half-reactions gives the balanced ***net ionic equation*** for the reaction:

$$5\ Fe^{++} + MnO_4^- + 8\ H^+ \rightarrow 5\ Fe^{+++} + Mn^{++} + 4\ H_2O$$

The net ionic equation emphasizes the fact that although various "spectator ions" are necessary to preserve electrical neutrality, the actual redox reaction remains the same whether one uses $FeSO_4$ or $FeCl_2$, $KMnO_4$ or $NaMnO_4$, H_2SO_4 or HCl. If we wish, we may add the appropriate "spectator ions" in order to obtain an equation showing the formulas of actual compounds:

$$5\ FeSO_4 + KMnO_4 + 4\ H_2SO_4 \rightarrow$$
$$2\tfrac{1}{2}\ Fe_2(SO_4)_3 + MnSO_4 + \tfrac{1}{2}\ K_2SO_4 + 4\ H_2O$$

Doubling this equation to eliminate the fractional coefficients leaves us with the same equation that we obtained by the oxidation number change method:

$$10\ FeSO_4 + 2\ KMnO_4 + 8\ H_2SO_4 \rightarrow 5\ Fe_2(SO_4)_3 + 2\ MnSO_4 + K_2SO_4 + 8\ H_2O$$

As another example, let us derive the equation representing the oxidation of chromite ion by hypochlorite ion in alkaline (OH^-) solution:

$$CrO_2^- \rightarrow CrO_4^{--}$$
$$ClO^- \rightarrow Cl_2^0$$

To balance the half-reaction for the oxidation of CrO_2^-, since the reaction is being carried out in basic solution, we add OH^- ions (4 of them in this case) to the side which has the ion with the smaller proportion of oxygen, and an appropriate number of H_2O molecules to the other side:

$$\underbrace{\underset{(-4)}{4\ OH^-} + \underset{(-1)}{CrO_2^-}}_{(-5)} \rightarrow \underbrace{\underset{(-2)}{CrO_4^{--}} + \underset{(0)}{2\ H_2O}}_{(-2)}$$

Adding up the total charges on each side shows us that 3 electrons are lost for every chromite ion oxidized.

The other half-reaction is similarly balanced, again adding OH^- and H_2O as needed:

$$\underbrace{\underset{(0)}{2\ H_2O} + \underset{(-2)}{2\ ClO^-}}_{(-2)} \rightarrow \underbrace{\underset{(0)}{Cl_2} + \underset{(-4)}{4\ OH^-}}_{(-4)}$$

Two electrons are seen to be gained in the reduction of two hypochlorite ions to molecular chlorine.

Multiplying the oxidation half-reaction by 2, and the reduction half-reaction by 3, balances the electrons lost and gained:

$$8\ OH^- + 2\ CrO_2^- \rightarrow 2\ CrO_4^{--} + 4\ H_2O$$
$$6\ H_2O + 6\ ClO^- \rightarrow 3\ Cl_2 + 12\ OH^-$$

$$8\ OH^- + 2\ CrO_2^- + 6\ H_2O + 6\ ClO^- \rightarrow 2\ CrO_4^{--} + 4\ H_2O + 3\ Cl_2 + 12\ OH^-$$

Cancelling those substances which appear in equal numbers on both sides of the expression affords the balanced net ionic equation for the reaction:

$$2\ CrO_2^- + 2\ H_2O + 6\ ClO^- \rightarrow 2\ CrO_4^{--} + 3\ Cl_2 + 4\ OH^-$$

A more complex example, which is quite difficult to balance by the oxidation number change method, is the equation for the oxidation of arsenic(III) sulfide (As_2S_3) by a nitrate in acid solution. In this reaction, both the arsenic(III) and sulfide ions are oxidized, the former to AsO_4^{---} the latter to SO_4^{--}:

$$2\ As^{+++} \rightarrow 2\ AsO_4^{---}$$
$$3\ S^{--} \rightarrow 3\ SO_4^{--}$$

The two half-expressions are balanced as before, adding H_2O and H^+ as needed:

$$8\,H_2O + 2\,As^{+++} \rightarrow 2\,AsO_4^{---} + 16\,H^+$$

(0) (+6) (−6) (+16)

(+6) loss of 4 e⁻ → (+10)

$$12\,H_2O + 3\,S^{--} \rightarrow 3\,SO_4^{--} + 24\,H^+$$

(0) (−6) (−6) (+24)

(−6) loss of 24 e⁻ → (+18)

Adding the two oxidation reactions gives:

$$20\,H_2O + As_2S_3 \rightarrow 2\,AsO_4^{---} + 3\,SO_4^{--} + 40\,H^+ + 28\,e^-$$

The oxidizing agent, which is NO_3^-, is reduced to NO. Balancing the half-reaction in the usual manner affords

$$4\,H^+ + NO_3^- \rightarrow NO + 2\,H_2O$$

(+4) (−1) (0) (0)

(+3) gain of 3 e⁻ → (0)

To balance the electrons lost in the oxidation reactions against the electrons gained in the reduction, the combined oxidation reaction must be multiplied by 3, and the reduction reaction by 28:

$$60\,H_2O + 3\,As_2S_3 \rightarrow 6\,AsO_4^{---} + 9\,SO_4^{--} + 120\,H^+ + 84\,e^-$$

$$84\,e^- + 112\,H^+ + 28\,NO_3^- \rightarrow 28\,NO + 56\,H_2O$$

Adding these two half-reactions and cancelling where possible yields the complete balanced net ionic equation:

$$4\,H_2O + 3\,As_2S_3 + 28\,NO_3^- \rightarrow 6\,AsO_4^- + 9\,SO_4^{--} + 28\,NO + 8\,H^+$$

Equivalent Weights of Redox Reagents 5.8

In Sec. 5.2 it was shown that the equivalent weight of an element deposited in an electrolysis reaction is equal to the atomic weight of the element divided by the number of electrons which it gains or loses. Deposition of one equivalent weight of an element corresponds to the transfer of one faraday of electricity, or in other words to the gain or loss of one mole of electrons. Electrolysis is a special case of oxidation-reduction in which the anode and cathode serve respectively as the oxidizing and reducing agent. Redox reactions other than electrolysis also involve the transfer of electrons. In a redox reaction, the transfer of one mole of electrons corresponds to the reaction of one equivalent weight of the oxidizing agent with one equivalent weight of the reducing agent. The equivalent weight of a redox reagent is equal to its formula weight divided by the number of electrons transferred in the reaction per mole of the reagent. For example, in the oxidation reaction

$$Fe^{++} \rightarrow Fe^{+++} + e^-$$

one mole of electrons is lost for every mole of Fe^{++} which is oxidized. The equivalent weight of an iron(II) salt which is being oxidized to iron(III) is therefore equal to its formula weight. In the reduction

$$5\ e^- + MnO_4^- + 8\ H^+ \rightarrow Mn^{++} + 4\ H_2O$$

five moles of electrons are gained for every mole of MnO_4^- reduced, and the equivalent weight of the permanganate compound is one-fifth of its formula weight. Considering the entire redox reaction,

$$10\ FeSO_4 + 2\ KMnO_4 + 8\ H_2SO_4 \rightarrow 5\ Fe_2(SO_4)_3 + K_2SO_4 + 2\ MnSO_4 + 8\ H_2O$$

we see that one equivalent weight (151.9/1 = 151.9 g) of $FeSO_4$ is just sufficient to reduce one equivalent weight (158.0/5 = 31.6 g) of $KMnO_4$. The oxidation of Fe^{++} to Fe^{+++} may also be carried out using potassium dichromate, $K_2Cr_2O_7$, rather than $KMnO_4$. The half-reaction for the reduction of the dichromate ion is

$$6\ e^- + 14\ H^+ + Cr_2O_7^{--} \rightarrow 2\ Cr^{+++} + 7\ H_2O$$

Since in this case six moles of electrons are gained per mole of dichromate reduced, the equivalent weight of $K_2Cr_2O_7$ in this reaction is 294.2/6 = 49.0 g.

The equivalent weight of a particular redox reagent is not necessarily the same in every reaction in which it takes part. An oxidizing agent, for example, may be reduced to a greater or less extent depending upon reaction conditions, and its equivalent weight will vary accordingly. For instance, we have seen above that under acid conditions MnO_4^- is reduced to Mn^{++}:

$$5\ e^- + MnO_4^- + 8\ H^+ \rightarrow Mn^{++} + 4\ H_2O$$

and therefore the equivalent weight of $KMnO_4$ is one-fifth of its formula weight (158.0/5 = 31.6 g) when it is used as an oxidizing agent in an acid solution. Under basic conditions, however, MnO_4^- is reduced to solid MnO_2:

$$3\ e^- + 2\ H_2O + MnO_4^- \rightarrow MnO_2 + 4\ OH^-$$

three moles of electrons being transferred per mole of permanganate reduced. Thus, when $KMnO_4$ is used as an oxidizing agent in basic solution, for example to oxidize sulfide ions to free sulfur,

$$4\ H_2O + 2\ MnO_4^- + 3\ S^{--} \rightarrow 2\ MnO_2 + 8\ OH^- + 3\ S$$

its equivalent weight is 158.0/3 = 52.7 g.

Faraday's paper "On Electrochemical Decomposition," published in the *Philosophical Transactions of the Royal Society* (1834), appears in the Dampiers' book *Readings in the Literature of Science* (Harper & Row, New York, 1959), beginning on p. 118. In this paper the terms *electrode, electrolyte, electrolysis, cation,* and *anion,* which Faraday developed in collaboration with the Rev. William Whewell, appear for the first time. Following the paper by Faraday, on p. 127, is the paper that Arrhenius published in 1887 describing his ionic dissociation theory.

In 1951 James R. Irving interviewed Robert W. Vicarey, who was then 93 years old and who as a boy had known and worked for Michael Faraday. Mr. Vicarey's personal recollections of Faraday during this interview are presented in the *J. Chem. Ed.* **28,** 323 (1951). "Faraday's Electrochemical Laws and the Determination of Equivalent Weights," by Rosemary G. Ehl and Aaron J. Ihde, *J. Chem. Ed.* **31,** 226 (1954), describes the skepticism with which Faraday's work was greeted by J. J. Berzelius. Faraday's contribution to the theory of electrolytic solutions is discussed by O. J. Drennan, *J. Chem. Ed.* **42,** 679 (1965). A description of the Royal Institution, where Faraday had his laboratory, is given by K. D. C. Vernon, *J. Chem. Ed.* **34,** 607 (1957).

Chapter 5 of *The Development of Modern Chemistry*, by Aaron J. Ihde (Harper & Row, New York, 1964), is a good, short presentation of the early history of electrochemistry and Berzelius' electrical theory of chemical bonding.

Questions and Problems

5.1 How does ionization account for (a) electrical conductance of molten salts and (b) electrical conductance of many aqueous solutions?

5.2 Why is it that the hydrogen ion rather than the sodium ion is reduced at the cathode during the electrolysis of aqueous sodium chloride? Write the cathode reaction.

5.3 In the electrolysis of copper(II) sulfate, why is it that oxygen is liberated at the anode? Write the anode reaction.

5.4 Why does the solution around the cathode become basic during the electrolysis of sodium sulfate solution? Why does the solution around the anode become acidic?

5.5 Why does the presence of a small amount of sulfuric acid dissolved in water markedly speed up the rate of electrolytic decomposition of water?

5.6 Define (a) coulomb, (b) ampere, (c) faraday, and (d) mole of electrons.

5.7 State Faraday's law of electrolysis.

5.8 How are the relative electronegativities of elements used in assigning oxidation numbers?

5.9 Distinguish between valence and oxidation state.

5.10 Determine the oxidation number of:

(a) S in H_2S, SO_2, SO_3, $Na_2S_2O_3$, $Na_2S_4O_6$, H_2SO_4

(b) N in N_2O, NO, N_2O_3, N_2O_4, HNO_3, HNO_2, NH_3, N_2H_4, NH_2OH

(c) P in PCl_3, P_4O_{10}, $POCl_3$, HPO_3, H_3PO_4, $Mg_2P_2O_7$, $Ca_3(PO_4)_2$

(d) As in As_4O_6, As_2S_5, H_3AsO_3, H_3AsO_4, AsH_3

(e) Cl in HCl, $HClO$, $HClO_2$, $HClO_3$, $HClO_4$, Cl_2O_7

(f) I in CuI, HIO_3, H_5IO_6, IF_7
(g) C in CH_4O, C_2H_4O, CH_2O, CO, $H_2C_2O_4$, CO_2, H_2CO_3
(h) Cr in $CrCl_3$, $Ca(CrO_2)_2$, K_2CrO_4, $K_2Cr_2O_7$, $H_2Cr_3O_{10}$
(i) B in HBO_2, H_3BO_3, $Na_2B_4O_7$
(j) O in Na_2O, Na_2O_2, OF_2

5.11 From its position in the periodic table, predict the maximum positive oxidation state to be expected for (a) scandium, (b) titanium, (c) vanadium, (d) gallium, (e) germanium, (f) arsenic, (g) selenium, (h) bromine.

5.12 Balance the following oxidation-reduction equations by the oxidation number change and ion-electron methods:

(a) $Cu + H^+ + NO_3^- \rightarrow Cu^{++} + NO_2 + H_2O$
(b) $Cu + H^+ + NO_3^- \rightarrow Cu^{++} + NO + H_2O$
(c) $Sb + H^+ + NO_3^- \rightarrow Sb_4O_6 + NO + H_2O$
(d) $H_2S + H^+ + NO_3^- \rightarrow S + NO + H_2O$
(e) $I_2 + H^+ + NO_3^- \rightarrow HIO_3 + NO_2 + H_2O$
(f) $S_2O_3^{--} + I_2 \rightarrow S_4O_6^{--} + I^-$
(g) $Br_2 + CO_3^{--} \rightarrow Br^- + BrO_3^- + CO_2$
(h) $HClO_3 \rightarrow HClO_4 + ClO_2 + H_2O$
(i) $H_2O_2 + MnO_4^- + H^+ \rightarrow Mn^{++} + H_2O + O_2$
(j) $C_2O_4^{--} + MnO_4^- + H^+ \rightarrow CO_2 + Mn^{++} + H_2O$

5.13 Complete and balance the following reactions, each of which occurs in acid solution:

(a) $Fe^{++} + Cr_2O_7^{--} \rightarrow Fe^{+++} + Cr^{+++}$
(b) $Mn^{++} + BiO_3^- \rightarrow MnO_4^- + Bi^{+++}$
(c) $Cr^{+++} + MnO_4^- \rightarrow Cr_2O_7^{--} + Mn^{++}$
(d) $As_4O_6 + MnO_4^- \rightarrow AsO_4^{---} + Mn^{++}$
(e) $IO_3^- + I^- \rightarrow I_2$
(f) $Mo^{+++} + MnO_4^- \rightarrow MoO_4^{--} + Mn^{++}$

5.14 Complete and balance the following reactions, each of which occurs in alkaline solution:

(a) $NO_2 \rightarrow NO_3^- + NO_2^-$
(b) $MnO_4^- + ClO_2^- \rightarrow MnO_2 + ClO_4^-$
(c) $Cl_2 \rightarrow ClO_3^- + Cl^-$
(d) $Zn + NO_3^- \rightarrow Zn(OH)_4^{--} + NH_3$

5.15 How many grams each of hydrogen and oxygen are liberated when a steady current of 2 amperes of electricity is passed through a dilute solution of sulfuric acid for 30 min?

5.16 For how long must a steady current of 2 amperes flow through an electrolytic cell to decompose 1 mole of water?

5.17 If 0.3 g of hydrogen is liberated by a certain current in 10 min, how long will it take the same current to deposit 15 g of gold from a gold plating bath? (The atomic weight of gold is 197.2 and its valence is 3.)

5.18 The exact measurement of the quantity of electricity used in an electrochemical process may be determined by placing a silver coulometer in the circuit of the experimental cell so that the current passes first through one cell then through the other, i.e., cells are in series.

(a) What quantity of electricity is used by any electrochemical process for every gram of silver deposited in a silver coulometer?
(b) If 0.895 of silver is deposited by a steady current flowing for 10 minutes, what is the current strength?
(c) How many grams of silver are deposited per coulomb of electricity consumed?

5.19 In a copper coulometer, 0.593 g of copper is deposited by a current of 2 amperes in 15 minutes. Calculate the atomic weight of copper.

5.20 Aluminum is produced industrially by the electrolysis of a molten solution of purified alumina, Al_2O_3, in cryolite, Na_3AlF_6. The cathode reaction, $Al^{+++} + 3\,e^- \rightarrow Al$, takes place at the carbon lining of the electrolytic cell upon which the aluminum collects. Oxygen is discharged at and reacts with carbon anodes that are lowered into the melt. The anode reaction is $C + 2\,O^{--} \rightarrow CO_2 + 4\,e^-$.

(a) How many grams of aluminum are produced by this process when 2 million coulombs pass through?
(b) What is the corresponding weight loss of the anode?

5.21 Determine the equivalent weight of the oxidizing and reducing agents in the reactions given in questions 5. 12(a), (d), (f), (i); 5. 13(a), (d), (e); 5. 14(b).

"Don't you think that
young Marsden . . . ought to begin
a small research?"

——Hans Geiger to Ernest Rutherford, 1909

6

THE NUCLEAR ATOM

When they thought about it at all, most chemists and physicists of the nineteenth century pictured the atom as a microscopic billiard ball: hard, indivisible, and unchanging. This simple picture was far from adequate, for it offered no explanation of chemical properties. Why do elements have different valences? Why do they form compounds at all? What holds compounds together? How can one account for the periodic law? The apparent inability of the atomic theory to provide answers to such questions led some scientists to doubt that atoms even existed. A useful concept, perhaps, but like Santa Claus, more imaginary than real.

Today, when atoms in some cases can even be made visible (Fig. 6.1), no one seriously questions their reality. But we now know the atom to be a complex microcosm composed of still smaller particles obeying their own unique set of physical laws. Knowledge of atomic structure leads to an understanding of chemical behavior, and from this understanding comes the ability to predict the properties of the elements.

The unraveling of the structure of the atom is a continuing story to which many people have contributed. If it can be said to have a beginning, it started in the 1890's, with Röntgen's discovery of X-rays and Thomson's investigation of the discharge of electricity through gases at low pressure. In this chapter we will follow the story from that beginning through the events leading up to Marsden's experiment and the discovery of the atomic nucleus, Moseley's determination of the nuclear charge, and the identification of the electron, proton, and neutron—three subatomic particles which together suffice to account for the chemical properties of the elements.

Fig. 6.1 Field ion micrograph of a platinum crystal showing individual atoms. The actual diameter of each atom shown is about 2.8 Å. (Courtesy of Professor Erwin W. Mueller, Pennsylvania State University.)

6.1 Cathode Rays

A potential difference of 10,000 volts is barely enough to cause a noisy spark to jump a fraction of an inch through the air. At pressures near 1 torr, current under the same voltage flows silently over a distance of several feet, and the residual gas glows with a characteristic color, as in the familiar neon sign. Lowering the pressure still further causes the glow to fade, until, at a pressure of about 10^{-4} torr, it practically disappears, although the electricity continues to travel between the electrodes. A screen coated with zinc sulfide and placed between the electrodes lights up on the side facing the negative electrode, or cathode. Evidently, whatever is carrying the electric current comes from the cathode and possesses enough energy to make the zinc sulfide glow when it strikes it (Fig. 6.2).

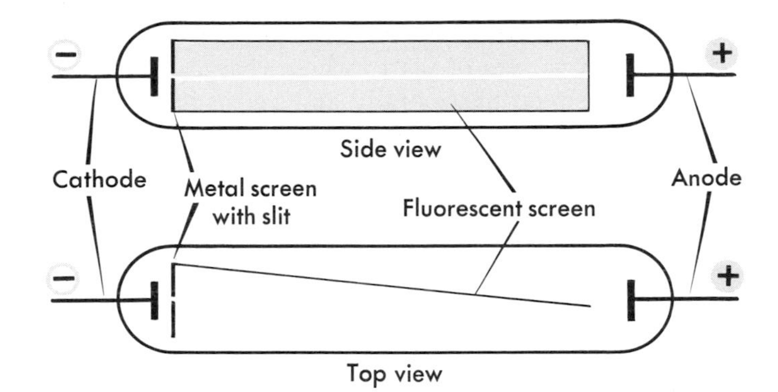

Fig. 6.2 Simple cathode ray tube.

Cathode rays, as they are called, normally travel in a straight line. If the positive electrode, or anode, is sealed into the side of the tube rather than the end, the cathode rays continue right past it, striking the end of the tube and causing the glass to glow, or *fluoresce*. A metal plate with a small hole, placed in front of the cathode, stops all but a thin pencil of the rays, which makes a bright spot at the end of the tube. Bringing a magnet alongside the tube deflects the beam and causes the spot to move. The direction of the deflection is exactly what one would expect if the beam carried a negative charge (Fig. 6.3a). If the rays are passed between oppositely charged plates, the beam is attracted by the positive plate. Again the spot moves, once more showing that the cathode rays are negatively charged (Fig. 6.3b).

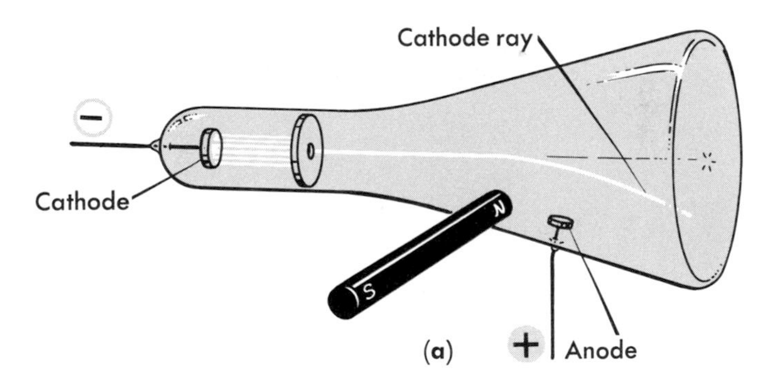

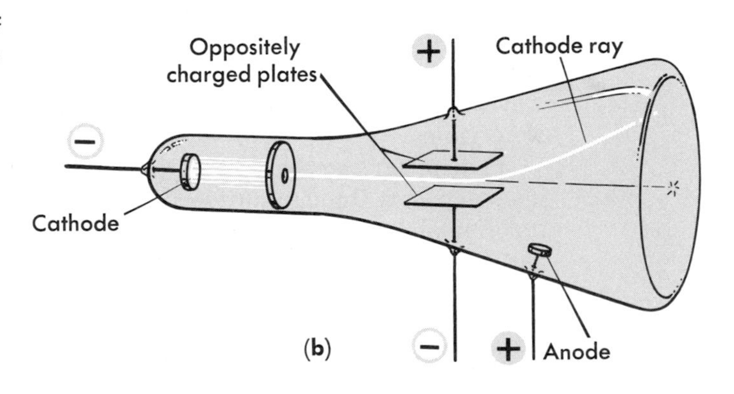

Fig. 6.3 Deflection of cathode ray (a) in a magnetic field and (b) in an electrical field.

The familiar television tube is essentially a cathode ray tube equipped with two sets of plates whose charges can be varied so as to cause the beam to sweep horizontally and vertically over a fluorescent screen on the face of the tube (Fig. 6.4).

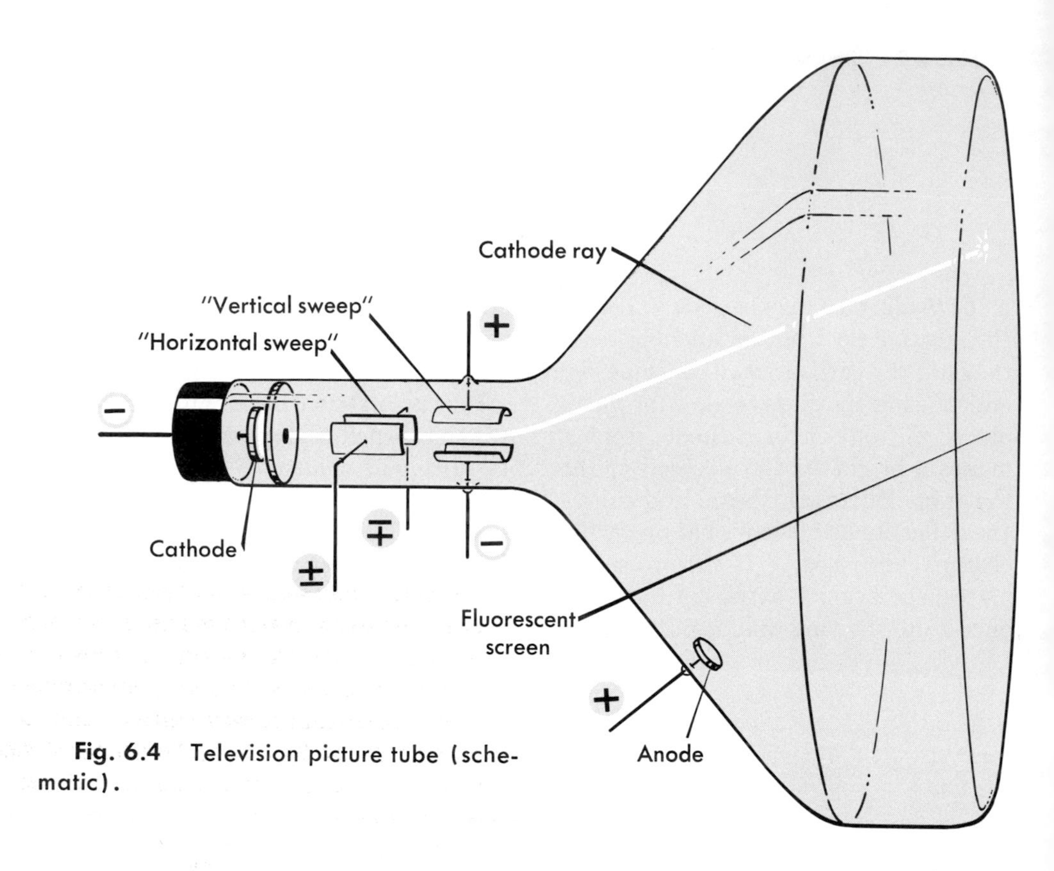

Fig. 6.4 Television picture tube (schematic).

6.2 Electrons

The fact that the cathode ray carries a charge suggests that it is composed of matter, and its behavior is typical of a stream of negatively charged particles. In 1897, J. J. Thomson, working at the Cavendish Laboratory, Cambridge, England, set about trying to learn something of the nature of these particles. Thomson's apparatus (Fig. 6.5) consisted of a cathode-ray tube fitted with a set of charged plates and an external electromagnet. A paper scale was pasted on the end of the tube to measure the amount by which the cathode rays were deflected as the magnetic and electrical fields were varied.

The greater the charge on a particle, the greater is the force exerted on it as it passes through an electrical field. How much it is deflected from its original path depends upon the magnitude of this force, the mass of the particle, and its speed. A heavy particle is deflected less than a light one moving at the same speed. A fast-moving particle spends less time in the electrical field, and therefore undergoes less of a deflection than a slow-moving one which has the same mass and charge. In other words, the

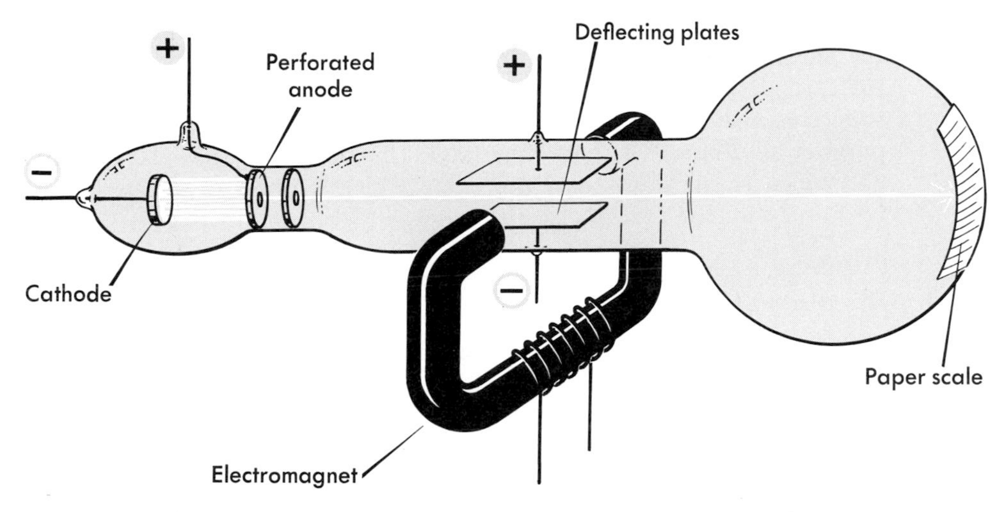

Fig. 6.5 Thomson's apparatus for determining the ratio of charge to mass (e/m) for cathode ray particles.

amount of deflection in an electrical field is directly proportional to the charge, and inversely proportional to both the mass and the speed of the particle. Provided that the speed of the particle is known, the ratio, e/m, between its charge e and its mass m may be calculated from the angle through which the particle is deflected in a given electrical field.

The situation is somewhat different in the case of a charged particle moving in a magnetic field. A magnetic field has no effect if the particle is stationary, but if it is moving, the particle experiences a force perpendicular both to its path and to the magnetic field. The faster the particle moves, the greater this force becomes. Therefore, while *the amount of deflection in a magnetic field is also directly proportional to the charge and inversely proportional to the mass, the deflecting force exerted on the particle is in this case directly proportional to its speed.*

No spreading of the cathode ray is observed when it is deflected by electrical and magnetic fields of varying strength, so apparently all of the particles of which it is composed have the same e/m and are all moving at the same speed. Thomson observed the deflection of the beam when the magnet alone was turned on and then adjusted the charge on the plates until the fluorescent spot on the end of the tube returned to its original position. Under these conditions, the magnetic and electrical forces acting on the particles were equal in magnitude:

$$Hev = Ee$$

and

$$v = E/H$$

where H and E represent the strengths of the magnetic and electrical fields, respectively, and v is the speed of the particles. Since E and H were both known, Thomson could now calculate v, and from it evaluate e/m. He performed the experiment a large number of times, obtaining in every case the same value for e/m, -1.76×10^8 coulombs per gram,* irrespective of the nature of both the residual gas in the tube and the metal out of which the cathode was made. In the paper describing his experiment, Thomson suggested that these particles were all identical and present as constituent parts of all atoms. A short time later, the Dutch physicist H. A. Lorentz christened them "electrons," the name which had already been suggested by Stoney for the unit of electrical charge (Sec. 5.2).

6.3 The Mass of the Electron

Thomson's work showed that the electron either had a very small mass or was very highly charged. Which was the actual case could not be decided with certainty until the actual charge on the electron was determined. This was done in a very ingenious manner by R. A. Millikan at the University of Chicago in 1908. In this experiment he sprayed oil droplets from an atomizer into the apparatus shown schematically in Fig. 6.6. The air

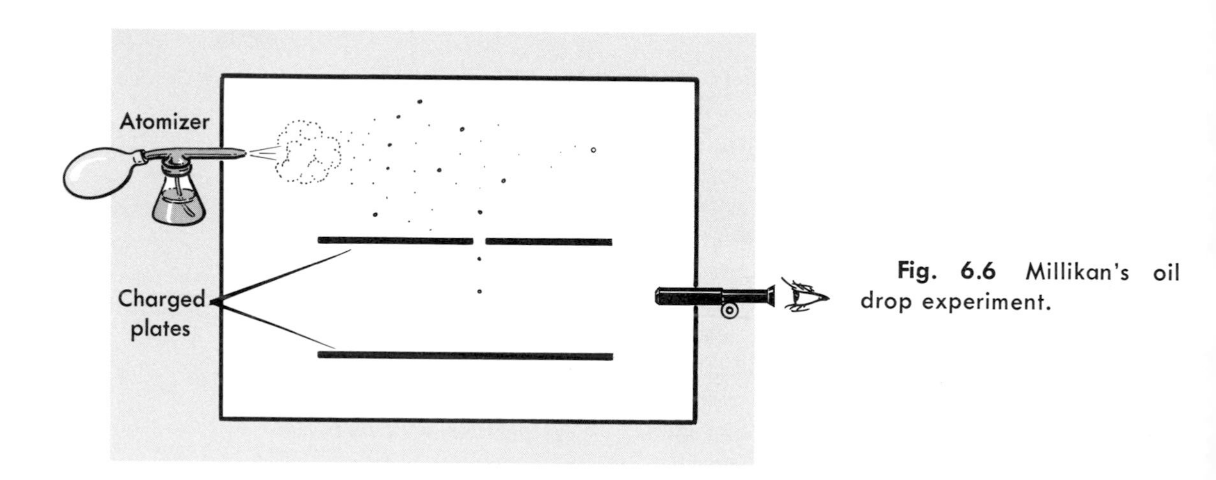

Fig. 6.6 Millikan's oil drop experiment.

between the plates was then exposed briefly to X-rays (Sec. 6.7), which had been shown to have the effect of dislodging electrons from the air molecules. Some of these electrons were picked up by the oil droplets, which then acquired a negative charge. By adjusting the charge on the plates, Milliken was able to attract one of these droplets to the positive plate just strongly enough to counteract the pull of gravity and cause the droplet to remain stationary. As might be expected, the charge on the plates necessary to accomplish this was inversely proportional to the charge on the oil droplet and directly proportional to its mass. The mass of the droplet could be calculated, and knowing this, Millikan was able to determine its charge.

He found, by repeating the experiment a number of times, that although the charge on different droplets varied, it was always some whole-number multiple of -1.60×10^{-19} coulomb. Apparently this value is the smallest

* The negative sign refers merely to the sign of the electrical charge, which is negative.

charge that any one oil drop can have, and consequently it must correspond to the charge on a single electron. From this, and the value of e/m determined by Thomson, the mass of an electron can be computed as follows:

$$m = \frac{-1.60 \times 10^{-19} \text{ coulomb}}{-1.76 \times 10^{8} \text{ coulomb/g}} = 9.1 \times 10^{-28} \text{ g}$$

Example 6.1

Given that one faraday is equal to 96,500 coulombs, calculate Avogadro's number.

Solution: It was shown in Chapter 5 that the faraday corresponds to the charge on one mole of electrons. Dividing the total charge in a faraday by the charge on a single electron will give the number of electrons in a mole, which is equal to Avogadro's number.

$$\text{Avogadro's number} = \frac{9.65 \times 10^{4} \text{ coulombs/mole}}{1.60 \times 10^{-19} \text{ coulomb/electron}} = 6.03 \times 10^{23} \text{ electrons/mole}$$

The presently accepted value of Avogadro's number, based on the most accurate measurements, is 6.02257×10^{23}.

Positive Rays 6.4

Even before Thomson determined the nature of the negative particles streaming away from the cathode of a discharge tube, a number of physicists had speculated that there might also be positive particles traveling in the opposite direction, that is, toward the cathode. Their presence was demonstrated in 1886 by the German physicist Eugen Goldstein, using a discharge tube with a perforated cathode (Fig. 6.7). When the current

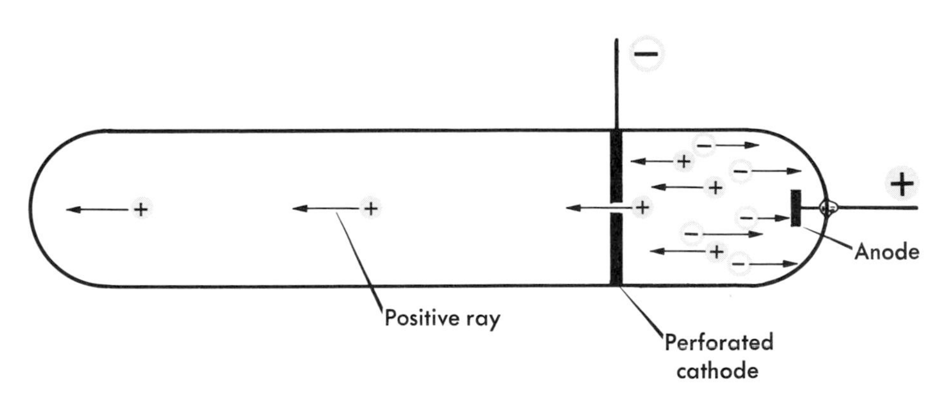

Fig. 6.7 Positive ray tube.

was turned on, a ray analogous to the cathode ray could be detected in the region behind the cathode. Like the cathode ray, it was deflected by a magnetic or electrical field, but in the opposite direction, which showed that it was composed of positively charged particles. In 1913, Thomson and F. W. Aston measured the charge-to-mass ratio of these particles by a method similar to that used before to determine e/m for the electron. Most significant, the value of the ratio was found not to be a constant, as it was in the case of the cathode ray, but to depend upon what residual gas was present in the tube. The largest values of e/m were obtained when the gas was hydrogen. When gases of higher molecular weight were placed in the tube, smaller values were obtained, corresponding to the greater mass of the molecules. The implication was clear to Thomson and Aston. The atom was not a simple sphere, as it had been pictured since the time of Dalton, but was itself composed of at least two parts, one of which was the electron. When the fast-moving electrons of the cathode ray collide with molecules of gas, they may occasionally do so with sufficient energy to dislodge additional electrons from the atoms. The atoms are originally electrically neutral, so the loss of a negative particle causes them to acquire a positive charge and to be attracted by the cathode. Most of the ions strike the cathode, but a few coast through the hole and appear on the other side as the positive ray. The lightest positive ray particle observed is the hydrogen ion, that is, a hydrogen atom from which an electron has been lost.

6.5 Isotopes

It soon became apparent that the e/m ratios of positive ray particles generated from different gases differ in a manner that can be accounted for if (1) the charges on the particles are always some whole-number multiple of the unit charge on the electron, and (2) their masses are some whole-number multiple of the mass of the hydrogen atom. No value of e/m corresponding to a particle possessing either fractional mass or charge was ever obtained. Instead, for example, when Thomson examined neon gas, he obtained values corresponding to masses of 20 and 22, but none corresponding to the experimentally determined atomic weight, which is 20.183.

Aston designed an improved positive ray apparatus, or ***mass spectrograph,*** which permitted more accurate sorting of ions according to their mass (Fig. 6.8). By deflecting the positive rays in both an electrical and a

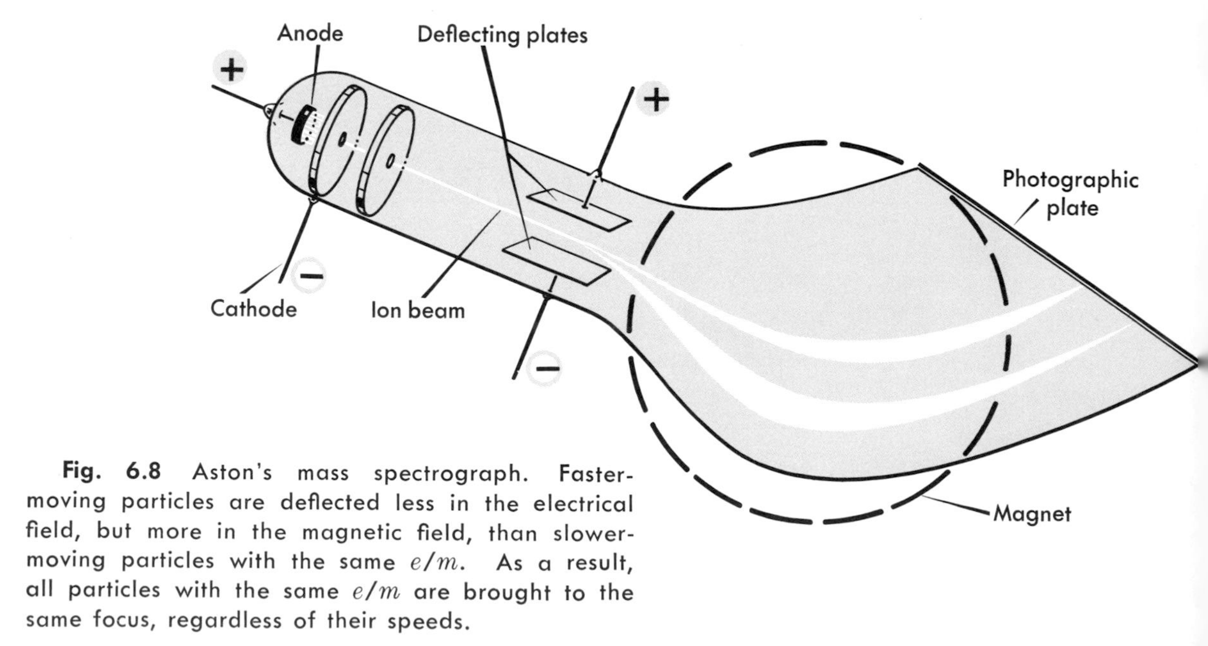

Fig. 6.8 Aston's mass spectrograph. Faster-moving particles are deflected less in the electrical field, but more in the magnetic field, than slower-moving particles with the same e/m. As a result, all particles with the same e/m are brought to the same focus, regardless of their speeds.

magnetic field, all particles with the same e/m, regardless of how fast they were moving, were brought to a focus at the same place on a photographic plate.* From the darkening of the plate, measured with an instrument called a densitometer, the relative amounts of particles having different masses could be determined. Aston was able to show that contrary to Dalton's assumption, atoms of the same element did not necessarily all have the same mass. Most elements are mixtures of atoms all of which have the same chemical properties, but which differ somewhat in mass. *Atoms which are of the same element, but which have different masses, are known as **isotopes*** (from the Greek for "same place," i.e., in the periodic table). An element's atomic weight is the weighted average of those of the individual isotopes, all of whose atomic weights are very nearly integral multiples of that of hydrogen. Since for most naturally occurring elements this average atomic weight always has the same value, one must conclude that in those cases the relative proportions of the various isotopes are always the same.

Example 6.2

Mass spectrometry shows that ordinary chlorine consists of two isotopes of mass 35 and 37 amu, in the relative proportions of 77.3% and 22.7%, respectively. Calculate the atomic weight of ordinary chlorine from this information.

Solution: The atomic weight of the ordinary isotopic mixture is the weighted average of the atomic weights of the isotopes, calculated as follows;

$$\begin{aligned} 0.773 \times 35 &= 27.1 \\ 0.227 \times 37 &= \underline{\ \ 8.4} \\ & \quad 35.5 \text{ amu} \end{aligned}$$

The Proton 6.6

Thomson had shown that the negative part of the atom was associated with particles of very small mass: the electrons. Now it was apparent that the positive part of the atom was associated with much heavier particles, seemingly the same as hydrogen ions. These particles, with a mass about 1840 times that of the electron, were named ***protons*** by Ernest Rutherford. The hydrogen atom is composed of a single proton and an electron. Other atoms contain larger numbers of protons, together with equal numbers of electrons in order to preserve electrical neutrality.

Example 6.3

The charge-to-mass ratio, e/m for the proton, is found experimentally to be 9.65×10^4 coulombs/g. Calculate the mass of the proton.

Solution:

$$\frac{e}{m} = 9.65 \times 10^4 \text{ coulombs/g}$$

* Slower-moving particles are deflected more by an electrical field, but less by a magnetic field than faster-moving ones (Sec. 6.2). By adjusting the magnitudes of the respective fields, the two effects can be made to cancel one another, so that the amount of deflection is determined solely by e/m.

$$m = \frac{1.60 \times 10^{-19} \text{ coulomb}}{9.65 \times 10^{4} \text{ coulombs/g}}$$

$$= 1.66 \times 10^{-24} \text{ g}$$

Example 6.4

From the mass of the proton determined in Example 6.3, calculate Avogadro's number.

Solution: The mass of one mole of hydrogen gas is equal to the mass of one hydrogen molecule multiplied by the number of molecules in a mole (Avogadro's number). Therefore,

$$\text{Avogadro's number} = \frac{\text{mass of one mole of hydrogen gas}}{\text{mass of one } H_2 \text{ molecule}}$$

Within the limitation of three significant figures, the mass of a molecule of H_2 is twice the mass of a proton. Therefore,

$$\text{Avogadro's number} = \frac{2.02 \text{ g/mole}}{(2)(1.66 \times 10^{-24} \text{ g/molecule})}$$

$$= 6.08 \times 10^{23} \text{ molecules/mole}$$

The discrepancy between the value obtained here and that calculated in Example 6.1 reflects the uncertainty in the third significant figure of the data in each case.

6.7 The Discovery of Radioactivity

Just two years prior to Thomson's study of the nature of cathode rays, Wilhelm Conrad Röntgen discovered by accident that the anode, or for that matter even the glass of the discharge tube, emitted secondary rays of an unusually penetrating sort when struck by the cathode ray. Röntgen had been experimenting, for another reason, with a discharge tube covered with black paper, and he noticed that a sample of barium platinocyanide on the laboratory bench near the tube glowed when the current was turned on. Intrigued by this, he investigated further and found that these ***X-rays,*** as he called them for want of a better name, caused fluorescence in a large number of minerals. They also darkened photographic film in the same manner as light, and could penetrate not only black paper, but flesh, casting a shadow image of the bones within. Röntgen's publication in 1895 of an X-ray photograph of the bones of the hand caused an immediate sensation in medical and scientific circles, and within a year a number of supply houses were advertising X-ray tubes (Fig. 6.9).

When Henri Becquerel learned in Paris of the discovery of X-rays and of Röntgen's observation that these rays caused certain minerals to emit visible light, he decided to study whether the process could be reversed, that is, whether these same minerals might absorb visible light and then emit X-rays. He wrapped a number of photographic plates in black paper, placed a sample of a mineral known to fluoresce under X-rays upon each plate, and then left them out in the bright sunlight for several hours. He then developed the plates and found, as he had expected, that several of

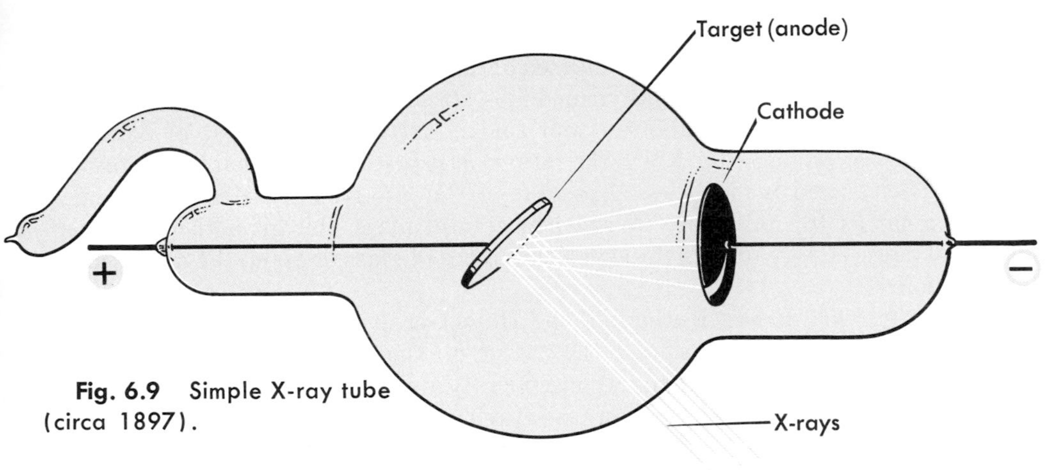

Fig. 6.9 Simple X-ray tube (circa 1897).

them were fogged. A few of the mineral samples, those that contained uranium, had indeed emitted X-rays. If the weather had not then taken a turn for the worse, that might have been the end of it. Becquerel would have drawn the obvious, and incorrect, conclusion that the minerals were fluorescing in the X-ray region, as he had predicted that they would. Instead, just as he was about to repeat the experiment to confirm his observations, it began to rain. Becquerel put the plates and mineral samples away in a drawer to wait for a sunny day. When the weather finally cleared five days later, Becquerel remembered his samples, but for some reason decided to develop the plates before exposing the samples to the light. Much to his surprise, the same uranium minerals which had fogged the plates when exposed to the light had again fogged the plates, even though they had been left in the dark. Becquerel reasoned correctly that the radiation emitted by the minerals had nothing to do with their exposure to light but was an intrinsic property of the minerals themselves.

Following Becquerel's discovery, Pierre and Marie Sklodowska Curie studied this phenomenon, which they called ***radioactivity,*** and found that the intensity of the radiation emitted by uranium compounds depended only upon the amount of uranium present. The Curies also observed that thorium and its salts emitted radiation similar to that of uranium, and some time later they isolated two new radioactive elements, *polonium* (named for Mme. Curie's native land, Poland) and *radium*, from the mineral pitchblende. A fuller discussion of radioactivity and the transformations undergone by radioactive elements will be given in Chapter 20.

Radioactive Emission 6.8

Only a few of the elements are naturally radioactive, and they emit radiation of three principal types, called respectively *alpha* (α), *beta* (β), and *gamma* (γ) *rays*. The first two are recognized as charged particles from their behavior in a magnetic or electrical field. *Gamma rays* have neither charge nor measureable mass, and they are in fact electromagnetic radiation (light) similar to X-rays, but of extremely high energy. Like X-rays, they can pass through matter and blacken photographic film, but because of their greater energy, they are more penetrating, being stopped only by several inches of lead or several feet of concrete. The β*-rays* carry a negative charge and are composed of electrons traveling at nearly the speed of light. Moving at this tremendous speed, they are able to penetrate a sheet of aluminum about 1 mm thick. *Alpha rays* consist of positively charged particles for which the ratio e/m is just one-half that of the proton. Their speed is much less than that of the β-particles, but still may be as great as 10^4 miles/sec. With their greater mass, this gives them sufficient kinetic energy to pass through a thin piece of glass or about 0.1 mm of metal foil.

In 1908, Ernest Rutherford and Hans Geiger determined that the charge on the α-particle was twice the charge on the proton. With e/m one-half that of the proton, its mass consequently was 4 amu, which suggested that the α-particle was actually a fast-moving He^{++} ion, a supposition that was proved by Rutherford in the following way. A sample of a known α-emitter (the element radon) was sealed into a thin-walled glass tube through which the α-particles could pass (Fig. 6.10). This tube was then placed inside an

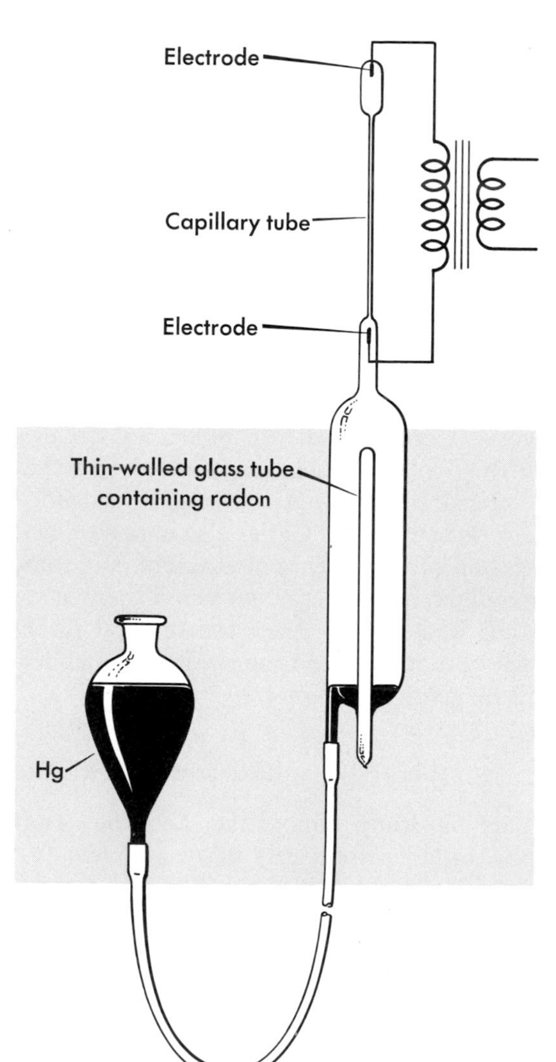

Fig. 6.10 Rutherford's apparatus for identifying the α-particle.

evacuated vessel. After a time, a small quantity of gas appeared in the outer tube. This gas was then compressed into a narrow glass capillary by raising the mercury reservoir attached to the apparatus. When an electric discharge was passed through the capillary, the gas glowed with the characteristic colors of the helium spectrum (Sec. 7.2). If helium gas was placed in the inner tube instead of radon, no helium spectrum was obtained. Clearly, it was not a matter of helium gas diffusing through the glass, but of helium ions being fired through the wall of the tube in the form of α-particles.

Discovery of the Nucleus 6.9

The atoms in a piece of metal have been shown by X-ray diffraction (Sec. 9.9) to be very nearly touching one another, so in order for α- or β-particles to penetrate a metal foil they must pass right through at least some of the atoms. This means that the atoms themselves are actually mostly empty space. The relatively heavy, high-energy α-particle would be barely affected by collision with an electron, but would be expected to be deflected slightly if it approached closely to a proton, which is positively charged and much more massive than an electron. If the protons are distributed uniformly throughout the volume of the atom, an α-particle will suffer a large number of small deflections, some in one direction, some in another, but the chance of there being any large excess of deflections in any one direction will be very small (Fig. 6.11). As a result, some scattering of

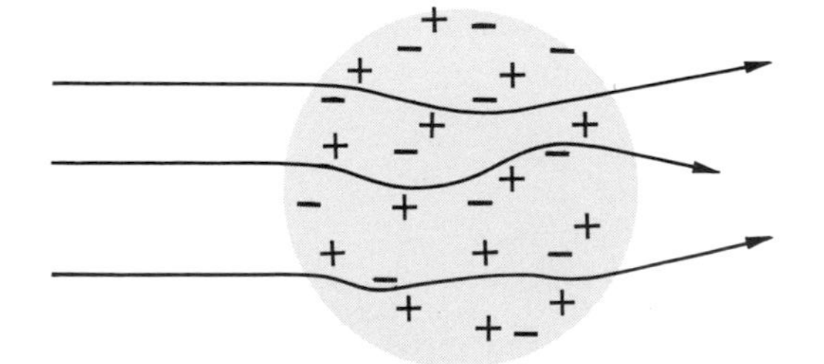

Fig. 6.11 Scattering of α-particles by an atom in which the positive and negative charges are evenly distributed.

the particles should occur, but the likelihood of any particles being scattered over large angles should be almost nonexistent. As a rough analogy, consider a .22-caliber bullet being fired through a well-shaken paper bag containing a small number of pebbles and an equal number of grains of sand. Hitting a grain of sand (electron) will have almost no effect, but collision with a pebble (proton) will turn the bullet (α-particle) slightly from its course.

In 1908, using the apparatus shown in Fig. 6.12, Hans Geiger measured the scattering of α-particles as they passed through a metal foil by observing the flashes of light which occurred as the particles struck the zinc sulfide screen mounted across the end of the evacuated tube. He found, as expected, that the number of particles scattered through a given angle decreased rapidly as the angle increased (Fig. 6.13). The following year a young graduate student, Ernest Marsden, was given the job of detecting

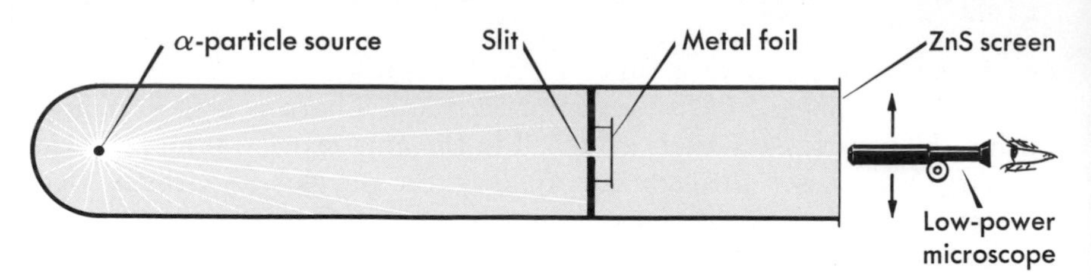

Fig. 6.12 Apparatus used by Hans Geiger to measure α-particle scattering.

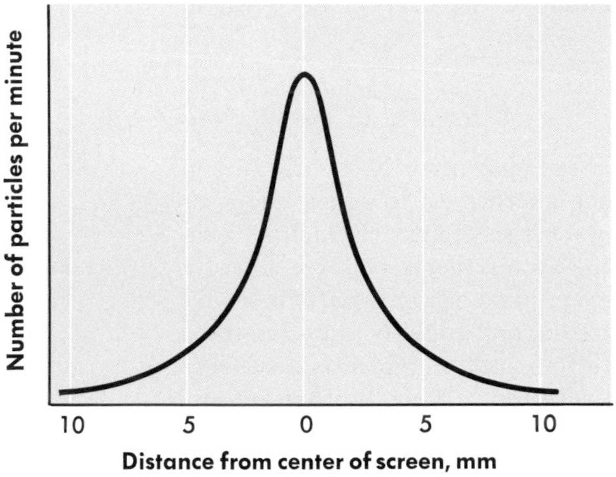

Number of particles per minute

10 5 0 5 10

Distance from center of screen, mm

Fig. 6.13 Results of Geiger's experiment on the scattering of α-particles by gold foil.

whether any α-particles were scattered through large angles. For the reasons already given, Rutherford did not believe this to be very likely. Marsden constructed the apparatus shown in Fig. 6.14, which allowed scattering angles as great as 180° to be measured. The subsequent developments are best described in Rutherford's own words.

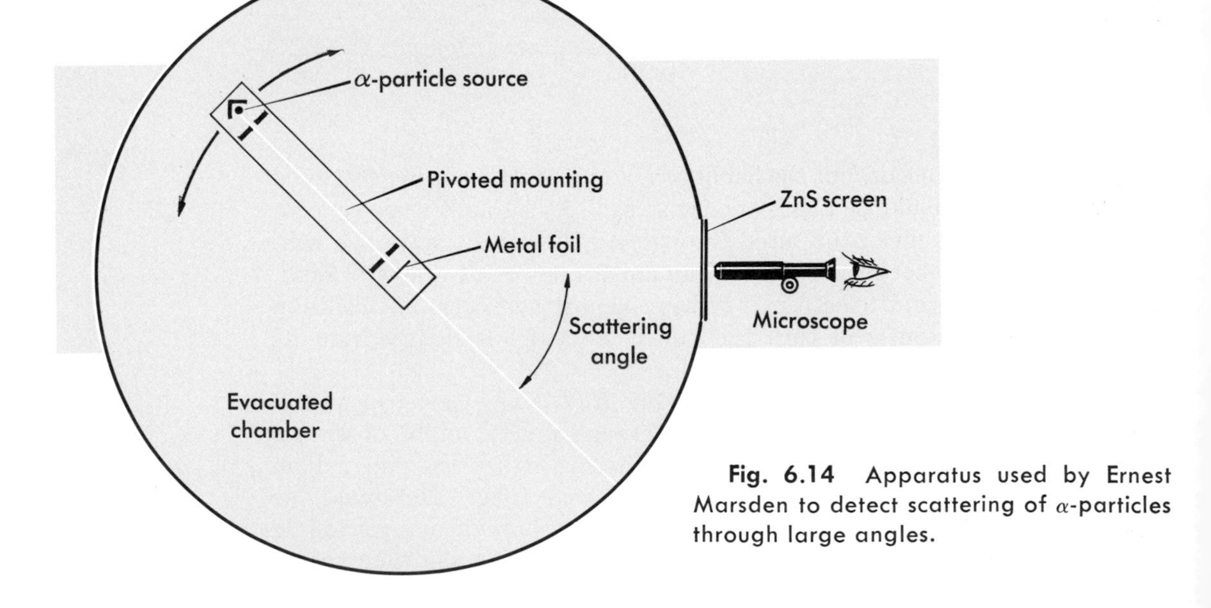

Fig. 6.14 Apparatus used by Ernest Marsden to detect scattering of α-particles through large angles.

> Then I remember two or three days later Geiger coming to me in great excitement and saying, "We have been able to get some of the alpha particles coming backwards. . . ." It was quite the most incredible event that has ever happened to me in my life. It was almost as incredible as if you fired a 15-inch shell at a piece of tissue paper and it came back and hit you.

There was only one way that Rutherford could see to account for the scattering of α-particles through wide angles, and that was to assume that the positive part of the atom, representing practically all of its mass, is concentrated in one place. This positive ***nucleus*** must be extremely small to account for the rarity with which wide-angle scattering occurs. Most of the α-particles pass through the atom without coming close enough to the nucleus to be deflected. A few approach near enough to be turned through small angles, and on rare occasions they come close enough to be turned backwards (Fig. 6.15). For the atom to be electrically neutral, the nucleus must be surrounded by electrons, thinly distributed through the remaining atomic volume.

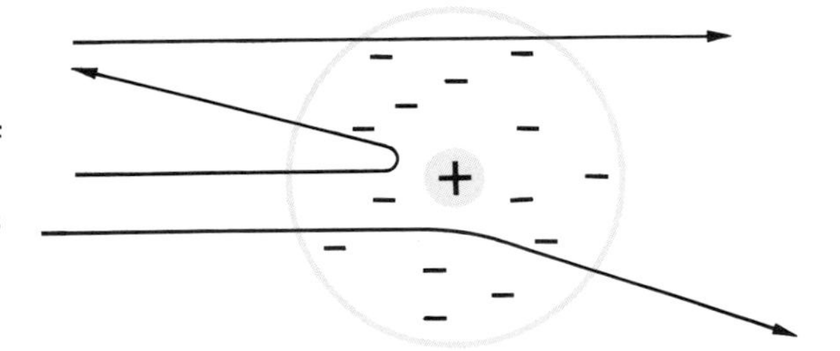

Fig. 6.15 Scattering of α-particles by an atom in which most of the mass is concentrated in a small positive nucleus.

The Charge on the Nucleus 6.10

Electromagnetic radiation, which includes X-rays and radio waves as well as visible light, is propagated in the form of waves traveling at a constant speed c, equal to 2.998×10^{10} cm/sec in a vacuum. The frequency ν of the radiation is equal to the number of waves passing a given point in one second, and depends upon wavelength λ. This is expressed by

$$\nu = \frac{c}{\lambda}$$

The wave character of electromagnetic radiation is represented in Fig. 6.16.

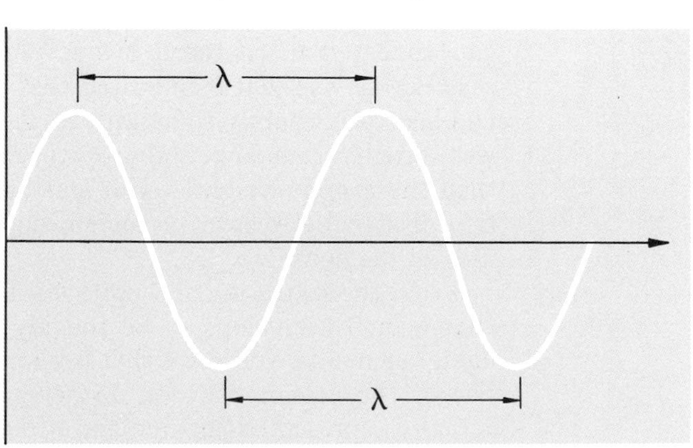

Fig. 6.16 Representation of radiation of wavelength λ being propagated in the direction of the arrow.

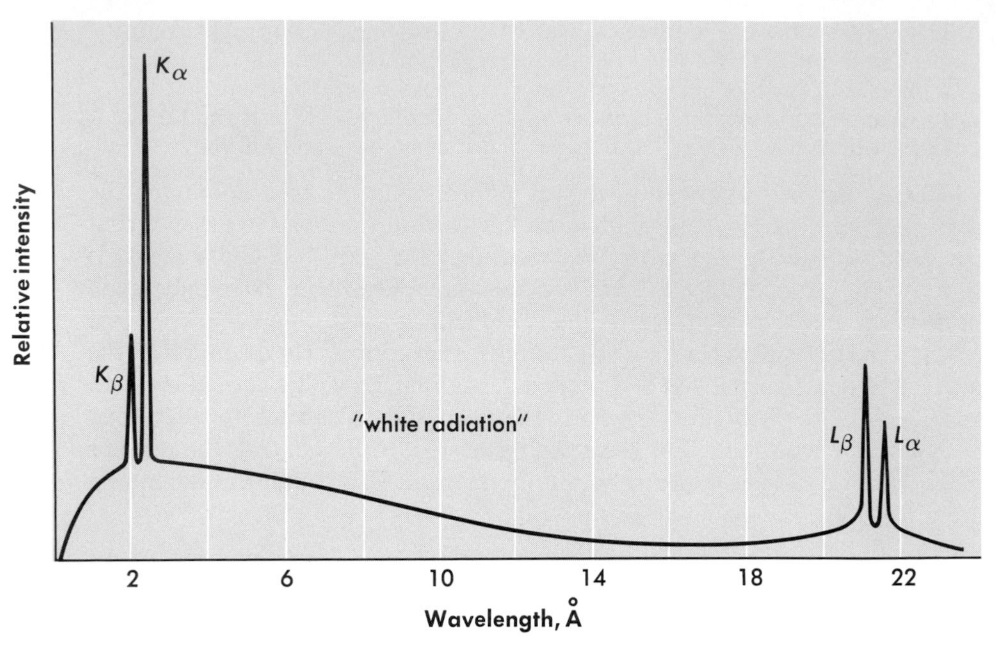

Fig. 6.17 Plot of intensity versus wavelength of the X-rays emitted by a chromium target.

When a substance is bombarded by cathode rays, it emits X-rays consisting of a continuous low-intensity background of so-called "white radiation," upon which is superimposed intense emission at several frequencies characteristic of the substance emitting the X-rays. In a plot of intensity versus wavelength, the latter appear as sharp peaks, designated K and L in Fig. 6.17.

In 1913, H. G. J. Moseley measured the wavelength of the characteristic K and L radiation emitted by various elements. He found that the wavelength decreases, or in other words the frequency increases, in a regular manner in passing from one element to the next one in order in the periodic table (Fig. 6.18). Most significant, a plot of atomic number against the square root of the frequency is a straight line (Fig. 6.19). Wherever a gap, representing a missing element, existed in the periodic table, a corresponding gap appeared in the straight-line plot. What made this relationship so remarkable was that it indicated that the atomic number, which heretofore had been used simply to indicate an element's position in the periodic table, was actually a fundamental property of the element, more important in fact than the atomic weight. This was almost like discovering that a correlation existed between a person's occupation and the number on the front door of his house!

From the scattering of α-particles, Rutherford had estimated the positive charge on the nucleus to be roughly one-half the atomic weight for the lighter elements, and somewhat less for heavier ones. As this was about the size of the atomic number, Moseley concluded that the atomic number actually represented the number of positive charges on the nucleus. Each

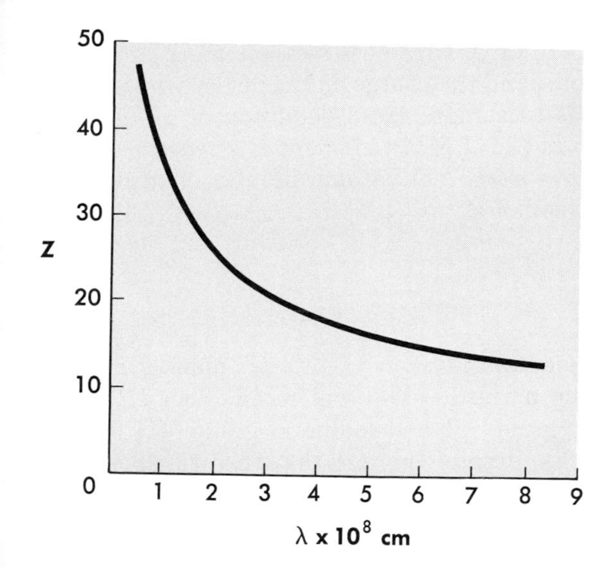

Fig. 6.18 Plot of the wavelength of the characteristic K_α radiation versus atomic number (Z) for elements from Al ($Z = 13$) to Ag ($Z = 47$).

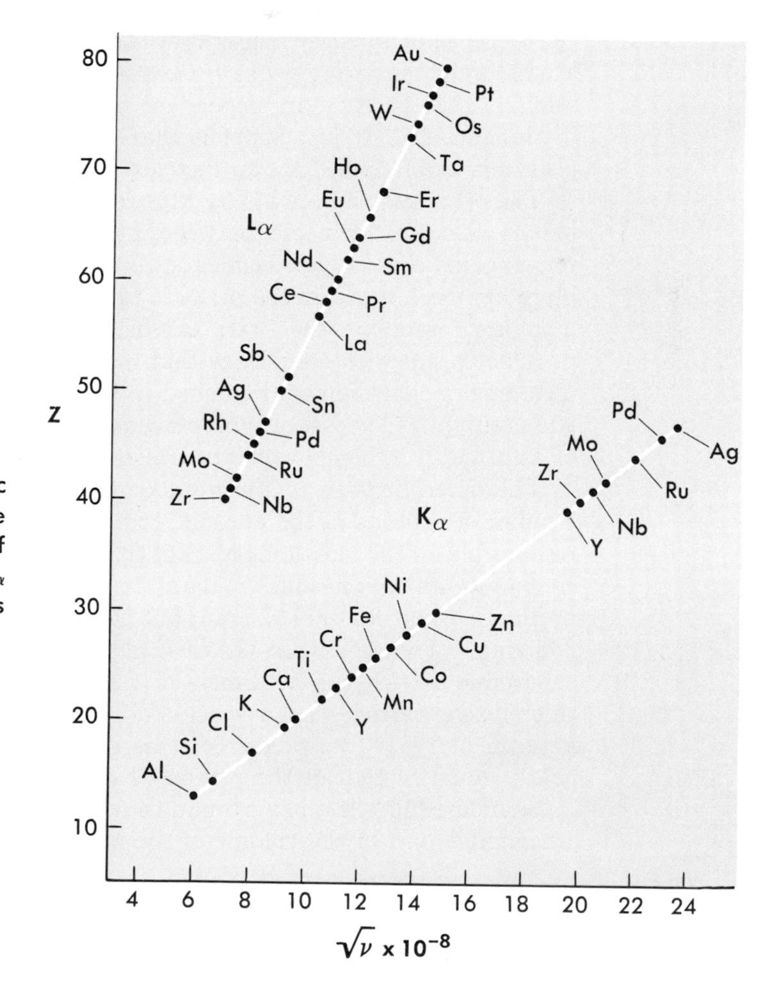

Fig. 6.19 Plot of atomic number Z versus the square root of the frequency ν of characteristic K_α and L_α radiation, using Moseley's data.

successive element in the periodic table thus possesses one more proton in its nucleus than the preceding one, and the charge on the nucleus determines what element it is. This leads to a more exact definition of an element than the operational one given in Sec. 1.3: *An **element** is a substance all of whose atoms have the same atomic number.* The atomic number of an element is usually represented by the symbol Z.

6.11 The Neutron

The discovery of the fundamental nature of the atomic number cleared up two problems while creating a third. You will recall (Sec. 4.2) that Mendeleev placed tellurium in group VI and iodine in group VII on the basis of their chemical properties, despite the fact that the atomic weight of tellurium is greater than that of iodine. Argon presented a similar case when it was discovered, since it was obviously a member of group 0, although its atomic weight fell between those of potassium and calcium. Cobalt and nickel also appear out of order on the basis of their atomic weights. These apparent exceptions to the periodic law, which had perplexed chemists for forty years, immediately disappear with the restatement of the law as a consequence of Moseley's discovery. Rather than being a function of the atomic weights, *the properties of the elements vary periodically with the atomic number*, that is, they are dependent upon the number of positive charges in the nucleus. It just happens that in most cases an increase in nuclear charge is accompanied by an increase in atomic weight.

The other problem solved by Moseley's work was that of the exact number of chemical elements between hydrogen and uranium. It must be remembered that only 83 elements were known in 1913, and no satisfactory place had been found in the periodic table for the elements between lanthanum and hafnium—the "rare earths," or lanthanides. Now it became possible to say with confidence that exactly nine spaces for nine elements, including one lanthanide, remained in the periodic table between hydrogen and uranium. The last of these places was filled in 1940 with the production of astatine by α-bombardment of bismuth (Sec. 20.4).

The determination of the number of positive particles, and hence the number of protons in the nucleus, created a problem concerning what was responsible for the remaining mass of the atom. The 92 electrons of uranium contribute an infinitesimal amount to the mass of the atom, and the 92 protons account for only 92 amu; but the atomic weight of uranium is about 238 amu. To account for the missing mass, Rutherford suggested a third subatomic particle having a mass of 1 amu, but no charge. The search for this elusive particle ended successfully with Chadwick's detection of the ***neutron*** in 1932. As predicted, this uncharged particle has a mass very nearly equal to that of the proton (Table 6.1).

Summarizing, the atom is found to consist of a minute nucleus, occupying a negligible part of the volume of the atom* but possessing nearly all of its

* Atoms have diameters of roughly 10^{-8} cm, and their nuclei are about 10^{-12} cm across. Imagine an atom magnified until its nucleus was as large as the sun. Its diameter would then be twice as great as that of the entire solar system.

TABLE 6.1 Principal Subatomic Particles

Name	Absolute Charge (coulomb)	Relative Charge	Relative Mass (amu)
Electron	-1.60×10^{-19}	-1	0.000548
Proton	$+1.60 \times 10^{-19}$	$+1$	1.00728
Neutron	0	0	1.00867

mass. In the nucleus are found two kinds of particles: protons and neutrons, each with a mass of approximately 1 amu. The number of protons is equal to the atomic number; the number of neutrons equals the difference between the atomic number and the atomic weight. Within the remaining volume of the atom are the electrons, equal in number to the number of protons in the nucleus.

Example 6.5

An isotope of thallium ($Z = 81$) has a mass of 203 amu. How many protons and neutrons are in the nucleus? How many electrons surround the nucleus in the neutral atom?

Solution: Since the atomic number is 81, there are 81 protons in the nucleus. The number of neutrons is equal to the difference between the atomic weight and the atomic number: $203 - 81 = 122$ neutrons. The nucleus is surrounded by 81 electrons, their number being equal to the number of protons in the neutral atom.

The existence of isotopes (Sec. 6.5) can now be understood in terms of the composition of the nucleus. Two atoms may have the same number of protons, but different numbers of neutrons in their nuclei. Since chemical properties depend upon the number of protons in the nucleus, these two atoms are both atoms of the same element, but because they have different numbers of neutrons, they have different atomic weights. They are, in other words, isotopes. The isotopes of an element are distinguished by having different numbers of neutrons in their nuclei. This gives them different atomic weights, but has little or no effect on their chemical properties.

Reading Suggestions 6.12

Those interested in a more detailed account, largely in the investigator's own words, of the earlier research leading up to the present-day concept of atomic structure should read *The Structure of Atoms*, by J. J. Lagowski (Volume G-1 in the paperback series *Classic Researches in General Chemistry*, Houghton Mifflin Co., Boston, 1964). From reading this short (118 pp.) book, one can arrive at a better appreciation of the role of experiment in the development of science. Thomson's account of his determination of the nature of cathode rays is reprinted on pp. 132–144 of *Readings in the Literature of Science* by W. C. and M. Dampier (Harper & Row, New York, 1959). Immediately following Thomson's paper, beginning on p. 145 of the Dampiers' book, is F. W. Aston's paper on isotopes and atomic weights, in which he describes the first mass spectrograph, and two papers by H. G. J. Moseley on X-ray spectra and atomic numbers. The history of this period comes alive in *Rutherford and the Nature of the Atom*, by E. N. da C. Andrade, who worked under Rutherford at the University of Manchester (Doubleday Anchor Books, Garden City, 1964).

Not all nineteenth century chemists were convinced that the atom was indivisible, as J. H. Scott points out in an article in *J. Chem. Ed.* **36,** 64 (1959). In 1816, William Prout suggested that all atoms were composed of hydrogen, which could be considered the "protyle," or prime matter, of the ancients. Prout's hypothesis, which foreshadowed the discoveries of nearly a century later, is discussed in articles by O. T. Benfey (*J. Chem. Ed.* **29,** 78 (1952)) and by R. Siegfried (*J. Chem. Ed.*, **33,** 263 (1956)).

A history of the search for the elusive neutron, which because of its lack of charge was difficult to detect, is given by V. Lavrakas, *J. Chem. Ed.* **29,** 281 (1952).

Questions and Problems

6.1 Name and briefly describe the three principal types of radiation from radioactive elements.

6.2 J. J. Thomson's model of the atom, proposed in 1898, pictured it as a sphere of positive electricity in which the electrons were embedded "like raisins in a plum pudding." Show how the experiment of Rutherford and Geiger on the scattering of α-particles is inconsistent with Thomson's model.

6.3 What are isotopes? How does the existence of isotopes account for the fact that most atomic weights are not whole numbers? Describe the principle of the mass spectrograph, and tell how it can be used to determine the existence of isotopes of an element.

6.4 Name and describe (charge and mass) the three major components of the atom.

6.5 Complete the following table:

Symbol	*Z*	Mass Number	Protons	Neutrons	Electrons
Ca			20	20	
	41	93			
Tb		151			65
U		238		146	
P		31	15		

6.6 There are three naturally occurring isotopes of magnesium: $^{24}_{12}Mg$, $^{25}_{12}Mg$, and $^{26}_{12}Mg$. From the atomic weights and relative abundances of these isotopes as given below, calculate the atomic weight of the natural isotopic mixture:

Isotope	Atomic Weight, amu	% Natural Abundance
$^{24}_{12}Mg$	23.99	78.70
$^{25}_{12}Mg$	24.99	10.13
$^{26}_{12}Mg$	25.98	11.17

6.7 The principal isotope of iron contains 26 protons and 30 neutrons in its nucleus. Using the data given in Table 6.1, calculate the relative mass (in amu) of this isotope. The actual isotopic mass, determined by mass spectroscopy, is 55.9349 amu. How does this compare with the calculated mass? What can you say about the difference, if any, in the two values?

6.8 The difference between the calculated and observed masses of an isotope is called the *mass defect*, and it corresponds to the energy released in the formation of the atoms from protons, neutrons, and electrons. From the calculated and observed masses of the iron isotope in problem 6.7, calculate the energy in kilocalories released in the formation of 1 mole of iron atoms.

6.9 Account for the fact that the mass spectrum of water shows peaks corresponding to mass numbers of 1, 16, 17, 18, 19, and 20, with the following relative intensities:

Mass Number	Relative Intensity
1	0.1
16	1.0
17	21.
18	100.
19	0.15
20	0.22

The relative abundances of the natural isotopes of hydrogen and oxygen are given below:

Hydrogen		Oxygen	
Mass Number	% Natural Abundance	Mass Number	% Natural Abundance
1	99.985	16	99.759
2	0.015	17	0.037
		18	0.204

What further refinement of your interpretation of the mass spectrum is possible in the light of this information?

Things on a very small scale
behave like nothing that you have
any direct experience about.

——Richard Feynman

7 ARRANGEMENT OF ELECTRONS IN ATOMS

Opposite charges attract one another. This being the case, then what keeps the negative electrons of an atom from falling into the positive nucleus? The most obvious suggestion is that the atom resembles a miniature solar system. Just as the centrifugal force on the orbiting planets balances the gravitational attraction of the sun, centrifugal force on the orbiting electrons balances the coulombic attraction of the nucleus. This picture is appealing in its simplicity, but unfortunately it possesses a fatal defect. Previous experience with moving charges predicts that such a structure would be inherently unstable and could exist for no more than an instant. According to classical physics, a charged particle moving in a curved path should radiate energy. Therefore an electron in a planetary orbit would be expected to lose energy and spiral into the nucleus. Obviously, this does not happen. Attempts to account for the observed stability of atoms led to the discovery that subatomic particles behave quite differently from macroscopic objects. The story of this discovery is the subject of this chapter.

The "Solar System" Atom 7.1

Let us consider the simplest possible atom, that of hydrogen, consisting of one electron and one proton. Imagine the electron traveling uniformly

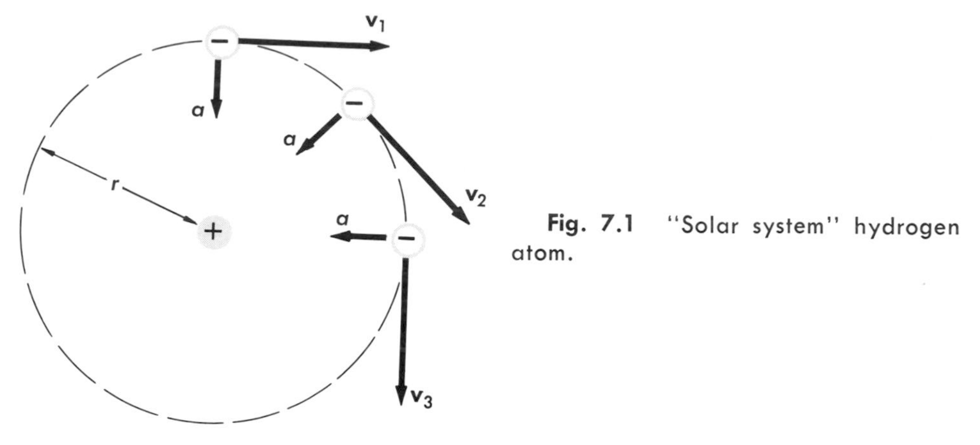

Fig. 7.1 "Solar system" hydrogen atom.

around the proton in a circular orbit whose radius is r. Our picture of the atom will then look like Fig. 7.1. At any instant, the velocity of the electron may be represented by a vector **v**, tangent to the circle and with its origin at the electron. As the electron moves around the nucleus, its accompanying velocity vector continuously changes direction. By definition, any change in velocity constitutes an acceleration. Since the velocity of an object is a vector quantity possessing both magnitude and direction (see footnote, page 62), an acceleration results from a change in either one. Thus an object moving uniformly in a curved path undergoes constant acceleration with respect to the focus of the curve. If the curve is a circle, the acceleration a is equal to $\mathbf{v}^2/r$.

Fig. 7.2 Acceleration in uniform circular motion.

The idea of a body undergoing acceleration as it moves in a circle with a constant speed may be a little hard to visualize at first. A simple illustration may give it more reality. Figure 7.2 shows a toy locomotive on a circular track. As the engine goes around the track, its shadow on the wall moves back and forth, speeding up—accelerating—toward the center, and slowing down at the edges. The shadow has effectively sorted out the engine's velocity component across the circle, and the engine is seen to be undergoing a periodic motion, or oscillation, relative to the center of the circle.

If instead of a toy train on a track we have an electron in an orbit, the picture is similar, but with a very important difference. An electron carries a charge, and an oscillating charge generates a constantly varying electromagnetic field, resulting in the emission of electromagnetic radiation. This is familiar to any amateur radio operator, who knows that an alternating current of electrons oscillating in the antenna at 1020 kilocycles per second generates the radio waves which put KDKA on the air.

The emitted radiation represents energy which must be given up by the electron. As it loses energy, the electron will move closer and closer to the nucleus, finally colliding with it. The situation is similar to that of an artificial earth satellite, which as it collides with occasional gas molecules and bits of cosmic dust gradually loses energy and slowly spirals back to earth. Classical mechanics thus predicts that an atom composed of electrons orbiting around a nucleus is doomed to destruction. In fact, however, an atom is quite stable and does not normally radiate energy. The model which we would derive from classical theory is completely at variance with the fact of the atom's stability, and we are forced to conclude that matter on a small scale obeys a different set of rules.

The first indication of how this confict between theory and observation might be resolved came about through a reconsideration of atomic spectra. These had been studied and used for analytical purposes since the invention of the prism spectroscope by Bunsen and Kirchhoff in 1859, but little was known about the fundamental processes which give rise to these spectra.

Atomic Spectra 7.2

An element, vaporized and brought to incandescence in a flame, an electric arc, or a discharge tube, emits light of characteristic color by which it may be identified. A Bunsen burner flame is colored yellow by sodium salts, red by strontium, violet by potassium. In a discharge tube, neon glows orange-red, helium pink, and so on. The different colors represent light of different wavelengths. Passing the light through a prism spreads it out into a ***spectrum*** (Fig. 7.3), light of longer wavelength being bent, or refracted, to a smaller degree than light of shorter wavelength. The spectrum of an incandescent gas is seen to consist of a number of lines—a so-called ***line spectrum*** (Fig. 7.4). Each element emits light of a limited number of definite wavelengths, and thus exhibits a characteristic line spectrum. It is also found that if light of all wavelengths (i.e., "white" light), is passed through the vapors of an element at low pressure, certain frequencies are absorbed which are found to correspond exactly to lines in the emission spectrum. The ***absorption spectrum,*** as this is called, is the reverse of the emission spectrum, and it consists of a series of dark lines superimposed on a

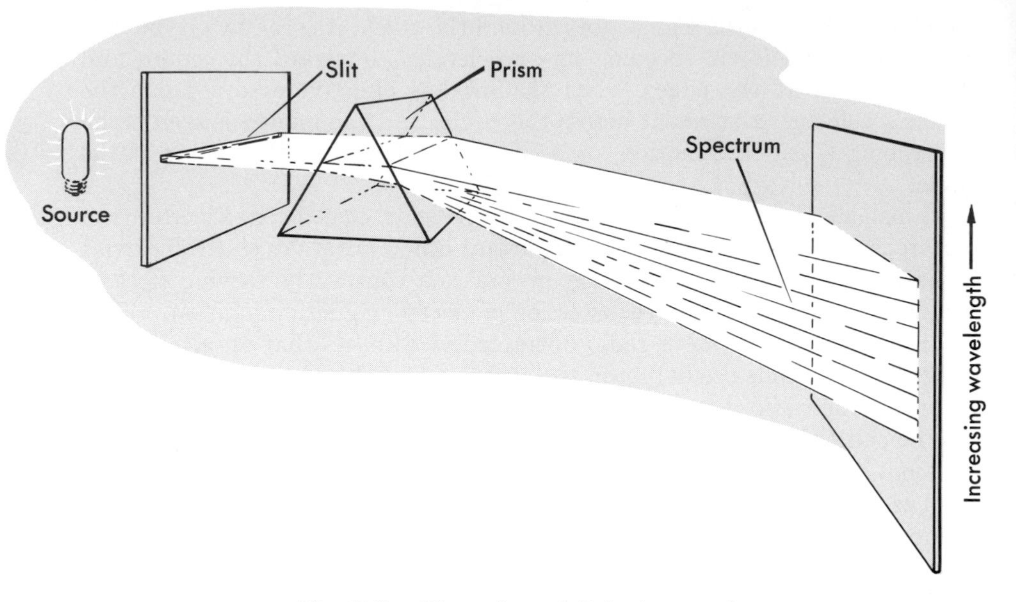

Fig. 7.3 Dispersion of light by a prism.

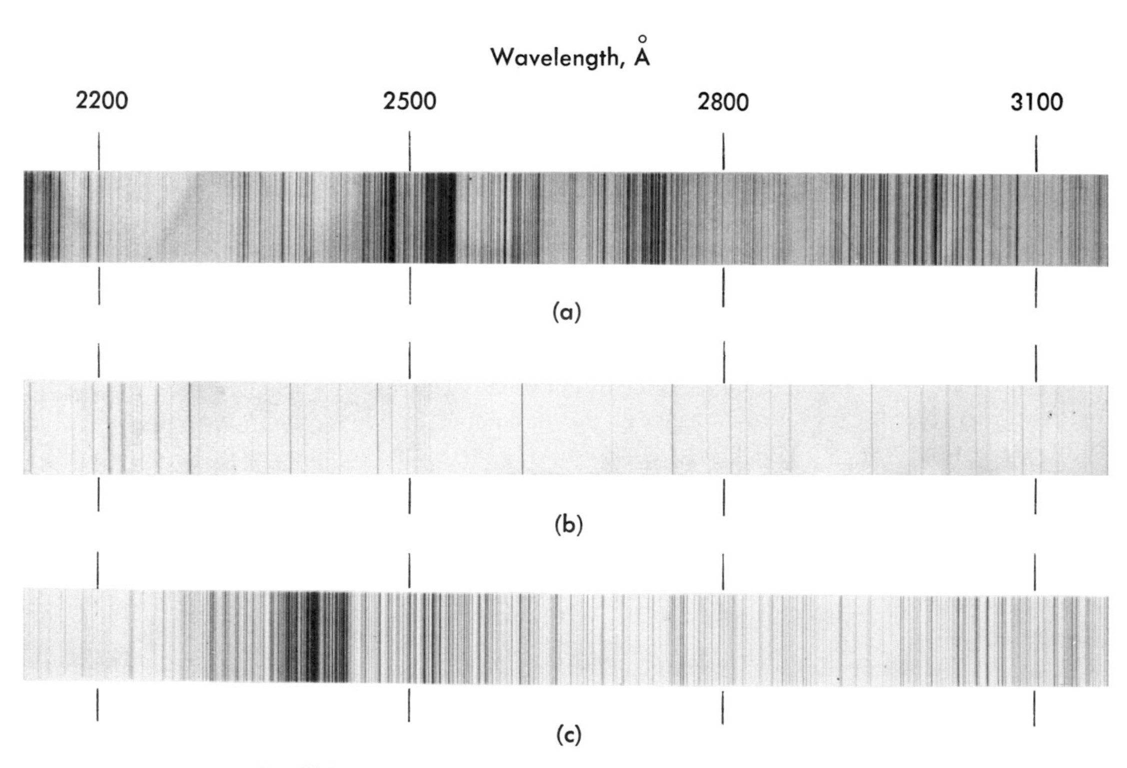

Fig. 7.4 Line emission spectra of (a) iron, (b) copper, and (c) cobalt between 2125 and 3175 Å. (Courtesy of Professor Gerald Spielholtz, Lehman College.)

continuous background.* Every line in the absorption spectrum also appears in the emission spectrum, although the latter may show additional lines as well. Any one element always exhibits the same spectrum, and if the light from two or more incandescent elements is passed simultaneously through a prism, the resulting spectra will be superimposed without interfering with one another. Few lines, if any, coincide in the spectra of different elements, and by referring to standard tables of spectral lines, the various elements in a mixture may be identified even though present in extremely small amounts.

The lines in the spectrum of an element are not haphazardly distributed, but are seen to occur in groups, or series, in which the wavelengths of the lines bear a mathematical relationship to one another. In each series the lines converge, that is, the separation between them decreases regularly as their wavelength decreases, reaching a limiting value beyond which the spectrum becomes continuous (Fig. 7.5). The significance of this convergence will shortly become apparent.

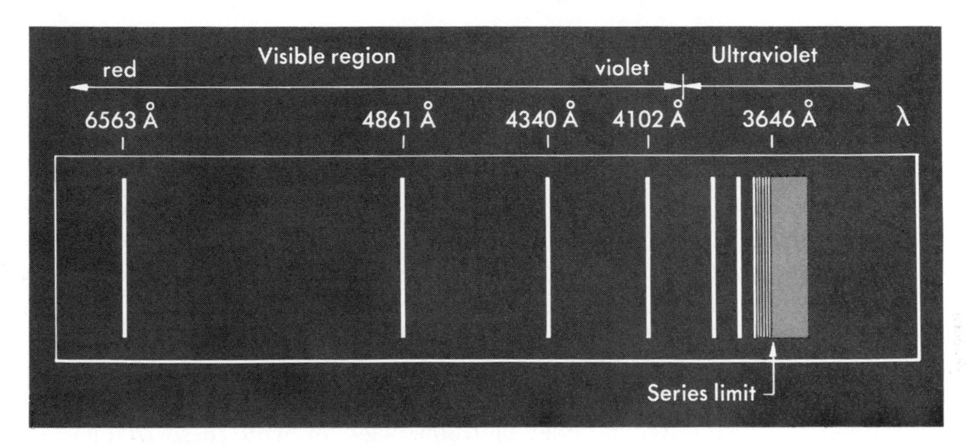

Fig. 7.5 The Balmer series of the hydrogen spectrum.

In 1885, J. J. Balmer observed that the wavelengths of the four bright lines in the visible portion of the hydrogen spectrum fit the expression

$$\frac{1}{\lambda} = R\left(\frac{1}{n_1^2} - \frac{1}{n_2^2}\right)$$

where $R = 109{,}678\ \text{cm}^{-1}$ (the "Rydberg constant" for hydrogen), $n_1 = 2$, and n_2 has the values 3, 4, 5, and 6, respectively, for the four lines. As other series of lines were recognized in the ultraviolet and infrared regions of the spectrum, they too were found to obey the same relationship (Table 7.1).

* The dark lines which appear superimposed on the solar spectrum—the Fraunhofer lines—correspond to the absorption spectra of the elements in the sun's atmosphere. A study of these lines in 1868 revealed one which was not present in the spectrum of any known element. In this way helium (from Greek *helios*, the sun) was discovered in the sun's atmosphere almost thirty years before it was found on the earth.

TABLE 7.1 Spectral Series for Hydrogen

Series Name	n_1	n_2	Wavelength of First Series Line, Å	Region of Spectrum
Lyman	1	2, 3, 4, . . .	1,216	Ultraviolet
Balmer	2	3, 4, 5, . . .	6,563	Visible
Paschen	3	4, 5, 6, . . .	18,751	Infrared
Brackett	4	5, 6, 7, . . .	40,500	Infrared
Pfund	5	6, 7, 8, . . .	75,980	Infrared

The factors R/n^2 are called the ***spectral terms*** (τ) for hydrogen. The spectral terms for elements other than hydrogen are more complex, but in all cases the wavelengths of the spectral lines appear in convergent series that have the general mathematical form

$$\frac{1}{\lambda} = \tau_1 - \tau_2$$

7.3 Energy Levels in the Atom

When atoms are "excited," for example, by being heated in a flame, they absorb energy. Light is a form of energy, and one can reason that the emission of light represents the release of excess energy by the excited atoms as they return to the unexcited state, or ***ground state.*** Similarly, one can conclude that the energy of light absorbed by gaseous atoms serves to raise the atoms from the ground state to some ***excited state*** or states. It is not immediately obvious, however, why emission and absorption of light should occur at only a limited number of frequencies, or why these frequencies should bear any sort of simple relationship to one another.

In 1900, Max Planck showed that in its interactions with matter, light and other forms of electromagnetic radiation behave as though their energy were delivered in the form of discrete packages, or ***quanta.*** The amount of energy in one of these packages depends upon the frequency of the light, and it is given by the expression

$$E = h\nu = \frac{hc}{\lambda}$$

where ν is the frequency, and the proportionality constant h, known as ***Planck's constant of action,*** has the value 6.63×10^{-27} erg-sec. An object can absorb or emit light energy only in multiples of whole quanta, never in any fractional amount. G. N. Lewis likened the quantum to an "atom" of light, and renamed it the ***photon.***

Planck's relationship can be used to calculate the energies corresponding to several of the lines in the hydrogen spectrum. Example 7.1 shows how this can be done.

Example 7.1

Calculate the energy in electron volts (eV) of the photon whose wavelength is 6563 Å (1.00 eV = 1.60×10^{-12} erg).

Solution:

$$E = h\nu = \frac{hc}{\lambda}$$

$$E = \frac{(6.63 \times 10^{-27} \text{ erg-sec})(3 \times 10^{10} \text{ cm/sec})}{6.563 \times 10^{-5} \text{ cm}}$$

$$= 3.03 \times 10^{-12} \text{ erg}$$

$$= \frac{3.03 \times 10^{-12} \text{ erg}}{1.60 \times 10^{-12} \text{ erg/eV}} = 1.89 \text{ eV}$$

The results of these calculations are given in Table 7.2, which also includes the values of n_1 and n_2 in the Balmer equation (Sec. 7.2) for the various spectral lines.

TABLE 7.2 Calculated Energies Related to Lines in the Hydrogen Spectrum

Series	Wavelength of Spectral Line, Å	n_1	n_2	Energy of Photons, eV
Paschen	18,751	3	4	0.67
	12,818	3	5	0.97
Balmer	6,563	2	3	1.89
	4,861	2	4	2.56
	4,340	2	5	2.86
Lyman	1,216	1	2	10.23
	1,026	1	3	12.12
	973	1	4	12.79
	950	1	5	13.10

Examination of Table 7.2 shows that a remarkable relationship exists among the energies of the various spectral lines. The difference between the calculated energies for any two lines in a given spectral series is the same as the difference between the energies calculated for the two lines in any other series which have the same values for n_2. For example, the difference between the energies calculated for the two lines in the Lyman series at 1026 Å ($n_1 = 1$; $n_2 = 3$) and at 973 Å ($n_1 = 1$; $n_2 = 4$) is $12.79 - 12.12 = 0.67$ eV. This is the same as the difference between the energies calculated for the lines at 6563 Å ($n_1 = 2$; $n_2 = 3$) and 4861 Å ($n_1 = 2$; $n_2 = 4$) in the Balmer series ($2.56 - 1.89 = 0.67$ eV). Not only that, but it is equal to the energy calculated for the line in the Paschen series at 18,751 Å for which the values of n_1 and n_2 are the same as the respective values of n_2 for the two other pairs of lines.

This relationship is hardly the result of coincidence. Rather, it suggests that there exists for the atom a limited number of permitted energy levels. An atom can gain or lose energy by absorption or emission of light only if the quantity involved is equal to the difference in energy between two such levels. The frequency of the photon absorbed or emitted in the process is

$$\nu = \frac{(E_2 - E_1)}{h}$$

where E_2 and E_1 are the respective energies of the higher and lower levels. The energy of the atom is said to be *quantized.* The integers (n) in the Balmer equation (Sec. 7.2) designate the permitted energy levels and are known as the ***principal quantum numbers.*** The lowest energy level is that for which $n = 1$; higher quantum numbers represent higher energy levels.* Each line in the spectrum of an element represents an energy transition between two permitted levels. Since the number of energy levels is limited, the number of frequencies at which lines can appear in the spectrum is likewise limited. The relationships among the energy levels of the hydrogen atom, the principal quantum numbers, and the spectral lines are shown in Fig. 7.6.

Example 7.2

Calculate the wavelength of the line in the hydrogen spectrum which appears when an excited hydrogen atom drops from the fourth to the second energy level.

Solution:

$$\frac{1}{\lambda} = 109{,}678 \text{ cm}^{-1}\left(\frac{1}{2^2} - \frac{1}{4^2}\right)$$

$$= 109{,}678 \text{ cm}^{-1}\left(\tfrac{1}{4} - \tfrac{1}{16}\right)$$

$$= 109{,}678 \text{ cm}^{-1}\left(\tfrac{3}{16}\right) = 20{,}564.7 \text{ cm}^{-1}$$

$$\lambda = 4862.70 \text{ Å}$$

7.4 The Bohr Model of the Atom

In 1913, the Danish physicist Niels Bohr suggested that the atomic energy levels represent orbits in which the electrons of the atom are allowed to travel. The larger the radius of the orbit, the greater the energy of the electron in that orbit. An electron occupying a permitted orbit is said to be in a ***stationary state*** in which it does not radiate energy, despite the contrary prediction of classical theory. Electrons can change in energy only by jumping from one allowed orbit or stationary state to another. In doing so, they gain or lose energy in quantities exactly equal to the difference in the energies of the respective stationary states. Exciting atoms in an electric arc, a discharge tube, or a flame raises some of their electrons from their ground states to other states of higher energy. Later, as the electrons return to lower energy states, this energy is re-emitted as light, giving rise to the various lines of the emission spectrum. Electrons may also be raised to higher energy states by the absorption of light of the appropriate frequencies.

* The letters K, L, M, . . . are often used in referring to the energy levels for which the respective values for n are 1, 2, 3, ...

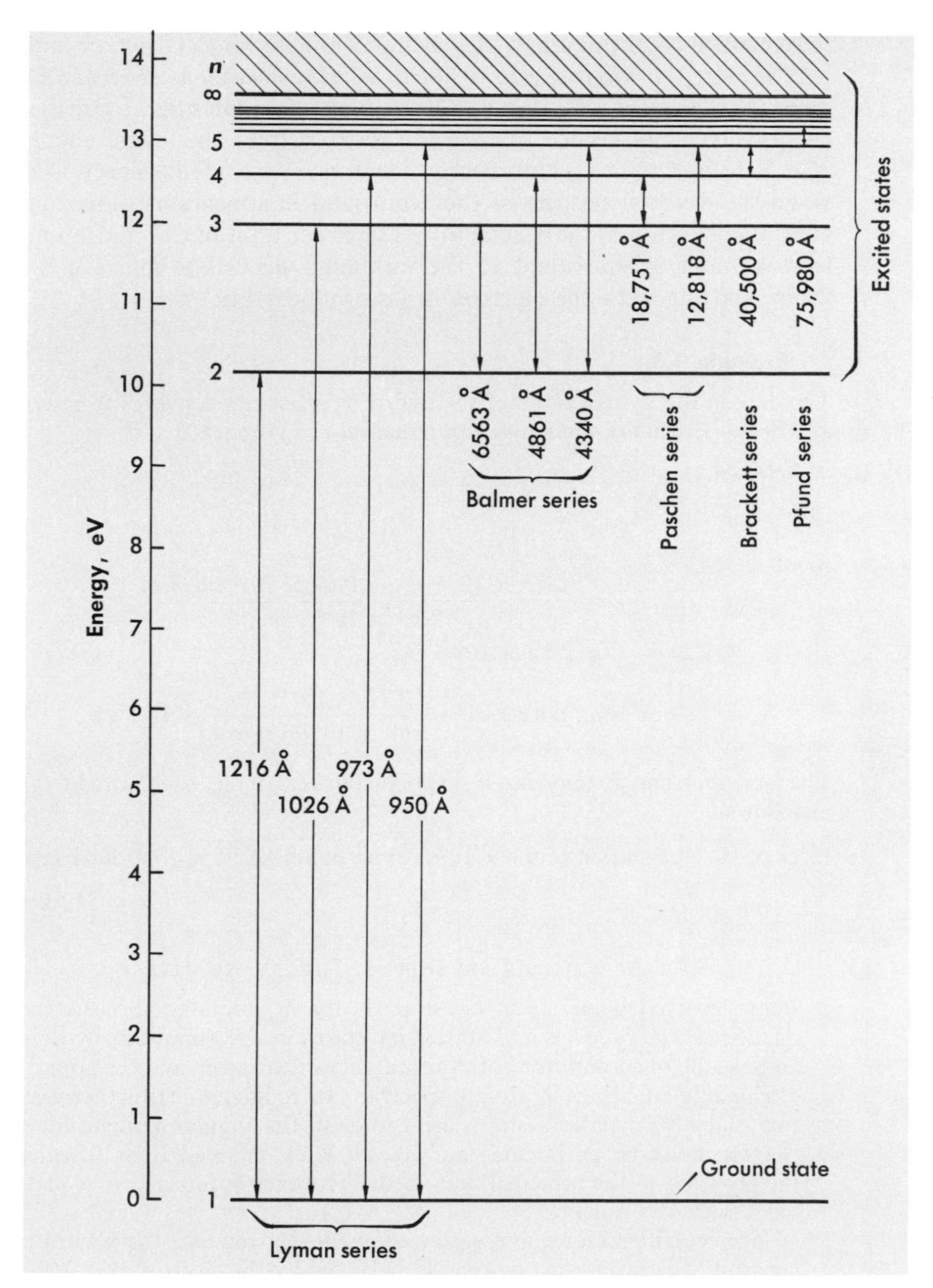

Fig. 7.6 Energy levels in the hydrogen atom.

Since the energies of the stationary states within the atom are fixed, the dark lines of the resulting absorption spectrum appear at the same frequencies as the bright lines of the emission spectrum. An electron which is completely separated from the atom is no longer constrained in any stationary state, and may gain or lose energy in any amount. Hence, each series of spectral lines ends in a continuum, representing complete dissociation, or ionization.

The energy, in electron volts, required to bring about ionization of an isolated atom in the gaseous state is known as its ***ionization potential.*** For hydrogen, this is the energy needed to raise the electron from the lowest energy level, $n = 1$, to an infinitely high energy level, $n = \infty$. This energy is released when the electron returns to the atom, and it appears as radiation in the continuous region of the spectrum. The lower limit of the continuum in the Lyman series is equivalent to the minimum needed to ionize a hydrogen atom, starting with the electron in its ground state, $n = 1$.

Example 7.3

The lines in the Lyman series of the hydrogen spectrum converge to a series limit at 919 Å. Calculate the ionization potential of hydrogen.

Solution:

$$E = \frac{hc}{\lambda}$$

$$= \frac{(6.63 \times 10^{-27}\ \text{erg-sec})(3 \times 10^{10}\ \text{cm/sec})}{9.19 \times 10^{-6}\ \text{cm}}$$

$$= 2.17 \times 10^{-11}\ \text{erg}$$

$$\text{Ionization potential} = \frac{2.17 \times 10^{-11}\ \text{erg}}{1.60 \times 10^{-12}\ \text{erg/eV}} = 13.5\ \text{eV}$$

The ionization energy may also be expressed in kcal/mole, which can be calculated as follows:

$$(2.17 \times 10^{-11}\ \text{erg/atom})(6.02 \times 10^{23}\ \text{atoms/mole})\ (2.39 \times 10^{-11}\ \text{kcal/erg}) = 312\ \text{kcal/mole}$$

The Application of Bohr's Theory to Hydrogen

Bohr departed boldly from classical theory in assuming the existence of quantized energy levels and stationary states in the atom, but by doing so he was able to account for both the stability of the atom and the appearance of characteristic lines in atomic spectra. Introducing one further assumption, namely, that for a stable orbit to exist, the angular momentum of the electron must be an integral multiple of $h/2\pi$, enabled Bohr to calculate the positions of the principal lines in the hydrogen spectrum, in good agreement with experiment.

The centrifugal force mv^2/r exerted on an electron as it travels in a circular orbit of radius r must be exactly balanced by the electrostatic attraction between it and the nucleus. Both the electron and the nucleus of the hydrogen atom ($Z = 1$) bear a charge of magnitude e. Therefore,

$$\frac{mv^2}{r} = \frac{e^2}{r^2} \qquad (1)$$

Applying the so-called "quantum condition," namely that the angular momentum $mvr = nh/2\pi$, allows the speed v of the electron to be calculated for each value of n, as follows:

$$mvr = \frac{nh}{2\pi} \qquad (n = 1, 2, 3, \ldots) \tag{2}$$

$$v = \frac{nh}{2\pi mr} \tag{3}$$

Substituting for v in Equation (1) gives

$$\frac{m}{r}\left(\frac{nh}{2\pi mr}\right)^2 = \frac{e^2}{r^2} \tag{4}$$

$$r = \frac{n^2h^2}{4\pi^2me^2} \tag{5}$$

Using the values for m and e obtained previously (Secs. 6.2 and 6.3),

$$e = 1.60 \times 10^{-19} \text{ coulomb} = 4.8 \times 10^{-10} \text{ electrostatic unit (esu)}$$
$$m = 9.1 \times 10^{-28} \text{ g}$$

the radius of the smallest orbit of the hydrogen atom, that for which $n = 1$, can be calculated thus:

$$r = \frac{(1)h^2}{4\pi^2me^2} = \frac{(6.63 \times 10^{-27})^2}{(4)(3.14)^2(9.1 \times 10^{-28})(4.8 \times 10^{-10})^2} = 0.53 \text{ Å}$$

The total energy within the atom consists of the sum of the kinetic energy, $\frac{1}{2}mv^2$ of the electron, and the potential energy $-e^2/r$ which arises from the coulombic attraction between the electron and the proton, i.e.,

$$E_{\text{total}} = E_k + E_p = (\tfrac{1}{2}mv^2) + (-e^2/r) \tag{6}$$

From Equation (1),

$$mv^2 = \frac{e^2}{r} \tag{7}$$

$$E_{\text{total}} = \frac{e^2}{2r} - \frac{e^2}{r} = \frac{-e^2}{2r} \tag{8}$$

Substituting the value of r obtained in Equation (5),

$$E_{\text{total}} = -\left(\frac{2\pi^2e^4m}{h^2}\right)\left(\frac{1}{n^2}\right) \tag{9}$$

The negative sign means that the energy of a hydrogen atom is less than that of a proton and electron separated by an infinite distance; that is, the hydrogen atom does not spontaneously dissociate.

The difference in energy between two permitted orbits whose quantum numbers are n_1 and n_2, from Equation (9) is

$$E_2 - E_1 = \left(-\frac{2\pi^2e^4m}{n_2^2h^2}\right) - \left(-\frac{2\pi^2e^4m}{n_1^2h^2}\right) \tag{10}$$

$$= \frac{2\pi^2e^4m}{h^2}\left(\frac{1}{n_1^2} - \frac{1}{n_2^2}\right) \tag{11}$$

From the Planck relationship (Sec. 7.3),

$$E_2 - E_1 = h\nu = \frac{hc}{\lambda}$$

and

$$\frac{1}{\lambda} = \frac{2\pi^2 e^4 m}{h^3 c}\left(\frac{1}{n_1^2} - \frac{1}{n_2^2}\right) \qquad (12)$$

Equation (12) has the same form as the Balmer equation (Sec. 7.2), and indeed, evaluation of the expression

$$\frac{2\pi^2 e^4 m}{h^3 c}$$

will show it to be equal to the empirically determined Rydberg constant.

7.5 Subsidiary Quantum Numbers

Bohr's theory correctly predicts the wavelengths of the principal lines in the hydrogen spectrum, but it does not account for the fact that many of the lines in an atomic spectrum which at first glance appear to be single lines can be further resolved into closely spaced groups. The existence of this "fine structure" implies that the principal energy levels consist of groups of sublevels which differ slightly in energy. Three subsidiary quantum numbers, in addition to the principal quantum number n, have been found necessary to describe fully the energy state of each electron in a given atom. These are:

1. **The azimuthal quantum number** l, which may take any integral value from $l = 0$ to $l = (n - 1)$. Thus, if $n = 1$, l can have only one value, $l = 0$; whereas if $n = 3$, l may have the values 0, 1, and 2. The azimuthal quantum number was originally associated with the eccentricity of the electronic orbit, which it was assumed could be elliptical as well as circular. The letters *s*, *p*, *d*, and *f* are commonly used to denote energy levels for which $l = 0, 1, 2$, and 3, respectively.*

2. **The magnetic quantum number** m, whose values depend upon those of l. The magnetic quantum number may have any integral value from $+l$ to $-l$, including 0. Thus, if $l = 0$, $m = 0$; if $l = 2$, m may have five values: $-2, -1, 0, +1, +2$. This subsidiary quantum number was introduced in order to account for the further splitting of spectral lines when an element is excited in a magnetic field, and was associated with the orientation in space of the electronic orbits relative to one another.

3. **The spin quantum number** s. In certain respects, an electron in an atom behaves as though it were spinning on its own axis. Each sublevel of the atom is therefore further split into two levels according to the direction of the electron's spin. For each value of m there are two values of s, namely, $s = +\frac{1}{2}$ and $s = -\frac{1}{2}$.

* The letters *s*, *p*, *d*, and *f* come from the terms used by spectroscopists to describe the corresponding lines in the spectrum: *s*harp, *p*rincipal, *d*iffuse, and *f*undamental. These terms were never particularly descriptive, but the letters have been retained as a convenient shorthand device.

The ***Pauli exclusion principle,*** enunciated by Wolfgang Pauli in 1925, states that *no two electrons belonging to the same atom can have all four of their quantum numbers the same.* This is like saying that no two electrons can occupy the same place at the same time, since the motion of the electron about the nucleus, and hence its location, is determined by its energy state, which in turn is fully described in terms of its four quantum numbers. By applying the exclusion principle it is possible to calculate the maximum number of electrons which can be accommodated in each principal energy level of the atom as well as in each sublevel. For example, if $l = 0$, corresponding to an s sublevel, $m = 0$, and s may be either $+\frac{1}{2}$ or $-\frac{1}{2}$. An s sublevel, therefore, can accommodate only two electrons whose spins must be opposite, or *paired.* If $l = 1$ (the p sublevel), m may have any one of three values, -1, 0, and $+1$, for each of which s may be $+\frac{1}{2}$ or $-\frac{1}{2}$. Thus a p sublevel can hold up to three pairs of electrons for a maximum total of six. A d sublevel, for which $l = 2$, has five possible values for m: -2, -1, 0, $+1$, $+2$, and can therefore accommodate five pairs of electrons, or 10 altogether. Similarly, an f sublevel ($l = 3$) can hold a maximum of 14 electrons: seven pairs, each corresponding to one of the seven possible values of m.

When the principal quantum number $n = 1$, l may have only one value, zero, and hence only two electrons are permitted in the first principal energy level, both of which are designated s. If $n = 2$, there are two possible values for l, 0 and 1, and eight electrons can be accommodated: two in the $2s$ sublevel, and six in the $2p$. When $n = 2$, the s, p, and d sublevels may be occupied, allowing a maximum total of $2 + 6 + 10 = 18$ electrons. The next level, for which $n = 4$, may hold as many as 32 electrons, distributed among the $4s$, $4p$, $4d$, and $4f$ sublevels. The possible combinations of quantum numbers from $n = 1$ through $n = 4$ are summarized in Table 7.3.

TABLE 7.3 Quantum Number Combinations

n	l	m	s	Designation	Total Combinations	
1	0	0	$\pm\frac{1}{2}$	1s	2	
2	0	0	$\pm\frac{1}{2}$	2s	2	8
2	1	-1, 0, $+1$	$\pm\frac{1}{2}$	2p	6	
3	0	0	$\pm\frac{1}{2}$	3s	2	
3	1	-1, 0, $+1$	$\pm\frac{1}{2}$	3p	6	18
3	2	-2, -1, 0, $+1$, $+2$	$\pm\frac{1}{2}$	3d	10	
4	0	0	$\pm\frac{1}{2}$	4s	2	
4	1	-1, 0, $+1$	$\pm\frac{1}{2}$	4p	6	32
4	2	-2, -1, 0, $+1$, $+2$	$\pm\frac{1}{2}$	4d	10	
4	3	-3, -2, -1, 0, $+1$, $+2$, $+3$	$\pm\frac{1}{2}$	4f	14	

It may be seen from the foregoing that *the maximum number of electrons that can occupy any principal energy level is $2n^2$.* The maximum number of electrons that can be accommodated in each principal level therefore increases in the order 2, 8, 18, 32, 50, . . . as n increases from 1 to 5, ... Since it happens that no known atom has more than 32 electrons in any one principal energy level, for the present, at least, we need not concern ourselves with sublevels beyond f.

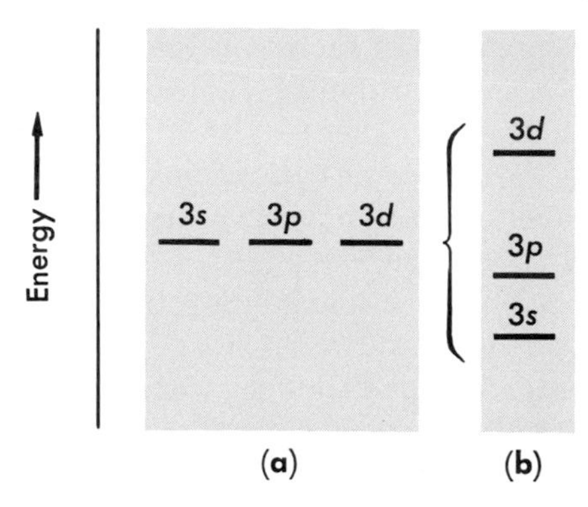

Fig. 7.7 Energy sublevels in (a) single-electron atom (hydrogen) and in (b) multielectron atom.

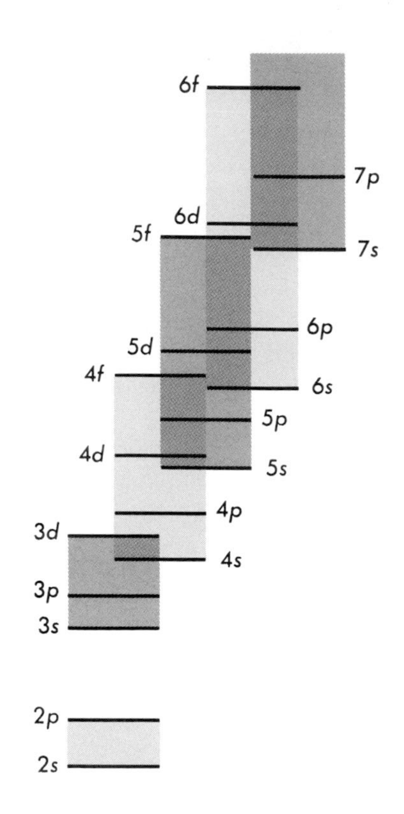

Fig. 7.8 Energy levels in multielectron atoms.

In the absence of an external magnetic field, the various sublevels within any principal energy level of the hydrogen atom are all of the same energy. In atoms possessing more than one electron, which means all neutral atoms other than hydrogen, each electron finds itself in a magnetic and electrical field created by the presence of the other electrons. In these atoms, as a result, levels which have the same value for n, but different values for l, possess slightly different energies (Fig. 7.7). For example, the energy of a $2p$ electron is somewhat greater than that of a $2s$. The $3d$ level represents a higher energy than the $3p$, which in turn is at a higher level than the $3s$. Splitting of the principal energy levels into sublevels results in overlapping among those for which n is greater than 2. While the actual energies and the degree of overlap will, of course, differ for each individual element, in general the relative energies of the various occupied sublevels increase in the order shown in Fig. 7.8.

Electronic Configuration and the Periodic Table 7.7

The electrons of an atom which is in its ground, or unexcited state all occupy the lowest energy levels available. The electronic arrangement of the atoms in their ground states can be deduced in almost every case by imagining that an atom is built up by starting with a bare nucleus having a positive charge equal to the atomic number of the element, and then adding electrons one by one until their number equals the nuclear charge. Each successive electron is assumed to enter the unoccupied level of lowest energy, starting with the $1s$.

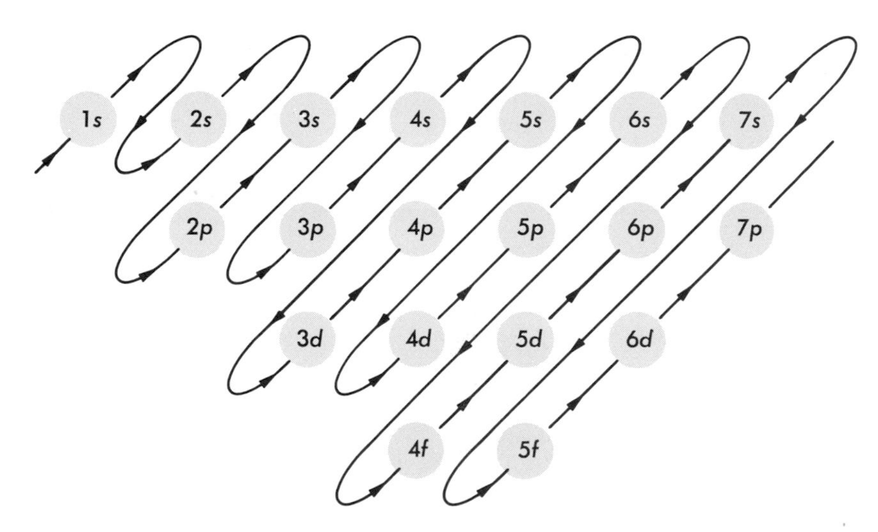

Fig. 7.9 Order of occupancy of electronic energy levels.

The order in which the various levels are occupied during this "building up" (*aufbau*) process is given by Fig. 7.8: $1s$, $2s$, $2p$, $3s$, $3p$, $4s$, $3d$, $4p$, $5s$, $4d$, $5p$, $6s$, $4f$, $5d$, $6p$, $7s$, $5f$, $6d$, $7p$. A convenient way to remember the order of occupancy is to list the levels in columns according to n (Fig. 7.9). When this is done, the diagonal lines describe the order in which electrons will be found in the majority of cases to enter the successive energy levels.

Now suppose that we follow the aufbau principle to predict the electronic configurations of the elements as we proceed through the periodic table. The first period is composed of just hydrogen and helium. Hydrogen has one proton in the nucleus ($Z = 1$), and a single electron in the lowest, or $1s$ energy level. Helium has one more proton in the nucleus and an additional electron. The second electron of helium also enters the $1s$ level, but the exclusion principle requires that its spin be opposite to that of the first. The electronic configurations of these elements are represented in either of two ways:

Z		Configuration		1s
1	H	$1s^1$	*or*	↑
2	He	$1s^2$	*or*	↑↓

In the notations $1s^1$ and $1s^2$ the superscripts refer to numbers of electrons and must never be mistaken for exponents. The small arrows ↑ and ↓ represent the relative spins of the electrons.

Following helium, the first element of the second period is lithium, for which $Z = 3$. Two of the three electrons of the lithium atom can be accommodated in the $1s$ level. The third, however, must enter the next higher level, which is the $2s$.

Z			1s	2s	2p		
3	Li	$1s^2\ 2s^1$	↑↓	↑	_	_	_

Proceeding in the same fashion for beryllium and boron, we obtain

Z			1s	2s	2p		
4	Be	$1s^2\ 2s^2$	↑↓	↑↓	_	_	_
5	B	$1s^2\ 2s^2\ 2p^1$	↑↓	↑↓	↑	_	_

The $2p$ is further subdivided into three levels corresponding to the three values (-1, 0, $+1$) possible for m. These three sublevels are normally of the same energy and are described as being *degenerate*. When we come to carbon, the sixth electron has the choice of pairing up with the other $2p$ electron, taking the opposite spin, or it may instead enter one of the other unoccupied degenerate sublevels. It has been shown experimentally that both p electrons of carbon in the ground state have their spins the same, or *parallel*. For their spins to be parallel, the two electrons must occupy separate p sublevels:

Z			1s	2s	2p		
6	C	$1s^2\ 2s^2\ 2p^2$	↑↓	↑↓	↑	↑	_

This behavior is general, and is expressed in ***Hund's rule of maximum multiplicity:*** *Where two or more electrons occupy an energy level with a given value of l, they will if possible assume parallel spins.* We can now predict the electronic configurations of the remaining members of the second period as follows:

Z			1s	2s	2p		
7	N	$1s^2\,2s^2\,2p^3$	↑↓	↑↓	↑	↑	↑
8	O	$1s^2\,2s^2\,2p^4$	↑↓	↑↓	↑↓	↑	↑
9	F	$1s^2\,2s^2\,2p^5$	↑↓	↑↓	↑↓	↑↓	↑
10	Ne	$1s^2\,2s^2\,2p^6$	↑↓	↑↓	↑↓	↑↓	↑↓

The completion of the second period, you will notice, coincides with the filling of the $2p$ level.

The next period again begins with an alkali metal, in this case sodium. Lithium and sodium resemble one another chemically, and now their chemical similarity is seen to be paralleled by a similarity in their electronic configurations: each has a single s electron in its highest principal energy level, and all of the lower levels are fully occupied:

Z			1s	2s	2p			3s	3p		
11	Na	$1s^2\,2s^2\,2p^6\,3s^1$	↑↓	↑↓	↑↓	↑↓	↑↓	↑	_	_	_

This similarity among the electronic configurations of the third and second period elements is found throughout the period. The period ends with the next noble gas, argon, corresponding to the filling of the $3p$ level:

Z			3s	3p		
12	Mg	$3s^2$	↑↓	_	_	_
13	Al	$3s^2\,3p^1$	↑↓	↑	_	_
14	Si	$3s^2\,3p^2$	↑↓	↑	↑	_
15	P	$3s^2\,3p^3$	↑↓	↑	↑	↑
16	S	$3s^2\,3p^4$	↑↓	↑↓	↑	↑
17	Cl	$3s^2\,3p^5$	↑↓	↑↓	↑↓	↑
18	Ar	$3s^2\,3p^6$	↑↓	↑↓	↑↓	↑↓

It is now becoming apparent that *similarities in properties are a reflection of similarities in electronic configuration.* The periodic recurrence of similar properties is associated with the periodic recurrence of similar arrangements of electrons.

Proceeding to the fourth period we find that because of the overlap between energy levels, the next two electrons enter the $4s$ level. The $3d$, with its capacity for 10 electrons, remains empty:

Z			3s	3p			3d					4s
19	K	$3s^2\,3p^6\,3d^0\,4s^1$	↑↓	↑↓	↑↓	↑↓	_	_	_	_	_	↑
20	Ca	$3s^2\,3p^6\,3d^0\,4s^2$	↑↓	↑↓	↑↓	↑↓	_	_	_	_	_	↑↓

With the filling of the 4*s* level at calcium, the next electron enters the 3*d* in scandium, the first of 10 *transition elements*, corresponding to the progressive filling of the 10 vacancies in the 3*d* level:

Z			3s	3p			3d					4s
21	Sc	$3s^2\ 3p^6\ 3d^1\ 4s^2$	↑↓	↑↓	↑↓	↑↓	↑	_	_	_	_	↑↓
22	Ti	$3s^2\ 3p^6\ 3d^2\ 4s^2$	↑↓	↑↓	↑↓	↑↓	↑	↑	_	_	_	↑↓
23	V	$3s^2\ 3p^6\ 3d^3\ 4s^2$	↑↓	↑↓	↑↓	↑↓	↑	↑	↑	_	_	↑↓
24	Cr	$3s^2\ 3p^6\ 3d^5\ 4s^1$	↑↓	↑↓	↑↓	↑↓	↑	↑	↑	↑	↑	↑
25	Mn	$3s^2\ 3p^6\ 3d^5\ 4s^2$	↑↓	↑↓	↑↓	↑↓	↑	↑	↑	↑	↑	↑↓
26	Fe	$3s^2\ 3p^6\ 3d^6\ 4s^2$	↑↓	↑↓	↑↓	↑↓	↑↓	↑	↑	↑	↑	↑↓
27	Co	$3s^2\ 3p^6\ 3d^7\ 4s^2$	↑↓	↑↓	↑↓	↑↓	↑↓	↑↓	↑	↑	↑	↑↓
28	Ni	$3s^2\ 3p^6\ 3d^8\ 4s^2$	↑↓	↑↓	↑↓	↑↓	↑↓	↑↓	↑↓	↑	↑	↑↓
29	Cu	$3s^2\ 3p^6\ 3d^{10}\ 4s^1$	↑↓	↑↓	↑↓	↑↓	↑↓	↑↓	↑↓	↑↓	↑↓	↑
30	Zn	$3s^2\ 3p^6\ 3d^{10}\ 4s^2$	↑↓	↑↓	↑↓	↑↓	↑↓	↑↓	↑↓	↑↓	↑↓	↑↓

The electronic configurations of these 10 elements agree with what we would predict in all but two cases. Chromium has the ground-state configuration $3d^5\ 4s^1$ rather than the expected $3d^4\ 4s^2$; copper has the arrangement $3d^{10}\ 4s^1$ instead of the predicted $3d^9\ 4s^2$. Evidently there is a special stability associated with degenerate levels which are either exactly half filled or completely filled. We will encounter other examples of this later on.

With the 3*d* level filled, the next six electrons enter the 4*p*, and we have the remaining six representative elements. Again the period is terminated by a noble gas, this time krypton:

Z			3d					4s	4p		
31	Ga	$3d^{10}\ 4s^2\ 4p^1$	↑↓	↑↓	↑↓	↑↓	↑↓	↑↓	↑	_	_
32	Ge	$3d^{10}\ 4s^2\ 4p^2$	↑↓	↑↓	↑↓	↑↓	↑↓	↑↓	↑	↑	_
33	As	$3d^{10}\ 4s^2\ 4p^3$	↑↓	↑↓	↑↓	↑↓	↑↓	↑↓	↑	↑	↑
34	Se	$3d^{10}\ 4s^2\ 4p^4$	↑↓	↑↓	↑↓	↑↓	↑↓	↑↓	↑↓	↑	↑
35	Br	$3d^{10}\ 4s^2\ 4p^5$	↑↓	↑↓	↑↓	↑↓	↑↓	↑↓	↑↓	↑↓	↑
36	Kr	$3d^{10}\ 4s^2\ 4p^6$	↑↓	↑↓	↑↓	↑↓	↑↓	↑↓	↑↓	↑↓	↑↓

The fifth period is built up in the same fashion as the fourth. Once more, the first two members of the period, rubidium and strontium, are representative elements, corresponding to the addition of two electrons to the 5*s* level. These are followed by another series of 10 transition elements as electrons are added one by one, filling up the 4*d* level. The next six electrons enter the 5*p* level, giving us the six remaining representative elements of the period, beginning with indium and ending with xenon:

Z			4d					5s	5p		
37	Rb	$4d^0\ 5s^1$		_	_	_	_	↑	_	_	_
38	Sr	$4d^0\ 5s^2$	_	_	_	_	_	↑↓	_		_
39	Y	$4d^1\ 5s^2$	↑	_	_	_	_	↑↓	_	_	_
40	Zr	$4d^2\ 5s^2$	↑	↑	_	_	_	↑↓	_	_	_
·	·	· · ·	·	·	·	·	·	·	·	·	·
47	Ag	$4d^{10}\ 5s^1$	↑↓	↑↓	↑↓	↑↓	↑↓	↑	_	_	_
48	Cd	$4d^{10}\ 5s^2$	↑↓	↑↓	↑↓	↑↓	↑↓	↑↓	_	_	_
49	In	$4d^{10}\ 5s^2\ 5p^1$	↑↓	↑↓	↑↓	↑↓	↑↓	↑↓	↑	_	_
50	Sn	$4d^{10}\ 5s^2\ 5p^2$	↑↓	↑↓	↑↓	↑↓	↑↓	↑↓	↑	↑	_
·	·	· · ·	·	·	·	·	·	·	·	·	·
53	I	$4d^{10}\ 5s^2\ 5p^5$	↑↓	↑↓	↑↓	↑↓	↑↓	↑↓	↑↓	↑↓	↑
54	Xe	$4d^{10}\ 5s^2\ 5p^6$	↑↓	↑↓	↑↓	↑↓	↑↓	↑↓	↑↓	↑↓	↑↓

The sixth period is composed of 32 elements: 8 representative, 10 transition, and 14 inner-transition—the ***lanthanides.*** Now that we have seen that the 8 representative elements of each period correspond to the progressive filling of *s* and *p* levels, and the 10 transition elements to the filling of a *d*, it is not difficult to surmise that the 14 inner-transition elements correspond to the filling of an *f* level which as we know has a capacity of 14 electrons. The energies of the 4*f* and 5*d* levels lie quite close together, however, so that following cesium and barium, which have the expected configurations $5s^2\ 5p^6\ 6s^1$ and $5s^2\ 5p^6\ 6s^2$, the addition of the next 14 electrons shows some irregularities:

Z			4f							5s	5p			5d					6s
55	Cs	$4f^0\ 5s^2\ 5p^6\ 5d^0\ 6s^1$	_	_	_	_	_	_	_	↑↓	↑↓	↑↓	↑↓	_	_	_	_	_	↑
56	Ba	$4f^0\ 5s^2\ 5p^6\ 5d^0\ 6s^2$	_	_	_	_	_	_	_	↑↓	↑↓	↑↓	↑↓	_	_	_	_	_	↑↓
57	La	$4f^0\ 5s^2\ 5p^6\ 5d^1\ 6s^2$	_	_	_	_	_	_	_	↑↓	↑↓	↑↓	↑↓	↑	_	_	_	_	↑↓
58	Ce	$4f^1\ 5s^2\ 5p^6\ 5d^1\ 6s^2$	↑	_	_	_	_	_	_	↑↓	↑↓	↑↓	↑↓	↑	_	_	_	_	↑↓
59	Pr	$4f^3\ 5s^2\ 5p^6\ 5d^0\ 6s^2$	↑	↑	↑	_	_	_	_	↑↓	↑↓	↑↓	↑↓	_	_	_	_	_	↑↓
60	Nd	$4f^4\ 5s^2\ 5p^6\ 5d^0\ 6s^2$	↑	↑	↑	↑	_	_	_	↑↓	↑↓	↑↓	↑↓	_	_	_	_	_	↑↓
61	Pm	$4f^5\ 5s^2\ 5p^6\ 5d^0\ 6s^2$	↑	↑	↑	↑	↑	_	_	↑↓	↑↓	↑↓	↑↓	_	_	_	_	_	↑↓
62	Sm	$4f^6\ 5s^2\ 5p^6\ 5d^0\ 6s^2$	↑	↑	↑	↑	↑	↑	_	↑↓	↑↓	↑↓	↑↓	_	_	_	_	_	↑↓
63	Eu	$4f^7\ 5s^2\ 5p^6\ 5d^0\ 6s^2$	↑	↑	↑	↑	↑	↑	↑	↑↓	↑↓	↑↓	↑↓	_	_	_	_	_	↑↓
64	Gd	$4f^7\ 5s^2\ 5p^6\ 5d^1\ 6s^2$	↑	↑	↑	↑	↑	↑	↑	↑↓	↑↓	↑↓	↑↓	↑	_	_	_	_	↑↓
65	Tb	$4f^9\ 5s^2\ 5p^6\ 5d^0\ 6s^2$	↑↓	↑↓	↑	↑	↑	↑	↑	↑↓	↑↓	↑↓	↑↓	_	_	_	_	_	↑↓
66	Dy	$4f^{10}\ 5s^2\ 5p^6\ 5d^0\ 6s^2$	↑↓	↑↓	↑↓	↑	↑	↑	↑	↑↓	↑↓	↑↓	↑↓	_	_	_	_	_	↑↓
67	Ho	$4f^{11}\ 5s^2\ 5p^6\ 5d^0\ 6s^2$	↑↓	↑↓	↑↓	↑↓	↑	↑	↑	↑↓	↑↓	↑↓	↑↓	_	_	_	_	_	↑↓
68	Er	$4f^{12}\ 5s^2\ 5p^6\ 5d^0\ 6s^2$	↑↓	↑↓	↑↓	↑↓	↑↓	↑	↑	↑↓	↑↓	↑↓	↑↓	_	_	_	_	_	↑↓
69	Tm	$4f^{13}\ 5s^2\ 5p^6\ 5d^0\ 6s^2$	↑↓	↑↓	↑↓	↑↓	↑↓	↑↓	↑	↑↓	↑↓	↑↓	↑↓	_	_	_	_	_	↑↓
70	Yb	$4f^{14}\ 5s^2\ 5p^6\ 5d^0\ 6s^2$	↑↓	↑↓	↑↓	↑↓	↑↓	↑↓	↑↓	↑↓	↑↓	↑↓	↑↓	_	_	_	_	_	↑↓

Following ytterbium, successive electrons enter the $5d$ level and then the $6p$, giving a regular transition series of 10 elements, followed by the six remaining representative elements of the period:

Z			5d					6s	6p		
71	Lu	$5d^1\ 6s^2$	↑	—	—	—	—	↑↓	—	—	—
72	Hf	$5d^2\ 6s^2$	↑	↑	—	—	—	↑↓	—	—	—
73	Ta	$5d^3\ 6s^2$	↑	↑	↑	—	—	↑↓	—	—	—
74	W	$5d^4\ 6s^2$	↑	↑	↑	↑	—	↑↓	—	—	—
75	Re	$5d^5\ 6s^2$	↑	↑	↑	↑	↑	↑↓	—	—	—
76	Os	$5d^6\ 6s^2$	↑↓	↑	↑	↑	↑	↑↓	—	—	—
77	Ir	$5d^7\ 6s^2$	↑↓	↑↓	↑	↑	↑	↑↓	—	—	—
78	Pt	$5d^9\ 6s^1$	↑↓	↑↓	↑↓	↑↓	↑	↑	—	—	—
79	Au	$5d^{10}\ 6s^1$	↑↓	↑↓	↑↓	↑↓	↑↓	↑	—	—	—
80	Hg	$5d^{10}\ 6s^2$	↑↓	↑↓	↑↓	↑↓	↑↓	↑↓	—	—	—
81	Tl	$5d^{10}\ 6s^2\ 6p^1$	↑↓	↑↓	↑↓	↑↓	↑↓	↑↓	↑	—	—
82	Pb	$5d^{10}\ 6s^2\ 6p^2$	↑↓	↑↓	↑↓	↑↓	↑↓	↑↓	↑	↑	—
83	Bi	$5d^{10}\ 6s^2\ 6p^3$	↑↓	↑↓	↑↓	↑↓	↑↓	↑↓	↑	↑	↑
84	Po	$5d^{10}\ 6s^2\ 6p^4$	↑↓	↑↓	↑↓	↑↓	↑↓	↑↓	↑↓	↑	↑
85	At	$5d^{10}\ 6s^2\ 6p^5$	↑↓	↑↓	↑↓	↑↓	↑↓	↑↓	↑↓	↑↓	↑
86	Rn	$5d^{10}\ 6s^2\ 6p^6$	↑↓	↑↓	↑↓	↑↓	↑↓	↑↓	↑↓	↑↓	↑↓

The seventh period, which to date is incomplete, appears to correspond closely to the sixth. The representative elements francium and radium are followed by 14 ***actinides,*** which form another inner-transition series in which the $5f$ level is being completed. Lawrencium, element 103, seems, as expected, to be the first member of a regular transition series of ten elements corresponding to the filling of the $6d$ level. Six more representative elements should follow these (assuming that they could all exist), the seventh period ending with the hypothetical noble element 118.

The periodic system was developed by Mendeleev on a purely empirical basis. Now we can see that this system, with its division of the elements into periods and groups, representative, transition, and inner-transition elements, arises naturally as a result of the existence within the atoms of energy levels, each of which has a definite capacity for electrons. The periodic relationship among the properties of the elements and their atomic numbers is seen to be a consequence of the periodic recurrence of electronic configurations as successive levels are filled in regular order.

7.8 Uncertainty

Bohr's theory of atomic structure shows how atomic spectra are to be interpreted in terms of quantized energy levels within the atom, and when applied to hydrogen and other one-electron systems such as He^+, Li^{++}, and

Be^{+++}, it accurately predicts the positions of the spectral lines. Attempts to apply it to multi-electron systems are, however, uniformly unsuccessful. It soon becomes apparent that there are fundamental defects in the theory which cannot be resolved by introducing new assumptions or additional quantum numbers. Nevertheless, in its departure from classical theory it represents a bold step and an important advance in the understanding of the nature of the atom. Without the Bohr theory to build on, with its postulates of energy quantization and stationary states, it is doubtful whether we would have progressed much beyond Rutherford's model of the atom. The defects in the Bohr model are the result mainly of not going far enough, and of trying to retain too much of a mechanical, "clockwork" picture of the atom. No logical reason is offered for the quantization of energy within the atom, and the model has an artificial character about it which is not completely satisfying.

Implicit in the Bohr theory is the assumption that both the location of an object and its momentum can be precisely known at the same time, that is, that at any moment one can know exactly where something is, where it came from, and where it is going. This presents no difficulty with large objects. By observing the motion of the planets today, we can predict exactly where they will be hundreds or thousands of years from now. When dealing with extremely small particles such as electrons, however, this assumption is unjustified.

In order to locate something, we must observe it in some way. If we want to know its position accurately, our method of observation must be one which will not measurably disturb the object being observed. For example, we might locate a small table in a dark room by feeling for it with a cane, but not by swinging at it with an axe. After hitting it with the axe, we would know where the table had been, but not where it, or the pieces of it, were going.

More often, we look for something not with a cane or an axe, but with a beam of light. Provided that the object being observed is appreciably larger than the wavelength of the light being used, its image will be sharp and it can be precisely located. A smaller object, on the other hand, scatters the light instead of reflecting it. Its image is fuzzy and its position uncertain. By using light of shorter wavelengths, smaller objects can be seen, but this poses a serious problem with a particle as small as an electron. According to the Planck relationship (Sec. 7.3), as the wavelength of light decreases, the energy of the photons increases. Photons of light with a wavelength approaching atomic dimensions, that is, about 1 Å, have an energy of the order of 10^4 eV—far more than enough to knock all of the electrons out of the atom altogether. In effect, in probing for an electron with a ray of light we find ourselves in the position of looking for that table not with a cane, or even an axe, but with a cannon!

The problem is an insurmountable one. The more precisely we know where an electron is at a given instant, the less we know about where it came from or where it is going. On the other hand, we can determine its motion more exactly, but only at the expense of not knowing where it is. This dilemma is expressed in the Heisenberg ***uncertainty principle***. In 1926, Werner Heisenberg showed that *the product of the uncertainty in the position*

(Δp) and in the momentum (Δq) of a body is of the order of Planck's constant of action:

$$(\Delta p)(\Delta q) \approx h$$

For objects of ordinary size, this uncertainty is so small as to be completely negligible. When it comes to electrons, the uncertainty may no longer be ignored, and the best that we can hope to do is to estimate the probability of finding the electron in a given region in space. The peculiar behavior of light, which appears sometimes to be a wave and other times to be a stream of particles, offers a clue to the way in which this probability may be estimated.

7.9 The Dual Nature of Light

Certain aspects of the behavior of light are best accounted for by attributing to it the nature of a wave. Among them are those which give rise to the phenomena of ***diffraction*** and ***interference.*** Light originating at one point (a "point source": a small lamp filament is a fair approximation) and shining through an aperture in an opaque screen projects an image of the opening on the other side. If the opening is large, its image is sharp, and the source, the edge of the opening, and the edge of the image all lie on a straight line (Fig. 7.10a). If the aperture is small—a pinhole, for example—the light ray is bent, or *diffracted* as it passes through, spreading out on the other side, and the edges of the image appear out of focus (Fig. 7.10b).

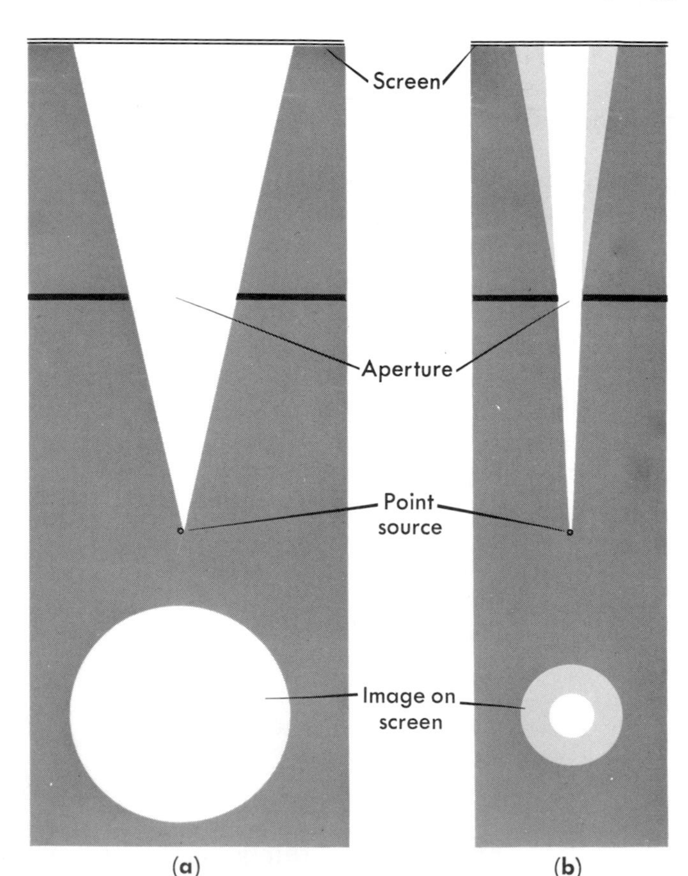

Fig. 7.10 Diffraction of light with (a) large aperture and (b) small aperture.

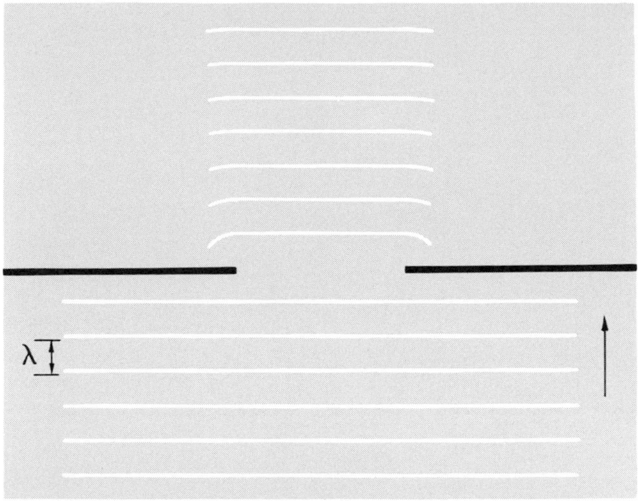

Fig. 7.11 Wave train of wavelength λ passing through large opening.

Diffraction is typical wave behavior and is observed with water waves as well as with light rays. Visualize a series of parallel waves approaching some barrier which has an opening in it considerably wider than the distance between wave crests (Fig. 7.11). This could be a series of water waves passing a breakwater, or a light ray passing through a hole in a screen. As the waves come out the other side of the opening, they spread out slightly at the edges. The reason for this is that a wave crest cannot be chopped off abruptly at the edges but necessarily must taper off gradually, just as a sugar cube under a tablecloth does not make a cubical bump in the cloth, but instead one with sloping sides. Because all parts of a wave crest are moving at the same speed, the edges assume a curved appearance.

Where the opening is large, as in the preceding case, the spreading at the edges of the waves is so small compared with their width as to be barely noticeable. If instead the opening is small, approaching one wavelength or less in width, this is no longer true. The diffracted portion becomes a major part of the wave, which spreads out in a wide arc (Fig. 7.12).

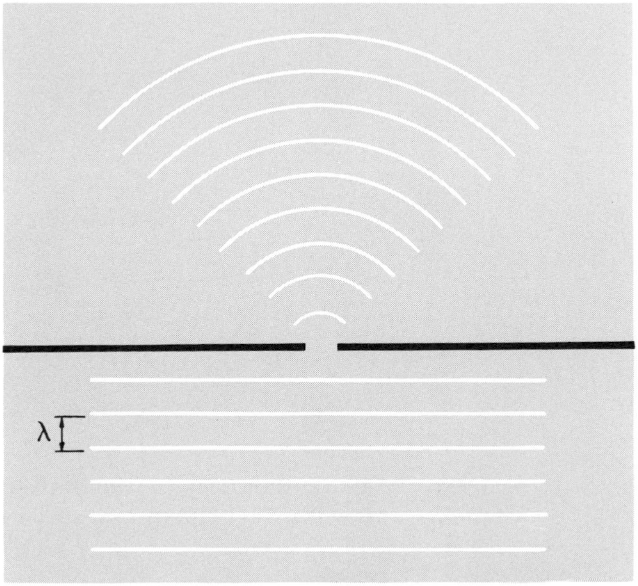

Fig. 7.12 Spreading (diffraction) of waves passing through a small opening.

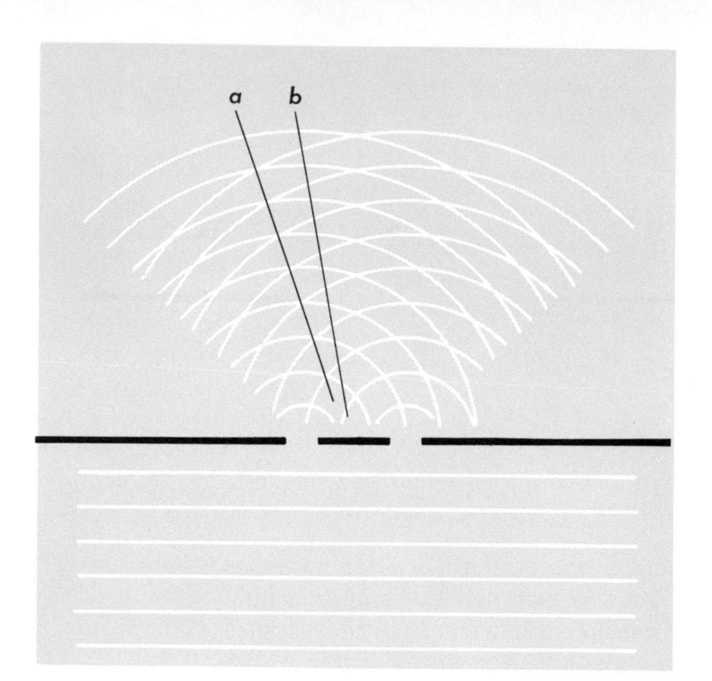

Fig. 7.13 Interference of waves diffracted through a pair of small openings.

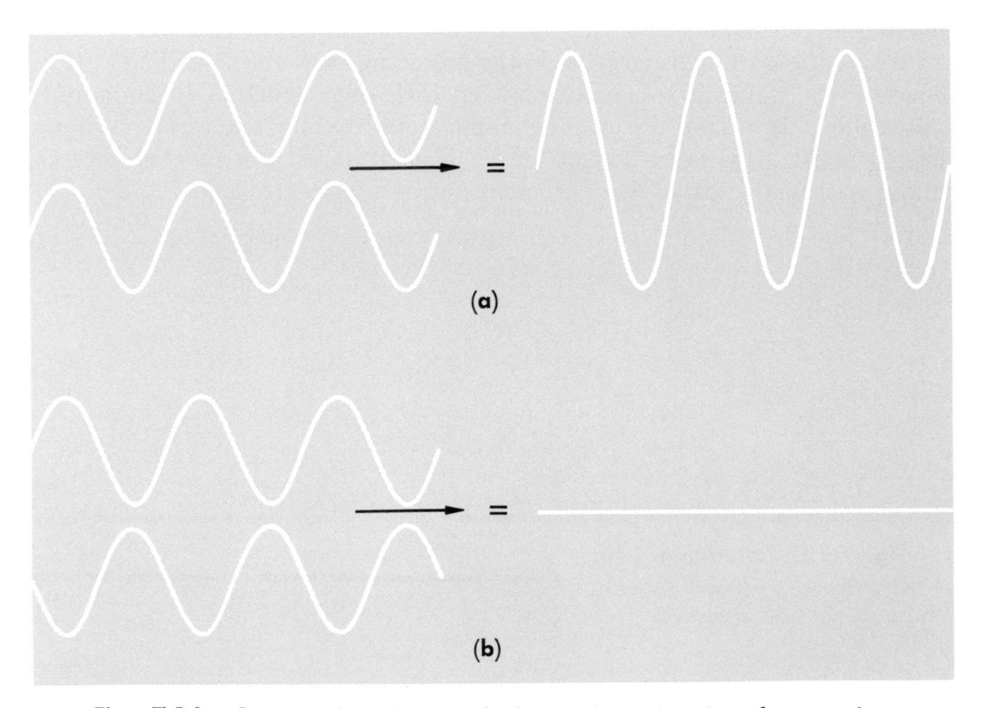

Fig. 7.14 Constructive (a) and destructive (b) interference between waves. The waves in (a) are said to be *in phase;* those in (b) are *out of phase.*

Suppose now that the wave train passes through two such small holes placed a short distance apart (Fig. 7.13). On the other side of the barrier, two wave trains appear, each again in the form of a set of ever-widening arcs. Where the waves having their origin at one hole intersect with those originating at the other, as along line *a* of the figure, we have the phenomenon known as ***constructive interference,*** or ***reinforcement.*** Along this line, the crests and troughs of one wave train exactly coincide with—are "in phase" with—the crests and troughs of the other. The result is reinforcement and an increase in the intensity, or ***amplitude,*** of the wave in that direction (Fig. 7.14a). Between these points of intersection, for example along line *b* of Fig. 7.13, the wave trains are "out of phase," crests coinciding with troughs and troughs with crests (Fig. 7.14b). The result is ***destructive interference*** and a decrease in amplitude. If the waves are light waves, we see not the images of two small holes, but a pattern of light and dark regions known as a ***diffraction pattern*** (Fig. 7.15).

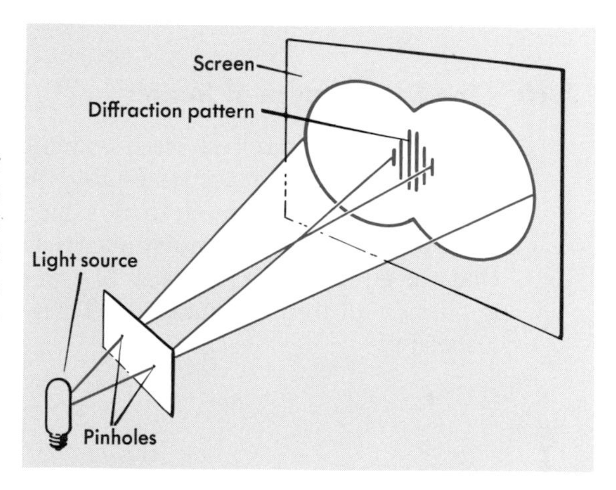

Fig. 7.15 Diffraction. Light from a single source passes through two pinholes and illuminates a screen. In the region illuminated by light from both pinholes, a series of light and dark lines—a diffraction pattern—appears.

In other respects, a beam of light behaves like a stream of particles. It can be demonstrated, for example, that light impinging upon a surface exerts a small but measurable pressure. Pressure, being a force, implies that there is a mass undergoing acceleration, and the existence of mass requires the existence of a particle or particles possessing that mass. The particle of light is evidently the photon, which we know to be the unit of light energy (Sec. 7.3).

Energy is equivalent to mass, the equivalence being given by the familiar Einstein equation (Sec. 1.8)

$$E = mc^2$$

If we insert into this expression the energy of the photon calculated from the Planck relationship (Sec. 7.3), we obtain the equation

$$mc^2 = h\nu$$

from which the apparent mass of the photon may be calculated:

$$m = \frac{h\nu}{c^2}$$

Since $\nu = c/\lambda$, this may also be written

$$m = \frac{h}{\lambda c}$$

Example 7.4

Calculate the mass of a photon of light which has a wavelength of 6863 Å.

Solution:

$$m = \frac{h}{\lambda c} = \frac{(6.63 \times 10^{-27} \text{ erg-sec})}{(6.863 \times 10^{-5} \text{ cm})(3.0 \times 10^{10} \text{ cm/sec})}$$
$$= 0.32 \times 10^{-32} \text{ erg-sec}^2/\text{cm}^{2*}$$
$$= 3.2 \times 10^{-33} \text{ g}$$

By comparison, the mass of the electron (Sec. 6.3) is about 10^6 times that of a photon of visible light.

7.10 The Dual Nature of Matter

If light can manifest itself sometimes as a wave and sometimes as a stream of particles, reasoned Louis de Broglie in 1924, then perhaps ordinary matter behaves in a similar dual fashion. There should, in other words, be a wave associated with a moving particle such as an electron. Let us assume that the equation for the mass of a photon derived in the preceding section applies to all forms of matter. Then, for a particle of mass m, moving at a speed v:

$$m = \frac{h}{\lambda v}$$

$$\lambda = \frac{h}{mv}$$

This equation can now be used to calculate the wavelength of the "particle wave."

Example 7.5

The electrons in Thompson's apparatus for determining e/m (Sec. 6.2) were found to be moving at a speed of 2.6×10^9 cm/sec. Calculate their associated wavelength.

Solution:

$$\lambda = \frac{h}{mv} = \frac{(6.63 \times 10^{-27} \text{ erg-sec})}{(9.1 \times 10^{-28} \text{ g})(2.6 \times 10^9 \text{ cm/sec})}$$
$$\lambda = 2.8 \times 10^{-9} \text{ cm} = 0.28 \text{ Å}$$

* The curious quantity erg-sec²/cm² is simply the gram in disguise:

$$\text{erg} = \text{dyne-cm}$$
$$\text{dyne} = \text{g-cm/sec}^2$$
$$\text{erg} = \text{g-cm}^2/\text{sec}^2$$
$$\therefore \text{erg-sec}^2/\text{cm}^2 = \text{g-cm}^2\text{-sec}^2/\text{cm}^2\text{-sec}^2 = \text{g}$$

If it is true that matter has a wave character, as does light, then, like light, it should exhibit the typical phenomena of diffraction and interference associated with waves. A beam of particles—electrons, for example—should give rise to a diffraction pattern after passing through a set of apertures of the appropriate size. For electrons, these apertures should best be less than 0.5 Å in diameter, and they should be about that same distance apart.

X-rays, which have a wavelength of the order of that calculated for the electrons in Example 7.5, are diffracted upon passing through a crystal such as quartz or sodium chloride. The distances between atomic nuclei in these crystals are close to the wavelength of the X-rays. The electrons of each atom are set into oscillation by the fluctuating electrical and magnetic field of the X-rays, causing them immediately to re-emit X-rays of the same wavelength, and these radiate from the atom in all directions. Each atom thus serves as a point source of X-rays in much the same manner as would a set of apertures in front of the X-ray beam (Fig. 7.16).

Fig. 7.16 Diffraction of X-rays by atoms in a crystal.

In 1927, C. J. Davisson and L. H. Germer at the Bell Telephone Laboratories passed a beam of electrons through a crystal of nickel and obtained a typical diffraction pattern, thus fully confirming de Broglie's assumptions regarding the wave nature of matter. Since then, the experiment has been repeated many times, and electron-diffraction patterns have been obtained with all sorts of crystals.

The electron microscope affords further and perhaps even more striking evidence of the wave nature of matter. In this device, a beam of electrons, focused by a set of magnets, passes through the specimen and forms a

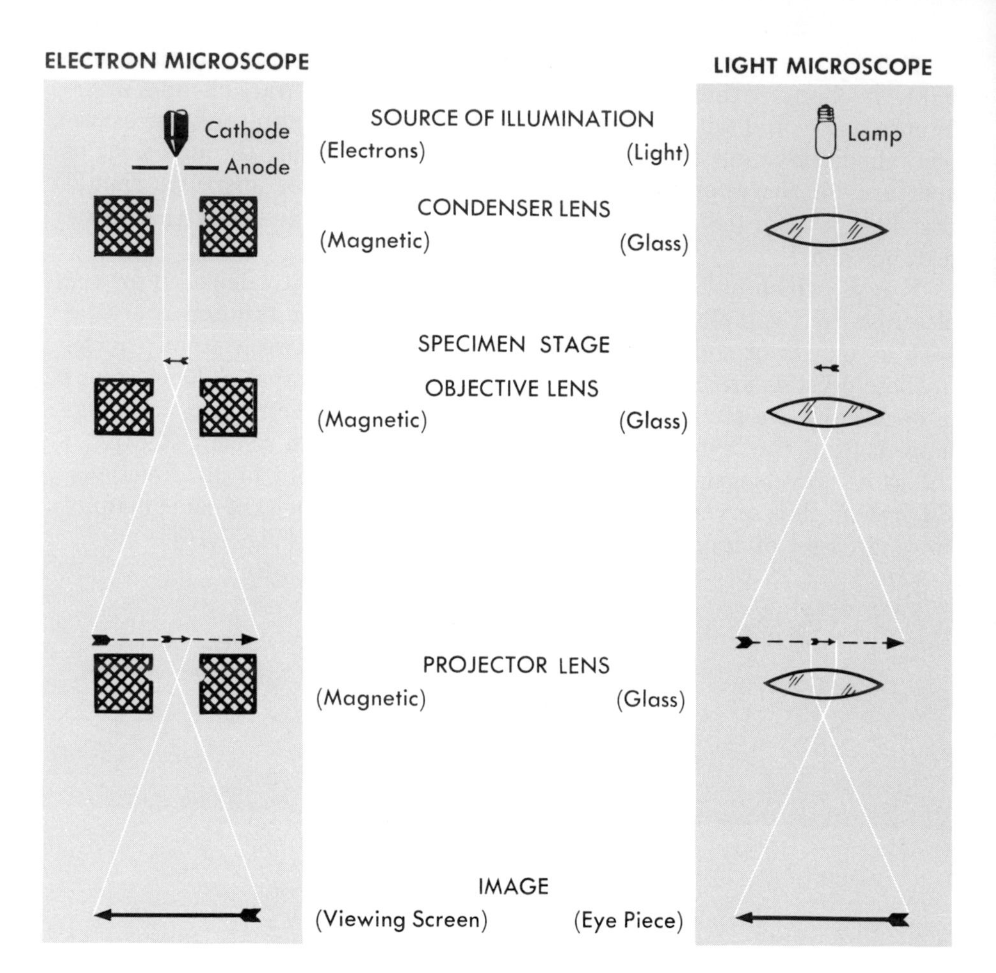

Fig. 7.17 Comparison of the optical system of an electron microscope with that of a light microscope. (Courtesy Radio Corporation of America.)

visible image of it on a fluorescent screen (Fig. 7.17). The short wavelength associated with the electron beam permits the examination of specimens smaller than the wavelength of visible light.

The wavelength of a material object decreases with its mass. For objects greater than subatomic dimensions, therefore, the wavelength becomes so small that diffraction, interference, and other wave phenomena are unobservable. This is just as well, for otherwise we might some day find ourselves passing through two doors simultaneously and ending up as a diffraction pattern on the other side!

7.11 Application of Wave Theory to the Atom

The peculiar restrictions on the energy of an electron within an atom begin to make sense as soon as the wave character of the electron is taken into account. Once ***boundary conditions*** are imposed on a wave, that is, once a wave is confined in some way, it can no longer have just any frequency,

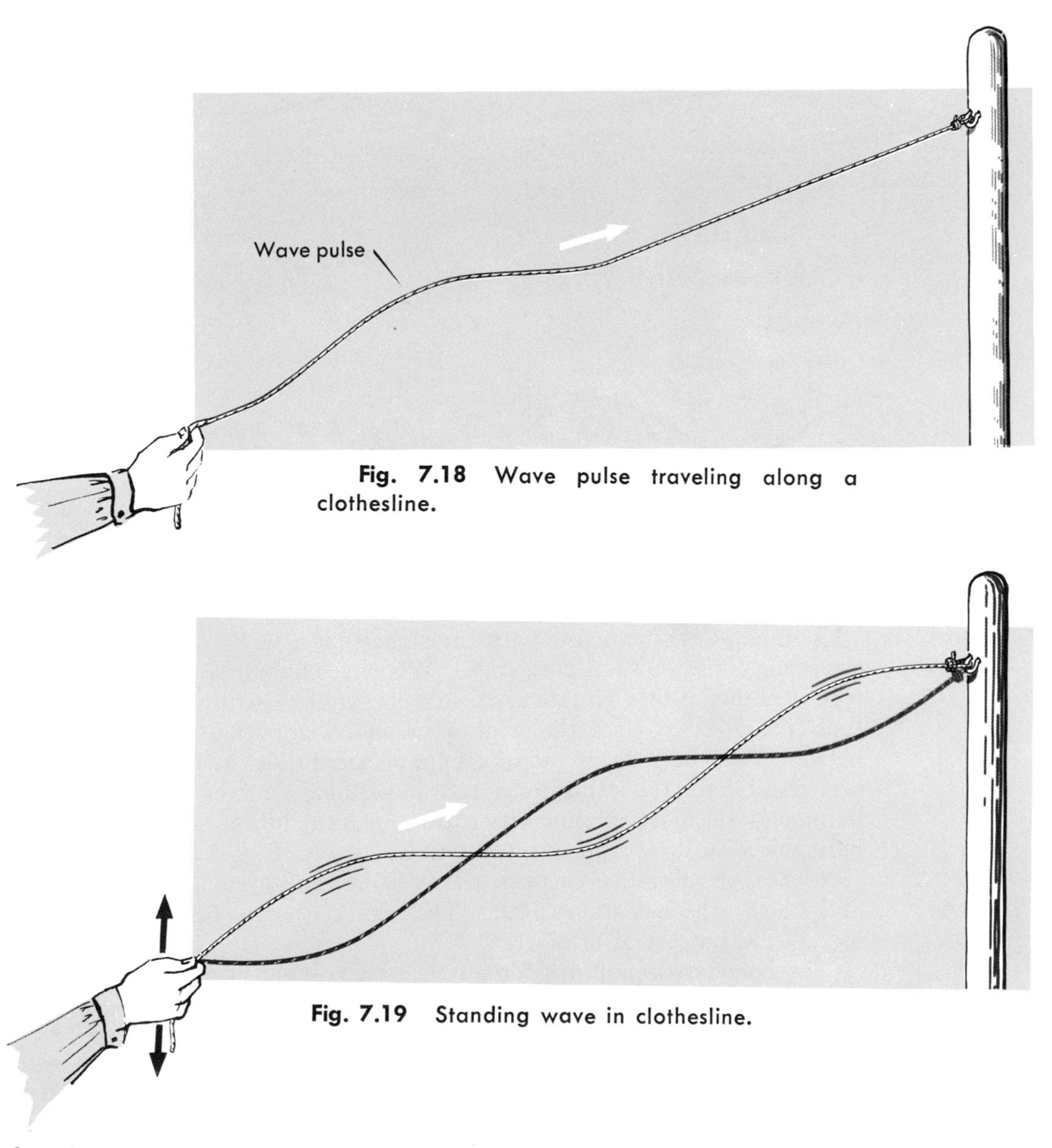

Fig. 7.18 Wave pulse traveling along a clothesline.

Fig. 7.19 Standing wave in clothesline.

but is restricted to those frequencies which permit establishment of a ***standing wave.*** To understand the idea of a standing wave, think of a piece of clothesline tied to a pole at one end (Fig. 7.18). When the other end is shaken, a wave pulse travels along the rope until it reaches the pole, where it is reflected, and returns. At all points along the rope, the amplitude of the reflected wave is opposite to that of the original one. In other words, where a crest appeared in the wave as it traveled toward the pole, a trough appears on the way back, and vice versa. By shaking the end of the rope with the right frequency, it is possible to keep the waves traveling in each direction in phase, so that the wave form appears to remain stationary. The result is a ***standing wave*** (Fig. 7.19). A standing wave can result only if the wavelength fits exactly between the ends of the rope.

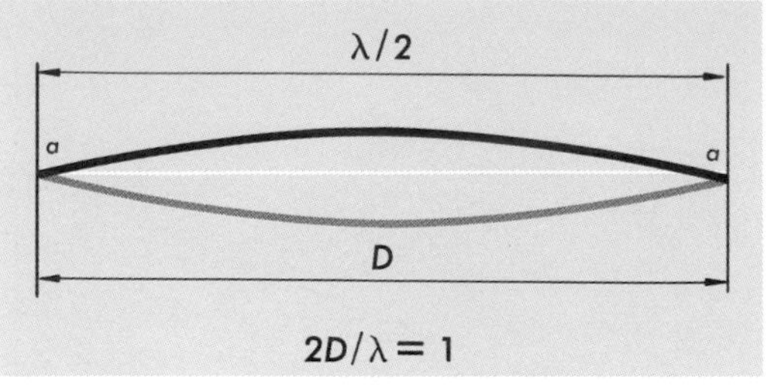

(a) Fundamental

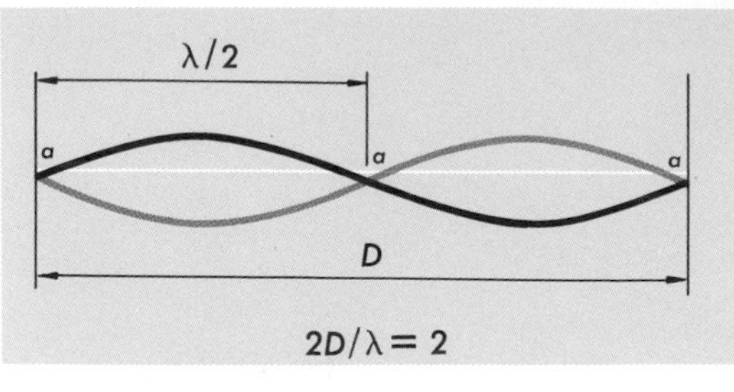

(b) 1st harmonic

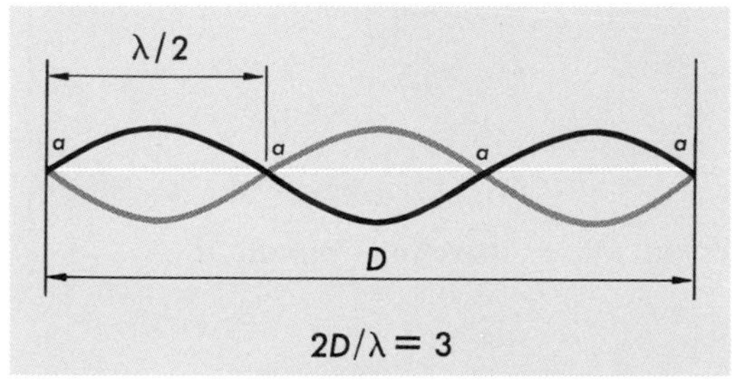

(c) 2nd harmonic

Fig. 7.20 Standing waves in a violin string. The *a*'s are *nodes*.

A similar situation exists with the strings on a violin or guitar. Here the string is tied down at both ends. When it is bowed or plucked, setting it into motion, it may vibrate as an entirety, giving rise to the fundamental tone (Fig. 7.20a). Here, the point of maximum amplitude is at the center, between two *nodes*, or points of minimum amplitude, at the ends. It is also possible for the string to vibrate in segments, producing the various harmonics: the first harmonic with two segments and three nodes, the second harmonic with three segments and four nodes, etc. (Fig. 7.20b and c). In each case, the distance between the ends of the string must be exactly divisible by the half-wavelength. That is, $2D/\lambda$ may be equal to 1, 2, 3, . . . , n, but not $1\frac{1}{2}$ or $6\frac{7}{8}$.

The boundary conditions for an electron moving in a Bohr orbit are determined by the size of the orbit. An electron can occupy a given orbit only if the circumference is exactly divisible by the wavelength of the electron. Otherwise, after going once around the orbit, the electron wave will end up out of phase with itself, leading to destructive interference (Fig. 7.21). This will cause the wave to cancel itself, which is equivalent to saying that the electron will be annihilated, and this, of course, is unacceptable. Therefore, for an orbit to be permissible,

$$2\pi r = n\lambda$$

Since

$$\lambda = \frac{h}{mv}$$

$$2\pi r = \frac{nh}{mv}$$

and

$$mvr = \frac{nh}{2\pi}$$

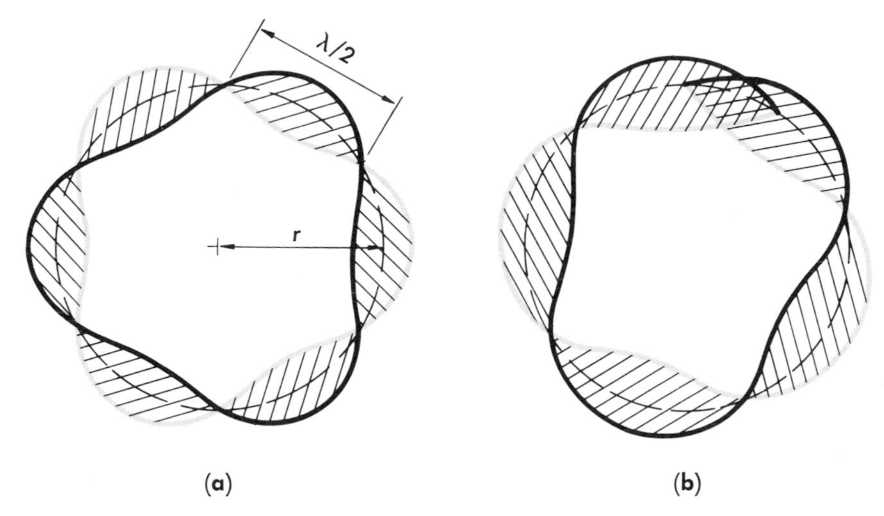

Fig. 7.21 Waves confined to a circle of radius r. (a) $n\lambda = 2\pi r$, wave in phase; (b) $n\lambda \neq 2\pi r$, wave interferes destructively with itself.

This expression is identical with Equation (2), and it is now seen that Bohr's a priori assumption that the angular momentum of an electron must be an integral multiple of $h/2\pi$ is a necessary consequence of the electron's wave nature.

Atomic Orbitals 7.12

In the above discussion, it was assumed for the sake of simplicity that the electron was moving in a circular Bohr orbit. In the light of the uncertainty principle, however, this assumption is unwarranted. The actual way in which the electron moves about the nucleus cannot be known. Nevertheless, no matter what the actual motion of the electron may be, whether in two dimensions or three, boundary conditions exist by virtue of the electron's association with the atom. The strict relationship between the energy of an electron and its motion about the nucleus, derived above for a circular orbit, remains valid.

Any wave is a periodic disturbance of some sort, which may be described in terms of its wave function ψ, a mathematical expression* representing the variation in time and space of the amplitude of a wave. Figure 7.22 represents an instantaneous plot of ψ versus the distance from one end of a vibrating string. We see that the sign of the wave function at a given point along the string may be either positive or negative, depending upon whether the string at that point is above or below the mid-line through the nodes. Whether it is positive or negative, all points along the string for which the values of the wave functions have the same sign are moving in the same direction. There is a node at any point where $\psi = 0$.

Whether the sign of the wave function at a given point is positive or negative, the wave constitutes a disturbance of some sort at that point.

* The mathematical form of this expression need not concern us at this time.

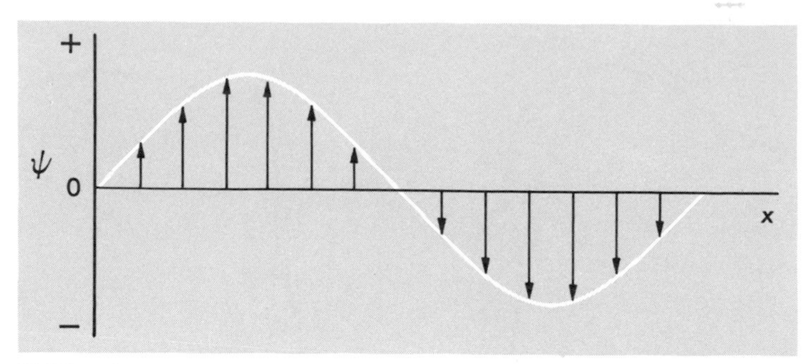

Fig. 7.22 Instantaneous plot of ψ vs. the distance x at time t, where ψ is a function of both x and t.

The intensity of the disturbance is a function of the amplitude of the wave. The average intensity, which is a measure of the probability that the disturbance will be felt at a particular place at a given time, is given by the square of the wave function. Although the wave function expressing the amplitude may be negative as well as positive, the square of the function will always be positive (Fig. 7.23).

By substituting the corresponding energy for the wavelength in the equation for the propagation of a wave in three dimensions, Erwin Schrödinger was able to obtain an equation whose solution yields values of ψ^2 for the electron. Physically real solutions for ψ^2 are obtained only when the energy of the electron has certain definite values. These values are determined by the set of quantum numbers which we introduced earlier. The probability of finding an electron at any distance r from the nucleus is given by a plot of the quantity $4\pi r^2\psi^2$, known as the ***radial distribution function,*** against r. This is shown for the hydrogen atom in Fig. 7.24.

Examination of Fig. 7.24 brings out several points worth noting. The electron of the hydrogen atom in the ground state is seen to spend most

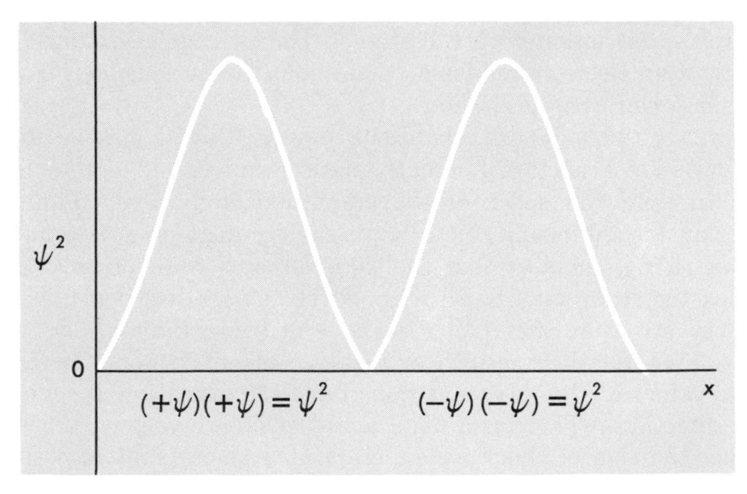

Fig. 7.23 Instantaneous plot of ψ^2 vs. x at time t. Except when it equals zero, the square of the wave function is always positive for every value of x.

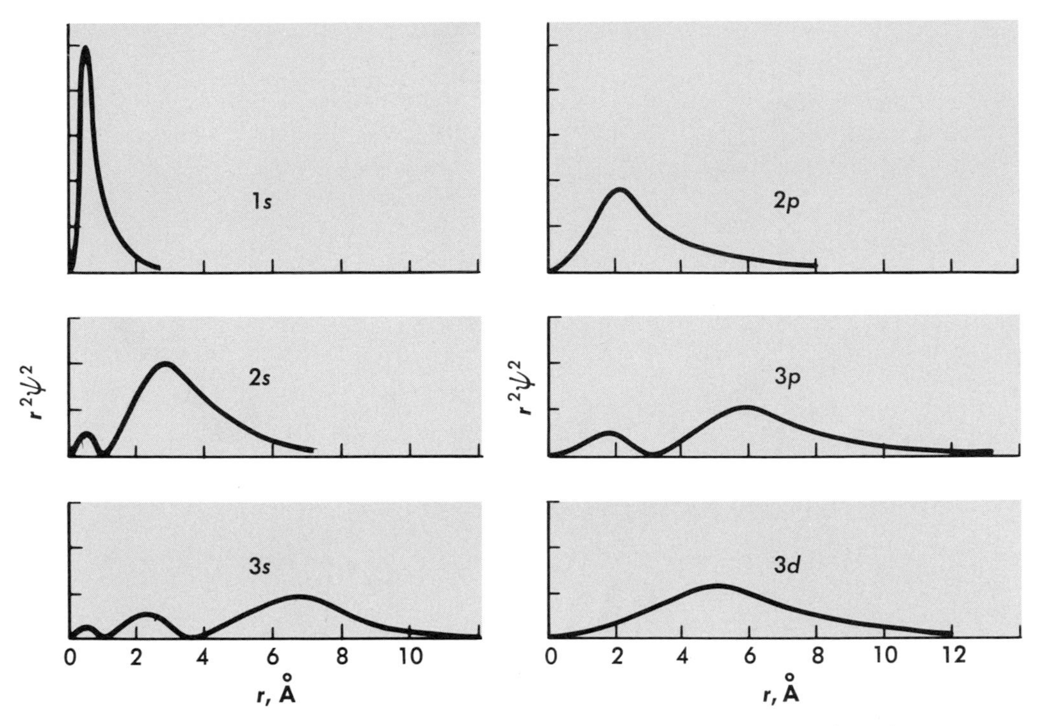

Fig. 7.24 Plot of the radial distribution function against r for the hydrogen atom.

of its time at a distance of about 0.53 Å from the nucleus. This distance is the same as the radius which Bohr calculated for the smallest electronic orbit of the hydrogen atom (Sec. 7.4). Electrons in higher energy states spend more of their time at a greater distance from the nucleus. Furthermore, among electrons with the same principal quantum number, those in the s level spend more of their time closer to the nucleus than do the p electrons, and these in turn penetrate closer to the nucleus on the average than those in the d level.

The region in space about the nucleus of an atom in which an electron with a given set of quantum numbers is most likely to be found is known as an ***atomic orbital.*** An atomic orbital (abbreviated AO) does not have sharp boundaries. Rather, the mathematical probability of finding an electron in a given region decreases gradually with distance from the nucleus, attaining a value of zero only at an infinite distance. Nevertheless, from a plot of ψ^2 in three dimensions, it is possible to draw a surface within which there is, for example, a 90% probability of finding the electron and in this way picture the shape of the orbital. Orbital diagrams drawn in this manner are shown in Fig. 7.25. Exact solution of the Schrödinger equation has not been achieved for atoms of greater complexity than helium, but approximate solutions have been obtained which indicate that the general shapes of the various types of atomic orbitals are the same for all atoms. All s orbitals, that is, those for which $l = 0$, are spherically symmetrical, with the probability of finding

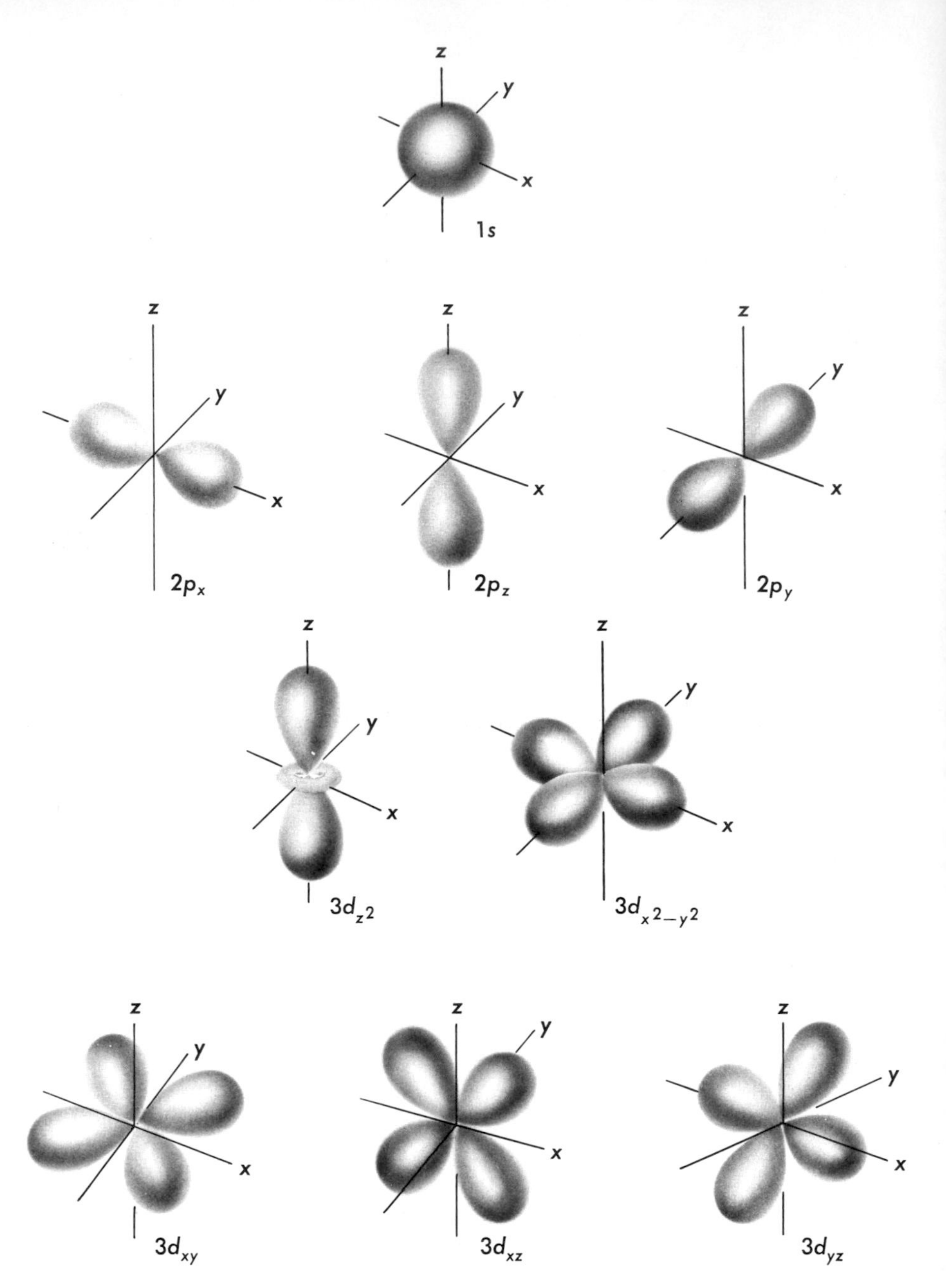

Fig. 7.25 Representations of the *s*, *p*, and *d* orbitals of the hydrogen atom.

the electron varying in the same fashion in all directions. This is not the case with *p* ($l = 1$), *d* ($l = 2$), or *f* ($l = 3$) orbitals. For example, in a *p* orbital, the region in which there is the greatest probability of finding the electron—the region of greatest ***electron density***—is composed of two roughly spherical domains, one on either side of the nucleus, with a common axis along one of the three spatial coordinates and a node (no probability of finding the electron) at the nucleus. The threefold degeneracy of the *p* orbitals can now be understood. There are three *p* orbitals, one for each of the three spatial coordinates. These will ordinarily be of equal energy. In a magnetic field, however, this degeneracy disappears, and the energies of the three p orbitals are slightly different, depending upon whether they are aligned with the magnetic field, or perpendicular to it.

Each orbital may be occupied by no more than two electrons, whose spins must be opposite. It must be kept clearly in mind that whether it is occupied by one electron or a pair, an orbital will have the same shape. For example, a single electron in a p orbital occupies *both* lobes of the orbital. If a p orbital should contain a pair of electrons, each one occupies each lobe of the orbital with the same probability.

The probability of finding an electron belonging to a given atom reaches zero only at an infinite distance from its nucleus. There is, therefore, a finite though small probability that the electron might be detected at a very great distance from the atom. In this respect, one must conclude that the atomic orbitals, and hence the atom itself, extend over all of space. We begin to find ourselves returning to the idea that matter is continuous. The density of this matter continuum varies from place to place. Those regions of highest density, corresponding to a high probability of detecting mass, are what we have in mind when we speak of atoms and molecules.

Reading Suggestions 7.13

Mr. Tompkins in Wonderland, by George Gamow (Cambridge University Press, London, 1960), is a most entertaining, as well as scientifically correct approach to the quantum, the uncertainty principle, and relativity. In a series of dreams, Mr. Tompkins finds himself traveling in lands where certain physical constants have vastly different values from the usual ones. His adventures on a tiger hunt in a jungle where Planck's constant is 1 erg-sec, and a gazelle undergoes diffraction running through a grove of bamboo, are not only very funny, but can perhaps give one a better appreciation of quantum restrictions than would any number of mathematical proofs.

Another longer and somewhat more serious—although far from stuffy—book, which will bring the reader a long way toward understanding the peculiar behavior of matter on a small scale, is *The Strange Story of the Quantum,* by Banesh Hoffmann (Dover Publications, Inc., New York, 1959).

A brief account of the development of the Bohr model of the atom, including the modifications introduced by Sommerfeld, is presented in Chapter 5 of *The Structure of Atoms,* by J. J. Lagowski (Houghton Mifflin Company, Boston, 1964). A more complete discussion of the Bohr model and the aufbau principle will be found in Chapters 2 and 3 of *Electronic Structure and Chemical Bonding,* by Donald K. Sebera (Blaisdell Publishing Company, Waltham, Mass., 1964). An exceptionally clear presentation of the wave mechanical model of the atom is given in Chapters 5 and 6. The serious student of chemistry will find this inexpensive paperback a valuable addition to his personal library. Also highly recommended is *An Introduction to Modern Chemistry* by M. J. S. Dewar (Oxford University Press, New York, 1965).

Questions and Problems

7.1 How did Niels Bohr account for the fact that a gaseous element heated to incandescence exhibits a line spectrum rather than emitting light of all wavelengths?

7.2 Applying the "aufbau" principle, and following the order of occupancy given in Fig. 7.9, predict the ground state electronic configuration of gadolinium (**Gd**, $Z = 64$). Of what significance is any discrepancy between the predicted electronic configuration of the element and that given in Section 7.7?

7.3 What is the relationship between the electronic configurations of the elements and the periodic law? In what way does their electronic configuration distinguish the transition metals from the representative elements? Account for the fact that there are 14 lanthanide elements. How can we be certain that there are no more than 14 actinides?

7.4 How is the Bohr model of the atom in conflict with the uncertainty principle of Heisenberg?

7.5 Show how ascribing the characteristics of a wave to the electron accounts for the quantization of atomic energy levels and the quantum restriction on the angular momentum of electrons in an atom.

7.6 Define atomic orbital, and distinguish clearly between an orbital and a Bohr orbit.

7.7 By applying the "aufbau" principle, predict the ground-state electronic configurations of the elements whose atomic numbers are respectively 20, 43, 52, 54, 65, 76, 87, 98, and 105. On the basis of their electronic configurations, classify each as a representative, transition, lanthanide, or actinide element.

7.8 The yellow "*D*" line at 5890 Å in the emission spectrum of sodium corresponds to the difference in energy between the $3s$ and $3p$ electronic levels in the atom. Calculate the energy difference in electron volts.

7.9 What is the energy in electron volts of infrared radiation which has a wavelength of 3.1×10^{-4} cm?

7.10 Calculate the wavelength of the line in the Balmer series of the hydrogen spectrum which corresponds to the energy emitted when an excited electron drops from the seventh to the second energy level.

7.11 Using the data given in Table 7.2, and the ionization potential of hydrogen calculated in Example 7.3, calculate the wavelength of the series limit in the Balmer series of the hydrogen spectrum.

7.12 It is possible to bring about dissociation of a chemical bond by irradiating it with light of the proper wavelength. What wavelength of light corresponds to the energy, 103.1 kcal/mole, necessary to dissociate the **H—Cl** bond?

7.13 What is the wavelength of the matter wave associated with a 140-g baseball thrown at a speed of 1800 cm/sec?

7.14 The wavelengths of the lines in the sodium spectrum are found to fit the expression

$$\frac{1}{\lambda} = R_{\text{Na}}\left(\frac{1}{(n_e'')^2} - \frac{1}{(n_e')^2}\right)$$

where $R_{\text{Na}} = 109{,}735\ \text{cm}^{-1}$, while n_e'' and n_e' are nonintegral "effective quantum numbers." The principal series in the spectrum of sodium arises from transitions of the outermost electron between the $3s$ level, with an effective quantum number $n_e'' = 1.627$, and various excited states. Calculate (a) the wavelength at the series limit ($n_e' = \infty$), (b) the ionization potential corresponding to loss of the $3s$ electron, and (c) the ionization energy in kcal/mole.

Ans. (a) 2420 Å, (b) 5.14 eV, (c) 118 kcal/mole

And seest not, therefore, how it matters much
After what order are set the primal germs,
And with what other germs they all are mixed,
And what the motions that they give and get?

—Lucretius, *Of the Nature of Things*, 58 B.C.*

8

ELECTRONS AND CHEMICAL PROPERTIES

An element exhibits its chemical properties by combining with other elements to form compounds. A compound is made up of aggregates of atoms in definite relative proportions, held together by chemical bonds. The composition of these aggregates depends upon the number of bonds which their components can form; their properties are determined largely by the nature of the bonds. A bond exists between two atoms if it takes energy to separate them. If to do this requires more than about 10 kcal of energy per mole of bonds, then the atoms may form an aggregate stable enough to be recognized as a chemical compound. The energy (usually expressed in kcal/mole) which is needed to disrupt the bonds and separate the atoms is called the ***bond energy.*** Chemical bonds generally have energies in excess of 40 kcal/mole.

The first hint that chemical bonding is electrical in nature came from the electrochemical experiments of Davy, Faraday, and others. With the recognition of the electron as an essential part of the atom came the suggestion that this particle might play an important rôle in chemical bonding. That electrons are involved in a very special way in the formation of

* From the translation by William Ellery Leonard. A Dutton Everyman Paperback, E. P. Dutton & Co., Inc., New York, 1957. By permission of the publishers.

chemical bonds was made obvious by the discovery that the periodic recurrence of similar chemical properties has its parallel in the periodic recurrence of similar electronic configurations.

There are two main types of chemical bond: the ***covalent bond,*** in which two atoms share a pair of electrons between them, and the ***ionic bond,*** which results from the transfer of an electron from one atom to another with the formation of positive and negative ions. The dividing line between these two types of bond is not always sharp, and covalent bonds may have some degree of so-called *ionic character*. We shall begin our discussion of chemical bonding by considering the formation of the simplest neutral molecule, H_2. The bond in molecular hydrogen is the prototype of the covalent bond, and the processes involved in its formation are essentially those that take part in the formation of a covalent bond between any two atoms.

8.1 Covalent Bonding

Picture two hydrogen atoms approaching one another. As the distance between them decreases, each electron begins to feel the attraction not only of its own nucleus, but also that of the other atom as well. Because of this, the electrons begin to spend more of their time in the region between the two nuclei where the attractive forces are greatest, and their orbitals become somewhat distorted (Fig. 8.1). Provided that the two electrons have opposite spins, at still smaller distances their orbitals start to merge, or overlap,

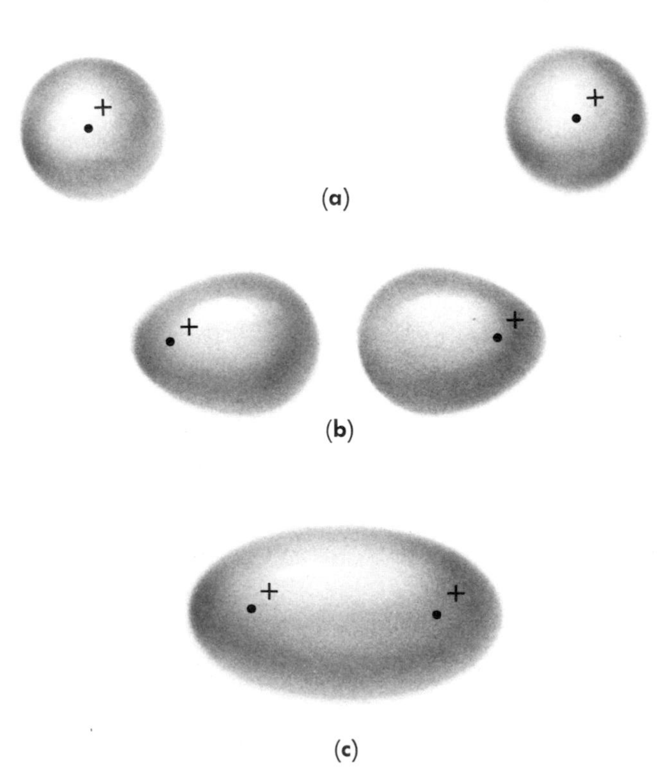

Fig. 8.1 Covalent bond formation. (a) Two isolated hydrogen atoms. (b) Distortion of orbitals resulting from attraction between the nucleus of one atom and the electron of the other. (c) Overlapping of electronic orbitals with formation of a covalent bond.

which means simply that there is now a chance of finding each electron in the vicinity of either nucleus. The electrons are now free to travel about both nuclei, and the resulting mutual attractions of the two electrons and the two nuclei have the effect of binding the atoms together. *The pair of electrons is said to be shared by the two atoms.* Because each electron is now held in the system by twice the charge that attracted it in the hydrogen atom, its potential energy, and therefore that of the entire system, is lowered. The result is a ***covalent bond.*** A covalent bond is usually represented by a line drawn between the symbols of the atoms joined by the bond, as in the following examples:

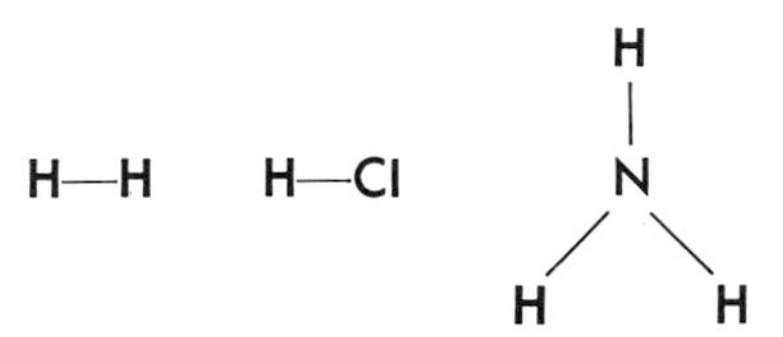

In Fig. 8.2, the change in the potential energy of the system which takes place during the formation of a covalent bond is shown as a function of the distance between the nuclei of the atoms. At large distances, the energy is simply that of two isolated hydrogen atoms. Like a ball rolling downhill, all systems tend toward a state of minimum potential energy. Lowering the potential energy therefore is equivalent to increasing the

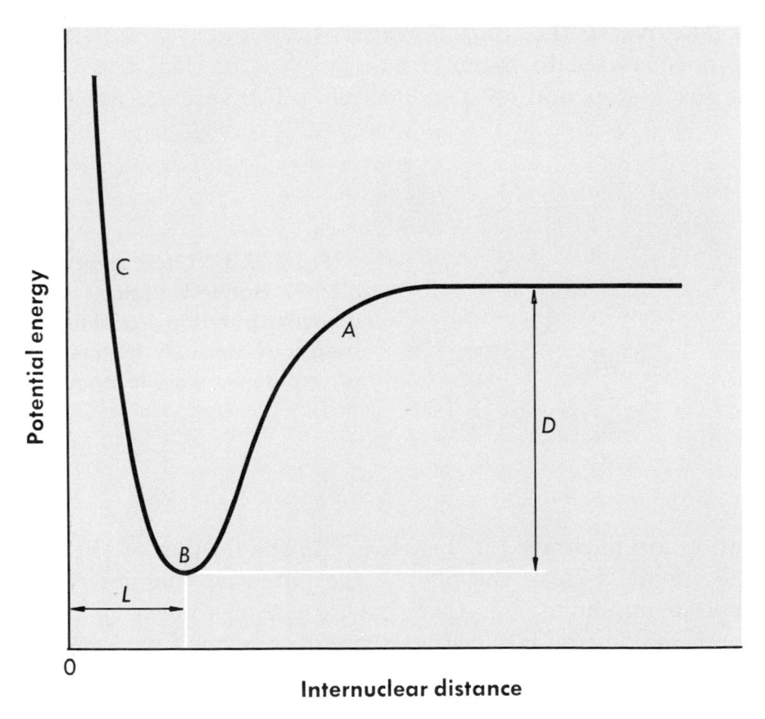

Fig. 8.2 Change in potential energy with distance between atoms. The minimum in the curve corresponds to bond formation.

stability of the system. At some point A, the electronic orbitals begin to overlap and the mutual attraction between the atoms leads to a decrease in potential energy. This continues until at a distance represented by point B, the potential energy of the system is at a minimum. Forcing the atoms closer together results in an increase in potential energy because of repulsion between the two nuclei, which becomes important at short distances. The curve therefore rises steeply at C. The internuclear distance L, at which the potential energy of the system is at a minimum, corresponds to the average bond length. To lift the system out of the potential energy "well," and redissociate the atoms requires at least the amount of energy represented by D. This energy, which is equal also to that released during the formation of the bond, is called the ***bond dissociation energy,*** or simply the ***bond energy.*** The average bond length L, and the bond energy D, are characteristic of the atoms joined by the bond.

Bonded atoms do not remain at a fixed distance from one another. A portion of the total kinetic energy of a molecule is associated with the motions of individual atoms, causing them to oscillate, or vibrate, as though they were balls attached by springs. As two bonded atoms oscillate, the distance between them is first less, then more than the average bond length. As they move closer together, the increasing repulsion between their nuclei causes them to slow down and finally stop, their kinetic energy of motion being converted into potential energy of repulsion. They then reverse direction, speeding up as potential energy is converted into kinetic until, when the distance between them is equal to the average bond length, the kinetic energy is at a maximum and the potential at a minimum. Attractive forces take over as the atoms move still farther apart. Kinetic energy of motion is converted to potential energy of attraction, and the atoms again slow down, stop, and reverse direction. The various changes during

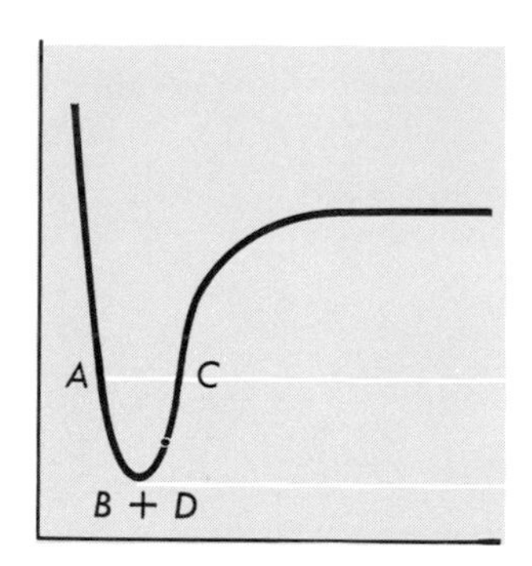

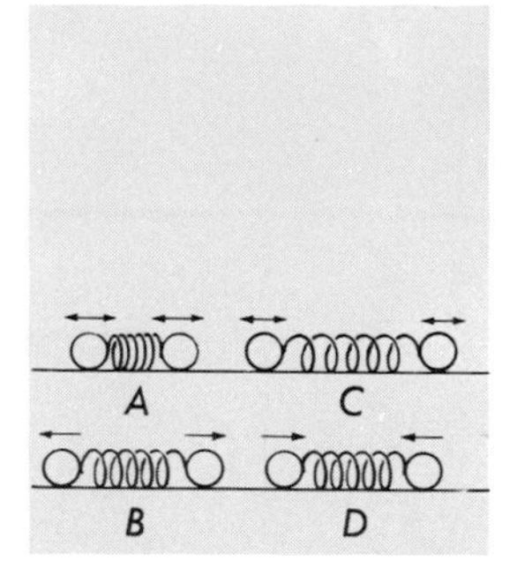

Fig. 8.3 Oscillation of covalently bonded atoms: A and C, maximum potential, minimum kinetic energy; B and D, minimum potential, maximum kinetic energy.

one oscillation are illustrated in Fig. 8.3. At the bottom of the potential energy well (point B-D on the figure), the potential energies of the two atoms are at a minimum, but their kinetic energies are at a maximum, and they are moving rapidly, either toward or away from one another. The distance between the atoms at this point is equal to the average bond distance. At point A the atoms have moved closer together. Their potential energy has increased at the expense of their kinetic energy, and the atoms are about to reverse direction and move apart. At C the atoms have moved apart. Their potential energy is the same as at A, their kinetic energy is again at a minimum, and they are about to move toward one another. If the total kinetic energy of a molecule is increased, more of this energy becomes associated with the individual atoms, causing them to oscillate more and more violently. Eventually, their maximum potential energy at the end of an oscillation may become greater than the bond energy, and the bond will be broken.

Molecular Orbitals 8.2

In Chapter 7 (Secs. 7.11 and 7.12) it developed that because of the wave aspect of the electron, an atomic orbital corresponds to a three-dimensional standing wave. Like any waves, a pair of overlapping atomic orbitals will interfere with one another. This interference may be constructive or destructive, according to whether the waves are in phase or out of phase in the region where they overlap. The result of constructive interference is reinforcement, which is equivalent to an increase in the probability of finding an electron in that region—an increase in the *electron density*, so to speak. Destructive interference, on the other hand, results in a decrease in the electron density in the region of overlap. This is represented schematically in Fig. 8.4.

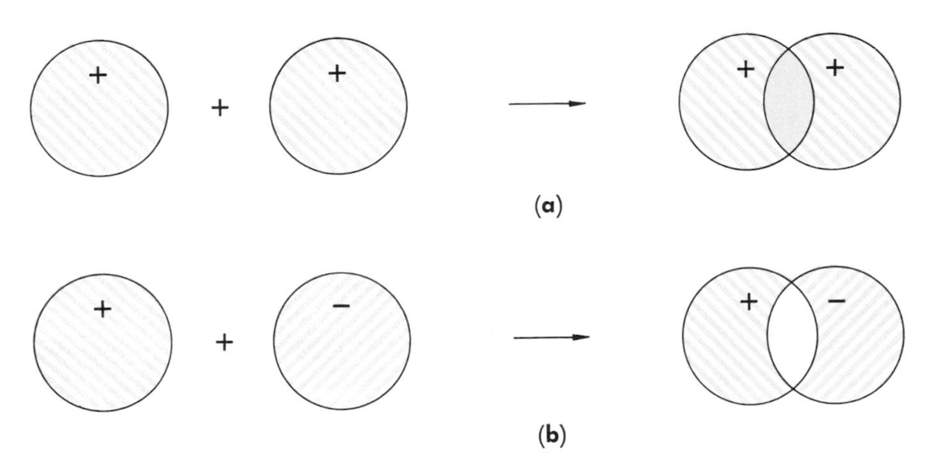

Fig. 8.4 Constructive (a) and destructive (b) interference between s orbitals.

The phase of a wave at a given point is represented by the sign of its wave function ψ at that point. When two waves A and B interfere, the result of their interference is a new pattern for which the wave function Ψ_{A-B} can be obtained by combining the individual wave functions ψ_A and ψ_B:

$$\Psi_{A\text{-}B} = \psi_A + \psi_B$$

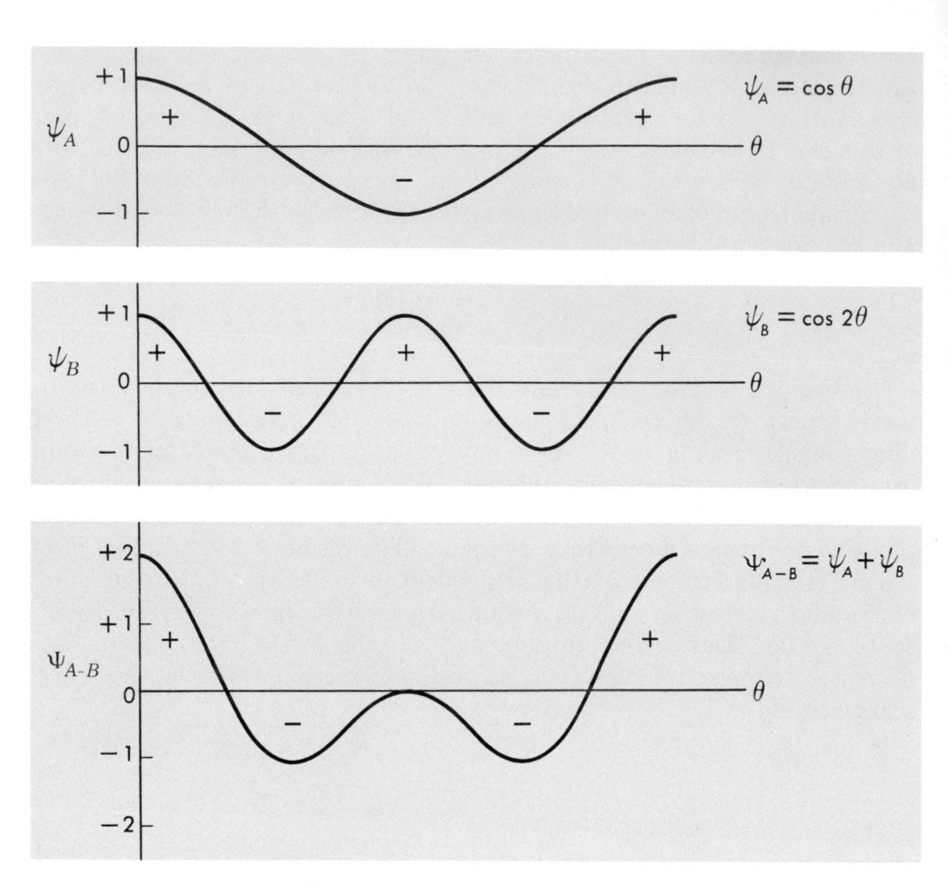

Fig. 8.5 Interference between waves in two dimensions.

Wherever ψ_A and ψ_B have the same sign, the combination $\Psi_{A\text{-}B}$ is numerically larger than either ψ_A or ψ_B, and the result is constructive interference. If ψ_A and ψ_B have opposite signs, making $\Psi_{A\text{-}B}$ smaller numerically, there is destructive interference. This is shown for a pair of simple two-dimensional cosine waves in Fig. 8.5.

Returning to our example of two interacting hydrogen atoms, we see that the overlapping of their respective atomic orbitals gives rise to two new orbitals, each of which includes both nuclei. *Orbitals of this sort, covering more than one nucleus, are called* ***molecular orbitals*** (abbreviated MO). The wave functions $\Psi_{A\text{-}B}$ and $\Psi^{\star}_{A\text{-}B}$ for the two MO's are calculated by respectively adding and subtracting the wave functions ψ_A and ψ_B for the individual atomic orbitals:†

$$\Psi_{A\text{-}B} = \psi_A + \psi_B$$
$$\Psi^{\star}_{A\text{-}B} = \psi_A - \psi_B$$

† The difference between two functions of the same sign is equivalent to the addition of two functions of opposite sign; that is,

$$\Psi^{\star}_{A\text{-}B} = \psi^{+}_{A} + \psi^{-}_{B} = \psi^{+}_{A} - \psi^{+}_{B}$$

The squares of the MO wave functions measure the probability of finding the electrons in a given region in space surrounding both nuclei, and the shapes of the molecular orbitals are described by three-dimensional plots of Ψ^2 and $\Psi^{\star 2}$, just as the shape of an atomic orbital is described by plotting ψ^2 (Sec. 7.12).

Expressed in this way, the calculation of a molecular orbital would seem to be a simple arithmetical operation. The symbol ψ, however, is a deceptively innocent-appearing representation of what is in fact a very complex mathematical expression. Exact solutions for Ψ have not been obtained even for so simple a molecule as H_2. Fortunately, fairly good approximate solutions are possible enabling us to draw the general shapes of the MO's and to determine their relative energies. The shapes of the MO's obtained by the overlap of two $1s$ atomic orbitals are shown in Fig. 8.6.

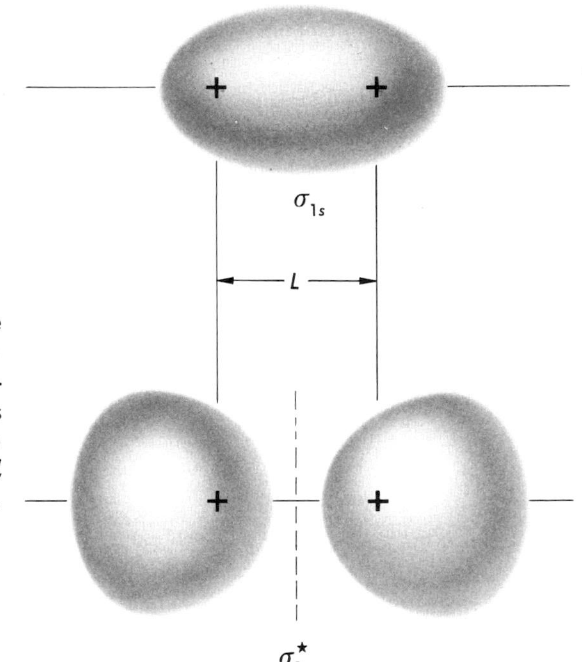

Fig. 8.6 Diagram showing the approximate shapes of σ_{1s} (bonding) and $\sigma^{\star}_{1s}$ (antibonding) molecular orbitals. The internuclear distance is given by L. The dashed line in the lower diagram represents a *nodal plane* between the lobes of the orbital.

Both MO's are seen to have ***cylindrical symmetry,*** that is, rotation of the orbitals about the axes shown has no effect upon their appearance. A molecular orbital with cylindrical symmetry is called a σ (sigma) MO.

The σ MO formed by constructive interference between the two s orbitals is calculated to be roughly sausage shaped, with the probability of finding the electrons greatest in the region between the nuclei. The attraction of the nuclei for the electrons is greatest in this region, and as a result, the electrons in the σ MO have a lower potential energy than they did when they occupied separate atomic orbitals. Constructive interference between the atomic orbitals has, in other words, resulted in the formation of a covalent bond, and the σ MO as a consequence is called a *bonding* MO.

The $\sigma^\star$ MO possesses a ***nodal plane*** between the nuclei, which means there is no probability of finding the electrons in the region where their potential energy would be at a minimum. Not surprisingly, this represents a higher energy state than would be the case if the two electrons were on isolated atoms. No stable bond results—in fact, the atoms tend to dissociate—and the $\sigma^\star$ is therefore called an *antibonding* MO. The relative potential energies of the 1*s* atomic orbitals and the σ_{1s} and $\sigma^\star_{1s}$ MO's are shown in Fig. 8.7.

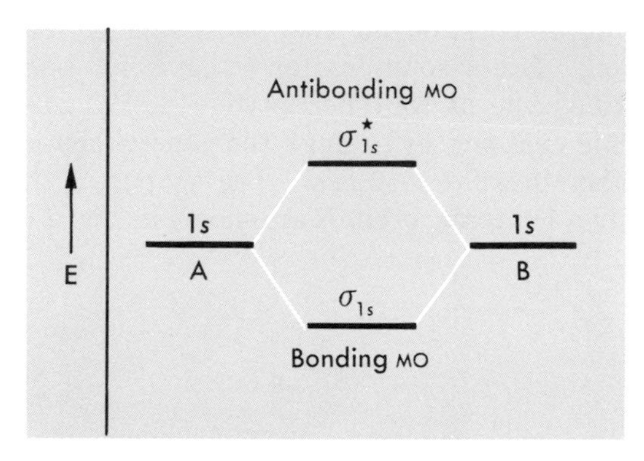

Fig. 8.7 Relative energies of 1*s*, σ_{1s}, and $\sigma^\star_{1s}$ orbitals.

We see that the combination of two atomic orbitals results in the formation of two molecular orbitals: a lower energy bonding MO and a higher energy antibonding MO. Since all systems tend, where possible, toward a state of minimum potential energy, electrons will not ordinarily occupy the antibonding MO if a vacancy exists in a lower energy bonding MO.

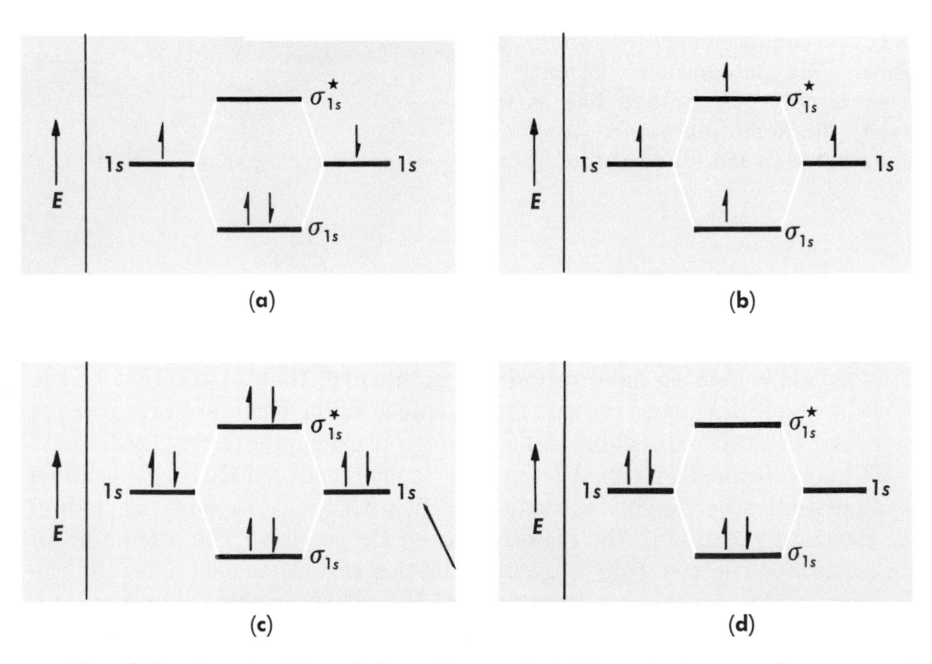

Fig. 8.8 Covalent bond formation. (a) Two electrons, spins opposed, stable bond formed. (b) Two electrons, parallel spins, no bonding. (c) Four electrons, no bonding. (d) Two electrons, both from the same atom, coordinate covalent (dative) bond.

Like an atomic orbital, each MO can accommodate two electrons, which must have opposite spins. The formation of a molecule of H_2 from two **H** atoms whose electrons have their spins opposed can be represented on an energy diagram, as in Fig. 8.8a. The two electrons enter the bonding MO as a pair, leaving the antibonding MO vacant. If the electrons have parallel spin, one of them is forced to enter the antibonding MO, leading to the situation shown in Fig. 8.8b. There is no net decrease in potential energy over a system consisting of two isolated hydrogen atoms, and no stable molecule results.

It is interesting to compare this case with that of two helium atoms. Here again we have two MO's, but this time we have four electrons to fill them. Two enter the bonding MO, but the other two are forced into the higher-energy antibonding MO. Again there is no net decrease in potential energy, and no stable bond is formed. This is the situation shown in Fig. 8.8c.

The usual requirement for the formation of a stable covalent bond is seen to be an available low-energy MO plus a pair of electrons to fill it. Generally this requirement will be met by a pair of atoms each of which possesses an atomic orbital occupied by a single electron. There is nothing, however, to prevent a bond from being formed where both electrons come from the same atom. This is shown in Fig. 8.8d. Here, of the two atomic orbitals which have overlapped to form the bond, one originally contained a pair of electrons, while the other was empty. The result is called a ***coordinate covalent bond,*** or ***dative bond.*** A coordinate covalent bond, once formed, is no different from any other covalent bond. When there is reason to emphasize the fact that the electron pair of the bond came entirely from one of the two atoms, the bond may be represented by an arrow pointing away from the atom which has furnished the bonding pair of electrons:

$$\begin{array}{ccccc} & \mathrm{H} & & \mathrm{F} & \\ & | & & | & \\ \mathrm{H}- & \mathrm{N} & \rightarrow & \mathrm{B} & -\mathrm{F} \\ & | & & | & \\ & \mathrm{H} & & \mathrm{F} & \end{array}$$

An alternative representation,

$$\begin{array}{ccccc} & \mathrm{H} & & \mathrm{F} & \\ & | & & | & \\ \mathrm{H}- & \mathrm{N}^{+} & - & {}^{-}\mathrm{B} & -\mathrm{F} \\ & | & & | & \\ & \mathrm{H} & & \mathrm{F} & \end{array}$$

reflects the fact that the donor atom, nitrogen in the case above, no longer has full possession of the pair of electrons as it did prior to formation of the bond. The nitrogen therefore has acquired a positive "formal charge," and the acceptor atom, boron in this instance, now has a share in more electrons than before, giving it a negative "formal charge."

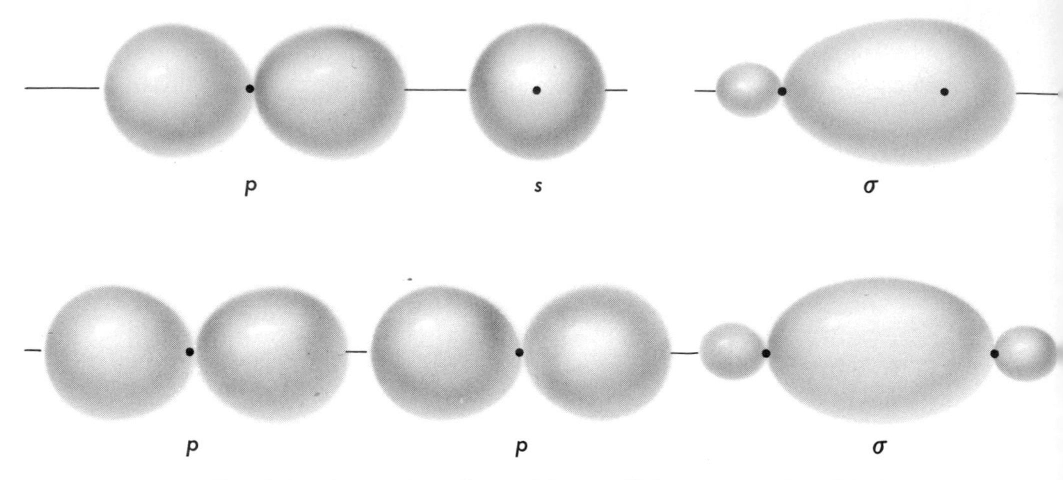

Fig. 8.9 Sigma bonding orbitals utilizing *p* atomic orbitals.

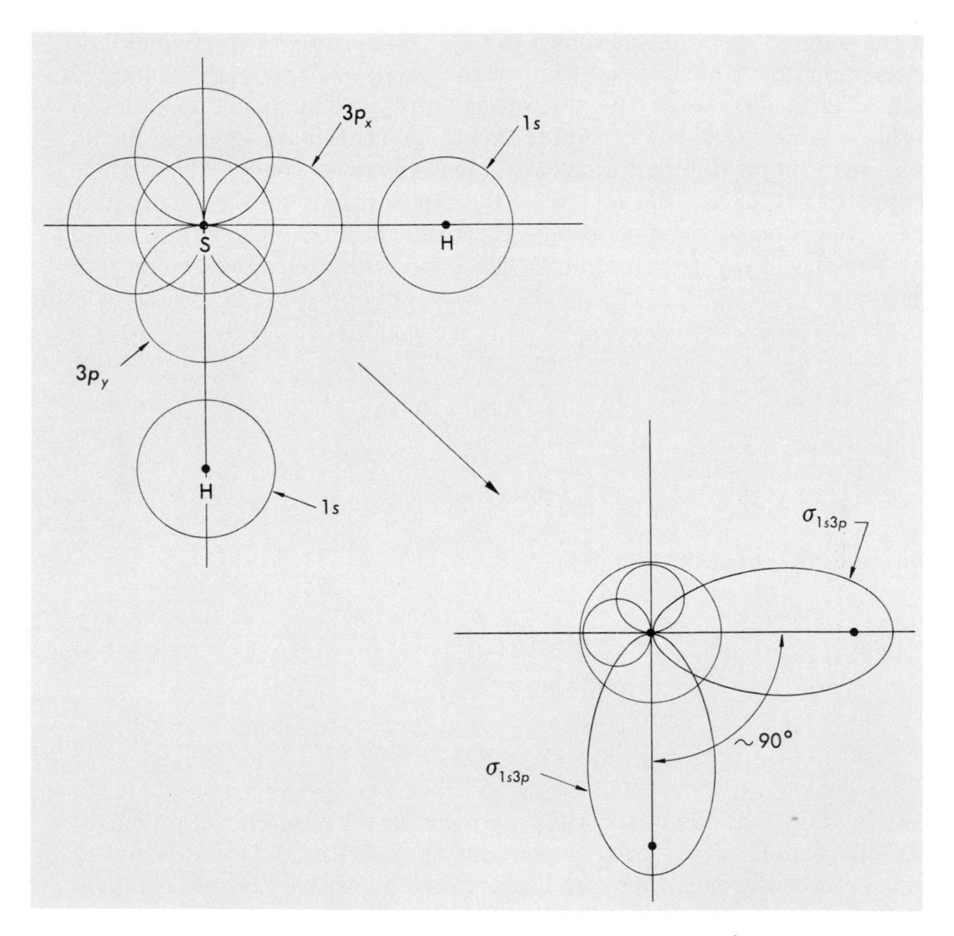

Fig. 8.10 Formation of the H_2S molecule.

Orientation of Covalent Bonds in Space 8.3

The strongest bond is formed when the atomic orbitals are able to overlap to the maximum extent in forming a molecular orbital. When the two electrons which form the bond are originally in spherically symmetrical *s* orbitals, the bond may be formed in any direction. When the atomic orbitals have a directional character, however, as is the case if *p* or *d* orbitals are used, the requirement of maximum overlap leads to preferential formation of the bond along a major axis common to both atomic orbitals (Fig. 8.9). An atom which forms more than one covalent bond, utilizing *p* or *d* orbitals, will form these bonds at definite angles to one another, corresponding in general to the angles between the atomic orbitals. As a result, a covalent molecule has a definite shape, or ***structure.*** The H_2S molecule shown in Fig. 8.10 is a simple example. Here the angle between the two H—S bonds is very nearly 90°, the same angle as that between the two 3*p* atomic orbitals of the sulfur.

Interatomic repulsions or geometric requirements may sometimes cause a distortion of the normal bond angles. Where this distortion causes a decrease in the orbital overlap, the result is a weakening of the bond.

Polar Covalent Bonds—Electronegativity 8.4

Two identical atoms joined by a covalent bond share equally in the electrons of the bond. That is to say, the variation in electron density is uniform across the bond, and the probability of finding an electron in a given region about one nucleus is the same as the probability of finding it in the corresponding location about the other (Fig. 8.11). If the two atoms are of different elements, however, the electrons of the bond will generally be attracted more strongly by one of the nuclei than by the other. As a result, the region of greatest "electron density"—the region in which there is the greatest probability of finding the electrons of the bond—will not be exactly midway between the nuclei but will be closer to the nucleus which exerts the greater attraction for the electrons (Fig. 8.12). One end of the bond is therefore negative relative to the other end. The bond possesses a negative pole and a positive pole, and hence it is said to be a ***polar bond.*** The polar nature of the bond is often indicated by the symbols $\delta+$ and $\delta-$, which represent ***partial charges.*** For example,

$$\overset{\delta^+}{\mathrm{H}}\text{—}\overset{\delta^-}{\mathrm{Cl}} \qquad \overset{\delta^+}{\mathrm{C}}\text{—}\overset{\delta^-}{\mathrm{O}} \qquad \overset{\delta^-}{\mathrm{N}}\text{—}\overset{\delta^+}{\mathrm{H}}$$

Of the two atoms joined by a polar covalent bond, the one showing the greater attraction for the electrons of the bond is described as being more *electronegative* than the other, since it has become the negative pole of the bond. The term electronegativity is a relative one. There are methods available which in many cases allow the polarity of a covalent bond to be estimated (cf. Sec. 8.8). Two elements that form highly polar bonds with one another must have greatly different electronegativities. If each of

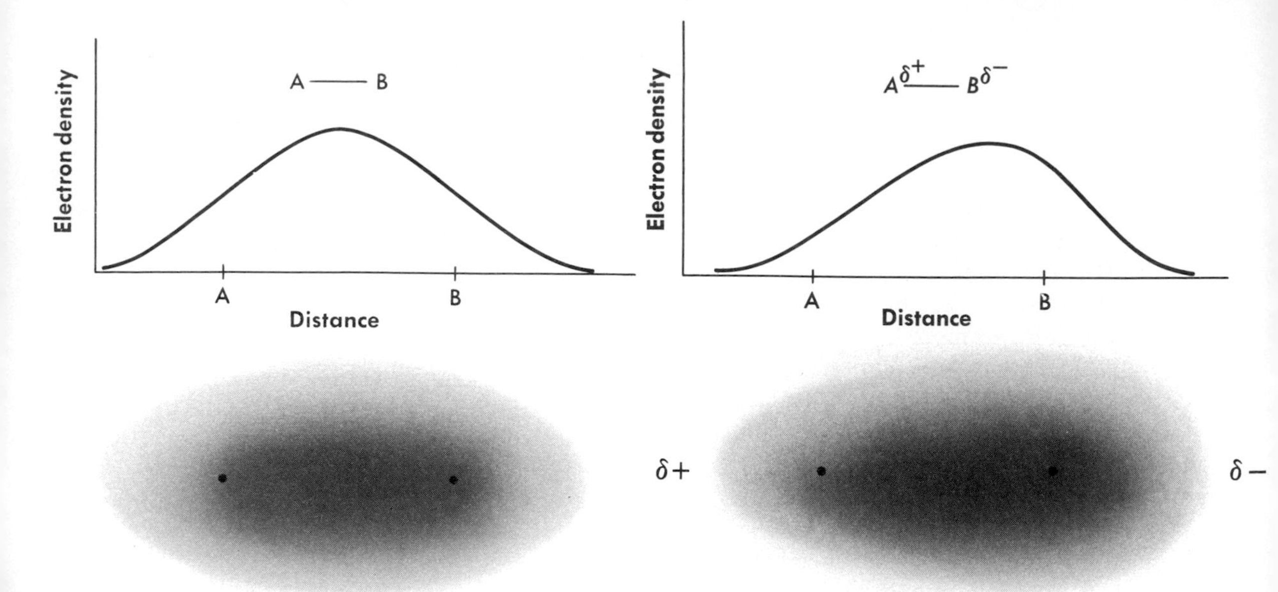

Fig. 8.11 Variation in electron density with distance across a bond between identical atoms. The electron distribution is uniform, and the greatest probability of finding an electron lies in the region exactly midway between the two nuclei.

Fig. 8.12 Variation in electron density with distance across a bond between different atoms. The nucleus of atom B attracts electrons more strongly than that of A. The electrons of the bond spend more of their time in the vicinity of B which is therefore said to be more electronegative than A.

these elements forms less polar bonds with the same third element, then the relative electronegativity of the third element must be intermediate between those of the other two. In this fashion, the relative electronegativities of all of the elements may be compared.

We find that as a general rule the relative electronegativities of the elements *increase* with increasing atomic number *from left to right across a*

I A	II A	III B	IV B	V B	VI B	VII B	VIII			I B	II B	III A	IV A	V A	VI A	VII A
H 2.2																
Li 1.0	Be 1.6											B 2.0	C 2.6	N 3.0	O 3.4	F 4.0
Na 0.9	Mg 1.3											Al 1.6	Si 1.9	P 2.2	S 2.6	Cl 3.2
K 0.8	Ca 1.0	Sc 1.4	Ti 1.5	V 1.6	Cr 1.7	Mn 1.6	Fe 1.8	Co 1.9	Ni 1.9	Cu 1.9	Zn 1.7	Ga 1.8	Ge 2.0	As 2.2	Se 2.6	Br 3.0
Rb 0.8	Sr 1.0	Y 1.2	Zr 1.3							Ag 1.9	Cd 1.7	In 1.8	Sn 2.0	Sb 2.0		I 2.7
Cs 0.8	Ba 0.9															

Fig. 8.13 Pauling electronegativities of the elements.

period, and *decrease* with increasing atomic number *from top to bottom in a group* of the periodic table. The most electronegative element, therefore, is fluorine, in the upper right-hand corner of the table (the group 0 elements, being very nearly inert, are not assigned electronegativities). Several numerical scales of relative electronegativities have been devised, among them that of Pauling. On the Pauling scale, the most electronegative element, fluorine, is arbitrarily assigned an electronegativity of 4.0. Smaller numbers are then assigned to the other elements in proportion to their electronegativities as compared with that of fluorine. A periodic table showing a number of the more important elements together with their Pauling electronegativities is shown in Fig. 8.13. Note that those elements with the lowest values are the same ones that we generally think of as metals.

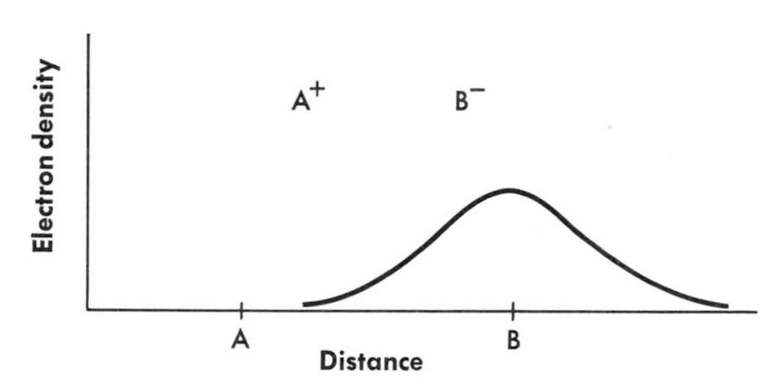

Fig. 8.14 Ionic bonding. The more electronegative atom, B, has taken complete possession of the bonding pair, thereby acquiring a negative charge. This leaves A positively charged, and the attraction between the ions constitutes the bond.

Ionic Bonding 8.5

Ionization represents the extreme example of bond polarity. When two elements combine which have electronegativities differing by two or more units on the Pauling scale, electrons can be effectively transferred from the atoms of one element to those of the other. The electrons of each bonding pair now spend all of their time in the vicinity of the more electronegative atom which thus acquires a full negative charge (Fig. 8.14). The atom which lost its electron is left with a positive charge. *The strong electrostatic attraction between the two oppositely charged ions constitutes the* ***ionic bond.*** In contrast to a covalent bond, a purely ionic bond has no directional character. Whereas in a covalent compound each atom is bound to certain specific other atoms to form a molecule, *in an ionic compound no*

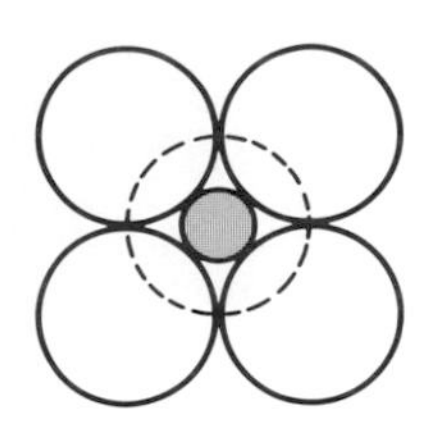

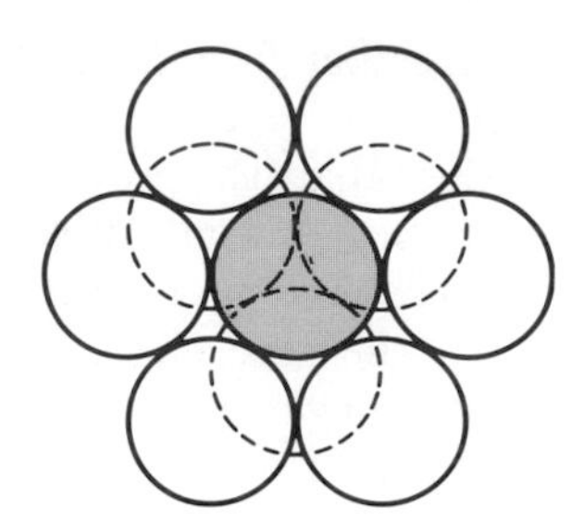

Fig. 8.15 Close packing of spheres. The small central sphere on the left can be in simultaneous contact with no more than 6 of the larger ones (4 in the plane shown, 1 above, and 1 below). The large sphere on the right can touch as many as 12 others at the same time (6 shown, 3 above, and 3 below).

true molecules exist. An ion behaves like a charged sphere, exerting its attraction for other ions uniformly in all directions. In the solid state each ion attracts and surrounds itself with ions of opposite charge to an extent dictated less by its charge than by the requirements of close packing of spheres (Fig. 8.15). In most cases, this means that, depending upon their relative sizes, each ion will be surrounded by four, six, or more oppositely charged ions and equally bound to each of them. The requirement of electrical neutrality determines the relative numbers of positive and negative ions. The formula of an ionic compound thus does not represent a molecule of the compound, but simply expresses the molar proportions of the constituent elements.

8.6 Ionization Potential

The ionization potential was defined in Sec. 7.4 as the energy, measured in electron volts, required to bring about ionization of an element in the gaseous state. Successive electrons can be removed from the atoms of an element up to the total number originally present. Thus an element will have first, second, third and subsequent ionization potentials corresponding to the successive removal of the first, second, third, and subsequent electrons. Each successive ionization potential is larger than the preceding one because it involves removing an electron from an ion with a greater positive charge.

It should not be too surprising to find that the electronegativities of the elements and their first ionization potentials parallel one another rather closely (Figs. 8.16 and 8.17). Generally speaking, the more tightly an element holds onto its own electrons, as measured by its ionization potential, the more it might be expected to attract the electrons of a bond. Conversely, elements with low ionization potentials should be expected to have small electronegativities. The relative inertness of the noble gases despite their high ionization potentials can be accounted for on the basis of their lack of unfilled orbitals to accommodate additional electrons—except in higher-energy levels, in which the electrons would usually be held too loosely to form a stable bond.

How difficult it is to remove an electron from an atom depends upon the combined effect of several factors. The most important of these are the charge on the nucleus, the orbital occupied by the electron, and the presence of electrons in orbitals closer to the nucleus. Within a period, each succeeding element has one additional positive charge in the nucleus. The greater charge means greater attraction for the electrons, leading to the observed

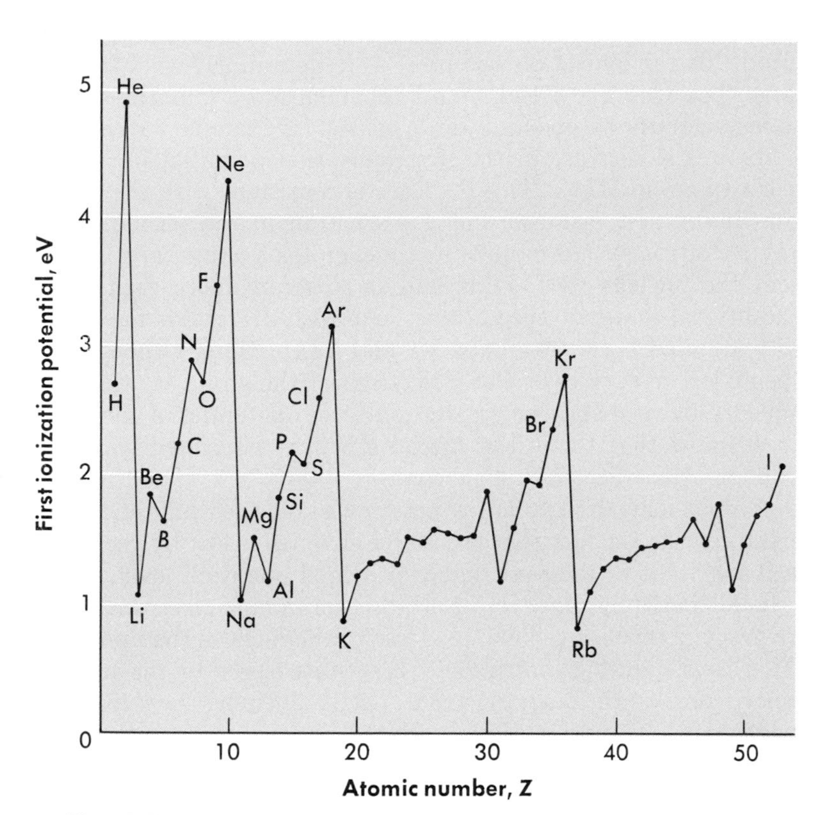

Fig. 8.16 Plot of the variation in the first ionization potential against the atomic number.

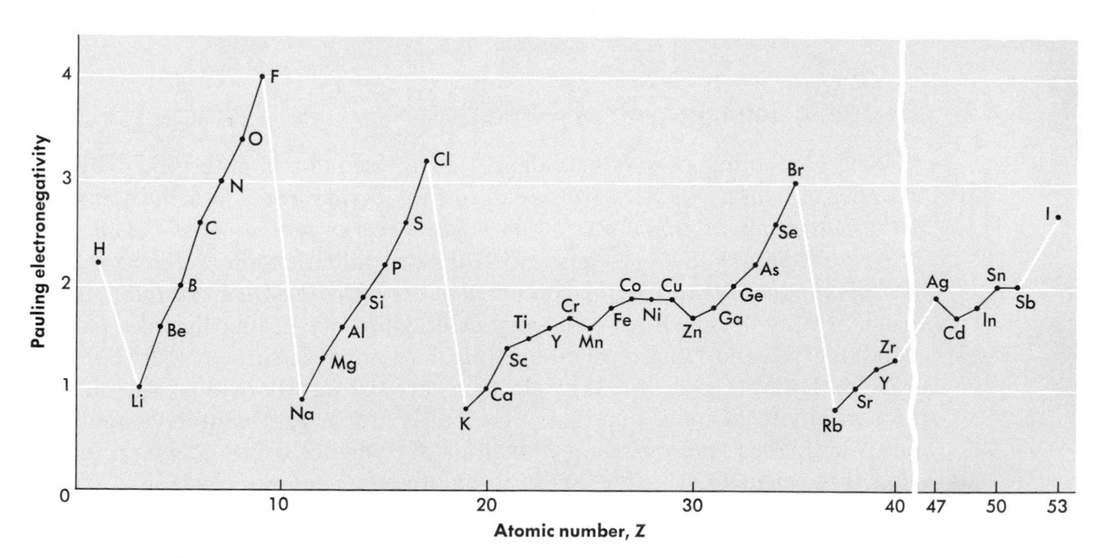

Fig. 8.17 Plot of Pauling electronegativities against atomic number.

trend toward higher ionization potential with increasing atomic number across a period. If the ionization potential were determined solely by the nuclear charge, however, the trend would be much more uniform than is actually the case. In the second and third periods, for example, rather than an increase there is a decrease in the first ionization potential in passing from group IIA to group IIIA. This decrease is consistent with the loss of an *s* electron in the first instance and a *p* electron in the second. The higher-energy *p* electron spends more of its time, on the average, at a greater distance from the nucleus (Sec. 7.12) and is therefore more easily lost, despite the additional charge on the nucleus. Another decrease in ionization potential will be noted between groups VA and VIA. Here, although a *p* electron is being lost in each case, the *p* electrons of the group VA elements are in half-filled sublevels, and the greater ionization potential of these elements again suggests that there is a special stability associated with this electronic configuration (Sec. 7.7).

The sharp drop in ionization potential between a noble gas and the following alkali metal reflects the fact that the electron which is lost by the alkali metal when it ionizes is in the next higher principal quantum level. This means that there is an additional set of orbitals containing electrons which on the average spend most of their time closer to the nucleus than does the electron which is lost during ionization. Electrons closer to the nucleus exert a repulsive force on the outer electrons, partly shielding them from the nuclear attraction. The more occupied orbitals of lower energy there are between the outermost electron and the nucleus, the greater is this shielding effect and the less tightly the electron is held. One result of this is that the first ionization potential of a representative A-group element is usually smaller than that of the element with the same group number in the preceding period. The trend is therefore toward decreasing ionization potential from top to bottom in a representative group. Among the transition elements, this factor of shielding is not always sufficient to overcome the effect of the increased nuclear charge, and the ionization potentials of those elements vary in an irregular manner.

8.7 Electronic Configuration and Valence

The combining power, or valence, of an element is determined by the number of bonds which its atoms can form. *Bond formation usually involves only those electrons which occupy the highest-energy orbitals of the atom when it is in its ground state.* These electrons are called ***valence electrons,*** and *the orbitals they occupy in the ground state are called* ***valence orbitals.*** Electrons in fully occupied lower-energy orbitals do not ordinarily take part in bonding. Overlapping of filled orbitals does not result in covalent bonding (Sec. 8.2), and these low-energy electrons are too tightly held by the nucleus to participate in ionic bonding. Generally, for a representative element, only the highest-energy *s* and *p* orbitals are valence orbitals, which means that these elements can possess from one to eight valence electrons. Occasionally a *d* orbital which is vacant in the ground state of the atom can be used in bonding. Transition elements can utilize partially occupied *d* and *f* orbitals as well. In the convenient notation introduced by G. N. Lewis in

1915, the valence electrons are shown as dots surrounding the symbol of the element, which is used to represent the atom's nucleus and remaining electrons. Some examples of Lewis symbols, together with the ground-state configurations of the elements are given in Table 8.1.

TABLE 8.1 Electronic Configurations and Lewis Symbols for the Elements from Lithium Through Argon.

Lewis Symbol	Valence Orbitals					Lewis Symbol						Valence Orbitals			
	1s	2s	2p				1s	2s	2p			3s	3p		
Li·	↑↓	↑	_	_	_	Na·	↑↓	↑↓	↑↓	↑↓	↑↓	↑	_	_	_
Be:	↑↓	↑↓	_	_	_	Mg:	↑↓	↑↓	↑↓	↑↓	↑↓	↑↓	_	_	_
·B:	↑↓	↑↓	↑	_	_	·Al:	↑↓	↑↓	↑↓	↑↓	↑↓	↑↓	↑	_	_
·Ċ:	↑↓	↑↓	↑	↑	_	·Ṡi:	↑↓	↑↓	↑↓	↑↓	↑↓	↑↓	↑	↑	_
·Ṅ: (·)	↑↓	↑↓	↑	↑	↑	·Ṗ: (·)	↑↓	↑↓	↑↓	↑↓	↑↓	↑↓	↑	↑	↑
:Ȯ: (·)	↑↓	↑↓	↑↓	↑	↑	:Ṡ: (·)	↑↓	↑↓	↑↓	↑↓	↑↓	↑↓	↑↓	↑	↑
·F̈: (··)	↑↓	↑↓	↑↓	↑↓	↑	·C̈l: (··)	↑↓	↑↓	↑↓	↑↓	↑↓	↑↓	↑↓	↑↓	↑
:N̈e: (··)	↑↓	↑↓	↑↓	↑↓	↑↓	:Är: (··)	↑↓	↑↓	↑↓	↑↓	↑↓	↑↓	↑↓	↑↓	↑↓

Now let us examine some of the individual elements, taking them in groups as they appear in the periodic table, and ask whether we can correlate the numbers and kinds of bonds they form with their electronic configurations.

(a) The Halogens. The elements of group VIIA are known collectively as the ***halogens*** (from the Greek, meaning salt-former). The halogens exhibit a valence of one in the majority of their compounds. With seven valence electrons, they each have one half-occupied p orbital which can accommodate one additional electron. Depending upon the relative electronegativity of the other element, the halogen may either form a covalent bond or take complete possession of the added electron and become a negative ion. Fluorine, for example, has the electronic configuration $1s^2\ 2s^2\ 2p^5$. This allows two fluorine atoms to combine with formation of a covalent bond as follows:

$$:\overset{\cdot\cdot}{\underset{\cdot\cdot}{F}}\cdot + {}^{\times}\overset{\times\times}{\underset{\times\times}{F}}{}^{\times}_{\times} \rightarrow :\overset{\cdot\cdot}{\underset{\cdot\cdot}{F}}{}^{\cdot}_{\times}\overset{\times\times}{\underset{\times\times}{F}}{}^{\times}_{\times}$$

All of the other halogens combine with one another in similar manner, and the free elements exist as diatomic molecules under ordinary conditions:

$$:\overset{\cdot\cdot}{\underset{\cdot\cdot}{Cl}}:\overset{\cdot\cdot}{\underset{\cdot\cdot}{Cl}}: \qquad :\overset{\cdot\cdot}{\underset{\cdot\cdot}{Br}}:\overset{\cdot\cdot}{\underset{\cdot\cdot}{Br}}: \qquad :\overset{\cdot\cdot}{\underset{\cdot\cdot}{I}}:\overset{\cdot\cdot}{\underset{\cdot\cdot}{I}}:$$

A covalent bond can also be formed between different halogen atoms to give an interhalogen compound such as **ClF**, **BrF**, **BrCl**, **ICl**, and **IBr**. Single covalent bonds with varying degrees of polarity are also formed between halogen atoms and atoms of other nonmetals. The bond between a halogen and a hydrogen atom is appreciably polar, the electrons spending much more of their time in the vicinity of the more electronegative halogen atom. The polarity, or ionic character, of the bond increases as the electronegativity of the halogen increases from iodine to fluorine. In aqueous solution, energy released by reaction between the water molecules and the hydrogen ions formed promotes complete ionization of the compound.

Elements with low ionization potentials, such as the active metals, lose their electrons completely to the halogen, and bonds with these elements are ionic:

$$\mathrm{Na}\cdot + \cdot\ddot{\underset{\cdot\cdot}{\mathrm{F}}}: \rightarrow \mathrm{Na}^+ :\ddot{\underset{\cdot\cdot}{\mathrm{F}}}:^-$$

$$\mathrm{Mg}: + 2\cdot\ddot{\underset{\cdot\cdot}{\mathrm{Cl}}}: \rightarrow :\ddot{\underset{\cdot\cdot}{\mathrm{Cl}}}:^- \quad \mathrm{Mg}^{++} :\ddot{\underset{\cdot\cdot}{\mathrm{Cl}}}:^-$$

After using its unpaired valence electron to form one bond, an atom of **Br**, **Cl** or **I** can utilize its remaining valence electrons in coordinate covalent bonding with electronegative atoms possessing vacant orbitals. Such bonding exists, for example, in three of the four oxy- acids of chlorine:

$$\mathrm{H{-}O{-}}\ddot{\underset{\cdot\cdot}{\mathrm{Cl}}}: \qquad \mathrm{H{-}O{-}}\ddot{\underset{\cdot\cdot}{\mathrm{Cl}}}\rightarrow\mathrm{O} \qquad \mathrm{H{-}O{-}}\overset{\cdot\cdot}{\underset{\underset{\mathrm{O}}{\downarrow}}{\mathrm{Cl}}}\rightarrow\mathrm{O} \qquad \mathrm{H{-}O{-}}\overset{\overset{\mathrm{O}}{\uparrow}}{\underset{\underset{\mathrm{O}}{\downarrow}}{\mathrm{Cl}}}\rightarrow\mathrm{O}$$

(b) Oxygen and Sulfur. Each of these elements has six valence electrons distributed as follows:

		2s	2p	
O	$2s^2\ 2p^4$	⇅	⇅ ↑ ↑	
		3s	**3p**	**3d**
S	$3s^2\ 3p^4\ 3d^0$	⇅	⇅ ↑ ↑	_ _ _ _ _

Each element can use its two half-occupied *p* orbitals to form two covalent bonds with hydrogen and other nonmetals:

$$\mathrm{H{:}\ddot{\underset{\cdot\cdot}{O}}{:}H} \qquad \mathrm{{:}\ddot{\underset{\cdot\cdot}{Cl}}{:}\ddot{\underset{\cdot\cdot}{O}}{:}\ddot{\underset{\cdot\cdot}{Cl}}{:}} \qquad \mathrm{H{:}\ddot{\underset{\cdot\cdot}{S}}{:}H} \qquad \mathrm{{:}\ddot{\underset{\cdot\cdot}{Cl}}{:}\ddot{\underset{\cdot\cdot}{S}}{:}\ddot{\underset{\cdot\cdot}{Cl}}{:}}$$

Their compounds with active metals are generally ionic:

$$\mathrm{Na}^+ \quad :\ddot{\underset{\cdot\cdot}{\mathrm{S}}}:^= \quad \mathrm{Na}^+ \qquad\qquad \mathrm{Mg}^{++} \quad :\ddot{\underset{\cdot\cdot}{\mathrm{O}}}:^=$$

Sulfur forms compounds such as SCl_4, SF_4, and SF_6, in which bond formation can involve "promotion" of one or two electrons into normally vacant *3d* orbitals:

	3*s*	3*p*			3*d*					
S(IV)	⇅	↑	↑	↑	↑	_	_	_	_	SCl_4, SF_4
S(VI)	↑	↑	↑	↑	↑	↑	_	_	_	SF_6

Both oxygen and sulfur can form coordinate covalent bonds, either by accepting a pair of electrons, as in the oxy- acids of chlorine shown above, or by donating a pair as in the reaction of water with a hydrogen ion to produce the ***hydronium ion*** H_3O^+:

$$\text{H—}\ddot{\underset{\cdot\cdot}{\text{O}}}\text{—H} + \text{H}^+ \rightarrow \left[\begin{array}{c}\text{H}\\ \uparrow\\ \text{H—}\underset{\cdot\cdot}{\text{O}}\text{—H}\end{array}\right]^+$$

(c) Nitrogen and Phosphorus. These elements have the valence orbital configuration

		2*s*	2*p*							
N	$2s^2\ 2p^3$	⇅	↑	↑	↑					
		3*s*	3*p*			3*d*				
P	$3s^2\ 3p^3\ 3d^0$	⇅	↑	↑	↑	_	_	_	_	_

The presence of three half-occupied *p* orbitals allows them to form three covalent bonds by sharing electrons with other atoms, as in the hydrides ammonia and phosphine:

Except in a few active metal nitrides, such as Li_3N and Mg_3N_2, the simple ions N^{3-} and P^{3-} apparently do not exist in compounds of these elements. As the negative charge on an ion becomes greater, its attraction for additional electrons naturally becomes less, and simple ions with a charge greater than -2 are relatively rare.

Nitrogen forms halides of the type NX_3, of which all but the trifluoride are extremely unstable. Phosphorus not only forms stable trihalides: PF_3, PCl_3, PBr_3, and PI_3, but by utilizing *d* orbitals can give the pentahalides PF_5, PCl_5, and PBr_5. Phosphorus, however, does not form a pentaiodide. The large size of the iodine atoms may make it difficult for five of them to get close enough to the phosphorus atom to form stable bonds. Both nitrogen and phosphorus can donate a pair of electrons to a coordinate covalent bond:

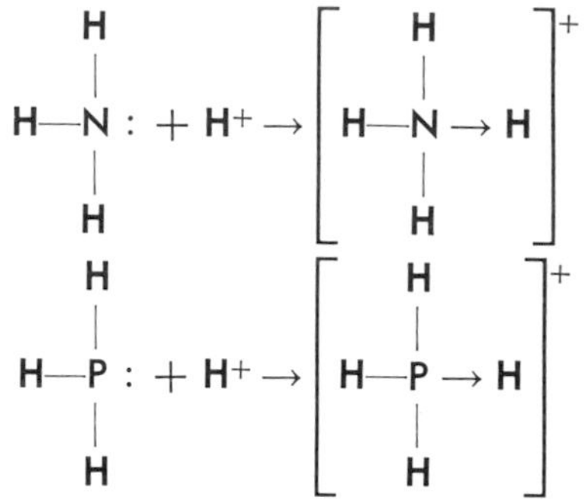

$$\begin{array}{c}H\\|\\H\text{—}N:\\|\\H\end{array} + H^{+} \rightarrow \left[\begin{array}{c}H\\|\\H\text{—}N \rightarrow H\\|\\H\end{array}\right]^{+}$$

$$\begin{array}{c}H\\|\\H\text{—}P:\\|\\H\end{array} + H^{+} \rightarrow \left[\begin{array}{c}H\\|\\H\text{—}P \rightarrow H\\|\\H\end{array}\right]^{+}$$

(d) Alkali and Alkaline Earth Metals. The elements of groups IA and IIA—the alkali and alkaline earth metals—possess one and two valence electrons, respectively. These electrons are lost with comparative ease, as indicated by the low ionization potentials of these elements (Table 8.2), and the metals therefore exist as positive ions in nearly all of their compounds.

TABLE 8.2 Ionization Potentials of the Alkali and Alkaline Earth Metals

	Ionization Potential, eV			Ionization Potential, eV	
Element	First	Second	Element	First	Second
Li	5.36	75.3	Be	9.28	18.1
Na	5.12	47.1	Mg	7.61	15.0
K	4.32	31.7	Ca	6.11	11.9
Rb	4.16	27.4	Sr	5.67	11.0
Cs	3.87	23.4	Ba	5.19	9.95

The first ionization potentials of the alkaline earth metals (group IIA) as expected, are greater than those of the corresponding alkali metals, since in going from group IA to group IIA an additional proton has been added to the nucleus. It is not surprising then that an alkaline earth metal is somewhat less active than the alkali metal in the same period. The second ionization potentials of the alkaline earths represent loss of the second valence electron and are very much less than those of the alkali metals, which correspond to the loss of an electron from an orbital with a lower principal quantum number. The alkaline earths as a result form dipositive ions, exhibiting a valence of two, while the valence of the alkali metals is one.

It may be disturbing to note that the second ionization potential of magnesium, for example, is greater than that of krypton (Table 8.4), yet magnesium readily forms Mg^{++} ions in its compounds while krypton is virtually unreactive. It is important to realize that the ionization potential is only one of a number of factors affecting the reactivity of an element. The comparative properties of similar elements or groups of elements can sometimes be predicted on the basis of ionization potentials alone, as we have just done in predicting the valences of the alkali and alkaline earth metals, but this can easily be carried too far. Remember that ionization potentials are measured under very artificial conditions, with the element by itself in the gaseous state. In a chemical reaction, the element is in the presence of the element with which it is reacting, and there may also be a solvent present as well as other molecules and ions. Thus, for example, magnesium readily loses two electrons to chlorine largely because the energy released as a result of the strong mutual attraction between the doubly charged Mg^{++} ion and the Cl^{-} ions more than makes up for the energy needed to ionize the magnesium in the first place. If the positive ion were singly charged, one would expect no more than half as much energy to be available as a result of interionic attraction, and this would not be adequate to make up for a first ionization potential as large as that of krypton.

(e) Boron and Aluminum. Of the three valence electrons which these elements possess, one occupies a *p* orbital in the isolated atom, and the other two are in an *s*. The ionization potentials corresponding to the successive loss of each of these three electrons are given in Table 8.3.

TABLE 8.3 Ionization Potentials of Boron and Aluminum

	Ionization Potential, eV		
Element	First	Second	Third
B	8.26	25.0	37.8
Al	5.96	18.7	28.3

The total energy required to remove all three electrons is probably too great to permit the elements to exist as simple +3 ions, with the possible exception of aluminum in AlF_3. The first ionization potentials of boron and aluminum are less than those of beryllium and magnesium (Table 8.2), and one might ask why they do not ordinarily lose just the *p* electrons to give the ions $:B^+$ and $:Al^+$. Apparently the promotion of an *s* electron to a vacant *p* orbital, followed by the formation of three covalent bonds, releases more energy overall and hence leads to a more stable system than the loss of a single *p* electron to give one ionic bond. In this connection, it is interesting to note that the heaviest member of group IIIA, thallium, forms well-defined ionic compounds in which it is present as the Tl^+ ion. The electronegativity of aluminum is low, and its bonds with elements such as chlorine are appreciably polar and may become ionic if additional energy is furnished, for example, through reaction with a solvent (Sec. 10.3).

(f) Group IVA. All the members of this group have the ground-state configuration $ns^2\ np^2$ and exhibit valences of 2 and 4. Compounds in which carbon and silicon are in the lower valence state are rare. Germanium, tin, and lead, however, form a number of compounds in which only the *p* electrons are used in bonding. In the oxides and halides of Pb(II) and Sn(II), the two bonds appear to be largely ionic.

It is possible to unpair the *s* electrons and to "promote" one of them to the vacant *p* orbital:

$$\begin{array}{cccccccccc} s & & p & & & & s & & p & \\ \underline{\uparrow\downarrow} & \underline{\uparrow} & \underline{\uparrow} & \underline{\ } & \rightarrow & \underline{\uparrow} & \underline{\uparrow} & \underline{\uparrow} & \underline{\uparrow} \end{array}$$

This leaves the atom with four half-occupied valence orbitals, allowing it to form four covalent bonds. All of the group IVA elements exhibit a covalence of 4. Carbon and silicon are too electronegative to lose just the *p* electrons to give +2 ions. Formation of 4, rather than 2, covalent bonds is energetically favored, and carbon and silicon are almost always tetravalent in their compounds. Tin and lead, with their smaller electronegativities, have a choice of forming either two ionic bonds or four covalent ones. Of all of the group IVA elements, lead has the greatest tendency to exist as a dipositive Pb^{++} ion. A more complete discussion of the properties of these elements will be found in Chapter 16.

(g) The Noble Gases. The noble gases are characterized by an almost complete lack of chemical properties, which shows that they have little or no inclination to lose, gain, or share electrons. The high first ionization potentials of these elements make it unlikely that they would lose electrons in chemical reactions to form positive ions (Table 8.4). At the same time,

TABLE 8.4 First Ionization Potentials of the Noble Gases

Element	First Ionization Potential, eV
He	24.46
Ne	21.47
Ar	15.68
Kr	13.93
Xe	12.08
Rn	10.70

although they hold their own electrons very tightly, they exert little attraction toward the electrons of other atoms. Before an atom can accept and hold one or more electrons, and become a negative ion, it must have orbital vacancies available to accommodate them. All the noble gases except helium, which has a fully occupied 1*s* orbital with two electrons, have 8 valence electrons and no unoccupied or partly occupied low-energy orbitals. An electron placed in a vacant higher-energy orbital would be held too loosely for bonding.

For the same reason, the lack of available low-energy orbitals, the noble gases do not ordinarily share electrons to form covalent bonds. We saw in Sec. 8.2 that the formation of a covalent bond to which each atom contributes one electron involves the overlapping of two atomic orbitals, each containing one electron, to form a bonding MO occupied by a pair of electrons. All the orbitals of the noble gases are either completely filled or completely empty, and there are no half-filled orbitals available for bond formation.

For many years most chemists firmly believed that the noble gases were absolutely inert, and various "explanations" were offered for their lack of chemical properties. In 1962, Niel Bartlett, at the University of British Columbia, oxidized gaseous oxygen with the vapor of platinum hexafluoride, obtaining a compound which was apparently $(O_2)^+(PtF_6)^-$. Realizing that the ionization potential of the oxygen molecule is nearly identical to that of the xenon atom, he then tried mixing xenon gas with PtF_6. He obtained an immediate reaction, and a solid product that he formulated as $XePtF_6$. Following the preparation of this substance, which appears to be a mixed covalent fluoride of xenon and platinum, rather than an ionic compound as was first assumed, a rather large number of compounds have been formed in which xenon is joined by covalent bonds with fluorine or oxygen. The fluorides XeF_2, XeF_4, and XeF_6 are prepared readily and in excellent yield from the gaseous elements by simply heating them together. In general, higher temperatures and higher fluorine pressures favor the formation of the higher fluorides. Thus at about 200°C in the presence of a large excess of xenon, the major product is XeF_2, while a 1:20 mixture of Xe and F_2 heated many hours at 60–100 atm and 300°C affords a better than 95% yield of XeF_6. Reaction of XeF_6 with water vapor produces $XeOF_4$ and XeO_3:

$$XeF_6 + H_2O \rightarrow 2\ HF + XeOF_4$$

$$XeOF_4 + 2\ H_2O \rightarrow 4\ HF + XeO_3$$

The compound $XeOF_4$ is a remarkably stable, colorless liquid which freezes at about −30°C. It reacts slowly with the silica of glass or quartz containers to give XeO_3:

$$XeOF_4 + SiO_2 \rightarrow SiF_4 + XeO_3$$

The trioxide is quite soluble in water, and solutions of XeO_3 have been suggested for use as oxidizing agents. While its solutions are fairly stable, the dry solid is dangerously and unpredictably explosive. KrF_2 and possibly KrF_4 have been reported, but krypton, as might be expected, is less reactive than xenon. Radon appears more reactive than xenon and seems to form fluorides, but the radioactivity of the element complicates the study of its chemistry.

The ground-state configuration of xenon is $5s^2$, $5p^6$, $5d^0$. Provided that sufficient energy were available, it might be possible to "promote" one or more electrons from the $5p$ to the $5d$ level. The energy for this process could come from that released during bond formation. In this way, a xenon atom can make as many as six half-filled orbitals available for bonding (Table 8.5).

TABLE 8.5 Possible Use of 5*d* Orbitals by Xenon

Oxidation State	Electronic Configuration 5s	5p	5d	Compound
Xe^{O}	⥮	⥮ ⥮ ⥮	_ _ _ _ _	Xe
Xe^{II}	⥮	⥮ ⥮ 1	1 _ _ _ _	XeF_2
Xe^{IV}	⥮	⥮ 1 1	1 1 _ _ _	XeF_4
Xe^{VI}	⥮	1 1 1	1 1 1 _ _	XeF_6

The objection has been raised to this that the energy difference between the $5p$ and $5d$ orbitals of xenon is too great. Instead, it has been suggested that the bonds between xenon and fluorine are "three-center bonds" resulting from the overlapping of three p orbitals: one from the xenon, and one from

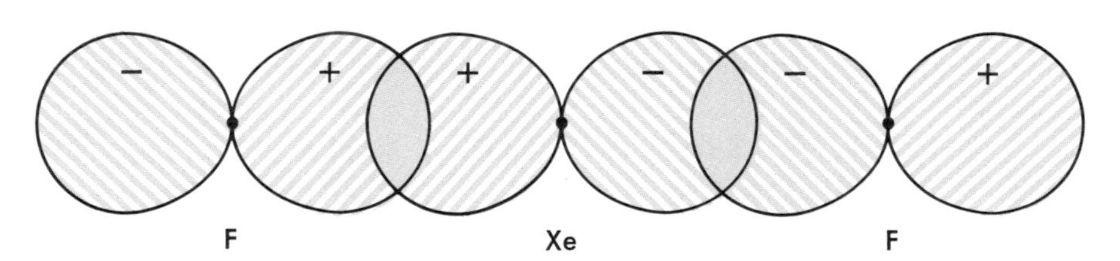

Fig. 8.18 Representation of the formation of a "three-center bond" by overlap of three *p*-orbitals.

each of two fluorine atoms (Fig. 8.18). Where the sum of two AO's consists of two MO's, one bonding and one antibonding, the sum of three AO's is three MO's. Again, one of these is bonding and one antibonding. The third, however, has the same energy as that of the AO's of the two fluorine atoms at the ends of the bond. Two of the four electrons of the bond enter the bonding MO, and the other two the nonbonding MO (Fig. 8.19). The electrons in the nonbonding MO contribute nothing to the strength of the bond, but neither do they weaken it. The result is that the three atoms are bound together by the equivalent of one covalent bond.

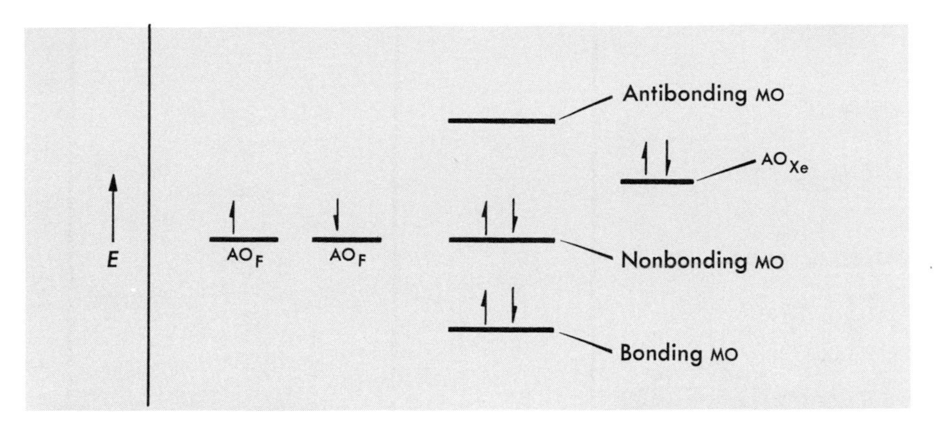

Fig. 8.19 Occupancy of bonding, nonbonding, and antibonding MO's in XeF_2, assuming a three-center bond.

Bonds between xenon and oxygen very possibly are coordinate covalent. In this case, it is not necessary to postulate either use of 5*d* orbitals or three-center bonds:

$$
\begin{array}{ccc}
\ddot{\underset{\cdot\cdot}{:O}}:\ddot{\underset{\cdot\cdot}{Xe}}:\ddot{\underset{\cdot\cdot}{O}}: & \equiv & :\ddot{\underset{\cdot\cdot}{O}}\leftarrow \ddot{Xe}\rightarrow \ddot{\underset{\cdot\cdot}{O}}: \\
\quad :\underset{\cdot\cdot}{O}: & & \downarrow \\
 & & :\underset{\cdot\cdot}{O}:
\end{array}
$$

Dipole Moment 8.8

In Sec. 8.4 it was seen that a bond between two atoms of different electronegativities is polar insofar as the electron density is concentrated in the vicinity of the more electronegative atom. The "centers of gravity," so to speak, of positive and negative charge do not coincide, and the resulting separation of charges constitutes a ***dipole.*** The presence of polar bonds in a molecule, with their accompanying dipoles, may cause the molecule as a whole to possess a ***dipole moment,*** the size of which depends upon the magnitude of the charges and the distance between them. The dipole moment is measured in ***debye units,*** one debye (D) being defined as the dipole moment resulting from two opposite charges of 10^{-10} esu separated by a distance of 1 Å. (For comparison, the charge on an electron is equivalent to 4.8×10^{-10} esu.)

Two oppositely charged plates separated by an insulator form a ***capacitor.*** The greater the potential that can be placed on the plates of the capacitor before the insulator breaks down and permits current to flow, the greater is the capacitor's ***capacitance.*** A polar molecule, that is, one possessing a dipole moment, when placed between the plates of a capacitor will tend to

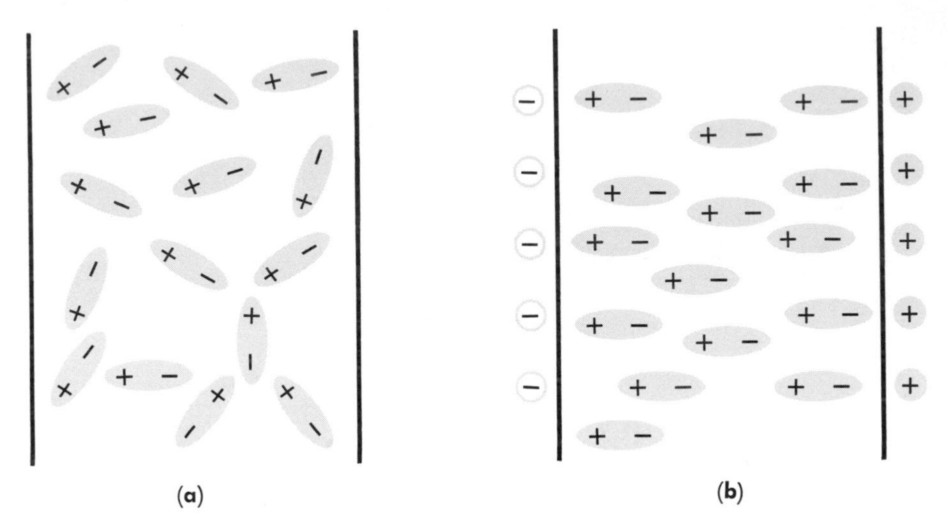

Fig. 8.20 Orientation of polar molecules between the plates of a capacitor. (a) Capacitor plates uncharged. (b) Capacitor plates oppositely charged.

orient itself with its positive end directed toward the negative plate of the capacitor and its negative end opposite the positive plate (Fig. 8.20). The partial charges of the polar molecule have the effect of neutralizing the charges on the capacitor plates to some degree, with the result that the capacitance is increased. The dipole moment of a substance can be calculated by comparing the capacitance when the substance is placed between the plates with the capacitance when the plates are separated by a vacuum.

The dipole moment is a vector quantity. For a simple diatomic molecule such as **HCl**, the dipole moment of the molecule is the same as the bond moment:

$$\overset{\delta^+}{\mathrm{H}}\text{—}\overset{\delta^-}{\mathrm{Cl}}$$
$$\underset{1.03\,\mathrm{D}}{\longmapsto}$$

The dipole moment of a polyatomic molecule containing more than one polar bond is equal to the vector sum of the individual bond moments. The measurement of dipole moments can in many cases afford a clue to the shape of a molecule. The water molecule, for example, might be linear,

$$^{\delta^+}\mathrm{H}\text{—}^{\delta^-}\mathrm{O}^{\delta^-}\text{—}\mathrm{H}^{\delta^+}$$
$$\underset{0\ \mathrm{D}}{\longmapsto\longleftarrow\!\!\dashv}$$

in which case the two bond moments, being equal in magnitude and opposite in direction, should cancel one another to give a resultant moment of zero.

Water has, in fact, a dipole moment of 1.85 D. To account for this large moment, one is forced to conclude that the water molecule is bent.

In contrast, the lack of a dipole moment for boron trifluoride suggests that all four atoms are in the same plane, with the fluorines arranged symmetrically around the boron.

Hybrid Orbitals 8.9

It is important never to make the mistake of picturing an atomic or molecular orbital as some kind of container into which one or more electrons can be placed. An orbital is a representation of the region about an atom in which an electron with a given energy is most likely to be found. The probability of finding the electron at a given point is determined by treating the electron as a wave and calculating—perhaps one might better say approximating—the amplitude of the wave from the value of the wave function at that point. Where an atom possesses more than one electron, the total probability of finding an electron at a given point in the vicinity of the atom—that is, the electron density at that point—is the sum of the probabilities of finding each of the individual electrons at that point.

Imagine, if you will, a hypothetical atom with two valence electrons just prior to the formation of two covalent bonds. We will suppose that the atom is in an excited state with one of the electrons in an s orbital and the other in a p. We may describe the region in space occupied by these two electrons either in terms of the separate s and p orbitals, or we may combine the two wave functions to obtain what are called ***hybrid orbitals.*** The combination of the wave functions is shown pictorially in Fig. 8.21. Depending upon whether the respective wave functions for the s and p orbitals are in phase to the right of the vertical axis shown in the diagram and out of phase to the left, or vice versa, the electron density ($\Psi_{sp}^2 = [\psi_s + \psi_p]^2$) will be greater on one side or the other. Therefore, by combining two atomic orbitals on the same atom we have obtained two hybrid orbitals, each consisting of one large lobe and one small one with a node at the nucleus. These hybrid orbitals, which are seen to have their regions of greatest electron density pointing in opposite directions, are called sp orbitals, since they are derived from the combination of one s orbital with one p.

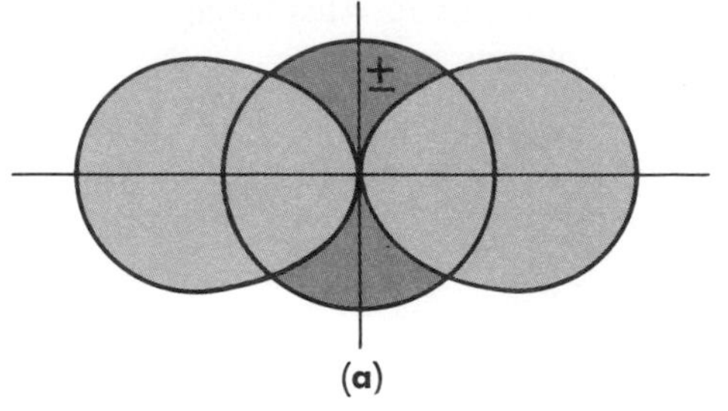

Fig. 8.21 Orbital hybridization. (a) One s and one p orbital. (b) Resulting equivalent sp hybrid orbitals.

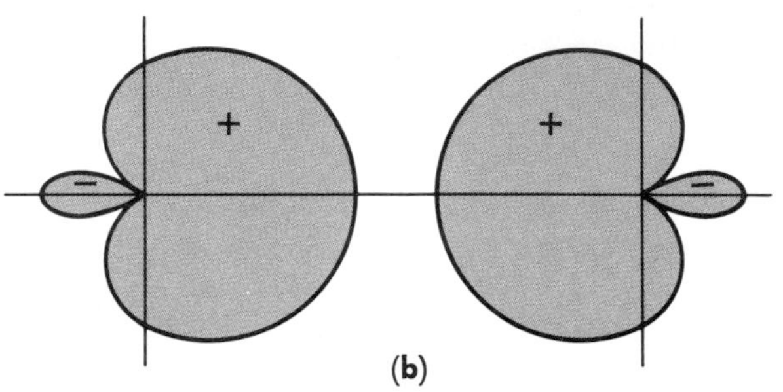

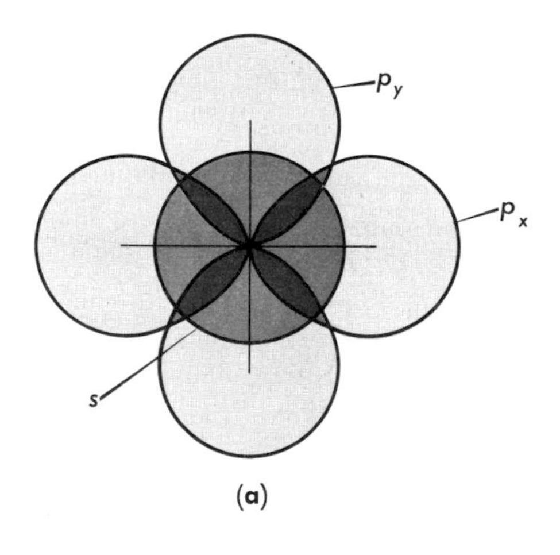

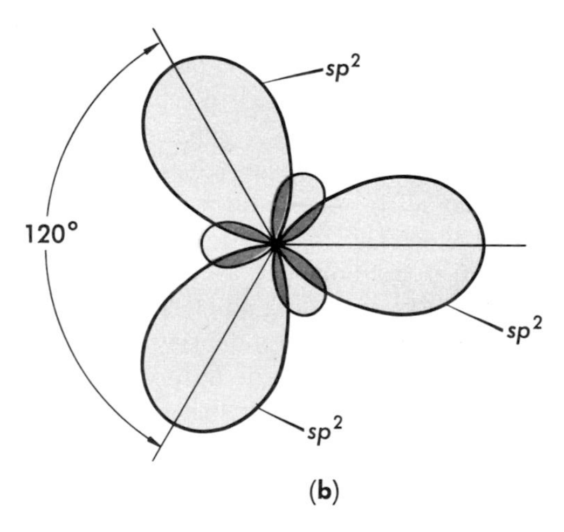

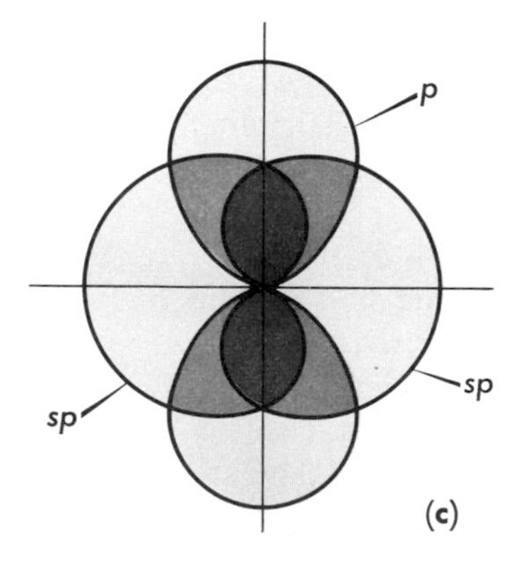

Fig. 8.22 Three ways of picturing the electron density distribution about an atom with the configuration ns^1 np^2. (a) One electron in an s orbital; two electrons in p orbitals. (b) Three electrons in equivalent sp^2 hybrid orbitals. (c) Two electrons in equivalent hybrid sp orbitals; one electron in a p orbital.

Hybridizing orbitals must be recognized for what it is: something done by the chemist, not by the atom. Whether we describe the region in space occupied by the electrons of an atom in terms of *s*, *p*, *d*, and *f* orbitals or in terms of hybrid orbitals has no more effect on the electrons than describing green as a mixture of blue and yellow has on the color. For example, the electron density about a hypothetical atom with three electrons in *s*, p_x, and p_y orbitals may be expressed in terms of simple or hybrid orbitals. Depending upon the point of view, the three electrons may be described as occupying one *s* and two *p* orbitals; one *p* and two hybrid *sp* orbitals; or three sp^2 hybrid orbitals (Fig. 8.22). According to circumstances, we will find each of these viewpoints useful.

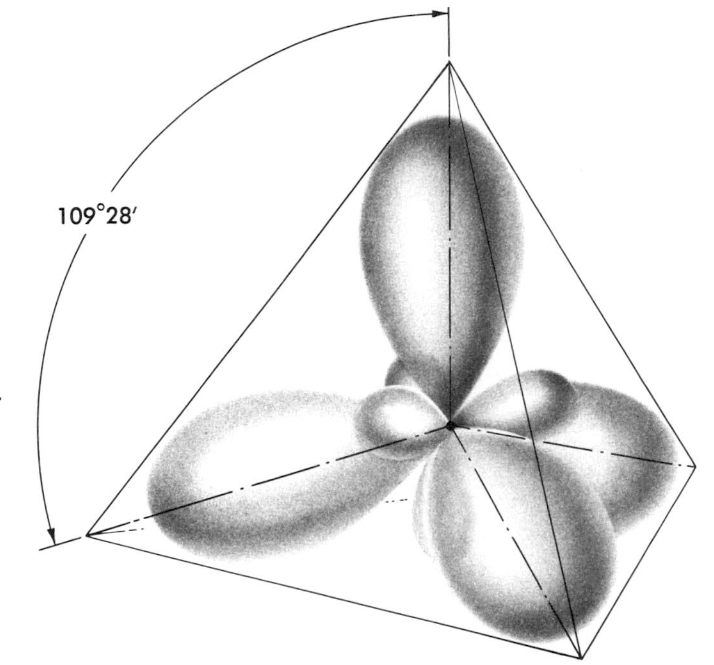

Fig. 8.23 sp^3 hybrid orbitals.

The combination of one *s* and three *p* orbitals results in four equivalent sp^3 orbitals at angles of 109° 28′ to one another, that is, directed toward the corners of an imaginary tetrahedron (Fig. 8.23). Additional hybrid orbitals result from interaction of *d* orbitals with *s* and *p* orbitals. A summary of the most frequently considered hybrid orbitals and their geometries is given in Table 8.6 on page 196.

The concept of orbital hybridization is especially useful in understanding and predicting the shapes of covalent molecules. Because of the overlapping of electronic orbitals there will be electron density maxima at definite angles about the nucleus. Stable bonds to other atoms can best be formed at these preferred angles, which we predict to be approximately 90°, 109°, 120°, and 180°, corresponding to the various types of orbital hybridization. At other angles, the electron density will be less, and weaker

TABLE 8.6 Hybrid Orbitals		
Hybridization	Geometry	
sp	Linear	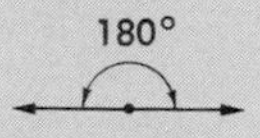 180°
sp^2	Trigonal, planar	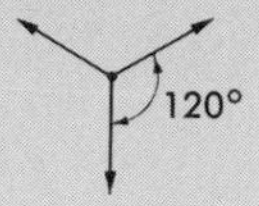 120°
sp^3	Tetrahedral	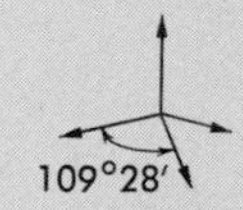 109°28′
dsp^2	Square planar	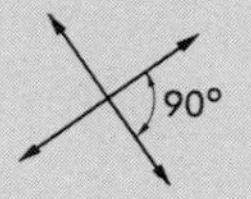 90°
dsp^3	Trigonal, bipyramidal	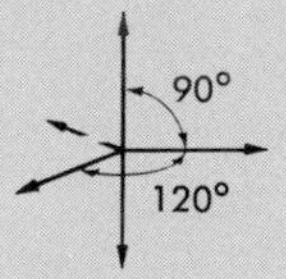 90° 120°
d^2sp^3	Octahedral	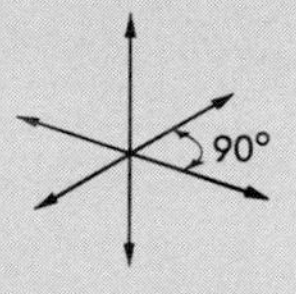 90°

bonds should result. Mutual repulsions among the groups bonded to a central atom will generally cause bonds to be formed at those angles which permit the groups to take positions as far as possible from one another. An unshared electron pair on the central atom counts as a group in this particular sense. Thus we would expect a molecule in which the central atom is united with two other groups to be linear; with three groups, trigonal, with four groups, tetrahedral; and with six, octahedral.

8.10 Multiple Bonds

Two atoms can in some cases be joined by two or three covalent bonds. For example, two carbon atoms are joined by a double bond in ethylene, C_2H_4, and by a triple bond in acetylene, C_2H_2. A triple bond is also present between the atoms in the nitrogen molecule, N_2.

In ethylene, each carbon atom is joined to three other atoms: one carbon and two hydrogens. The bonds to these atoms lie at angles to one another

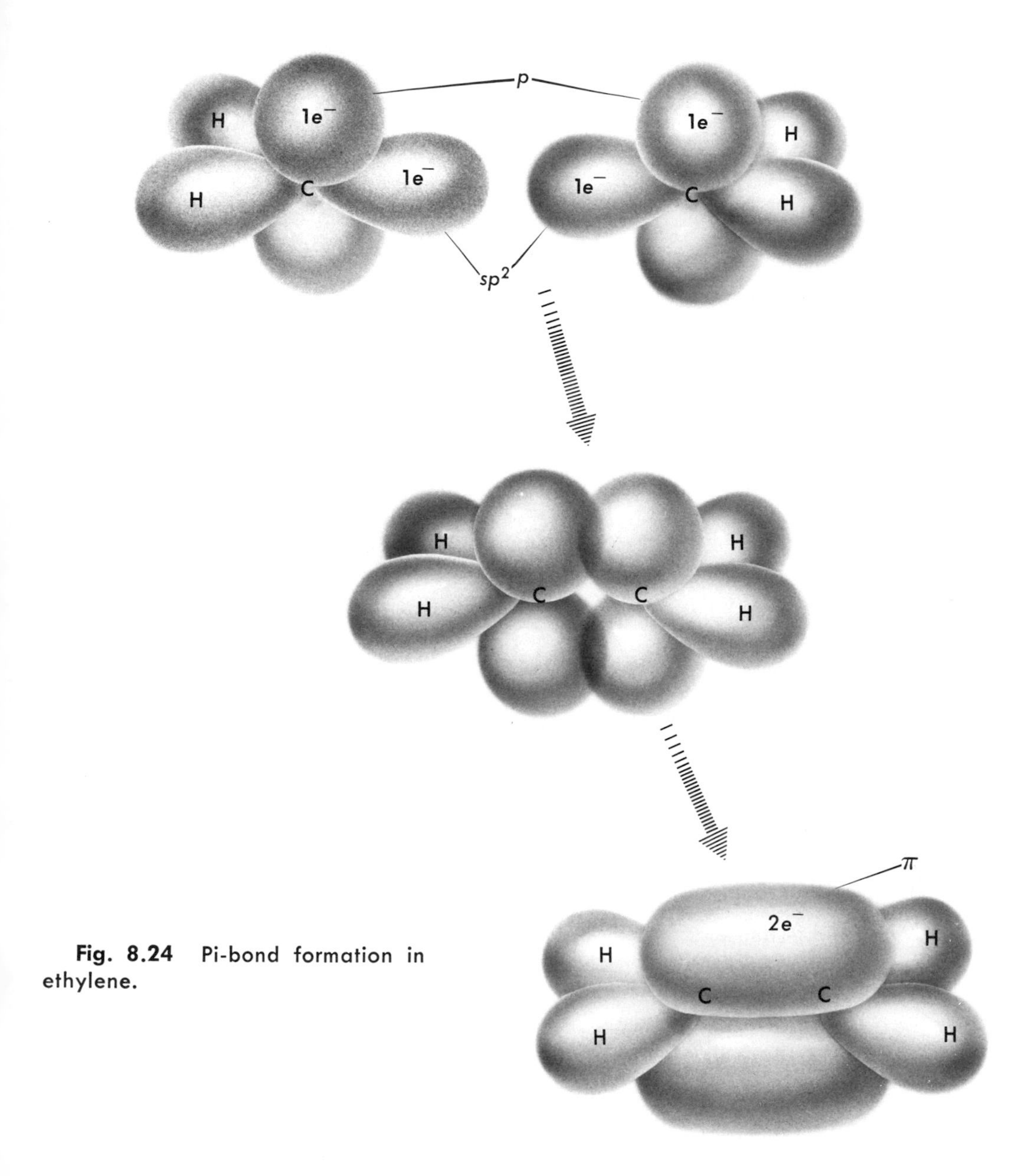

Fig. 8.24 Pi-bond formation in ethylene.

of very nearly 120°. If we picture the formation of these bonds in terms of the utilization of sp^2 orbitals by the central carbon, we can consider the remaining electron on each carbon atom to occupy a p orbital. Formation of a bond between the two carbon atoms brings the two p orbitals into a position in which they overlap, giving a second covalent bond (Fig. 8.24). The bond that results from the overlap of two p orbitals along a line perpendicular to the orbital axes is called a ***pi bond,*** or π bond. Unlike a σ bond, a π bond is not cylindrically symmetrical but possesses a nodal plane along its major axis. The overlapping of the orbitals to form a π bond is less efficient than that in the σ bond formed by the overlap of the sp^2 orbitals of the two

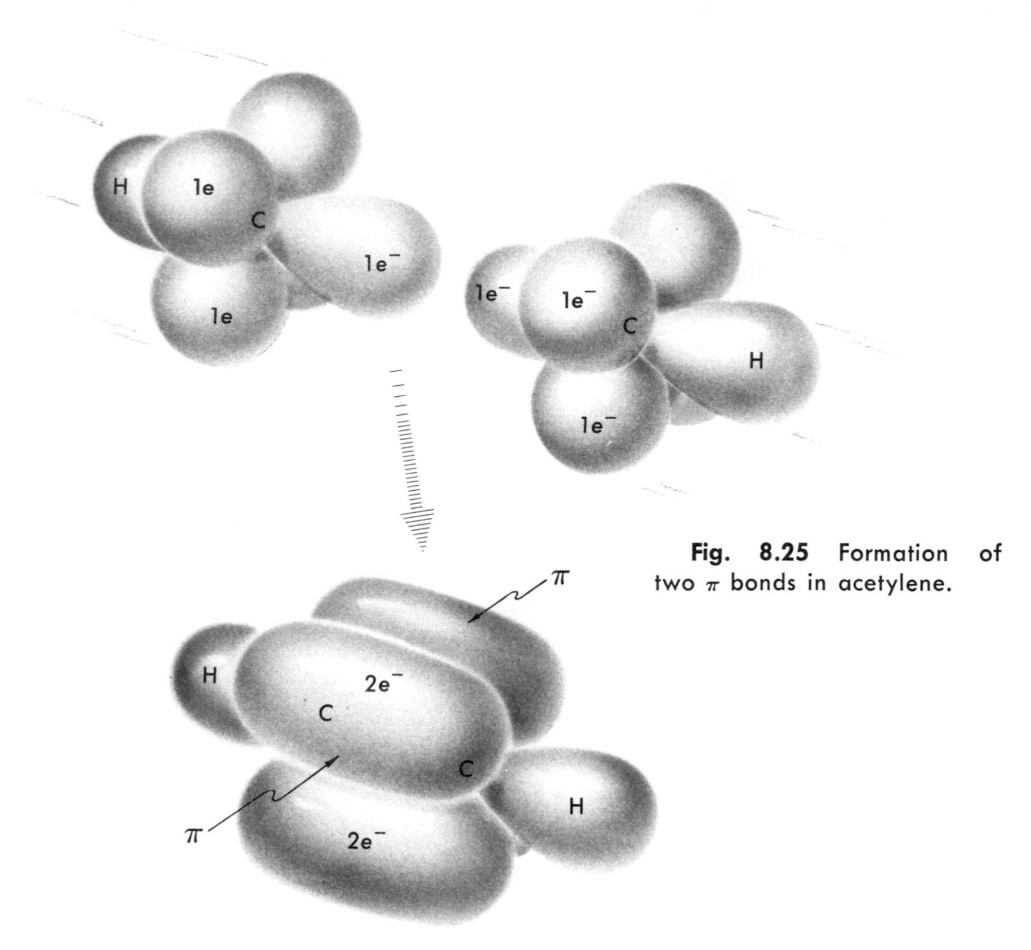

Fig. 8.25 Formation of two π bonds in acetylene.

carbon atoms. Consequently, of the two bonds between the carbon atoms, the π is not as strong as the σ.

In acetylene, the molecule is linear; the carbon atoms are pictured as using *sp* orbitals to form bonds with the hydrogen atoms and with each other. This leaves each carbon atom with two half-occupied *p* orbitals which overlap to give two π bonds (Fig. 8.25). The bonding in N_2 is very similar to that in acetylene, with the exception that the outer *sp* orbitals, rather than being utilized in bonding, are occupied by unshared electron pairs.

8.11 Reading Suggestions

The Chemical Bond, by J. J. Lagowski (Volume G-2 of the series, *Classic Researches in General Chemistry*, Houghton Mifflin Co., Boston, 1966), presents the development of the theory of chemical bonding from earliest times to the present. Much of the text of this book is taken directly from classic papers in the field. The modern theory is outlined only briefly, however. A much more complete nonmathematical approach to the chemical bond and molecular orbital theory is the brief monograph (144 pp) *Chemical Bonding*, by Audrey L. Companion (McGraw-Hill Book Co., New York, 1964). Somewhat in the same vein is *Chemical Bonding and the Geometry of Bonding*, by George E. Ryschkewitsch (Reinhold Publishing Corp. New York, 1963). *The Chemical Bond*, by Linus

Pauling (Cornell University Press, Ithaca, N.Y., 1967), a paperback abridgment of Pauling's classic *The Nature of the Chemical Bond*, is recommended for more advanced students.

An exceptionally clear discussion of hybrid orbitals appears in Chapter 7 of *Electronic Structure and Chemical Bonding*, by Donald K. Sebera (Blaisdell Publishing Co., Waltham, Mass., 1964). Chapter 8 of the same book is a good nonmathematical approach to molecular orbital theory. Also recommended for supplementary reading is Chapter 6, on atomic and molecular structure, of M. J. S. Dewar's *An Introduction to Modern Chemistry* (Oxford University Press, New York, 1965).

The Noble Gases, by Howard H. Claassen (D. C. Heath and Co., Boston, 1966), is an interesting and thorough review of the preparation and properties of these compounds, and includes a discussion of bonding in xenon compounds. Three interesting articles on the subject of the noble gases appear in the April 1964 issue of the *Journal of Chemical Education:* "The Chemistry of the Noble Gases," by Herbert H. Hyman (*J. Chem. Ed.*, **41,** 175 (1964)); "Bonding in Xenon Hexafluoride," by Joyce J. Kaufman (*ibid.*, p. 183); and " 'Compounds'(?) of the Noble Gases Prior to 1962," by Cedrick L. Chernick (*ibid.*, p. 185).

Questions

8.1 Define: covalent bond, ionic bond, bond energy, molecular orbital (MO), bonding MO, antibonding MO, coordinate covalent bond, polar covalent bond.

8.2 What is the usual requirement for the formation of a stable covalent bond? How is a coordinate covalent, or dative bond, formed? Is there any essential difference between a covalent bond and a coordinate covalent bond?

8.3 Under what conditions are the strongest covalent bonds formed? What effect does this have on the shapes of covalent molecules?

8.4 Arrange the bonds between the following pairs of atoms in order of increasing polarity: (a) Na and Cl; (b) H and O; (c) H and S; (d) C and Cl; (e) Sn and Cl; (f) Zn and S; (g) H and Rb; (h) N and N; (i) P and N; (j) F and O. Use the symbols $\delta+$ and $\delta-$ to indicate the direction in which each bond is polarized.

8.5 Account for the way in which the first ionization potentials of the representative elements vary (a) within a period and (b) within a group.

8.6 What are valence electrons? Write Lewis symbols for the representative elements of the fourth period.

8.7 Describe what is meant by three-center bonding. If bonding in XeF_2 is of this type, what should be the shape of the molecule? Would the compound be expected to have a dipole moment?

8.8 If we assume the bonds in XeO_3 to be coordinate covalent, what shape should we predict for the molecule? Should the compound have a dipole moment?

8.9 Account for the fact that the second ionization potential of magnesium is larger than the first, but not so large as the second ionization potential of sodium. How is this related to the valences exhibited by these elements?

8.10 How is it possible for a molecule to contain polar bonds and yet not possess a dipole moment? Carbon-oxygen bonds are appreciably polar, yet carbon dioxide has no dipole moment. What does this indicate regarding the shape of the molecule? Do all linear molecules have zero dipole moment? Explain.

8.11 What shape would you predict for each of the following molecules and ions?

SF_6	SO_4^{--}	ClO_2^-	ClO_4^-	$Co(NH_3)_6^{+++}$
PBr_3	ClO^-	ClO_3^-	$AlCl_3$	$SnCl_4$

8.12 Distinguish clearly between sigma and pi bonds.

8.13 What is meant by a hybrid orbital? Name the hybrid orbitals utilized by the central atom in each of the following molecules or ions:

H_2O	$Al(OH)_6^{---}$	CH_4
ClO_4^-	$Zn(NH_3)_4^{++}$ (square planar)	BF_3
		BeH_2

8.14 How is it that phosphorus can form both a trichloride and a pentachloride while nitrogen can form only a trichloride? What is the maximum number of covalent bonds which a nitrogen atom can form? In the light of your answer would you expect nitrogen to form a tetrachloride? Explain.

8.15 By applying the "aufbau" principle (Chapter 7) predict the electronic configurations of the elements whose atomic numbers are respectively 19, 33, 49, 56, 63, and 73. From your answer in each case deduce the class to which the element belongs—metal, nonmetal, transition metal, lanthanide, or actinide, its most probable valence, and the type of bond—ionic or covalent—which it would be expected to form with chlorine.

8.16 Draw electron-dot (Lewis) formulas for the following molecules and ions:

PH_3	$BrCl$	NO_2^-	SnO	$PbCl_4$
SF_6	N_2	NO_3^-	SO_4^{--}	$AlCl_6^{---}$

8.17 Account for the fact that although the bonds about each carbon atom in 1,2-dichloroethane ($CH_2Cl—CH_2Cl$) are arranged tetrahedrally, the compound as a whole has no dipole moment.

8.18 There are three different compounds, A, B, and C, all with the molecular formula $C_2H_2Cl_2$. Both A and B react with hydrogen to form 1,2-dichloroethane:

$$C_2H_2Cl_2 + H_2 \rightarrow CH_2Cl—CH_2Cl$$

Compound A has a dipole moment of 1.89 D; compound B has no dipole moment. Assign structures to compounds A, B, and C.

They move in the void
and catching each other up jostle together,
and some recoil in any direction that may chance,
and others become entangled with one another
in various degrees according to
the symmetry of their shapes and sizes
and positions and order,
and they remain together . . .

—Simplicius, *De Caelo,* 6th century B.C.

9

GASES, LIQUIDS AND SOLIDS

The gas law relationships described in Chapter 3 represent an ideal which is never fully attained. An ***ideal gas,*** or ***perfect gas,*** that is, *one which obeys the ideal gas laws exactly under all conditions*, exists only in imagination. All real gases deviate more or less from ideal behavior. Provided that the pressure is not much above atmospheric and the temperature not much below 0°C, this deviation is usually small, allowing us to make good use of the gas laws in calculations. At high pressures, low temperatures, or both, however, the discrepancy between ideal and real gas behavior may become quite large. In this chapter we shall see that this discrepancy is the result of two factors neglected in our earlier discussion of the kinetic molecular theory. These factors are the volume of the molecules themselves, and the existence of attractive forces—usually small ones—between them.

At sufficiently high pressures and low enough temperatures, all gases can be liquefied. Lowering the temperature still further will cause the liquid to solidify. A gas is easily compressed because its molecules are relatively far apart and can readily be pushed closer together. In contrast, liquids and solids are almost incompressible, suggesting that their particles for the most part are in contact with one another. Solids are further distinguished from

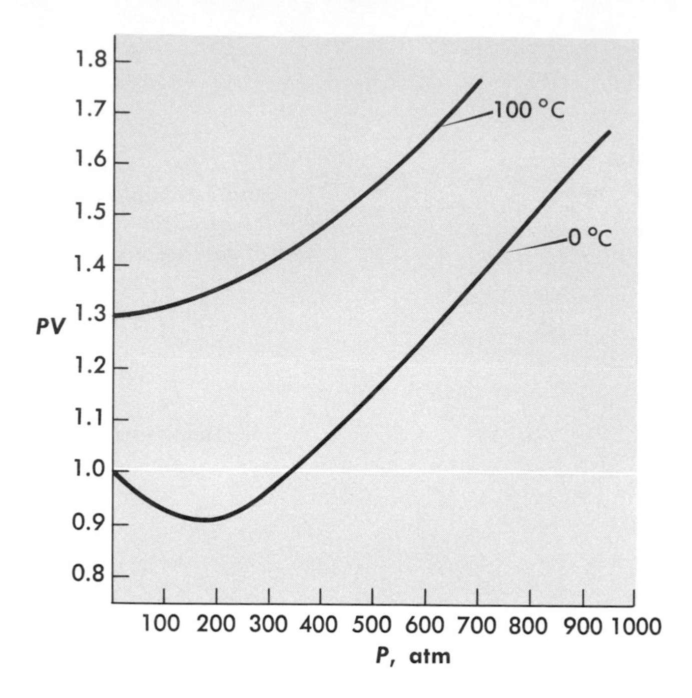

Fig. 9.1 Plot of PV vs. P for oxygen at 0° and 100°C.

liquids not so much by their rigidity as by their ***crystallinity,*** or ***regularity of form,*** which as we shall see reflects an orderly arrangement of their ultimate particles.

In this chapter, we shall consider the nature and characteristics of real gases, liquids, and solids, transitions among these states of matter, and the internal forces which determine their behavior.

9.1 Real Gases

Suppose that we have one liter of oxygen measured at standard conditions. According to Boyle's law, if we increase the pressure, keeping the temperature at 0°C, the volume of the gas should decrease in proportion so that the product PV remains constant. Actually, up to about 300 atm the volume

TABLE 9.1 Values of *PV* for Oxygen at 0°C and Various Pressures

	Calculated from Boyle's Law		Observed	
P (atm)	*V* (liters)	*PV*	*V* (liters)	*PV*
1.0	1.0	1.0	1.0	1.0
100	0.010	1.0	0.0093	0.93
200	0.0050	1.0	0.0046	0.92
300	0.0033	1.0	0.0032	0.96
400	0.0025	1.0	0.0026	1.0
500	0.0020	1.0	0.0023	1.2
1000	0.0010	1.0	0.0017	1.7

of the gas, and hence the value of PV, is found to be *less* than that predicted by Boyle's law, while at higher pressures it is *greater* than predicted (Fig. 9.1 and Table 9.1).

The smaller-than-predicted volume of the gas up to 300 atm indicates that some attraction must exist between the molecules. This attraction draws the molecules together and causes them to occupy less space than they would otherwise. The Dutch physicist J. D. van der Waals first recognized the existence of these attractions, which are now known as ***van der Waals forces.*** At constant temperature, increasing the pressure on a gas brings the molecules closer together. This increases the effectiveness of the van der Waals attractions, which operate only over short distances, and as a result the value of PV at first decreases with increasing pressure.

At still higher pressures, another factor, the size of the molecules themselves, must be considered. Compressing a gas causes an increase in pressure because the molecules, being closer together, travel a shorter distance between collisions. Collisions with other molecules and with the walls of the container are more frequent, and this is felt as an increase in pressure. At low pressures, where the molecules are far apart, they can be treated as dimensionless points, and the distances between them may be assumed to be the same as the distances between their centers. This assumption becomes less valid as the average distance between molecules decreases. At high pressures, the average radii of the molecules make up a substantial part of the distance between their centers. The distance traveled between collisions is therefore less than it would be if the molecules had no dimensions (Fig. 9.2). This results in more frequent collisions and, for a given volume of gas, a greater pressure than that calculated from Boyle's law.

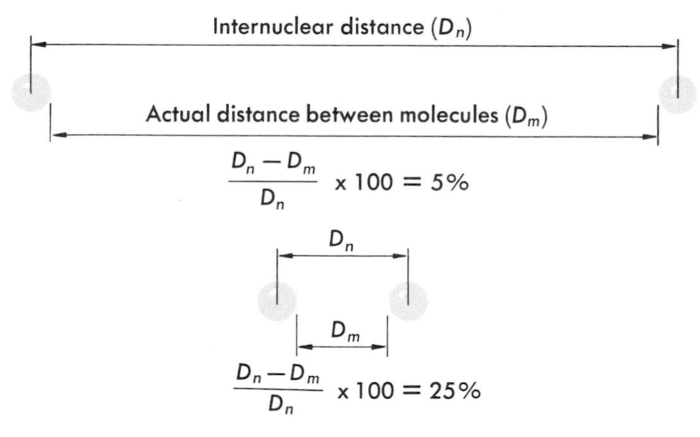

Fig. 9.2 Neglecting the size of the molecules introduces a smaller error at low pressures when the molecules are farther apart.

At 100°C, a plot of PV versus P for oxygen shows no minimum such as it shows at 0° (Fig. 9.1). At higher temperatures the relatively weak van der Waals forces are negligible compared with the average kinetic energy of the molecules, and therefore only the factor of molecular size has any noticeable effect on the value of PV.

In 1873, van der Waals introduced two empirical corrections into the perfect gas equation to allow for intermolecular attractions and for the finite volume of the molecules, permitting accurate calculation of P-V-T relationships for real gases over a wide range of temperatures and pressures. The form of the van der Waals equation is

$$(P + a/V^2)(V - b) = nRT$$

where a and b are constants experimentally determined for each gas. The first correction term a/V^2 adjusts for the attractive forces between the molecules and becomes smaller as the volume increases and the molecules move farther apart. The volume of the molecules themselves is introduced by the second term b. Tables giving the values of a and b for various gases appear, for example, in the *Handbook of Chemistry and Physics.*

Intermolecular attractions usually increase with increasing size and complexity of the molecules, and a plot of PV versus P for a gas such as carbon dioxide shows a pronounced minimum even at relatively high temperatures (Fig. 9.3). At low temperatures, the intermolecular attractions may be

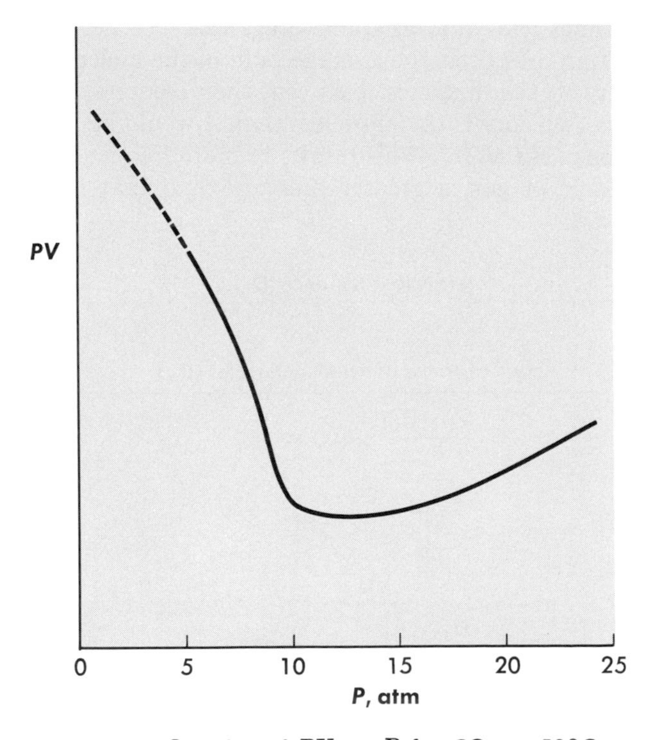

Fig. 9.3 Plot of PV vs. P for CO_2 at 50°C.

sufficient to cause the slow-moving molecules to stick together, with the result that the gas may condense to a liquid or solid. The weaker the van der Waals forces between the molecules, the lower is the temperature at which condensation begins to occur. For this reason gases with small, simple molecules usually have very low liquefaction temperatures, and those with larger molecules generally liquefy at higher temperatures. For example, in order to be converted to liquid at a pressure of one atmosphere, hydrogen must be cooled below −253°C, and helium below −269°C. On the other hand, ammonia and sulfur dioxide, with their larger and more complex molecules, become liquid at much higher temperatures: −33°C and −10°C, respectively.

The Nature of van der Waals Forces 9.2

Under the heading of van der Waals forces are included all of the various attractive forces which exist between neutral molecules. These forces are relatively weak, seldom exceeding 4 to 5 kcal/mole, but they nevertheless play a significant role in determining the physical properties of substances. Essentially, these forces arise from the attraction between the nuclei of one molecule and the electrons of another. If unpaired electrons or vacant orbitals are present, this attraction may result in covalent bonding (Sec. 8.1). If not, the result is van der Waals attraction.

When two molecules are brought close to one another, both attractive and repulsive forces become operative between them (Fig. 9.4). Both of

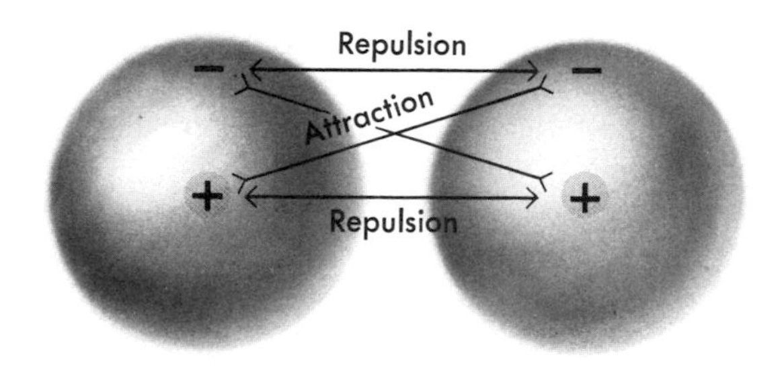

Fig. 9.4 Forces between molecules at short distances.

these forces are effective only over short distances and decrease rapidly as the distance increases. As it happens, the repulsive forces diminish with distance more rapidly than the attractive ones, leading to a net attraction at short distances. This makes up the major part of the van der Waals forces between molecules.

In addition, if the molecules are polar, there will be some contribution from dipole-dipole interaction. The positive end of one molecule will attract the negative end of another, and the molecules will tend to orient themselves accordingly (Fig. 9.5). In a mixture of molecules of different substances, some of which are polar while the others are not, the presence of the polar molecules may cause an ***induced,*** or temporary, polarization of the others, resulting in attraction between the permanent and induced dipoles (Fig. 9.5b). Molecules in which a dipole can be induced in this way are

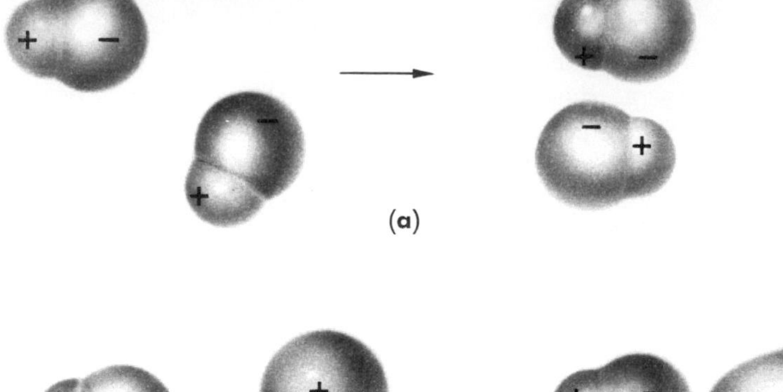

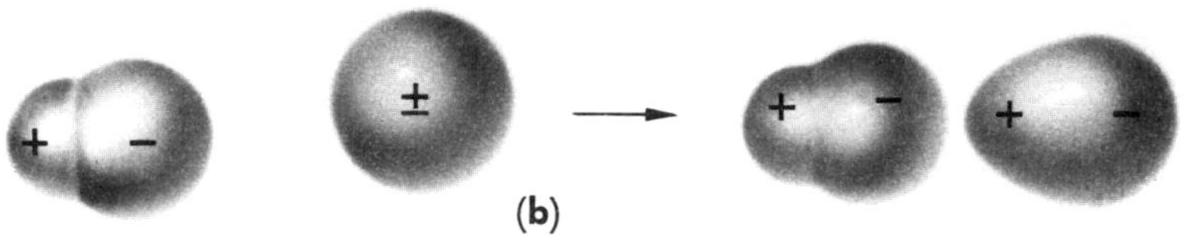

Fig. 9.5 Dipole-dipole interaction: (a) permanent; (b) induced.

said to be ***polarizable.*** Dipole-dipole interactions usually make only a minor contribution to the overall van der Waals attractions, but in certain circumstances may become more important.

Among compounds which are chemically similar, the van der Waals attractive forces increase with increasing molecular weight. For this reason, the greater the molecular weight of a compound the more likely it is to be a liquid or solid at ordinary temperatures. This is the case, for example, among the paraffin hydrocarbons. All of these compounds are nonpolar, chemically similar, and have the general formula C_nH_{2n+2} (e.g.: CH_4, C_2H_6, $C_{10}H_{22}$). The first four of these compounds, that is, those for which n is 1, 2, 3, or 4, are gases at room temperature. From C_5H_{12} through $C_{17}H_{36}$ they are liquids with regularly increasing boiling points, and from $C_{18}H_{38}$ on they are all solids. In a series such as this, the attractive force per atom is essentially constant, but as more and more atoms are attached to one another, the total attractive force per molecule will, of course, increase (Fig. 9.6).

Attractive Force

Per Atom	Per Molecule
1	1
1	2
1	3
1	6

Fig. 9.6 Van der Waals attraction between molecules. Assuming the attraction between atoms in adjacent rows to remain constant, the attraction between molecules is seen to increase as more atoms are included in each. This is an oversimplification of the actual situation, but the general trend will be as shown.

Van der Waals attractions are also found to increase if the number of atoms per molecule is unchanged but the number of electrons increases. For example, the boiling points of the group IVA hydrides become progressively higher as one descends through the group because of the greater attractions which exist among the molecules with more electrons (Table 9.2).

TABLE 9.2 Boiling Points of the Hydrides of Group IVA

Compound	Mol. Wt.	No. of Electrons	Boiling Point (1 atm)
CH_4	16.0	10	−164
SiH_4	32.1	18	−112
GeH_4	76.6	36	−90
SnH_4	122.7	54	−52

This trend is often obscured by the presence of other factors, such as a change in bond type within the molecule as one descends through a group, and the variation in properties is not always as regular as in the example shown.

Liquefaction of Gases 9.3

At relatively high temperatures, a plot of P vs. V for a sample of gas is a smooth curve (curve I, Fig. 9.7). At lower temperatures, however, the

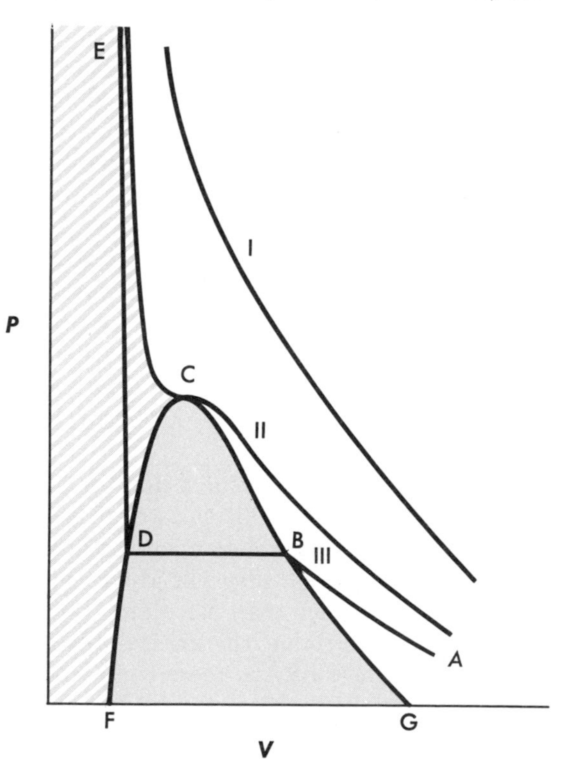

Fig. 9.7 Plots of P vs. V for a sample of gas at three temperatures.

curve consists of three parts (curve III, Fig. 9.7). The first of these is a gently sloping segment *AB* corresponding to large volumes and low pressures. At higher pressures the curve changes suddenly to a horizontal straight line *BD*, signifying a drastic change in volume with no accompanying change in pressure. This change in volume is accompanied by liquefaction of the gas. The pressure remains constant until all of the gas has been converted to liquid. A liquid is very nearly incompressible, so the last part of the curve, *DE*, which represents the very small change in the volume of the liquid as the pressure is increased, rises almost vertically. At higher temperatures, greater pressures are required to cause the gas to liquefy. At these higher pressures the difference between the volume of the gas and that of the liquid becomes less, and the ends of the horizontal portion of the curve *BD* approach one another along the curve *FCG*, finally meeting at *C*. Point *C* is called the ***critical point.*** The pressure at the critical point is the ***critical pressure;*** the temperature is the ***critical temperature.*** The values of its critical constants are characteristic physical properties of each gas.

There is no sharp demarcation between gas and liquid at the critical point. Their densities are the same, and they are, for all practical purposes, indistinguishable. A gas cannot be liquefied above its critical temperature. Below its critical temperature, it can be liquefied by the application of sufficient pressure. In Fig. 9.7 the region above and to the right of curve II corresponds to temperatures above the critical temperature. The shaded region on the left corresponds to conditions of P, V, and T under which the substance can exist only as a liquid. Only under those conditions described by the region under curve *FCG* can both liquid and vapor be present simultaneously in equilibrium with one another.

A gas which is below its critical temperature is often called a ***vapor.*** Gases such as CO_2, NH_3, and HCl have critical temperatures above ordinary room temperature. When compressed into a gas tank or cylinder, therefore, they liquefy, and the conditions within the cylinder are described by some point under the curve *FCG*. If gas is drawn from the cylinder, the pressure within remains constant until all the liquid has evaporated. The cylinder pressure therefore offers no information regarding the amount of gas remaining. Gases such as H_2, N_2, and He have critical temperatures far below room temperature and are known as ***permanent gases.*** At ordinary temperatures, a cylinder of one of these substances contains only gas, and the pressure within the cylinder is almost exactly proportional to the amount of gas it contains. Thus if a full tank of nitrogen were under a pressure of 1600 $lb/in.^2$, a reading of 400 $lb/in.^2$ after the tank had been used would mean that 25% of the gas remained.

The critical constants for a number of gases, together with their molar volumes at standard conditions, are given in Table 9.3. Note that the gases with the highest critical temperatures have the smallest molar volumes. This is to be expected, since the attractive forces which are responsible for a gas having a smaller than calculated volume at low temperatures are also those which determine the critical temperature. The greater the intermolecular attractions, the more compressible the gas should be at low temperatures and the higher will be its critical temperature. A comparison of Table 9.3 and Fig. 9.8 will show this to be the case.

TABLE 9.3 Critical Constants and Molar Volumes of Gases

Gas	T_c (°C)	P_c (atm)	Molar Volume (liters) at STP
He	−267.9	2.26	22.43
H_2	−239.9	12.8	22.43
Ne	−228.7	25.9	22.41
N_2	−147.1	33.5	22.40
CO	−139	35	22.40
O_2	−118.8	49.7	22.39
CH_4	−82.5	45.8	22.38
CO_2	31.1	73.0	22.26
HCl	51.4	81.6	22.24
H_2S	100.4	88.9	22.14
NH_3	132.4	111.5	22.09
Cl_2	144	76.1	22.06

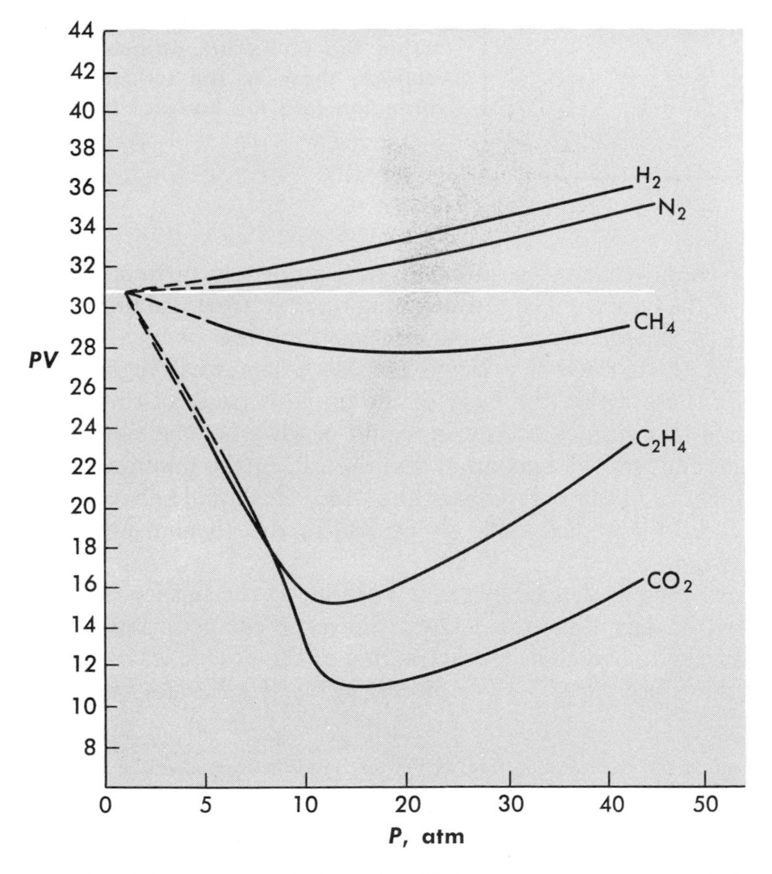

Fig. 9.8 Plots of PV against P for various gases at 50°C.

9.4 The Liquid State

Molecules of a liquid, like those of a gas, are in constant motion, and at the same temperature the average kinetic energies of gas and liquid molecules are the same. Unlike those of a gas, however, the molecules of a liquid are all very nearly touching one another, and their motion accordingly is much more restricted. Diffusion is therefore much slower in a liquid than it is in a gas. Because so little of its volume is empty space, a liquid is virtually incompressible and its volume is affected comparatively little by changes in pressure or temperature.

A molecule within the body of a liquid is surrounded by other molecules and attracted by them more or less equally in all directions (Fig. 9.9). It is under no compulsion to move in any particular direction, and its motion is almost completely random. The situation is quite different at the surface of the liquid. A molecule at the surface is not completely surrounded by other molecules of the liquid. The forces acting upon it are unbalanced, with the result that it experiences a net attraction into the body of the liquid. Molecules at the surface of a liquid possess a somewhat higher potential energy than those within the body of the liquid because of this attraction. To minimize this surface energy, a liquid tends where possible toward a shape which encloses the maximum volume within the minimum surface—ideally, a sphere. The result is that the surface of a liquid behaves as though it were a tightly stretched skin, giving rise to the phenomenon known as ***surface tension.***

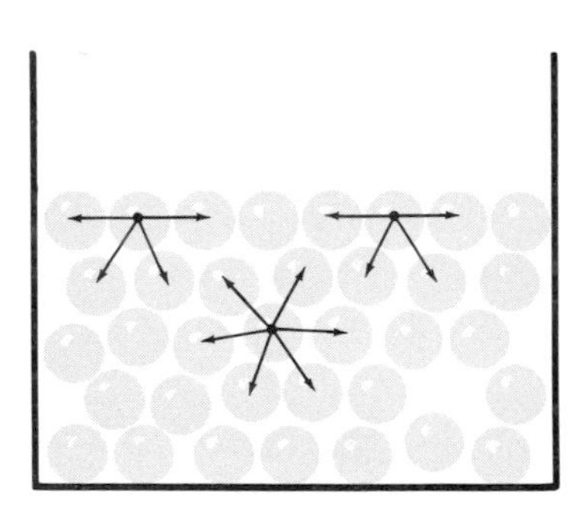

Fig. 9.9 Surface tension. Molecules within the liquid are attracted in all directions; those at the surface feel a net attraction into the body of the liquid.

Because of the unbalanced forces, a molecule at the surface is not equally free to move in any direction. Only the most energetic molecules have sufficient energy to overcome the attraction of the others, leave the surface, and enter the vapor phase.* *The process by which molecules leave the liquid*

* A ***phase*** is a homogeneous portion of matter, uniform throughout in chemical composition and physical state. It need not be a pure substance—a solution, for example, is a single liquid phase. A phase may be subdivided without creating new phases—a spoonful of sugar is a single solid phase. A glass of soda and ice contains three phases: solid (ice), liquid (soda), and gas (CO_2). An added scoop of ice cream, assuming it to be homogeneous, would be a fourth phase.

and enter the vapor state is called ***evaporation.*** Since the less energetic molecules are left behind during evaporation, the temperature of the remaining liquid will decrease unless heat is added from another source. The cooling effect of evaporation is familiar to everyone. In warm weather we perspire freely, and the moisture on the skin carries away excess heat as it evaporates. In cooler weather, when heat must be conserved, we perspire less, and in this way body temperature is maintained within safe limits.

The amount of energy required to maintain 1 g of a liquid at a constant temperature during evaporation is called the ***heat of vaporization.*** The heat of vaporization is characteristic of the particular liquid and varies somewhat with temperature. The heat of vaporization of water at various temperatures is given in Table 9.4.

TABLE 9.4 Heat of Vaporization of Water at Various Temperatures

Temperature, °C	0	20	40	60	80	100
Heat of Vaporization, cal/g	595.4	584.9	574.2	562.8	555.1	538.7

If heat is added to an evaporating liquid at a faster rate than it is removed by the molecules entering the vapor state, the temperature of the liquid rises, and at the same time the rate of evaporation increases. Eventually a point is reached at which evaporation occurs within the body of the liquid as well as at the surface, and the liquid is said to boil. Addition of more heat to a boiling liquid increases the rate of evaporation, but does not cause any further rise in temperature.

Vapor Pressure 9.5

A liquid placed in an open container will continue to evaporate until all of it is converted to vapor. In a closed container, evaporation proceeds to a limited degree, after which there is no further apparent change. There is a simple explanation for this. In a closed container, the partial pressure of the vapor, which depends upon the number of vapor molecules in the available volume, increases as the liquid evaporates. An increase in the partial pressure means that the vapor molecules are colliding more frequently with all of the surfaces surrounding the vapor, including the surface of the liquid. Each time a vapor molecule strikes the surface of the liquid, the likelihood is that it will stay there and re-enter the liquid phase. A state is soon reached in which the rate at which the molecules return to the liquid is equal to the rate at which they evaporate. *With two opposing processes occurring at the same rate, the system is now in a state of* ***dynamic equilibrium.*** This is shown diagrammatically in Fig. 9.10. *The partial pressure of a vapor in dynamic equilibrium with the liquid is known as the **vapor pressure** of the liquid.* A simple way to measure the vapor pressure of a liquid at room temperature is to introduce a small quantity of the liquid above the mercury in a barometer tube (Fig. 9.11). The liquid evaporates into the vacuum above the mercury, and the pressure of its vapor forces the mercury level downward. Provided that a small amount of liquid remains so that equilibrium is

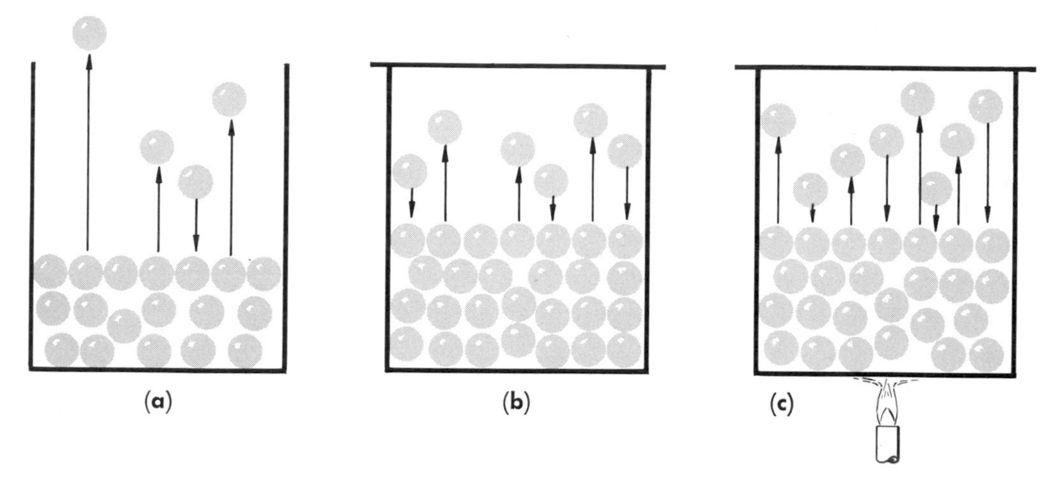

Fig. 9.10 Vapor pressure. (a) Open container: rate of evaporation > rate of condensation, equilibrium not attainable. (b) Closed container: rate of evaporation = rate of condensation, system in dynamic equilibrium. (c) Closed container at higher temperature than at (b); rate of evaporation = rate of condensation, but both greater than in (b). Vapor pressure increased.

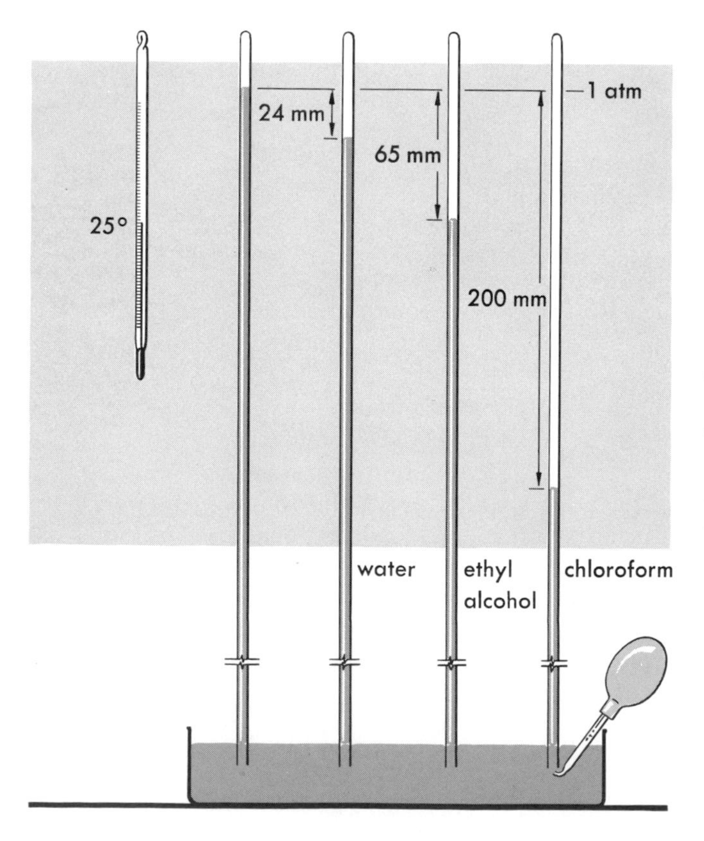

Fig. 9.11 Measurement of the vapor pressures of water, ethyl alcohol, and chloroform at 25°C. The weight of the small amount of liquid floating on the mercury in each tube introduces a negligible error into the observed depression of the mercury level.

attained, the depression of the mercury column will be equal to the vapor pressure of the liquid in torr.*

The vapor pressure of a liquid is determined by the attractive forces within the liquid and by the average kinetic energy of the molecules, and it is unaffected by the presence of other gases or vapors. Whether the liquid evaporates into a vacuum, or into another gas such as the atmosphere, its vapor pressure at a given temperature remains the same. The partial pressure of a gas confined over a liquid is therefore equal to the total pressure less the vapor pressure of the liquid. We have already made use of this principle in calculating the dry volume of a gas collected over water (Sec. 3.5).

The greater the rate of evaporation, the greater will be the pressure of the vapor when equilibrium is attained. Increasing the temperature raises the average kinetic energy and increases the number of molecules which possess the energy needed to evaporate. The vapor pressure of a substance therefore always increases with temperature (Fig. 9.12). A plot of vapor pressure

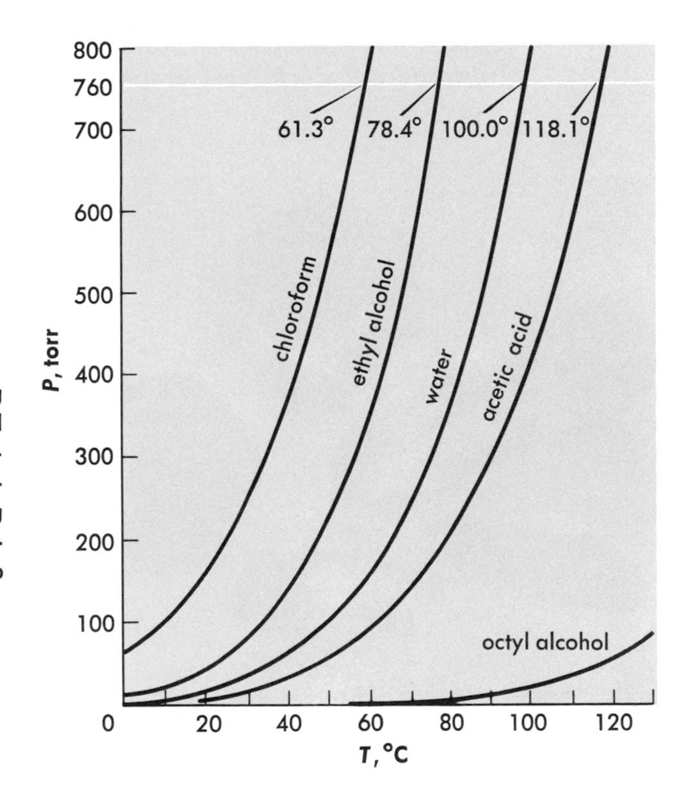

Fig. 9.12 Curves showing the vapor pressures of several substances at various temperatures. The temperatures indicated are the normal boiling points at which the vapor pressures of the liquids are equal to 1 atm (760 torr).

against temperature is a curve which rises more and more steeply, terminating at the critical point, at which all of the molecules have sufficient energy to overcome the intermolecular attractions in the liquid.

* The weight of the liquid floating on its surface also contributes to the force pushing the level of the mercury downward, but if only a drop of liquid is present, and the density of the liquid is low, its contribution is negligible.

Whenever the vapor pressure of a liquid is equal to the external pressure on its surface, the liquid boils (Sec. 9.4). The ***normal boiling point*** *is defined as the temperature at which the vapor pressure of the liquid is 1 atm.* A liquid can be made to boil at a lower temperature by lowering the pressure. Advantage is often taken of this in the laboratory. By lowering the pressure, an unstable compound, which might otherwise decompose at its normal boiling point, may be safely distilled, or a compound with a very high boiling point at a pressure of 1 atm may be distilled at a more convenient temperature. For example, octyl alcohol, which has a normal boiling point of 195°, will boil at 115° when the pressure has been reduced to 40 torr (Fig. 9.12).

9.6 Solids

In distinguishing a true solid from a liquid, far more important than rigidity is the property of ***crystallinity.*** Examination of a solid such as salt or sugar shows it to be composed of crystals of regular and characteristic shape. The exterior of a crystal consists of a number of flat surfaces, or ***crystal faces,*** which meet at definite angles (Fig. 9.13). The angles are

Fig. 9.13 Photograph of some well-formed natural crystals. Clockwise, starting in foreground: calcite (Iceland spar, $CaCO_3$), two pieces of quartz (rock crystal, SiO_2), halite (rock salt, NaCl), and iron pyrite ("fool's gold," FeS_2).

always exactly the same between corresponding faces of different crystals of a given substance formed under similar conditions. These ***interfacial angles*** are characteristic physical properties of the substance and can, in fact, be used for its identification. A crystal may be cut or ground to give flat or curved surfaces at any angle, but when broken, it will cleave along natural ***cleavage planes*** parallel to the faces of the original crystal (Fig. 9.14). In addition, although there is an almost limitless number of substances which form crystals, every crystal is found to belong to one of six major crystal systems, based upon its having one of a limited number of possible geometric shapes.

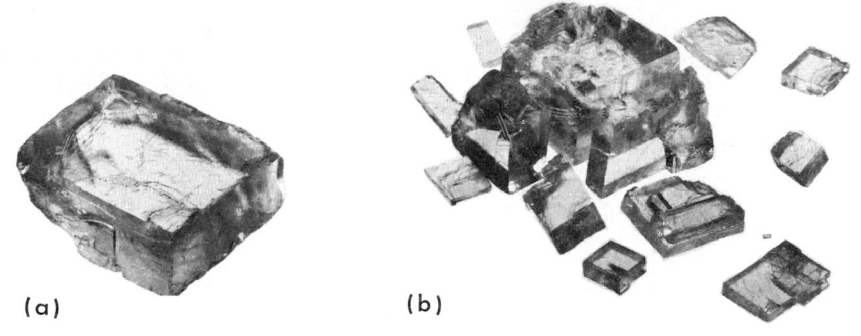

Fig. 9.14 Calcite crystal (a) before cleavage and (b) after being shattered by a sharp blow.

The Crystal Lattice 9.7

As early as 1784, R. J. Haüy recognized that the observed regularity in crystal form must arise from a regularity in the arrangement of the fundamental units of which crystals are composed. It is this internal order, more than anything else, which distinguishes a true solid from a liquid. Amorphous, apparent solids, such as glasses and certain plastics, have rigidity but do not possess internal order and lack crystallinity. They may be thought of more as liquids with very high viscosity (resistance to flow) than as true solids. The fundamental units of a crystal, which may be atoms, molecules, or ions, are not free to move from place to place, but vibrate about fixed points in the crystal. These points create a three-dimensional pattern, or ***crystal lattice,*** and are therefore called ***lattice points*** (Fig. 9.15).*

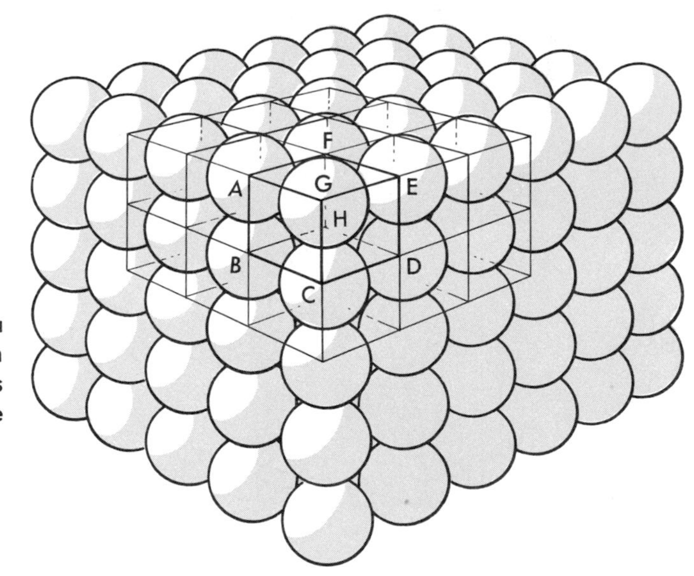

Fig. 9.15 Structure of a simple crystal showing a portion of the crystal lattice. Points *A-H* are lattice points at the corners of a unit cell.

* Often, in real crystals, a few of the lattice points will be unoccupied. An ion or molecule may in some cases migrate from an adjacent lattice point to the unoccupied one. This very restricted motion permits a certain amount of slow diffusion within the crystal, but its crystalline form is retained at all times.

The lattice is seen to be composed of *basic repeating units*, or ***unit cells***, *by whose repetition the entire crystal lattice may be generated.* This is similar to the repetition of a simple unit of design in a wallpaper pattern, but repeating in three dimensions (Fig. 9.16).

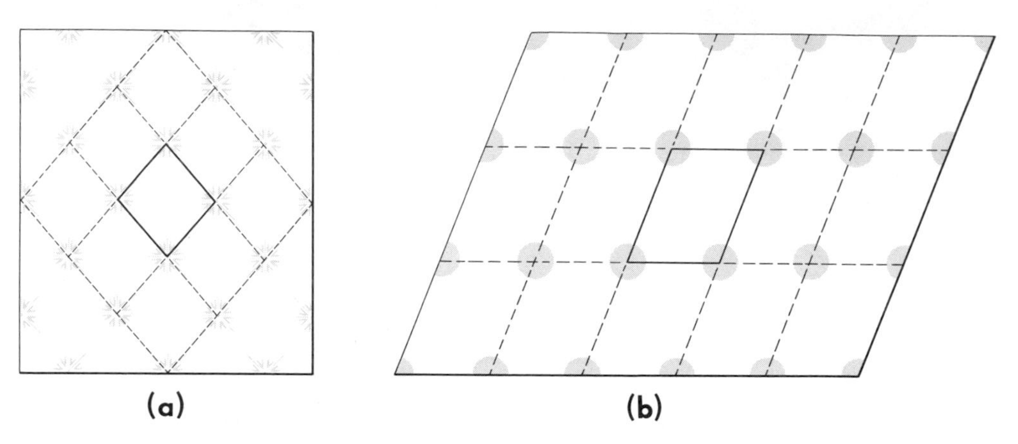

Fig. 9.16 Unit cells in two dimensions: (a) wallpaper; (b) cross section of crystal lattice.

9.8 Crystal Systems

The size and shape of the unit cell is fully described in terms of three major axes, the length of the unit cell along each axis, and the angles between the axes (Fig. 9.17). When these lengths and angles are specified, six possi-

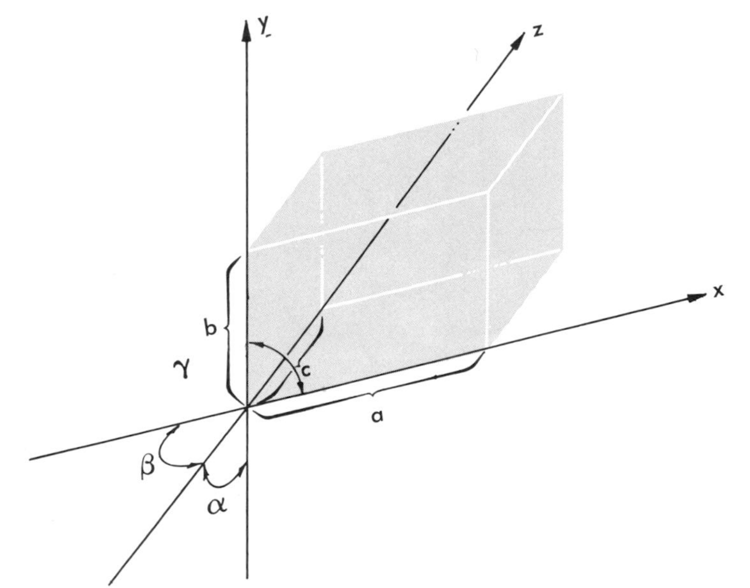

Fig. 9.17 Unit cell: x, y, and z are the major crystal axes which intersect at angles α, β, and γ; a, b, and c are the unit distances determined by the size of the unit cell.

bilities result, according to whether or not the unit lengths are equal, and whether or not the angles are 90°. These are the six ***major crystal systems:***

Cubic (isometric) System:

$a = b = c$

$\alpha = \beta = \gamma = 90°$

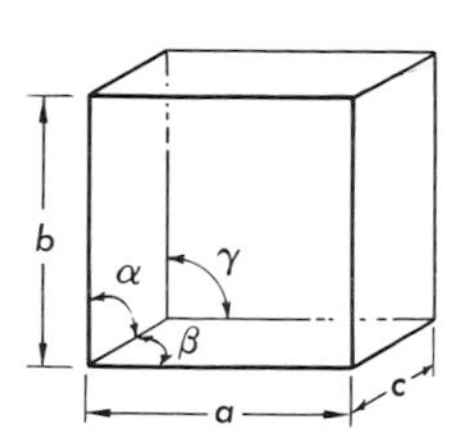

Tetragonal System:

$a = b \neq c$

$\alpha = \beta = \gamma = 90°$

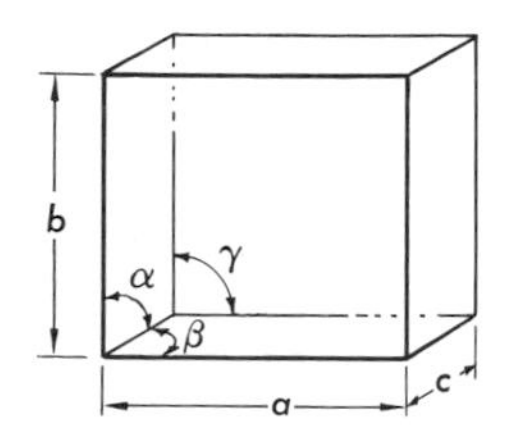

Orthorhombic System:

$a \neq b \neq c$

$\alpha = \beta = \gamma = 90°$

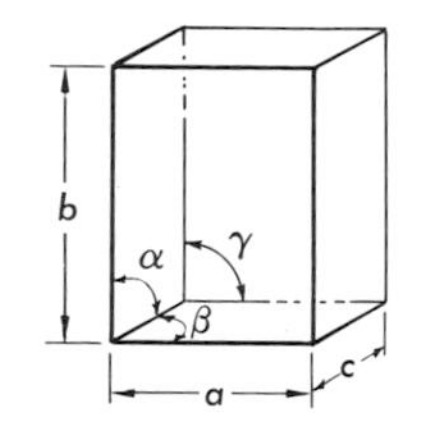

Monoclinic System:

$a \neq b \neq c$

$\alpha = \beta = 90°; \gamma \neq 90°$

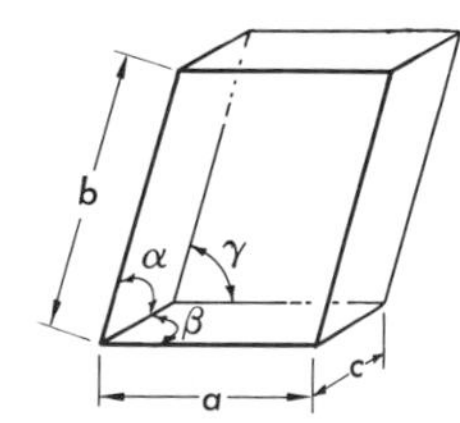

Triclinic System:

$a \neq b \neq c$

$\alpha \neq \beta \neq \gamma \neq 90°$

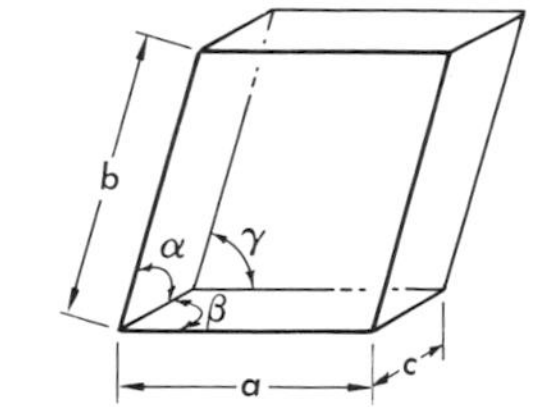

Hexagonal System:

$a = b \neq c$

$\alpha = \beta = 90°; \gamma = 120°$

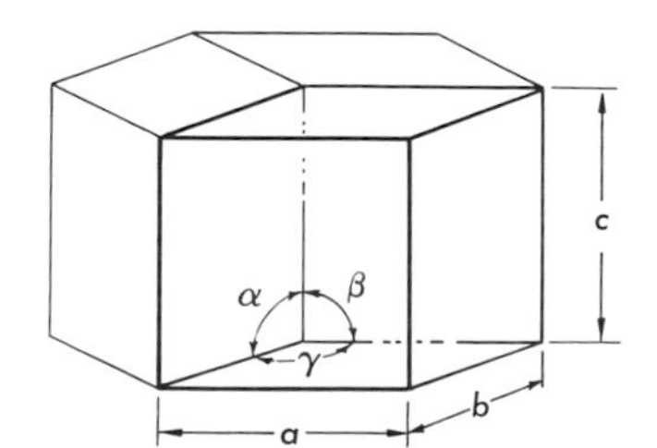

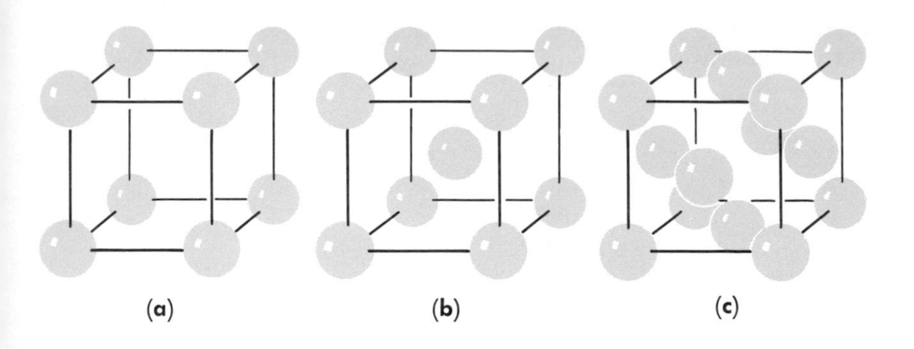

Fig. 9.18 Cubic lattices: (a) simple, or primitive; (b) body-centered; (c) face-centered.

If the atoms or molecules of the substance occupy only the lattice points at the corners of the unit cells, the crystal lattice is said to be *simple*, or *primitive*. The geometric centers of the unit cells are occupied in a *body-centered* lattice. If the centers of the unit cell faces are occupied, the lattice is *face centered*. Diagrams of the three types of lattices are shown for the cubic system in Fig. 9.18.

9.9 Lattice Planes

The lattice points in a crystal are arranged in layers. *A plane drawn through the crystal connecting all of the lattice points in one of these layers is a* ***lattice plane.*** Numerous lattice planes may be drawn through a crystal, but only at certain definite, characteristic angles which depend upon the dimensions of the unit cell (Fig. 9.19). Any one of these planes may serve as a crystal face, and in fact, each face of the crystal must lie along some one

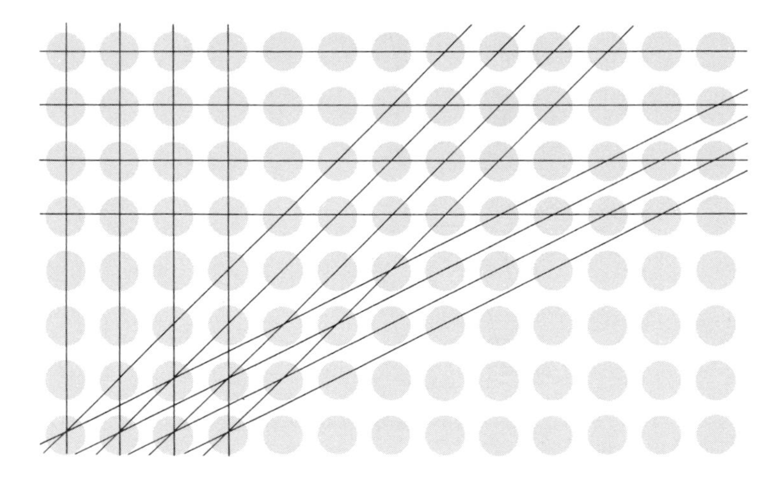

Fig. 9.19 Lattice planes. The layer of atoms shown is one lattice plane. Lines may be drawn connecting the atoms in this plane. These lines meet at very definite angles, the values of which are determined by the unit cell dimensions. If extended through the crystal, each of these lines defines a lattice plane.

of the possible lattice planes. The characteristic interfacial angles and cleavage planes of a crystal (Sec. 9.6) are a consequence of this requirement. Conditions during the formation of a crystal will generally favor the development of faces along certain of the lattice planes, and this will be reflected in the final shape of the crystal. The crystal shape is thus determined by, but is not necessarily the same as, the shape of the unit cell (Fig. 9.20).

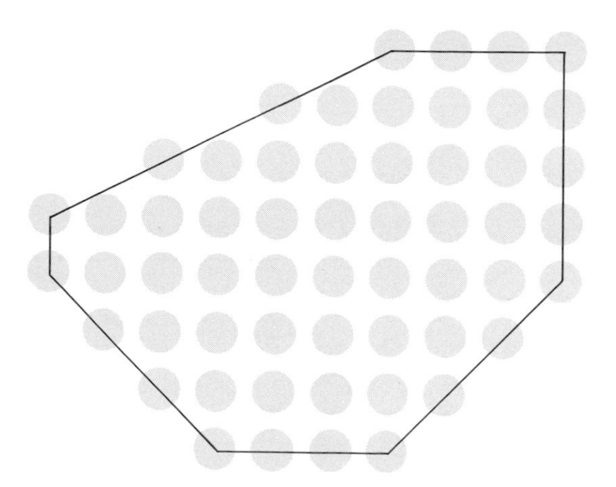

Fig. 9.20 Crystal shape. Each crystal face lies along a lattice plane. The shape of the crystal depends upon the shape of the unit cell, but it is not necessarily the same as that of the unit cell.

The distances between the various lattice planes in the crystal may be determined by taking advantage of their ability to reflect X-rays. When a beam of X-rays of a single wavelength strikes the surface of a crystal, part of the beam is reflected from the top layer of molecules or ions, while part penetrates the surface and is reflected from the next layer. After reflection, the part of the beam which has penetrated the surface has traveled a greater distance than that reflected from the top layer. Only if this additional distance traveled is equal to some whole number of wavelengths will the two parts of the beam remain in phase after reflection. If the beams remain in phase, with the crests and troughs coinciding, a strong reflection is observed as a result of constructive interference (Sec. 7.9). If the beams are out of phase, the result is destructive interference, and weak reflection or none at all (Fig. 9.21).

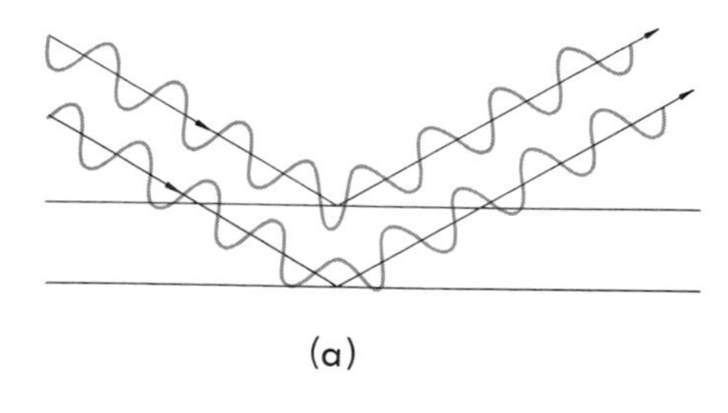

(a)

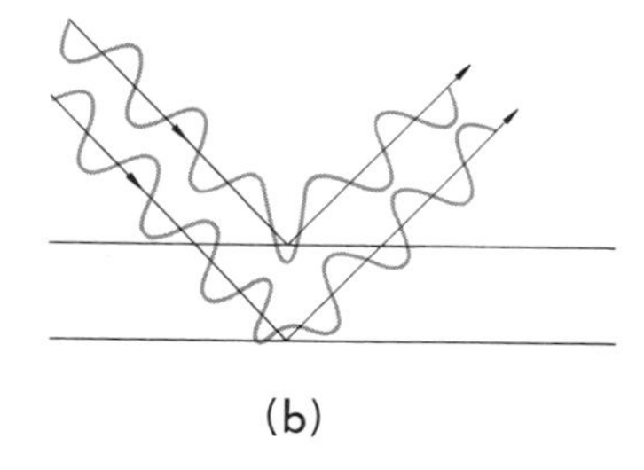

(b)

Fig. 9.21 Reflection of X-rays by crystal lattice planes; (a) strong reflection, beam in phase; (b) weak reflection, beam out of phase.

A simple relationship exists among the wavelength of the X-rays λ, the angle of reflection θ, and the interplanar distance d (Fig. 9.22). When conditions are right for a strong reflection,

$$AO + OB = \mathbf{n}\lambda$$

where $\mathbf{n} = 1, 2, 3 \ldots$

$$\sin \theta = \frac{AO}{d}$$

Since $AO = OB$

$$\mathbf{n}\lambda = 2d \sin \theta$$

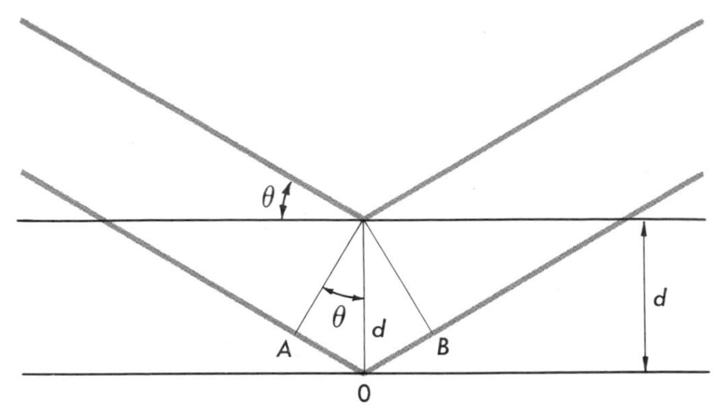

Fig. 9.22 Determination of interplanar distance in a crystal.

This relationship is known as the ***Bragg equation,*** named for W. H. Bragg and his son, W. L. Bragg, who developed this method of crystal structural analysis. For each interplanar distance there will be several angles θ, corresponding to different values for $\mathbf{n}$, at which reflection will occur. The integer $\mathbf{n}$ is known as the ***order of reflection.*** Assignment of the proper value to $\mathbf{n}$ is usually not difficult. In most cases the first-order reflections are the most intense. Where any doubt exists, the Bragg equation is solved for reflections of different order from the same set of planes. If the correct values are chosen for $\mathbf{n}$, the same interplanar distance will be obtained in each case.

One way to measure θ experimentally is to mount the crystal on a rotating holder at the center of a circular camera (Fig. 9.23). The crystal is rotated

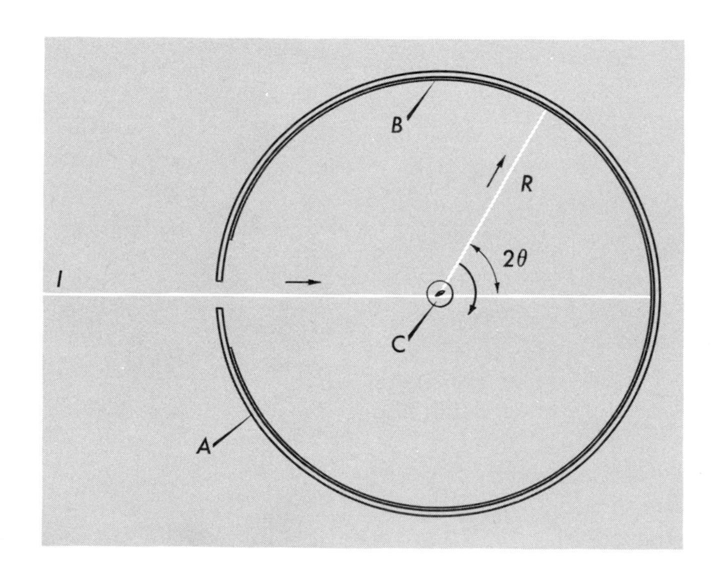

Fig. 9.23 Camera for X-ray crystal analysis. A, circular camera; B, photographic film; C, rotating crystal mount; I, incident ray; R, reflected ray.

in the X-ray beam, and each time a set of lattice planes is in the correct orientation to satisfy the Bragg relationship, a reflected beam shoots out, making a spot on the film. From the dimensions of the camera and the positions of the spots on the developed film, the Bragg angles θ can be derived and from them the internal dimensions of the crystal.

The molecules or atoms in the interior of a crystal continue to oscillate about their average lattice positions as the temperature is increased, but their oscillations become progressively more violent. Finally, a temperature is reached at which the motion of the molecules or atoms is so violent that the orderly arrangement characteristic of a crystal is lost, and the substance becomes a liquid. The molecules of a pure substance are either arranged in orderly fashion or they are not, so that the melting of a pure solid occurs sharply and at a precise temperature: the ***melting point.*** The melting point is affected to some degree by the pressure, but not usually to the same extent as is the boiling point, and not always in the same manner. Where the density of the liquid at the melting point is less than that of the solid, as is usually the case, the melting point is found to rise with increasing pressure. In some cases, most notably water, the density of the liquid is greater than that of the solid, and therefore increasing the pressure lowers the melting point.

During the melting of a solid the temperature remains constant at the melting point until all of the solid has liquefied. Any energy added to the system at this point goes not to raise the temperature but to melt more of the solid. *The melting of a substance at constant temperature is accompanied by absorption of the* ***heat of fusion.*** For water at its melting point (0°C at 1 atm), the heat of fusion is about 79 cal/g.

Theoretically, the melting of a solid should be a completely reversible process, and the liquid, upon cooling, should solidify at the same temperature at which the solid melts. In fact, most pure liquids can be "supercooled" to temperatures considerably below their normal melting points without solidifying. Shaking the supercooled liquid, adding a bit of foreign matter or a crystal of the solid, or otherwise disturbing the liquid will usually induce crystallization. At the same time, the release of the heat of fusion during crystallization causes the temperature to rise to the melting point, where it remains until all of the liquid has solidified (Fig. 9.24).

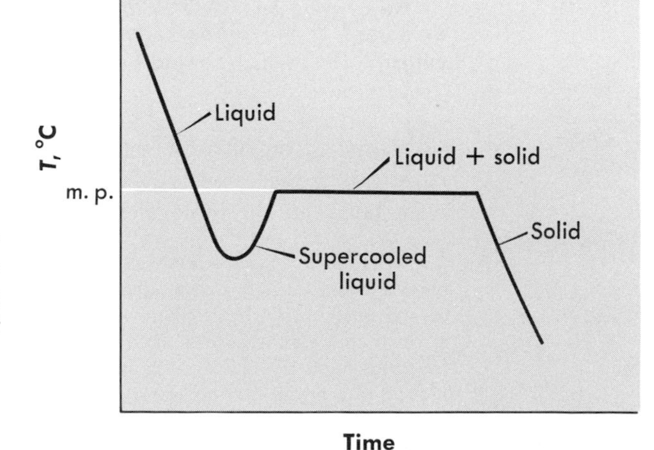

Fig. 9.24 Time-temperature cooling curve for a substance which exhibits supercooling. Heat is being removed from the system at a constant rate throughout.

The phenomenon of supercooling arises from the fact that, in order to solidify, not only must the kinetic energy of the molecules be lowered sufficiently, but the molecules must also arrange themselves in the unique, orderly pattern typical of the crystal. This is often difficult unless some matrix is present to attract and hold a few of the slower-moving molecules and form a nucleus for further crystal growth. The best matrix for this purpose is the surface of a crystal of the solid in which the molecules are already properly arranged, although often a speck of dust or glass, the surface of a small air bubble, or a crystal of some other substance will serve the purpose.*

It should not be surprising to find that substances with large, complex, or irregularly shaped molecules are most prone to supercooling. These molecules must not only be placed at the lattice points of the crystal, but must also be very precisely oriented in order to fit together. The more "knobs" there are on the molecule, the harder it will be to arrange them just right (Fig. 9.25).

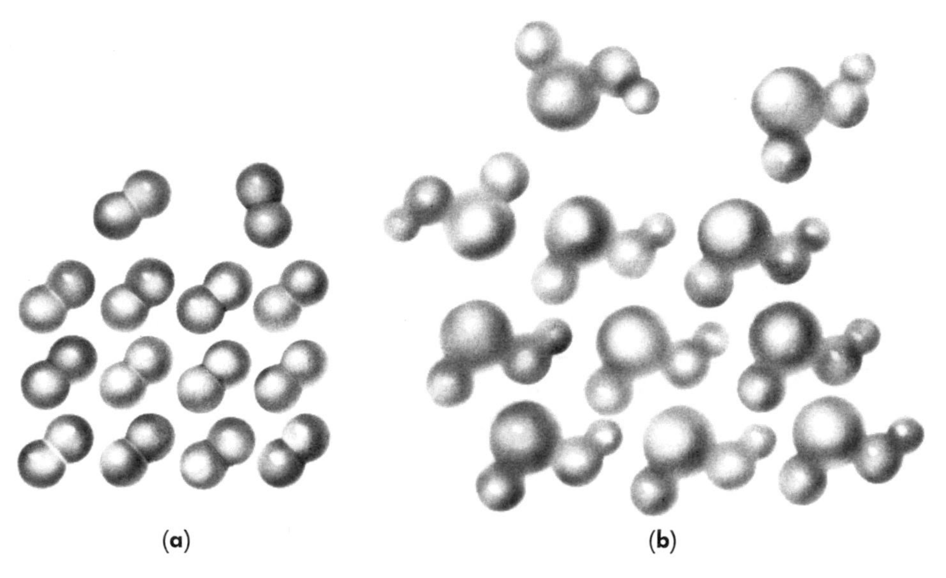

Fig. 9.25 Crystallization. The simple molecules in (a) are more readily arranged in the proper orientation for crystallization than the complex molecules in (b), which should be more prone to supercooling.

Evaporation of most solids is imperceptible at ordinary room temperature, but some, especially those in which only weak van der Waals forces exist between the molecules, exhibit appreciable vapor pressures. As in a

* It is not uncommon, among organic chemists especially, to find that a certain substance may crystallize easily in one laboratory and not in another because of the presence of tiny crystal nuclei in the atmosphere of one laboratory which are absent in the other. Each time an intractable substance is crystallized in a particular laboratory it usually becomes that much easier to crystallize it the next time. The authors know of one chemist who, before he moved to a brand new laboratory in a new building "preseasoned" it by spraying the room liberally with a solution of most of the chemicals from his old laboratory, which had been well broken in through many years of use.

liquid, the attraction of the other molecules may sometimes be insufficient to prevent a more energetic molecule at the surface from passing into the vapor state. *The passage of molecules directly from the solid to the vapor state without liquefaction is called* ***sublimation.*** The partial pressure of the vapor in equilibrium with the solid is the vapor pressure of the solid. The vapor pressure of a solid increases with temperature in the same manner as does the vapor pressure of a liquid, and for the same reason: at higher temperatures a larger fraction of the molecules possess enough energy to overcome the attractive forces at the surface of the crystal.

The vapor pressures of some substances reach one atmosphere at temperatures below the normal melting points of the solids. When crystals of these substances are heated, they pass directly into the vapor state without melting. The temperature rises to the sublimation temperature—the temperature at which the vapor pressure of the solid is 1 atm—and then remains constant until all of the solid has been converted to vapor. Cooling the vapors redeposits the solid, often as very pure, well-formed crystals. Best known of the solids whose sublimation temperatures lie below their melting points is solid carbon dioxide, or Dry Ice, which has a vapor pressure of 1 atm at $-78.2°C$. Many solids with relatively low vapor pressures can be readily sublimed by lowering the external pressure, much as a liquid can be boiled at low temperature under reduced pressure (Sec. 9.5). High-melting solids are often freed of nonvolatile impurities by this process of *vacuum sublimation.*

Phase Diagrams 9.11

A plot of the conditions of pressure and temperature under which two or more physical states of a substance can exist in dynamic equilibrium is known as a ***phase diagram.*** A typical phase diagram, showing the conditions of equilibrium among the solid, liquid, and vapor states, will look about like Fig. 9.26. The diagram is seen to be divided into three regions, which correspond to

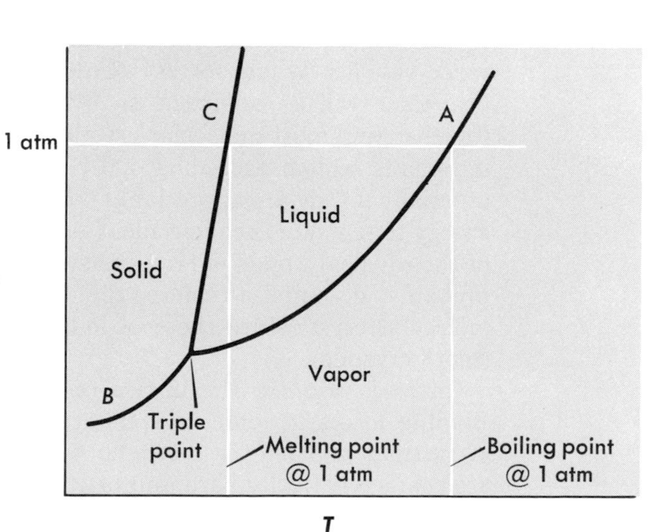

Fig. 9.26 Typical phase diagram.

the three physical states. Under any set of conditions which fall within one of these three regions, the substance will exist at equilibrium only in the corresponding physical state. The boundaries separating the regions represent those conditions under which two physical states of the substance can exist in equilibrium with one another. Curve A will be recognized as the vapor pressure curve for the liquid; curve B is the vapor pressure curve for the solid. At points along C, solid and liquid are in equilibrium in the absence of vapor. Where the three curves meet is known as the ***triple point.*** *At the triple point, and only at that point, all three phases, solid, liquid, and vapor, can exist simultaneously in a state of dynamic equilibrium*—that is, only at the triple point can the processes of melting and solidification, evaporation and condensation all take place at the same time and at the same rate. The normal melting or freezing point is defined at 1 atm as shown on the diagram, and does not coincide with the triple point, although the difference in the two temperatures is usually small. It will be noted that under conditions wholly within one of the three regions, both pressure and temperature may be varied independently, within limits, without causing a change in state or disturbing the equilibrium. Along any of the three curves, A, B, or C, representing equilibrium between two phases, once either the pressure or temperature is specified, the other is automatically fixed if the equilibrium is to be maintained. Where three phases are in equilibrium—at the triple point—both temperature and pressure are fixed, and a change in either of these will result in a departure from equilibrium conditions.

9.12 Types of Crystals

Crystals may be classified as *molecular*, *ionic*, *covalent*, or *metallic*, according to the nature of the fundamental units occupying the lattice points and the forces which bind them together in the crystal.

The lattice points in *molecular crystals* are occupied by *molecules*. The atoms within the molecules are joined by covalent bonds, but the molecules themselves are bound to one another within the crystal only by relatively weak van der Waals forces. Unless the molecules are very large, a few kcal/mole will be sufficient to overcome the forces holding the crystal together, and most molecular crystals are soft and easily broken, with melting points seldom exceeding 300°C. If the molecules are very large, and especially if they are appreciably polar as well, it may take as much or more energy to separate the molecules from one another as it would to break some of the covalent bonds joining the atoms. In that event, the substance will probably decompose before the crystal melts. Familiar examples of molecular crystals are those of iodine (Fig. 9.27), sugar, and naphthalene (moth crystals).

In *ionic crystals*, the lattice points are occupied by *ions* (Fig. 9.28). Binding forces in ionic crystals are ionic bonds—the strong electrostatic attractions which exist between oppositely charged ions. Ionic crystals are characteristically hard and brittle, with melting points usually in excess of 600°C.

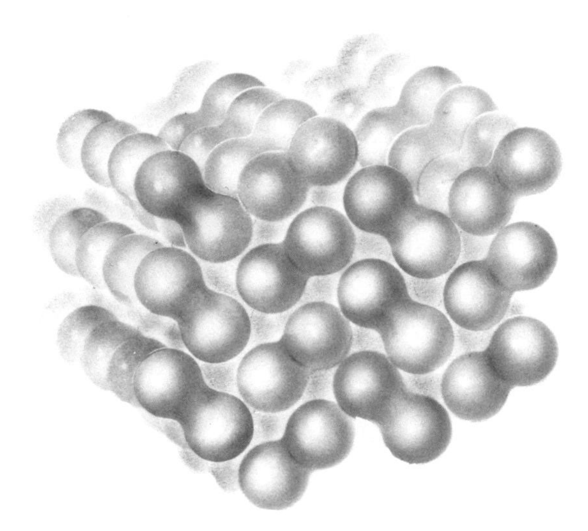

Fig. 9.27 Structure of an iodine crystal.

Fig. 9.28 Sodium chloride crystal lattice.

All of the atoms of a *covalent crystal* are bound to one another by *covalent bonds*, making the entire crystal a single macromolecule. Since covalent bond energies are usually of the order of 40 to 100 kcal/mole, the total binding energy in a covalent crystal is very large, and very high melting points are the rule. The enormous difference between the melting points of carbon dioxide ($-56.6°$ at 5.2 atm) and of silicon dioxide (1610°C at 1 atm) results from the different nature of the crystals. Solid carbon dioxide is a molecular crystal composed of individual CO_2 molecules. In the covalent silicon dioxide crystal, each silicon atom is bound to four oxygen atoms by covalent bonds to form an extended three-dimensional network (Fig. 9.29). The formula SiO_2 represents merely the atomic ratio; no individual molecules with this formula are present in the crystal.

In a *metallic crystal*, the lattice points are occupied by *atoms*. Bonding is uniform throughout the crystal and is of a type known as ***metallic bonding***. The electrons that participate in metallic bonding are not localized, as they would be, for example, in a typical covalent bond, but apparently they are able to move easily from one atom to another throughout the crystal. This

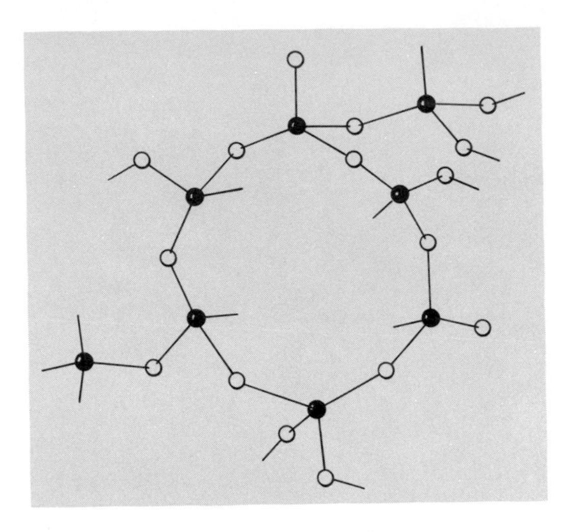

Fig. 9.29 Portion of the SiO_2 crystal lattice.

is evident from the good electrical conductivity typical of metals, a property not shared by molecular, ionic, or covalent crystals. Metallic and covalent bonding are related inasmuch as both can be considered to arise from the overlapping of atomic orbitals, but metallic bonding is sufficiently unique to warrant further discussion in the next section.

9.13 Bonding in Metals

Metals form crystals in which the atoms typically are arranged in a face-centered cubic, hexagonal close-packed, or body-centered cubic array. The face-centered cubic and hexagonal close-packed lattices correspond to the closest possible packing of identical spheres (like a pile of cannon balls alongside a monument), and in them each metal atom is surrounded by 12 nearest neighbors (Fig. 9.30). In the body-centered cubic lattice, each atom is surrounded by 14 others: eight nearest neighbors at the corners of the unit cell, and six others only slightly farther away (Fig. 9.31). Consideration of their electronic configurations makes it clear that none of the metals has sufficient valence electrons to form 12 or 14 ordinary covalent bonds. We have a real problem, for example, in trying to account for the fact that lithium, with only one valence electron per atom, nevertheless crystallizes in a body-centered cubic lattice in which each atom is bound tightly enough to 14 other atoms to give the crystal a melting point of 186°C.

We might expect an atom of lithium to use its one valence electron to form a single covalent bond with one other atom:

$$\mathrm{Li}\cdot + \cdot\mathrm{Li} \rightarrow \mathrm{Li} : \mathrm{Li}$$

and Li_2 molecules do appear to exist in the gaseous state. In the solid, however, the 2*s* orbital containing the valence electron of each atom overlaps with the corresponding orbitals of all of the atoms adjacent to it. The result is a set of molecular orbitals embracing all of the atoms in the crystal.

You will recall from Chapter 8 that the interaction of two atomic orbitals

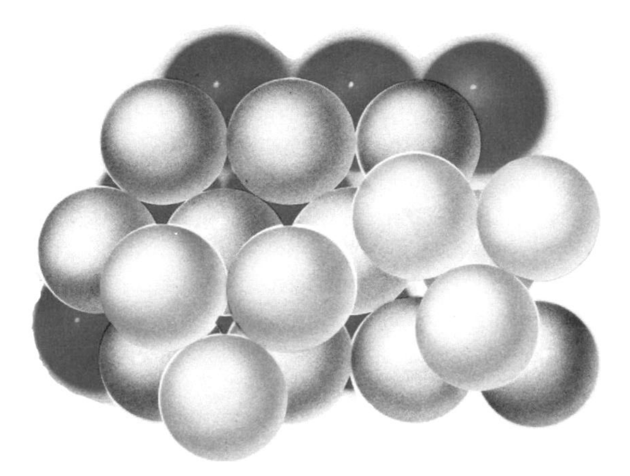

Fig. 9.30 Close packing of spheres. The atoms of the third layer may lie above the triangular spaces between the atoms of the first, as on the left side of the figure, resulting in an *abcabc* pattern and a face-centered cubic lattice. Alternatively, the atoms of the third layer may lie directly above those of the first, as on the right. The latter corresponds to an *ababab* pattern and a hexagonal close-packed lattice. In either pattern, each atom is surrounded by 12 equidistant nearest neighbors.

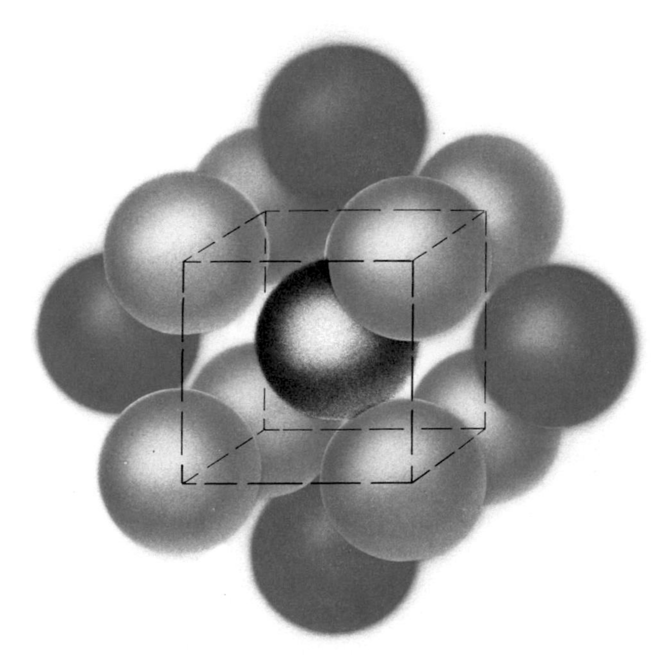

Fig. 9.31 Body-centered cubic lattice. The eight nearest neighbors (white) and four of the six next nearest neighbors (gray) to the central (black) atom are shown.

affords two molecular orbitals, one bonding and one antibonding, and that the result of the interaction of three AO's is three MO's. However many AO's are combined, the principle of ***orbital conservation*** is obeyed: if 2, 3, 4, . . . , n AO's interact, the result is 2, 3, 4, . . . , n MO's, no two of which will have exactly the same energy. If n is 10^{23}, for example, as it would be in a crystal of lithium containing 10^{23} atoms, the result will be a band of 10^{23} closely spaced energy levels. This is shown diagrammatically in Fig. 9.32. Each of these levels can hold two electrons, so the total capacity of a band consisting of 10^{23} levels is 2×10^{23} electrons. Only one electron is contributed by each lithium atom, so that ordinarily just the lower half of the energy band is occupied. The mutual attraction between the electrons in these occupied orbitals and the atoms at the lattice points serves to hold the crystal together.

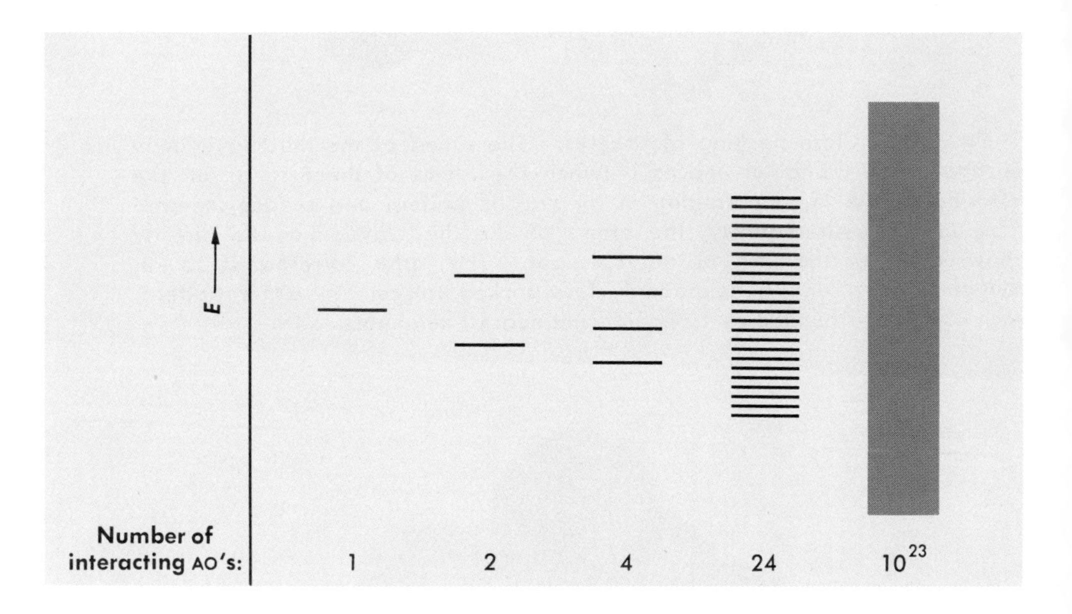

Fig. 9.32 Interaction of AO's to form MO's. When the number of interacting AO's is large, the energies of the resultant MO's are spread out to form a band of closely spaced levels.

The band picture of metallic crystals can account for the electrical conductivity of metals. Because the difference in energy between the highest occupied and lowest unoccupied levels is so small, hardly any energy is required to lift an electron into the lower levels of the otherwise empty portion of the band, which therefore probably always contains some electrons. A potential difference applied across the crystal will cause these electrons to move toward the region of lower potential. At the same time, other electrons can enter the vacancies left in the lower part of the band, and in this way a flow of electrons, or electrical current, can be maintained as long as a potential difference exists.

Electrons can also be excited into the upper portion of the band by the absorption of electromagnetic radiation, or light. Because the energy levels are so closely spaced, photons of nearly any energy, corresponding to almost all frequencies of light, can be absorbed and then re-emitted by the electrons responsible for metallic bonding. As a consequence, most metals have no color of their own, but faithfully reflect (absorb and re-emit) all colors of light, thus showing a typical metallic luster.

A metal such as magnesium with two valence electrons might be expected to be nonconducting, since interaction of the filled $3s$ valence orbitals will lead to a completely filled energy band. Evidently in this case the filled $3s$ band overlaps with the vacant band created by the interaction of the $3p$ orbitals to give a partially filled conduction band similar to that in lithium (Fig. 9.33).

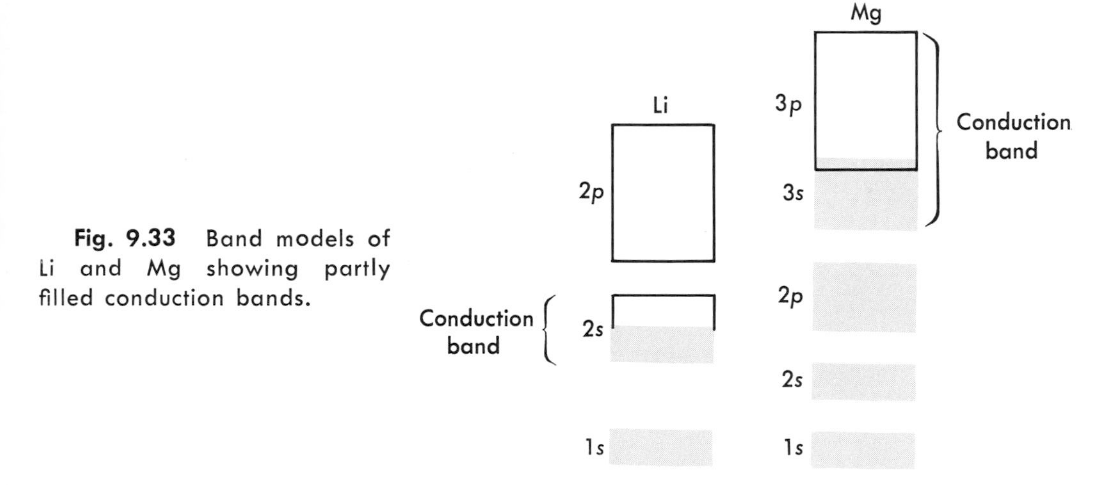

Fig. 9.33 Band models of Li and Mg showing partly filled conduction bands.

One may reasonably ask at this point why it is that hydrogen with its single valence electron does not form metallic crystals the same as lithium. A clue is afforded by the electronegativities of the elements. All the elements which we consider to be metals and which are known to form metallic crystals have relatively low electronegativities: generally less than 2.0 on the Pauling scale (Fig. 8.13). We might conclude that the electrons in a covalent bond between two atoms of low electronegativity—for example in a molecule of Li_2—would be loosely held, and not so rigidly confined to the region between the atomic nuclei as they would be if the electronegativity of the atoms were greater. The molecular orbital containing the electrons of the bond may be thought of as extending a greater distance from each atom on the side opposite the bond than would otherwise be the case. Another atom or molecule can therefore approach closely enough for the corresponding orbitals to interact before repulsion between the nuclei prevents the atoms from coming any closer to one another. A bonding MO between two more electronegative atoms such as hydrogen is more nearly restricted to the region between the atoms. Internuclear repulsion will prevent another atom from approaching close enough to permit any appreciable orbital interaction.

The foregoing seems to imply that if it were possible to force the molecules closer together the bonding in solid hydrogen might become metallic, and indeed this appears to be the case. Experimental evidence suggests that at extremely high pressures bonding in all solids tends to become metallic.

9.14 Water

The properties of water are so familiar to everyone that we are likely to be unaware of just how remarkable its properties actually are. Water is the closest thing we have to a universal solvent. No other substance that is liquid at ordinary temperatures can dissolve as great a variety of substances as water can. Water is essential to the existence of life as we know it, since all life processes take place in water solution. It is one of the very few substances which expand, rather than contract, upon freezing; that is, its density at the melting point is greater as a liquid than as a solid. As a result, ice floats on water, a fortunate occurrence, for otherwise lakes and rivers would freeze solid from the bottom up as soon as the temperature went below 0°C. Not only would this be a calamity for the fish, but even with all that ice, we could not go ice-skating.

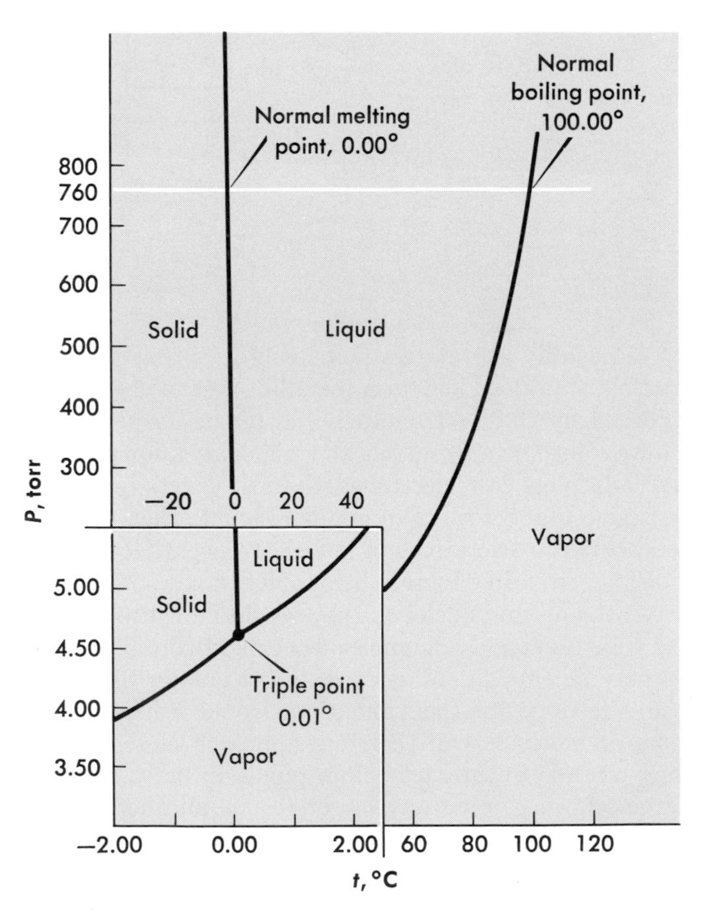

Fig. 9.34 Phase diagram for water.

The melting point of a substance like water, which expands when it freezes, is lowered by applying pressure. A glance at the phase diagram for water (Fig. 9.34) will show this to be the case. The triple point for water is reached at 0.01°C and 4.58 torr. With increasing pressure, the solid-liquid curve slants to the left, toward lower temperature. At 760 torr (1 atm) ice melts at 0°C—the so-called "normal" melting point—and the melting point continues to fall as the pressure rises. At 1000 atm, for example, the melting point of ice is about −10°C. A skater's entire weight, applied through the small area of a skate blade, exerts considerable pressure on the surface of the ice. This causes the surface to melt directly under the blade, and the skater sails along not on the ice, but on a lubricating film of water. The ice is slipperiest when the temperature is just below freezing. Skating on extremely cold ice is like skating on a piece of glass.

The most commonplace property of water, the fact that it is a liquid at ordinary temperatures, is actually quite remarkable. Judging from its molecular weight, and the properties of the other group VIA hydrides, we might expect water to be a gas with a liquefaction temperature of about −100°C, something which it most obviously is not. A plot of the boiling

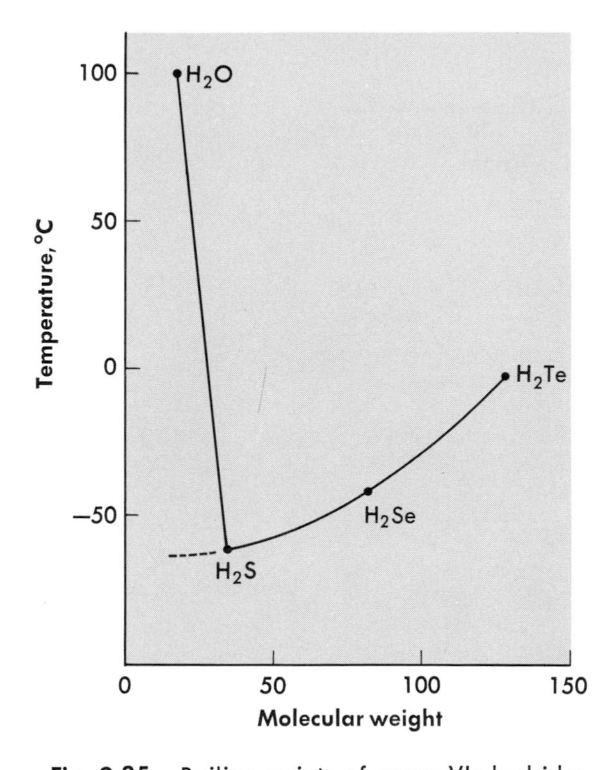

Fig. 9.35 Boiling points of group VIA hydrides.

points of water and the hydrides of the other elements of group VIA is presented in Fig. 9.35. It will be seen that except for water, all these hydrides are gases at room temperature, and that their boiling points increase regularly as their molecular weights increase. The exceptionally high boiling point of water suggests that there must be appreciable intermolecular attractions present in water which are not present in the other hydrides. These attractions cannot be accounted for simply on the basis of the polarity of water which, although large, is right in line with those of the other group VIA hydrides (Fig. 9.36). The same sort of strong intermolecular association is found in NH_3 and **HF** as in H_2O, and the boiling points of these compounds are also unexpectedly high (Fig. 9.37). It is notable that the three elements **N**, **O**, and **F**, whose hydrides show exceptionally high boiling points, are also the three most electronegative elements (Sec. 8.4). Because they

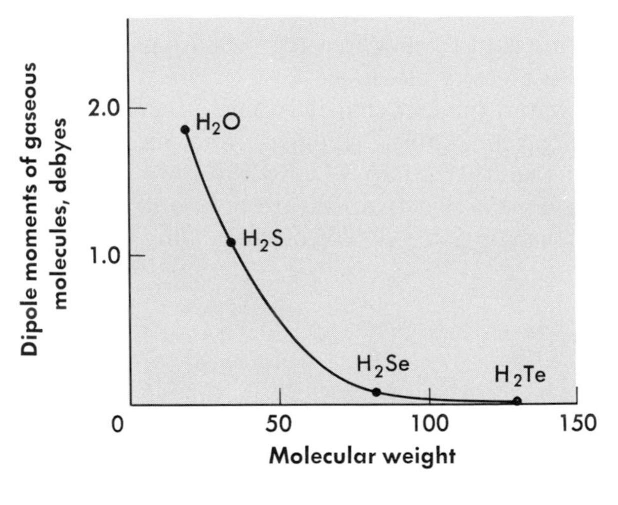

Fig. 9.36 Dipole moments of group VIA hydrides.

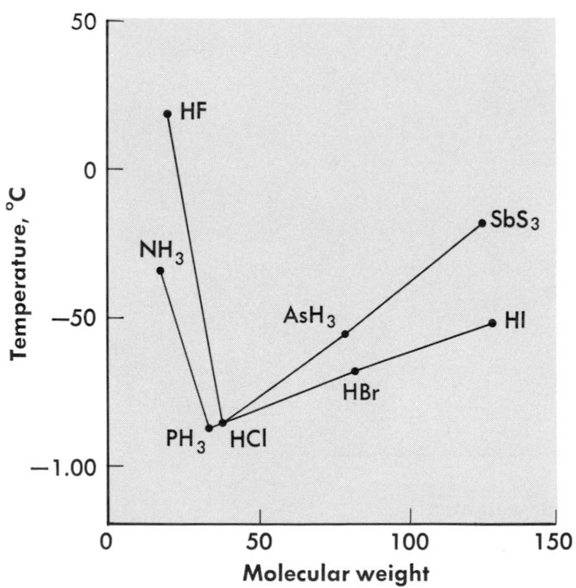

Fig. 9.37 Boiling points of the hydrides of groups VA and VIIA.

are so electronegative, they apparently attract the electrons of the covalent bond to such an extent as to leave the hydrogen nucleus almost completely exposed. The almost-bare hydrogen nucleus is attracted to the region of high electron density about the electronegative atom of another molecule.

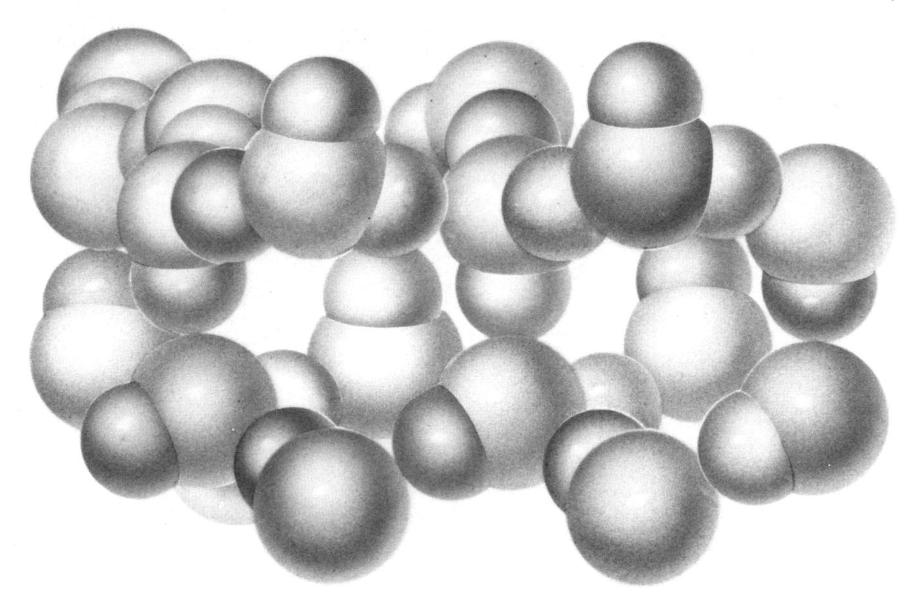

Fig. 9.38 A portion of the ice crystal.

Hydrogen is the smallest of all atoms, and therefore it is possible for its nucleus to come very close to the electronegative atom of the other molecule.

The resulting electrostatic attraction, while weak compared to a covalent bond, is much stronger than the usual attraction between dipoles, or ordinary van der Waals forces, and for this reason it is called a ***hydrogen bond.*** The energy required to dissociate the hydrogen bonds in water has been estimated to be about 4 to 7 kcal/mole. The exceptionally large heats of fusion and vaporization of water are accountable at least in part on the basis of the additional energy needed to separate water molecules because of the presence of hydrogen bonding. On a hot day the water in the ocean or a lake absorbs a great deal of heat but warms up only slightly, while the sand on the beach may become too hot to walk on. At night, the sand quickly cools off, but the water temperature changes very little. It is this ability to absorb a large amount of heat in warm weather and release it slowly later on, which results in the moderating effect that large bodies of water have on the climate of coastal areas.

Hydrogen bonding is also responsible for the low density of ice relative to water at the melting point. Because of hydrogen bonding, the molecules in an ice crystal are not packed together as closely as possible, but rather are arranged in an open-work lattice enclosing a considerable amount of empty space (Fig. 9.38). When the crystal melts, many of the hydrogen bonds are disrupted and the open-work structure begins to collapse. With less open space between the molecules, the liquid is more dense than the solid. That some partial structure is retained in the liquid is indicated by the fact that the density of the liquid continues to increase up to about 4°C, after which the normal expansion with temperature, observed in any substance as a result of increased thermal motion of the molecules, begins to dominate (Fig. 9.39).

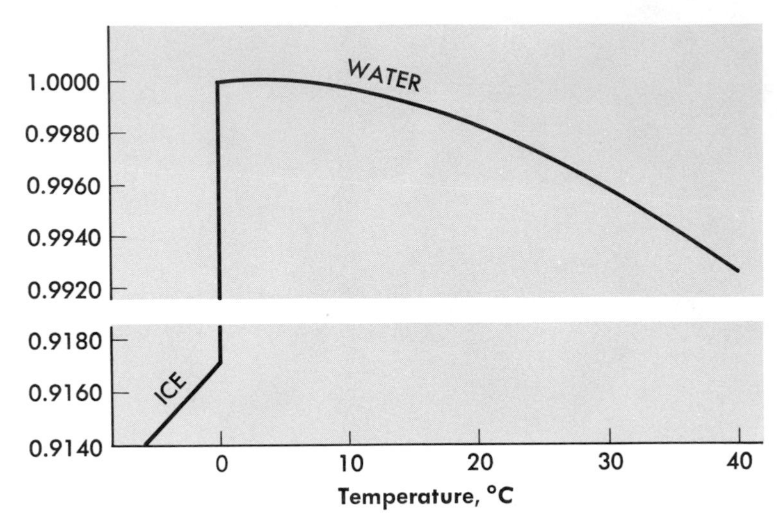

Fig. 9.39 Density of solid and liquid water from —6° to 40°C.

9.15 Reading Suggestions

The reasoning behind the van der Waals equation (Sec. 9.1) and a not-too-difficult mathematical discussion of why it works is given by E. S. Swinbourne in an article in *J. Chem. Ed.* **32,** 366 (1955).

The assignment of a crystal to one of the six major crystal systems solely on the basis of the lengths of the crystal axes and the angles between them can lead to error in a few cases. This is pointed out by Karol J. Mysels in *J. Chem. Ed.* **34,** 40 (1957).

Most ionic crystal lattices are based upon the principle of closest possible packing of spheres; the exact arrangement of the ions in the crystal being determined largely by the relative sizes of the ions and their charges. The derivation of the standard ionic crystal structures is presented in a beautifully illustrated article by William G. Gehman in *J. Chem. Ed.* **40,** 54 (1963).

A good, short discussion of X-ray diffraction methods for crystal structure determination will be found in Chapters 2 and 3 of *Physical Methods for Determining Molecular Geometry,* by Wallace S. Brey, Jr. (Selected Topics in Modern Chemistry Series, Reinhold Publishing Corp., New York, 1965), although the few mathematical expressions introduced in the section on complete structure determination are more confusing than helpful.

The nature of the hydrogen bond, and its effect on the physical properties of substances, including a description of hydrogen bonding in proteins, is discussed in the short final chapter of *The Chemical Bond,* by Linus Pauling (Cornell University Press, Ithaca, N.Y., 1967).

Questions and Problems

9.1 Tell how each of the following properties is related to the strength of the attractive forces between the molecules of a substance: normal boiling point; normal freezing point; critical temperature; heat of vaporization; molar volume in the gaseous state at STP.

9.2 Explain why a liquid is cooled by evaporation. Why does raising the temperature of a liquid cause an increase in its equilibrium vapor pressure?

9.3 The heat of vaporization of any substance normally becomes less as the temperature rises. Why should this be so?

9.4 What is meant by an ideal gas? How do real gases differ from ideal gases? What are van der Waals forces? What effect does the existence of van der Waals forces have on the compressibility of a gas?

9.5 In what respect does a true solid differ from a glass? What is a supercooled liquid? Why should substances whose molecules are large or complex be more prone to supercooling than simple substances?

9.6 Define vapor pressure. What is meant by dynamic equilibrium? What is the vapor pressure of a substance at its normal boiling point? Is it possible to boil a liquid at a temperature other than its normal boiling point? If so, how? What is the process called by which a solid is converted directly into vapor without passing through the liquid state?

9.7 An orbiting space explorer, in a state of weightlessness, spills a glass of water, which floats about the cabin of the space ship in the form of spherical drops. Why should all of the drops be spherical?

9.8 Referring to Fig. 9.34, tell what will happen to a sample of water initially at 60°C and a pressure of 760 torr under the following circumstances. In each case, describe any phase changes which take place, as well as the temperature and pressure at which they occur.

(a) The temperature is raised to 110°C.
(b) The temperature is reduced to 0°C, and the pressure is then increased to 800 torr.
(c) The temperature is first lowered to −1°C, and the pressure is then increased to 800 torr.
(d) The pressure is first decreased to 3 torr, and the temperature is then lowered to −1°C.
(e) The pressure is decreased to 100 torr, and the temperature is then lowered to 0.00°C.

9.9 Prepare a table comparing molecular, ionic, covalent, and metallic crystals with respect to the units occupying the lattice points of the crystal, the type of bonding within the crystal, and the relative strength of bonding in the crystal.

9.10 Under what conditions are hydrogen bonds formed? How can hydrogen bonding account for the abnormally high boiling point of water and the low density of ice at 0°C relative to liquid water at the same temperature?

9.11 From Fig. 9.35 and 9.37, estimate what would be the boiling points of water, ammonia, and hydrogen fluoride in the absence of hydrogen bonding.

9.12 Identify the crystal system to which each of the following substances belongs:

Substance	Lattice Constants (a, b, c in Å; α, β, γ in degrees)					
	a	b	c	α	β	γ
Na_3AlF_6	5.39	5.59	7.76	90°	90° 11′	90°
C (graphite)	1.42	1.42	3.35	90°	90°	120°
C (diamond)	3.56	3.56	3.56	90°	90°	90°
$ZnSO_4$	4.71	6.73	8.51	90°	90°	90°
$Na_2B_4O_7 \cdot 10\ H_2O$	12.30	11.82	10.61	90°	106° 35′	90°
H_3BO_3	7.04	7.04	6.56	92° 30′	101° 10′	120°
KPb_2Br_5	8.14	8.14	14.1	90°	90°	90°
Zn	2.66	2.66	4.93	90°	90°	120°

9.13 Account for the following:

(a) Carbon dioxide is a gas, but silicon dioxide is a solid.
(b) Iodine crystals are soft and easily crushed, while sodium iodide crystals are hard and brittle.
(c) Metal surfaces exhibit a characteristic luster.
(d) Many high-molecular-weight covalent solids decompose before they melt.
(e) Metals are good conductors of electricity.

9.14 Account for the following:

(a) Dimethyl ether ($H_3C—O—CH_3$, mol wt 46) is a gas (b.p. −25°C) while ethyl alcohol ($H_3C—CH_2—OH$, mol wt 46) is a liquid (b.p. 78.5°C).
(b) Thioacetic acid ($H_3C—C({=}O)—SH$) has a higher molecular weight than acetic acid ($H_3C—C({=}O)—OH$), but its boiling point is about 30° lower.

9.15 Acetic acid is a covalent compound with the structure

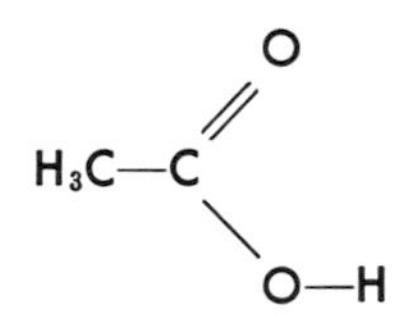

Although the molecular weight of acetic acid, calculated from the formula, is 60, the density of acetic acid vapor at a temperature slightly above the boiling point (118.5°C) corresponds to a molecular weight of about 120. Account for this in terms of hydrogen bonding. What is the probable structure of the species whose molecular weight is 120?

9.16 When 1000 ml of a certain gas at 1 atm pressure is put under a pressure of 84 atm, keeping the temperature constant, the volume becomes 4.7 ml. What should the volume become according to Boyle's law? Briefly account for any discrepancy.

9.17 Use the following data to construct a properly labeled pressure-temperature phase diagram for carbon dioxide.

Equilibrium Vapor Pressure of CO_2 at Various Temperatures

(a) Solid CO_2

Temperature, °K	200	202	204	206	208	210	212	214
Pressure, atm	1.55	1.81	2.12	2.44	2.82	3.27	3.76	4.32

(b) Liquid CO_2

Temperature, °K	220	225	230	235	240	245	250	255
Pressure, atm	5.95	7.30	8.85	10.7	12.7	15.1	17.7	20.6

Critical temperature: 304°K
Critical pressure: 73 atm
Triple point: 216°K
Vapor pressure at triple point: 5.1 atm
Melting point at critical pressure: 218°K

9.18 First-order reflection of X-radiation from a Cu target by adjacent layers of ions in a crystal of NaCl occurs at 15° 54′. If the ionic layers are 2.81 Å apart in the crystal, calculate the wavelength of the radiation.

9.19 Using X-rays with a wavelength of 1.66 Å from a nickel target, first-order reflection from adjacent carbon layers in a crystal of graphite occurs at 14° 18′. Calculate the distance between layers in the crystal. At what angle will the second-order reflections appear?

9.20 Neon crystallizes in the cubic system at 24°K, with a unit cell 4.5 Å on an edge. The density of the solid at the same temperature is 1.45 g/cm³. (a) How many atoms, or their equivalent (e.g., four half-atoms is equivalent to two whole atoms), lie within the unit cell? (b) What type of cubic lattice, simple, body centered, or face centered, does this correspond to? (c) What is the shortest distance between the centers of any two neon atoms in the solid? The effective atomic radius is equal to half that distance.
Ans. (a) 4 atoms/unit cell (b) face centered lattice (c) 3.18 Å, atomic radius, 1.59 Å

9.21 Vanadium metal (atomic weight 50.942 g/mole) forms body-centered cubic crystals with a unit cell 3.011 Å on an edge and a density of 5.96 g/cm³. From these data calculate Avogadro's number.

The most sensual and exciting of
the sciences, Chemistry. Even in its
modern austerity, a chemical laboratory
is the most fascinating place in the world
to those lucky enough to possess
strong curiosity and sense of smell.

—William Bolitho, in *Twelve Against the Gods* [1929]
Cagliostro (and Seraphina)

10 SOLUTIONS

A chemist spends much of his time working with mixtures of substances. A pure substance has a definite, fixed composition, but the composition of a mixture may vary. Depending upon the degree of subdivision of its components, a mixture may appear to be either heterogeneous or homogeneous. The components of a heterogeneous mixture are present as separate phases that can be distinguished from one another either by eye or under a microscope. The components of a homogeneous mixture are subdivided into particles of about molecular size and uniformly mixed, so that the entire mixture is a single phase. ***Homogeneous mixtures*** are better known as ***solutions.*** Substances in solution often behave quite differently from the same substances in the pure state. Because of this, and also because most chemical reactions are carried out in solution, knowledge of the general properties of solutions is of great practical importance to the chemist.

Types of Solutions 10.1

Gases, unless they react to form new substances, mix uniformly with one another in all proportions. All mixtures of gases are solutions. Since at ordinary conditions gas molecules are relatively far apart and move pretty much independently of one another, a ***gaseous solution*** is for the most part no different physically from a pure gas. Common air, composed of about 79 mole-% N_2,* 20 mole-% O_2, and 1 mole-% Ar, CO_2, H_2O, and

* That is, 79% of the molecules in a given sample of air are N_2.

various other gases and vapors, is the most familiar example of a gaseous solution.

Liquids dissolve a variety of other liquids, gases, and solids to form ***liquid solutions.*** Because the molecules in a liquid are in intimate contact, they are less independent of one another than they are in a gas, and the properties of a substance may be modified appreciably by placing it in liquid solution. The properties of liquid solutions, and most particularly aqueous solutions—those in which water is present, usually as the major component—are of greatest importance to us, and will be considered in detail in this chapter.

Two or more substances may crystallize together to form a ***solid solution.*** Just as in a crystal of a pure substance, the atoms or molecules in a solid solution are arranged in a regular fashion, but the different kinds of atoms or molecules are randomly distributed among the lattice points. Substances whose atoms or molecules are of similar structure and chemical type are most apt to form solid solutions in one another. Pairs of salts such as $NaH_2PO_4 \cdot H_2O$ and $NaH_2AsO_4 \cdot H_2O$, which have similar formulas and form the same type of crystal—so-called ***isomorphous salts***—often crystallize together from aqueous solution to give crystals in which the ions of both salts are present in solid solution. Many alloys such as brass (zinc and copper) and sterling silver (silver and copper) are solid solutions. Others, however, are heterogeneous mixtures of microscopic crystals of the pure components. Copper-lead and zinc-cadmium alloys are of this type. Intermetallic compounds of definite composition, Mg_2Sn and KBi_2, for example, are also known.

Most solid solutions are ***substitutional solutions,*** in which the atoms, molecules, or ions of the various components are all located at the lattice points of the crystal. In a solid ***interstitial*** solution all of the lattice points of the crystal are taken up by one component, while the atoms or molecules of the other component fit into the interstices, or voids between them (Fig. 10.1). Since these interstices are usually small, interstitial solutions are most likely to involve small atoms such as hydrogen. Platinum and palladium, for example, form interstitial solutions with hydrogen, each metal dissolving many times its own volume of the gas. Much larger atoms and even molecules may sometimes be accommodated by substances which

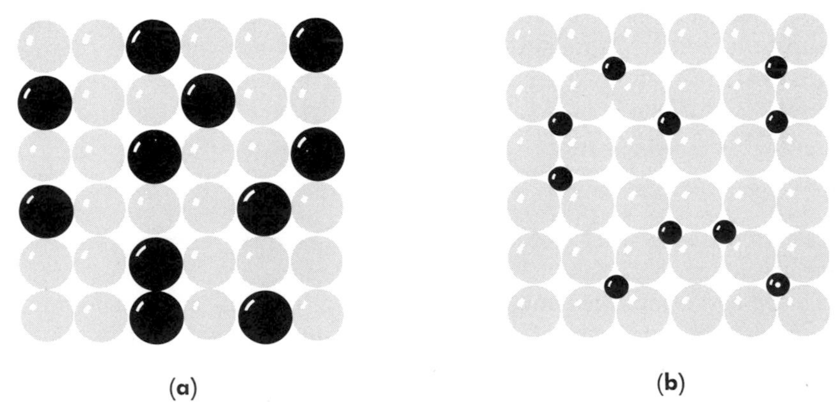

Fig. 10.1 Solid solutions: (a) substitutional; (b) interstitial.

crystallize in lattices containing large voids. Xenon, for example, forms a solid "hydrate" in which the xenon atoms are held in the cage-like voids of the ice lattice.

When a solid or a gas is dissolved in a liquid to form a liquid solution, the original liquid is usually referred to as the ***solvent,*** and the solid or gas is considered to be the ***solute.*** For example, in club soda, water is the solvent, CO_2 the solute; in brine, water is again the solvent and NaCl is the solute. If both components were originally in the same physical state, that is, both gases, both liquids, or both solids, then the one present in larger amount is usually considered the solvent and the other becomes the solute.

Concentration 10.2

The terms *concentrated* and *dilute*, often used in reference to solutions, are purely relative and convey little useful information. Since most of the important properties of solutions depend upon their concentrations, it is important to be able to express the concentration of a solution in a meaningful, quantitative fashion. The concentration of a solution can be described quantitatively in several ways.

(a) Weight Percent. Although weight percent is a very common way of expressing concentration, this is probably the least useful from the chemist's point of view. The ***weight percent*** *is equal to the number of grams of solute present in 100 g of solution.* For example, a 10% solution of sodium carbonate contains 10 g of Na_2CO_3 in every 100 g of solution:

$$\frac{10 \text{ g } Na_2CO_3}{100 \text{ g solution}} \times 100 = 10\%$$

Likewise, 5 g of Na_2CO_3 dissolved in 45 g of water is also a 10% solution:

$$\frac{5 \text{ g } Na_2CO_3}{5 \text{ g } Na_2CO_3 + 45 \text{ g } H_2O} \times 100 = 10\%$$

or, in general,

$$\frac{\text{g solute}}{\text{g solution}} \times 100 = \% \text{ solute}$$

It is often necessary in the laboratory to determine the quantity of solute present in a given amount of a solution whose composition is given in weight percent. This is easily done if the density of the solution is known or can be determined.

Example 10.1

How many grams of HCl are present in 250 ml of commercial 37% hydrochloric acid which has a density of 1.19 g/ml?

Solution: 250 ml × 1.19 g/ml = 297 g solution

$$297 \text{ g} \times \frac{37 \text{ g}}{100 \text{ g}} = 110 \text{ g HCl}$$

(b) Molarity. *The number of moles of solute per liter of solution is equal to the* ***molarity*** *of the solution.* For example, a solution of

1 mole (106 g) of Na_2CO_3 in 1 liter of solution is 1 molar (1 M),

2 moles (212 g) of Na_2CO_3 in 1 liter of solution is 2 M,

0.5 mole (53 g) of Na_2CO_3 in 1 liter of solution is 0.5 M,

0.5 mole (53 g) of Na_2CO_3 in 0.5 liter of solution is 1 M.

Example 10.2

What is the molarity of a solution prepared by dissolving 10.0 g of Na_2CO_3 in enough water to give a final volume of 200 ml?

Solution: One mole of Na_2CO_3 weighs 106 g. The number of moles of Na_2CO_3 in the solution is therefore 10.0 g/106 g/mole. Dividing the number of moles by the volume *in liters* gives the molarity of the solution:

$$\frac{10.0 \text{ g}}{106 \text{ g/mole}} \times \frac{1}{0.200 \text{ liter}} = 0.472 \text{ mole/liter} = 0.472\ M$$

Expressing solution concentrations in terms of molarity affords a convenient way to measure out a definite number of moles of solute. Equal volumes of all solutions with the same molarity contain the same number of moles of solute. Moreover, *the number of moles of solute in a given volume of solution is equal to the product of the molarity of the solution times its volume in liters:*

$$\text{Moles of solute} = M \times \text{liters}$$

In the laboratory, volumes of solutions are more often measured in milliliters. Multiplying the molarity of a solution by its volume in milliliters gives the number of ***millimoles*** (1 mmole = 0.001 mole):

$$\text{mmoles of solute} = M \times \text{ml}$$

Example 10.3

How many grams of $CuSO_4 \cdot 5\ H_2O$ are needed to prepare 300 ml of a 0.30 M solution of the salt?

Solution: One mole of $CuSO_4 \cdot 5\ H_2O$ weighs 249.7 g.

(0.30 liter)(0.30 mole/liter)(249.7 g/mole) = 22 g $CuSO_4 \cdot 5\ H_2O$ required

One is frequently called upon in the laboratory to prepare a solution of a specified molarity from a solution of the same substance with a different molarity. For example, the "dilute" acids and bases on the laboratory bench are usually 6 M, but an experiment will often call for solutions that are 2 M, 0.5 M, 0.1 M, and so on. Adding more solvent to a given amount of solution changes the molarity of the solution, but the number of moles or millimoles of solute present remains the same. This means that

$$M_A \times V_A = M_B \times V_B$$

where V is the volume of the solution in liters or milliliters, and the subscripts A and B refer to the solution before and after addition of more solvent. The use of this relationship is illustrated in the following example.

Example 10.4

How can a chemist prepare 30 ml of 1.5 M HCl using the 6 M acid which is on the shelf?

Solution: To do this, he needs to take that volume of 6 M acid which contains the same number of mmoles of HCl as there are in 30 ml of 1.5 M acid, and then add enough water to make the final volume 30 ml.

$$1.5\ M \times 30\ \text{ml} = 6\ M \times V$$

$$7.5\ \text{ml} = V$$

Therefore, by diluting 7.5 ml of 6 M HCl to a final volume of 30 ml, the chemist will obtain the 1.5 M solution he needs.

(c) Normality. The ***normality*** of a solution is defined as *the number of equivalents of solute per liter of solution.* A liter of 1-normal (1 N) solution therefore contains 1 equivalent of solute. The equivalent weight of a substance depends upon the reaction in which it is taking part. In Sec. 5.8 the equivalent weight of a redox reagent was shown to be equal to its formula weight divided by the number of electrons transferred in the reaction per mole of reagent. This is summarized in Table 10.1 for some common redox reagents.

TABLE 10.1 Equivalent Weights of Redox Reagents

Reagent	Reaction	Formula Weight	Electrons Transferred per Mole	Equivalent Weight
$FeSO_4$	$Fe^{++} \rightarrow Fe^{+++}$	151.9	1	151.9 g
$KMnO_4$	$MnO_4^- \rightarrow Mn^{++}$	158.0	5	31.6 g
$KMnO_4$	$MnO_4^- \rightarrow MnO_2$	158.0	3	52.7 g
$K_2Cr_2O_7$	$Cr_2O_7^{--} \rightarrow 2\ Cr^{+++}$	294.2	6	49.0 g
HNO_3	$NO_3^- \rightarrow NO_2$	63.0	1	63.0 g
HNO_3	$NO_3^- \rightarrow NO$	63.0	3	21.0 g

The equivalent weight of an acid or base in aqueous solution is taken as the amount in grams equal to its formula weight divided by the number of moles of replaceable H^+ or OH^- ions per mole of acid or base. A 1 N solution of an acid is therefore 1 M in H^+; a 0.5 N solution of a base is 0.5 M in OH^-, and so on. Since it is usually the molar concentrations of the H^+ and OH^- that we are interested in, and not those of the other ions that may be present, concentrations of acids and bases are most often expressed in terms of normality. Equivalent weights of some common acids and bases are given in Table 10.2.

Some simple applications of the normality concept in chemical analysis are illustrated in the following examples.

TABLE 10.2 Equivalent Weights of Acids and Bases

Acid or Base	Formula Weight	Moles of Replaceable H^+ or OH^-/mole	Equivalent Weight
HCl	36.5	1	36.5 g
HNO_3	63.0	1	63.0 g
H_2SO_4	98.1	2	49.1 g
H_3PO_4	98.0	3	32.7 g
$NaOH$	40.0	1	40.0 g
$Ca(OH)_2$	74.1	2	37.1 g

Example 10.5

A chemist needs 500 ml of 0.100 N H_2SO_4. How can he prepare this from some 6.00 M H_2SO_4 which he has?

Solution: There are 2 moles of replaceable H^+ per mole of H_2SO_4: therefore 6.00 M H_2SO_4 is 12.0 N. The number of ***milliequivalents*** (1 meq = 0.001 eq) of solute is equal to the volume of the solution in milliliters times its normality. The volume of 12.0 N H_2SO_4 which contains the same number of meq as does 500 ml of 0.100 N acid is calculated as follows:

$$0.100\ N \times 500\ \text{ml} = 12.0\ N \times V$$

$$4.17\ \text{ml} = V$$

By taking 4.17 ml of 6.00 M (12.0 N) H_2SO_4 and diluting it to a final volume of 500 ml, the chemist will obtain the 0.100 N solution he needs.

Example 10.6

50.0 ml of the 0.100 N H_2SO_4 prepared above reacts exactly with (neutralizes) 30.0 ml of a solution of $NaOH$. What is the normality of the $NaOH$ solution?

Solution: To react exactly with one another, the two volumes of solution must have contained the same number of milliequivalents of acid and of base, respectively. Therefore,

$$0.100\ N \times 50.0\ \text{ml} = N \times 30.0\ \text{ml}$$

$$0.167\ \text{meq/ml} = N$$

The $NaOH$ solution is 0.167 N.

Example 10.7

A sample of 0.500 g of impure oxalic acid ($H_2C_2O_4$) is exactly neutralized by 50.0 ml of 0.167 N $NaOH$. What is the percentage of oxalic acid in the sample?

Solution: In 50.0 ml of 0.167 $NaOH$ there are $50.0 \times 0.167 = 8.35$ meq of base. For it to be exactly neutralized, the sample must contain the same number (8.35) of milliequivalents of oxalic acid. The formula weight of oxalic acid is 90.0 g. With 2 moles of replaceable H^+ per mole, the equivalent weight of the acid is $90.0/2 = 45.0$ g, and 1 meq weighs $45.0/1000 = 0.0450$ g. The sample therefore contained

$$8.35\ \text{meq} \times 0.045\ \text{g/meq} = 0.376\ \text{g}$$

and the percentage of oxalic acid in the sample was

$$\frac{0.376}{0.500} \times 100 = 75.2\%$$

(d) Mole Fraction. The ***mole fraction*** *of any one component of a solution is the ratio of the number of moles of that component to the total number of moles of all components in the solution.*

Example 10.8

A solution is prepared from 50.0 g of ethyl alcohol (C_2H_5OH) and 100 g H_2O. Calculate the mole fraction of each component.

Solution: The molecular weight of C_2H_5OH is 46.0, that of H_2O is 18.0. The solution therefore contains 50.0/46.0 = 1.09 moles of alcohol and 100/18.0 = 5.56 moles of water, a total of 6.65 moles.

$$\text{Mole fraction } C_2H_5OH = \frac{1.09}{6.65} = 0.164$$

$$\text{Mole fraction } H_2O = \frac{5.56}{6.65} = 0.836$$

The sum of the mole fractions of all components in a solution is always equal to 1, as it is in this example.

Because the number of moles of gas present in a given volume is proportional to its partial pressure, the mole fraction of a gas in a mixture of gases can be determined by dividing its partial pressure by the total pressure.

Example 10.9

A gas is collected over water at 25°C and 750 torr. What is the mole fraction of water vapor in the gas at equilibrium?

Solution: The vapor pressure of water, which is its partial pressure in the mixture at equilibrium, is 23.8 torr.

$$\text{Mole fraction } H_2O = \frac{23.8 \text{ torr}}{750 \text{ torr}} = 0.0318$$

This means that in this mixture 318 of every 10,000 molecules, or about 1 in 32, are water molecules.

(e) Molality. The ***molality*** *of a solution is equal to the number of moles of solute dissolved in* 1000 g *of solvent.** In dilute aqueous solutions the mole fraction of a solute and its molality are almost exactly proportional. In 1000 g of water there are 55.6 moles of H_2O. Adding a fraction of a mole of solute to such a large number of moles of water has an almost negligible effect upon the total number of moles in the solution, and doubling the

* It is very important not to confuse molality with molarity. Because the volume of 1000 g of H_2O is almost exactly 1 liter, the molality of a dilute aqueous solution, in which the volume of the solute is negligible, is very nearly the same as its molarity. For a more concentrated solution, or one in another solvent, however, the molality and molarity may be very different.

molality of a dilute aqueous solution doubles the mole fraction of the solute as well. For example, in a 1.00 molal (1.00 *m*) solution, the mole fraction of solute is

$$\frac{1.00}{1.00 + 55.6} = 0.0177$$

If the molality is doubled to 2.00 *m*, the mole fraction of the solute is

$$\frac{2.00}{2.00 + 55.6} = 0.0347$$

which is nearly a two-fold increase in the mole fraction.

The proportionality between molality and mole fraction does not hold so well for more concentrated solutions or for solutions in solvents of high molecular weight. For instance, 1000 g of carbon tetrachloride (CCl_4, mol. wt. = 154) contains only 6.49 moles. Similar doubling of the molality of a CCl_4 solution from 1.00 *m* to 2.00 *m* results in a significantly less than two-fold increase in the mole fraction:

$$\frac{2.00}{2.00 + 6.49} = 0.134$$

$$\frac{2.00}{2.00 + 6.49} = 0.236$$

Plots of molality against mole fraction for solutions in water and in carbon tetrachloride are shown in Fig. 10.2. The plot is nearly a straight line for water solutions up to 5 *m* but shows a pronounced curve for CCl_4 solutions above 0.1 *m*.

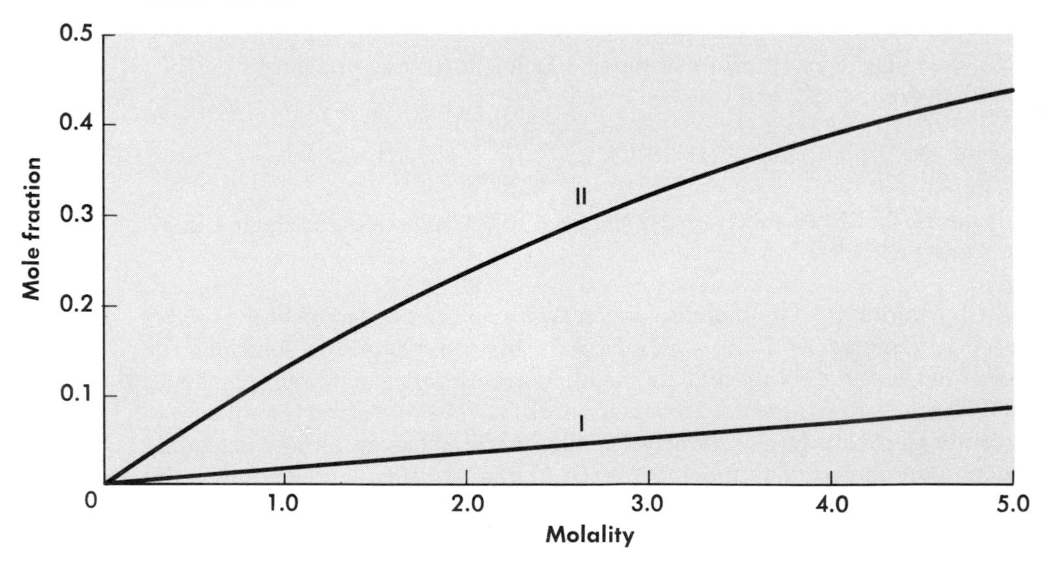

Fig. 10.2 Molality as a function of mole fraction for a solute in water (curve I) and in carbon tetrachloride (curve II).

The Nature of the Solution Process 10.3

Dispersing one substance in another to form a solution usually requires that the particles of each substance be separated from one another in order to let the particles of the other fit in between. This means overcoming those intermolecular, interatomic, or interionic attractive forces which exist in each of the substances. These may be anything from van der Waals forces and hydrogen bonds to strong chemical bonds, whether covalent, ionic, or metallic. The energy to overcome these forces must be supplied somehow if solution is to take place. Most, if not all, of this energy must come from whatever attraction the particles of one substance may have for those of the other. These may be small compared to those which are to be overcome, in which case solution is likely to be difficult and solubility limited, or they may be large, in which case the substances are more likely to dissolve readily in one another. If more energy is required to disperse the substances than is released by their interaction, the additional energy needed must come from outside the mixture, and the process of solution in such a case will be heat-absorbing, or ***endothermic.*** If more energy is released by interaction between the components of the solution than is needed to disperse them in solution, then the extra energy is given off as heat to the surroundings and the process is said to be ***exothermic.***

A common rule for predicting solubility in liquids is expressed in the saying, "Like dissolves like." In more scientific language this means that polar solvents like water are better able to dissolve other polar substances, and nonpolar solvents like carbon tetrachloride are better able to dissolve other nonpolar substances than the other way around. Let us look at some simple examples to see why this should be so.

Benzene, C_6H_6, a nonpolar hydrocarbon, mixes with carbon tetrachloride in all proportions to form solutions. In both liquids the only attractive forces between the molecules are of the van der Waals type. These forces are relatively weak and of nearly the same magnitude in each liquid, as indicated by the low and almost identical boiling points of the two substances (C_6H_6, b.p. 80.1°C; CCl_4, b.p. 76.8°C). We should not be surprised to find that the intermolecular forces existing in the solution are quite similar to those in the pure liquids. There is thus no energy barrier to prevent the two types of molecules from mixing freely with one another.

Nonpolar molecular solids also are generally quite soluble in nonpolar liquids. The mere fact that these substances are solids, however, suggests that the intermolecular forces in the pure solids are greater than those that exist in their solutions. A solid might be expected to be less soluble in a given solvent than would be a chemically similar substance which is liquid at the same temperature.

In contrast to its solubility in carbon tetrachloride, benzene is almost completely insoluble in the polar solvent water. The difficulty here lies in attempting to overcome the relatively strong attractive forces between water molecules. The weak van der Waals forces which might be present between water and benzene molecules are not enough to compensate for the energy needed to disrupt the hydrogen bonds between the water molecules.

A solute possessing some degree of polarity may associate strongly enough with a polar solvent to lead to solubility. Molecules of alcohol and sugar, for example, possess highly polar —**OH** groups and are soluble in water by virtue of their ability to form hydrogen bonds with that solvent. The forces of molecular association between two polar substances may be so great in some instances as to result in a reaction to yield oppositely charged ions:

$$HCl + H_2O \rightarrow H_3O^+ + Cl^-$$

$$NH_3 + H_2O \rightarrow NH_4^+ + OH^-$$

$$HC_2H_3O_2 + H_2O \rightarrow H_3O^+ + C_2H_3O_2^-$$

Those ionic solids which dissolve in polar solvents such as water do so despite the large interionic forces which must be overcome in order to disrupt the crystal. At the surface of the crystal lattice the positive ions strongly attract the negative oxygens of the polar water molecules, while the negative ions attract the hydrogens of the water. This ion-dipole attraction is accompanied by the release of energy called ***heat of hydration*** (or ***heat of solvation*** if the solvent is something other than water). This energy goes at least partly to increase the kinetic energy of the ions, causing them to vibrate more violently about the lattice points. If the heat of hydration is sufficient, it may cause the ions to leave the lattice points entirely and pass into solution as hydrated ions (Fig. 10.3). The ions of sodium chloride solution are each associated with, or hydrated by, at least six water molecules.

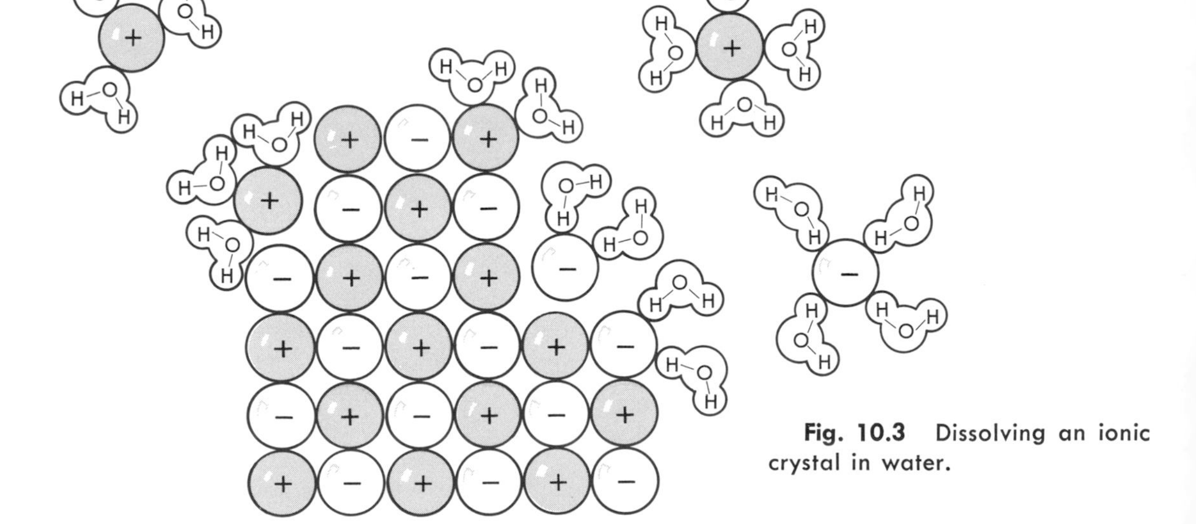

Fig. 10.3 Dissolving an ionic crystal in water.

Whereas all gases and many liquids are completely miscible in all proportions, the solubility of a solid in a liquid may sometimes be very large but is seldom unlimited. If a solid is added continuously and at constant temperature to a liquid in which it is soluble, its concentration in the solution will increase up to a limiting value beyond which no further increase in concentration can take place, and any additional solid will remain undissolved. At this point the solution is said to be *saturated.* The process of solution does not cease when a solution attains saturation. Rather, a state of dynamic equilibrium is established in which undissolved solute is passing into the dissolved state at the same rate at which dissolved solute is returning to the undissolved state. The situation is reminiscent of the dynamic equilibrium that exists between liquid and vapor in a closed container (Sec. 9.5). A ***saturated solution*** *is defined as one which can exist in equilibrium with undissolved solute.* That dynamic equilibrium does indeed exist can be demonstrated by suspending a crystal with a damaged, irregular face in a saturated solution of the same substance. After a time, the regular form of the crystal will be restored, but the mass of the crystal will be found to have remained unchanged.

Different substances vary widely in their limiting solubilities. A solute that is very soluble in water will give a saturated solution which is also concentrated, while a sparingly soluble substance will give a saturated solution which is dilute. In an ***unsaturated solution*** the concentration of the solute in the solution is less than its limiting solubility at that temperature. If more undissolved solute is added to such a solution, it will pass into solution at a faster rate than the dissolved solute comes out. As the concentration of the solution increases, the rate at which dissolved solute redeposits also increases until equilibrium is attained.

Temperature and Solubility 10.4

The solubility of a particular solute in a given solvent varies with temperature. The effect of temperature changes on solubility in a given solvent varies widely from one solute to another, usually in a rather unpredictable way, so that it must be determined experimentally in each case. Curves showing the variation in solubility with temperature for a number of common substances in water solution are plotted in Fig. 10.4. The maximum solubility of any one of the solutes in equilibrium with undissolved solid at a given temperature may be read directly from its solubility curve. The curve for KNO_3 shows that the solubility of this salt increases rapidly with increasing temperature. The solubility of $NaCl$ on the other hand increases only very slightly over the same temperature range (from 36 g/100 g H_2O at 0°C to 39 g/100 g H_2O at 100°C). A break in the solubility curve indicates some change in the structure of the solute, often accompanied by a change in the degree of hydration.

Gases usually become less soluble in water as the temperature rises, and water can be freed of most dissolved gases by boiling it for a short time. The little bubbles that appear in a glass of water that has been standing a while are formed from dissolved air which has been driven out of solution as the water has warmed up. Gas molecules are widely separated and have little effect upon one another, whereas in solution the molecules are close together and are more likely to exert an attraction for one another. Gases therefore frequently undergo a decrease in potential energy in entering solution, and the process is an exothermic one. As a general rule (***Le Chate-***

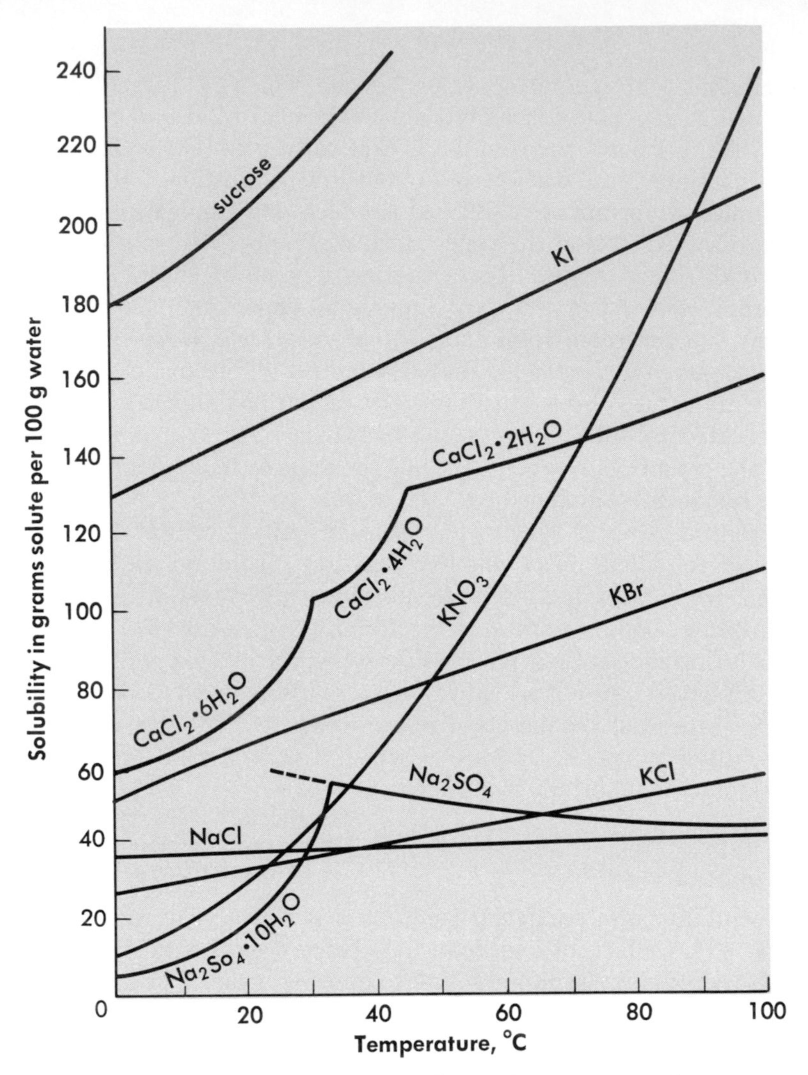

Fig. 10.4 Solubility curves for various compounds.

lier's principle), *when a system in a state of dynamic equilibrium is disturbed in some way, a reaction occurs which tends to offset the effect of the disturbance.* Thus, lowering the temperature will favor the process which releases heat; raising the temperature will favor the process which absorbs heat. If solution of a gas is an exothermic process, then we should expect the gas to become less soluble as the temperature rises, in accord with observation. While as a general rule gas solubility decreases with temperature, there are exceptions. In solvents other than water, and in water at several hundred degrees and elevated pressure, some gases become more soluble as the temperature rises. Factors other than those mentioned above must come into play in these cases.

If the dissolving of a solid in a liquid merely involves the dispersal of the solute in the solvent with little or no chemical or physical interaction or "association" between the molecules of solute and solvent, then the process can be regarded as analogous to the fusion of the solid, a process which is always endothermic. The solid will absorb heat from its surroundings in passing from the solid state to what is in effect a liquid state, and in accord with Le Chatelier's principle, the solubility of the solid will increase with rising temperature. If solution is accompanied by association with the solvent, then whether the solution process is exothermic or endothermic will depend upon the relative magnitudes of the forces holding the crystal lattice together and the associative forces within the solution. For example, more energy may be required to overcome the electrostatic forces within an ionic crystal than is available from the heat of hydration of the ions. Solution of such a crystal is an endothermic process, and the solubility of the salt rises with temperature. If the process is highly endothermic, meaning that the forces within the crystal lattice are very much stronger than the forces of association with the solvent, the solubility curve of the salt will rise very steeply. The curve for KNO_3 (Fig. 10.4) is a case in point. When such salts are dissolved in water, the solution may become very cold because of absorption of heat from the surroundings. Where the process is only slightly endothermic, the solubility curve, like that of $NaCl$ (Fig. 10.4), will show only a slight rise.

Where the change of state from solid to solution is accompanied by a sufficiently large degree of chemical association between solute and solvent, the overall process may be exothermic. In accord with Le Chatelier's principle, the solubility of the solute will decrease with increasing temperature.

The solubility curve of sodium sulfate decahydrate ($Na_2SO_4 \cdot 10\ H_2O$) is an interesting case. Below 32.4°C the crystals that dissolve are made up of ions that are already partially hydrated in the solid. Only a small degree of additional hydration occurs upon solution, and the solution process is endothermic, the solubility increasing with rising temperature. At 32.4° the remaining solid hydrate undergoes a transition, or change, to the anhydrous salt Na_2SO_4. Provided that the transition temperature is maintained long enough to allow the crystals of decahydrate to be converted to the anhydrous salt, it is the anhydrous salt dissolving at temperatures above 32.4°. Solution now involves a greater degree of hydration of the ions. The energy liberated by this chemical interaction is in excess of the energy required to break up the crystal lattice. The overall process is therefore exothermic above 32.4°C, and above this temperature the solubility of the salt decreases with rising temperature.

When two liquids dissolve in one another, the heat of solution is usually small and frequently endothermic. Since the solution process in this case does not involve any change in state, the accompanying heat of solution, if any, that is observed must arise largely from the energy change resulting from chemical association between solute and solvent. Because the heat of solution involved when two liquids are mixed is usually small, the effect of temperature on the solubility of partially miscible liquids is generally correspondingly small. In most cases the limiting saturation solubility of each liquid in the other increases slowly as the temperature rises. With rising temperature the concentration of each liquid dissolved in the other increases until eventually the two solutions have the same composition and can no longer be distinguished. The temperature at which this occurs is known as the ***critical solution temperature,*** and at or above this temperature the two liquids are completely miscible.

There are some cases in which the mixing of two liquids is accompanied by the evolution of a large amount of heat. The dilution of concentrated sulfuric acid with water is a familiar example. Here it is good practice to add the acid slowly to the water, rather than the other way around, and stir the mixture well. Otherwise the heat of solution may cause local boiling where the two liquids are in contact, spattering the acid around dangerously. Examples such as this involve some chemical reaction between the liquids. With sulfuric acid the main reaction is

$$H_2SO_4 + H_2O \rightarrow H_3O^+ + HSO_4^-$$

followed by reactions of hydration of the ions produced, generating still more heat.

10.5 Pressure and Solubility

The effect of pressure on the solubility of solids and liquids is generally negligible. However, for gases, unless they react chemically with the solvent, their solubility in liquids is directly proportional to their partial pressures above the solution. This dependence of gas solubility on pressure is known as ***Henry's law.*** Like other laws describing the behavior of gases, it holds strictly only at relatively low pressures. Henry's law again illustrates the general applicability of Le Chatelier's principle to systems in dynamic equilibrium. When the stress of increased pressure is applied, more gas dissolves, lowering its partial pressure and thus relieving the stress on the system. Even gases which react appreciably with the solvent, although they may not obey Henry's law particularly well, are nevertheless more soluble at high pressures. An example is carbon dioxide, which reacts with water to some degree, forming carbonic acid:

$$CO_2 + H_2O \rightarrow H_2CO_3$$

Carbonated beverages are saturated solutions of CO_2 under pressure. When a soda bottle is opened, relieving the pressure, bubbles of CO_2 form in the liquid and the gas continues to escape until equilibrium is attained between the dissolved CO_2 and that in the atmosphere. Chemical reactions between liquids and gases are frequently carried out under pressure to take advantage of the increased solubility of the gas.

10.6 Supersaturated Solutions

When one cools a saturated solution of a solute whose solubility increases with temperature, excess solute should come out of solution at such a rate that the solution remains saturated at all times as the temperature decreases. In many instances, however, if the solution is left undisturbed, the excess solute over that required for saturation does not separate at the lower temperature but remains in the dissolved state. The solution then contains a higher concentration of solute than it would if it were in equilibrium with undissolved solute at the same temperature, and it is described as being ***supersaturated.*** A supersaturated solution is in a metastable state, that is, it may remain unchanged for a long time if it is not disturbed, but once the excess solute begins to separate, the process continues until equilibrium is reached.

A supersaturated solution cannot exist for long in the presence of undissolved solute, so that crystallization from such a solution can usually be started by adding a crystal of the solute as a "seed." The phenomenon of supersaturation is reminiscent of the supercooling of a liquid and arises from similar causes (Sec. 9.10). As would be expected, complex substances are often most prone to form supersaturated solutions because the probability of the individual particles colliding in just the right orientation to begin to build the crystal lattice is small unless an appropriate matrix is present. Again, as with a supercooled liquid, an air bubble, a piece of dirt, a chip of glass, or a crystal of some other substance of similar structure may sometimes serve to induce crystallization. Sometimes, to the exasperation of the chemist, the solute may separate to become a supercooled liquid ("oil out"), leaving him still with the problem of getting the often sticky gunk to crystallize.

Partition Between Solvents—Extraction 10.7

Two liquids which are immiscible or only partially miscible in one another form a two-phase system which can be used to advantage for the selective separation of one substance from a mixture. If a solute is brought in contact with such a two-phase system, it dissolves in both liquids and distributes itself so that the ratio between its concentration in one solvent (C_A) and its concentration in the other (C_B) is constant at any fixed temperature. This ratio is called the ***distribution coefficient,*** or the ***partition coefficient,*** for the substance between the two solvents. Unless the substance is soluble in all proportions in one or the other of the solvents, the distribution coefficient is generally approximately equal to the ratio between the limiting solubilities (S_A/S_B) of the substance in the two solvents at the same temperature:

$$\frac{C_A}{C_B} = \frac{S_A}{S_B} = K$$

Iodine, for example, is about 85 times as soluble in carbon tetrachloride at 25°C as it is in water. The distribution coefficient C_{CCl_4}/C_{H_2O} for iodine between these two solvents at that temperature is therefore 85. If an equal volume of carbon tetrachloride is added to an aqueous solution of iodine and the mixture is shaken vigorously, the iodine is extracted into the CCl_4 layer until an equilibrium distribution of iodine between the two solvents is attained. Upon standing, the denser CCl_4, colored violet by the iodine, settles to the bottom of the container (Fig. 10.5). Analysis will show that $\frac{85}{86}$ of the total quantity of iodine has passed into the CCl_4 layer. Repeating the process with a fresh portion of CCl_4 will extract $\frac{85}{86}$ of the iodine remaining after the first extraction, and in this way the concentration of iodine in the aqueous layer can eventually be reduced to a negligible amount.

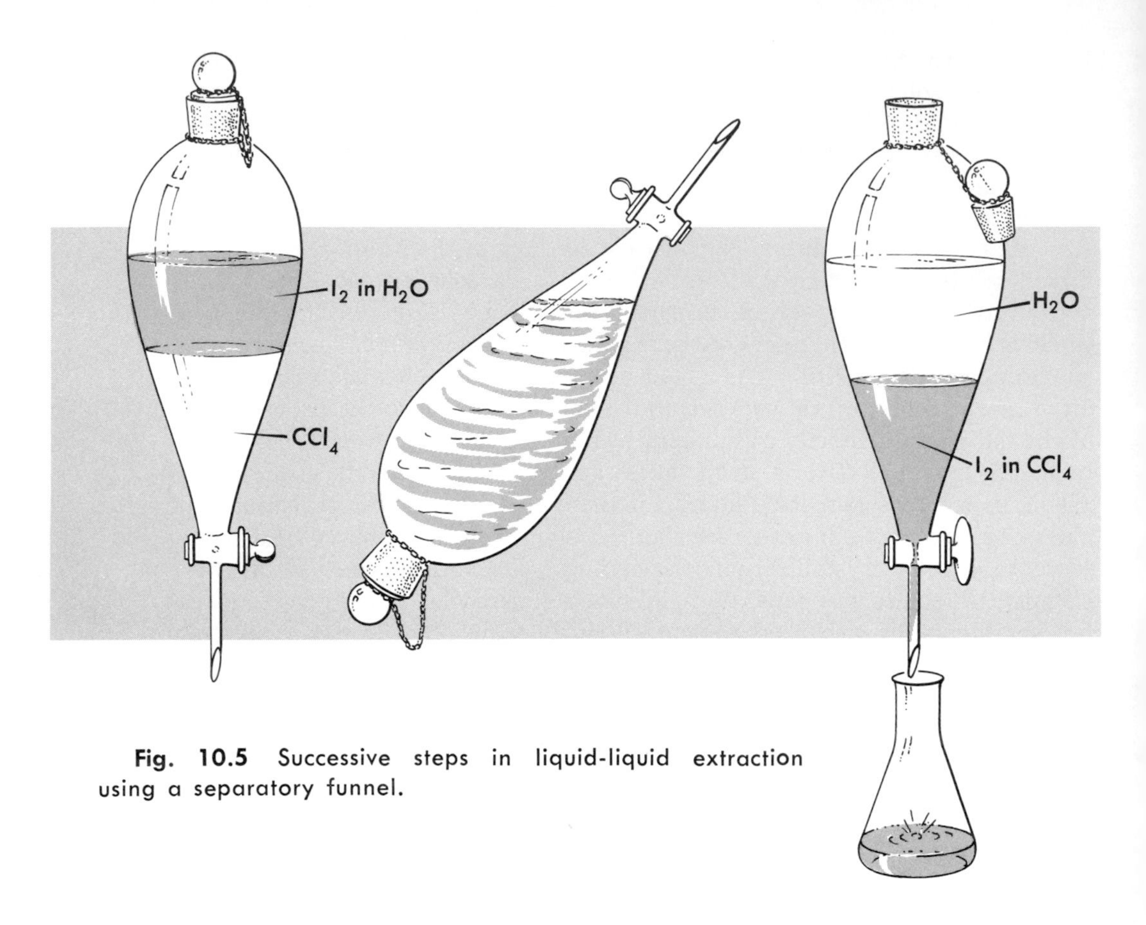

Fig. 10.5 Successive steps in liquid-liquid extraction using a separatory funnel.

If the substances present in a mixture possess different distribution coefficients between two immiscible or partially miscible liquid solvents, the process of extraction can be used to separate them. Where the distribution coefficients are very different, a single extraction may be enough to effect almost complete separation. If, on the other hand, the difference in coefficients is small, or if there are more than two substances present in the mixture, then a number of successive extractions may be required, perhaps using a succession of different solvents, in order to achieve the desired degree of separation.

10.8 Vapor Pressure of Solutions

When a solute is dissolved in a liquid solvent, the vapor pressure of the solvent is lowered, and the amount by which it is lowered depends upon the amount of solute added. Evidently the escape of solvent molecules from the surface is hindered by the presence of the solute. If the solute itself is volatile, then both components exhibit lower vapor pressures than they would in the pure state, and the total vapor pressure of the solution is the sum of the partial pressures of the two components. When the solute is nonvolatile, or nearly so, as is usually the case with solutes which are solids in the pure state, the vapor pressure of the solution is only that exerted by the solvent molecules and is always less than the equilibrium vapor pressure of pure solvent. This can be demonstrated by placing a beaker containing an aqueous solution of a nonvolatile solute alongside a beaker of pure water and covering both beakers with a bell jar (Fig. 10.6). With the passage of

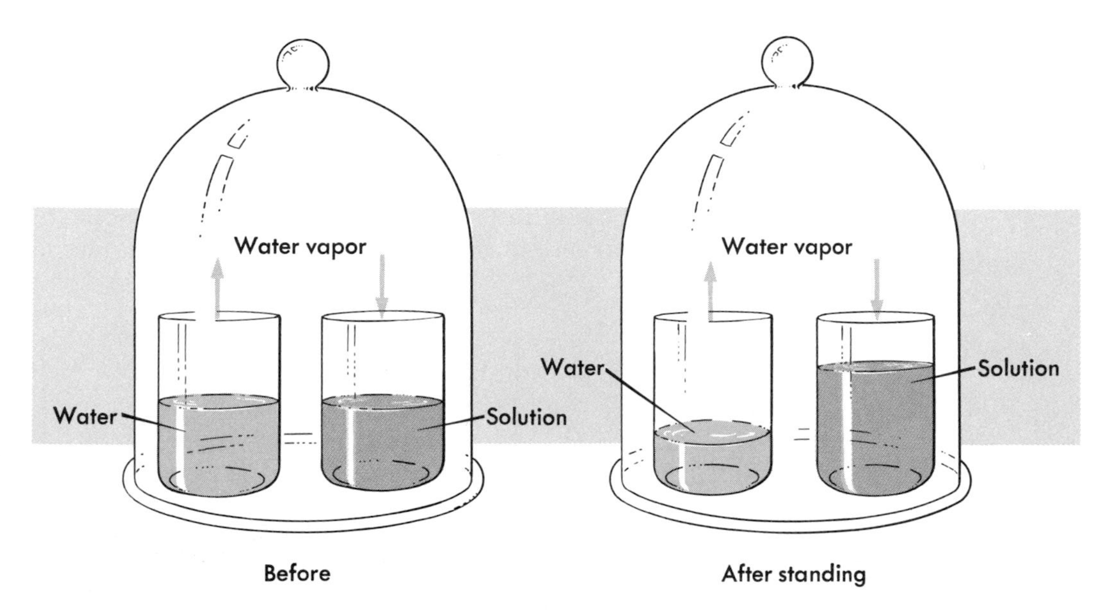

Fig. 10.6 Transfer of solvent in a closed system.

time, the level in the beaker containing the solution is seen to rise, while that of the pure water falls. Evaporation takes place at a faster rate from the pure solvent than from the solution, with the result that the partial pressure of water vapor in the bell jar is always greater than the vapor pressure of the solution so long as any pure water remains in the beaker. Hence, water vapor condenses on the surface of the solution faster than it evaporates from it. This in turn keeps the partial pressure of the water vapor below the equilibrium vapor pressure of pure water, so that in the other beaker, molecules leave the surface at a faster rate than they return. The result is that water continuously passes from one beaker to the other through the atmosphere in the bell jar until all of it has been transferred to the beaker containing the solution, leaving the other one dry.

Raoult's Law 10.9

Where the attractive forces between solvent and solute molecules are small, and of about the same order as the forces which exist in the pure components, there is little or no heat of solution when the components are mixed. The molecules of solute and solvent behave virtually independently of one another, and the solution is said to approach ***ideality***. *The vapor pressure of a volatile component of an ideal solution is proportional to its mole fraction:*

$$P_A = X_A P_A^0$$

where P_A is the vapor pressure of A above a solution in which its mole fraction is X_A, and P_A^0 is the vapor pressure of pure liquid A at the same temperature. This law, first expressed by François Raoult in 1881, is known as ***Raoult's law.*** Deviations from Raoult's law are observed with nonideal solutions, but if the solutions are dilute, the deviations are usually small.

Since the effect of the presence of a solute is always to lower the vapor pressure of the solvent, Raoult's law may be restated as follows: *the lowering of the vapor pressure of a solvent is directly proportional to the mole fraction of the solute.* It is easy enough to see why this should be so. If the mole fraction of solute, for example, is 0.25, then there are only 0.75 times as many solvent molecules at the surface where they can enter the vapor phase as there would be in the pure solvent (Fig. 10.7). The rate at which solvent

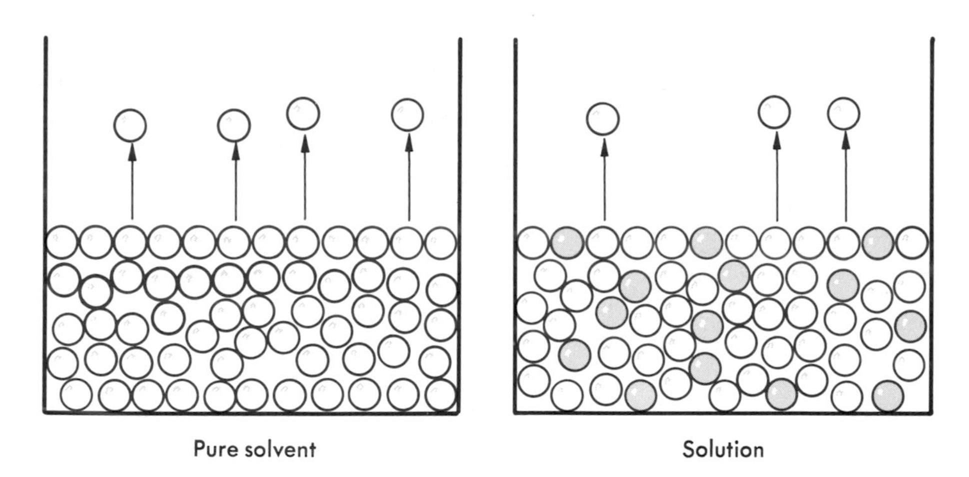

Fig. 10.7 Raoult's law. The rate of evaporation of the solvent, and hence its vapor pressure, decreases in proportion to the mole fraction of the solute.

molecules evaporate, which determines the magnitude of the vapor pressure, is therefore only 0.75 times as great in the solution as in the pure solvent. The vapor pressure as a result is lowered by 25%, an amount proportional to the mole fraction of the solute. In a dilute solution, a proportionality exists between the mole fraction of the solute and its molality (Sec. 10.2e). Therefore, in dilute solutions the vapor pressure of the solvent is lowered by an amount directly proportional to the molality of the solute. Since the lowering of the vapor pressure of one component of a solution by the presence of another depends only upon the relative numbers of each kind of molecule in the solution and not on their nature, it is called a ***colligative property*** of the solution (from Latin *colligare,* to collect).

The normal boiling point of a liquid is the temperature at which its vapor pressure is 1 atm. The presence of a nonvolatile solute lowers the vapor pressure of the solvent at any temperature so that in order to boil the solution it is necessary to heat it above the boiling point of the pure solvent

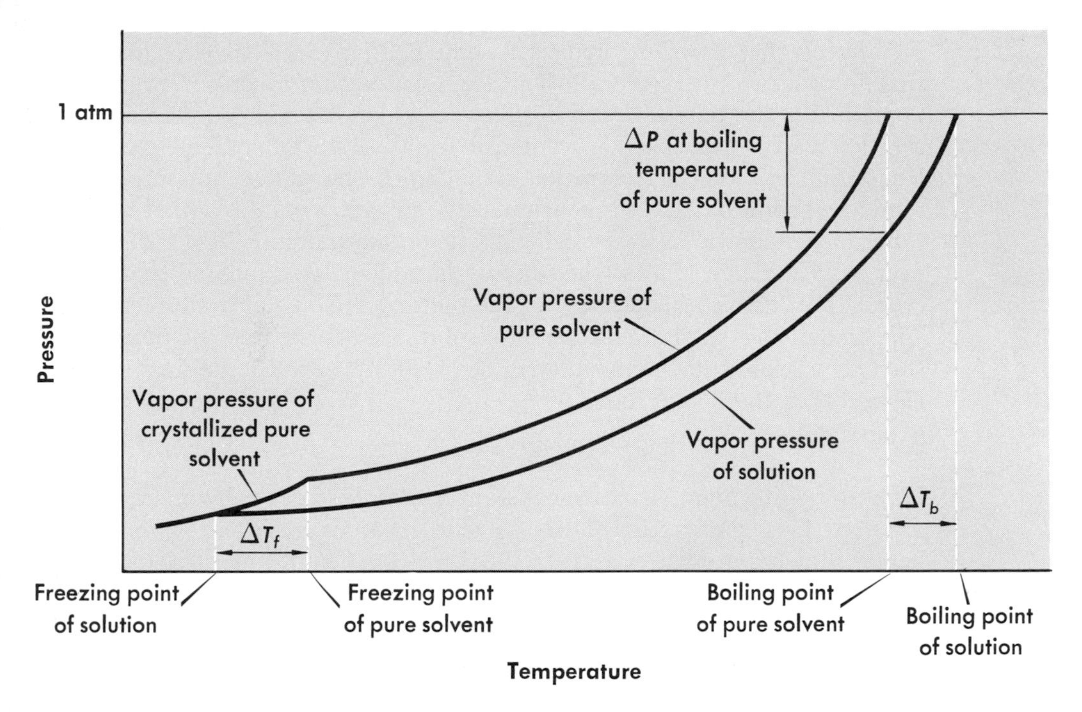

Fig. 10.8 **Diagram showing the lowering of the vapor pressure by the presence of a nonvolatile solute and its effect on the boiling and freezing points of the solution.**

(Fig. 10.8). The boiling point of a solution of a nonvolatile substance will be higher than that of the pure solvent by an amount in proportion to the lowering of the vapor pressure caused by the presence of the solute. Assuming a dilute solution and ideal behavior, the lowering of the vapor pressure, and hence the elevation of the boiling point, will be proportional to the molality of the solute,

$$\Delta T_{\mathrm{b}} = mK_{\mathrm{b}}$$

where ΔT_{b} is the difference between the boiling point of the solution and that of the pure solvent, m is the molality of the solution, and K_{b} is the ***molal boiling point elevation constant*** for the solvent. The value of K_{b} is characteristic for each solvent, and is *the amount in °C by which the boiling point of the solvent is raised by the presence of 1 mole of nonvolatile solute in 1000 g of solvent.*

Most solids are able to dissolve only negligible amounts of other substances, so that when a solution freezes, crystals of the pure solvent usually separate at first, with the solute remaining in the liquid phase. Again, because the presence of solute lowers the vapor pressure at all temperatures, the vapor pressure of the pure solid at its normal freezing point is greater than that of the solution at the same temperature (Fig. 10.8). Unless the vapor pressure of the solid phase is the same as that of the liquid, the two cannot exist together, for the same reason that solution and solvent cannot remain together very long under the same bell jar (Sec. 10.8). This means that in order to freeze the solution, the temperature must be lowered to a point below the normal freezing point at which the vapor pressure of the solution and of the solid solvent are equal. As the solvent crystallizes from solution, the concentration, and hence the vapor pressure, of the remaining solution changes continuously, so that a solution freezes over a range of temperatures rather than at a single sharp point. The range, however, will be fairly small if the solution is sufficiently dilute, so that we are reasonably justified in speaking of the melting "point" of a dilute solution. The amount by which the presence of solute lowers the freezing point of the solvent is related to the molality of the solution in the same way as is the elevation of the boiling point:

$$\Delta T_f = mK_f$$

Like the boiling point elevation constant, the ***molal freezing point depression constant*** K_f is characteristic of the solvent. Values of K_b and K_f for a number of solvents are listed in Table 10.3.

TABLE 10.3 Molal Boiling Point Elevation and Freezing Point Depression Constants

Solvent	B.p., °C	K_b, °C	F.p., °C	K_f, °C
Acetic acid	118.5	3.07	16.7	3.9
Benzene	80.1	2.53	5.5	5.12
Camphor	208.5	5.95	178.4	39.7
Carbon tetrachloride	76.8	5.02	−22.9	31.8
Naphthalene	218.0	5.65	80.2	6.9
Water	100.0	0.51	0.0	1.86

10.10 Determining Molecular Weight from Colligative Properties

Dilute solutions of nonvolatile nonelectrolytes behave according to Raoult's law, providing a way to determine the molality of such solutions experimentally by comparing their boiling or freezing points with those of the pure solvents. This then furnishes us with a method for estimating the molecular weights of many substances whose vapor densities cannot be obtained. Molecular weights determined in this way are approximate, since nearly all solutions deviate in some degree from ideal behavior.

Example 10.10

A solution containing 1.05 g of glucose dissolved in 25.0 g of water boils at 100.12°C. Calculate the molecular weight of glucose.

Solution: The elevation in the boiling point ΔT_b caused by the presence of the glucose is 100.12 − 100.00 = 0.12°C. From Table 10.3, the molal boiling point elevation constant K_b for water is 0.51°C. The molality of the solution is therefore

$$\frac{\Delta T_b}{K_b} = \frac{0.12°}{0.51°} = 0.23\ m$$

The solution contains 1.05 g of glucose in 25.0 g of water; therefore in 1000 g of water there would be

$$\frac{1.05\text{ g}}{25.0\text{ g}} \times 1000 = 42.0\text{ g}$$

Since the solution is 0.23 *m*, 42.0 g of glucose must be 0.23 mole, and the approximate molecular weight of glucose is then:

$$\frac{42.0\text{ g}}{0.23\text{ mole}} = 183\text{ g/mole}$$

It is possible to combine all of these operations into one step as follows:

$$\text{Mol. wt.} = \frac{\text{g solute}}{\text{g solvent}} \times 1000 \times \frac{K_b}{\Delta T_b} = \frac{1.05\text{ g}}{25.0\text{ g}} \times 1000 \times \frac{0.51°}{0.12°} = 183\text{ g/mole}$$

Most nonpolar solids are fairly soluble in melted camphor, which because of its especially large K_f is a particularly desirable solvent for determining molecular weights by freezing point depression. The determination of molecular weight using camphor as a solvent is known as the ***Rast method*** and is illustrated in the following example.

Example 10.11

A sample of a solid nonelectrolyte weighing 0.044 g was mixed with 0.625 g of camphor in a small test tube. The tube was heated quickly until the mixture of solids just melted to a clear solution; then it was cooled. The mixture was removed from the test tube and powdered, and a sample of it was tightly packed into a capillary melting point tube. The sample was heated slowly in a suitable apparatus, and the melting point of the mixture, assumed to be the same as its freezing point, was taken as the temperature at which a clear solution, free of solid, was obtained. For this sample, this temperature was found to be 163.3°C. Using the same apparatus, the melting point of pure camphor was found to be 176.0°C. Calculate the molecular weight of the compound.

Solution: The depression of the melting (or freezing) point is 176.0 − 163.3 = 12.7°. The discrepancy between the melting point of camphor determined here and that given in Table 10.3 indicates an error intrinsic in the apparatus. Provided that the same apparatus is used to obtain the melting point of the solution, each melting point should be in error by the same amount, so that the two errors cancel. Using the value of K_f from the table,

$$\text{Mol. wt.} = \frac{0.044\text{ g}}{0.625\text{ g}} \times 1000 \times \frac{39.7°}{12.7°} = 220\text{ g/mole}$$

If the molecular weight of the solute is known, the relationships derived from Raoult's law can also be used to estimate the boiling point or freezing point of a solution of known concentration or to estimate the concentration required to give a solution which will boil or freeze at any desired temperature within certain limits. For example, the amount of ethylene glycol ($C_2H_6O_2$, mol. wt. 62) required per 1000 g of water to produce a radiator coolant that will not freeze at −18.6°C (−1.5°F) can be calculated as follows:

$$K_f\ (H_2O) = 1.86°$$

$$\text{Molality required} = \frac{\Delta T_f}{K_f} = \frac{18.6°}{1.86°} = 10\ m$$

$$10\ \text{moles}/1000\ \text{g} \times 62\ \text{g/mole} = 620\ \text{g}/1000\ \text{g}\ H_2O$$

Calculations made on the basis of such large concentrations are of course very likely to be in error by a considerable margin because of deviations from Raoult's law on the part of concentrated solutions. Experimentally it is found that a 10 m solution of ethylene glycol freezes somewhat below $-18.6°$C, and when it does freeze, the ice crystals which separate make the remaining solution even more concentrated, so that the freezing point continues to drop.

10.11 Deliquescence and Efflorescence

When a solid is exposed to moist air, some of the molecules of water vapor striking the surface of the solid may remain there because of mutual forces of attraction between the water molecules and the solid. If the solid is one which is very soluble in water, it may dissolve in the water layer which forms on its surface, producing a very concentrated solution whose vapor pressure may be less than the partial pressure of water vapor in the air. If this takes place, then water will condense onto the surface layer faster than it evaporates from it and more solid will dissolve. The solution will remain saturated so long as undissolved solid is present. After all of the solid has dissolved, water will continue to condense into the solution until the vapor pressure of the solution is equal to the partial pressure of the water vapor in the air. This process, by which a soluble substance spontaneously absorbs water and dissolves when in contact with moist air, is called ***deliquescence.*** Sodium hydroxide is a striking example of a deliquescent compound. Pellets of $NaOH$, left exposed on the laboratory bench, become coated with a layer of moisture almost immediately. Magnesium chloride is another very deliquescent substance. A trace of $MgCl_2$, present as an impurity in table salt, will absorb enough water in damp weather to cause the crystals to stick together and clog up the salt shaker. The removal of this impurity is the secret of free-flowing salt.

Many ionic substances, and some nonionic ones, crystallize with a definite proportion of ***water of hydration*** bound within the crystal lattice. The water of hydration is bound reversibly in the crystal, and a hydrate exerts a definite vapor pressure. For example, at moderate temperatures the hydrate $CuSO_4 \cdot 5\ H_2O$ decomposes reversibly, forming the lower hydrate according to the equation

$$CuSO_4 \cdot 5\ H_2O \rightleftharpoons CuSO_4 \cdot 3\ H_2O + 2\ H_2O$$

At 25°C, the partial pressure of water vapor in equilibrium with the two hydrates is 7.8 torr. At this equilibrium pressure, the rate of decomposition of the pentahydrate equals its rate of formation from the trihydrate. If crystals of the pentahydrate are left exposed to an atmosphere in which the partial pressure of water vapor is less than the equilibrium vapor pressure, they will lose water spontaneously, a process known as ***efflorescence,*** and form the lower hydrate. On the other hand, the trihydrate, kept in an atmosphere in which the partial pressure of water vapor is above the equilibrium vapor pressure, will absorb water until the pentahydrate is formed. The vapor pressure of a hydrate, like that of water itself, increases with increasing temperature, and most hydrated salts unless they decompose can be completely dehydrated by heating them.

A substance which absorbs water from the air, whether or not it is sufficiently soluble to deliquesce, is described as being ***hygroscopic.*** Hygroscopic substances which absorb water to form solutions or hydrates with very low vapor pressures are often employed as drying agents, or ***desiccants.*** The deliquescent salt calcium chloride is used for this purpose, for example, to dehumidify damp basements, and in the laboratory to maintain a dry atmosphere in a desiccator jar for storing chemicals.

Osmosis 10.12

Membranes of certain substances often exhibit a selective permeability toward solutions, that is, they may permit the passage of one component of a solution while impeding or preventing the passage of others. Examples of such ***semipermeable membranes*** are such things as parchment paper, collodion, and animal and plant membranes, including cell walls. A perfectly semipermeable membrane is one which permits the passage of only one component of a solution while completely preventing the passage of all others. The gelatinous chemical copper ferrocyanide, $Cu_2Fe(CN)_6 \cdot xH_2O$, precipitated within the pores of an earthenware cup, gives a supported membrane which is mechanically strong and nearly perfectly semipermeable to the water component of many aqueous solutions.

Suppose that we have a solution, say of sugar in water, on one side of such a semipermeable membrane and pure water on the other. Water can diffuse in both directions through the membrane, but passage of sugar molecules is prevented. Because the concentration of water molecules at the interface with the membrane is less on the side with the solution, the rate of diffusion of water through the membrane will be less from solution to pure solvent than in the opposite direction. The result is *a net transfer of solvent from the region of low* (in this case, zero) *solute concentration to the region of higher concentration, a process known as* ***osmosis.***

The apparatus shown in Fig. 10.9 is one form of *osmometer.* In this apparatus, the passage of solvent from the inner tube into the solution contained in the outer tube causes the water level in the capillary tube at A to drop. By applying pressure at B, however, it is possible to increase the rate of diffusion of solvent from the solution into the pure solvent so that it becomes equal to the rate of diffusion in the opposite direction, and in this way to maintain the water level stationary in A. The mechanical pressure which is just sufficient to accomplish this is defined as the ***osmotic pressure*** of the solution. At constant temperature, the osmotic pressure Π of a dilute solution is directly proportional to its concentration c. If the concentration of the solution is expressed in moles per liter and V is taken as the volume of

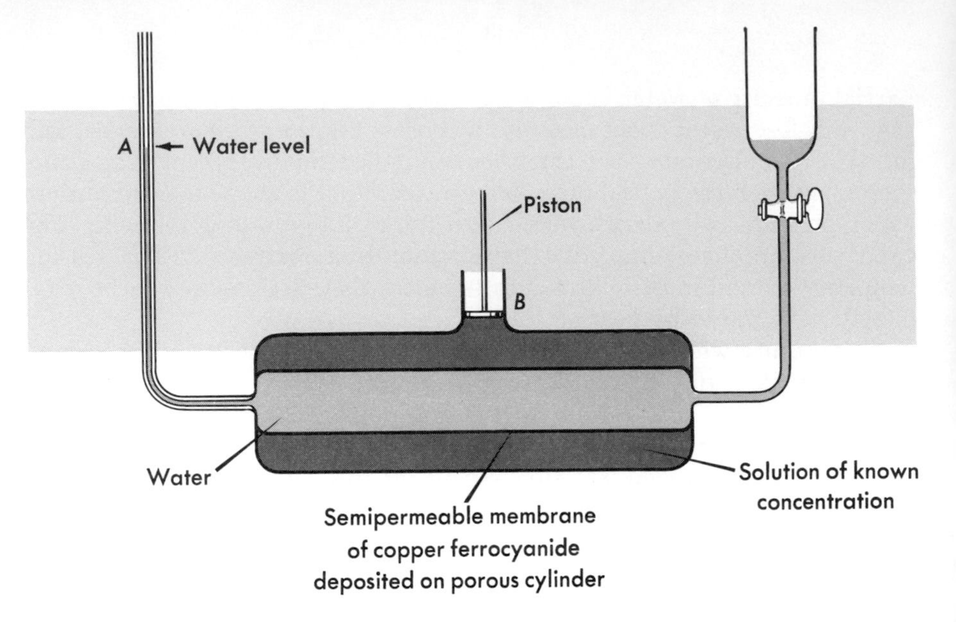

Fig. 10.9 Osmometer.

an equally concentrated solution containing 1 mole of solute, then $c = 1/V$, and the proportionality may be expressed as:

$$\Pi V = \text{constant}$$

At constant concentration it is found that the osmotic pressure of a dilute solution is very nearly proportional to the absolute temperature, that is,

$$\frac{\Pi}{T} = \text{constant}$$

In appearance, these two expressions are reminiscent of the laws of Boyle and Charles, only with the osmotic pressure of a solution substituted for the pressure of a gas. Combining both expressions leads to the van't Hoff equation:

$$\Pi V = RT$$

where R is a constant. Evaluation of R shows it to have the same value, 0.082 liter-atm/deg-mole, as the universal gas law constant. This implies that Avogadro's principle is applicable to the osmotic pressure of dilute solutions, i.e., *equal numbers of molecules of different solutes dissolved in the same volume of solution give the same osmotic pressure at the same temperature.* It also implies that for dilute solutions the osmotic pressure that results from a given concentration of solute is equal to the gas pressure that would result from an equal concentration of molecules in the gaseous state at the same temperature. This is in general borne out by experiment. The osmotic pressures of 0.1 M solutions of nonelectrolytes at 0°C average close to 2.24 atm. Thus the calculated osmotic pressure of a 1 M solution is 22.4 atm at 0°, which is also the pressure which, according to Boyle's law, would be exerted at that temperature by 1 mole of gas compressed into a volume of 1 liter. The van't Hoff law actually is valid only for quite dilute solutions. Deviations of 10% or more are not uncommon for 1 M solutions.

The van't Hoff equation has been applied to the determination of molecular weights of larger molecules such as those of proteins and other polymeric substances. This method is more suitable for substances of this sort than methods based on the boiling point elevation or freezing point depression. Solutions of quite low molar concentration exhibit appreciable osmotic pressures, while the differences in their boiling and freezing points from those of the pure solvent may be too small to measure with any degree of accuracy. For molecular weight determination, the van't Hoff equation is usually used in the form

$$\Pi V = \frac{g}{M} RT$$

where g is the number of grams of solute present in 1 liter of solution, and M is the molecular weight to be determined.

Osmosis plays a very important role in the physiological functioning of animals and plants. The transport of water in and out of living cells, for example in the absorption of water by the root cells of plants, the rise of sap in trees, and the functioning of the kidney, all depend upon osmosis. If animal or plant cells are placed in an aqueous solution having a lower concentration of solute than that of the fluid in the cell (***hypotonic solution***), water diffuses into the cells, causing them to swell and eventually to rupture. On the other hand, if the cells are immersed in a solution of higher solute concentration (***hypertonic solution***), water diffuses out of the cells, causing them to shrink. Red blood cells are very sensitive to these effects, and injections into the blood stream must be made using solutions that have the same osmotic pressure (***isotonic solutions***) as that of the solution inside the red cells. All materials that are injected into the blood stream are therefore placed in an isotonic physiological saline solution containing 0.9% NaCl.

Solutions with Two Volatile Components 10.13

According to Raoult's law, at any particular temperature, each component in an ideal solution exerts a partial vapor pressure equal to the vapor pressure of the pure component multiplied by its mole fraction in the solution. The total vapor pressure of the solution is the sum of the partial vapor pressures of its components. In Fig. 10.10 we see that the partial vapor pressure of each component increases linearly as its mole fraction in the solution increases. The total vapor pressure of the solution, which is the sum of the two partial pressures, also lies along a straight line and, regardless of the concentration, always has a value intermediate between the vapor pressures of the pure components. If the temperature of an ideal solution having a particular concentration is changed, the partial vapor pressures of each component, and hence the total vapor pressure of the solution, change correspondingly, increasing with increasing temperature until the total vapor pressure becomes equal to the external atmospheric pressure. At that point the solution boils.

Assuming that equilibrium exists between the liquid and vapor phases, if one of the components of the solution has a higher vapor pressure than

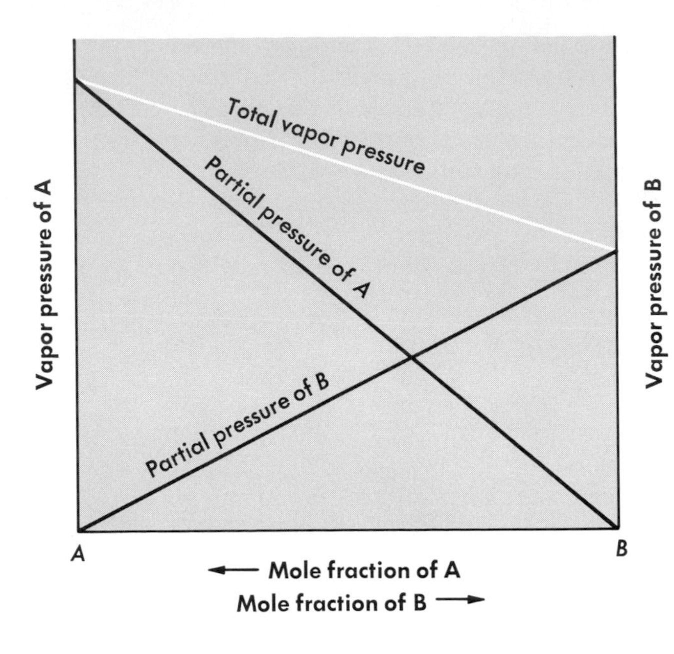

Fig. 10.10 Vapor pressure at constant temperature of various solutions of two components which form an ideal solution.

the other, then at all temperatures, including the boiling temperature, the concentration of the more volatile component is greater in the vapor than it is in the liquid. This can be shown to be the case as follows: Consider a solution containing 0.4 mole fraction of carbon tetrachloride and 0.6 mole fraction of chlorobenzene at 100°C. At this temperature the vapor pressure of carbon tetrachloride is 1457 torr; that of chlorobenzene is 293 torr. This solution exhibits ideal behavior, so that the partial vapor pressure of each component can be calculated from Raoult's law:

$$p_A = 0.4 \times 1457 = 582.8 \text{ torr}$$

$$p_B = 0.6 \times 293 = 175.8 \text{ torr}$$

The total vapor pressure of the solution is the sum of the partial pressures, $p_A + p_B = 758.6$ torr, which is the pressure under which this solution boils at 100°C. In Sec. 10.2(d) it was shown that the mole fraction of any component of a mixture of gases is equal to the partial pressure of that component divided by the total pressure. Therefore, taking X_A and X_B to represent the mole fractions of carbon tetrachloride and chlorobenzene, respectively, in the vapor phase:

$$X_A = \frac{p_A}{p_A + p_B} = \frac{582.8 \text{ torr}}{758.6 \text{ torr}} = 0.77$$

$$X_B = \frac{p_B}{p_A + p_B} = \frac{175.8 \text{ torr}}{758.6 \text{ torr}} = 0.23$$

This shows that with a liquid composition which is 40 mole-% in carbon tetrachloride (mole-% = mole fraction × 100) and 60 mole-% chlorobenzene, the vapor in equilibrium with the liquid at 100° is 77 mole-% carbon tetrachloride and only 23 mole-% chlorobenzene. In other words, the vapor is nearly twice as rich in the more volatile component than is the liquid at the same temperature.

Curves showing the compositions of liquid and vapor in equilibrium as a function of the boiling point at constant pressure for carbon tetrachloride–chlorobenzene solutions are shown in Fig. 10.11. The diagram is typical

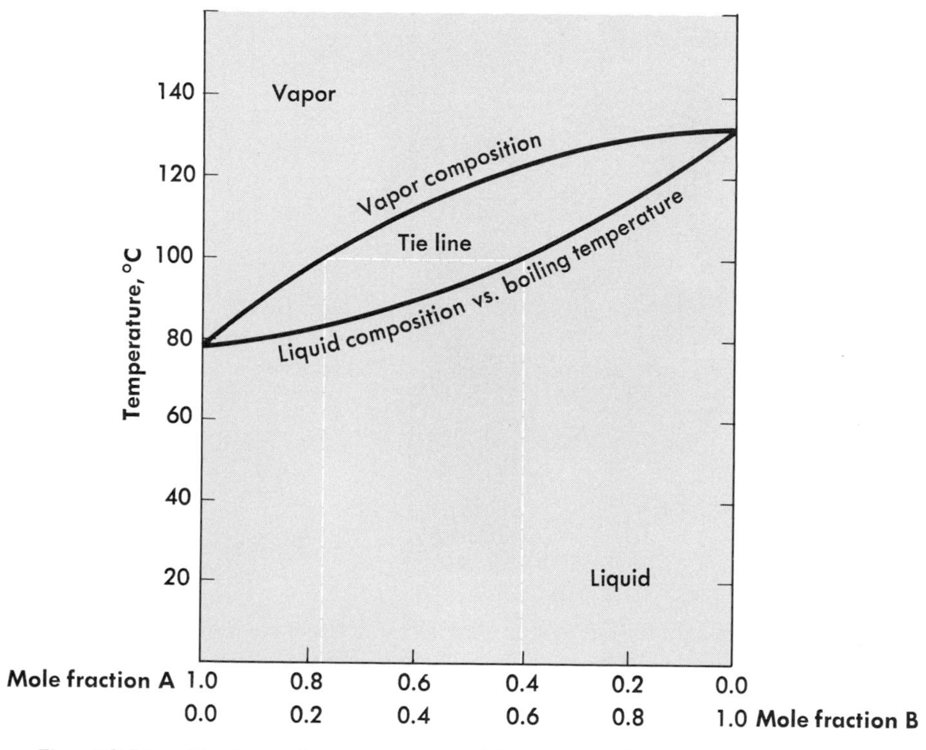

Fig. 10.11 Liquid and vapor composition curves for carbon tetrachloride – chlorobenzene solution at constant pressure.

for liquid systems which approach ideality. A horizontal tie line drawn from any point on the liquid curve to the vapor curve gives the composition of the vapor in equilibrium with the liquid at that temperature. It can be seen from the diagram that so long as both components are present in the liquid, the vapor in equilibrium with the liquid at the boiling temperature is always richer in the lower boiling component.

If, at the boiling temperature of a particular liquid mixture, the vapor is removed and a new liquid-vapor equilibrium established, the newly formed vapor will again be richer in the more volatile, lower boiling component. The liquid left behind necessarily becomes richer in the less volatile, higher boiling component, and its boiling temperature increases. In the process known as ***fractional distillation,*** the components of a liquid mixture are separated from one another by taking advantage of the difference in their volatilities. The process consists of subjecting the mixture to a series of successive distillations. In each distillation step, the liquid is boiled and the vapors are led to another part of the apparatus, where they are cooled and condensed to a liquid having a higher concentration of the more volatile component than the original mixture. The bubble plate column (Fig. 10.12a) is one form of apparatus designed for this purpose. At each level,

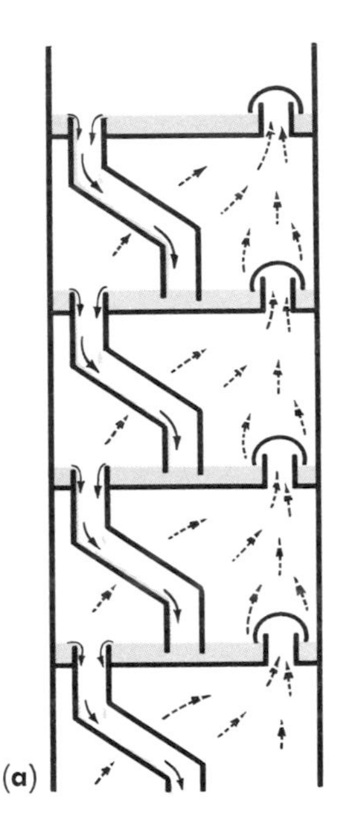

Fig. 10.12 Fractionating columns: (a) bubble plate column; (b) packed column.

or ***plate,*** in this column the vapor that rises to the next higher plate is richer in the more volatile component, and the liquid that overflows onto the next lower plate is enriched in the less volatile component. The more volatile substance therefore moves upward in the column during operation while the less volatile moves downward. Eventually, if enough plates are used, the pure lower-boiling fraction may be removed from the top of the column and the higher-boiling component at the bottom. Columns of this design are widely used in the petroleum industry for separating the various fractions—gasoline, kerosene, lubricating oils, fuel oil, etc.—from crude and refined petroleum. In a packed column, which as its name implies is simply a long tube packed with some kind of inert material, essentially the same process occurs as in the bubble plate column, except that it takes place continuously rather than in a series of steps.

Only a limited number of liquid–liquid solutions obey Raoult's law over the entire range of composition. Most solutions deviate from the law, the magnitude of the deviation depending upon the nature of the components. Where the molecular structure of the components is such that the forces of attraction between unlike molecules are greater than those between like molecules, the solution process is accompanied by the evolution of heat. In such cases the partial pressure of each component, and the total vapor pressure of the solution, is less than would be predicted from Raoult's law because the strong forces of attraction between unlike molecules decrease the "escaping tendency" of both kinds of molecules. This type of behavior

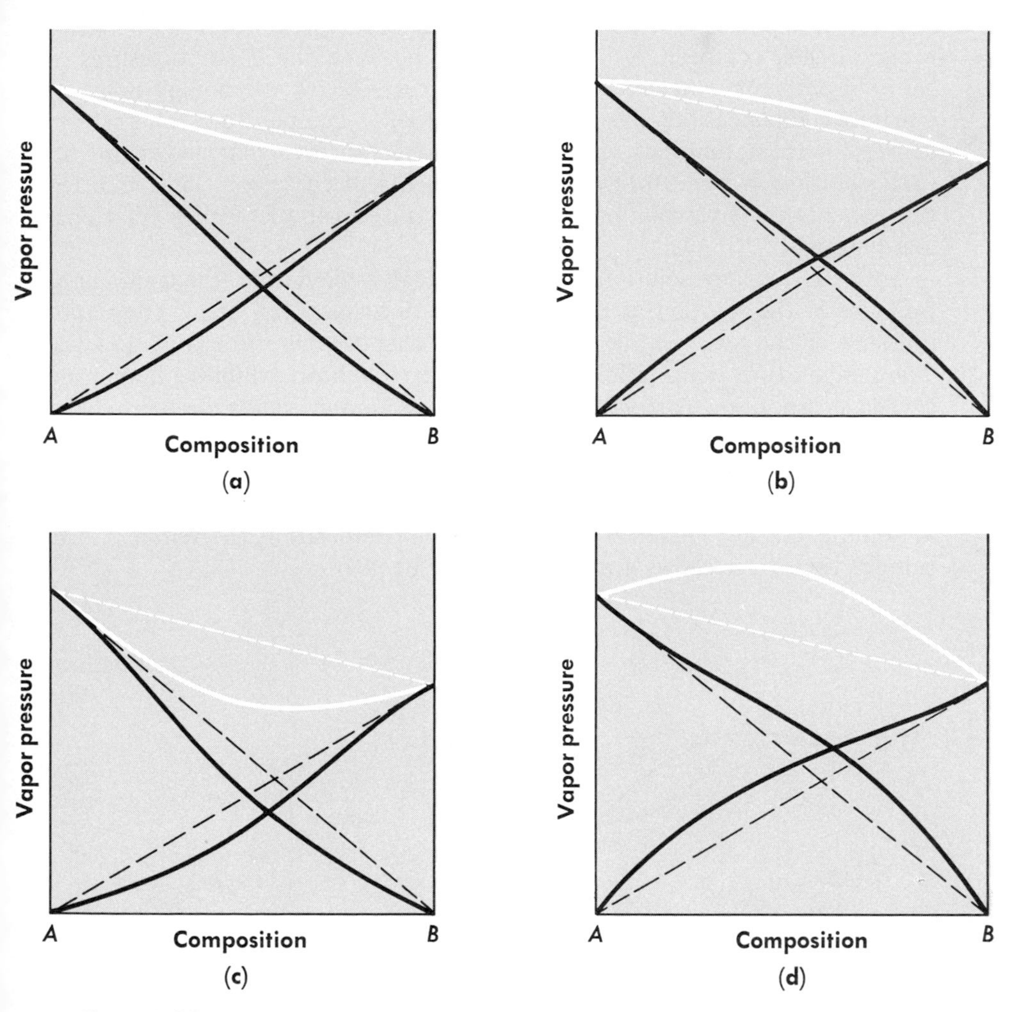

Fig. 10.13 Vapor pressure–composition curves at constant temperature showing (a) negative deviation with no minimum vapor pressure, (b) positive deviation with no maximum, (c) negative deviation with minimum, and (d) positive deviation with maximum.

is referred to as ***negative deviation*** from ideality, and it leads to a vapor pressure-composition diagram of the type shown in Fig. 10.13a. When the forces of attraction between unlike molecules are less than those between molecules of the same kind, the solution process is accompanied by absorption of heat. In these cases the partial pressure of each component, as well as the total vapor pressure of the solution, is greater than predicted because the stronger forces of attraction between like molecules cause each component to tend to "squeeze" the other out of solution, thus increasing the tendency of the squeezed component to escape. This leads to ***positive deviation,*** and a vapor pressure-composition diagram of the type in Fig. 10.13b. Solutions like these, which exhibit positive or negative deviation from ideal behavior, but for which the total vapor pressure over the entire range of their composition is intermediate between the vapor pressures of the two pure components, boil at temperatures below the boiling point of one pure component but above that of the other. Temperature-composition curves for these solutions are similar in appearance to that shown for an ideal solution in Fig. 10.11. The components of these solutions, like the components of ideal solutions, can be separated completely by fractional distillation.

In some cases, for solutions exhibiting negative deviation, the total vapor pressure of the solution at certain compositions may fall below the vapor pressure of the less volatile component at that temperature (Fig. 10.13c). The temperature-composition curve for such a solution exhibits a maximum at the composition corresponding to the minimum vapor pressure (Fig. 10.14a). Likewise, a solution showing positive deviation may have a total vapor pressure greater than that of the more volatile component (Fig. 10.13d). For a solution of this sort, the vapor pressure attains a maximum at some particular composition, and at this composition the temperature-composition curve shows a minimum (Fig. 10.14b).

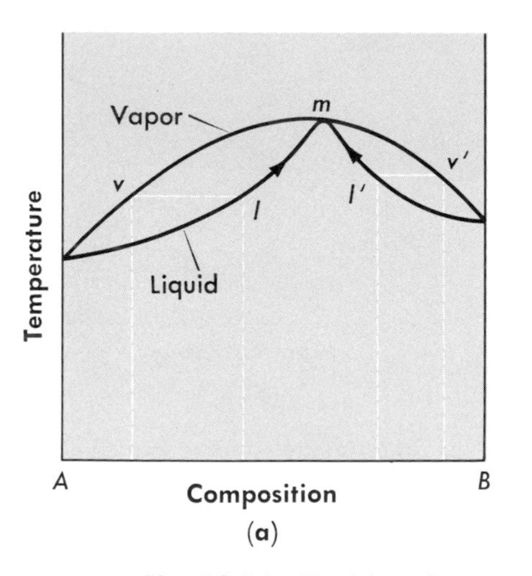

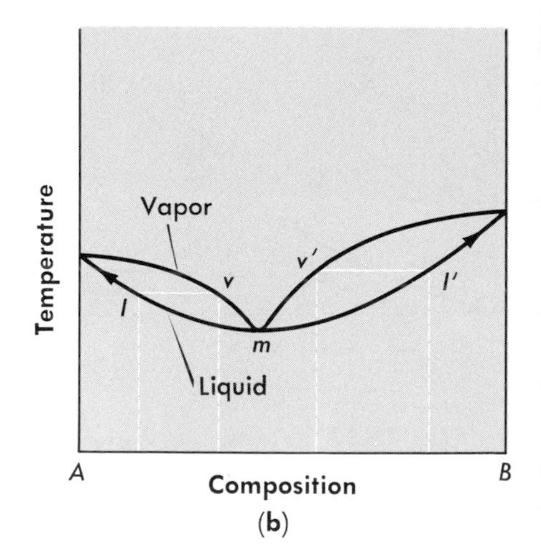

Fig. 10.14 Liquid and vapor composition curves for (a) solution exhibiting a maximum boiling azeotrope and (b) solution exhibiting a minimum boiling azeotrope.

The particular solution composition which corresponds to the maximum or minimum on the temperature-composition or boiling point diagram is called an ***azeotropic mixture,*** or ***azeotrope.*** Upon distillation, the composition and boiling temperature of an azeotrope remain unchanged because the vapor and liquid phases in equilibrium have the same composition. The components of an azeotrope therefore cannot be separated by distillation. A solution whose composition does not correspond to that of the azeotrope can be separated by fractional distillation into one pure component and the azeotrope. For example, if a solution with the liquid composition l in

Fig. 10.14a is distilled, the vapor v in equilibrium with the liquid is richer in component A than is the liquid. The residual solution therefore becomes enriched in B, and if the vapor is continuously removed, the boiling point of the residue rises as its composition moves along the liquid composition curve from l to m. Fractional distillation of this mixture thus results in final separation into pure A and the constant boiling azeotrope. Similarly, a solution with a composition represented by l' can be separated into pure B and the azeotrope.

Hydrogen chloride in water is an example of a system with a maximum boiling point. At 1 atm, the azeotrope boils at 108.58°C and contains 20.222% **HCl**. Constant-boiling **HCl** can be used as a concentration standard for preparing acid solutions of known concentration (standard solutions). An example of a solution with a minimum boiling point is that of ethyl alcohol and water. For this system, the azeotrope (1 atm) boils at 78.13°C and contains 95.57% by weight of alcohol. Fractional distillation of aqueous solutions of ethyl alcohol containing less than 95.57% of the alcohol cannot yield a distillate any richer in alcohol than the azeotrope.

Solutions of Electrolytes 10.14

Solutions of electrolytes are characterized by their ability to conduct an electric current (Sec. 5.1). The conductivity of an electrolyte in solution is measured in terms of its equivalent conductance Λ, which is defined as the total conductivity in reciprocal ohms (ohms^{-1} or mhos) of a volume of solution containing one equivalent weight of solute placed between two parallel electrodes which are 1 cm apart and sufficiently large to contain all of the solution between them.* Experimentally, it is found that different electrolytes vary in their equivalent conductance, and the equivalent conductance of any one electrolyte increases with dilution, reaching a limiting maximum value at infinite dilution.

Solutions of electrolytes exhibit abnormal colligative properties. The colligative effect of an electrolyte solution is always greater than that of a solution of a nonelectrolyte of the same molal concentration. The ratio between the observed lowering of the vapor pressure, elevation of the boiling

* For a given electrolyte solution the conductance varies directly with the area of the electrodes and inversely with the distance between them. To compare the conductivity of different solutions, the dependence upon electrode dimensions and spacing is eliminated by calculating the specific conductance k, which is related to the measured conductance L by the equation

$$k = L\frac{l}{A},$$

where l is the distance between the electrodes in centimeters, and A is the electrode area in square centimeters. Thus, the specific conductance is the conductance that would be obtained using electrodes with an area of 1 cm² spaced 1 cm apart. The equivalent conductance is related to the specific conductance by the expression

$$\Lambda = k\left(\frac{1000}{c}\right)$$

where c is the concentration of the solution in equivalents/liter.

point, depression of the freezing point, or osmotic pressure of the solvent in an electrolyte solution and the corresponding value for an equally concentrated ideal solution of a nonelectrolyte is known as the ***van't Hoff factor*** and is designated by the letter i in each case. Thus,

$$\frac{\Delta p_{\text{vapor}}}{(\Delta p_{\text{vapor}})_0} = i$$

$$\frac{\Delta T_{\text{b}}}{(\Delta T_{\text{b}})_0} = i$$

$$\frac{\Delta T_{\text{f}}}{(\Delta T_{\text{f}})_0} = i$$

$$\frac{\Pi}{(\Pi)_0} = i$$

where the subscript zero refers in each instance to the effect produced by a solute which is a nonelectrolyte. The van't Hoff factor i increases with dilution, approaching a limiting value of 2, 3, or 4 at infinite dilution, depending upon the nature of the electrolyte.

10.15 The Arrhenius Theory

The theory which Svante Arrhenius proposed in 1887 to account for both the electrical conductivity and the abnormal colligative properties of electrolyte solutions was described briefly in Sec. 5.3. You will recall that, according to this theory, when an electrolyte is dissolved in water it immediately dissociates to some degree into oppositely charged fragments which we call ions. Dissociation is assumed to be favored by dilution, reaching a value of 100% at infinite dilution. The theory predicts that the equivalent conductance should increase with dilution, since dilution is accompanied by an increase in the number of current-carrying ions that become available per equivalent of dissolved solute. The van't Hoff factor i increases with dilution for the same reason, namely, that the total number of particles—ions in this case—present in the solution per mole of solute dissolved increases with dilution. The limiting integral value of i, equal to 2, 3, or 4, may be taken as representing dissociation at infinite dilution into 2, 3, or 4 moles of ions per mole of solute.

10.16 Strong and Weak Electrolytes

Examination of Table 10.4 reveals that different electrolytes differ markedly in their ability to conduct electricity in solution. KCl and HCl have large equivalent conductances at all concentrations and are known as ***strong electrolytes.*** Acetic acid ($HC_2H_3O_2$) and ammonium hydroxide (NH_4OH)* exhibit small equivalent conductances except at infinite dilution and are examples of ***weak electrolytes.*** Among both strong and weak electrolytes the equivalent conductance increases with decreasing concen-

* See Sec. 13.2.

TABLE 10.4 Equivalent Conductance of Electrolytes in Water at 25°C

Concentration, eq/liter	Λ, ohms^{-1} KCl	HCl	$HC_2H_3O_2$	NH_4OH
0.000[a]	149.86	426.16	390.7	271.4
0.001	146.95	421.36	49.2	34.0
0.010	141.27	412.00	16.3	11.3
0.100	128.96	391.32	5.2	3.6
1.000	111.9	332.8	—	—

[a] By extrapolation.

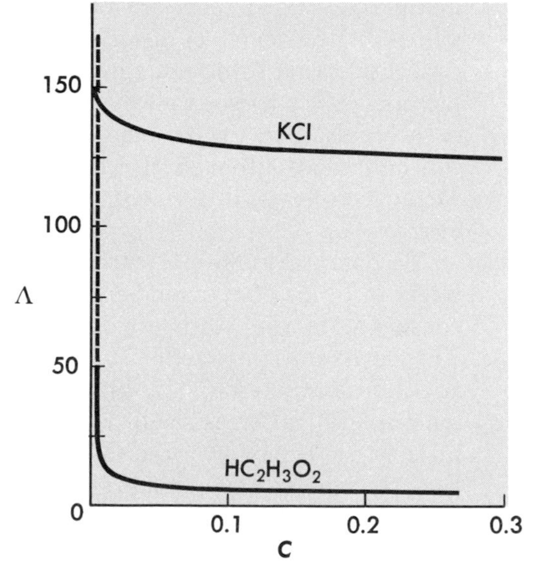

Fig. 10.15 Variation of equivalent conductance of a strong electrolyte (KCl) and a weak electrolyte ($HC_2H_3O_2$) with concentration.

tration. This is also shown graphically for KCl and $HC_2H_3O_2$ in Fig. 10.15. Strong electrolytes show a comparatively small change in conductivity with dilution, however, while weak electrolytes show a large increase in conductivity at very low concentrations. All ionic compounds, which includes almost all salts and strong bases, are strong electrolytes. Some polar covalent compounds are also strong electrolytes in solution because they react almost completely with water and are largely dissociated into ions in the process. The strong acids, such as HCl, HNO_3, H_2SO_4, and $HClO_4$ belong to this class of strong electrolytes. Weak electrolytes include most organic acids (Sec. 17.3), carbonic acid (H_2CO_3), boric acid (H_3BO_3), hydrosulfuric acid (H_2S), a very few salts (e.g., Hg_2Cl_2), and ammonia and its organic derivatives, the amines.

If it is assumed that the increase in equivalent conductance with dilution is caused solely by the increase in the number of ions present per equivalent of dissolved solute, and that the solute is completely dissociated at infinite dilution, the apparent degree of dissociation α of an electrolyte can be calculated simply from the ratio Λ/Λ_0, where Λ_0 is the equivalent conductivity at infinite dilution. The degree of dissociation may also be calculated from values of the van't Hoff factors. Taking n as the number of ions formed per molecule of solute, the total number of moles i of all kinds of particles (dissociated and undissociated) present per mole of solute dissolved is

$$i = (1 - \alpha) + n\alpha$$

and

$$\alpha = \frac{i - 1}{n - 1}$$

10.17 Defects in the Arrhenius Theory

For weak electrolytes, the values of α obtained by each of the two methods described above are found to be in good agreement. However, the values for the degree of dissociation of strong electrolytes as obtained from conductance ratios do not agree with those calculated from the van't Hoff factors. Since these two ways of calculating the degree of dissociation are each based upon the assumptions of the Arrhenius theory, one is led to conclude that although the theory is essentially valid for solutions of weak electrolytes, it does not correctly account for the behavior of strong electrolytes.

The Arrhenius theory attempts to explain the behavior of electrolytes solely in terms of the number of dissolved particles and does not take into consideration the possible existence of interionic attractions in solution. The electrostatic attraction between ions in solution must affect their distribution and motion. In dilute solutions of weak electrolytes, where the ionic concentration is small, the effect of interionic attraction contributes little to the behavior of the solution, and the Arrhenius theory is valid for those solutions. The situation with respect to strong electrolytes is quite different. To begin with, it is now known that ionic salts are completely ionized in the crystalline state and undergo no further ionization in solution. Other strong electrolytes, even though not ionic in the pure state, nevertheless are completely ionized in solution even at fairly high concentration. The ionic concentration in solutions of strong electrolytes is therefore large compared to that in equimolar solutions of weak electrolytes. The effect of inter-ionic attraction is also larger as a result, and contributes appreciably to the behavior of these solutions, becoming more pronounced as the concentration increases.

10.18 The Debye-Hückel Theory of Interionic Attraction

According to the Debye-Hückel theory, oppositely charged ions tend to become associated in solution, and the degree of association increases with increasing concentration and increasing ionic charge. This results in a lowering of the *effective* ionic concentration, which accounts for the fact that the van't Hoff factor for strong electrolytes depends upon concentration

TABLE 10.5 Van't Hoff Factors for Various Strong Electrolytes

Molality	KCl	HCl	$MgSO_4$	K_2SO_4	$CoCl_2$	$K_4Fe(CN)_6$
0.0005	—	—	—	—	—	3.92
0.0010	—	1.98	—	2.84	2.91	3.82
0.0050	1.96	1.95	1.69	2.77	2.80	3.51
0.0100	1.94	1.94	1.62	2.70	2.75	3.31
0.0500	1.88	1.90	1.42	2.45	2.64	3.01
0.1000	1.86	1.89	1.32	2.32	2.62	2.85
0.2000	1.83	1.90	1.22	2.17	2.66	2.69

and charge (Table 10.5). With dilution, the degree of ionic association decreases with increasing distance between ions, and the effective ionic concentration approaches the actual ionic concentration of 2, 3, or 4 times Avogadro's number of ions per mole. The van't Hoff factors therefore approach limiting integral values at infinite dilution, where interionic attractions disappear.

Apart from the association between ions that results in a lowering of the effective particle concentration, interionic attraction also results in a decrease in ionic mobility because each ion attracts oppositely charged ions and repels like charged ions. Each ion is therefore surrounded by an "atmosphere" of oppositely charged ions which acts as a drag on its rate of migration through the solution under the influence of an electrical potential. The reduction in the mobility of an ion which results might be compared to the reduction in the mobility of a convict wearing a ball and chain on his ankle. The drag effect becomes less pronounced as the concentration is reduced until at extreme dilution it virtually disappears and the equivalent conductance reaches a limiting value.

Reading Suggestions 10.19

For a more detailed discussion of the nature of liquids and solutions than can be given here, see *Liquids and Solutions* by Dale Dreisbach (Volume G-3 in the series *Classic Researches in General Chemistry*, Houghton Mifflin Co., Boston, 1966). Chapter 5 of *The Mole Concept in Chemistry*, by William F. Kieffer (*Selected Topics in Modern Chemistry* series, Reinhold Publishing Corp., New York, 1962), dealing with the properties of liquid solutions, includes a number of illustrative examples based upon the colligative properties of solutions. The rôle played by the solvent in chemical reactions in solution is discussed in Chapter 1 of *Chemistry in Non-aqueous Solvents* by Harry H. Sisler (*Selected Topics in Chemistry* series, Reinhold Publishing Corp., New York, 1961). The behavior of solutes in a number of less familiar solvent systems is presented in an exceptionally clear fashion in the remaining chapters of this book.

The history of the Rast method and the use of camphor as a solvent in determining molecular weights by the depression of the freezing point is presented in a paper by Elwood R. Shaw and Earle R. Caley, *J. Chem. Ed.* **35,** 355 (1958). A fascinating early history of the process of distillation, by A. J. Liebmann, appears in *J. Chem. Ed.*, **33,** 166 (1956).

Questions and Problems

10.1 In view of what is meant by solution as described in the introductory paragraph of this chapter, is it possible to have a solution of a liquid in a gas? Why is a fog not a solution?

10.2 How does one account for the solubility of hydrogen in platinum?

10.3 What determines whether the process of dissolving a solid in a liquid is exothermic or endothermic?

10.4 Provide an explanation for the fact that the solubility of certain solids in water increases with rising temperature while for others the solubility decreases with rising temperature.

10.5 Account for the breaks in the solubility curves appearing in Fig. 10.4.

10.6 How can one demonstrate that a dynamic equilibrium exists between a saturated solution and an excess of undissolved solute?

10.7 Why do some solids deliquesce while others do not? If deliquescence of a compound is to occur, what conditions must be met?

10.8 Provide an explanation for the lowering of the vapor pressure of a liquid by a nonvolatile solute in terms of the kinetic molecular theory.

10.9 Suggest why the osmotic pressure of a solution should be proportional to its molecular concentration.

10.10 What are colligative properties and what gives rise to them?

10.11 State Raoult's law and explain why it does not apply to concentrated solutions and solutions of electrolytes.

10.12 What will happen to the contents of a beaker containing ice and a beaker containing a 1 molal sugar solution when both are placed under a bell jar and held at a temperature of (a) 0°C, (b) −1.86°C, (c) −4.0°C?

10.13 Define the term milliequivalents in terms of (a) normality and milliliters, (b) milligrams and equivalent weight.

10.14 When is the molality of a solute proportional to its mole fraction? Explain why the proportionality exists.

10.15 Calculate the molarity of each of the following solutions:
- (a) 4.9 g H_2SO_4 in 1.0 liter of solution.
- (b) 80 mg $NaOH$ in 80 ml of solution.
- (c) 85 g H_3PO_4 in 100 ml of solution.
- (d) 6.30 g $H_2C_2O_4 \cdot 2\ H_2O$ in 500 ml solution.

10.16 Calculate the normality of each solution listed under problem 10.15.

10.17 Concentrated nitric acid is 70% HNO_3 and has a density of 1.42 g/ml. Calculate the molarity of concentrated nitric acid.

10.18 What volumes of concentrated nitric acid (15.8 *M*) and of water are mixed to prepare 500 ml of 0.100 *M* HNO_3?

10.19 A 10.0% solution of H_3PO_4 has a density of 1.053 g/ml. What is (a) the molarity and (b) the molality of this solution?

10.20 An 85% solution of H_3PO_4, syrupy phosphoric acid, has a density of 1.689 g/ml. What is (a) the molarity and (b) the molality of this solution?

10.21 In what volume of solution should 1.000 g of $KBrO_3$ (molecular weight 167) be dissolved in order to prepare a 0.1000 *N* solution of $KBrO_3$ to be employed in the reaction

$$BrO_3^- + 6\,I^- + 6\,H^+ \rightarrow Br^- + 3\,I_2 + 3\,H_2O$$

What is the molarity of the $KBrO_3$ solution?

10.22 The reaction by which the percentage of Mo_2O_3 in an ore sample is quantitatively determined is

$$5\,Mo^{+++} + 3\,MnO_4^- + 8\,H_2O \rightarrow 5\,MoO_4^{--} + 3\,Mn^{++} + 16\,H^+$$

(a) How many grams of $KMnO_4$ (mol. wt. = 158) must be dissolved in a liter of solution to make it 0.1000 *N*? (b) What is the equivalent weight of Mo_2O_3?

10.23 0.1022 g of an unknown acid H_2X is neutralized by 40.00 ml of a 0.1500 *N* NaOH solution. (a) What is the equivalent weight of this acid? (b) What is the atomic weight of X?

10.24 204.2 mg of pure potassium acid phthalate, $KHC_8H_4O_4$, is exactly neutralized by titration with 39.22 ml of NaOH solution. What is the normality of the NaOH solution?

10.25 A 1.000-g sample containing oxalic acid, $H_2C_2O_4$, requires 41.10 ml of 0.1020 *N* NaOH for neutralization. Find the percentage of oxalic acid in the sample.

10.26 (a) A 0.200 g sample of a pure organic acid, m.p. = 153°C, requires 30.49 ml of 0.1020 *N* NaOH for its complete neutralization. What is the equivalent weight of the organic acid? (b) Organic acids that melt within ±2.0°C from the observed melting point of 153° are:

	Molecular Weight	No. of Replaceable H^+
adipic acid	166	2
p-nitrophenylacetic acid	181	1
2,4-dichlorobenzoic acid	191	1
citric acid	192	3
m-bromobenzoic acid	201	1
2,4,6-trimethybenzoic acid	164	1

What acid has this analytical procedure revealed the sample to be?

10.27 When a mixture of 54 mg of an unknown compound and 520 mg of camphor is heated to form a melt that is then allowed to cool slowly, the first crystallization from solution occurs at 156.9°C. What is the molecular weight of the unknown? The camphor used in the experiment was itself found to freeze at 178.6°C.

10.28 A solution containing 4.00 g of sucrose (a nonelectrolyte) in 50.0 g of water freezes at −0.435°C. Calculate the molecular weight of sucrose.

10.29 Calculate the weights of (a) methanol, CH_4O, and (b) ethylene glycol, $C_2H_6O_2$, that must be dissolved per liter of water to just prevent the formation of ice at −10°C.

10.30 A solution of 0.465 g of aniline, a nondissociated solute, in 10.0 g of benzene, freezes at 2.94°C. Calculate the molecular weight of aniline.

10.31 (a) The osmotic pressure created by 2.0 g of a protein per 100 ml of solution is found to be equal to 22 torr (22/760 atm). What is the molecular weight of the protein? (b) What is the molar concentration of the solution and (c) by how much would the freezing point of water be depressed by this concentration of solute? *Ans.* (a) 17,000, (b) 1.2×10^{-3}, (c) 0.002°C

10.32 Solutions of carbon tetrachloride (CCl_4) in chlorobenzene (C_6H_5Cl) exhibit ideal behavior. At 50°C, the vapor pressure of carbon tetrachloride is 317.1 torr, and that of chlorobenzene is 42.0 torr. What is the vapor pressure at 50°C of a solution containing 50 g of each liquid, and what is the composition, expressed in terms of mole fraction, of carbon tetrachloride in the vapor in equilibrium with the solution? *Ans.* 145.6 torr; 0.915

10.33 Benzene and toluene form ideal solutions. At 100°C, the vapor pressure of benzene is 1357 torr, and that of toluene is 558 torr. Calculate the mole fraction of benzene in the solution which will boil at 100°C at 1 atm, and in the vapor which is in equilibrium with the solution at that temperature.

Ans. Mole fraction benzene in liquid = 0.253
Mole fraction benzene in vapor = 0.451

10.34 From the values of equivalent conductances given in Table 10.4, calculate the percent dissociation at 25°C of (a) 0.100 *N* acetic acid, (b) 0.010 *N* acetic acid.

All the King's horses and all the King's men
Couldn't put Humpty Dumpty together again.

——Mother Goose

11 INTRODUCTORY THERMODYNAMICS

Poor Humpty Dumpty learned two fundamental laws of nature the hard way during his celebrated fall: (1) things fall down; (2) it's awfully hard to unscramble an egg. These two laws are in constant operation, not only on eggs, but on everything around us. For example, a truck parked at the top of a hill will roll to the bottom of its own accord if its brakes slip. As it rolls, the potential energy it possessed by virtue of its position at the top of the hill is converted into kinetic energy. When it reaches the bottom it is in a state of lower potential energy than it was at the top. In its travels, the truck may run into a building, reducing it to rubble, but if it runs into a pile of rubble it is not likely to change it into a building. Experience tells us that objects tend to roll downhill and that a random, or disordered, arrangement of objects is usually more probable than an orderly one. Expressed more elegantly, this principle states that the most probable state of a system* is one of maximum disorder and minimum potential energy. The two tendencies, toward maximum disorder and minimum potential energy, often operate at cross purposes, that is, the most disordered state of a system is not necessarily the state of lowest potential energy. In such a case, the most probable final state of the system is determined by which of the two tendencies predominates under a given set of conditions.

Thermodynamics is the study of the interrelationships among the energy

* *A **system** is any isolated collection of materials whose interactions we happen to be investigating.* A system may be as large as the universe or as small as a single atomic nucleus. In the example above, the system consists of the truck, the hill, and the building. In the laboratory, the most common system is a beaker of reacting chemicals.

changes which accompany chemical and physical processes. These energy changes generally result in a transfer of heat between the system and its surroundings. From quantitative measurements of this heat transfer, together with a knowledge of thermodynamics, it is often possible to obtain an insight into the nature of a reaction process and in many cases to predict the course of a reaction in the absence of experimental data.

11.1 Heat of Reaction

The amount of heat evolved or absorbed during a chemical reaction is called the ***heat of reaction.*** If heat is evolved, as for example when hydrogen burns in oxygen, the reaction is described as ***exothermic.*** A reaction accompanied by the absorption of heat is said to be ***endothermic.*** Clearly, if a system *evolves* heat during a reaction, it must contain *less* heat after the reaction than it did before. Conversely, if it *absorbs* heat during a reaction, it will contain *more* heat after the reaction is complete. For a reaction carried out at constant pressure, for example, in an open beaker, the heat of reaction is equal to the change in the ***heat content,*** or ***enthalpy*** H of the system:

$$\text{Heat of reaction at constant pressure} = H_2 - H_1 = \Delta H$$

where H_1 and H_2 are the respective heat contents of the system before and after the reaction. *An exothermic reaction is accompanied by a decrease in enthalpy, and the sign of* ΔH *is therefore negative. An endothermic reaction involves an increase in enthalpy and a positive value for* ΔH.

The heat content of a substance depends to some extent upon its physical state and its temperature. Water vapor, for example, contains more heat per mole than liquid water at the same temperature because heat is required to evaporate the liquid (heat of vaporization, Sec. 9.4). Liquid water at 100°C has a larger heat content per mole than liquid water at 25°C because heat is required to raise the temperature of any substance. Because of this, when writing a thermodynamic equation in which the heat of reaction is expressed, it is necessary to specify the temperature and the physical states of all of the reactants and products. The equation

$$H_2(g) + \tfrac{1}{2}\, O_2(g) \rightarrow H_2O(l) \quad \Delta H_{298} = -68.32 \text{ kcal}$$

states that when one mole of hydrogen gas and one-half mole of oxygen gas react at 298°K (25°C) to form one mole of liquid water, 68.32 kcal of heat are liberated as the heat of reaction.

In the absence of catalysts hydrogen and oxygen do not react to any detectable extent at 25°C, and therefore the enthalpy change for this reaction cannot readily be measured directly at that temperature. The heat of reaction at one temperature can, however, be calculated from that obtained at a different temperature provided that the heat capacities C of all of the reactants and products are known. The heat capacity of an object is a measure of the amount of heat required to raise its temperature by a given amount. *The* ***molar heat capacity*** *of a substance is the amount of heat in calories required to raise the temperature of 1 mole of that substance 1°C.* The heat capacity per gram is also known as the ***specific heat*** (Sec. 1.10).

Suppose that we are able to measure ΔH at some temperature t_2 for the reaction

$$\text{Reactants} \rightarrow \text{Products}$$

for which we wish to determine ΔH at some other temperature t_1. The law of conservation of energy requires that the same total amount of energy should be absorbed or evolved whether the reactants are heated to t_2 and then allowed to react at that temperature, or whether the reaction takes place initially at t_1, after which the products are heated to t_2. The heat absorbed in raising the temperature of the reactants from t_1 to t_2 will be equal to the product of the heat capacity of the reactants multiplied by the change in temperature Δt, where $\Delta t = t_2 - t_1$. Similarly, the heat absorbed in heating the products from t_1 to t_2 will be equal to the product of the heat capacity of the products multiplied by Δt:

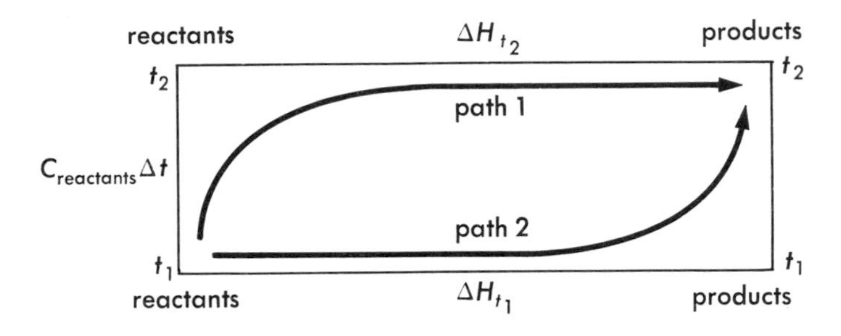

Thus,

$$\text{Total heat change (path 1)} = C_{\text{reactants}}\,\Delta t + \Delta H_{t_2}$$

$$\text{Total heat change (path 2)} = C_{\text{products}}\,\Delta t + \Delta H_{t_1}$$

$$\text{Total heat change (path 1)} = \text{total heat change (path 2)}$$

$$C_{\text{reactants}}\,\Delta t + \Delta H_{t_2} = C_{\text{products}}\,\Delta t + \Delta H_{t_1}$$

$$\Delta H_{t_1} = \Delta H_{t_2} + (C_{\text{reactants}} - C_{\text{products}})\Delta t$$

The measured heat of reaction may be different if a reaction is carried out in a closed vessel rather than an open one, especially if any of the reactants or products are gases. In an open vessel, the system is free to expand or contract as required to maintain the pressure constant. If the system expands, however, it performs work.* Conversely, work must be done on the system to cause it to contract. By definition, work is the product of a force multiplied by a distance. If the volume of a system under an external pressure of p dynes/cm^2 changes from V_1 cm^3 to V_2 cm^3, the product of the pressure multiplied by the change in volume,

$$p\Delta V = \frac{(\text{dynes})(\text{cm}^3)}{(\text{cm}^2)} = \text{dynes (force)} \times \text{cm (distance)}$$

is equal to the work performed. If the volume increases during the reaction, $V_2 > V_1$, $p\Delta V$ is *positive*, and work is performed *by* the system. If there is

* This is convincingly illustrated in an automobile engine, where the expansion of the burning gases furnishes the work needed to move the car.

a decrease in volume, $V_1 > V_2$, $p\Delta V$ is *negative*, and work is done *on* the system. It takes energy to do work, so this work corresponds to energy evolved or absorbed by the system, but since it is not in the form of heat, it is not measured as part of the enthalpy change. The difference between the observed enthalpy change at constant pressure and the ***total energy change*** ΔE that the system undergoes during a reaction corresponds to the work done by or on the system:

$$\Delta H - \Delta E = p\Delta V$$

Example 11.1

At 1 atm, ΔH_{298} for the reaction

$$H_2(g) + \tfrac{1}{2}\,O_2(g) \rightarrow H_2O(l)$$

is -68.32 kcal per mole of water formed. Calculate ΔE_{298} for this reaction.

Solution: Applying the combined gas law equation, the total initial volume of the reactant H_2 and O_2 is calculated to be 3.67×10^4 cm³. The final volume of the water ($d \approx 1$ g/cm³) is about 18 cm³. ΔV is therefore $(18 - 3.67 \times 10^4) \approx -3.67 \times 10^4$ cm³; $p = 1$ atm $= 1.01 \times 10^6$ dynes/cm².

$$p\Delta V = \frac{(1.01 \times 10^6 \text{ dynes/cm}^2)(-3.67 \times 10^4 \text{ cm}^3)}{(4.18 \times 10^7 \text{ dynes-cm/cal})} = -0.89 \text{ kcal}$$

$$\Delta E = \Delta H - p\Delta V$$

$$\Delta E = -68.32 + 0.89 = -67.43 \text{ kcal}$$

The amount of energy actually lost by the system is seen to be less than the heat evolved at constant pressure. This is as we would expect, since part of the energy lost as heat was replaced by the work done on the system as its volume decreased.

If a reaction is carried out in a sealed vessel so that the volume cannot change, $p\Delta V = 0$, and $\Delta H = \Delta E$. Most reactions in which all reactants and products are liquids or solids involve negligible volume changes, so that for all practical purposes, ΔH and ΔE may be assumed to be equal in those particular cases also. It is well to remember that it is not the pressure *of* the gas, but rather the pressure *on* the gas, that is, the pressure against which the gas is working, which determines the amount of work done. Therefore in the special case of free expansion into a vacuum, since $p = 0$, no work is done and $\Delta H = \Delta E$.

The work done by or on a system may be in some form other than that of expansion or contraction. Mechanical and electrical work are familiar examples. In any event, however, whatever the form in which the work appears, the total change in the internal energy ΔE of a system is equal to the quantity of heat q added to the system less the work w performed by the system on its surroundings:

$$\Delta E = q - w$$

This equation amounts to a mathematical expression of the ***law of conservation of energy,*** also known as the ***first law of thermodynamics.*** ΔE depends only on the initial and final states of the system and is called a ***state function.*** On the other hand, q and w depend upon the manner in which the change is carried out, each varying with the other in such a way that ΔE remains constant.

It is frequently inconvenient or impossible to measure the heat of a particular reaction directly, but it can readily be calculated, provided that the heat contents of all of the reactants and products are known. Although the absolute heat content of a substance cannot readily be determined, it is possible to measure the change in heat content when a substance is formed from its constituent elements. *The change in heat content when one mole of a substance is formed from its elements in their standard states is called the* ***heat of formation*** *of that substance. A substance is described as being in its* ***standard state*** *when it is in its stable form at* 298°K (25°C) *and* 1 atm *pressure.* By convention, *the heat contents of all elements in their standard states are arbitrarily taken as zero.* Following this convention, the heat content of a substance becomes equivalent to its heat of formation. The symbol ΔH_f^0 is used to represent the ***standard heat of formation,*** the superscript zero indicating that all reactants and products are in their stable forms at 1 atm and 298°K. For any reaction, then, the heat of reaction is equal to the difference between the heats of formation of the products and the reactants.

Example 11.2

Given the following heats of formation:

	ΔH_f^0
CH_4	−17.89 kcal/mole
CH_3OH	−57.02 kcal/mole
H_2O	−68.32 kcal/mole

calculate ΔH_{298}^0 for the hypothetical reaction

$$CH_4(g) + H_2O(l) \rightarrow CH_3OH(l) + H_2(g)$$

Solution: The heat of formation ΔH_f^0 for elemental hydrogen in its standard state is zero; thus,

$$\Delta H_{298}^0 = (-57.02 + 0) - (-17.89 - 68.32) = 29.19 \text{ kcal}$$

Since ΔH is positive, the reaction is endothermic.

The standard heat of formation of a substance may be measured directly, or it may be calculated from the heat of a reaction in which the substance takes part, provided that the heats of formation of all of the other reactants and products are known. For example, given that ΔH_f^0 for $SO_3(l)$ and $H_2O(l)$ are −104.67 and −68.32 kcal/mole respectively, and $\Delta H_{298}^0 =$ −20.92 kcal for the reaction

$$SO_3(l) + H_2O(l) \rightarrow H_2SO_4(l)$$

ΔH_f^0 for $H_2SO_4(l)$ can be calculated as follows:

$$\Delta H_{298}^0 = (\Delta H_{f\,H_2SO_4}^0) - (\Delta H_{f\,SO_3}^0 + \Delta H_{f\,H_2O}^0)$$

$$\Delta H_{f\,H_2SO_4}^0 = (-20.92) + (-104.67 - 68.32)$$

$$\Delta H_{f\,H_2SO_4}^0 = -193.91 \text{ kcal}$$

Heats of formation are most often calculated from heats of combustion, which are readily obtained for most substances. Advantage is taken of two thermodynamic principles, both of which are direct consequences of the law of conservation of energy. The first of these, mentioned in passing in Sec. 11.1, is known as ***Hess' law of constant heat summation,*** which states that *ΔH and ΔE for a reaction depend only upon the initial and final states of the system* and are independent of any intermediate steps through which the reaction may pass. This means that whether methane, for example, is formed directly from its elements:

$$C(s) + 2\ H_2(g) \rightarrow CH_4(g) \qquad \Delta H_f^0 = -17.89 \text{ kcal}$$

or by an equivalent series of reactions:

$$\begin{array}{rl}
C(s) + O_2(g) \rightarrow CO_2(g) & \Delta H_{298}^0 = -94.05 \text{ kcal} \\
2\ H_2(g) + O_2(g) \rightarrow 2\ H_2O(l) & \Delta H_{298}^0 = 2(-68.32) \text{ kcal} \\
CO_2(g) + 2\ H_2O(l) \rightarrow CH_4(g) + 2\ O_2(g) & \Delta H_{298}^0 = +212.80 \text{ kcal} \\
\hline
C(s) + 2\ H_2(g) \rightarrow CH_4(g) & \Delta H_f^0 = -17.89 \text{ kcal}
\end{array}$$

the system undergoes the same total change in heat content. The second principle is that the values of ΔH for a forward reaction and its reverse have the same numerical value but opposite signs. This means, for example, that if ΔH_{298}^0 for the reaction

$$C_2H_5OH(l) + 3\ O_2(g) \rightarrow 2\ CO_2(g) + 3\ H_2O(l)$$

is -327.0 kcal, then ΔH_{298}^0 for the reverse reaction

$$2\ CO_2(g) + 3\ H_2O(l) \rightarrow C_2H_5OH(l) + 3\ O_2(g)$$

must be $+327.0$ kcal.

To illustrate the way in which these principles are applied, let us calculate the heat of formation of ethyl alcohol from the heats of combustion of the alcohol and of its constituent elements:

$$\begin{array}{rl}
C_2H_5OH(l) + 3\ O_2(g) \rightarrow 2\ CO_2(g) + 3\ H_2O(l) & \Delta H_{298}^0 = -327.0 \text{ kcal} \\
C(s) + O_2(g) \rightarrow CO_2(g) & \Delta H_{298}^0 = -94.1 \text{ kcal} \\
H_2(g) + \frac{1}{2}\ O_2(g) \rightarrow H_2O(l) & \Delta H_{298}^0 = -68.3 \text{ kcal}
\end{array}$$

The heat of formation of C_2H_5OH is equal to ΔH_{298}^0 for the reaction

$$2\ C(s) + 3\ H_2(g) + \frac{1}{2}\ O_2(g) \rightarrow C_2H_5OH(l)$$

This reaction is the summation of the following three reactions for which the values of ΔH_{298}^0 can be obtained from the heats of combustion given above:

$$2\,C(s) + 2\,O_2(g) \rightarrow 2\,CO_2(g) \qquad \Delta H^0_{298} = 2(-94.1)\text{ kcal}$$

$$3\,H_2(g) + \tfrac{3}{2}\,O_2(g) \rightarrow 3\,H_2O(l) \qquad \Delta H^0_{298} = 3(-68.3)\text{ kcal}$$

$$2\,CO_2(g) + 3\,H_2O(l) \rightarrow C_2H_5OH(l) + 3\,O_2(g) \qquad \Delta H^0_{298} = 327.0\text{ kcal}$$

$$2\,C(s) + 3\,H_2(g) + \tfrac{1}{2}\,O_2(g) \rightarrow C_2H_5OH(l) \qquad \Delta H^0_{298} = -66.1\text{ kcal}$$

Not only heats of formation, but heats of other reactions can be calculated by the application of Hess' law, as illustrated in the following example.

Example 11.3

Given:

$$C_2H_5OH(l) + 3\,O_2(g) \rightarrow 2\,CO_2(g) + 3\,H_2O(l) \qquad \Delta H^0_{298} = -327.0\text{ kcal}$$

$$C_2H_4(g) + 3\,O_2(g) \rightarrow 2\,CO_2(g) + 2\,H_2O(l) \qquad \Delta H^0_{298} = -337.3\text{ kcal}$$

Calculate ΔH^0_{298} for the reaction

$$C_2H_4(g) + H_2O(l) \rightarrow C_2H_5OH(l)$$

Solution: The reaction for which ΔH^0_{298} is to be determined is seen to be equivalent to the sum of the reactions

$$C_2H_4(g) + 3\,O_2(g) \rightarrow 2\,CO_2(g) + 2\,H_2O(l) \qquad \Delta H^0_{298} = -337.3\text{ kcal}$$

$$3\,H_2O(l) + 2\,CO_2(g) \rightarrow C_2H_1OH(l) + 3\,O_2(g) \qquad \Delta H^0_{298} = +327.0\text{ kcal}$$

$$C_2H_4(g) + H_2O(l) \rightarrow C_2H_5OH(l) \qquad \Delta H^0_{298} = -10.3\text{ kcal}$$

Bond Energies 11.3

The enthalpy change accompanying the dissociation of a diatomic molecule can often be measured experimentally, and it is a measure of the strength of the bond (Sec. 8.1). Thus it may be seen from the values of ΔH for the reactions

$$H_2(g) \rightarrow 2\,H(g) \qquad \Delta H_{298} = 104.2\text{ kcal}$$

$$Cl_2(g) \rightarrow 2\,Cl(g) \qquad \Delta H_{298} = 57.9\text{ kcal}$$

that it takes more energy to break the **H—H** bond, which must therefore be stronger than the **Cl—Cl** bond. Now the reaction between hydrogen and chlorine to give hydrogen chloride,

$$\tfrac{1}{2}\,H_2(g) + \tfrac{1}{2}\,Cl_2(g) \rightarrow HCl(g) \qquad \Delta H_{298} = -22.1\text{ kcal}$$

involves the breaking of one **H—H** and one **Cl—Cl** bond and formation of an **H—Cl** bond. The heat evolved in the formation of **HCl** must therefore be equal to the energy released in forming the **H—Cl** bond less that required to break the bonds in the hydrogen and chlorine molecules (Fig. 11.1). Formation of one mole of **HCl** requires first that the energy needed to dissociate one-half mole of H_2 and one-half mole of Cl_2 be furnished. Subtracting this energy from the heat of formation of **HCl** leaves -103.1 kcal as the energy

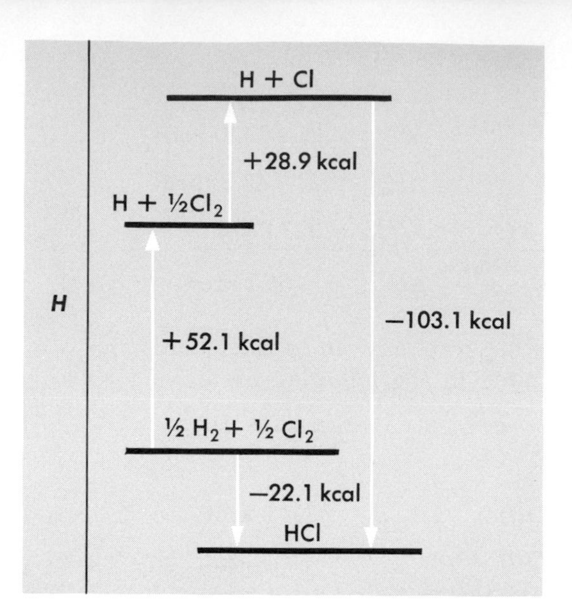

Fig. 11.1 Enthalpy diagram for the reaction $\frac{1}{2}\ H_2 + \frac{1}{2}\ Cl_2 \rightarrow HCl$.

released in forming a bond between a hydrogen atom and a chlorine atom. Thus ΔH_{298} for the reaction

$$HCl(g) \rightarrow H(g) + Cl(g) \qquad \Delta H_{298} = 103.1 \text{ kcal}$$

which is the energy needed to dissociate the bond, is 103.1 kcal. This energy we will call the ***bond energy.***

Bond energies for bonds between many pairs of atoms may be calculated in similar fashion. For example, the formation of methane from its elements

$$C(graphite) + 2\ H_2(g) \rightarrow CH_4(g) \qquad \Delta H_f^0 = -17.9 \text{ kcal}$$

may be visualized as taking place in the following steps:

$$C(graphite) \rightarrow C(g) \qquad \Delta H_{298} = 170.9 \text{ kcal}$$

$$2\ H_2(g) \rightarrow 4\ H(g) \qquad \Delta H_{298} = 208.4 \text{ kcal}$$

$$C(g) + 4\ H(g) \rightarrow CH_4(g) \qquad \Delta H_{298} = -17.9 - (170.9 + 208.4)$$

$$= -397.2 \text{ kcal}$$

ΔH_{298} for the reaction

$$CH_4(g) \rightarrow C(g) + 4\ H(g)$$

is then +397.2 kcal. The average energy required to break each C—H bond is one-fourth of this, or 99.3 kcal, and this may be taken as the average C—H bond energy.* Values of some bond energies are given in Table 11.1.

* It must be emphasized that the C—H bond energy obtained in this way is only an average value and that the actual enthalpy changes for removal of successive hydrogens from methane differ from this average value. Recent experimental work gives the following approximate values for the successive dissociation steps:

$$CH_4(g) \rightarrow CH_3(g) + H(g) \qquad \Delta H_{298} = 101 \text{ kcal}$$

$$CH_3(g) \rightarrow CH_2(g) + H(g) \qquad \Delta H_{298} = 88 \text{ kcal}$$

$$CH_2(g) \rightarrow CH(g) + H(g) \qquad \Delta H_{298} = 124 \text{ kcal}$$

$$CH(g) \rightarrow C(g) + H(g) \qquad \Delta H_{298} = 80 \text{ kcal}$$

Fortuitously, the value for the removal of the first hydrogen is close to the average.

TABLE 11.1 Bond Energies (kcal/mole)

Bond	ΔH_{298}	Bond	ΔH_{298}
H—H	104	C—C	83
H—F	135	C=C	147
H—Cl	103	C≡C	194
H—Br	88	C—Cl	79
O=O	118	C—N	70
O—H	111	N≡N	226
C—H	99	N—H	93
C—O	84	Cl—Cl	58
C=O	170	Br—Br	46

If one assumes that the energy required to dissociate a bond between two given atoms is the same regardless of the compound in which the bond is present, it is possible to use average bond energy values such as those given in the table to estimate the energy required to break all of the bonds in a compound and dissociate it completely into atoms. For example, ethyl alcohol, C_2H_5OH, has the structure

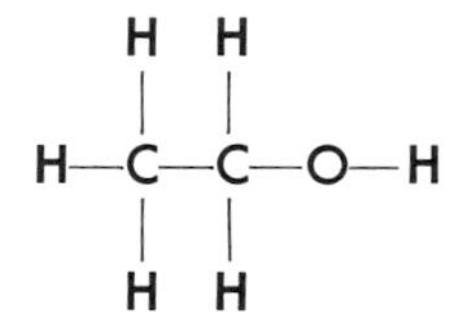

in which there are 1 C—C, 1 C—O, 1 O—H, and 5 C—H bonds. Using the bond energies given in Table 11.1, the energy required to break all the bonds in the compound is calculated to be

$$\begin{aligned} 1 \times 83 &= 83 \\ 1 \times 84 &= 84 \\ 1 \times 111 &= 111 \\ 5 \times 99 &= \underline{495} \\ & 773 \text{ kcal/mole} \end{aligned}$$

This, then is the calculated enthalpy change for the reaction

$$C_2H_5OH(g) \rightarrow 2\ C(g) + 6\ H(g) + O(g) \qquad \Delta H_{298} = 773 \text{ kcal}$$

From this dissociation energy, the dissociation energies of H_2 and O_2 and the heat of sublimation of carbon, it is possible to estimate the heat of formation of gaseous ethanol:

$$\begin{aligned} &3\ H_2(g) \rightarrow 6\ H(g) && \Delta H_{298} = 3 \times 104 = && 312 \text{ kcal} \\ &\tfrac{1}{2}\ O_2(g) \rightarrow O(g) && \Delta H_{298} = \tfrac{1}{2} \times 118 = && 59 \text{ kcal} \\ &2\ C(graphite) \rightarrow 2\ C(g) && \Delta H_{298} = 2 \times 171 = && 342 \text{ kcal} \\ &2\ C(g) + 6\ H(g) + O(g) \rightarrow C_2H_5OH(g) && \Delta H_{298} = && -773 \text{ kcal} \\ \hline &3\ H_2(g) + \tfrac{1}{2}\ O_2(g) + 2\ C(graphite) \rightarrow C_2H_5OH(g) && \Delta H_{298} && = -60 \text{ kcal} \end{aligned}$$

The calculated heat of formation in this case, -60 kcal/mole, is in good agreement with the experimental value, which is -56 kcal/mole. Such good agreement is obtained in many cases, but not in all. A substantial difference between the calculated and experimental values suggests a difference in the nature of the bonding in the compound from that assumed on the basis of its formula.

11.4 Enthalpy and Stability

If energy is released in forming a compound from its elements, that is, if its heat of formation is negative, it will require at least as much energy to decompose the compound into its elements. The more negative a compound's heat of formation, the more difficult it should be to decompose it, since more energy will be required. A compound which is hard to decompose is stable, and the harder it is to decompose the compound the more stable it is. We saw in Sec. 11.2 that ΔH for any reaction is equal to the difference between the heats of formation of the products and the reactants. This being the case, it is evident that the total heat of formation of the products of any exothermic reaction must be more negative than that of the reactants, and in that sense, the products of an exothermic reaction should be more stable than the reactants (Fig. 11.2).

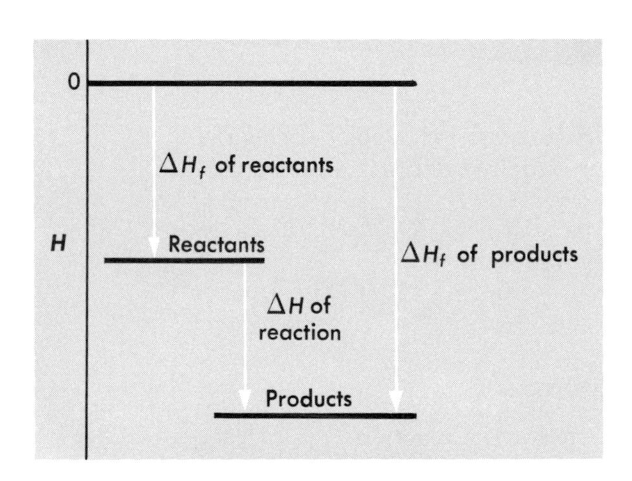

Fig. 11.2 Enthalpy diagram for an exothermic reaction.

As we know from experience, all systems tend whenever possible to "roll downhill" to a state of greater stability. Attaining a state of greater stability is a *spontaneous process*, which means that once the process is started, it will continue of its own accord until the more stable state is reached. Once the brakes are released, the truck will roll downhill by itself. The reverse process is not spontaneous. The truck won't roll back uphill unless energy is continuously supplied by burning fuel in the engine, nor will a chemical reaction proceed to give less stable products unless energy is constantly supplied to the reacting system from its surroundings.

This would seem to imply that every exothermic process, once started, should be self-sustaining, and that no endothermic process could be spontaneous.* This is definitely not true. Many exothermic reactions are spontaneous, but there are also many which are not. On the other hand, there are endothermic processes, such as the melting of ice at temperatures above 0°, which do take place spontaneously. Furthermore, endothermic reactions tend to become spontaneous at high temperatures. Exothermic reactions are less likely to occur spontaneously at high temperatures. From the foregoing it is apparent that *a system in the state of minimum enthalpy is not necessarily in the state of maximum thermodynamic stability.*

Probability, Entropy, and Thermodynamic Stability 11.5

The driving force behind any spontaneous chemical or physical change is the attainment of a state of greater thermodynamic stability. The relative thermodynamic stability of a system in a given state depends upon two factors, one of which is the enthalpy. The second factor is a measure of the disorder, or randomness, of the system. Generally speaking, the most stable state is that of minimum enthalpy *and* maximum disorder. Both factors must be considered in determining the relative stability of the system. A reaction that results in a large decrease in enthalpy may be favored even at the expense of a certain decrease in randomness. Conversely, an endothermic reaction may occur spontaneously if it is accompanied by a large enough increase in randomness. Anyone who has ever tried to keep a neat desk knows that all things tend toward a state of maximum disorder. The desk seems to become messy of its own accord—that is, spontaneously—but it requires continuing effort to keep it neat. A neat desk, then is in a higher energy state than a messy one. The energy exerted in arranging things in orderly fashion does not increase their potential energy, however, and cannot be recovered or put to any useful purpose. If the papers on the desk are set afire, they will produce exactly the same amount of heat, regardless of whether or not they happen to be arranged alphabetically.

This universal tendency toward maximum disorder or randomness is a reflection of the greater probability of a disordered state. Picture a box which contains one white marble and is shaken so that the marble moves about at random. We can expect the marble to be in the left half of the box about half of the time and in the right half the rest of the time. In other words, the probability of finding the white marble in a particular half of the box is 1/2. Now add a black marble to the box. There are now four equally probable arrangements of the two marbles in the box:

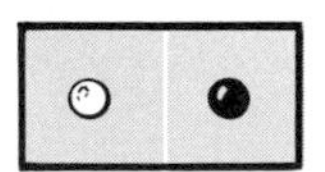
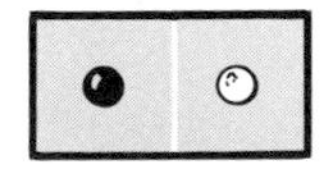
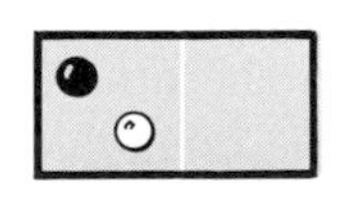
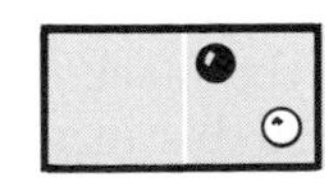

* Describing a reaction as spontaneous implies nothing regarding the rate at which it takes place. A spontaneous reaction may proceed rapidly or immeasurably slowly. Thus the reaction $N_2 + 3\ H_2 \rightarrow 2\ NH_3$ is spontaneous as the term is used here, yet a mixture of nitrogen and hydrogen may be kept for years at room temperature without any detectable amount of ammonia being formed. The rate at which a chemical reaction occurs is controlled by other factors, which will be discussed in Chapter 12.

There is still one chance in two that the white marble will be in the left half of the box, but there is only one chance in four, a smaller probability, that the black marble will be in the right half of the box when the white marble is in the left. If we put two white and two black marbles in the box, there are three possible arrangements of the white marbles. The probability of the white marbles being in a particular one of these arrangements is one in three, or 1/3:

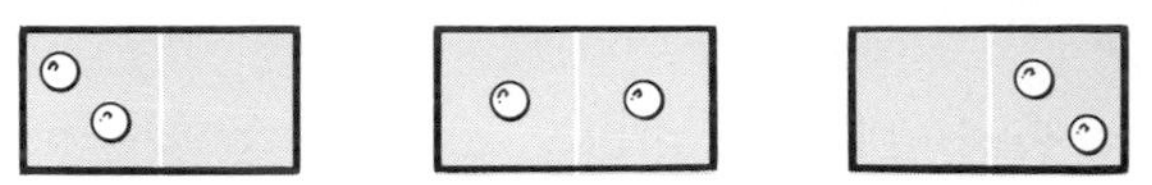

There are also three possible arrangements of the black marbles, each of which again has a probability of 1/3:

Combining these gives us nine (3 × 3) equally probable arrangements for the four marbles:

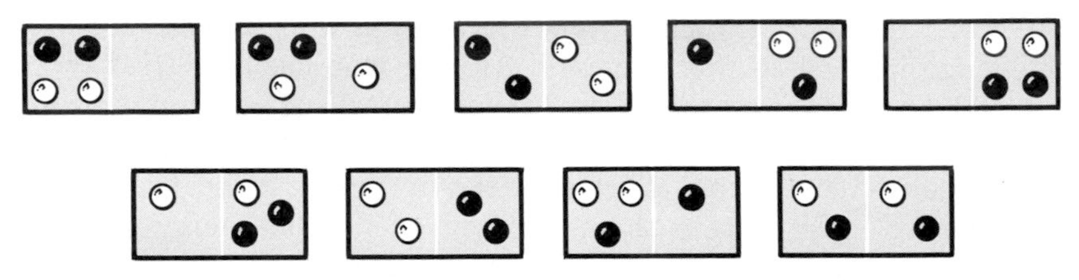

The probability of the marbles being in any one of these nine arrangements, both white marbles on the left and both black marbles on the right, for example, is seen to be one in nine (1/3 × 1/3). Similarly, it can be shown that the probability of a particular arrangement of four white marbles is 1/5. The probability of a given arrangement of four black marbles is also 1/5, and the probability of all eight marbles being in a given arrangement is 1/5 × 1/5, or 1/25. From this we can derive the general relationship for the probability of a given arrangement of marbles:

$$\text{Probability} = \frac{1}{n_1 + 1} \times \frac{1}{n_2 + 1}$$

where n_1 and n_2 are the numbers of white and black marbles, respectively. It is easy to see that as the number of marbles is increased, there is less and less chance that all of the white ones will be found in one half of the box and all of the black ones in the other.

It is this increase in probability with increasing disorder which is the driving force behind such phenomena as the spontaneous, uniform mixing of gases. Suppose that instead of black and white marbles we have two vessels filled with gas and connected by a stopcock. The first vessel contains one mole (6.02×10^{23} molecules) of one gas, and the second vessel contains one mole of some other gas. When the stopcock is opened, what is the probability that the gases will remain unmixed? From the expression we derived above, we can calculate that the probability of all of the molecules of one gas remaining in one container and all the other molecules remaining in the other is equal to

$$\frac{1}{(6.02 \times 10^{23}) + 1} \times \frac{1}{(6.02 \times 10^{23}) + 1} = \frac{1}{3.62 \times 10^{47}}$$

This means that there is only one chance in 362,000,000,000,000,000,000,-000,000,000,000,000,000,000,000,000 that the molecules will not mix. Any event with such a small probability of occurrence is about as close to impossible as an event can be. Conversely, the spontaneous mixing of the gases is a near certainty.

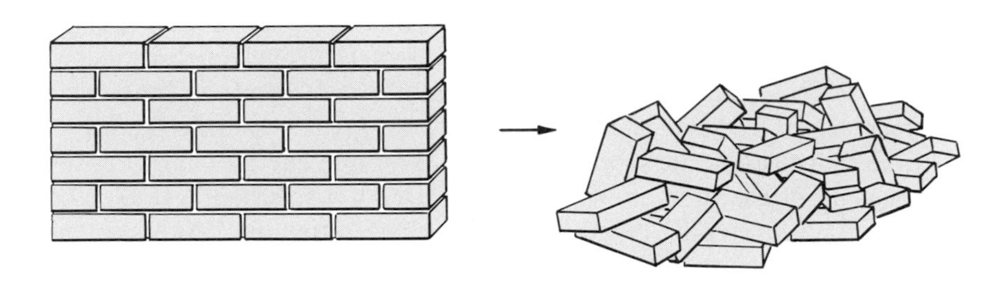

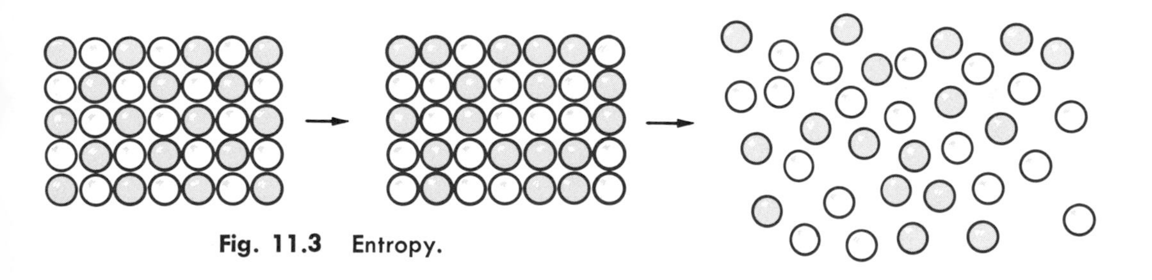

Fig. 11.3 Entropy.

The degree of randomness or disorder in a system is described in terms of the ***entropy*** S of the system. The more highly ordered the system, the lower its entropy; the more randomly the components of the system are arranged the greater is its entropy (Fig. 11.3). To decrease the entropy of a system requires the expenditure by the system of a certain amount of energy. Returning to the box of marbles, the mixing of the marbles is spontaneous, but their unmixing is not. One has to exert effort to sort out the marbles, putting all of the black ones on one side and all of the white ones on the other. Furthermore, if the box is being shaken, imparting kinetic energy to the marbles, it will take much more effort to sort them out than if the box is stationary. The more violently the box is shaken, the harder it will be to sort out the marbles and keep them sorted. The quantity of energy q_r involved in bringing about a given entropy change is thus proportional to the kinetic energy of the system. If the system consists of molecules, their kinetic energy in turn is proportional to the absolute temperature, and the relationship becomes

$$q_r = T\Delta S$$

11.6 Free Energy

The relative stabilities of two possible states of a system can now be defined in terms of two energy factors, one the difference in their enthalpies ΔH, and the other the energy $T\Delta S$ determined by the difference in their entropies. The more stable state will be the one for which the difference between the two energy factors, $\Delta H - T\Delta S$, is a minimum. This difference,

$$\Delta G = \Delta H - T\Delta S$$

is called the ***Gibbs free energy change,*** after J. Willard Gibbs, an American physicist whose work in the latter part of the nineteenth century laid the foundations of chemical thermodynamics. A reaction that results in a decrease in free energy leads to a state of greater thermodynamic stability and hence can occur spontaneously. The free energy change is therefore a measure of the spontaneity, or *feasibility*, of a reaction. If ΔG is negative, the reaction tends toward greater thermodynamic stability, and once started it will be self-sustaining. If ΔG is positive, the reaction leads toward decreasing stability and cannot occur spontaneously. If ΔG is zero, the reaction can go equally well in either direction, and the system must therefore be in a state of equilibrium. To summarize,

ΔG negative: reaction can occur spontaneously
ΔG positive: reaction cannot occur spontaneously
ΔG zero: system at equilibrium

We can now begin to understand how an endothermic reaction which cannot occur at low temperatures may proceed at higher temperatures. ΔH and ΔS for a given process or reaction usually change very little with temperature. If ΔS is positive, however, $T\Delta S$ will increase with temperature and at sufficiently high temperatures may become larger than ΔH, making ΔG negative. Consider, for example, the dissociation of water into hydrogen and oxygen at 1 atm:

$$H_2O(g) \rightarrow H_2(g) + \tfrac{1}{2} O_2(g)$$

A system in which the atoms are distributed among $1\frac{1}{2}$ moles of gas is more disordered than one in which they are present in only one mole. Dissociation of water therefore results in an increase in entropy, and ΔS for this reaction is positive, its value in this particular case being nearly constant at 14 cal/°K over a wide range of temperatures. Over the same temperature range, ΔH for this endothermic reaction is also nearly constant at about 58 kcal. At 300°K,

$$\Delta G = 58 - 300(0.014) = 54 \text{ kcal}$$

The ΔG is positive, and dissociation of water would not be expected to occur at that temperature. At 5000°K on the other hand,

$$\Delta G = 58 - 5000(0.014) = -12 \text{ kcal}$$

Here ΔG is negative, and water dissociates spontaneously into its elements. By setting ΔG equal to zero we can calculate the temperature at which the system

$$H_2O(g) \rightleftharpoons H_2(g) + \tfrac{1}{2} O_2(g)$$

will be in a state of equilibrium at 1 atm:

$$\Delta G = 0 = 58 - T(0.014)$$

$$T \approx 4150°K$$

Frequently an exothermic reaction will be accompanied by a decrease in entropy, and such a reaction will cease to be spontaneous above a certain temperature. This is the case, for example, for the reverse of the reaction above, namely, the combination of hydrogen and oxygen to form water:

$$H_2(g) + \tfrac{1}{2} O_2(g) \rightarrow H_2O(g)$$

This reaction ceases to be spontaneous above 4150°K, the temperature above which the dissociation reaction was found to be spontaneous.

The relationship among free energy, enthalpy, and entropy changes holds for physical as well as chemical processes. The freezing of water is an exothermic process, yet water does not freeze above 0°C (273°K). The ΔH for the process

$$H_2O(l) \rightarrow H_2O(s)$$

averages about -1.44 kcal/mole between 0° and 100°C. Crystallization always involves a decrease in entropy because the atoms are more highly ordered in the crystal lattice than they are in the liquid. ΔS is therefore negative, its value in this instance being approximately -5.3 ***entropy units*** (1 e.u. = 1 cal/°K). At room temperature, that is, at about 25°C (298°K),

$$\Delta G = -1.44 - 298(-0.0053) = +0.14 \text{ kcal}$$

The ΔG is positive, and water does not freeze, but instead, ice melts. At 0°C (273°K),

$$\Delta G = -1.44 - 273(-0.0053) = 0.00$$

The $\Delta G = 0$, and ice and water are in equilibrium at the melting point. Below 0°, say at -10°C (263°K),

$$\Delta G = -1.44 - 263(0.0053) = -0.05 \text{ kcal}$$

The ΔG is negative, and the freezing process becomes spontaneous.

Reversible and Irreversible Processes—The Second Law 11.7

We saw in Sec. 11.1 that the amount of work performed by a system undergoing a change varies according to the manner in which the change is carried out. It is easy enough to see that the least amount of work the system can do is no work at all, as in the case of a gas expanding freely into a vacuum. There must also be some upper limit to the work which can be performed. Imagine a sample of gas expanding at constant temperature T against some external pressure p. If $p = 0$, $p\Delta V = 0$, and no work is done by the system. If the pressure on the gas is increased, the work it performs during expansion increases also, but only up to a point. When the external pressure becomes equal to the pressure of the gas, expansion is no longer possible, and the system again performs no work. Any further increase in the external pressure will result in work being done on the system rather than by it. We may conclude that *the greatest amount of work will be performed by this system if the external pressure is at all times only infinitesimally less than the pressure of the gas.* An infinitesimal increase in the pressure on the system will cause the process to reverse direction. Therefore, *a process taking place under conditions such that the greatest amount of work is done by the system is described as a* ***reversible process.*** Carried out under any other conditions, the process is irreversible, and less work is done.

Reversible and irreversible processes are not limited to those involving work of expansion, as they are in the example above. Any process that performs work does so by acting against some opposing force, and whatever this force may be, in theory at least, if not often in practice, it may be made infinitesimally less than that exerted by the system so that the process operates reversibly.

The quantity of heat q_r transferred between the system and its surroundings during a process taking place reversibly at temperature T and performing an amount of work w_r, is given by the first law:

$$q_r = \Delta E + w_r$$

From this, the entropy change for the process may be calculated:

$$\Delta S = \frac{q_r}{T}$$

Now let us return for a moment to our expanding gas. We can see that the final state of the gas after it expands is the same, whether or not it performed any work during the expansion process. The increase in disorder, or entropy, of the gas must therefore be the same regardless of how the process is carried out. From this we can conclude that *whether a system undergoes a given change by a reversible process or an irreversible one, the entropy change of the system is the same and is given by* q_r/T.

Whatever quantity of heat may be gained by the system undergoing change, that same quantity of heat must be lost by the system's surroundings, and by the same token, any heat lost by the system is gained by the surroundings. As a result, the surroundings also undergo a change in entropy, the magnitude of which depends upon the quantity of heat transferred. If the process takes place in a reversible manner, the entropy change for the surroundings is

$$\Delta S_{\text{sur}} = \frac{-q_r}{T}$$

the negative sign signifying that the effect on the surroundings is in the opposite direction from that on the system, that is, if the entropy of the system increases, that of the surroundings decreases, and vice versa. The total entropy change for both a system and its surroundings is

$$\Delta S_{tot} = \Delta S_{sys} + \Delta S_{sur}$$

In a process which is taking place reversibly,

$$\Delta S_{tot} = \frac{q_r}{T} + \frac{-q_r}{T} = \frac{q_r - q_r}{T} = 0$$

If, on the other hand, the process is carried out in an irreversible fashion, the work done by the system is less than w_r, and the heat transferred, q_{irr}, differs accordingly from q_r:

$$q_{irr} = \Delta E + w_{irr}$$

In an exothermic process, where q and ΔE are negative, q_{irr} turns out to be *more negative* than q_r; in an endothermic process, q and ΔE are positive, and q_{irr} is *less positive* than q_r. Now in an irreversible process, while the change in the entropy of the system is still given by q_r/T, *the entropy change on the part of the surroundings is determined by the amount of heat transferred*, i.e.,

$$\Delta S_{sur} = \frac{-q_{irr}}{T}$$

In a process occurring irreversibly, therefore,

$$\Delta S_{tot} = \frac{q_r - q_{irr}}{T}$$

Whether q_{irr} is more negative or less positive than q_r, the result is the same,

$$\frac{q_r - q_{irr}}{T} > 0$$

from which it follows that *the total entropy change resulting from a process carried out irreversibly is always greater than zero.* Thus,

For any process occurring reversibly, $\Delta S_{tot} = 0$

For any process occurring irreversibly, $\Delta S_{tot} > 0$

These two statements are a summary of the ***second law of thermodynamics.*** Another way of stating the second law is as follows: *No process can take place which results in a net decrease in the entropy of the universe.* This means an automobile cannot run backwards, taking in its exhaust through the tail pipe and pumping gasoline back into the tank. Humpty Dumpty fell down, but a scrambled egg will not fall up. Every process that occurs at a measurable rate must take place irreversibly, leading us to the inevitable conclusion that while the total energy of the universe is constant, its entropy constantly increases. The natural trend of the universe is therefore toward increasing disorder, and continuous effort is necessary if any local degree of order is to be maintained.

11.8 Absolute Entropy—the Third Law

In Sec. 11.2 we saw how the heat of reaction could be calculated from the heats of formation of the reactants and products. If there were some way to determine the entropy change during the reaction, then the change in free energy, which measures the spontaneity, or feasibility, of the reaction, could be calculated from the relationship

$$\Delta G = \Delta H - T\Delta S$$

It is usually not possible to measure ΔS directly, but it can be calculated from the absolute entropies of the products and reactants:

$$\Delta S = S_{\text{products}} - S_{\text{reactants}}$$

This calculation is based on the postulate known as the ***third law of thermodynamics:*** *The entropy of any pure crystalline substance at 0°K is zero.* The assumption here is that at absolute zero, 0°K, all molecular motion has ceased, and a pure crystal at that temperature is in the most ordered state possible. Increasing the temperature causes an increase in the entropy of the substance. For each infinitesimal increase in the temperature of the substance, its entropy increases by an amount determined by the quantity of heat absorbed in the process. This is given by the heat capacity of the substance at that temperature. If a change in state, such as fusion or vaporization, takes place, the corresponding increase in entropy is calculated from the heat of fusion or heat of vaporization. The total entropy change the substance undergoes as its temperature is raised from 0°K to some chosen temperature is its absolute entropy at that temperature. *The absolute entropy for a substance in its standard state at 25°C (298°K) is called its* ***standard entropy*** S^0. The standard entropy is usually evaluated by plotting C_p/T as a function of T from 0° to 298°K, where C_p represents the heat capacity at constant pressure (1 atm) of the substance at each temperature. The area under the curve then equals ΔS^0. Tables of standard entropies are available from the National Bureau of Standards and are included in most chemical handbooks.

Example 11.4

Given the following standard heats of formation and standard entropies,

	ΔH_f^0 (kcal/mole)	S^0 (cal/°K)
C_2H_6	−20.24	54.85
C_2H_4	12.50	52.54
H_2	0.00	31.21

predict whether the reaction

$$C_2H_6(g) \rightarrow C_2H_4(g) + H_2(g)$$

is feasible at 25°C (298°K).

Solution:

$$\Delta H^0_{298} = \Delta H^0_f \text{ (products)} - \Delta H^0_f \text{ (reactants)}$$
$$= (12.50 + 0.00) - (-20.24) = 32.74 \text{ kcal}$$
$$\Delta S^0_{298} = S^0_{298} \text{ (products)} - S^0_{298} \text{ (reactants)}$$
$$= (52.54 + 31.21) - (54.85) = 28.9 \text{ cal/°K}$$
$$\Delta G^0_{298} = \Delta H^0_{298} - T\Delta S^0_{298} \qquad (T = 298\text{°K})$$
$$= 32.74 - 298(0.0289) = 24.13 \text{ kcal}$$

Since the free energy change is positive for this reaction at 298°K, the reaction is not feasible at that temperature.

Example 11.5

Assuming that ΔH and ΔS do not change appreciably with temperature, calculate the temperature above which the reaction in Example 11.4 becomes spontaneous.

Solution: The reaction will become spontaneous above the equilibrium temperature, that is, above the temperature at which $\Delta G = 0$.

$$\Delta G = 0 = 32.7 - (0.029)T$$
$$T = 1130\text{°K or } 857\text{°C}$$

The reaction should be spontaneous at temperatures above approximately 857°C.

Methods for determining ΔG experimentally will be discussed in later sections.

Free Energy Changes and Concentration 11.9

In our discussion up to now we have said little about concentration, and we have assumed for purposes of calculation that all gaseous reactants and products were at 1 atm of pressure and have avoided problems dealing with liquid solutions. However, a little thought will lead us to conclude that although such functions as ΔH and ΔE should be independent of concentration* the same is not true of ΔG because of its dependence on ΔS. Reducing the concentration of molecules increases their freedom of motion and hence their entropy. Both the free expansion of a gas and the diffusion of a solute from a region of high to one of low concentration are spontaneous processes, because both lead to an increase in the entropy of the system. Generally speaking, the spontaneity of a reaction will be favored by carrying it out under conditions which lead to a decrease in concentration. The quantitative relationship between the standard free energy change, measured with all reactants at ***unit activities*** (solids and liquids in their standard states, gases at 1 atm, and solutions at an effective concentration of 1 mole/liter) and the free energy change at other concentrations will be developed in Chapter 14 (Sec. 14.9).

* In practice they are affected by concentration to a slight and variable degree because of the presence of intermolecular forces of the sort that lead to nonideal behavior on the part of gases, liquids, and solutions.

11.10 Reading Suggestions

At this point, two books can be read with considerable profit. The first of these, *Chemical Energy*, by Laurence E. Strong and Wilmer J. Stratton (Selected Topics in Modern Chemistry Series, Reinhold Publishing Corp., New York, 1965), is a very clear presentation of elementary thermodynamics, expanding on the subjects introduced in this chapter in a manner requiring only a rudimentary knowledge of mathematics. Particularly interesting is Chapter 7, the final chapter of the book, in which practical applications of thermodynamic principles to chemical reactions are illustrated. The other book is *The Second Law*, by Henry A. Bent (Oxford University Press, New York, 1965). This is a most remarkable, lively, and entertaining volume, filled with personal vignettes and anecdotes of and about many of the great chemists and physicists who laid the foundations of thermodynamics. The style of the book is unconventional and makes for delightful reading and an almost painless introduction to the subject. The first part of the book, a 110-page introduction to classical thermodynamics, will be of greatest interest to the beginning student and employs only simple mathematics. Detailed answers are given for the problems, of which there are a great many.

More advanced students will want to read the rest of Professor Bent's book, and those with some knowledge of calculus will find a rigorous but still lucid treatment of the subject in *Basic Chemical Thermodynamics*, by Jürg Waser (W. A. Benjamin, Inc., New York, 1966).

Questions and Problems

11.1 Show that the product $p\Delta V$ represents work.

11.2 For each of the following exothermic reactions, predict whether the heat evolved at constant pressure will be greater than, less than, or nearly the same as the amount of heat evolved at constant volume.

$$2\,CO(g) \rightarrow CO_2(g) + C(s)$$

$$\tfrac{1}{2}\,H_2(g) + \tfrac{1}{2}\,Cl_2(g) \rightarrow HCl(g)$$

$$\tfrac{1}{2}\,H_2(g) + \tfrac{1}{2}\,Cl_2(g) \rightarrow HCl(aq) \quad (aq = \text{aqueous solution})$$

$$SO_3(g) + H_2O(l) \rightarrow H_2SO_4(l)$$

$$NH_3(g) + HCl(g) \rightarrow NH_4Cl(s)$$

$$CuS(s) + 1\tfrac{1}{2}\,O_2(g) \rightarrow CuO(s) + SO_2(g)$$

$$(C_2H_5)_2O(l) + H_2O(l) \rightarrow 2\,C_2H_5OH(l)$$

$$Ca(OH)_2(s) + CO_2(g) \rightarrow CaCO_3(s) + H_2O(g)$$

$$Ca(OH)_2(s) + CO_2(g) \rightarrow CaCO_3(s) + H_2O(l)$$

11.3 What is meant by a spontaneous process? Are all exothermic processes spontaneous? Under what conditions may an endothermic process become spontaneous? Does every spontaneous process necessarily take place at a measurable rate?

11.4 Account for the fact that most dissociation reactions become spontaneous at high temperatures.

11.5 Which of the following statements are correct for a reversible process in a state of equilibrium?

(a) The system is performing maximum work.
(b) $\Delta G = 0$
(c) $\Delta G = \Delta H$
(d) $\Delta H = T\Delta S$
(e) ΔS is always negative.

11.6 Which of the following statements are correct for a process which is occurring spontaneously?

(a) ΔS is always negative
(b) $\Delta H < T\Delta S$
(c) $\Delta G > 0$
(d) $\Delta G < 0$
(e) The process is occurring reversibly.

11.7 Which of the following statements are correct with respect to a process taking place in a reversible manner?

(a) The system performs maximum work.
(b) The total entropy change undergone by the system and its surroundings is zero.
(c) $\Delta S_{\text{system}} = q_r/T$
(d) $\Delta S_{\text{surroundings}} = -q_r/T$
(e) $\Delta S_{\text{total}} > 0$

11.8 Show that for any process ΔS_{total} is equal to, or greater than zero.

11.9 Which of the following reactions are accompanied by an increase, and which by a decrease in entropy?

	ΔH_{298} (kcal)
$ZnS(s) + 2\,O_2(g) \rightarrow ZnSO_4(s)$	−183.6
$S(s) + 1\frac{1}{2}\,O_2(g) \rightarrow SO_3(g)$	−91.5
$H_2(g) + I_2(s) \rightarrow 2\,HI(g)$	+11.8
$CaO(s) + CO_2(g) \rightarrow CaCO_3(s)$	−42.5
$HgO(s) \rightarrow Hg(l) + \frac{1}{2}\,O_2(g)$	+21.7
$6\,H_2(g) + P_4(s) \rightarrow 4\,PH_3(g)$	+8.8

Which of these reactions would be expected to become increasingly spontaneous at higher temperatures? At lower temperatures? Which reactions, if any, are not feasible at any temperature?

11.10 ΔH_{298} for the reaction

$$H_2(g) + \tfrac{1}{2}\,O_2(g) \rightarrow H_2O(l)$$

is −68.3 kcal. Using the value 9.7 kcal/mole for the heat of vaporization of water at 100°C, and the average heat capacities given below, calculate ΔH for the reaction

$$H_2(g) + \tfrac{1}{2}\,O_2(g) \rightarrow H_2O(g)$$

at 500°C

	$H_2(g)$	$O_2(g)$	$H_2O(g)$	$H_2O(l)$
Average heat capacity (cal/mole-degree)	6.9	6.9	7.8	18

11.11 Given:

	ΔH_f^0 (kcal/mole)		ΔH_f^0 (kcal/mole)
$H_2O(l)$	-68.32	$Na_2CO_3(s)$	-270.3
$CO_2(g)$	-94.05	$NaC_2H_3O_2(s)$	-169.8
$CO(g)$	-26.42	$C_2H_2(g)$	$+54.19$
$SO_2(g)$	-70.96	$C_6H_6(l)$	$+19.82$
$SO_3(l)$	-104.67	$C_2H_5OH(l)$	-66.36
$Fe_2O_3(s)$	-196.5	$HC_2H_3O_2(l)$	-116.4

Calculate ΔH_{298}^0 for each of the following reactions:

(a) $3\ C_2H_2(g) \rightarrow C_6H_6(l)$

(b) $Fe_2O_3(s) + 3\ CO(g) \rightarrow 2\ Fe(s) + 3\ CO_2(g)$

(c) $2\ HC_2H_3O_2(l) + Na_2CO_3(s) \rightarrow 2\ NaC_2H_3O_2(s) + H_2O(l) + CO_2(g)$

(d) $C_2H_5OH(l) + O_2(g) \rightarrow HC_2H_3O_2(l) + H_2O(l)$

(e) $2\ SO_2(g) + O_2(g) \rightarrow 2\ SO_3(l)$

11.12 Calculate ΔE_{298} for the following reactions:

(a) $N_2(g) + 3\ H_2(g) \rightarrow 2\ NH_3(g)$ $\quad \Delta H_{298}^0 = -21.9$ kcal

(b) $2\ SO_3(l) \rightarrow 2\ SO_2(g) + O_2(g)$ $\quad \Delta H_{298}^0 = +44.4$ kcal

11.13 Calculate the standard heat of formation of sucrose ($C_{12}H_{22}O_{11}$), given that its heat of combustion in the standard state at 1 atm is -1348.9 kcal/mole.

11.14 Use the bond energies given in Table 11.1 to estimate ΔH_{298} for the chlorination of ethylene:

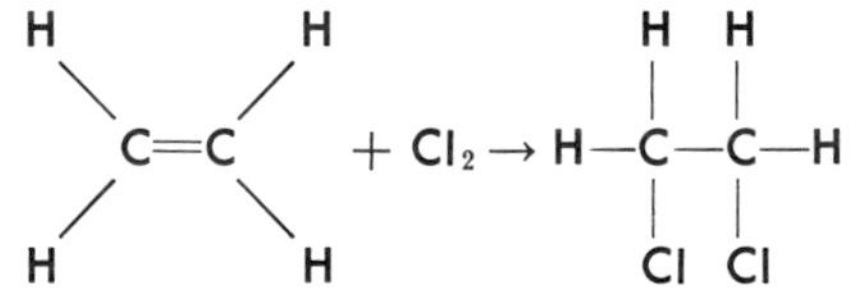

```
H         H                  H  H
 \       /                   |  |
  C == C      + Cl2 -> H -- C -- C -- H
 /       \                   |  |
H         H                  Cl Cl
```

11.15 According to August Kekulé (1865), the benzene molecule consists of a ring of six carbon atoms joined to one another alternately by single and double bonds, and to hydrogen atoms by single bonds:

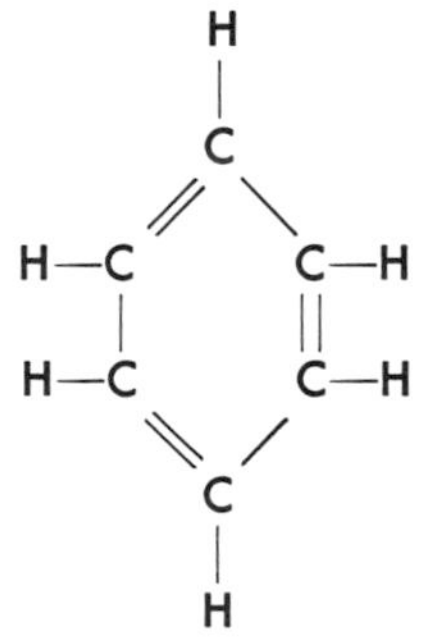

```
          H
          |
          C
        //  \
   H -- C      C -- H
        |      ||
   H -- C      C -- H
        \\  /
          C
          |
          H
```

Using the bond energies given in Table 11.1, calculate the heat of formation of benzene. *Ans.* 54 kcal/mole

11.16 Calculate the heat of formation of benzene from its experimentally determined heat of combustion, which is −789.1 kcal/mole. How does the value obtained in this case compare with that calculated in problem 11.15? Discuss the possible significance of any discrepancy.
Ans. 19.8 kcal/mole. See Section 17.10

11.17 Assuming that ΔH and ΔS for the reaction

$$N_2(g) + 3\ H_2(g) \rightarrow 2\ NH_3(g)$$

are approximately constant at −22 kcal and −47 cal/°K, respectively, over a wide range of temperatures, calculate the temperature at which the three gases are in equilibrium, each at a pressure of 1 atm.

11.18 Rhombic sulfur, which is the stable form of the element at room temperature, undergoes a transition to the monoclinic form at 95.5°C, absorbing 0.071 kcal/mole in the process. Calculate the entropy change for the transition

$$S(\text{rhombic}) \rightarrow S(\text{monoclinic})$$

11.19 From the heats of formation and standard entropies given below, and assuming that ΔH and ΔS do not change appreciably with temperature, estimate the temperature above which the reaction

$$CaCO_3(s) \rightarrow CaO(s) + CO_2(g)$$

becomes spontaneous at 1 atm.

	ΔH_f^0 (kcal/mole)	S^0 (cal/°K)
$CaCO_3(s)$	−288.5	22.2
$CaO(s)$	−151.9	9.5
$CO_2(g)$	−94.1	51.5

11.20 Given the following standard heats of formation and standard entropies for cyanic acid, urea, and ammonia, each in 1 M aqueous solution at 298°K, calculate ΔG_{298} for the reaction:

$$HCNO(1\ M) + NH_3(1\ M) \rightarrow CO(NH_2)_2(1\ M)$$

	ΔH_f^0 (kcal/mole)	S^0 (cal/°K)
cyanic acid ($HCNO$)	−35.1	43.6
urea ($CO(NH_2)_2$)	−76.3	41.6
ammonia (NH_3)	−19.3	26.3

11.21 The molar heat of combustion of benzoic acid (mol. wt. 122.12) at constant volume (ΔE_{298}) is −770.9 kcal/mole. Combustion of 0.5000 g of benzoic acid in a constant volume (bomb) calorimeter causes a temperature rise of 2.160°C. Calculate the total heat capacity of the calorimeter. *Ans.* 1461.3 cal/°C

11.22 Combustion of 0.4520 g of naphthalene ($C_{10}H_8$, mol. wt. 128.18) in the calorimeter described in problem 11.21 causes a temperature rise of 2.961°C. Calculate ΔE_{298} and ΔH_{298} (1 atm) for the reaction:

$$C_{10}H_8(s) + 12\ O_2(g) \rightarrow 10\ CO_2(g) + 4\ H_2O(l)$$

Ans. $\Delta E_{298} = -1227.0$ kcal, $\Delta H_{298} = -1228.1$ kcal

11.23 Mercury (at. wt. 200.6 amu) melts at −38.9°C and boils at 356.6°C. The heat of fusion at the melting point and the heat of vaporization at the boiling point of the element are 2.82 cal/g and 65.0 cal/g, respectively. For each process, fusion and vaporization, calculate ΔS. What do the values of ΔS indicate regarding the relative degree of order among the mercury atoms in the solid, liquid, and vapor states?

Ans. $\Delta S_{\text{fusion}} = 2.42$ cal/deg
$\Delta S_{\text{vaporization}} = 20.7$ cal/deg

If one of the factors of any system in chemical equilibrium varies, the whole system will be modified in such a way that— provided there is only one variation involved— a modification in the opposite direction to the considered factor will occur.

——Henri Louis Le Chatelier, 1884

12 REACTION RATES AND CHEMICAL EQUILIBRIUM

The sign of the free energy change indicates the direction in which a reaction tends to go but says nothing about how fast it will take place. Among several possible reactions, all with about the same negative value for ΔG, one may be over in an instant, another may proceed at a slow, measurable rate, and still another may show no signs of taking place even after years or centuries have elapsed. Reactants are not changed into products by magic; a lot happens in between. Molecules collide, bonds break, new bonds form. There may be many steps, many arrangements and rearrangements of atoms involved in the journey from reactants to products. Whether the journey is easy or hard, fast or slow, depends not on the final outcome but on what happens along the way. Knowing only the overall free energy change for a reaction, we are like a bicyclist who knows that San Francisco is downhill from Denver but is unaware of the Rocky Mountains in between.

The branch of chemistry which deals with the study of reaction rates is known as ***chemical kinetics.*** Several factors are found to influence the rate of a chemical reaction. These are, besides the nature of the reactants themselves, the *concentration of the reactants*, the *temperature*, and the presence of certain other substances known as ***catalysts.*** By studying the influence of each of these factors in turn the kineticist is often able to obtain clues to the nature of the intermediate steps, that is, the ***mechanism,*** by which reactants are converted to products. Knowledge of how a chemical reaction takes place can lead to improved conditions for carrying it out and can also suggest other possible reactions that might otherwise never be attempted.

12.1 Concentration

Consider a reaction in which a single molecule dissociates into products:

$$A \rightarrow \text{products}$$

The rate of this reaction may be measured by measuring how fast A is being used up. Suppose that at a given temperature, on the average 10% of the A molecules present dissociate each minute. If we start out with 1 mole of A in a volume of 1 liter, 10% of it, or 0.1 mole, will have dissociated after 1 min. If instead we had 2 moles—twice as many as before—in the same volume, after 1 min 0.2 mole—twice as much—would have dissociated. Similarly, if our initial concentration of A were 3 moles/liter, after 1 min 0.3 mole would have dissociated, and so on. In other words, the number of moles of A in one liter which dissociate in 1 minute, that is, the ***rate of dissociation*** of A, is directly proportional to its molar concentration:

$$\text{rate} = k[A]$$

where k is a proportionality constant, or *rate constant* for the reaction and $[A]$ represents the concentration of A in moles/liter.

Most chemical processes are not simple dissociations but involve two or more molecules reacting together. The reaction

$$A + B \rightarrow \text{products}$$

will serve as a generalized example. For any products at all to be formed in this reaction, molecules of A and B must come in contact—collide—with one another. Not every collision between A and B need necessarily lead to reaction, but it seems reasonable to assume that the greater the number of collisions in a given period of time, the greater the probability that reaction will occur.

What are the chances that a molecule of A will collide with one of B at a given instant? It will depend on how many molecules of B are present. If there are no B molecules present at all, then there is no chance that A will bump into one of them. If there are a few B molecules around, then there are a few chances of collision; if there are a great many B molecules, there are a great many chances that A will hit one of them. The same holds for B. The more molecules of A present, the more likely a B molecule is to collide with one.

Let's take a closer look at this, even at the risk of seeming to overstress an obvious point. Imagine that we have 4 molecules of A mixed with 4 molecules of B in some small volume. Each A molecule has 4 chances of colliding with a B at a given instant, and since there are 4 A's, there are $4 \times 4 = 16$ chances altogether that an A will hit a B:

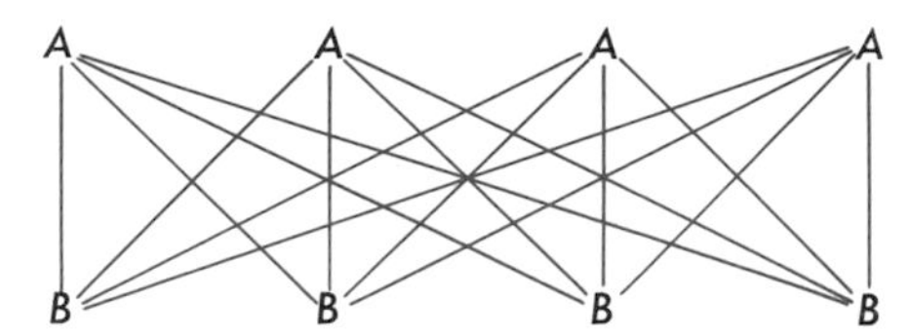

Now suppose that we double the concentration of A from 4 to 8 molecules in the same volume. Each A molecule still has 4 chances of colliding with a B, but because there are 8 A molecules, the total number of collision possibilities is $8 \times 4 = 32$:

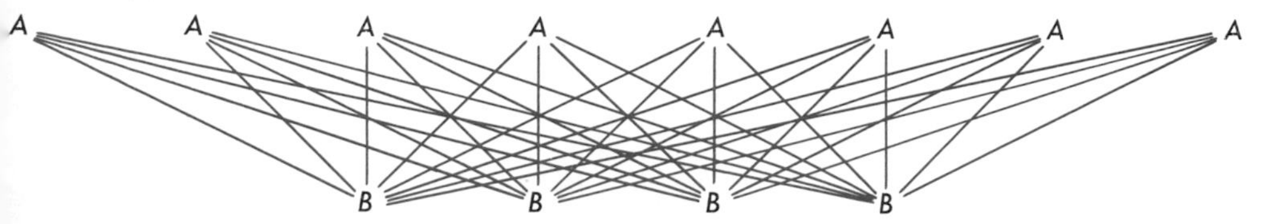

If both concentrations are doubled from 4 to 8, then the chances of collision are quadrupled to $8 \times 8 = 64$:

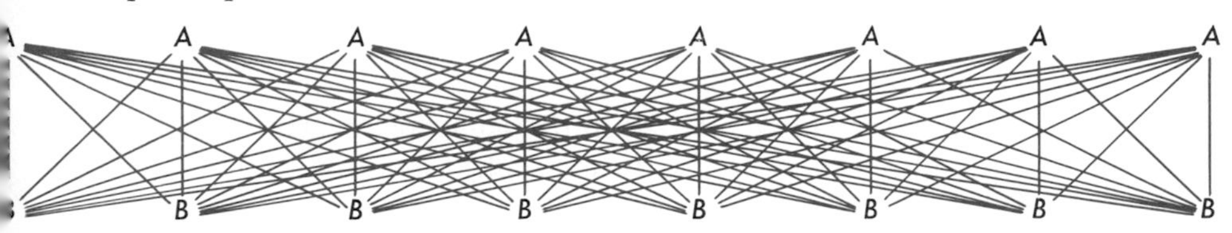

The chances of collision between A and B therefore depend upon the product of their concentrations. The greater the chance of collision, the more actual collisions will take place in a given period of time. Assuming that the rate of reaction is proportional to the rate at which the molecules collide, we come to the conclusion that the rate of reaction is also proportional to the product of the molar concentrations of the reacting species:

$$\text{Rate} = k[A][B]$$

How about a case where two molecules of the same kind react with one another?

$$2\,A \rightarrow \text{products}$$

Suppose this time that we have 8 A molecules in some given volume. Starting with any one of them we find that at any moment it has 7 distinct chances of colliding with another molecule:

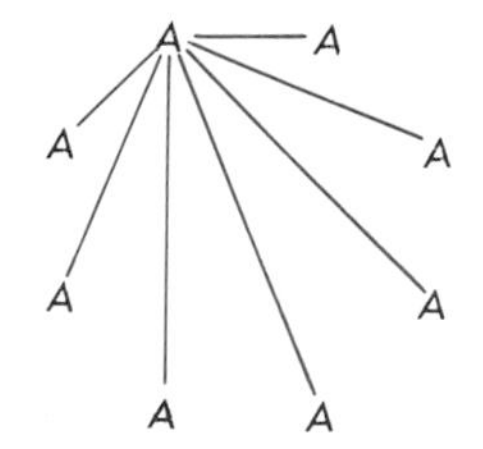

The next molecule has 6 additional chances of collision, besides collision with the first molecule, which has already been counted:

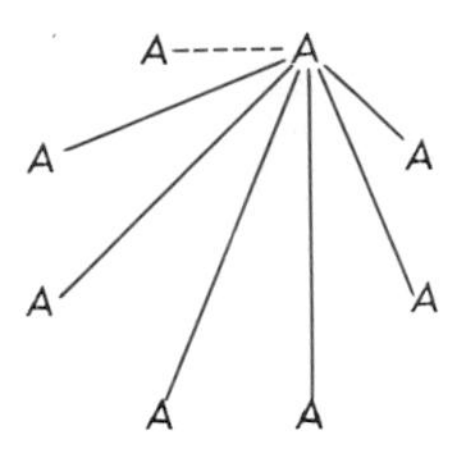

The third molecule has 5 additional chances; the fourth, 4 additional, and so forth. Altogether, the total collision possibilities are:

$$7 + 6 + 5 + 4 + 3 + 2 + 1 = 28$$

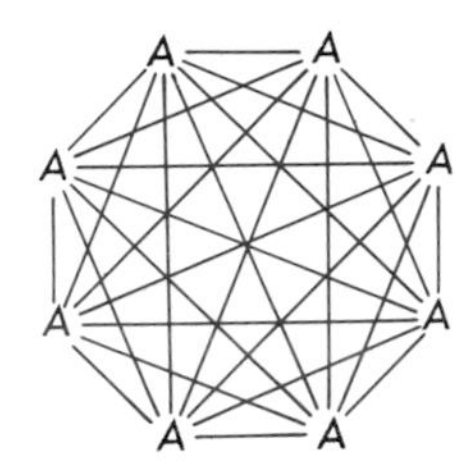

If there were twice as many molecules in the same volume, the total number of collision possibilities among the 16 molecules would be:

$$15+14+13+12+11+10+9+8+7+6+5+4+3+2+1=120$$

In general, N molecules have

$$(N - 1) + (N - 2) + (N - 3) + \cdots + 1 = (N)(N - 1)/2$$

separate chances of collision. The actual number of collisions occurring in a given time should then be proportional to $(N)(N - 1)$. In any real case, the number of molecules N will be very large, so that for all practical purposes $(N - 1) = N$ and $(N)(N - 1) = N^2$. If the rate of reaction is proportional to the rate at which collisions take place, which depends in turn on the value of N^2, then, since the number of molecules of A in a given volume is proportional to the molar concentration $[A]$,

$$\text{rate} = k[A]^2$$

For reactions which occur as a result of simultaneous collision of 3 molecules:

$$(1) \qquad A + B + C \rightarrow \text{products}$$

$$(2) \qquad 2\,A + B \rightarrow \text{products}$$

$$(3) \qquad 3\,A \rightarrow \text{products}$$

reasoning similar to that above leads to the rate expressions:

$$(1) \quad \text{Rate}_1 = k_1[A][B][C]$$

$$(2) \quad \text{Rate}_2 = k_2[A]^2[B]$$

$$(3) \quad \text{Rate}_3 = k_3[A]^3$$

Reaction Order 12.2

*The **order** of a reaction is the sum of all of the exponents appearing in the rate expression for the reaction.* Thus, the reaction

$$2\ N_2O_5 \rightarrow 4\ NO_2 + O_2 \qquad \text{Rate} = k_1[N_2O_5]$$

is first order;

$$H_2 + I_2 \rightarrow 2\ HI \qquad \text{Rate} = k_2[H_2][I_2]$$

is second order; and the reaction

$$2\ NO + O_2 \rightarrow 2\ NO_2 \qquad \text{Rate} = k_3[NO]^2[O_2]$$

is third order.

From the discussion in the preceding section, it might appear that the rate expression and order of a reaction could be deduced from the coefficients of the reactants appearing in the balanced equation. Consideration of the decomposition of N_2O_5,

$$2\ N_2O_5 \rightarrow 4\ NO_2 + O_2$$

which has been shown experimentally to be a first-order reaction, should be enough to disabuse one of that possible misconception. In fact, an obvious relationship between the stoichiometry of a reaction and its order exists only for simple reactions occurring in a single step. Most experimentally observable chemical reactions occur through a series of several simple reactions each of which proceeds at its own characteristic rate. The overall reaction rate and order will depend, usually in unpredictable fashion, upon the relative rates of the several steps, their reaction orders, and the molecular species taking part in each. For this reason, *the rate expression*, and from it the reaction order, *must be determined experimentally in every case.*

The rate of reaction may be measured by following the appearance or disappearance of some reacting species, or the change in some physical property of the reaction system, as a function of time. For example, the rate of hydrolysis of ethyl acetate:

$$C_2H_3O_2C_2H_5 + NaOH \rightarrow NaC_2H_3O_2 + C_2H_5OH$$

may be determined by periodically removing samples of the reaction mixture and adding them to dilute HCl, converting the $NaC_2H_3O_2$ to acetic acid, which is analyzed. The gas-phase dissociation of ethylamine,

$$C_2H_5NH_2 \rightarrow C_2H_4 + NH_3$$

can be followed by measuring the increase in volume at constant pressure, or the increase in pressure at constant volume, as the reaction proceeds, since two moles of gas are produced for every mole of gas dissociated. The rate of pyrolysis of methane to carbon at temperatures between 1000° and 1100°C,

$$CH_4(g) \rightarrow C(s) + 2\ H_2(g)$$

has been determined by measuring the drop in resistance as carbon is deposited on a surface between two electrodes.

The proper rate expression is arrived at by trial and error. One way is to measure the reaction rates at a number of different reactant concentrations. The values of the corresponding rates and concentrations are then inserted in a postulated rate expression, which is then solved for k. If the proper rate expression is chosen, the same value for k will be obtained in each case. If not, the process is repeated, trying another postulated expression until one is found which gives a constant value for k at all reactant concentrations.

12.3 Reaction Mechanism

Whatever the mechanism by which N_2O_5 dissociates into NO_2 and O_2, the fact that the reaction follows first-order kinetics means that it cannot be a simple collision between two molecules of N_2O_5 to give the final products. The reaction may, however, take place in a series of steps, one of them much slower than the others. The reaction cannot proceed any faster than its slowest step, which therefore controls the overall rate. Should the rate-controlling step involve only a single molecule of N_2O_5, this would account for the observed reaction order. A mechanism has been proposed for this reaction consisting of the following steps:

$$(1) \qquad N_2O_5 \rightleftharpoons NO_2 + NO_3$$

$$(2) \qquad NO_2 + NO_3 \rightarrow NO_2 + O_2 + NO$$

$$(3) \qquad NO + NO_3 \rightarrow 2\ NO_2$$

If step (1) were rate-controlling, this would readily account for the overall first-order rate. Present indications are, however, that although the reaction does appear to proceed according to the proposed mechanism, the slow step is actually step (2). Evidently step (1) is reversible, going about equally well in either direction, with the result that N_2O_5 disappears from the mixture only as fast as NO_2 and NO_3 react in step (2).

Nitric oxide reacts as follows with hydrogen in the gas phase at 800°C:

$$2\ NO + 2\ H_2 \rightarrow N_2 + 2\ H_2O$$

Doubling the concentration of NO in the mixture causes a fourfold increase in the initial rate of this reaction, which shows it to be second order in NO. The reaction is first order in H_2, however, since doubling the concentration of that reactant results only in a doubling of the initial reaction rate. The overall reaction therefore is third order with the rate expression:

$$\text{Rate} = k[\text{NO}]^2[\text{H}_2]$$

This suggests that the rate-controlling step is a reaction involving a simultaneous collision among two molecules of NO and one of H_2, perhaps the following:

$$2\ \text{NO} + \text{H}_2 \rightarrow \text{N}_2 + \text{H}_2\text{O}_2$$

accompanied by the fast step:

$$\text{H}_2\text{O}_2 + \text{H}_2 \rightarrow 2\ \text{H}_2\text{O}$$

It does not follow that because a proposed mechanism is consistent with the observed reaction kinetics it must necessarily be the mechanism by which the reaction takes place. There may be several possible mechanisms which can be written, all of them consistent with experiment, only one of which is likely to be the correct one. The reaction between NO and H_2, for example, could just as well proceed as follows:

$$2\ \text{NO} + \text{H}_2 \rightarrow \text{N}_2\text{O} + \text{H}_2\text{O} \qquad \text{(slow)}$$

$$\text{N}_2\text{O} + \text{H}_2 \rightarrow \text{N}_2 + \text{H}_2\text{O} \qquad \text{(fast)}$$

Choosing among several reasonable mechanisms is not always easy and may entail finding a way to detect the presence of some transient species in the reaction mixture. For instance, the detection of either H_2O_2 or N_2O in the mixture would permit a choice to be made between the two mechanisms given for the NO-H_2 reaction. Because most reaction intermediates are present in extremely small amounts and have very short lifetimes, their detection may be accompanied by great experimental difficulty, and failure to detect an intermediate species does not necessarily rule out a proposed mechanism.

The formation of HI from its elements is a classic example of a case where the generally accepted reaction mechanism later turned out to be incorrect. Since the turn of the century this reaction, which follows second-order kinetics, had been assumed to involve a simple collision between two molecules:

$$\text{H}_2 + \text{I}_2 \rightarrow 2\ \text{HI} \qquad \text{Rate} = k[\text{H}_2][\text{I}_2]$$

As recently as 1967, however, Dr. J. H. Sullivan of the Los Alamos Scientific Laboratory demonstrated that the reaction is considerably more complex and probably proceeds through one of the following series of steps:

$$\text{I}_2 \rightleftharpoons 2\ \text{I} \qquad \text{(reversible)}$$

$$2\ \text{I} + \text{H}_2 \rightarrow 2\ \text{HI} \qquad \text{(rate-controlling)}$$

or,

$$\text{I}_2 \rightleftharpoons 2\ \text{I} \qquad \text{(reversible)}$$

$$\text{I} + \text{H}_2 \rightarrow \text{IH}_2 \qquad \text{(fast)}$$

$$\text{IH}_2 + \text{I} \rightarrow 2\ \text{HI} \qquad \text{(slow, rate-controlling)}$$

12.4 Temperature

Raising the temperature increases the rate of any chemical reaction, whether the reaction is an endothermic or an exothermic one. Experimentally we find that a 10° rise in temperature approximately doubles the rates of many chemical reactions. Temperature is a measure of the average kinetic energy of the molecules. A rise in temperature corresponds to an increase in average kinetic energy, and we might suppose that the increase in kinetic energy is responsible for the faster reaction rate. A rise in temperature from 0° to 10°C increases the average kinetic energy by only $\frac{10}{273}$, or less than 4%, however, and at higher temperatures, the percentage increase is even less. This alone would not seem to be sufficient to account for the doubling of the reaction rate.

At higher temperatures, the molecules move faster and collide more frequently, but it can be shown that a 10° rise in temperature causes an increase of less than 2% in the collision frequency, again not enough to account for the reaction rate doubling. At room temperature and 1 atm pressure, the molecules in 1 ml of gas undergo a total of something like 10^{27} to 10^{28} collisions in 1 sec. Each individual molecule therefore is involved in more than one million collisions each second. Clearly, if every collision led to reaction, any chemical reaction would be virtually instantaneous. Evidently, only a small fraction of the total collisions taking place are effective in bringing about reaction. If we assume that for a collision to be effective the molecules colliding must together possess a certain minimum kinetic energy, then we are able to account for the observed effect of temperature on the rate of reaction. *This minimum kinetic energy which the molecules must possess in order to react we will call the* ***activation energy*** *of the reaction.*

The distribution of molecular kinetic energies is shown in Fig. 12.1 for two temperatures where $T_2 > T_1$. If the minimum energy required for reaction to take place is E_a, then the number of molecules possessing at least this energy at each temperature is given by the area of the shaded region under each curve. We can see from this how a relatively small increase in the average kinetic energy can result in a large increase in the number of molecules which possess the necessary activation energy. As the number of molecules with the necessary energy increases, the rate of reaction increases proportionately. It is found experimentally that the rate constant k increases regularly with temperature, a plot of log k against $1/T$ being a straight line with a slope proportional to E_a. This affords a way of determining the activation energy for any reaction for which k can be calculated from experimental data measured at at least two temperatures.

Like the mountains between Denver and San Francisco, the requirement that the reacting molecules possess at least the minimum activation energy acts as a barrier to what otherwise might be a downhill trip from reactants to products. The existence of this activation energy barrier is evidence that the reaction process must pass through some intermediate *activated state* of higher energy than either the reactants or products. The activation energy can sometimes be related to the energy of some simple process. For example, the thermal decomposition of methane to carbon is first order with an activation energy equal to the **C—H** bond energy, suggesting, but by no

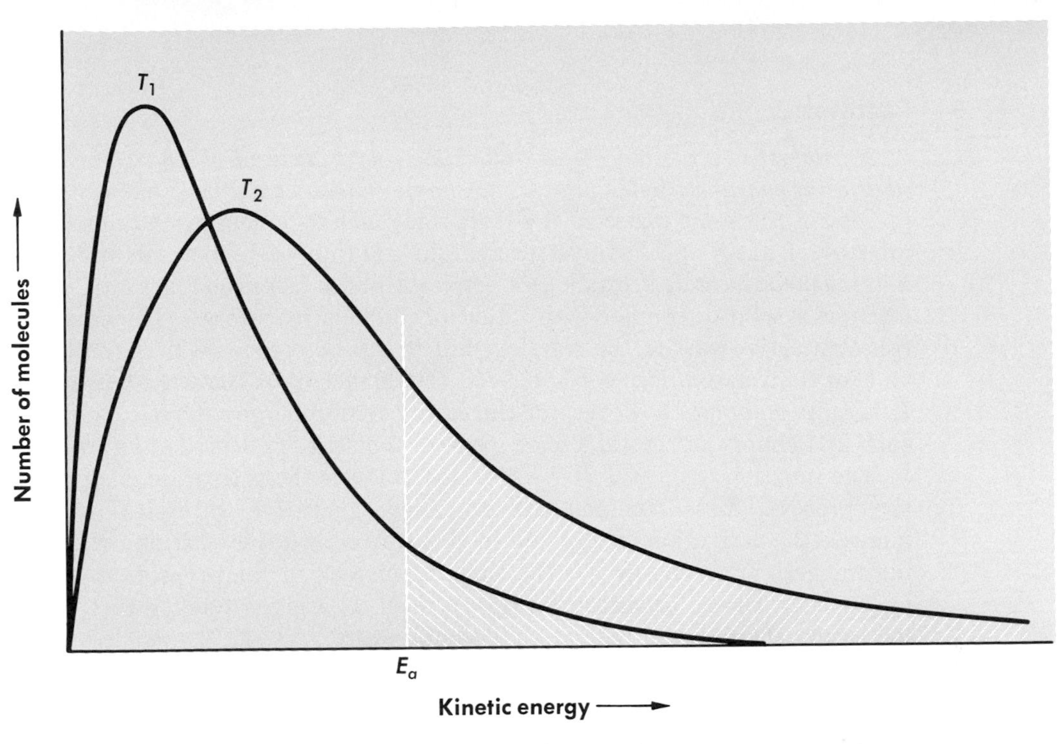

Fig. 12.1 Distribution of molecular kinetic energies at two temperatures, $T_2 > T_1$.

means proving, that E_a for this reaction may be the heat of reaction for the rate-controlling step:

$$CH_4 \rightarrow CH_3 + H$$

In most cases all that can be said about the activated state is that it consists of some arrangement of atoms which is less stable than either the reactants or products, and in which some bonds are in the process of being broken while others are being formed. The relationship between the activation energy and the actual heat of reaction is shown for an exothermic reaction in Fig. 12.2, and for an endothermic reaction in Fig. 12.3.

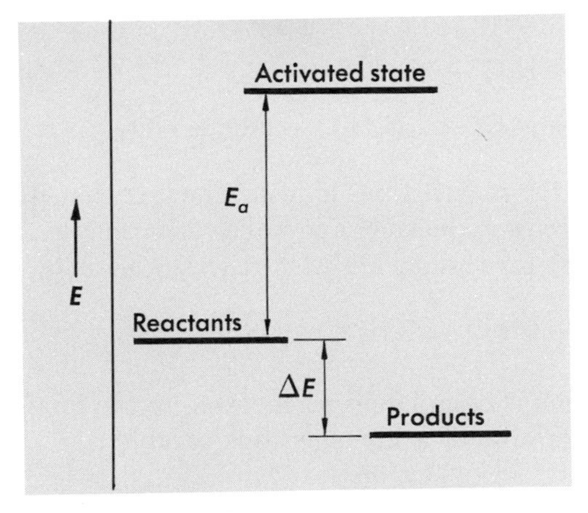

Fig. 12.2 Energy diagram for an exothermic reaction, ΔE negative.

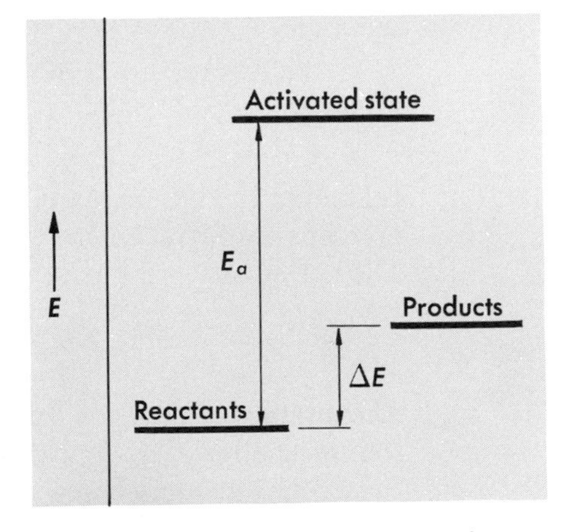

Fig. 12.3 Energy diagram for an endothermic reaction, ΔE positive.

12.5 Catalysis

A ***catalyst*** *is a substance which alters the rate of a chemical reaction without itself being consumed in the process.* A **homogeneous catalyst** is one which is present in the same phase as the reactants, such as a gaseous catalyst in a mixture of gases or a catalyst present in solution with the reactants. A ***heterogeneous catalyst*** exists as a separate phase from the reactants, most often as a solid in contact with liquid or gaseous reactants. The catalyst takes an active part in the reaction, but it can be recovered in its entirety and for that reason does not appear in the equation for the overall process. It is quite common, however, for the catalyst to undergo a physical change such as a change in crystal size or form, or a change in degree of hydration.

The function of a catalyst is generally to lower the activation energy for the process. Less common are so-called "negative catalysts" which increase the activation energy and in this way retard the reaction. Lowering the activation energy has the effect of increasing the proportion of the molecules with the necessary energy to react at a given temperature, thus increasing the reaction rate at that temperature.

One way in which a catalyst can operate is by providing an alternative, easier path by which the reaction may be carried out—a trail around the mountain, so to speak, rather than directly over the summit. For example, sulfuric acid may be prepared as follows:

$$2\ SO_2 + O_2 \rightarrow 2\ SO_3$$

$$SO_3 + H_2O \rightarrow H_2SO_4$$

In the absence of a catalyst, the first of these reactions, the oxidation of SO_2 to SO_3, although feasible, has a very high activation energy and does not occur to any appreciable extent at moderate temperatures.* In the old ***lead chamber process*** for sulfuric acid manufacture (Sec. 18.16c), the reactants SO_2, O_2, and H_2O are mixed with NO and NO_2. The mechanism of the ensuing reaction is only partly understood, but the first identifiable product is nitrosylsulfuric acid, $HNSO_5$, which subsequently reacts with additional water to yield sulfuric acid:

$$NO + NO_2 + 2\ SO_2 + O_2 + H_2O \rightarrow 2\ HNSO_5$$

$$2\ HNSO_5 + H_2O \rightarrow 2\ H_2SO_4 + NO + NO_2$$

Whatever the intermediate steps in the reaction mechanism, the fact that it proceeds readily at room temperature is evidence of a low activation energy. The net equation is the same as that for the uncatalyzed reaction, namely,

$$2\ SO_2 + O_2 + 2H_2O \rightarrow 2\ H_2SO_4$$

The mixture of nitrogen oxides, which is completely regenerated in the final step of the reaction, is a typical example of a homogeneous catalyst.

* Since two moles of gas are being produced from three, we would predict that the entropy change for this reaction is negative and that at high temperatures, where the activation energy might be available, ΔG will become positive and the reaction will no longer be feasible.

The more modern ***contact process*** for sulfuric acid makes use of a heterogeneous solid catalyst of platinum metal or vanadium pentoxide to promote the direct oxidation of SO_2 to SO_3. The effectiveness of a heterogeneous catalyst appears to depend upon the adsorption of one or more of the reactants on the surface of the catalyst. Energy released as a result of the bonding of reactant molecules to the catalyst surface may serve to weaken a bond which is to be broken in the reaction and in this way lower the activation energy. The catalyst surface may also act as a matrix to hold the reactant molecule in an orientation particularly favorable to reaction with another molecule, thus increasing the probability that reaction will take place. Most catalysts are highly specific, and a substance that influences the rate of one reaction may have little or no effect on the rate of another, apparently similar reaction. It is seldom possible to predict beforehand, except sometimes in a very general way, what substance or type of substance will catalyze a particular reaction.

Although the presence of a catalyst affects the activation energy, and hence the rate of a chemical reaction, it has no effect on the total free energy change. For this reason, *a catalyst cannot be used to bring about a reaction under conditions for which the free energy change of the uncatalyzed reaction is unfavorable.*

Chemical Equilibrium 12.6

The rate of any chemical reaction at a given temperature is proportional to the concentrations of the reactants. For example, the rate of the reaction

$$H_2 + I_2 \rightarrow 2\ HI$$

is given by the expression

$$\text{Rate}_1 = k_1[H_2][I_2]$$

As H_2 and I_2 are consumed during the reaction, and their concentrations decrease accordingly, the reaction proceeds at a slower and slower rate. At the same time, the concentration of HI in the mixture increases. The rate of decomposition of HI, which is the reverse of its formation,

$$2\ HI \rightarrow H_2 + I_2$$

is given by

$$\text{Rate}_2 = k_2[HI]^2$$

and the more HI is formed by the forward reaction, the faster it decomposes back into its elements. With the forward reaction slowing down and the back reaction speeding up, eventually both reactions will end up going at the same rate. This is shown schematically in Fig. 12.4. When that happens, the system will be in a state of dynamic equilibrium, and unless something is done to disturb the equilibrium, the concentrations of H_2, I_2, and HI will undergo no further change.

At equilibrium,

$$\text{Rate}_1 = \text{Rate}_2$$

Substituting the corresponding expressions for the rates:

$$k_1[H_2][I_2] = k_2[HI]^2$$

and

$$\frac{k_1}{k_2} = \frac{[HI]^2}{[H_2][I_2]} = K_c$$

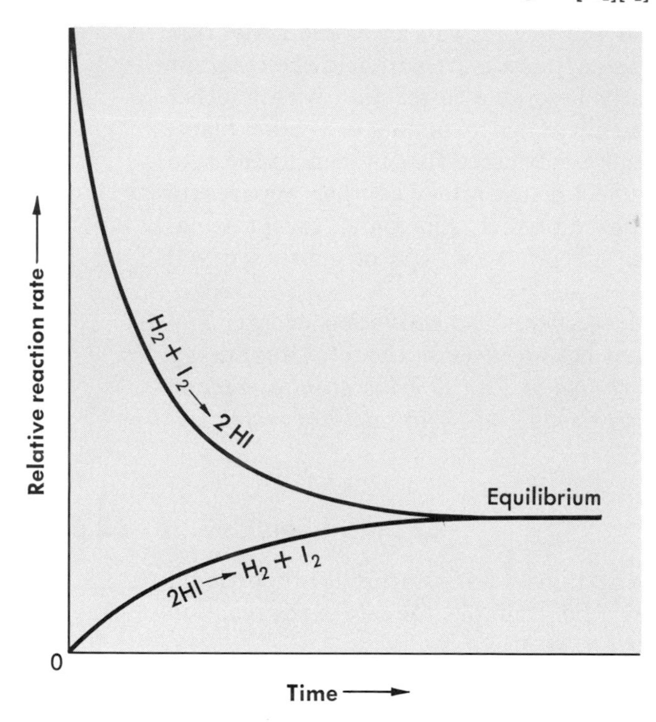

Fig. 12.4 Changes in relative reaction rates as the system $H_2 + I_2 \rightleftharpoons 2\,HI$ approaches equilibrium at 450°C. At time 0, $[H_2] = [I_2]$; $[HI] = 0$.

The constant K_c is known as the ***equilibrium constant*** for the reaction. The subscript c means that the value of the constant has been calculated from the molar concentrations of the reactants and products at equilibrium. At any one temperature, the equilibrium constant for a particular reaction has a single, unique value. Some experimental data are given in Table 12.1 for

TABLE 12.1 Equilibrium Data for the Reaction $H_2 + I_2 \rightleftharpoons 2\,HI$ at 458°C

	Concentration, moles/liter						
	Initially			At Equilibrium			
Experiment	H_2	I_2	HI	H_2	I_2	HI	$K_c = \frac{[HI]^2}{[H_2][I_2]}$
1	0.0123	0.00996	0.00	0.00384	0.00152	0.0169	48.5
2	0.0123	0.00878	0.00	0.00457	0.00106	0.0155	49.3
3	0.0120	0.00840	0.00	0.00458	0.00097	0.0149	49.5
4	0.00	0.00	0.0379	0.00421	0.00421	0.0294	48.8
5	0.00	0.00	0.0152	0.00170	0.00170	0.0118	48.5
6	0.00	0.00	0.0129	0.00143	0.00143	0.0100	48.8
						Average =	48.8

the hydrogen iodide equilibrium at 458°C, at which temperature all the reactants are in the gaseous state. You will note that no matter what the initial concentrations of the reactants may have been, by the time equilibrium is attained, their concentrations have changed in such a way that the same value is obtained for K_c.

The rate expressions are known for both the forward and reverse reactions in the case of the hydrogen iodide equilibrium, and when they are equated, the equilibrium expression can be obtained. For most chemical equilibria, neither the reaction mechanisms nor the appropriate rate expressions are known, yet the equilibrium expression can still be written so long as we have the balanced equation for the overall reaction. Consider the imaginary equilibrium

$$2\,A + 2\,B \rightleftharpoons C + 2\,D$$

If the forward reaction takes place in a single step consisting of a simultaneous collision of 2 molecules of A and 2 molecules of B, its rate will be given by the expression:

$$\text{Rate}_f = k_f[A]^2[B]^2$$

Likewise, if the reverse reaction occurs in a single step its rate is:

$$\text{Rate}_r = k_r[C][D]^2$$

and at equilibrium, when $\text{Rate}_f = \text{Rate}_r$,

$$k_f[A]^2[B]^2 = k_r[C][D]^2$$

and

$$\frac{k_f}{k_r} = K_c = \frac{[C][D]^2}{[A]^2[B]^2}$$

But suppose that the reaction proceeds through some unknown series of steps? Whatever the steps may be, we can safely say that if the reaction as a whole is reversible, both the forward and reverse reactions must pass through the same steps but in opposite directions. Each individual step is reversible, in other words, and at equilibrium will be going at the same rate in both directions.

Suppose that our reaction proceeds through the following two-step mechanism:

$$(1) \qquad 2\,A + B \rightleftharpoons C + Q$$

$$(2) \qquad Q + B \rightleftharpoons 2\,D$$

For step (1),

$$\text{Rate}_f = k_f[A]^2[B]$$

$$\text{Rate}_r = k_r[C][Q]$$

at equilibrium,

$$\text{Rate}_f = \text{Rate}_r$$

and

$$\frac{k_f}{k_r} = K_1 = \frac{[C][Q]}{[A]^2[B]}$$

Similarly for step (2):

$$\text{Rate}'_f = k'_f[Q][B]$$

$$\text{Rate}'_r = k'_r[D]^2$$

and at equilibrium,

$$\frac{k'_f}{k'_r} = K_2 = \frac{[D]^2}{[Q][B]}$$

The product of two constants is a third constant; therefore, multiplying K_1 by K_2 we obtain

$$K_1K_2 = K_c = \frac{[C][\not{Q}]}{[A]^2[B]} \times \frac{[D]^2}{[\not{Q}][B]}$$

$$K_c = \frac{[C][D]^2}{[A]^2[B]^2}$$

The equilibrium expression turns out to be the same whether we assume a one- or two-step mechanism. We will find, in fact, that no matter what mechanism we assume for this reaction, we will always arrive at the same equilibrium expression. For the general case,

$$a\,A + b\,B + \cdots \rightleftharpoons c\,C + d\,D + \cdots$$

$$K_c = \frac{[C]^c[D]^d[\cdots}{[A]^a[B]^b[\cdots}$$

When we write the equilibrium expression for a reversible reaction, by convention the concentrations of the reactants appearing to the right of the double arrow in the equation as written are placed in the numerator, and the concentrations of the reactants to the left are placed in the denominator. To avoid any ambiguity, the equation should be given any time the equilibrium constant is discussed.

Example 12.1

Write the equilibrium expression for the reaction

$$4\ HCl + O_2 \rightleftharpoons 2\ Cl_2 + 2\ H_2O$$

Solution:

$$K_c = \frac{[Cl_2]^2[H_2O]^2}{[HCl]^4[O_2]}$$

Because the molar concentration of a gas is proportional to its partial pressure, for gas-phase equilibria the equilibrium constant may be expressed either in terms of molar concentrations or in terms of partial pressures. The constant for the equilibrium

$$N_2 + 3\ H_2 \rightleftharpoons 2\ NH_3$$

for example, may be expressed as either

$$K_c = \frac{[NH_3]^2}{[N_2][H_2]^3}$$

or

$$K_p = \frac{(p_{NH_3})^2}{(p_{N_2})(p_{H_2})^3}$$

Only in those instances where the same number of moles of gas appear on both sides of the equation will K_c and K_p have the same numerical value. In any discussion of gaseous equilibria, therefore, it is most important to specify whether K_c or K_p is meant. It is also important to be consistent in calculating the equilibrium constant, that is to use all molar concentrations or all partial pressures in its calculation, and not some of each.

Example 12.2

A mixture of 0.0112 mole of H_2, and 0.00923 mole of I_2 was sealed in a 1-liter vessel and kept at 394°C until equilibrium was attained. At equilibrium, the mixture was found to contain 0.0159 mole of HI. Calculate K_c for the reaction; $H_2 + I_2 \rightleftharpoons 2\ HI$ at 394°C.

Solution: It is seen from the equation for the reaction that for every mole of HI formed, $\frac{1}{2}$ mole of H_2 and $\frac{1}{2}$ mole of I_2 are consumed. In this example, since 0.0159 mole of HI was formed, half that amount, 0.00795 mole, of each of the initial reactants was used up, leaving in the final mixture

$$0.0112 - 0.00795 = 0.0032 \text{ mole } H_2$$

$$0.00923 - 0.00795 = 0.00128 \text{ mole } I_2$$

Substituting these values in the equilibrium expression

$$K_c = \frac{[HI]^2}{[H_2][I_2]}$$

we obtain

$$K_c = \frac{(0.0159)^2}{(0.0032)(0.00128)} = 61.6$$

Example 12.3

A 0.010-mole sample of HI is sealed into a 1-liter vessel at 394°C. What will be the composition of the mixture in the vessel when equilibrium is attained?

Solution: For every mole of H_2 formed, 1 mole of I_2 is also produced and 2 moles of HI are consumed. Let $x = [H_2] = [I_2]$ at equilibrium. Then,

	Initial Concentration	At Equilibrium
HI	0.010 mole	0.010 − 2x mole
H_2	0.000 mole	x mole
I_2	0.000 mole	x mole

When we use the value of K_c calculated in Example 12.2, we get

$$61.6 = \frac{(0.010 - 2x)^2}{x^2}$$

Solving the resulting quadratic equation gives $x = 0.00103$. Therefore, there are 0.00103 mole H_2, 0.00103 mole I_2, and $0.010 - 0.0021 = 0.0079$ mole HI present at equilibrium.

Example 12.4

In 1924, during an investigation of the phosgene equilibrium

$$CO + Cl_2 \rightleftharpoons COCl_2$$

Bodenstein and Plaut placed Cl_2 at an initial partial pressure of 0.46 atm and CO at an initial partial pressure of 0.45 atm in a glass bulb which was sealed and heated at 395°C. At equilibrium, the total pressure of the gas mixture in the bulb was found to be 0.58 atm. Calculate K_p for this reaction at 395°C.

Solution: Because the volume remained constant throughout the experiment, the partial pressures are directly proportional to the number of moles of each gas present. Let x = partial pressure of $COCl_2$ in the equilibrium mixture. Since for every mole of $COCl_2$ formed, 1 mole of Cl_2 and 1 mole of CO are used up, x also represents the decrease in the partial pressures of each of these gases as a result of the reaction. Then,

	Initial Pressure (atm)	At Equilibrium (atm)
Cl_2	0.46	$0.46 - x$
CO	0.45	$0.45 - x$
$COCl_2$	0.00	x

Since the total pressure at equilibrium is 0.58 atm

$$P_{\text{tot}} = p_{Cl_2} + p_{CO} + p_{COCl_2}$$

$$0.58 = (0.46 - x) + (0.45 - x) + x$$

$$p_{COCl_2} = x = 0.33 \text{ atm}$$

$$p_{Cl_2} = (0.46 - 0.33) = 0.13 \text{ atm}$$

$$p_{CO} = (0.45 - 0.33) = 0.12 \text{ atm}$$

Therefore:

$$K_p = \frac{p_{COCl_2}}{p_{Cl_2} p_{CO}} = \frac{0.33}{(0.13)(0.12)} = 21$$

Example 12.5

From the data given in Example 12.4, calculate K_c for the reaction

$$CO + Cl_2 \rightleftharpoons COCl_2$$

at 395°C.

Solution: The molar concentration of any substance is n/V, where n is the number of moles of substance, and V is the volume it occupies. From the combined gas-law equation

$$pV = nRT$$

the molar concentration of a gas is found to be

$$n/V = p/RT$$

Hence,

$$K_c = \frac{[COCl_2]}{[Cl_2][CO]} = \frac{\dfrac{p_{COCl_2}}{RT}}{\dfrac{p_{Cl_2}}{RT} \times \dfrac{p_{CO}}{RT}}$$

$$K_c = \frac{p_{COCl_2}}{p_{Cl_2}p_{CO}} \times RT$$

$$K_c = K_pRT$$

At 395°C = 668°K

$$RT = 0.082(668) = 54.8$$

$$K_c = 21 \times 54.8 = 1.2 \times 10^3$$

Similar calculations will show that, in all homogeneous gaseous equilibria

$$K_c = K_p/(RT)^{\Delta n}$$

where Δn is the difference in the number of moles of gas appearing on the left and right sides of the equation, respectively. In the case of the phosgene equilibrium, $\Delta n = -1$, and, as we found above,

$$K_c = K_p/(RT)^{-1} = K_pRT$$

Heterogeneous Equilibria 12.7

A heterogeneous equilibrium exists when the reactants in equilibrium are present in different phases. The most common case is that of a solid in equilibrium with a gas or a liquid. An example is the equilibrium between calcium carbonate and its decomposition products, calcium oxide and carbon dioxide:

$$CaCO_3(s) \rightleftharpoons CaO(s) + CO_2(g)$$

The equilibrium expression for this reaction is

$$K = \frac{[CaO][CO_2]}{[CaCO_3]}$$

The molar concentration of a pure substance is proportional to its density,* which for a pure solid or liquid is a constant at any one temperature, being affected to only a negligible degree by changes in pressure. If the molar concentration of a solid is a constant, the above equilibrium expression becomes

$$K = \frac{k[CO_2]}{k'}$$

Collecting all of the constants on one side of the equation:

$$Kk'/k = K_c = [CO_2]$$

* The relationship is

$$\text{Molarity} = 1000(d/M)$$

where d is the density in grams per milliliter, M the molecular weight in gram/mole, and the factor 1000 is used to convert from milliliters to liters.

The equilibrium expression for this reaction in terms of partial pressures is similar in form:

$$K_p = p_{CO_2}$$

Although it may seem a bit strange to speak of the partial pressure of a pure solid or pure liquid within the solid or liquid phase, the partial pressure is a function of concentration, which is a constant for any pure solid or liquid. Therefore, no pressure term for either CaO or $CaCO_3$ appears in the equilibrium expression.

The principle developed for the $CaCO_3-CaO$ equilibrium holds true for any heterogeneous equilibrium. In the calculation of K_c or K_p for a heterogeneous equilibrium, concentration and pressure terms corresponding to pure solids or liquids present in different phases do not appear in the equilibrium expression.

Example 12.6

Write the equilibrium expressions in terms of concentrations and in terms of partial pressures for the reaction

$$CH_4(g) \rightleftharpoons C(s) + 2\ H_2(g)$$

Solution:

$$K_c = \frac{[H_2]^2}{[CH_4]}$$

$$K_p = \frac{p_{H_2}^2}{p_{CH_4}}$$

12.8 Effect of Concentration Changes on Equilibrium

From the form of the equilibrium expression it is apparent that the equilibrium of a reacting system will be disturbed by a change in the concentration of any one of the reactants. Consider the reaction

$$A + B \rightleftharpoons C + D$$

With the system in equilibrium, the concentrations of the reactants are fixed by the requirement that at equilibrium,

$$\frac{[C][D]}{[A][B]} = K_c$$

Suppose now that more of reactant A is added to the equilibrium mixture. This has the effect of increasing the denominator in the expression above so that it no longer equals K_c and the system is no longer in equilibrium. The value of the numerator must be increased in order to restore the equality. This can be interpreted as meaning that in order for this system to return to equilibrium after the addition of A, the concentrations of C and D must be increased also. The concentrations of C and D can increase only at the expense of those of A and B. The addition of A may be said to have caused a "shift in the position of equilibrium" in the forward direction, or to the right as the equation is written. Addition of B will have the same effect. By the same token, the addition of either C or D to the equilibrium mixture will cause the position of equilibrium to be shifted in the reverse direction, or to the left, toward the formation of greater amounts of A and B.

The effect on the equilibrium is exactly as one would expect from the change in the relative rates of the forward and reverse reactions as a result of a change in the concentration of one of the reactants. An increase in the concentration of one of the reactants will be accompanied by an increase in the rate of the process in which it takes part. This is shown in Fig. 12.5 for the **HI** equilibrium. At time t, **HI** is added to the equilibrium mixture, with the result that the rate at which **HI** is decomposing is increased over its rate at equilibrium and over that of the recombination reaction. As **HI** is consumed and more $\mathbf{H_2}$ and $\mathbf{I_2}$ are formed, the decomposition slows down and the

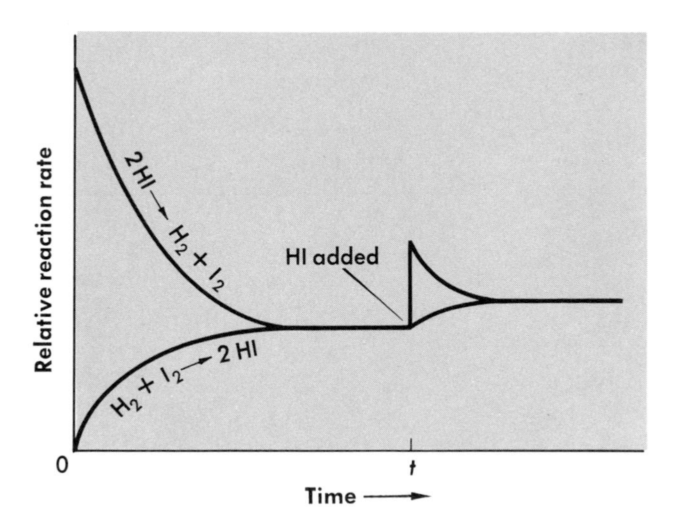

Fig. 12.5 Effect of adding HI to the system $H_2 + I_2 \rightleftharpoons 2\ HI$ at equilibrium. At time 0, $[H_2] = [I_2] = 0$. Temperature, 394°C.

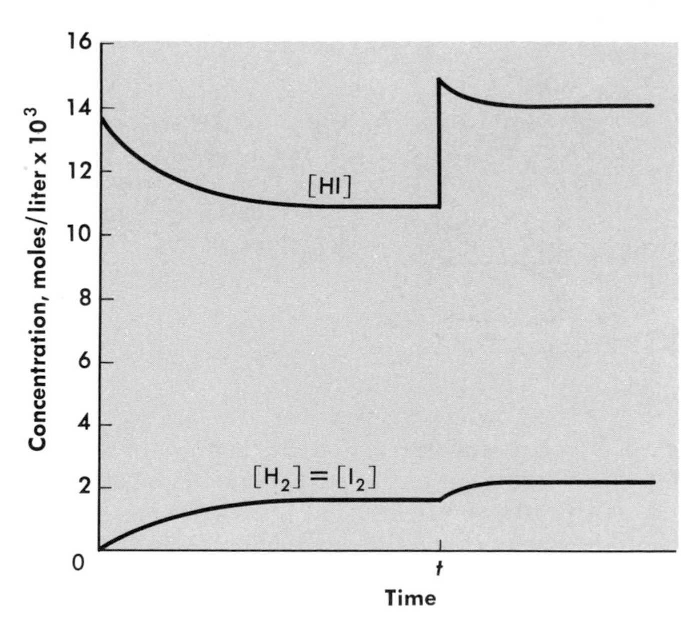

Fig. 12.6 Effect of adding HI on the concentrations of H_2 and I_2 at equilibrium. Temperature, 394°C.

recombination speeds up, until once again both rates are equal and equilibrium is restored. At the new equilibrium, however, both reactions are going faster than they were before. Analysis of the new equilibrium mixture shows it to contain more of the reactants H_2 and I_2 than it did prior to time t (Fig. 12.6). The composition of the equilibrium mixtures both before and after time t, as determined by analysis, are given in Table 12.2. Insertion of these values into the equilibrium expression is seen to give the same value for K_c in each case.

TABLE 12.2 Equilibrium Data for the Reaction $H_2 + I_2 \rightleftharpoons 2\ HI$ at 394°C, HI added to equilibrium mixture at time t

	Equilibrium Concentration, moles/liter			
	H_2	I_2	HI	K_c
Before time t	0.00140	0.00140	0.0108	59.5
After time t	0.00180	0.00180	0.0139	59.6

In Fig. 12.7 the effect of adding H_2 to the equilibrium mixture is shown. The result, as expected, is the displacement of the equilibrium toward the formation of more HI at the expense of the third reactant, I_2.

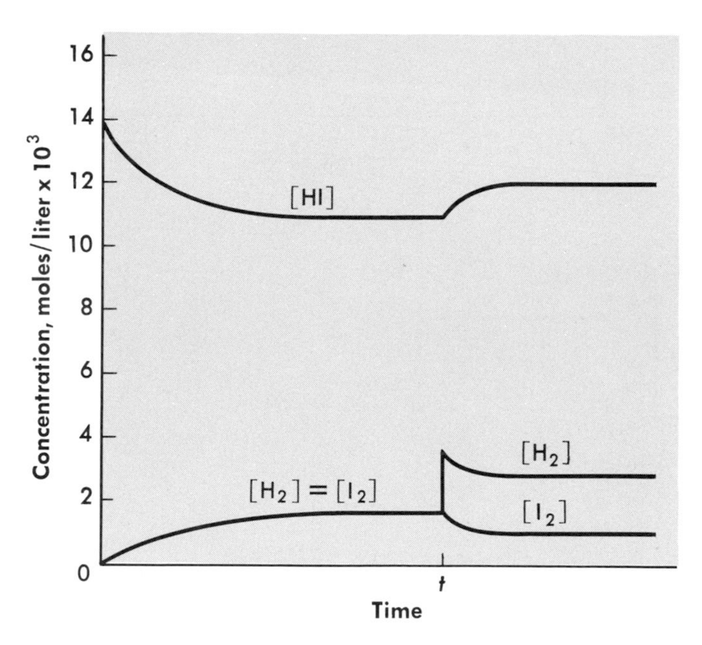

Fig. 12.7 Effect of adding H_2 to the system $H_2 + I_2 \rightleftharpoons 2\ HI$ at time t on the proportions of reactants present at equilibrium. Temperature, 394°C.

Removing a participant in a reversible reaction has the effect of displacing the equilibrium in the direction leading to the formation of more of the substance being removed. Advantage is often taken of this in forcing a reversible reaction to go completely in one direction by removing one of the products of the reaction as fast as it is formed. For example, the hydrolysis of ethyl acetate,

$$C_2H_3O_2C_2H_5 + H_2O \rightleftharpoons HC_2H_3O_2 + C_2H_5OH$$

proceeds to completion in the presence of NaOH, which converts the acetic acid as fast as it is formed into its sodium salt:

$$HC_2H_3O_2 + NaOH \rightarrow NaC_2H_3O_2 + H_2O$$

On the other hand, amyl alcohol may be almost completely converted to amyl acetate by carrying out the reaction under a fractionating column (Sec. 10.13). This permits the continuous removal, by distillation, of the water produced in the reaction:

$$C_5H_{11}OH + HC_2H_3O_2 \rightleftharpoons C_2H_3O_2C_5H_{11} + H_2O$$

Effect of Pressure on Systems in Equilibrium 12.9

The molar concentration of a gas at constant temperature is directly proportional to its partial pressure. Therefore, any change in the total pressure on a system in equilibrium has the effect of changing the molar concentrations of all of the gaseous reactants, with the possible result that the system may no longer be in equilibrium at the new pressure. The rates of both the forward and reverse reactions will be affected by the changes in concentrations accompanying a pressure change, but not necessarily to the same extent. Because of this, when equilibrium is finally restored at the new pressure, the relative concentrations of the reactants in the mixture may be different from what they were before the pressure was changed. In practice, it is found that for a reaction such as

$$N_2(g) + 3\ H_2(g) \rightleftharpoons 2\ NH_3(g)$$

in which fewer moles of gas appear on the right-hand side of the equation as written than appear on the left, an increase in pressure will favor the forward reaction over the reverse, resulting in an increase in the relative amount of products (NH_3 in this example) in the new equilibrium mixture. The increase in pressure in this case has caused a "shift" in the equilibrium to the right, as the equation is written. On the other hand, if more moles of gas appear on the right than on the left, as in the equation for the dissociation of PCl_5,

$$PCl_5(g) \rightleftharpoons PCl_3(g) + Cl_2(g)$$

then an increase in pressure will cause a shift in the equilibrium to the left. If the same number of moles of gas appears on both sides of the equation, as in

$$H_2(g) + I_2(g) \rightleftharpoons 2\ HI(g)$$

a change in pressure will have no effect on the position of the equilibrium.

Example 12.7

At 250°C and 1 atm, PCl_5 is 80% dissociated at equilibrium according to the reaction

$$PCl_5(g) \rightleftharpoons PCl_3(g) + Cl_2(g)$$

What will be the percentage dissociation of PCl_5 at 2 atm pressure and the same temperature?

Solution: The first step in the solution of this problem is to calculate K_p using the data obtained at 1 atm. Since 80% of the PCl_5 has dissociated at equilibrium, for every mole of PCl_5 originally present, 0.80 mole of PCl_3, 0.80 mole Cl_2, and 0.20 mole PCl_5 are present at equilibrium, a total of 1.80 moles altogether. Multiplying the mole fraction of each gas by the total pressure gives us the partial pressure of each gas at equilibrium:

$$p_{PCl_5} = \frac{0.20}{1.80} \times 1 = 0.11 \text{ atm}$$

$$p_{Cl_2} = p_{PCl_3} = \frac{0.80}{1.80} \times 1 = 0.45 \text{ atm}$$

$$K_p = \frac{p_{Cl_2}p_{PCl_3}}{p_{PCl_5}} = \frac{(0.45)^2}{0.11} = 1.8$$

Now let $x = p_{Cl_2} = p_{PCl_3}$ at equilibrium under a pressure of 2 atm; p_{PCl_5} is then equal to $(2 - 2x)$.

$$K_p = 1.8 = \frac{x^2}{(2 - 2x)}$$

$$x = 0.8 \text{ atm}$$

$$p_{PCl_5} = 2.0 - 1.6 = 0.4 \text{ atm}$$

The number of moles of gas in a given volume is proportional to its partial pressure; therefore, for every 0.4 mole of PCl_5 present at equilibrium there must also be 0.8 mole of PCl_3 and 0.8 mole of Cl_2. According to the equation for the reaction, the latter two gases were produced by the dissociation of 0.8 mole of PCl_5. Hence,

Percent dissociation

$$= \frac{(\text{moles } PCl_5 \text{ dissociated})}{(\text{moles } PCl_5 \text{ dissociated}) + (\text{moles } PCl_5 \text{ undissociated})} \times 100$$

$$= \frac{0.8}{0.8 + 0.4} \times 100 = 67\%$$

An increase in pressure is seen to shift the position of this equilibrium to the left, with the result that less of the PCl_5 dissociates.

12.10 Effect of Temperature Changes on Equilibrium

An increase in temperature may cause either an increase or a decrease in the value of the equilibrium constant for a reversible reaction, depending upon whether the forward or the reverse process is one which absorbs heat. In any reversible reaction, both processes must necessarily pass through the same intermediate activated state. Because of this, the activation energy in one direction is larger than that in the other, and the difference between the two activation energies is equal to the heat of reaction. This is shown in Fig. 12.8, again using the hydrogen iodide equilibrium for purposes of illustration. The reaction between H_2 and I_2 in the vapor state is exothermic,

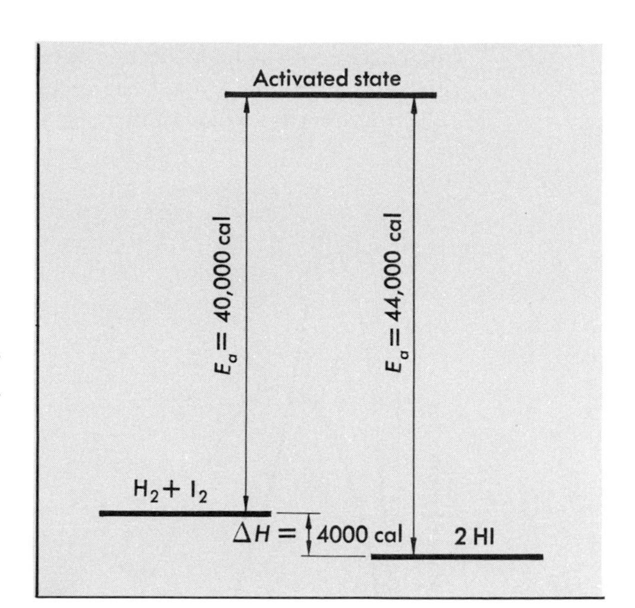

Fig. 12.8 Energy diagram for the reaction $H_2 + I_2 \rightleftharpoons 2\ HI$ at 298°C.

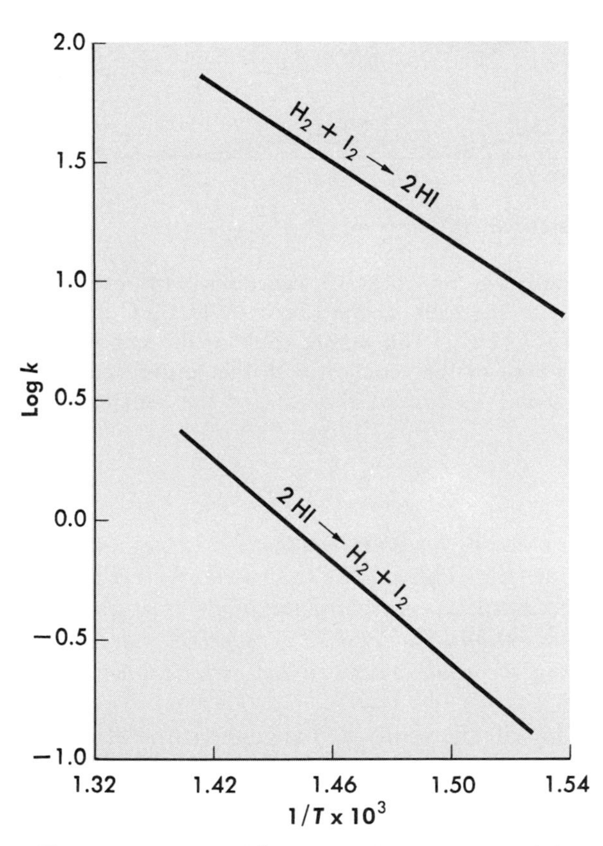

Fig. 12.9 Plot of the log of the rate constant against the reciprocal of the Kelvin temperature for the formation and decomposition of HI.

$\Delta H_{298} = -4000$ cal/mole. The decomposition of **HI** is, of course, endothermic by the same amount. From the diagram, one can see that the activation energy for the exothermic reaction is 4000 cal *less* than the activation energy for the endothermic one. A plot of the logarithms of the respective rate constants against the reciprocal of the absolute temperature (Fig. 12.9) reveals that while an increase in temperature increases the rate of both

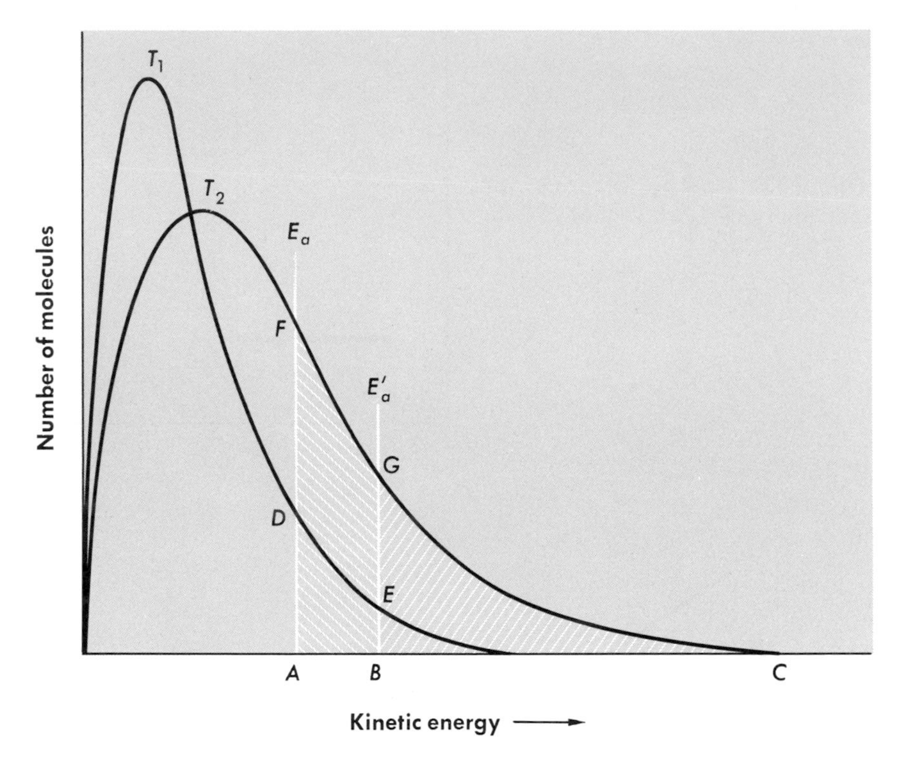

Fig. 12.10 Effect of temperature on rates of reactions with activation energies E_a and E'_a respectively. The ratio of the areas BGC/BEC is about twice the ratio of the areas AFC/ADC. This means that for the same rise in temperature from T_1 to T_2, the rate of the reaction with the larger activation energy should increase about twice as fast as the rate of the reaction with the smaller activation energy.

reactions, *the rate of the reaction having the greater activation energy increases more rapidly* than that of the other. This means that *a rise in temperature is accompanied by a shift in the equilibrium toward the products of the endothermic reaction*, that is, *in the direction in which heat is absorbed. A decrease in temperature causes a shift in the equilibrium in the direction leading to evolution of heat.*

A consideration of Fig. 12.10 will show why a change in temperature has a greater effect on the rate of the reaction with the higher activation energy. It can be seen from the diagram that an increase in temperature from T_1 to T_2 will result in a greater proportionate increase in the number of molecules which possess energy equal to or in excess of the greater activation energy. The relative numbers of molecules which have the necessary energy in each case are given by the respective areas under the curves.

Le Chatelier's Principle 12.11

The observed effects of concentration, pressure, and temperature changes are all consistent with the principle of Le Chatelier, which was mentioned earlier (Sec. 10.4) in connection with the influence of temperature on solubility. According to this principle, *when a stress is applied to a system in a state of dynamic equilibrium, a reaction will occur wherever possible in the direction which tends to offset the effect of the stress.* Le Chatelier's principle is of general applicability to any dynamic equilibrium, whether chemical or physical.

Catalysts and Equilibrium 12.12

The presence of a catalyst does not affect the position of the equilibrium. The role of the catalyst, as we have seen, is to lower the overall activation energy for the reaction. Whether or not it accomplishes this by causing the reaction to proceed by a different mechanism, the fact remains that if the reaction is reversible, both the forward and the reverse reactions must pass through the same activated state. Although the activation energies of the two reactions are lowered by the presence of the catalyst, both are lowered to the same extent. The rates of both the forward and reverse reactions are increased by exactly the same amount, so that the equilibrium position remains unchanged. A catalyst therefore cannot be used to change the relative proportions of reactants present in the mixture at equilibrium. The practical value of a catalyst results from its causing the system to attain equilibrium more rapidly under given conditions than would otherwise be the case.

The Haber process for the direct synthesis of ammonia from its elements serves as a classic example of the application of a catalyst in a reversible reaction. This process, which is the major source of industrial ammonia, is exothermic to the extent of about 21.9 kcal/mole of nitrogen converted:

$$N_2 + 3\ H_2 \rightleftharpoons 2\ NH_3 \qquad \Delta H_{298} = -21.9 \text{ kcal}$$

In accord with Le Chatelier's principle, high temperatures favor the dissociation of ammonia, which becomes nearly complete at temperatures above 700°C. The best yield of ammonia should therefore be obtained at low temperatures, but because of the high activation energy of the reaction, equilibrium is attained too slowly for the process to be of any practical use. The use of a specially treated iron catalyst lowers the activation energy sufficiently so that equilibrium is attained rapidly at temperatures low enough to give a reasonable yield of ammonia. A further improvement in yield is obtained by working at high pressures, since by the combination of nitrogen and hydrogen to give ammonia, 4 moles of gas are converted to 2 moles. At 500°C and 200 atm, a single pass of hydrogen and nitrogen in a 3:1 ratio yields a mixture containing a maximum of 20% NH_3. At 1000 atm, the maximum yield of ammonia per pass at the same temperature is about 57%.

12.13 Free Energy and Equilibrium

From the discussion of free energy in Chapter 11, we know that if the free energy change for a given reaction is negative, that for the reverse reaction must be positive. Therefore, if a reversible process is spontaneous in one direction, it cannot also be spontaneous in the opposite direction. How then, is it possible for such a process to be going in both directions at the same time, especially if the system has not yet attained equilibrium? The two opposing reactions are in a sense like a pair of heavy weights, one lying on the ground and the other suspended in midair. We can be certain that the weight which is up in the air is going to fall down of its own accord, that is, spontaneously. We can be equally certain that the other weight is not going to fall up. But hook the two weights together with a rope and pulley, and as the upper weight falls, it lifts the other one until equilibrium is reached with both weights off the ground. Some of the energy released by the spontaneous process has been used to furnish the energy needed to make the nonspontaneous process take place. Provided that the spontaneous process releases at least as much energy as the nonspontaneous one absorbs, both processes will occur at the same time.

Consider the reaction

$$A + B \rightleftharpoons C + D$$

for which the respective free energy changes for the forward and reverse reactions are ΔG_f and ΔG_r. Assume that only A and B are present initially and that ΔG_f is negative, that is, the reaction between A and B is spontaneous. As the reaction proceeds, and A and B are used up, ΔG_f, which depends on their concentrations (Sec. 11.9) becomes less negative and approaches zero. At the same time, as C and D increase in concentration, ΔG_r becomes less positive and also approaches zero. So long as $\Delta G_f + \Delta G_r$ is negative, the reaction between A and B is favored, and the system is not at equilibrium. Equilibrium is finally reached when $\Delta G_f = \Delta G_r = 0$.

12.14 Reading Suggestions

A good, simple introduction to modern chemical kinetics will be found in Chapter 8 of *An Introduction to Modern Chemistry*, by M. J. S. Dewar (Oxford University Press, New York, 1965). A more thorough, and also more mathematical treatment of the subject will be found in *Elementary Reaction Kinetics*, by J. L. Latham (Butterworths, London, 1964); in *Chemical Kinetics*, by G. M. Harris (Topics in Modern Chemistry Series, D. C. Heath and Co., Boston, 1966); and in *Modern Chemical Kinetics*, by H. and E. M. Eyring (Selected Topics in Modern Chemistry Series, Reinhold Publishing Co., New York, 1963). Also in the Selected Topics in Modern Chemistry series is the book *Principles of Chemical Equilibrium*, by Kelso Morris (Reinhold Publishing Co., New York, 1965). A discussion of heterogeneous equilibrium is presented in an article by Leonard C. Grotz in *J. Chem. Ed.* **40,** 479 (1963). R. T. Sanderson, in *J. Chem. Ed.* **41,** 13 (1964), presents a group of 27 principles which permit one to predict whether or not a particular chemical reaction is likely to occur under a given set of conditions. In an amusing article, *The Role of Chance in Chemical Investigation*, J. H. Wolfenden describes how a rude remark by Walter Nernst helped inspire Fritz Haber to develop the synthetic ammonia process which bears his name. Also in this article are the stories of Becquerel's problems with the Parisian weather (Sec. 6.7), Daguerre's accidental discovery of his photographic process, and the laboratory accident which resulted in the preparation of a hydrogenation catalyst of unprecedented activity.

Questions and Problems

12.1 (a) Graphically indicate the potential energy change during the course of a reaction of the type A → B, given the following conditions:

	Heat of Reaction	Energy of Activation
Case I	$\Delta E = -100$ kcal	$E_a = 50$ kcal
Case II	$\Delta E = -100$ kcal	$E_a = 100$ kcal
Case III	$\Delta E = +50$ kcal	$E_a = 75$ kcal

(b) Indicate the nature of the above reactions (exothermic or endothermic).
(c) Graphically indicate how the potential energy diagram for Case I is altered upon addition of a catalyst.
(d) What effect does the presence of a catalyst have on the value of E_a?

12.2 (a) Provide an explanation for the dependence of reaction rate on activation energy.
(b) Provide an explanation for the dependence of reaction rate on temperature.

12.3 During the course of a reaction, why is the concentration of a pure solid or pure liquid reactant considered to be invariant?

12.4 Under what circumstances are the values of K_c and K_p numerically equal? Why?

12.5 Compare and contrast the nature of the catalytic action in the "lead chamber" and "contact" processes for the manufacture of sulfuric acid.

12.6 Account for the fact that the rate of a surface-catalyzed unimolecular gaseous reaction is directly proportional to the pressure of the reacting gas, i.e., first order, at low pressure but becomes independent of the pressure, i.e., zero order, at higher pressures.

12.7 The rate of the reaction A + 2 B → C is equal to the specific rate constant k when [A] = 1 and [B] = 1. What will be the rate of the reaction when the concentration of C has reached 0.2 mole/liter?

12.8 The rate of the reaction A + B → AB is equal to the specific rate constant k when [A] = 0.5 and [B] = 2. What will be the rate of the reaction when the concentration of A has dropped to 0.1 mole/liter?

12.9 How much faster will the reaction $H_2 + I_2 \rightarrow 2\ HI$ proceed if the partial pressures of H_2 and I_2 are 2 atm each as compared with the rate when the pressures are each 0.5 atm at the same temperature?

12.10 When 0.00983 mole of HI is placed in a sealed 1-liter vessel and maintained at 394°C, it decomposes to yield 0.00101 mole each of H_2 and I_2 in equilibrium with HI. What is the value of K_c (a) for the decomposition of HI and (b) for the reaction of $H_2 + I_2$ at 394°C?

12.11 For the reaction $H_2 + I_2 \rightleftharpoons 2\ HI$ at 458°C, the equilibrium constant K_p = 48.8. If the initial partial pressure of H_2 and I_2 is 0.5 atm for each gas, what will be the partial pressure of each gas present when equilibrium is attained?

12.12 For the reaction $A + B \rightarrow C$ the following data are obtained:

Initial [A]	Initial [B]	Initial Rate
1.0 M	1.0 M	3×10^{-2}
0.1 M	1.0 M	3×10^{-3}
1.0 M	0.1 M	3×10^{-4}

(a) What is the rate law expression for the reaction?
(b) What is the numerical value for the rate constant?
(c) Speculate on a reasonable equation for the rate-determining step.

12.13 For the reaction $A + B + 2\ C \rightarrow 3\ D$ at 25°C, the following data were obtained:

Experiment	Initial [A]	Initial [B]	Initial [C]	Initial Rate of Formation of D
1	0.1 M	0.1 M	0.2 M	4×10^{-4} M/min
2	0.3 M	0.2 M	0.2 M	1.2×10^{-3}
3	0.1 M	0.3 M	0.2 M	4×10^{-4}
4	0.3 M	0.4 M	0.6 M	3.6×10^{-3}

(a) Write the rate law expression for the reaction.
(b) What is a plausible rate-determining step?
(c) What is the numerical value for the specific rate constant?
(d) In the case of experiment 4, compare the initial rate of reaction with the rate when exactly one-half the A present initially has been consumed. Assume the volume of the reaction mixture remains constant.
(e) In each of the experiments 2 and 4, what is the maximum concentration obtainable for D? Assume that the volume remains constant.
(f) When the reaction in each of the four experiments has proceeded to completion, which reactant or reactants if any, and in what concentration, remain unconsumed? Assume that the volume remains constant.

12.14 The relationship between energy of activation, E_a in calories, and the fraction of collisions that possess that energy is

$$10^{-E_a/4.6T} = \text{fraction of collisions with energy equal to or greater than } E_a.$$

For the gas phase attack of chlorine or bromine atoms on methane

$$CH_4 + Cl^{\cdot} \rightarrow HCl + CH_3^{\cdot} \qquad \Delta H = -1 \text{ kcal}, E_a = 4 \text{ kcal}$$

$$CH_4 + Br^{\cdot} \rightarrow HBr + CH_3^{\cdot} \qquad \Delta H = +15 \text{ kcal}, E_a = 18 \text{ kcal}$$

(a) Graphically show the potential energy change during the course of each of these two reactions.

(b) Calculate the fraction of the collisions that are effective for each of these two reactions at a temperature of 270°C.

(c) How many times greater is the reactivity of chlorine atoms than that of bromine atoms toward methane at 270°C?

(d) What fraction of the collisions is effective in the reaction between methane and bromine atoms at 300°C and how much faster is this reaction at 300°C than at 270°C?

(e) What fraction of the collisions is effective in the reaction between methane and chlorine atoms at 300°C and how much faster is this reaction at 300°C than at 270°C?

Ans. (b) 1 in 40 for $CH_4 + Cl^\cdot$
1 in 16,000,000 for $CH_4 + Br^\cdot$
(c) 400,000 times faster
(d) 1 in 6,800,000, 2.4 times faster
(e) 1 in 33, 1.2 times faster

12.15 At 400°C, $K_p = 1.64 \times 10^{-4}$ for the reaction $N_2 + 3\ H_2 \rightleftharpoons 2\ NH_3$. Calculate the value of K_c.

12.16 Ethyl alcohol and acetic acid react to form ethyl acetate and water according to the equation

$$C_2H_5OH + HC_2H_3O_2 \rightleftharpoons C_4H_8O_2 + H_2O$$

Data were obtained from three separate experiments:

Experiment	Initial Concentration (moles/liter)		Equilibrium Concentration (moles/liter)
	C_2H_5OH	$HC_2H_3O_2$	$C_4H_8O_2$
1	0.5	1.0	0.423
2	1.0	1.0	0.667
3	1.5	1.0	0.785

(a) Calculate the equilibrium constant for the reaction. (b) From the average value of K_c, calculate the concentration of ethyl acetate which would be present in the equilibrium mixture that would result from a fourth experiment in which the initial concentration of ethyl alcohol was 2.0 moles/liter, and that of acetic acid was 1.0 mole/liter. (c) Is the change in the equilibrium concentration of ethyl acetate from one experiment to the next in agreement with LeChatelier's principle?

Ans. (a) 4.0; (b) 0.848

12.17 The forward reaction for $AB + C \rightleftharpoons A + BC$ is exothermic by 5000 cal/mole and has an activation energy (uncatalyzed) of 10,000 cal/mole. When catalyzed, the activation energy of the reaction is lowered to 5000 cal/mole. What is the activation energy for the reverse reaction (a) when uncatalyzed, (b) when catalyzed? From the relationship that the fraction of collisions with energy equal to or greater than the activation energy is equal to $10^{-E_a/4.6T}$, calculate how many times faster (c) the forward reaction, and (d) the reverse reaction will proceed at 500°K when catalyzed than when no catalyst is used. (e) Are the results in agreement with the statements made in Section 12.12?

Ans. (c) and (d) 150 times faster

What am I, Life? A thing of watery salt
Held in cohesion by unresisting cells,
Which work they know not why, which never halt,
Myself unwitting where their Master dwells?

—John Masefield,
Sonnets, 14*

13 ACIDS, BASES AND SALTS— IONIC EQUILIBRIA

Three kinds of chemical substances, acids, bases, and salts, have been recognized since earliest times. The word ***acid*** (from the Latin term for sour) is descriptive of one of the most obvious properties which acids have in common—the sour taste of their water solutions. In addition, acids turn blue litmus red and cause characteristic changes in the colors of many other dyes. They also typically react with certain active metals with the liberation of free hydrogen gas. ***Bases*** have a bitter taste in water, and their aqueous solutions feel slippery, or "soapy." They turn red litmus blue, and their effects on the colors of other dyes are distinct from those of acids. Bases react with, or *neutralize*, acids; the product of neutralization is a ***salt.*** An acid or base is described as being *strong* or *weak* according to how pronounced is the fashion in which it manifests its characteristic properties.

In this chapter we will consider what makes an acid an acid and a base a base, and why some acids and bases are strong while others are weak. We shall also see how the principles of chemical equilibrium developed in Chapter 12 can be applied to control the acidity and basicity of solutions and the solubility of salts.

13.1 Acids

The French chemist Claude Louis Berthollet in 1798 showed that all typical acids contain hydrogen. Not all substances that contain hydrogen are acids, however, but only those which yield hydrogen ions in solution. Pure acids and solutions of acids in nonpolar solvents usually do not conduct electricity, but all acids are electrolytes in water solution. The stronger the acid, the more electrically conductive are its solutions. A typical acid, then, is a covalently bound substance which, in accord with the Arrhenius theory of electrolytic dissociation (Secs. 5.3 and 10.15), ionizes reversibly when dissolved in water, forming hydrogen ions and anions:

$$HA \rightleftharpoons H^+ + A^-$$

The relative strength of an acid, as well as its electrical conductivity in solution, depends upon how completely it ionizes at a given concentration.

The hydrogen ion, or proton, has the largest ratio of charge to radius of any ion, and hence its attraction for the highly polar water molecule is especially strong—so strong, in fact, that it leads to covalent bonding and formation of the hydronium ion:

$$H^+ + H_2O \rightarrow H_3O^+$$

In aqueous solution, all of the hydrogen ions are in the hydrated state, and the ionization of an acid in water is more correctly represented as follows:

$$HA + H_2O \rightleftharpoons H_3O^+ + A^-$$

Both the hydronium ions and the anions are undoubtedly further hydrated in the manner described in Sec. 10.3. The common properties of all aqueous acid solutions depend upon the presence of hydronium ions, and the greater the hydronium ion concentration the more strongly acidic is the solution.

An acid whose molecule possesses a single ionizable hydrogen is described as being a ***monoprotic acid.*** The strong acids HCl and HNO_3 are monoprotic, as is the weak acetic acid $HC_2H_3O_2$. In the latter case, of the four hydrogen atoms in the molecule, three are covalently bound to carbon and do not ionize. The remaining hydrogen, which is responsible for the acidity of this compound, is bonded to one of the oxygen atoms. The strong acid H_2SO_4 and the weak acid H_2S, each with two ionizable hydrogens, are ***diprotic acids.*** Phosphoric acid, H_3PO_4, is a ***triprotic acid.***

13.2 Bases

Substances that yield hydroxide ions in aqueous solution are bases. In this category are the active metal hydroxides whose van't Hoff factors (Sec. 10.14) show them to be completely ionized in solution. The highest concentrations of hydroxide ions, and hence the most basic solutions, are obtained by dissolving the very soluble alkali metal hydroxides in water.

Sparingly soluble hydroxides such as $Ca(OH)_2$ and $Mg(OH)_2$, even though completely ionized, yield saturated solutions which are only weakly basic, because the concentration of OH^- ions in these solutions is limited by the low solubility of the base.

Some covalent compounds, notably ammonia and its derivatives the amines, dissolve in water to give weakly basic solutions. Here, the hydroxide ions responsible for the basicity come not from the dissociation of the covalent compound, but rather from the solvent:

$$NH_3 + H_2O \rightleftharpoons NH_4^+ + OH^-$$

Despite the great solubility of ammonia in water, its solutions are very weakly basic, which shows that the equilibrium of the above reaction must lie far to the left.

Neutralization 13.3

The neutralization of one equivalent of any strong acid by one equivalent of any strong base is always accompanied by the evolution of the same amount of heat—13.7 kcal. This is to be expected, since the actual reaction taking place is the same in each case. By definition, a strong acid is one which reacts essentially completely with water to yield hydronium ions and anions:

$$HCl + H_2O \rightarrow H_3O^+ + Cl^-$$

$$HNO_3 + H_2O \rightarrow H_3O^+ + NO_3^-$$

$$HClO_4 + H_2O \rightarrow H_3O^+ + ClO_4^-$$

Any strong base is also completely ionized. When their solutions are mixed, the hydronium ions and hydroxide ions react with one another to form water. The remaining anions and cations are spectator ions and take no part in the reaction:

$$H_3O^+ + Cl^- + Na^+ + OH^- \rightarrow Na^+ + Cl^- + 2\,H_2O$$

$$H_3O^+ + Cl^- + K^+ + OH^- \rightarrow K^+ + Cl^- + 2\,H_2O$$

$$H_3O^+ + NO_3^- + Na^+ + OH^- \rightarrow Na^+ + NO_3^- + 2\,H_2O$$

$$H_3O^+ + ClO_4^- + K^+ + OH^- \rightarrow K^+ + ClO_4^- + 2\,H_2O$$

When the spectator ions are omitted, each of the above reactions becomes

$$H_3O^+ + OH^- \rightarrow 2\,H_2O \qquad \Delta H = -13.7 \text{ kcal}$$

When it comes to the neutralization of a weak acid or a weak base, the situation is quite different. The heat of neutralization of acetic acid by a strong base, for example, is -13.4 kcal per equivalent. The heat of neutralization of ammonia by a strong acid is -12.3 kcal per equivalent. The principal reaction taking place in the first instance is probably that between hydroxide ions and undissociated acetic acid molecules:

$$HC_2H_3O_2 + OH^- \rightarrow C_2H_3O_2^- + H_2O$$

In the second, it appears to be between ammonia molecules and hydronium ions:

$$NH_3 + H_3O^+ \rightarrow NH_4^+ + H_2O$$

Whether the acids and bases taking part are strong or weak, we see that in every case the process of neutralization involves the formation of water molecules.

13.4 Brønsted-Lowry Concept of Acids and Bases

From the foregoing, one may conclude that every reaction between an acid and a base involves the transfer of a proton from one molecule or ion to another. Carrying this a step further, J. N. Brønsted and N. Bjerrum in Denmark and, independently, T. M. Lowry in England viewed every transfer of a proton as being an acid-base reaction. In 1923 they proposed that an *acid* be defined as a ***proton donor,*** and a *base* as a ***proton acceptor.*** The reasonableness of this view is readily apparent. Take the reactions

$$HC_2H_3O_2 + OH^- \rightarrow C_2H_3O_2^- + H_2O$$

and

$$HC_2H_3O_2 + H_2O \rightarrow C_2H_3O_2^- + H_3O^+$$

for example. So far as the ionization of the acetic acid is concerned, both OH^- and H_2O are performing the same function. Therefore, if OH^- is a base, it is perfectly logical to call H_2O a base as well. The reaction of acetic acid with OH^- ions proceeds more nearly to completion than that with water, which reaches equilibrium after less than 2% of the molecules have ionized. Water is less disposed to gaining a proton than is OH^-. It is a *weaker proton acceptor*, and hence a *weaker base* than OH^-.

The reaction between an acid and a base always results in the formation of a new acid and a new base. The acid, by the act of donating a proton to the base, is itself converted to a proton acceptor, or base. At the same time, by accepting the proton, the base becomes an acid:

$$\underset{acid_1}{HC_2H_3O_2} + \underset{base_2}{H_2O} \rightarrow \underset{base_1}{C_2H_3O_2^-} + \underset{acid_2}{H_3O^+}$$

If an acid is weak, that is, if it does not readily lose a proton, the base formed from it—its *conjugate base*—should regain a proton readily. In other words, *a weak acid forms a strong conjugate base,* and conversely, *a strong acid forms a weak conjugate base:*

$$\underset{\text{weak acid}_1}{HC_2H_3O_2} + \underset{\text{weak base}_2}{H_2O} \rightarrow \underset{\text{strong base}_1}{C_2H_3O_2^-} + \underset{\text{strong acid}_2}{H_3O^+}$$

$$\underset{\text{weak acid}_1}{H_2O} + \underset{\text{weak base}_2}{NH_3} \rightarrow \underset{\text{strong acid}_2}{NH_4^+} + \underset{\text{strong base}_1}{OH^-}$$

$$\underset{\text{strong acid}_1}{HCl} + \underset{\text{weak base}_2}{H_2O} \rightarrow \underset{\text{strong acid}_2}{H_3O^+} + \underset{\text{weak base}_1}{Cl^-}$$

$$\underset{\text{strong acid}_1}{H_3O^+} + \underset{\text{strong base}_2}{OH^-} \rightarrow \underset{\text{weak acid}_2}{H_2O} + \underset{\text{weak base}_1}{H_2O}$$

In general, proton transfers, or ***protolytic reactions,*** are reversible and reach an equilibrium. The equilibrium conditions are determined by the relative proton-donating capacity (acidity) of the two acids and the relative proton-accepting capacity (basicity) of the two bases involved. Generally speaking, the position of the equilibrium will lie in the direction of the weaker acid-base pair.

The Brønsted-Lowry concept of acids and bases can also be applied to nonaqueous solvent systems such as liquid ammonia and glacial (anhydrous) acetic acid. Ammonium salts behave as typical strong acids in liquid ammonia solution, reacting with active metals, for example, with the liberation of hydrogen:

$$2\,NH_4^+ + Mg \rightarrow Mg^{++} + 2\,NH_3 + H_2$$

the reaction being perfectly analogous to the reaction of hydronium ions with an active metal in aqueous solution:

$$2\,H_3O^+ + Mg \rightarrow Mg^{++} + 2\,H_2O + H_2$$

The alkali metal amides such as $NaNH_2$ are typical strong bases in liquid ammonia, neutralizing ammonium salts as follows:

$$NH_4^+ + NH_2^- \rightarrow 2\,NH_3$$

The ammonium and amide ions occupy the same positions in the liquid ammonia system that hydronium and hydroxide ions occupy in the water system.

The acids $HClO_4$, HNO_3, and HCl are all of the same strength in water solution, in which they react almost completely with the solvent to form hydronium ions:

$$HClO_4 + H_2O \rightarrow H_3O^+ + ClO_4^-$$
$$HNO_3 + H_2O \rightarrow H_3O^+ + NO_3^-$$
$$HCl + H_2O \rightarrow H_3O^+ + Cl^-$$

The acid strengths of these and other strong acids in aqueous solution are therefore reduced, or "leveled," to that of the hydronium ion, which is the principal acid species present. Because all acids stronger than H_3O^+ react almost completely with water, the hydronium ion is the strongest acid that can exist in any significant concentration in aqueous solution.

Acids that show the same strength in aqueous solution because of the leveling effect can exhibit markedly different strengths in a solvent such as glacial acetic acid. Since acetic acid is a far weaker base than water, the reactions

$$HClO_4 + HC_2H_3O_2 \rightleftharpoons H_2C_2H_3O_2^+ + ClO_4^-$$
$$HNO_3 + HC_2H_3O_2 \rightleftharpoons H_2C_2H_3O_2^+ + NO_3^-$$
$$HCl + HC_2H_3O_2 \rightleftharpoons H_2C_2H_3O_2^+ + Cl^-$$

do not proceed as far to the right as do the reactions of these acids with water. The position of the equilibrium in each case is a measure of the relative strength of the acid. In the examples above, the relative acid strengths are in the order $HClO_4 > HNO_3 > HCl$.

Water exerts a leveling effect on strong bases as well as on strong acids. Any species such as NH_2^- or $C_2H_5O^-$, which is a stronger base than OH^-, will react completely with the solvent to form hydroxide ions:

$$NH_2^- + H_2O \rightarrow NH_3 + OH^-$$

$$C_2H_5O^- + H_2O \rightarrow C_2H_5OH + OH^-$$

In aqueous solution, therefore, just as H_3O^+ is the strongest acid, so is OH^- the strongest base that can exist in any appreciable concentration.

13.5 Lewis Concept of Acids and Bases

In order to accept the electron deficient proton and thus function as a base, a substance must possess a pair of electrons available for sharing with the proton to form a covalent bond. Every substance which is a base according to the Brønsted-Lowry definition therefore acts as an electron donor toward the proton. The proton, however, is not the only electron-deficient species able to accept an electron pair from a base. Accordingly, G. N. Lewis suggested that the definition of an *acid* be broadened to include any species capable of acting as an ***electron pair acceptor.*** A *base* is defined as an ***electron pair donor.*** Every substance which is a base according to the Lewis definition is a base under the Brønsted-Lowry concept as well, and vice versa. The Lewis definition of an acid, however, includes many electron deficient substances that possess no displaceable hydrogen and hence would not be acids in the Brønsted-Lowry sense.

Examples of some Lewis acid-base reactions are the following:

$$\underset{\text{base}}{H_3N:} + \underset{\text{acid}}{BF_3} \rightarrow H_3N:BF_3$$

$$\underset{\text{base}}{:\ddot{\underset{..}{Cl}}:^-} + \underset{\text{acid}}{AlCl_3} \rightarrow [AlCl_4]^-$$

$$\underset{\text{acid}}{Ag^+} + 2\,\underset{\text{base}}{:NH_3} \rightarrow [H_3N:Ag:NH_3]^+$$

$$\underset{\text{acid}}{H^+} + \underset{\text{base}}{:OH^-} \rightarrow H:OH$$

Of these, only the last is an acid-base reaction according to the Brønsted-Lowry concept.

Many reactions in nonpolar media may be considered as acid-base reactions according to the Lewis concept, which has therefore been found particularly useful in the study of organic chemistry (Chapter 17).

Self-Ionization, or Autoprotolysis 13.6

Water is a substance which is ***amphiprotic,*** or ***amphoteric,*** that is, it can perform the function of either an acid or a base according to the circumstances in which it finds itself. In fact, one molecule of water can act as an acid toward another molecule serving as a base, the result being the transfer of a proton and self-ionization, or ***autoprotolysis,*** of the water:

$$\underset{\text{acid}}{H_2O} + \underset{\text{base}}{H_2O} \rightleftharpoons \underset{\text{acid}}{H_3O^+} + \underset{\text{base}}{OH^-}$$

Because the autoprotolysis of water leads to the formation of a strong acid and a strong base, the equilibrium for this reaction lies far to the left. Nevertheless, the small residual conductivity of even the purest water is evidence of a slight degree of self-ionization. Other pure liquids may also undergo autoprotolysis, ammonia, for example:

$$\underset{\text{acid}}{NH_3} + \underset{\text{base}}{NH_3} \rightleftharpoons \underset{\text{acid}}{NH_4^+} + \underset{\text{base}}{NH_2^-}$$

and sulfuric acid:

$$\underset{\text{acid}}{(HO)_2SO_2} + \underset{\text{base}}{(HO)_2SO_2} \rightleftharpoons \underset{\text{acid}}{(HO)_3SO^+} + \underset{\text{base}}{HOSO_3^-}$$

Because of its importance as a solvent, however, we will focus our main attention on the ionization of water.

The calculated H_3O^+ concentration in absolutely pure water at 25°C is 10^{-7} mole/liter. Since for every H_3O^+ ion formed in the autoprotolysis one OH^- is produced as well, the concentration of OH^- in absolutely pure water at 25°C must also be 10^{-7} mole/liter. The equilibrium expression for the reaction

$$2\ H_2O \rightleftharpoons H_3O^+ + OH^-$$

is

$$\frac{[H_3O^+][OH^-]}{[H_2O]^2} = K_c$$

One liter of water at 25°C contains 55.6 moles. This is such a large figure in comparison with the amount which ionizes that the factor $[H_2O]^2$ is effectively constant. The above expression can therefore be written

$$[H_3O^+][OH^-] = K_c[H_2O]^2 = K_w$$

The constant K_w, known as the ***ion-product constant for water,*** is evaluated by substituting the values for the concentrations of the ions and solving the equation:

$$K_w = [H_3O^+][OH^-] = (10^{-7})(10^{-7}) = 10^{-14} \text{ at } 25°C$$

K_w increases rapidly with temperature. At 50°C, $K_w = 5.5 \times 10^{-14}$, and at 100°C, $K_w = 5.8 \times 10^{-13}$. Unless some other temperature is specified, however, it is generally understood that all measurements of ionic concentrations in water solution are made at or near 25°C, where $K_w = 10^{-14}$.

If an acid or base is dissolved in water, the H_3O^+ ion and OH^- ion concentrations can no longer be expected to remain equal. For example, if acid is added so that $[H_3O^+] = 0.1$ mole/liter, the increase in H_3O^+ concentration will, in accord with Le Chatelier's principle, cause the equilibrium $2\ H_2O \rightleftharpoons H_3O^+ + OH^-$ to be shifted to the left, with the result that the concentration of OH^- will be lowered to a value that can be calculated as follows:

$$(0.1)[OH^-] = 10^{-14}$$

$$[OH^-] = \frac{10^{-14}}{10^{-1}} = 10^{-13}$$

Example 13.1

What is the H_3O^+ concentration in a solution in which $[OH^-] = 10^{-3}$ mole/liter?

Solution:

$$[H_3O^+][OH^-] = K_w$$

$$[H_3O^+] = \frac{K_w}{[OH^-]}$$

$$[H_3O^+] = \frac{10^{-14}}{10^{-3}} = 10^{-11} \text{ mole/liter}$$

13.7 pH

In 1909, the Danish chemist S. P. L. Sørensen suggested that the relative acidity or basicity of an aqueous solution could be conveniently expressed in terms of the negative logarithm of the hydronium ion concentration, a function he called the *p*H:

$$p\text{H} = -\log [H_3O^+]$$

Taking the logarithm avoids the use of exponential numbers in expressing the hydronium ion concentration; the negative sign makes the *p*H a positive number for all concentrations of H_3O^+ up to and including 1 *M*.

The H_3O^+ concentration of a neutral solution is the same as that in pure water: 10^{-7} *M*. *A neutral solution therefore has a p*H *of 7.* An acid solution is one in which the H_3O^+ concentration is greater than 10^{-7} *M*, which means that *the p*H *of an acid solution is less than 7.* In a basic solution, the H_3O^+ concentration is less than 10^{-7}, and therefore *the p*H *of a basic solution is greater than 7.* The relationships among the H_3O^+ concentration, the *p*H, and the acidity or basicity of a solution are shown in Table 13.1.

A change of a single *p*H unit represents a 10-fold change in the hydronium

TABLE 13.1 Relationships Among $[H_3O^+]$, pH, Acidity and Basicity of Aqueous Solutions at 25°C

$[H_3O^+]$, mole/liter	pH	
$10^0 = 1$	0	Very acidic
10^{-1}	1	↑
10^{-2}	2	
10^{-3}	3	
10^{-4}	4	
10^{-5}	5	Weakly acidic
10^{-6}	6	↑
10^{-7}	7	Neutral
10^{-8}	8	↓
10^{-9}	9	Weakly basic
10^{-10}	10	
10^{-11}	11	
10^{-12}	12	
10^{-13}	13	↓
10^{-14}	14	Very basic

ion concentration. Halving the *p*H of a solution from 8 to 4, for example, causes not a doubling of the H_3O^+ concentration but a 10,000-times increase.

Example 13.2

What is the *p*H of a 0.02 *M* solution of HCl?

Solution: HCl is a strong acid; its solutions may be assumed to have H_3O^+ concentrations approximately equal to the concentration of the dissolved acid:

$$[H_3O^+] \approx [HCl] \approx 0.02\ M$$

$$pH = -\log(2 \times 10^{-2})$$

$$= -(0.3 - 2.0)$$

$$= 1.7$$

Example 13.3

What is the *p*H of a 0.03 *M* solution of NaOH?

Solution: Since NaOH is a strong base and completely ionized:

$$[OH^-] = [NaOH] = 0.03\ M$$

To determine the *p*H of the solution it is first necessary to calculate the H_3O^+ concentration:

$$[H_3O^+] = \frac{K_w}{[OH^-]} \doteq \frac{10^{-14}}{3 \times 10^{-2}}$$

$$= 3 \times 10^{-13}$$

$$pH = -\log(3 \times 10^{-13}) = -(0.5 - 13.0) = 12.5$$

Sørensen's convenient device has been extended to include pOH:

$$pOH = -\log [OH^-]$$

and pK:

$$pK = -\log K$$

where K is any equilibrium constant. Later we will use pK as a convenient way to express the relative strengths of weak acids and bases (see Sec. 13.8).

In any aqueous solution,

$$pH + pOH = pK_w = 14$$

This relationship somewhat simplifies the calculation of pH and $[H_3O^+]$, when $[OH^-]$ is given or can be determined, and the calculation of $[OH^-]$ when the pH is known.

Example 13.4

What is the pH of a 0.05 M solution of KOH?

Solution: As in Example 13.3, since KOH is a strong base, its concentration is equal to the OH^- concentration and

$$\begin{aligned} pOH &= -\log [OH^-] = -\log 5 \times 10^{-2} \\ &= -(0.7 - 2.0) \\ &= 1.3 \\ pH &= 14.0 - pOH \\ &= 14.0 - 1.3 \\ &= 12.7 \end{aligned}$$

Example 13.5

What is the OH^- concentration in a solution with a pH of 9.3?

Solution:

$$\begin{aligned} pOH &= 14.0 - 9.3 \\ &= 4.7 = -\log [OH^-] \\ \log [OH^-] &= -4.7 \\ \text{antilog } (-4.7) &= [OH^-] \end{aligned}$$

In order to take the antilog of -4.7, the mantissa (-0.7) must be converted to a positive value before it can be found in a table of logarithms. This can be done without changing the value of the logarithm by adding 1 to the mantissa while subtracting 1 from the characteristic:

$$-4.7 = (-4.0 - 1.0) + (-0.7 + 1.0) = -5.0 + 0.3$$

$$\text{antilog } (-4.7) = \text{antilog } (-5.0) \times \text{antilog } (0.3)$$

$$[OH^-] = 2 \times 10^{-5}$$

The equilibrium constant for the ionization of a weak acid in water

$$HA + H_2O \rightleftharpoons H_3O^+ + A^-$$

is given by the expression

$$K_c = \frac{[H_3O^+][A^-]}{[HA][H_2O]}$$

The amount of water consumed in the ionization of a weak acid in dilute solution is so small in comparison with its total molar concentration, which was shown in Sec. 13.6 to be about 55.6 M, that $[H_2O]$ can be taken as a constant and included in what is called the ***ionization constant*** for the acid:

$$K_a = \frac{[H_3O^+][A^-]}{[HA]}$$

The ionization constant for a weak base in dilute solution,

$$B + H_2O \rightleftharpoons BH^+ + OH^-$$

is given by

$$K_b = \frac{[BH^+][OH^-]}{[B]}$$

The size of the ionization constant is a measure of the relative strength of the acid or base. The greater the degree to which the acid or base ionizes at a given concentration, the stronger it is, and the larger is the value of its ionization constant.

Several methods are available for determining the ionization constant of a weak acid or base. Perhaps the most direct way is to measure the pH of its solution when exactly one-half of the acid or base has been neutralized. At the half-neutral point, one-half of the acid or base originally present has been converted to its completely ionized salt, leaving an equal number of moles unreacted. If we neglect any ionization of the unreacted acid or base, which will be very small in the presence of such a large concentration of its salt, then

For a weak acid at the half-neutral point:

$$[HA] = [A^-]$$

$$K_a = [H_3O^+]$$

$$pK_a = p\text{H}_{1/2}$$

For a weak base at the half-neutral point:

$$[BH^+] = [B]$$
$$K_b = [OH^-]$$
$$pK_b = pOH_{1/2}$$

Equilibrium constants may also be calculated from the degree of dissociation determined from measurements of equivalent conductance or from van't Hoff factors (Secs. 10.14–10.16). The following examples will illustrate the application of both methods.

Example 13.6

Using the equivalent conductance data given in Table 10.4, calculate the degree of dissociation of 0.100 M $HC_2H_3O_2$ at 25°C.

Solution: From Sec. 10.16 we know that the degree of dissociation α of a weak electrolyte at a given concentration is given by the ratio of its equivalent conductance Λ at that concentration to its equivalent conductance at infinite dilution:

$$\alpha = \frac{\Lambda}{\Lambda_0}$$

From Table 10.4, Λ for 0.100 M $HC_2H_3O_2$ is 5.2 ohms^{-1}, and Λ_0 is 390.7 ohms^{-1}. Thus,

$$\alpha = \frac{5.2 \text{ ohms}^{-1}}{390.7 \text{ ohms}^{-1}} = 0.0133$$

This means that at a concentration of 0.100 M, acetic acid dissociates to the extent of 1.33% at 25°C.

Example 13.7

Calculate the degree of dissociation of 0.010 M $HC_2H_3O_2$ at 25°C.

Solution: From Table 10.4, Λ for a 0.010 M solution of $HC_2H_3O_2$ is 16.3 ohms^{-1}, from which the degree of dissociation is calculated to be

$$\alpha = \frac{16.3 \text{ ohms}^{-1}}{390.7 \text{ ohms}^{-1}} = 0.0417$$

The effect of dilution has been to increase the degree of dissociation of the acid.

Example 13.8

The freezing point of a 0.100 m solution of $HC_2H_3O_2$ is −0.189°C. Calculate the degree of dissociation of the acid.

Solution: The van't Hoff factor i is given by the ratio of the observed freezing point depression ΔT_f of the electrolyte solution compared with the corresponding value $(\Delta T_f)_0$ for an equally concentrated solution of a nonelectrolyte (see Sec. 10.14):

$$\frac{\Delta T_f}{(\Delta T_f)_0} = i$$

Since 0.1 m acetic acid freezes at −0.189°C, $\Delta T_f = 0.189$. For a 0.100 m solution of a nonelectrolyte in water,

$$(\Delta T_f)_0 = 0.100 \times 1.86 = 0.186$$

$$\frac{\Delta T_f}{(\Delta T_f)_0} = \frac{0.189}{0.186} = 1.016 = i$$

The degree of dissociation of a weak electrolyte can be calculated from the van't Hoff factor, using the relationship

$$\alpha = \frac{i - 1}{n - 1}$$

where n is the number of ions formed per molecule that ionizes. In this instance, $n = 2$. Substituting for i and n in the above expression, we get

$$\alpha = 0.016$$

The degree of dissociation has been calculated here for a 0.100 m solution. Because a dilute aqueous solution has a density very close to 1 g/ml, its molality is very nearly the same as its molarity (Sec. 10.2). The value of α calculated above can therefore be assumed equal to the degree of dissociation of acetic acid in 0.100 M solution without introducing any serious error.

The degree of dissociation of weak electrolytes is small, resulting in van't Hoff factors only slightly larger than 1. Because of the difficulty of measuring small differences in temperature with sufficient precision, values of α calculated from freezing point depression or boiling point elevation are usually not as accurate as those obtained from conductivity measurements. Furthermore, measurements of colligative properties are necessarily made at the freezing point or boiling point of the solution, that is, close to 0° and 100°C, and are for that reason not exactly comparable to conductivity measurements which are generally made at 25°C.

Once the degree of dissociation is known, the ionization constant is readily calculated, as shown in the following example.

Example 13.9

Calculate the ionization constant for acetic acid using the values for α obtained in Examples 13.6 and 13.7.

Solution: If a number of moles C of a weak electrolyte is dissolved in a liter of solution, the amount which dissociates into ions is $C\alpha$. The amount remaining undissociated is $C - C\alpha$, and $C\alpha$ moles of each ion are formed. In this case,

$$\underset{(C - C\alpha)}{HC_2H_3O_2} + H_2O \rightleftharpoons \underset{C\alpha}{H_3O^+} + \underset{C\alpha}{C_2H_3O_2^-}$$

These values are introduced into the equilibrium expression for the ionization:

$$\frac{[H_3O^+][C_2H_3O_2^-]}{[HC_2H_3O_2]} = \frac{(C\alpha)^2}{(C - C\alpha)} = \frac{C\alpha^2}{1 - \alpha} = K_a$$

In Example 13.6, α was found to be 0.0133 in 0.100 M acetic acid solution, giving

$$K_a = \frac{(0.100)(0.0133)^2}{1 - (0.0133)}$$
$$= 1.79 \times 10^{-5}$$

In 0.010 M solution, the degree of dissociation of acetic acid, from Example 13.7, is 0.0417.

$$K_a = \frac{(0.010)(0.0417)^2}{1 - (0.0417)}$$

$$= 1.81 \times 10^{-5}$$

The two values for K_a, obtained at different acid concentrations, are seen to be in quite good agreement. When changes in ion mobilities with concentration are taken into account, the best value for the ionization constant for acetic acid at 25°C is 1.75×10^{-5}.

Acids that possess more than one ionizable hydrogen ionize in successive steps, each with its own ionization constant. The ionization constant for the first step is always the largest, and each successive ionization constant is smaller than the preceding one. The strong acid H_2SO_4 ionizes in two steps:

$$H_2SO_4 + H_2O \rightarrow H_3O^+ + HSO_4^-$$

$$HSO_4^- + H_2O \rightleftharpoons H_3O^+ + SO_4^{--}$$

The first step in the ionization is essentially complete, $K_{a_1} \approx \infty$. For the second ionization, which is incomplete,

$$K_{a_2} = \frac{[H_3O^+][SO_4^{--}]}{[HSO_4^-]} = 1.2 \times 10^{-2}$$

Phosphoric acid ionizes in three steps:

$$H_3PO_4 + H_2O \rightleftharpoons H_3O^+ + H_2PO_4^- \qquad K_{a_1} = 7.5 \times 10^{-3}$$

$$H_2PO_4^- + H_2O \rightleftharpoons H_3O^+ + HPO_4^{--} \qquad K_{a_2} = 6.2 \times 10^{-8}$$

$$HPO_4^{--} + H_2O \rightleftharpoons H_3O^+ + PO_4^{---} \qquad K_{a_3} = 4.8 \times 10^{-13}$$

Ionization constants of polyprotic acids are best measured by methods comparable to the measurement of pH at the half-neutral point. The partial neutralization of polyprotic acids forms ***acid salts***. Thus sodium hydrogen sulfate ($NaHSO_4$), also called sodium bisulfate, is the acid salt of sulfuric acid, formed by neutralizing only the first of the two ionizable hydrogens of the acid. Phosphoric acid forms two series of acid salts, the dihydrogen phosphates and monohydrogen phosphates (e.g., NaH_2PO_4 and Na_2HPO_4) in addition to the "normal" salts such as Na_3PO_4. Solutions of acid salts are not necessarily acidic. Some are, but others, because of hydrolysis (Sec. 13.13), may be neutral or even basic. They are, nevertheless, capable of reacting with and neutralizing additional base:

$$HSO_4^- + OH^- \rightarrow SO_4^{--} + H_2O$$

$$H_2PO_4^- + OH^- \rightarrow HPO_4^{--} + H_2O$$

$$HPO_4^{--} + OH^- \rightarrow PO_4^{---} + H_2O$$

Ionization constants of weak bases are obtained by the same general methods used for weak acids. The ionization constants, pK_a and pK_b, of a number of weak acids and bases are given in Tables 13.2 and 13.3.

TABLE 13.2 Ionization Constants of Weak Acids

Acid	Reaction	K_a(25°C)	pK_a
Acetic	$HC_2H_3O_2 + H_2O \rightleftharpoons H_3O^+ + C_2H_3O_2^-$	1.75×10^{-5}	4.76
Boric	$HBO_2 + H_2O \rightleftharpoons H_3O^+ + BO_2^-$	6×10^{-10}	9.2
Carbonic	$H_2CO_3 + H_2O \rightleftharpoons H_3O^+ + HCO_3^-$	4.5×10^{-7}	6.4
	$HCO_3^- + H_2O \rightleftharpoons H_3O^+ + CO_3^{--}$	5×10^{-11}	10.3
Chloroacetic	$HC_2H_2ClO_2 + H_2O \rightleftharpoons H_3O^+ + C_2H_2ClO_2^-$	1.4×10^{-3}	2.9
Dichloroacetic	$HC_2HCl_2O_2 + H_2O \rightleftharpoons H_3O^+ + C_2HCl_2O_2^-$	5×10^{-2}	1.3
Formic	$HCHO_2 + H_2O \rightleftharpoons H_3O^+ + CHO_2^-$	2×10^{-4}	3.7
Hydrocyanic	$HCN + H_2O \rightleftharpoons H_3O^+ + CN^-$	7.2×10^{-10}	9.1
Hydrofluoric	$HF + H_2O \rightleftharpoons H_3O^+ + F^-$	7×10^{-4}	3.2
Hydrosulfuric	$H_2S + H_2O \rightleftharpoons H_3O^+ + HS^-$	6×10^{-8}	7.2
	$HS^- + H_2O \rightleftharpoons H_3O^+ + S^{--}$	1×10^{-14}	14.0
Trichloroacetic	$HC_2Cl_3O_2 + H_2O \rightleftharpoons H_3O^+ + C_2Cl_3O_2$	2×10^{-1}	0.7

TABLE 13.3 Ionization Constants of Weak Bases

Base	Reaction	K_b(25°C)	pK_b
Ammonia	$NH_3 + H_2O \rightleftharpoons NH_4^+ + OH^-$	1.75×10^{-5}	4.76
Aniline	$C_6H_5NH_2 + H_2O \rightleftharpoons C_6H_5NH_3^+ + OH^-$	3.8×10^{-10}	9.4
Dimethylamine	$(CH_3)_2NH + H_2O \rightleftharpoons (CH_3)_2NH_2^+ + OH^-$	5×10^{-4}	3.3
Ethylamine	$C_2H_5NH_2 + H_2O \rightleftharpoons C_2H_5NH_3^+ + OH^-$	4.7×10^{-4}	3.3
Hydrazine	$N_2H_4 + H_2O \rightleftharpoons N_2H_5^+ + OH^-$	3×10^{-6}	5.5
Methylamine	$CH_3NH_2 + H_2O \leftrightarrows CH_3NH_3^+ + OH^-$	4.4×10^{-4}	3.4
Pyridine	$C_6H_5N + H_2O \rightleftharpoons C_6H_5NH^+ + OH^-$	1.4×10^{-9}	8.9
Silver hydroxide	$AgOH \rightleftharpoons Ag^+ + OH^-$	1.1×10^{-4}	4.0
Trimethylamine	$(CH_3)_3N + H_2O \rightleftharpoons (CH_3)_3NH^+ + OH^-$	6.3×10^{-5}	4.2

Calculations Using Ionization Constants 13.9

In aqueous solutions of acids the H_3O^+ concentration is in effect the sum of the concentrations of H_3O^+ produced in the dissociation of the acid plus that from the self-ionization of the water. So long as the acid is an appreciably stronger acid than water, which is almost always the case, the relatively high concentration of H_3O^+ resulting from its dissociation will shift the water equilibrium $2\ H_2O \rightleftharpoons H_3O^+ + OH^-$ almost entirely to the left. The H_3O^+ ions in the solution can therefore be considered as coming entirely from the acid, and their concentration can be calculated from the ionization constant of the acid alone.

Example 13.10

Calculate the H_3O^+ concentration, pH, and degree of dissociation of acetic acid in a 0.100 M solution.

Solution: The equation for the dissociation of acetic acid in water is

$$HC_2H_3O_2 + H_2O \rightleftharpoons C_2H_3O_2^- + H_3O^+$$

Let $x = [H_3O^+]$. Since 1 $C_2H_3O_2^-$ is formed for every H_3O^+ produced in the dissociation, $x = [C_2H_3O_2^-]$ also. The concentration of acid remaining undissociated at equilibrium, $[HC_2H_3O_2] = (0.100 - x)$. Substituting these values into the equilibrium expression gives

$$\frac{[H_3O^+][C_2H_3O_2^-]}{[HC_2H_3O_2]} = \frac{x^2}{(0.100 - x)} = K_a = 1.75 \times 10^{-5}$$

The exact solution can be obtained by solving this quadratic equation. However, if K_a/C, where C is the total concentration of the acid, is smaller than 10^{-4}, x is so much smaller than C that it can be neglected in comparison. The concentration of undissociated acid can then be taken equal to C without introducing any serious error in the result. We follow this procedure in the present example,

$$[HC_2H_3O_2] = (0.100 - x) \approx 0.100$$

and the equation above becomes

$$\frac{x^2}{0.100} = 1.75 \times 10^{-5}$$

$$x^2 = 1.75 \times 10^{-6}$$

$$x = [H_3O^+] = 1.33 \times 10^{-3}$$

$$pH = -\log [H_3O^+]$$

$$= -\log (1.33 \times 10^{-3}) = -(0.12 - 3)$$

$$= 2.88$$

The degree of dissociation α is the ratio of the concentration of the acid ionized to the total concentration of acid present. Since every H_3O^+ ion represents 1 ionized acid molecule,

$$\alpha = \frac{[H_3O^+]}{C} = \frac{1.33 \times 10^{-3}}{0.100} = 0.0133$$

The approximation used in Example 13.10 leads to the general equation

$$[H_3O^+] = \sqrt{K_aC}$$

where C is the concentration of the weak acid, neglecting the small amount of it which ionizes. Taking the negative logarithm of both sides converts this equation to

$$pH = \frac{pK_a - \log C}{2}$$

These equations are valid for solutions of pure weak acids in water provided K_a/C is less than 10^{-4}. As the following example shows, these approximations cannot be used if K_a/C is greater than 10^{-4}.

Example 13.11

Calculate the pH and degree of dissociation of the acid in a 0.100 M solution of dichloroacetic acid ($K_a = 5 \times 10^{-2}$; $pK_a = 1.3$).

Solution: K_a/C in this instance is equal to $5 \times 10^{-2}/10^{-1} = 5 \times 10^{-1}$. This is larger than 10^{-4}, and hence the quadratic equation must be solved.

$$HC_2HCl_2O_2 + H_2O \rightleftharpoons H_3O^+ + C_2HCl_2O_2^-$$

Let $x = [H_3O^+] = [C_2HCl_2O_2^-]$. Then

$$[HC_2HCl_2O_2] = (0.100 - x)$$

$$K_a = 5 \times 10^{-2} = \frac{[H_3O^+][C_2HCl_2O_2^-]}{[HC_2HCl_2O_2]}$$

$$= \frac{x^2}{(0.100 - x)}$$

$$x^2 + (5 \times 10^{-2})x - 5 \times 10^{-3} = 0$$

From the law for a quadratic equation,

$$x = \frac{-b \pm \sqrt{b^2 - 4ac}}{2a}$$

$$x = \frac{-(5 \times 10^{-2}) \pm \sqrt{(25 \times 10^{-4}) - 4(1)(-5 \times 10^{-3})}}{2(1)}$$

$$x = 0.05; \ -0.10$$

Since the H_3O^+ concentration must be a positive number, $[H_3O^+] = 0.05\ M$. It is clear that this is not a negligible quantity compared with the total concentration 0.100 M.

$$pH = -\log 0.05$$

$$= 1.3$$

$$\alpha = [H_3O^+]/C = 0.05/0.100$$

$$= 0.5$$

Dichloroacetic acid is therefore 50% dissociated in 0.100 M solution. If we had neglected the dissociation of the acid,

$$[H_3O^+] = \sqrt{K_aC} = \sqrt{(5 \times 10^{-2})(10^{-1})}$$

$$= 0.07\ M$$

the H_3O^+ concentration would have been in error by 40%.

The OH^- concentration and degree of dissociation of weak bases in dilute aqueous solution are calculated from their ionization constants in a similar manner.

Example 13.12

Calculate the pH of a 0.15 M solution of ammonia. $K_b = 1.75 \times 10^{-5}$.

Solution:

$$NH_3 + H_2O \rightleftharpoons NH_4^+ + OH^-$$

Let $x = [NH_4^+] = [OH^-]$. Then

$$[NH_3] = 0.15 - x$$

$$K_b = \frac{[NH_4^+][OH^-]}{[NH_3]}$$

$$1.75 \times 10^{-5} = \frac{x^2}{(0.15 - x)}$$

Since K_b/C in this instance is less than 10^{-4}, $(0.15 - x) \approx 0.15$, and

$$x = [OH^-] = \sqrt{K_bC} = \sqrt{(1.75 \times 10^{-5})(1.5 \times 10^{-1})}$$
$$= \sqrt{2.6 \times 10^{-6}}$$
$$= 1.6 \times 10^{-3}$$
$$pOH = -\log (1.6 \times 10^{-3})$$
$$= 2.8$$
$$pH = (14.0 - 2.8) = 11.2$$

13.10 Polyprotic Acids

Two equilibria are involved in the dissociation of a diprotic acid:

$$(1) \qquad H_2A + H_2O \rightleftharpoons H_3O^+ + HA^-$$

$$K_{a_1} = \frac{[H_3O^+][HA^-]}{[H_2A]}$$

$$(2) \qquad HA^- + H_2O \rightleftharpoons H_3O^+ + A^{--}$$

$$K_{a_2} = \frac{[H_3O^+][A^{--}]}{[HA^-]}$$

If K_{a_2} is very much smaller than K_{a_1} as is usually the case, the concentrations of H_3O^+ and HA^- can be calculated from the expression for the first dissociation step, neglecting any H_3O^+ coming from the second. The results of this calculation can then be used in the expression for the second step in order to find $[A^{--}]$.

Example 13.13

Calculate the concentration of sulfide ions S^{--} in a saturated solution of H_2S at 25°C. The values of K_{a_1} and K_{a_2} are given in Table 13.2.

Solution: At 25°C and 1 atm pressure, the concentration of H_2S in a saturated solution is approximately 0.1 M.

Let $x = [H_3O^+]$ from the first dissociation step. Because K_{a_2} is very much smaller than K_{a_1}, the further dissociation of HS^- can be neglected, and taking $[HS^-] = x$ will introduce no measurable error. Since the solution is being kept saturated at 1 atm, the H_2S concentration is unaffected by the ionization, and $[H_2S] = 0.1\ M$.

$$K_{a_1} = \frac{[H_3O^+][HS^-]}{[H_2S]}$$

$$6 \times 10^{-8} = \frac{x^2}{0.1}$$

$$x = 7.7 \times 10^{-5} = [H_3O^+] = [HS^-]$$

The very small value (1×10^{-14}) of K_{a_2} means that the concentration of HS^- is reduced, and the concentration of H_3O^+ is increased by a negligible amount as a result of the second dissociation step. We can therefore substitute the concentrations of these species calculated above into the expression for the second dissociation:

$$HS^- + H_2O \rightleftharpoons H_3O^+ + S^{--}$$

and solve for $[S^{--}]$, namely,

$$K_{a_2} = \frac{[H_3O^+][S^{--}]}{[HS^-]}$$

$$1 \times 10^{-14} = \frac{7.7 \times 10^{-5}[S^{--}]}{7.7 \times 10^{-5}}$$

$$[S^{--}] = 1 \times 10^{-14}$$

You will notice that in Example 13.13, $[S^{--}] = K_{a_2}$. In general, it is found that in any pure solution of a weak diprotic acid H_2A, the concentration of A^{--} is approximately equal to the second dissociation constant.

Similar calculations can be applied without undue complication in order to determine the concentrations of the various species that are present in a solution of a triprotic acid.

Example 13.14

Calculate the concentration of PO_4^{---} in a 0.10 M solution of H_3PO_4.

$$K_{a_1} = 7.5 \times 10^{-3}; \quad K_{a_2} = 6.2 \times 10^{-8}; \quad K_{a_3} = 4.8 \times 10^{-13}.$$

Solution: As in the preceding example, all of the H_3O^+ ions present in the solution may be assumed to come from the first dissociation step:

$$H_3PO_4 + H_2O \rightleftharpoons H_3O^+ + H_2PO_4^-$$

Let $x = [H_3O^+] \approx [H_2PO_4^-]$. Then

$$[H_3PO_4] = (0.10 - x)$$

$$\frac{[H_3O^+][H_2PO_4^-]}{[H_3PO_4]} = K_{a_1}$$

$$\frac{x^2}{(0.10 - x)} = 7.5 \times 10^{-3}$$

Solution of the quadratic equation, which is necessary in this case because K_a/C

is greater than 10^{-4}, shows that

$$x = [H_3O^+] = 0.024\ M$$

Neglecting any further ionization of $H_2PO_4^-$ as being insignificant, we find that its concentration is also 0.024 M. Substituting these values into the expression for the second dissociation step gives

$$H_2PO_4^- + H_2O \rightleftharpoons H_3O^+ + HPO_4^-$$

$$\frac{[H_3O^+][HPO_4^{--}]}{[H_2PO_4^-]} = K_{a_2}$$

$$\frac{0.024[HPO_4^{--}]}{0.024} = 6.2 \times 10^{-8}$$

$$[HPO_4^{--}] = 6.2 \times 10^{-8}$$

Introducing the values for $[H_3O^+]$ and $[HPO_4^{--}]$ into the expression for the third step,

$$HPO_4^{--} + H_2O \rightleftharpoons H_3O^+ + PO_4^{---}$$

we get

$$\frac{[H_3O^+][PO_4^{---}]}{[HPO_4^{--}]} = K_{a_3}$$

$$\frac{(2.4 \times 10^{-2})[PO_4^{---}]}{(6.2 \times 10^{-8})} = 4.8 \times 10^{-13}$$

$$[PO_4^{---}] = 1.2 \times 10^{-18}$$

13.11 Common Ion Effect

Addition of a strong acid to a solution of a weak one suppresses the degree of dissociation of the weak acid to such an extent that the concentration of H_3O^+ in the solution is determined almost entirely by that of the strong acid. Similarly, in a solution of a strong base, the dissociation of any weak base present is almost completely suppressed.

Example 13.15

A solution contains 0.10 mole/liter of $HC_2H_3O_2$ and 0.050 mole/liter of HCl. Calculate the degree of dissociation α of the $HC_2H_3O_2$ in the solution.

Solution: The ionization of the strong acid HCl is virtually complete; hence the concentration of H_3O^+ from the dissociation of HCl is 0.050 M. Let x equal the concentration of each ion formed by the dissociation of the acetic acid:

$$HC_2H_3O_2 + H_2O \rightleftharpoons H_3O^+ + C_2H_3O_2^-$$

Then,

$$[H_3O^+] = (0.050 + x)$$

$$[C_2H_3O_2^-] = x$$

$$[HC_2H_3O_2] = (0.10 - x)$$

$$\frac{[H_3O^+][C_2H_3O_2^-]}{[HC_2H_3O_2]} = K_a$$

$$\frac{(0.050 + x)(x)}{(0.10 - x)} = 1.75 \times 10^{-5}$$

In Example 13.10, the amount of acetic acid which dissociated was found to be negligible for purposes of calculation when acetic acid was the only acid present. In the present case, the dissociation should be even less because of the presence of the strong acid. Therefore, neglecting x added to or subtracted from larger numbers gives

$$\frac{0.050x}{0.10} = 1.75 \times 10^{-5}$$

$$x = [C_2H_3O_2^-] = 3.5 \times 10^{-5}\ M$$

$$\alpha = \frac{3.5 \times 10^{-5}}{0.10}$$

$$= 3.5 \times 10^{-4}$$

Compare this with the degree of dissociation of acetic acid in a pure solution at the same concentration, which was found in Example 13.10 to be 1.3×10^{-2}.

The use of a common ion from another source to control the degree of dissociation of a weak electrolyte, as in the preceding example, finds important application in the use of H_2S as a reagent for the selective precipitation of ions in qualitative analysis. It is possible to vary the sulfide ion concentration in a saturated solution of H_2S over a wide range by adjusting the acidity of the solution.

Example 13.16

In the sulfide scheme of qualitative analysis, the copper-arsenic group of cations are precipitated as their sulfides. In order to avoid precipitation of the nickel group cations at the same time, the sulfide ion concentration in the solution must be kept below $10^{-21}\ M$. At what *p*H should the precipitation be carried out?

Solution: The overall expression for the dissociation of H_2S to yield sulfide ions,

$$H_2S + 2\ H_2O \rightleftharpoons 2\ H_3O^+ + S^{--}$$

can be obtained by multiplying the equilibrium expressions for the two separate dissociation steps:

$$\frac{[H_3O^+][HS^-]}{[H_2S]} \times \frac{[H_3O^+][S^{--}]}{[HS^-]} = K_{a_1} \times K_{a_2} = K_{H_2S}$$

$$\frac{[H_3O^+]^2[S^{--}]}{[H_2S]} = 6 \times 10^{-22}$$

The concentration of H_2S in a saturated solution at ordinary laboratory conditions (approximately 25°C and 1 atm) can be taken as 0.1 M. The maximum S^{--} ion concentration allowed in this experiment is $10^{-21}\ M$. Introduce these values into the above expression and solve for $[H_3O^+]$ as follows:

$$\frac{[H_3O^+]^2(10^{-21})}{(10^{-1})} = 6 \times 10^{-22}$$

$$[H_3O^+]^2 = 6 \times 10^{-2}$$

$$[H_3O^+] = 2.5 \times 10^{-1}$$

$$pH \approx 0.6$$

This is the maximum pH permitted if precipitation of the nickel group is to be avoided. To insure satisfactory separation of the groups, precipitation of the copper-arsenic group is generally carried out in 0.3 M HCl solution ($pH \approx 0.5$).

The common ion effect can be used to advantage in adjusting the pH of a solution of weak acid or base to some desired value. The necessary common ion is supplied by adding a salt of the acid or base to the solution.

Example 13.17

How much NH_4Cl, when added to 1.0 liter of 0.10 M ammonia, will give a solution with a pH of 9?

Solution: A pH of 9 corresponds with a pOH of 5, and $[OH^-] = 10^{-5}\ M$. Since the solution is 0.10 M, $[NH_3] \approx 1.0 \times 10^{-1}$.

$$\frac{[NH_4^+][OH^-]}{[NH_3]} = \frac{[NH_4^+](10^{-5})}{(10^{-1})} = 1.75 \times 10^{-5}$$

$$[NH_4^+] = 1.75 \times 10^{-1}\ M$$

A pH of 9 requires the presence of 0.175 mole of NH_4^+ ions in 1.0 liter of 0.10 M ammonia solution. This concentration of NH_4^+ can be obtained by dissolving 0.175 mole, or about 9.4 g, of the almost completely ionized salt of NH_4Cl in the solution. The NH_4^+ produced in the equilibrium:

$$NH_3 + H_2O \rightleftharpoons NH_4^+ + OH^-$$

amounts to only 10^{-5} mole/liter and can be neglected.

13.12 Buffer Solutions

A solution of a weak acid or weak base in the presence of one of its salts (such as that described in Example 13.17) *is known as a* ***buffer solution.*** Buffer solutions resist changes in pH resulting from the addition of small amounts of acid or base. Typical is a solution of acetic acid and sodium acetate. The ionic salt furnishes acetate ions, the conjugate base of acetic acid, to the solution. Any strong acid added to this solution is neutralized by the base ($C_2H_3O_2^-$) present as follows:

$$C_2H_3O_2^- + H_3O^+ \rightarrow HC_2H_3O_2 + H_2O$$

Similarly, a strong base is neutralized by reaction with the undissociated acetic acid in the solution:

$$HC_2H_3O_2 + OH^- \rightarrow C_2H_3O_2^- + H_2O$$

In effect, the addition of either strong acid or strong base merely alters the ratio of the concentrations of the two components of the buffer system without appreciably changing the concentrations of H_3O^+ and OH^-. The buffering action will continue as long as the number of moles of H_3O^+ or OH^- added does not exceed the number of moles of $C_2H_3O_2^-$ or $HC_2H_3O_2$ present in the solution. Once either component of the buffer system is depleted, further addition of acid or base will cause a drastic change in the *p*H.

A solution of a weak base together with one of its salts, NH_3 and NH_4Cl for example, resists changes in *p*H in similar manner. Any added H_3O^+ is neutralized by the unreacted base in the solution:

$$NH_3 + H_3O^+ \rightarrow NH_4^+ + H_2O$$

The conjugate acid, NH_4^+, supplied by the dissolved salt, takes care of any OH^- ions:

$$NH_4^+ + OH^- \rightarrow NH_3 + H_2O$$

Example 13.18

Calculate the *p*H of a solution formed by adding 20.0 ml of 0.10 *M* NaOH to 50.0 ml of 0.10 *M* $HC_2H_3O_2$.

Solution: First calculate the concentrations of the various species that are present.

There were (50 ml × 0.10 *M*) = 5.0 mmoles of $HC_2H_3O_2$ present in the original solution before addition of the base. Adding (20 ml × 0.10 *M*) = 2.0 mmoles of NaOH neutralizes 2.0 mmoles of the acid. The final solution, which has a volume of (20 + 50) = 70 ml, therefore contains 2.0 mmoles of $C_2H_3O_2^-$ ions and (5.0 − 2.0) = 3.0 mmoles of unreacted $HC_2H_3O_2$. Thus,

$$[HC_2H_3O_2] = 3.0 \text{ mmoles}/70 \text{ ml}$$

$$[C_2H_3O^-] = 2.0 \text{ mmoles}/70 \text{ ml}$$

Neglect any further dissociation of $HC_2H_3O_2$ as being insignificant, and

$$\frac{[H_3O^+](2.0/70)}{(3.0/70)} = 1.75 \times 10^{-5}$$

$$[H_3O^+] = 1.75 \times 10^{-5}(3.0/2.0)$$

$$= 2.6 \times 10^{-5}$$

$$pH = 4.59$$

From this example we can derive, as the general equation for the concentration of H_3O^+ in a buffer solution consisting of a solution of a weak acid together with its salt, the expression

$$[H_3O^+] = K_a \frac{[HA]}{[A^-]}$$

or, alternatively,

$$[H_3O^+] = K_a \frac{n_a}{n_s}$$

in which n_a represents the number of mmoles of acid and n_s represents the mmoles of salt present in any given volume of solution.

Example 13.19

What will be the effect on the pH of adding 10.0 ml of 0.10 M HCl to the solution prepared in Example 13.18?

Solution: The added (10.0 ml $\times$ 0.10 M) = 1.0 mmole of HCl reacts with 1.0 mmole of $C_2H_3O_2^-$ to form an equal amount of $HC_2H_3O_2$. The final solution therefore contains 4.0 mmoles of $HC_2H_3O_2$ and 1.0 mmole of $C_2H_3O_2^-$.

$$[H_3O^+] = K_a \frac{n_a}{n_s}$$
$$= (1.75 \times 10^{-5})(4.0/1.0)$$
$$= 7.0 \times 10^{-5}$$
$$pH = 4.15$$

The addition of 10.0 ml of 0.10 M HCl to this buffer solution is seen to cause a change in the pH amounting to less than one-half unit. In contrast, the addition of that same amount of 0.10 M HCl to 70 ml of pure water yields a solution with a H_3O^+ concentration of

$$[H_3O^+] = \frac{(10.0 \text{ ml})(0.10\ M)}{(80.0 \text{ ml})} = 1.25 \times 10^{-2}$$

and a pH of 1.9.

Similarly, the expression

$$[OH^-] = K_b \frac{n_b}{n_s}$$

may be used to estimate the OH^- concentration in a buffer solution of a weak base.

13.13 Hydrolysis

The reaction between equivalent amounts of a strong acid such as HCl and a strong base such as NaOH results in a solution in which the concentrations of H_3O^+ and OH^- are the same as they are in pure water. The anion of the acid and the cation of the base act merely as "spectator ions" (Sec. 13.3). The water equilibrium is undisturbed by their presence, and the resulting salt solution is neutral. On the other hand, if a weak acid like $HC_2H_3O_2$ is neutralized with an equivalent amount of a strong base, the salt solution obtained is not neutral, but slightly basic. The anion, in this case ($C_2H_3O_2^-$), is a relatively strong base, being the conjugate base of a weak acid, and it reacts to a small extent with the water:

$$C_2H_3O_2^- + H_2O \rightleftharpoons HC_2H_3O_2 + OH^-$$

Because of this reaction the solution contains a slightly greater concentration of OH^- than of H_3O^+, making it slightly basic. *Any reaction between water and the ions of a salt dissolved in it is called* ***hydrolysis.***

A salt of a weak base and a strong acid, NH_4Cl for example, dissolved in pure water, gives a slightly acidic solution. Here it is the cation, which is the strong conjugate acid of a weak base, that is the species undergoing hydrolysis:

$$NH_4^+ + H_2O \rightleftharpoons NH_3 + H_3O^+$$

The equilibrium expression for anion hydrolysis,

$$A^- + H_2O \rightleftharpoons HA + OH^-$$

is

$$\frac{[HA][OH^-]}{[A^-]} = K_h$$

The constant K_h is known as the ***hydrolysis constant.*** The extent to which an anion undergoes hydrolysis, as measured by its hydrolysis constant, should be inversely proportional to the strength of its conjugate acid (i.e., the stronger the acid, the less its salt should hydrolyze) and directly proportional to the acid strength of the solvent (water). The relative acidity of an acid is given by its ionization constant; that of water is given by K_w:

$$K_h = \frac{K_w}{K_a} = [H_3O^+][OH^-] \times \frac{[HA]}{[H_3O^+][A^-]}$$

$$= \frac{[HA][OH^-]}{[A^-]}$$

Similarly, for the hydrolysis of a cation,

$$BH^+ + H_2O \rightleftharpoons B + H_3O^+$$

$$K_h = \frac{K_w}{K_b} = \frac{[B][H_3O^+]}{[BH^+]}$$

Example 13.20

Calculate the pH at the equivalence point when 50.0 ml of 0.10 M $HC_2H_3O_2$ is neutralized with 50.0 ml of 0.10 M $NaOH$.

Solution: At the equivalence point, 50.0 ml $\times$ 0.10 M = 5.0 mmoles of $HC_2H_3O_2$ has reacted with 50.0 ml $\times$ 0.10 M = 5.0 mmoles of OH^- to give 5.0 mmoles of $C_2H_3O_2^-$ dissolved in 100 ml of water. The concentration of $C_2H_3O_2^-$ in the solution before hydrolysis is therefore 5.0 mmoles/100 ml = 0.050 M. The equation for the hydrolysis is

$$C_2H_3O_2^- + H_2O \rightleftharpoons HC_2H_3O_2 + OH^-$$

$$K_h = \frac{K_w}{K_a} = \frac{[HC_2H_3O_2][OH^-]}{[C_2H_3O_2^-]}$$

Let x = $[HC_2H_3O_2]$ = $[OH^-]$. Then

$$[C_2H_3O_2^-] = (0.050 - x)$$

$$K_h = \frac{10^{-14}}{1.75 \times 10^{-5}} = 5.7 \times 10^{-10}$$

$$5.7 \times 10^{-10} = \frac{x^2}{(0.050 - x)}$$

Since K_h is small, the extent of hydrolysis is also small, and $(0.050 - x) \approx 0.050$. Then,

$$\frac{x^2}{0.050} = 5.7 \times 10^{-10}$$

$$x^2 = 2.9 \times 10^{-11} = [OH^-]^2$$

$$2(pOH) = -\log 2.9 \times 10^{-11} = 10.5$$

$$pOH = 5.3$$

$$pH = 8.7$$

When a weak acid is neutralized by a weak base, both ions of the salt formed are hydrolyzed. The pH of the salt solution will depend upon the relative strengths of the acid and base which react to form the salt. Ammonium acetate will serve as an example. The hydrolysis reactions are

$$NH_4^+ + H_2O \rightleftharpoons NH_3 + H_3O^+$$

$$C_2H_3O_2^- + H_2O \rightleftharpoons HC_2H_3O_2 + OH^-$$

Adding these two equations gives

$$NH_4^+ + C_2H_3O_2^- + 2\ H_2O \rightleftharpoons NH_3 + HC_2H_3O_2 + H_3O^+ + OH^-$$

Since the equilibrium,

$$2\ H_2O \rightleftharpoons H_3O^+ + OH^-$$

exists in aqueous solution in any case, it may be subtracted from the combined hydrolysis reaction to give

$$NH_4^+ + C_2H_3O_2^- \rightleftharpoons NH_3 + HC_2H_3O_2$$

for which the hydrolysis constant is

$$\frac{[NH_3][HC_2H_3O_2]}{[NH_4^+][C_2H_3O_2^-]} = K_h$$

The combined hydrolysis constant can be evaluated from the individual hydrolysis constants of the two ions:

$$\frac{[NH_3][H_3O^+]}{[NH_4^+]} = \frac{K_w}{K_b}$$

$$\frac{[HC_2H_3O_2][OH^-]}{[C_2H_3O_2^-]} = \frac{K_w}{K_a}$$

Rearrangement of these expressions gives

$$[H_3O^+] = \frac{K_w[NH_4^+]}{K_b[NH_3]}$$

$$[OH^-] = \frac{K_w[C_2H_3O_2^-]}{K_a[HC_2H_3O_2]}$$

Multiplying one by the other, we obtain

$$[H_3O^+][OH^-] = K_w = \frac{K_w[NH_4^+]}{K_b[NH_3]} \times \frac{K_w[C_2H_3O_2^-]}{K_a[HC_2H_3O_2]}$$

and rearranging terms yields the expression for the hydrolysis constant:

$$\frac{[NH_3][HC_2H_3O_2]}{[NH_4^+][C_2H_3O_2^-]} = \frac{K_w}{K_aK_b} = K_h$$

From this expression it can be seen that salts of weak acids and weak bases are quite extensively hydrolyzed, since the quotient of K_w divided by the product of two ionization constants must be relatively large, and that the smaller the values of K_a and K_b, that is, the weaker the acid and base, the greater will be the degree of hydrolysis of the salt. It can be shown that the H_3O^+ concentration in a solution of such a salt is given by the relationship,

$$[H_3O^+] = \sqrt{\frac{K_aK_w}{K_b}}$$

According to this, if $K_a = K_b$, which happens to be true for ammonium acetate, $[H_3O^+] = 10^{-7}$, and the solution of the salt is neutral in spite of hydrolysis. If $K_a > K_b$, $[H_3O^+] > 10^{-7}$, and the solution is acidic. On the other hand, if $K_b > K_a$, $[H_3O^+] < 10^{-7}$, and the solution is basic.

If any of the products of hydrolysis are of low solubility in water, they may precipitate, especially if the salt solution is fairly concentrated. Heavy metal salts, for example, often undergo appreciable hydrolysis in solution, with the formation of a precipitate of the hydroxide or oxide:

$$Bi^{+++} + 6\ H_2O \rightleftharpoons Bi(OH)_3\downarrow + 3\ H_3O^+$$

$$Hg^{++} + 3\ H_2O \rightleftharpoons HgO\downarrow + 2\ H_3O^+$$

Solutions of these salts in pure water will appear cloudy because of the presence of the precipitate. A clear solution is obtained by adding acid to force the equilibrium back toward the formation of the metal ions. If the products of hydrolysis are very insoluble, or if they are gases which escape to the atmosphere, the hydrolysis may proceed nearly to completion. For example, Al_2S_3 is completely hydrolyzed in water:

$$Al_2S_3 + 6\ H_2O \rightleftharpoons 2\ Al(OH)_3\downarrow + 3\ H_2S\uparrow$$

and any attempt to form it in solution results instead in the precipitation of $Al(OH)_3$ and the evolution of H_2S gas.

13.14 Indicators

The color change that litmus undergoes according to whether it is in contact with an acid or a base is familiar to nearly everyone. Litmus is an example of an ***acid-base indicator,*** a substance whose color depends upon the concentration of hydronium ions in solution. Indicators are used extensively to show whether solutions are acidic or basic and to detect, or *indicate*, the equivalence point in the quantitative neutralization, or ***titration,*** of acids and bases. An indicator is itself a weak acid or a weak base whose conjugate acid-base forms are of different colors. When the acid form of an indicator is represented by HIn, the equation for its dissociation in water is

$$HIn + H_2O \rightleftharpoons H_3O^+ + In^-$$

for which the equilibrium expression is

$$\frac{[H_3O^+][In^-]}{[HIn]} = K_{\text{ind}}$$

The amount of indicator generally used is so small that its dissociation does not measurably affect the H_3O^+ concentration of the solution. Instead, through the common ion effect, it is the latter which determines the ratio between the concentrations of HIn and In^- as follows:

$$[H_3O^+] = K_{\text{ind}} \frac{[HIn]}{[In^-]}$$

The color of the indicator will range from that of HIn through some intermediate shade to that of In^-, according to the relative proportions of the two species present in the solution. At a high concentration of H_3O^+ (low pH), the color observed will be that of HIn. At a low concentration of H_3O^+ (high pH), the color will be that of In^-. When $[H_3O^+] \approx K_{\text{ind}}$, $[HIn] \approx [In^-]$; an intermediate shade, the result of the mixture of the colors of the two species, will be observed.

In the case of the indicator methyl red, HIn is red, In^- is yellow, and $K_{\text{ind}} = 5.6 \times 10^{-6}$. A solution containing methyl red will appear orange (red + yellow) if $[H_3O^+] \approx 5.6 \times 10^{-6}$, that is, at a pH of 5.25. At a lower pH the color will be red; at a higher pH, yellow. The eye can detect the difference in color with certainty in most cases when one form of the indicator is present in ten-fold excess over the other. With methyl red, when

$$\frac{[\mathrm{HIn}]}{[\mathrm{In}^-]} = 10 \text{ or above}$$

the solution appears definitely red. The pH corresponding to this situation is readily calculated:

$$[\mathrm{H_3O^+}] = (5.6 \times 10^{-6})(10) = 5.6 \times 10^{-5}$$

$$p\mathrm{H} = 4.3$$

The solution will be definitely yellow when the above ratio is 0.1 or less:

$$[\mathrm{H_3O^+}] = (5.6 \times 10^{-6})(10^{-1}) = 5.6 \times 10^{-7}$$

$$p\mathrm{H} = 6.3$$

TABLE 13.4 Color Changes and *p*H Ranges for Some Common Indicators

Indicator	Color Change and *p*H Range				
Thymol blue	red	–	1.2– 2.8	–	yellow
Methyl orange	red	–	3.1– 4.4	–	yellow
Bromcresol green	yellow	–	3.8– 5.4	–	blue
Methyl red	red	–	4.2– 6.3	–	yellow
Bromthymol blue	yellow	–	6.0– 7.6	–	blue
Phenol red	yellow	–	6.8– 8.4	–	red
Thymol blue	yellow	–	7.0– 9.6	–	blue
Phenolphthalein	colorless	–	8.3–10.0	–	red
Thymophthalein	colorless	–	9.3–10.5	–	blue
Alizarin yellow	yellow	–	10.1–12.1	–	lilac

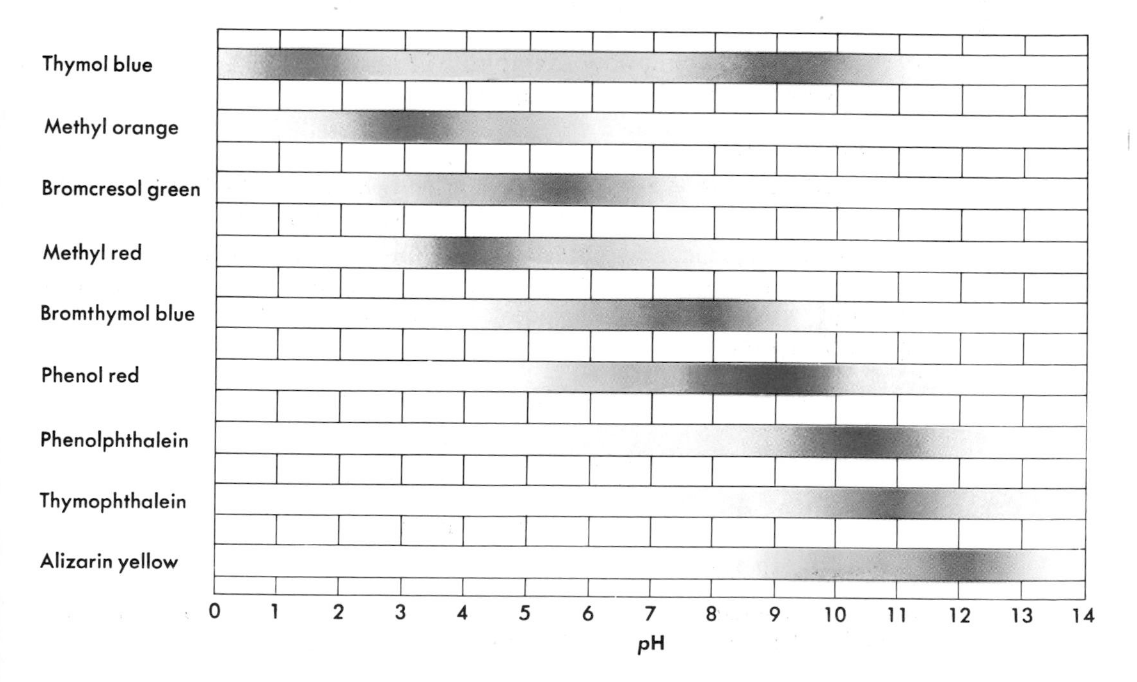

Fig. 13.1 Useful ranges of acid-base indicators.

With most indicators, as with methyl red, the change in color takes place over a range of about 2 *p*H units.

There are many acid-base indicators, each of which has its own particular ionization constant. For this reason, the *p*H range over which indicator color transitions take place vary from one indicator to another. The transition ranges for a number of common indicators are shown in Table 13.4 and Fig. 13.1 on p. 359. Thymol blue appears twice in the table, since it changes color over two distinct regions, corresponding to two separate ionization constants.

Indicator papers are made by impregnating filter paper with either a single indicator, covering a narrow range of *p*H, or with several indicators which, taken together, cover a broad *p*H range. Litmus paper changes from red to blue between *p*H 4.5 and *p*H 8.3.

13.15 Acid-Base Titrations

The quantitative analysis of acids and bases is carried out by means of titration. An acid or base to be analyzed is titrated by adding a base or acid of known concentration to it from a calibrated delivery tube called a *buret*. The equivalence point is detected from the color change of an added indicator. At the equivalence point,

$$\text{Milliequivalents of base} = \text{milliequivalents of acid}$$

The number of milliequivalents of base or acid taken is equal to the product of its normality times its volume in milliliters. If the purpose of the titration is to determine the normality of a solution of acid or base of unknown concentration, the relationship

$$N_{\text{base}} \times V_{\text{base}} = N_{\text{acid}} \times V_{\text{acid}}$$

is convenient. The following examples will illustrate the types of calculations involved in titration experiments.

Example 13.21

Neutralization of 0.4870 g of pure potassium acid phthalate ($KHC_8H_4O_4$) requires 23.4 ml of $NaOH$ solution. Calculate the normality of the base.

Solution: Potassium acid phthalate has 1 replaceable hydrogen; hence its equivalent weight is equal to its formula weight, which is 204.2 g. The milliequivalent weight is $\frac{1}{1000}$ of the equivalent weight, or 0.2042 g/meq. At the equivalence point,

$$\text{meq }(NaOH) = \text{meq }(KHC_8H_4O_4)$$

$$23.4\text{ ml}(N) = \frac{0.4870\text{ g}}{0.2042\text{ g/meq}}$$

$$N = 0.102\text{ meq/ml}$$

Example 13.22

What is the normality of an H_2SO_4 solution if 25.7 ml of it is needed to neutralize 31.2 ml of the 0.102 N base standardized in Example 13.21?

Solution: At the equivalence point,

$$N_{\text{base}} \times V_{\text{base}} = N_{\text{acid}} \times V_{\text{acid}}$$
$$(0.102)(31.2) = (N)(25.7)$$
$$0.124 = N_{\text{acid}}$$

Example 13.23

A 0.2460 g sample of washing soda neutralizes 34.6 ml of 0.124 N acid. What is the percentage of Na_2CO_3 in the sample?

Solution: The equation for the reaction of a carbonate with an acid is

$$CO_3^{--} + 2\ H_3O^+ \rightarrow 3\ H_2O + CO_2$$

The formula weight of Na_2CO_3 is 106.0 g. Since 1 mole of CO_3^{--} neutralizes 2 moles of acid, the equivalent weight of Na_2CO_3 in this reaction is one-half its formula weight; 53.0 g/eq; 0.0530 g/meq. At the equivalence point,

$$\text{meq (acid)} = \text{meq } (Na_2CO_3)$$
$$(0.124\ N)(34.6\ \text{ml}) = 4.29\ \text{meq}$$

The number of g of Na_2CO_3 in the sample equals the number of meq multiplied by the mass of 1 meq:

$$(4.29\ \text{meq})(0.0530\ \text{g/meq}) = 0.227\ \text{g}$$

and the percentage of Na_2CO_3 in the sample is

$$\frac{0.227}{0.246} \times 100 = 92.4\%$$

The operation is combined into one step as follows:

$$\frac{(V_{\text{titrant}})(N_{\text{titrant}})(\text{g/meq})}{(\text{g sample taken})} \times 100 = \%$$

$$\frac{(34.6\ \text{ml})(0.124\ N)(0.053\ \text{g/meq})}{(0.246\ \text{g})} \times 100 = 92.4\%\ Na_2CO_3$$

The pH of a solution changes continuously during the course of any titration. The change in pH as the titration proceeds may be followed by the use of a pH meter (Sec. 14.6), or it may be calculated by the methods illustrated earlier in this chapter. A plot of pH as a function of the volume of titrant added is called a ***titration curve.*** To illustrate the construction of such a curve, let us consider the titration of 50.00 ml of 0.1000 N HCl with 0.1000 N NaOH. Before any of the base is added, $[H_3O^+] = 0.1000\ M$, and $p\text{H} = 1.00$. The concentration of the acid decreases, and the pH rises as NaOH solution is continuously added. After 49.95 ml of base has been added, $(49.95\ \text{ml} \times 0.1000\ N) = 4.995$ meq of NaOH have reacted with 4.995 meq of HCl out of a total of $(50.00\ \text{ml} \times 0.1000\ N) = 5.000$ meq originally present. The solution at this point contains 4.995 meq NaCl and 0.005 meq unreacted HCl in a total volume of 99.95 ml. Since the NaCl has no effect on the pH of the solution, the pH can be calculated from the concentration of the HCl:

$$[H_3O^+] = \frac{0.005 \text{ meq}}{99.95 \text{ ml}} = 5 \times 10^{-5}\ M$$

$$pH = 4.30$$

At the equivalence point, when 50.00 ml of base has been added, the pH = 7.00, since the solution contains only $NaCl$. Adding 1 more drop (0.05 ml) of $NaOH$ results in a solution containing (0.05 ml × 0.1000 N) = 0.005 meq of excess base in a volume of 100.05 ml. Therefore,

$$[OH^-] = \frac{0.005 \text{ meq}}{100.05 \text{ ml}} = 5 \times 10^{-5}\ M$$

and the pH is now 9.70. A plot of a number of such pH calculations for various volumes of base added looks like the titration curve *a* in Fig. 13.2. The striking feature of this titration curve is the rapid rise in pH in the vicinity of the equivalence point. From 0.05 ml base before to 0.05 ml base beyond the equivalence point, the pH changes from 4.30 to 9.70. Thus any indicator which changes color within this pH range will be suitable for signaling the equivalence point within acceptable limits of two parts in 1000, or 0.2%. At higher concentrations of acid and base, the pH change is even more pronounced: from 3.30 to 10.70, for example, in the titration of 1.000 N HCl by 1.000 N $NaOH$. At lower concentrations there is less of a change in pH in passing the equivalence point, and the situation is less favorable for analytical purposes.

The titration of a weak acid by a strong base is represented by curve *b* of Fig. 13.2. In this example the acid is $HC_2H_3O_2$, the base is again $NaOH$. Initially, the pH of 0.1000 N $HC_2H_3O_2$ is 2.88, as we calculated in Example 13.10. Upon addition of $NaOH$, the concentration of $HC_2H_3O_2$ decreases as its conjugate base $C_2H_3O_2^-$ is formed, and the mixture constitutes a buffer solution. The pH at any point in the titration curve intermediate between the beginning of titration and the equivalence point corresponds to the continuously changing ratio of acid to salt during the course of the titration. In Example 13.18 it was found that the addition of 20.0 ml of 0.10 N $NaOH$ to 50.0 ml of 0.10 N $HC_2H_3O_2$ results in a solution with a pH of 4.59. Similar calculations will show that when the titration has progressed to the point where 49.95 ml of $NaOH$ has been added, the pH will be 7.74. At the equivalence point the pH is that of a solution of sodium acetate, found in Example 13.20 to be 8.7 for this concentration. Beyond the equivalence point, the solution contains excess OH^- which almost completely suppresses the hydrolysis of $C_2H_3O_2^-$, and the remainder of the curve has the same appearance as that part of the HCl titration curve. Again, there is a considerable rise in pH in the vicinity of the equivalence point, and any indicator that changes color in the range from pH 7.74 to pH 9.70 is suitable for this titration. The choice, however, is more limited than it was for the titration of a strong acid with a strong base.

The earliest portion of the acetic acid titration curve shows a minor inflection where the pH at first rises rather rapidly. This reflects the formation of the salt sodium acetate, which suppresses the ionization of acetic acid through the common ion effect. As more base is added, the pH rises more slowly because the base is now being added to a buffer solution. The maximum buffering effect occurs at the midpoint of the titration where the concentration of acetic acid equals that of the acetate ion. Closer to the equivalence point, the pH again begins to change rapidly, because of the dwindling concentration of acetic acid available for reaction with the added base. The shape of the titration curve of a given weak acid depends upon the concentration of the acid. For example, the titration of 0.01 N $HC_2H_3O_2$ with 0.01 N NaOH follows the curve shown by the dashed line in Fig. 13.2 *b*. At this lower concentration, the rate at which the pH changes in the vicinity of the equivalence point is more gradual, and the volume of titrant required to effect an observable color change on the part of the indicator will be larger than if the solutions are more concentrated. Because of this, the titration will be subject to a greater error. If the error is to be held to within a few tenths of one percent, the practical limit of feasibility for an acetic acid titration using a conventional indicator is a concentration of 0.01 N.

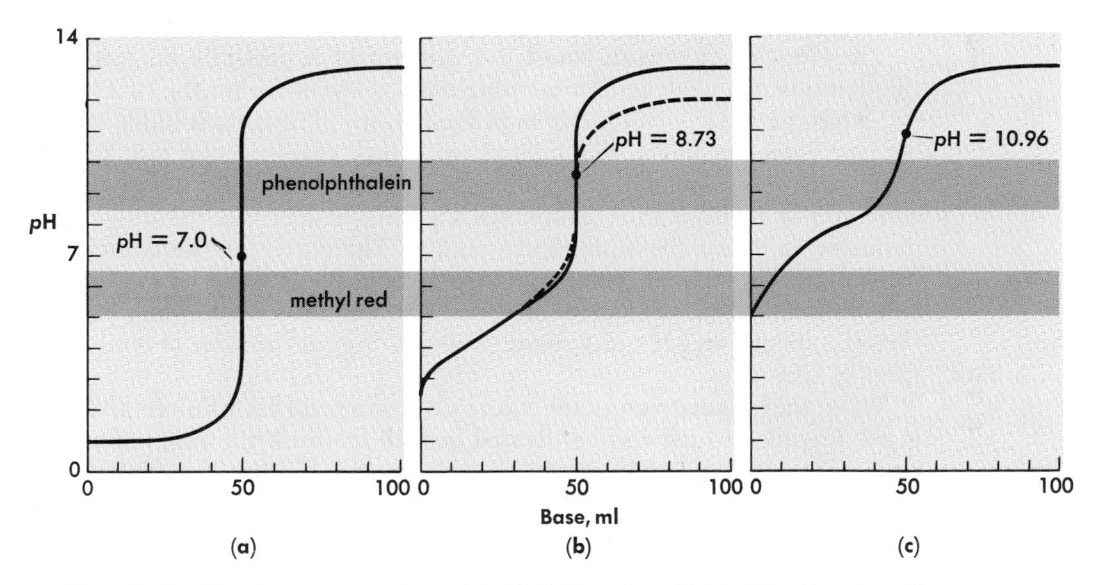

Fig. 13.2 Titration curves: (a) 0.1 N HCl — 0.1 N NaOH; (b) 0.1 N $HC_2H_3O_2$ — 0.1 N NaOH; (c) 0.1 N HBO_2 — 0.1 N NaOH.

For a given concentration, the weaker the acid (i.e., the smaller the value of K_a), the higher will be the pH throughout the course of the titration. The pH at equivalence will be higher because of the more extensive hydrolysis of the salt formed, and there will be a less rapid change in pH upon the addition of excess strong base just beyond the equivalence point. Thus the change in pH, as well as the change in color of an indicator whose range is centered at the equivalence point pH, may be so gradual that the equivalence point cannot be detected with any degree of accuracy. In practice, for 0.1 N solutions, the limit of feasibility for a conventional titration using an indicator is reached when $K_a \approx 10^{-6}$, or when $K_a[HA]$ at the start of titration is about 10^{-7}. The titration curve for 0.1 N HBO_2 ($K_a = 6 \times 10^{-10}$) is shown in Fig. 13.2c.

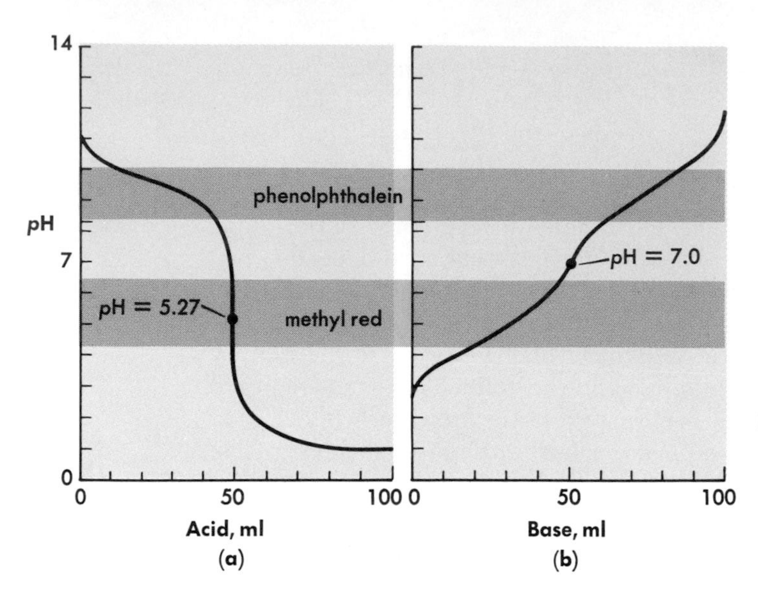

Fig. 13.3 Titration curves: (a) 0.1 N NH_3 — 0.1 N HCl; (b) 0.1 N $HC_2H_3O_2$ — 0.1 N NH_3.

The titration of a weak base by a strong acid is perfectly analogous to the titration of a weak acid by a strong base. The curve for the titration of 0.1 N NH_3 with 0.1 N HCl is shown in Fig. 13.3a. The most suitable indicator here is seen to be one like methyl red, which changes color at a slightly acid pH in the vicinity of the equivalence point at pH 5.26. A weak acid can never be satisfactorily titrated with a weak base or vice versa, using an indicator to detect the equivalence point. The curve for the titration of 0.1 N $HC_2H_3O_2$ with 0.1 N ammonia is shown in Fig. 13.3b. It can be seen from this curve that to change the color of an indicator whose range extends through about two pH units centered at pH 7 would require several milliliters of titrant.

When the ionization constant of an acid is so small that its direct titration is not feasible, its salt can be titrated instead, because the anion of a very weak acid is a moderately strong base. Consider the titration of 50.00 ml of 0.1000 N $NaBO_2$ by 0.1000 N HCl. The original salt solution is quite basic because of hydrolysis:

$$BO_2^- + H_2O \rightleftharpoons HBO_2 + OH^-$$

The OH^- concentration in this solution can be calculated as follows:

$$[OH^-] = \sqrt{\frac{K_w[A^-]}{K_a}}$$

$$= \sqrt{\frac{(10^{-14})(0.1000)}{(6 \times 10^{-10})}} = 1.3 \times 10^{-3}$$

$$pH = 11.1$$

Upon addition of HCl, the reaction

$$BO_2^- + H_3O^+ \rightarrow HBO_2 + H_2O$$

takes place, and the concentration of HBO_2 increases while that of BO_2^- decreases. At all points between the beginning of titration and the equivalence point, the solution is buffered by a continuously increasing ratio of HBO_2/BO_2^-, and the pH gradually diminishes. When 49.95 ml of HCl has been added, the solution contains 4.995 meq of HBO_2 and 0.005 meq $NaBO_2$ in 99.95 ml of solution:

$$[H_3O^+] = (6 \times 10^{-10}) \left(\frac{4.995}{0.005}\right)$$

$$= 6 \times 10^{-7}\ M$$

$$pH = 6.2$$

At the equivalence point, the pH of the solution is that of a 0.0500 N solution of HBO_2:

$$[H_3O^+] = \sqrt{(6 \times 10^{-10})(5 \times 10^{-2})}$$

$$= 5.5 \times 10^{-6}\ M$$

$$pH = 5.3$$

Beyond the equivalence point, the pH is calculated from the concentration of HCl in the solution. With 0.05 ml of 0.1000 N HCl in excess,

$$[H_3O^+] = \frac{0.005\ \text{meq}}{100.05\ \text{ml}} = 5 \times 10^{-5}\ M$$

$$pH = 4.3$$

The curve for this titration is shown in Fig. 13.4a, and that for the titration of sodium acetate with HCl is given in Fig. 13.4b. It can be seen from the figures that while the titration of $NaBO_2$ is feasible, that of $NaC_2H_3O_2$ is not. The solution at the equivalence point in the latter case has a pH of 3.03. Therefore, considerably more than 0.05 ml of HCl would have to be added in order to lower the pH by an additional unit. Generally speaking, if the acid can be satisfactorily titrated, its salt cannot be.

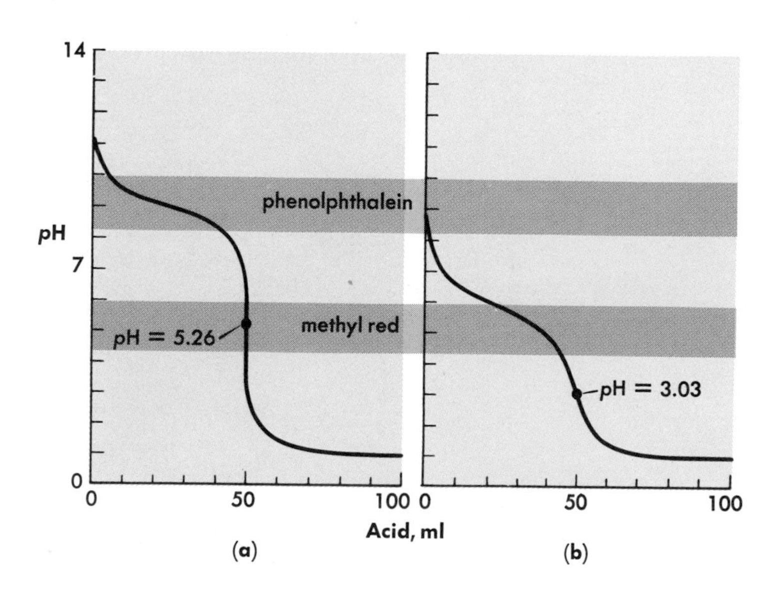

Fig. 13.4 Titration curves: (a) 0.1 N $NaBO_2$ — 0.1 N HCl; (b) 0.1 N $NaC_2H_3O_2$ — 0.1 N HCl.

13.16 Solubility Product and Precipitation

When a sparingly soluble salt such as silver chloride is placed in water, it dissolves until equilibrium is established between the resulting saturated solution of its ions and undissolved solid phase. The equilibrium condition is given by

$$AgCl(s) \rightleftharpoons Ag^+ + Cl^-$$

Since the concentration of a pure solid is constant (Sec. 12.7), the equilibrium expression in this case is

$$[Ag^+][Cl^-] = K_{sp}$$

The constant K_{sp} is known as the ***solubility product constant.*** The constancy of K_{sp} holds satisfactorily only for solutions of electrolytes at concentrations of 0.01 M or less. For saturated solutions at higher concentrations, the deviation from ideality as a result of interionic attraction becomes so great that the ion product is no longer even approximately constant.

In writing the solubility product expression for a salt yielding more than one ion of any single species in solution, the concentration of that ion is raised to a power equal to its coefficient in the equilibrium equation. For example,

$$Ag_2CrO_4 \rightleftharpoons 2\ Ag^+ + CrO_4^{--}$$

$$K_{sp} = [Ag^+]^2[CrO_4^{--}]$$

$$Al(OH)_3 \rightleftharpoons Al^{+++} + 3\ OH^-$$

$$K_{sp} = [Al^{+++}][OH^-]^3$$

The solubility product of a slightly soluble salt can be calculated as in the following example if its molar solubility in pure water is known.

Example 13.24

A saturated solution of BaF_2 at 25°C is 0.0065 M. Calculate K_{sp} for the salt.

Solution:

$$BaF_2 \rightleftharpoons Ba^{++} + 2\ F^-$$

$$[Ba^{++}][F^-]^2 = K_{sp}$$

Since a saturated solution of the completely ionized salt is $6.5 \times 10^{-3}\ M$, the concentration of Ba^{++} is $6.5 \times 10^{-3}\ M$ and that of the F^- is twice as much, i.e., $[F^-] = 1.3 \times 10^{-2}\ M$, because according to the equation for the solution process, two F^- ions are produced for every BaF_2 which dissolves. Substituting in the expression for the solubility product, we get

$$K_{sp} = (6.5 \times 10^{-3})(1.3 \times 10^{-2})^2$$
$$= 1.1 \times 10^{-6}$$

Because of the exceedingly small solubility of many electrolytes it is virtually impossible to measure their molar solubilities directly. However, the voltage of an electrochemical cell is related to the concentration of ions participating in the cell reaction. It is therefore possible, by measuring the voltage of a suitably chosen cell, to calculate the solubility and K_{sp} for a salt when they cannot be measured directly by any other means (Sec. 14.7). Solubility product constants of some sparingly soluble salts and ionic hydroxides frequently encountered in analytical chemistry are listed in Table 13.5.

TABLE 13.5 Solubility Product Constants (25°C)

Carbonates	K_{sp}	Sulfides	K_{sp}
$BaCO_3$	5.1×10^{-9}	CuS	8.7×10^{-36}
$CaCO_3$	7.2×10^{-9}	PbS	8.4×10^{-28}
$MgCO_3$	3.0×10^{-5}	CdS	7.0×10^{-27}
		HgS	8.6×10^{-52}
Chromates		CoS	5.0×10^{-22}
$PbCrO_4$	1.8×10^{-14}	NiS	1.8×10^{-21}
Ag_2CrO_4	1.3×10^{-12}	MnS	5.1×10^{-15}
Hydroxides		ZnS	1.1×10^{-21}
$Al(OH)_3$	2.0×10^{-32}		
$Cr(OH)_3$	8.0×10^{-31}	Halides	
$Fe(OH)_3$	3.0×10^{-38}	BaF_2	1.1×10^{-6}
$Mg(OH)_2$	1.1×10^{-11}	AgCl	1.8×10^{-10}
		AgBr	5.0×10^{-13}
Sulfates		AgI	9.8×10^{-17}
$BaSO_4$	1.0×10^{-10}	PbI_2	8.3×10^{-9}
$CaSO_4$	1.2×10^{-6}		
$PbSO_4$	1.7×10^{-8}		

Although a relationship exists between the solubility of a substance and its K_{sp}, the latter, being an equilibrium constant, is invariant at a given temperature, while the solubility of the substance depends upon whether it is the only solute present or is in the presence of some other electrolyte, especially one that is a source of a common ion. Once K_{sp} is provided for a compound, its solubility in pure water is readily calculated.

Example 13.25

Calculate the molar solubility of AgCl in pure water at 25°C.

Solution:

$$AgCl \rightleftharpoons Ag^+ + Cl^-$$

The salt is the only source of Ag^+ and Cl^-, and these must therefore be present in equal amounts. Let $x = [Ag^+] = [Cl^-]$. Then

$$[Ag^+][Cl^-] = K_{sp}$$

$$x^2 = 1.8 \times 10^{-10}$$

$$x = 1.3 \times 10^{-5}\ M$$

The molar solubility of AgCl is also $1.3 \times 10^{-5}\ M$, since 1 mole of AgCl produces 1 mole each of Ag^+ and Cl^- when dissolved.

Example 13.26

Calculate the molar solubility of Ag_2CrO_4 in pure water at 25°C.

Solution:

$$Ag_2CrO_4 \rightleftharpoons 2\ Ag^+ + CrO_4^{--}$$

The salt is the only source of Ag^+ and CrO_4^{--}; therefore, from the equation for the solution process, the concentration of Ag^+ must be twice that of CrO_4^{--}. Let $x = [CrO_4^{--}]$; $2x = [Ag^+]$, and

$$[Ag^+]^2[CrO_4^{--}] = K_{sp}$$

$$(2x)^2(x) = 1.3 \times 10^{-12}$$

$$[CrO_4^{--}] = x = 6.9 \times 10^{-5}$$

$$[Ag^+] = 2x = 1.4 \times 10^{-4}$$

The solubility of the salt Ag_2CrO_4 is equal to that of CrO_4^{--}: $6.9 \times 10^{-5}\ M$.

Because the product of the concentrations of the ions in a saturated solution is a constant, it follows that the addition of a salt that possesses an ion in common with one of the ions of the saturated solution places a stress on the equilibrium, and in order to maintain the equilibrium, the concentration of the other ion must decrease. Therefore, in the presence of a common ion, the solubility of a sparingly soluble electrolyte (measured from the concentration of the ions which it provides in solution) is less than its solubility in pure water.

Example 13.27

A 0.01 M solution of NaCl is saturated with AgCl. Calculate the solubility of AgCl in the solution.

Solution: Let x be the concentration of dissolved AgCl. Then $[Ag^+] = x$, and $[Cl^-] = 0.01 + x$. Substituting these values into the equilibrium constant expression for AgCl gives

$$(x)(0.01 + x) = 1.8 \times 10^{-10}$$

Neglecting the contribution of the AgCl to the concentration of the chloride ion, since x must be less than 1.3×10^{-5} (see Example 13.25), yields

$$0.01x = 1.8 \times 10^{-10}$$

$$x = 1.8 \times 10^{-8}\ M$$

In accord with Le Chatelier's principle, the solubility of AgCl is decreased by the presence of the common ion Cl^-.

The solubility product principle may be used to predict whether precipitation will or will not occur, given specified reagent concentrations. If, under a given set of conditions, the ion product of an electrolyte is smaller than its K_{sp}, its solution is unsaturated, no precipitate will form, and any precipitate present will dissolve until equilibrium is attained. If the ion product exceeds the value of K_{sp}, the solution is supersaturated, and precipitation will take place. When the ion product is equal to K_{sp}, the solution is saturated, and any precipitate present is in equilibrium with the solution.

Example 13.28

A solution is 0.1 M in $MgCl_2$ and 0.15 M in NH_3. Will $Mg(OH)_2$ precipitate?

Solution: The OH^- concentration in 0.15 M ammonia solution was calculated in Example 13.12 to be 1.6×10^{-3} M. $MgCl_2$ is completely ionized in solution; therefore $[Mg^{++}] = 0.1$ M.

$$Mg(OH)_2 \rightleftharpoons Mg^{++} + 2\ OH^-$$

$$[Mg^{++}][OH^-]^2 = (10^{-1})(1.6 \times 10^{-3})^2$$
$$= 2.6 \times 10^{-7}$$

The ion product, in this case 2.6×10^{-7}, is larger than K_{sp} for $Mg(OH)_2$, which is given in Table 13.5 as 1.1×10^{-11}. Therefore $Mg(OH)_2$ will precipitate from the solution.

Example 13.29

A solution is 0.1 M in $MgCl_2$, 0.15 M in NH_3, and 1.0 M in NH_4Cl. Will $Mg(OH)_2$ precipitate?

Solution: The solution is buffered.

$$[OH^-] = K_b \frac{[NH_3]}{[NH_4^+]} = 1.75 \times 10^{-5} \left(\frac{0.15}{1.0}\right)$$

$$[OH^-] = 2.6 \times 10^{-6}$$

$$[Mg^{++}][OH^-]^2 = (10^{-1})(2.6 \times 10^{-6})^2$$
$$= 6.9 \times 10^{-13}$$

This time the ion product, $6.9 \times 10^{-13} < 1.1 \times 10^{-11}$, and precipitation of $Mg(OH)_2$ will not occur.

Addition of aqueous ammonia to a solution containing Al^{+++}, Fe^{+++}, Cr^{+++}, and Mg^{++}, all at a concentration of about 0.1 M, will cause all four ions to precipitate as their hydroxides. In the presence of sufficient NH_4Cl, however, the concentration of OH^- is lowered, as in the previous example, to such an extent that $Mg(OH)_2$ does not precipitate, while the hydroxides of the other ions, with their much smaller K_{sp}'s, do separate from solution. This means of selective precipitation is used to separate Mg^{++} from the other three ions in the usual qualitative analytical scheme.

Reference to Table 13.5 will show that the K_{sp}'s for CuS, PbS, and HgS are all very much smaller than those for CoS, NiS, MnS, and ZnS. This difference in solubility is used to advantage in the separation of the copper-arsenic group of cations—

Hg^{++}, Pb^{++}, Bi^{+++}, Cu^{++}, Cd^{++}, As^{+++}, Sb^{+++}, and Sn^{++++}

all of whose sulfides have solubility product constants of 10^{-27} or less—from the nickel group—

$$Ni^{++}, \quad Co^{++}, \quad Mn^{++}, \quad \text{and } Zn^{++}$$

the sulfides of which have K_{sp}'s greater than 10^{-22}. If a solution containing any of these ions at a concentration about 0.1 M is made sufficiently acidic so that when saturated with H_2S the concentration of S^{--} is in the vicinity of 10^{-22} M, the K_{sp}'s of the copper-arsenic group sulfides will be exceeded, and these will precipitate while the nickel group will remain in solution.

As an example, consider the separation of Pb^{++} and Co^{++}, each at a concentration of 0.1 M, by controlled selective precipitation from an acidic solution saturated with H_2S. The applicable solubility product constants are

$$[Pb^{++}][S^{--}] = 8.4 \times 10^{-28}$$

$$[Co^{++}][S^{--}] = 5.0 \times 10^{-22}$$

In order to avoid precipitation of CoS, which is the least soluble of the nickel group sulfides, the S^{--} concentration must be less than

$$[S^{--}] = \frac{K_{sp}}{[Co^{++}]} = \frac{5.0 \times 10^{-22}}{10^{-1}} = 5.0 \times 10^{-21}\ M$$

In 0.3 M HCl, the concentration of S^{--} is given by

$$\frac{[H_3O^+]^2[S^{--}]}{[H_2S]} = 6 \times 10^{-22}$$

$$\frac{(3 \times 10^{-1})^2[S^{--}]}{(10^{-1})} = 6 \times 10^{-22}$$

$$[S^{--}] \approx 7 \times 10^{-22}\ M$$

Under these conditions neither CoS nor any other nickel group sulfides will precipitate. However, under the same conditions,

$$[Pb^{++}][S^{--}] = (10^{-1})(7 \times 10^{-22})$$

$$= 7 \times 10^{-23}$$

which is greater than 8.4×10^{-28}, and PbS precipitates. The concentration of Pb^{++} remaining in solution is

$$[Pb^{++}] = \frac{K_{sp}}{[S^{--}]}$$

$$= \frac{8.4 \times 10^{-28}}{7 \times 10^{-22}}$$

$$= 1.2 \times 10^{-6}$$

The precipitation is therefore essentially complete. Under these same conditions, all of the other still less soluble copper-arsenic group sulfides will also precipitate, and in this way the two groups of cations are effectively separated.

The Mohr method for the quantitative volumetric determination of chloride in solution depends upon the difference in solubilities of the two sparingly soluble salts $AgCl$ and Ag_2CrO_4. The chloride is precipitated as $AgCl$, with standardized $AgNO_3$ solution used as the precipitating agent. The indicator used is 0.002 M K_2CrO_4, and the equivalence point, or end point, is detected by the first appearance of an intensely red precipitate of Ag_2CrO_4.

The molar solubilities of $AgCl$ and Ag_2CrO_4 in pure water were calculated in Examples 13.25 and 13.26, and Ag_2CrO_4 was found to be several times more soluble than $AgCl$. The chloride therefore precipitates first during the analysis. In order for Ag_2CrO_4 to precipitate from a solution which is 0.002 M in CrO_4^{--}, the concentration of Ag^+ must be at least

$$[Ag^+] = \sqrt{\frac{K_{sp}}{[CrO_4^{--}]}}$$

$$= \sqrt{\frac{1.3 \times 10^{-12}}{2 \times 10^{-3}}}$$

$$= 2.6 \times 10^{-5}\ M$$

Substituting this value into the solubility product expression for $AgCl$ gives us as the concentration of Cl^- remaining in solution at the indicated end point,

$$[Cl^-] = \frac{K_{sp}}{[Ag^+]} = \frac{1.8 \times 10^{-10}}{2.6 \times 10^{-5}}$$

$$= 0.7 \times 10^{-5}$$

showing that precipitation of Cl^- is essentially complete by the time the red precipitate appears.

At the end point, the excess of Ag^+ over Cl^- is $(2.6 \times 10^{-5}) - (0.7 \times 10^{-5}) = 1.9 \times 10^{-5}$ mole/liter. This represents a titration error, since there should be no excess of Ag^+ over Cl^- at the equivalence point. If the volume at the end point is in the vicinity of 100 ml, and the titrant is 0.100 M $AgNO_3$, as is usual in the Mohr analysis, the titration error is the volume of 0.100 M $AgNO_3$ solution required to give an excess of 1.9×10^{-5} mole/l of Ag^+ in 100 ml of solution. That is,

$$(100\ \text{ml})(1.9 \times 10^{-5}\ \text{mole}) = 1.9 \times 10^{-3}\ \text{mmole}$$

of excess Ag^+. This corresponds to

$$\frac{1.9 \times 10^{-3}\ \text{mmole}}{0.100\ M} = 0.019\ \text{ml}$$

of 0.100 M $AgNO_3$ solution. The percentage error is the excess volume of titrant used divided by the total volume of the titrant. If the volume of

$AgNO_3$ used is about 50 ml the percentage error is about

$$\frac{0.019}{50} \times 100 = 0.04\%$$

which is negligibly small.

13.17 Reading Suggestions

Well worth reading at this point is Calvin Vander Werf's *Acids, Bases, and the Chemistry of the Covalent Bond* (Selected Topics in Modern Chemistry series, Reinhold Publishing Corp., New York, 1961). Written in a breezy style, this book is a thorough, but not overwhelming, presentation of the Brønsted-Lowry and Lewis concepts of acids and bases and their application to the study of chemical reactions. The book is concerned with the qualitative aspects of acid-base theory and is therefore completely nonmathematical. Another volume in the same Selected Topics series is *Chemistry in Non-Aqueous Solvents*, by Harry H. Sisler (Reinhold Publishing Corp., New York, 1961). Most chemists give very little thought to solvent systems other than water. Professor Sisler's book is a pleasant travel guide to a whole new world of interesting chemistry.

A brief history of *p*H is presented by Ferenc Szabadvary in an article, *Development of the pH Concept*, in *J. Chem. Ed.* **41,** 105 (1964). An interesting application of the Brønsted-Lowry concept to acid-base balance in respiration and kidney function is described by Arthur W. Devor in *J. Chem. Ed.* **31,** 425 (1954).

Questions and Problems

13.1 Hydrogen chloride in the gaseous or liquid state is a nonelectrolyte, yet in aqueous solution it is as strong an electrolyte as sodium chloride. Provide an explanation for this fact.

13.2 Provide an explanation for the equality of acidic strengths of equally concentrated solutions of aqueous $HClO_4$, H_2SO_4, and HCl solutions and for their different acid strengths when dissolved in glacial acetic acid.

13.3 Describe the acid-base behavior of ammonium chloride and sodium amide in liquid ammonia. Compare with the aqueous acid-base system.

13.4 What is meant by the words dibasic and diprotic as descriptive terms for acids?

13.5 What is meant by the terms Lewis acid and Lewis base? In what respect do these terms have any meanings that differ from the Brønsted-Lowry acid-base concept?

13.6 Provide an explanation for the fact that sulfur trioxide is a Lewis acid and show how it reacts with calcium oxide, a Lewis base, to yield the salt calcium sulfate.

13.7 Identify as Lewis or Brønsted-Lowry the acids and bases in each of the following reactions:

(a) $(BH_3)_2 + 2\ NH_3 \rightarrow 2\ H_3B{:}NH_3$

(b) $2\ Li^+H^- + (BH_3)_2 \rightarrow 2\ Li^+BH_4^-$

(c) $Li^+H^- + H_2O \rightarrow Li^+OH^- + H_2$

(d) $O^{--} + H_2O \rightarrow 2\ OH^-$

(e) $Br_2 + FeBr_3 \rightarrow Br^+ + FeBr_4^-$

13.8 What is meant by a neutralization reaction and heat of neutralization? Why is the heat (enthalpy) of neutralization a constant for the neutralization of strong acids by strong bases in aqueous solution?

13.9 What is meant by neutralization end-point? How can the end-point of a neutralization reaction be determined?

13.10 A 1.0 molal solution of NaCl freezes neither at −1.86°C nor at exactly −3.72°C. Why?

13.11 Why does a buffer solution resist change in hydrogen ion concentration?

13.12 Which of the acids listed in Table 13.2 taken along with its sodium salt would be the most suitable for utilization as a buffer with maximum buffering capacity at a *p*H of 3.7? What would be the ratio of the acid to the salt in this buffer solution?

13.13 Provide an explanation for the fact that an aqueous solution of ammonium acetate is neutral toward litmus while one of ammonium cyanide gives an alkaline reaction.

13.14 Explain why CuS can be precipitated from a solution containing Cu^{++} and Zn^{++} ions while ZnS cannot when the hydrogen ion concentration of the solution is 1.0 *M*.

13.15 Why are 2.0 ml of 0.1 *M* K_2CrO_4 added to the reaction flask in which an unknown chloride is analyzed by the Mohr method?

13.16 Why is the concentration of water omitted from the equilibrium constant expression for equilibria in which water is a reactant as well as the solvent?

13.17 Why is the normality of phosphoric acid three times its molarity in terms of its conversion to the normal salt while under titration conditions its normality is usually no more than twice its molarity?

13.18 At 0.01 *M* concentration a weak monoprotic acid dissociates to the extent of 0.1%. What is the K_a of this acid?

13.19 Calculate the (a) hydrogen ion concentration, (b) *p*H of a 0.01 *M* solution of acetic acid. (c) To what extent is 0.01 *M* acetic acid dissociated? Compare results with those given in examples 13.7 and 13.10. Are the results consistent with expectations?

13.20 Calculate the *p*H of (a) 0.1 *M* $Ba(OH)_2$ solution, (b) 0.1 *M* aqueous ammonia.

13.21 Calculate the sulfide ion concentration of saturated H_2S solutions whose total hydrogen ion concentrations have been adjusted to (a) 10^{-7} *M*, (b) 10^{-4} *M*, (c) 10^{-3} *M*, (d) 10^{-2} *M*, (e) 10^{-1} *M*, (f) 1.0 *M*.

13.22 Plot the results of problem 13.21 using $[H_3O^+]$ as ordinates, origin at 10^{-14}, and $[S^{-2}]$ as abscissas, with origin at 6×10^{-23}. On the same graph, plot $[H_3O^+]^2$ against $[S^{-2}]$. What relationship exists between the sulfide ion concentration of a saturated solution of H_2S and the hydrogen ion concentration of the solution?

13.23 (a) What is the *p*H of a solution that contains 1.20 g of acetic acid and 1.64 g of sodium acetate per 100 ml? (b) If 10 ml of 0.1 *N* HCl is added to the solution in (a), by how many *p*H units will the *p*H change?

13.24 A buffer solution with *p*H of 5.00 is to be prepared from acetic acid and sodium acetate. The sodium acetate must be 1 *M*. What should be the concentration of the acid?

13.25 (a) How many grams of sodium acetate must be added to 1.0 liter of 0.1 *N* acetic acid to give a solution whose $pH = 5$?

(b) If 1.0 ml of 10.0 *N* HCl is added to the above solution, what is the resulting pH?

(c) If 1.0 ml of 10.0 *N* HCl is added to 1.0 liter of water, what pH will result?

13.26 The K_{ind} of an indicator that is a weak monoprotic acid is 10^{-6}. What is the pH when the indicator is equally divided between its two colored forms?

13.27 An acid indicator of $K_{ind} = 10^{-9}$ is red in strongly acid solution and yellow in strongly basic solution. (a) What is the pH of a solution in which this indicator is 10% in its red form? (b) What color would the indicator show in a solution of pH 7?

13.28 The pH range for methyl orange color change is 3.1 to 4.4. (a) What is the hydrogen ion concentration of a solution in which methyl orange shows its intermediate color? (b) If the pH of this solution is due to the presence of acetic acid, what must its concentration be?

13.29 Fifty ml of 0.100 *N* acid HA ($K_a = 5 \times 10^{-6}$) is titrated with 0.100 *N* $NaOH$. (a) Calculate the pH when half of the acid has been neutralized. (b) Calculate the pH when 49.9 ml of base is added. (c) Calculate the pH at the equivalence point. (d) Calculate the pH when 50.1 ml of base is added. (e) What relationship exists between the pH as calculated in (a) and the pK_a of the acid? (f) Discuss the feasibility of the titration in terms of the above calculations.

13.30 Calculate the pH of a buffer solution made from equivalent concentrations of NaH_2PO_4 and Na_2HPO_4. The ionization constants for H_3PO_4 are $K_{a_1} = 7.5 \times 10^{-3}$, $K_{a_2} = 6.2 \times 10^{-8}$, $K_{a_3} = 4.8 \times 10^{-13}$.

13.31 In a liter of saturated solution of AgCl the concentrations of Ag^+ and Cl^- are each 1.3×10^{-5} *M*. What will be the concentration of Ag^+ when 0.05846 g of $NaCl$ (mol. wt. = 58.46) is added?

13.32 The solubility of PbI_2 (molecular weight = 461) is 0.059 g/100 ml. Calculate the K_{sp} for PbI_2.

13.33 The solubility of $BaCO_3$ is 7.1×10^{-5} moles per liter. Calculate its K_{sp}. Calculate the CO_3^{--} ion concentration that will result upon the addition of 2.08 g of $BaCl_2$ (molecular weight = 208) to 1 liter of saturated solution of $BaCO_3$.

13.34 To a solution which is 0.01 *M* in chloride ion and 0.001 *M* in bromide ion, 0.01 *M* silver nitrate solution is added drop by drop. Determine which silver salt will precipitate first.

13.35 A 0.3 *M* HCl solution, 0.01 *M* in Pb^{++} ion and 0.01 *M* in Ni^{++} ion, is saturated with H_2S (0.1 *M*) at room temperature. (a) Calculate the sulfide ion concentration in the solution. (b) Will PbS precipitate? (c) Will NiS precipitate?

13.36 Calculate (a) the hydrogen ion concentration, (b) the sulfide ion concentration of a saturated (0.1 *M*) solution of H_2S at 25°C. (c) If 1.3 g of $NiCl_2$ is added to 100 ml of solution that is kept saturated in H_2S by continuous passage of H_2S gas through the solution, will NiS precipitate? (d) Write the equation for the precipitation of $NiCl_2$ by H_2S. (e) What happens to the hydrogen ion concentration of the solution as precipitation occurs? (f) What effect does this change in H_3O^+ concentration have on the solubility of NiS? (g) In what direction must the *p*H of the solution be changed in order to obtain essentially complete precipitation of NiS?

Ans. (a) 7.7×10^{-5}, (b) 1×10^{-14}, (c) yes, (e) $[H^+]$ increases, (f) solubility increases, (g) to higher *p*H value

13.37 Hydrogen sulfide is added to separate 0.01 *M* solutions of the following ions: (a) Hg^{++}, (b) Cu^{++}, (c) Pb^{++}, (d) Ni^{++}, (e) Mn^{++}. What is the sulfide ion concentration when precipitation begins in each case? (f) If a solution 0.01 *M* each in Hg^{++}, Cu^{++}, Pb^{++}, Ni^{++}, and Mn^{++} is saturated with H_2S, which if any of the ions will remain unprecipitated? To what level of H_3O^+ concentration must the saturated solution of H_2S be adjusted to just prevent the precipitation of (g) 0.01 *M* Ni^{++}, (h) 0.01 *M* Pb^{++}?

Ans. (a) 8.6×10^{-50} (b) 8.7×10^{-34} (c) 8.4×10^{-26}
(d) 1.8×10^{-19} (e) 5.1×10^{-13} (f) MnS
(g) 1.8×10^{-2} (h) 710, an impossible condition

13.38 A solution contains 0.09 moles/liter of pandemonium nitrate ($Pn(NO_3)_2$; mol. wt. 209) and 0.04 moles/liter of delerium nitrate ($DeNO_3$; mol. wt. 129). A chemist wishes to separate the ions by using H_2S to precipitate one metal as the sulfide without precipitating the other. Within what range (maximum and minimum) should he adjust the *p*H of the solution? Which metal will precipitate? At room temperature, a saturated solution contains 0.0003 g of pandemonium sulfide per liter. A saturated solution of delerium sulfide contains 0.000052 g of the sulfide per liter.

Ans. *p*H range 2.75 to 6.05 for precipitation of delerium

13.39 Enough water was added to 5.85 g of NaCl and 0.194 g K_2CrO_4 to make 1 liter of solution. Into 100 ml of this solution solid $AgNO_3$ was added. (a) Calculate the concentration of Ag^+ necessary to start the precipitation of Ag_2CrO_4. (b) Calculate the concentration of Ag^+ necessary to start the precipitation of AgCl. (c) What is the composition of the permanent first precipitate formed? (d) What fraction of the Cl^- ion originally present before the addition of the $AgNO_3$ remains in solution as the Ag_2CrO_4 just begins to precipitate?

Ans. (a) 3.6×10^{-5}, (b) 1.8×10^{-9}, (c) AgCl, (d) 0.005%

Chemical affinity and electricity
are one and the same.

——Michael Faraday, 1833

14 ELECTROCHEMISTRY

We saw in Chapter 5 that a redox reaction involves the transfer of electrons from the substance being oxidized to the one being reduced. If the redox process is carried out in such a way that the reactants do not come into direct contact with one another, it is possible to cause the electrons being transferred to flow through an external circuit where they can be made to perform work. A device for accomplishing this is called an ***electrochemical cell.*** The amount of work obtainable from the cell is determined by the quantity of electricity flowing and the potential difference across the external circuit. This is determined by the cell voltage, which is closely related to the free energy change for the reaction process.

The Zinc-Copper Cell 14.1

If a strip of zinc is immersed in a solution of Cu^{++} ions, copper immediately begins to deposit on the zinc, and an equivalent amount of zinc dissolves. All the energy liberated as a result of the reaction appears in the form of heat. The overall reaction

$$Zn + Cu^{++} \rightarrow Zn^{++} + Cu$$

is the sum of two processes, one an *oxidation,*

$$Zn \rightarrow Zn^{++} + 2\ e^-$$

and the other a *reduction:*

$$Cu^{++} + 2\ e^- \rightarrow Cu$$

If the respective reactants (Zn, Zn^{++}) and (Cu, Cu^{++}) are separated so that the oxidizing agent (Cu^{++}) and reducing agent (Zn) are not in direct contact, electrons can be transferred from one to the other through a wire. At least a part of the total reaction energy in this case will be in the form of electrical energy.

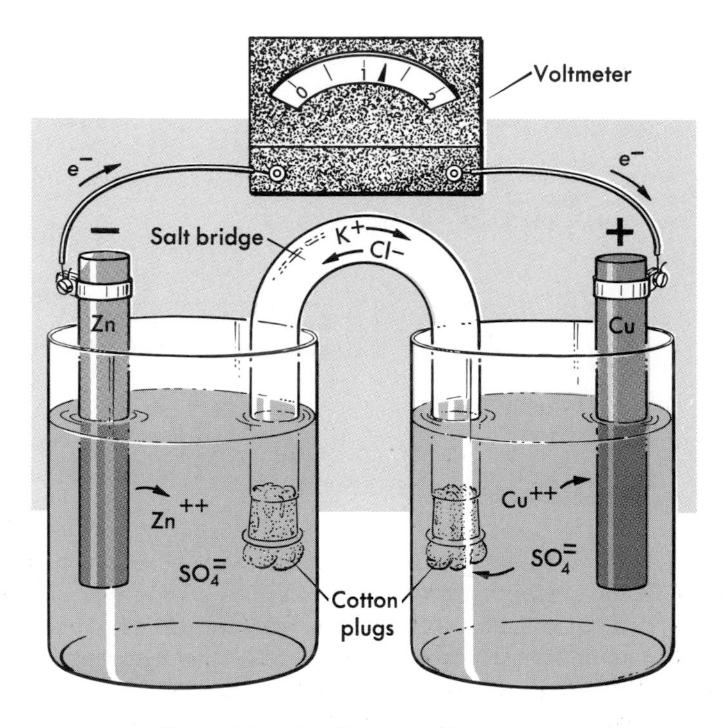

Fig. 14.1 Zn-Cu electrolytic cell.

A typical electrochemical cell making use of this reaction is shown in Fig. 14.1. The complete cell consists of two *half-cells*. Each half-cell consists of a piece of metal dipping into a solution of its ions. A salt bridge permits the flow of ions from one half-cell compartment to the other when the cell is in operation. A voltmeter placed in the external circuit measures the electromotive force (emf) of the cell. Even before the zinc and copper electrodes are connected in the circuit, a few of the atoms at the surface of each enter solution as hydrated cations. The electrons which they leave behind accumulate on the electrodes and give each of them a slight negative charge. Ions from the solution are attracted by the negative charge, and equilibrium is quickly established:

$$Zn \rightleftharpoons Zn^{++} + 2\ e^-$$

$$Cu \rightleftharpoons Cu^{++} + 2\ e^-$$

With the same concentration of electrolyte in each half-cell, the first of these equilibria lies further to the right. That is, zinc loses electrons more readily—is more easily oxidized—than copper. There is therefore a greater accumulation of electrons on the zinc than on the copper, and a potential difference exists between the electrodes as a result. When the electrodes are connected, electrons flow from the region of high potential (the Zn electrode) to that of low potential (the Cu electrode) through the external circuit. The Zn, Zn^{++} equilibrium is displaced toward the right (oxidation), and the Cu, Cu^{++} equilibrium toward the left (reduction). The circuit is completed by a flow of ions within the cell.

As Cu^{++} ions migrate toward and are discharged at the copper electrode, they are replaced by K^+ ions from the salt bridge, and these in turn by Zn^{++} ions from the other half-cell compartment. More Zn^{++} ions are supplied by the zinc electrode, which is continuously eaten away. The anions Cl^- (from the salt bridge) and SO_4^{--} migrate in the opposite direction, toward the zinc half-cell. Oxidation takes place at the zinc electrode, which is therefore the *anode*. It is also considered the negative pole of the cell, because electrons flow from it into the external circuit. The copper electrode, at which reduction occurs, is the *cathode*, and also the positive pole of the cell.

The overall cell reaction

$$Zn + Cu^{++} \rightleftharpoons Zn^{++} + Cu$$

is reversible and tends toward equilibrium. The equilibrium expression for this reaction is

$$K = \frac{[Zn^{++}]}{[Cu^{++}]}$$

From this it can be seen that the greater the concentration of Cu^{++} and the smaller that of Zn^{++}, the further away from equilibrium the cell will be and the greater will be the driving force behind the forward reaction. Since it is this which determines the emf of the cell, the cell voltage will be greatest when $[Zn^{++}]/[Cu^{++}]$ is at a minimum. During the operation of the cell, the concentration of Zn^{++} increases, that of Cu^{++} decreases, and the voltage accordingly drops, reaching zero at equilibrium. With pure zinc immersed in a 1 M solution of Zn^{++}, and pure copper in 1 M Cu^{++} at 25°C, the maximum emf produced by this particular cell, measured as described below, is 1.10 volts.

Free Energy and Cell Potential 14.2

The maximum potential difference between the electrodes of a cell is measured under conditions such that no current is actually flowing in the circuit. When current is flowing, part of the energy of the cell reaction, instead of appearing as electrical energy, is used to overcome the electrical resistance of the circuit, and the emf measured is less than the maximum. The maximum emf can be measured by connecting the cell in opposition to a potentiometer, a device which supplies a known emf that can be varied at

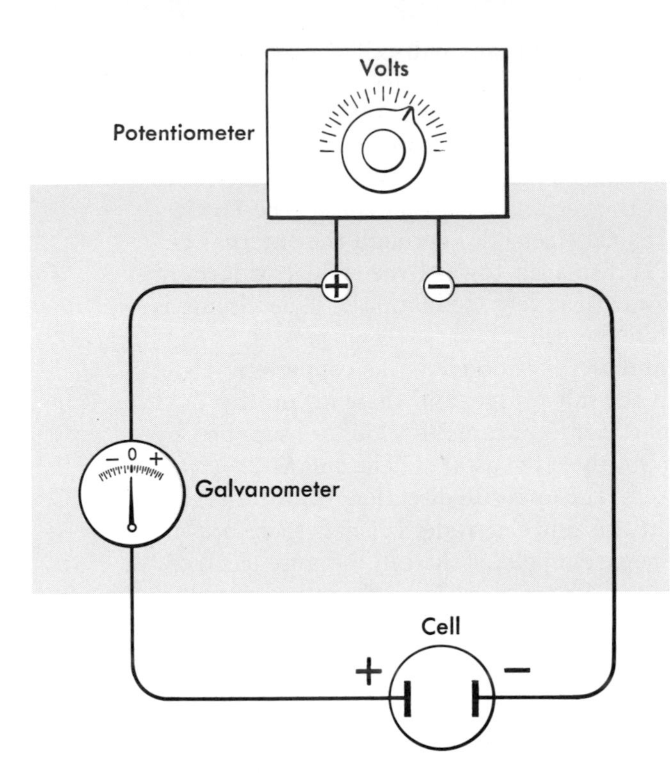

Fig. 14.2 Measuring cell emf with a potentiometer.

will. The experimental arrangement is shown diagrammatically in Fig. 14.2. The potentiometer voltage is adjusted until the galvanometer shows no deflection, indicating that no current is flowing in the circuit. At this point, the two opposing emf's are equal, and the voltage appearing on the potentiometer dial is the same as the maximum emf of the cell. The cell is operating under ***reversible conditions*** (Sec. 11.7), since the cell reaction can be caused to go in either the forward or reverse direction by an infinitesimal change in the opposing emf, and its capacity to perform work is therefore at a maximum.

A charge moving through a potential difference performs an amount of work equal to the magnitude of the charge in coulombs multiplied by the potential difference in volts. For one mole of reaction taking place in an electrochemical cell, the work done is

$$w = n\mathfrak{F}\mathcal{E}$$

where n is the number of moles of electrons transferred per mole of reaction, $\mathfrak{F}$ is the faraday, 96,500 coulombs/mole, and $\mathcal{E}$ is the cell potential. If the cell is operated reversibly, $\mathcal{E}$ is the maximum emf, and w is the maximum useful work that the cell can perform. Work of expansion, if any, is not included in w.

A system can perform work only if the process taking place is spontaneous, that is, only at the expense of the free energy of the system (Sec. 11.6). The free energy change is given by

$$\Delta G = \Delta H - T\Delta S$$

For an open system, such as an electrochemical cell, operating at constant pressure,

$$\Delta H = \Delta E + p\Delta V$$

Substituting for ΔE the quantity $(q - w)$ from the first law of thermodynamics (Sec. 11.1) gives

$$\Delta H = q - w + p\Delta V$$

and

$$\Delta G = q - w + p\Delta V - T\Delta S$$

If the system is one which is operating reversibly,

$$\Delta G = q_r - w_r + p\Delta V - T\Delta S$$

Since $\Delta S = q_r/T$ (Sec. 11.7),

$$\Delta G = -w_r + p\Delta V$$

$$-\Delta G = w_r - p\Delta V$$

The quantity $(w_r - p\Delta V)$ is equal to the total reversible work less any work of expansion of the system and corresponds to the maximum capacity of the system for useful work. For an electrical cell operating reversibly, it was shown above that

$$w_{\text{max}} = n\mathfrak{F}\mathcal{E}$$

and therefore,

$$\Delta G = -n\mathfrak{F}\mathcal{E}$$

This relationship affords us the simplest and most direct way of measuring ΔG for any reaction that can be arranged as an electrochemical cell.

Example 14.1

The emf of the Zn, 1.0 *M* Zn^{++}:1.0 *M* Cu^{++}, Cu electrochemical cell, measured at 25°C under conditions of zero current flow, is 1.10 volts. Calculate ΔG for the cell reaction under these conditions.

Solution:

$$\Delta G = -n\mathfrak{F}\mathcal{E}$$

$$= -(2)(96{,}500 \text{ coulombs})(1.10 \text{ volts})$$

$$= -212{,}000 \text{ volt-coulombs}$$

Since 1 volt-coulomb = 1 joule = 0.239 cal,

$$\Delta G = (-212{,}000 \text{ joules})(0.239 \text{ cal/joule})$$

$$= -50{,}700 \text{ cal}$$

$$= -50.7 \text{ kcal/mole of reaction}$$

Standard Electrode Potentials 14.3

The total free energy change for the cell reaction

$$Zn + Cu^{++} \rightarrow Zn^{++} + Cu$$

is the difference between the free energy changes for the two oxidation half reactions:

$$(1) \qquad \mathrm{Zn} \rightarrow \mathrm{Zn}^{++} + 2\ \mathrm{e}^-$$

$$(2) \qquad \mathrm{Cu} \rightarrow \mathrm{Cu}^{++} + 2\ \mathrm{e}^-$$

$$\Delta G_{\text{cell}} = \Delta G_1 - \Delta G_2$$

Since $\Delta G = -n\mathfrak{F}\mathcal{E}$,

$$\begin{aligned} -n\mathfrak{F}\mathcal{E}_{\text{cell}} &= -n\mathfrak{F}\mathcal{E}_1 - (-n\mathfrak{F}\mathcal{E}_2) \\ &= -n\mathfrak{F}\mathcal{E}_1 + n\mathfrak{F}\mathcal{E}_2 \\ &= -n\mathfrak{F}(\mathcal{E}_1 - \mathcal{E}_2) \end{aligned}$$

and

$$\mathcal{E}_{\text{cell}} = \mathcal{E}_1 - \mathcal{E}_2$$

where $\mathcal{E}_1$ and $\mathcal{E}_2$ correspond to the ***electrode potentials,*** that is, the individual contributions of each of the half-cells to the total emf of the cell.

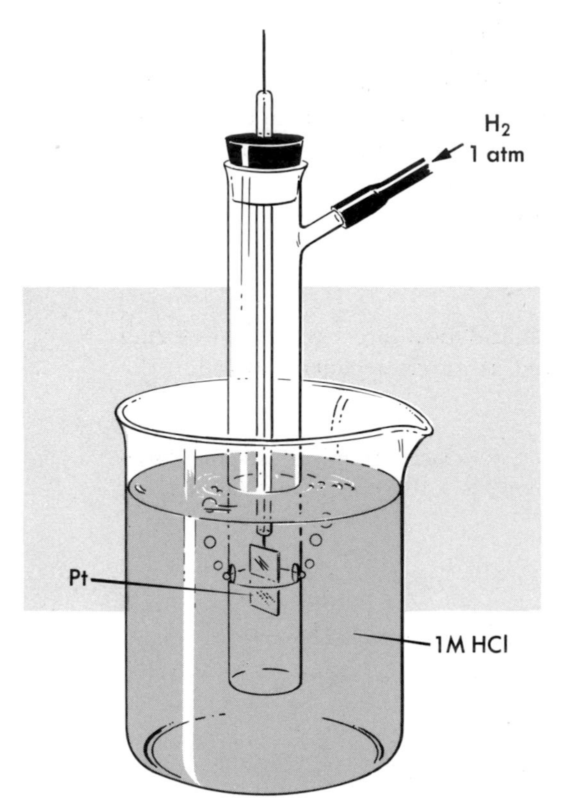

Fig. 14.3 Hydrogen electrode.

There is no way to measure the potential of half a cell directly. It is possible, however, to choose a particular half-cell as a reference standard and assign to it an arbitrary electrode potential. A cell can then be constructed from the reference standard and some other half-cell for which the electrode potential is to be determined. The relative electrode potential of that half-cell is then equal to the difference between the assigned reference potential and the measured emf of the cell. The reference standard chosen is the H_2, H_3O^+ half-cell, or *hydrogen electrode* (Fig. 14.3). The standard hydrogen electrode consists of a strip of platinum foil upon which finely divided platinum black has been deposited by electrolysis. The platinized platinum is immersed in an acid solution with an effective H_3O^+ ion concentration of 1 mole/liter, while at the same time it is kept in contact with and saturated by hydrogen gas supplied at a pressure of 1 atm. At 25°C the standard hydrogen electrode is arbitrarily assigned a potential of 0.00 volt. The half-cell reaction at the hydrogen electrode is

$$H_2 + 2\,H_2O \rightleftharpoons 2\,H_3O^+ + 2\,e^-$$

If a Zn, 1.0 *M* Zn^{++} half-cell is coupled to a standard hydrogen electrode, electrons flow from the zinc, which is therefore the negative pole, to the hydrogen electrode. The reaction

$$Zn + 2\,H_3O^+ \rightarrow Zn^{++} + H_2 + 2\,H_2O$$

is therefore spontaneous (ΔG negative, $\mathcal{E}$ positive) as written. As before,

$$\mathcal{E}_{cell} = \mathcal{E}_1 - \mathcal{E}_2$$

where $\mathcal{E}_1$ is the electrode potential for the half-cell in which oxidation takes place (this is always the half-cell containing the negative electrode—the zinc electrode in the present case). The electrode potential for the other half-cell, in which reduction is occurring, is $\mathcal{E}_2$. The measured cell potential is found to be 0.76 volt. Thus,

$$0.76 = \mathcal{E}_1 - 0.00$$

$$\mathcal{E}_1 = 0.76 \text{ volt}$$

This value, 0.76 volt, is the ***standard electrode potential**** $\mathcal{E}^0$ for the Zn, Zn^{++} half-cell.

The standard Cu, Cu^{++} electrode potential is determined in the same way by coupling a Cu, 1.0 *M* Cu^{++} half-cell to the standard hydrogen electrode. This time, electrons flow through the circuit from hydrogen to copper, which means that the reaction

$$H_2 + 2\,H_2O + Cu^{++} \rightarrow 2\,H_3O^+ + Cu$$

is spontaneous. The hydrogen electrode is negative in this case, and its half-cell potential is therefore $\mathcal{E}_1$. The copper electrode is positive, and its potential is accordingly subtracted from that of the hydrogen electrode to give the cell potential. The measured cell potential is 0.34 volt. Thus,

$$0.34 = 0.00 - \mathcal{E}_2$$

$$\mathcal{E}_2 = -0.34 \text{ volt}$$

which is the standard electrode potential for the Cu, Cu^{++} half-cell.

To summarize,

Reaction	$\mathcal{E}^0$ (volts)
$Zn \rightleftharpoons Zn^{++} + 2\,e^-$	0.76
$H_2 + 2\,H_2O \rightleftharpoons 2\,H_3O^+ + 2\,e^-$	0.00
$Cu \rightleftharpoons Cu^{++} + 2\,e^-$	−0.34

* Also known as the ***standard oxidation potential.***

Now let us use these standard electrode potentials to calculate the emf of the standard zinc-copper cell discussed in Sec. 14.1. *The electrode for which $\mathcal{E}$ is more negative (or less positive) is always the positive electrode of the cell, and its potential is always subtracted from that of the other electrode to obtain the cell potential.* Therefore, for the zinc-copper standard cell,

$$\begin{aligned}\mathcal{E}_{\text{cell}} &= 0.76 - (-0.34)\\ &= 1.10 \text{ volts}\end{aligned}$$

Standard electrode potentials for other half-cells are measured in similar manner. Since cell potentials vary with concentration and temperature, values of $\mathcal{E}^0$ are measured with all reactants at unit activity at 25°C. In practice, unit activity is taken as

(a) 1 *M* solution for all soluble reactants*
(b) Saturated solution for sparingly soluble reactants
(c) Gaseous reactants under constant pressure of 1 atm. Standard electrode potentials for a number of common half-cell reactions are given in Table 14.1.

Example 14.2

The common lead storage cell uses electrodes of **Pb** and **PbO_2** immersed in an electrolyte of dilute **H_2SO_4**. From the data in Table 14.1, determine (a) the standard cell potential at 25°C; (b) the net cell reaction; and (c) ΔG^0 for the net reaction.

Solution: After locating the electrodes in the first column of the table, we find the corresponding half-cell reactions and $\mathcal{E}^0$'s in the other two columns. These are:

		$\mathcal{E}^0$
(1)	$Pb(s) + SO_4^{--} \rightleftharpoons PbSO_4(s) + 2\ e^-$	0.35 volt
(2)	$PbSO_4(s) + 6\ H_2O \rightleftharpoons PbO_2(s) + 4\ H_3O^+ + SO_4^{--} + 2\ e^-$	−1.69 volts

The **$PbSO_4$**, **PbO_2** electrode; since it has the more negative $\mathcal{E}^0$, is the positive electrode of the cell. The cell potential is obtained by subtracting the $\mathcal{E}^0$ of the positive electrode from that of the negative electrode:

$$\begin{aligned}\mathcal{E}^0_{\text{cell}} &= \mathcal{E}^0_1 - \mathcal{E}^0_2\\ &= 0.35 - (-1.69)\\ &= 2.04 \text{ volts}\end{aligned}$$

Reduction takes place at the positive electrode; therefore, as the cell operates, reaction (1) proceeds in the forward direction as written; reaction (2) in the reverse direction:

(1) $Pb(s) + SO_4^{--} \rightarrow PbSO_4(s) + 2\ e^-$

(2) $2\ e^- + PbO_2(s) + 4\ H_3O^+ + SO_4^{--} \rightarrow PbSO_4(s) + 6\ H_2O$

Adding the two half-cell reactions gives the net cell reaction:

$$Pb(s) + PbO_2(s) + 4\ H_3O^+ + 2\ SO_4^{--} \rightarrow 2\ PbSO_4(s) + 6\ H_2O$$

* For nonideal solutions and solutions of electrolytes, this is an ***effective concentration*** of 1 *M*, taking into account necessary corrections for molecular and ionic interactions.

The standard free energy change for the cell reaction is calculated as follows:

$$\begin{aligned}\Delta G^0 &= -n\mathcal{F}\mathcal{E}^0 \\ &= -(2)(96{,}500 \text{ coulombs})(2.04 \text{ volts}) \\ &= -(394{,}000 \text{ joules})(0.239 \text{ cal/joule}) = -94{,}200 \text{ cal} \\ &= -94.2 \text{ kcal/mole of reaction}\end{aligned}$$

TABLE 14.1 Standard Electrode Potentials at 25°C

Electrode	Half-cell Reaction	$\mathcal{E}^0$ (volts)
$Li \mid Li^+$	$Li(s) \rightleftharpoons Li^+ + e^-$	3.05
$K \mid K^+$	$K(s) \rightleftharpoons K^+ + e^-$	2.92
$Ca \mid Ca^{++}$	$Ca(s) \rightleftharpoons Ca^{++} + 2\ e^-$	2.87
$Na \mid Na^+$	$Na(s) \rightleftharpoons Na^+ + e^-$	2.71
$Mg \mid Mg^{++}$	$Mg(s) \rightleftharpoons Mg^{++} + 2\ e^-$	2.37
$Al \mid Al^{+++}$	$Al(s) \rightleftharpoons Al^{+++} + 3\ e^-$	1.66
$Zn \mid Zn^{++}$	$Zn(s) \rightleftharpoons Zn^{++} + 2\ e^-$	0.76
$Fe \mid Fe^{++}$	$Fe(s) \rightleftharpoons Fe^{++} + 2\ e^-$	0.44
$Pb \mid PbSO_4(s), SO_4^{--}$	$Pb(s) + SO_4^{--} \rightleftharpoons PbSO_4(s) + 2\ e^-$	0.35
$Sn \mid Sn^{++}$	$Sn(s) \rightleftharpoons Sn^{++} + 2\ e^-$	0.14
$Pb \mid Pb^{++}$	$Pb(s) \rightleftharpoons Pb^{++} + 2\ e^-$	0.13
$H_2 \mid H_3O^+$	$H_2(g) + 2\ H_2O \rightleftharpoons 2\ H_3O^+ + 2\ e^-$	0.00
$Pt \mid Sn^{++}, Sn^{++++}$	$Sn^{++} \rightleftharpoons Sn^{++++} + 2\ e^-$	−0.14
$Ag \mid AgCl(s), Cl^-$	$Ag(s) + Cl^- \rightleftharpoons AgCl(s) + e^-$	−0.22
$Hg \mid Hg_2Cl_2(s), Cl^-$	$2\ Hg(l) + 2\ Cl^- \rightleftharpoons Hg_2Cl_2(s) + 2\ e^-$	−0.26
$Cu \mid Cu^{++}$	$Cu(s) \rightleftharpoons Cu^{++} + 2\ e^-$	−0.34
$I_2 \mid I^-$	$2\ I^- \rightleftharpoons I_2(s) + 2\ e^-$	−0.54
$Pt \mid Fe^{++}, Fe^{+++}$	$Fe^{++} \rightleftharpoons Fe^{+++} + e^-$	−0.77
$Ag \mid Ag^+$	$Ag(s) \rightleftharpoons Ag^+ + e^-$	−0.80
$NO \mid NO_3^-$	$NO(g) + 6\ H_2O \rightleftharpoons NO_3^- + 4\ H_3O^+ + 3\ e^-$	−0.96
$Br_2 \mid Br^-$	$2\ Br^- \rightleftharpoons Br_2(l) + 2\ e^-$	−1.07
$O_2 \mid H_2O$	$6\ H_2O \rightleftharpoons O_2 + 4\ H_3O^+ + 4\ e^-$	−1.23
$Cl_2 \mid Cl^-$	$2\ Cl^- \rightleftharpoons Cl_2(g) + 2\ e^-$	−1.36
$Pt \mid Ce^{+++}, Ce^{++++}$	$Ce^{+++} \rightleftharpoons Ce^{++++} + e^-$	−1.61
$PbSO_4(s) \mid PbO_2(s), SO_4^{--}$	$PbSO_4(s) + 6\ H_2O \rightleftharpoons PbO_2(s) + 4\ H_3O^+ + SO_4^{--} + 2\ e^-$	−1.69
$F_2 \mid 2\ F^-$	$2\ F^- \rightleftharpoons F_2(g) + 2\ e^-$	−2.87

Example 14.3

Copper dissolves in dilute HNO_3, forming Cu^{++} and NO. Calculate ΔG^0 for the net reaction.

Solution: From Table 14.1,

		$\mathcal{E}^0$
(1)	$Cu \rightleftharpoons Cu^{++} + 2\ e^-$	−0.34 volt
(2)	$NO + 6\ H_2O \rightleftharpoons NO_3^- + 4\ H_3O^+ + 3\ e^-$	−0.96 volt

Subtracting the more negative $\mathcal{E}^0$ from the less negative one gives

$$\mathcal{E}^0_{cell} = -0.34 - (-0.96)$$
$$= 0.62 \text{ volt}$$

To calculate ΔG^0 it is necessary to know the number of electrons transferred in the reaction. For this we need to know the overall balanced equation. The two half-reactions are:

Oxidation: $Cu \rightarrow Cu^{++} + 2\ e^-$

Reduction: $3\ e^- + NO_3^- + 4\ H_3O^+ \rightarrow NO + 6\ H_2O$

To balance the electrons lost in the oxidation against electrons gained in the reduction the first equation is multiplied by 3 and the second by 2:

$$3\ Cu \rightarrow 3\ Cu^{++} + 6\ e^-$$
$$6\ e^- + 2\ NO_3^- + 8\ H_3O^+ \rightarrow 2\ NO + 12\ H_2O$$

The overall reaction is

$$3\ Cu + 2\ NO_3^- + 8\ H_3O^+ \rightleftharpoons 3\ Cu^{++} + 2\ NO + 12\ H_2O$$

Six electrons are transferred, hence $n = 6$:

$$\Delta G^0 = -n\mathcal{F}\mathcal{E}^0$$
$$= -(6)(96{,}500 \text{ coulombs})(0.62 \text{ volt})(0.239 \text{ cal/joule})$$
$$= -89{,}400 \text{ cal}$$
$$= -89.4 \text{ kcal}$$

ΔG^0 per mole of Cu oxidized is one-third of this, or -29.8 kcal.

14.4 The Calomel Reference Electrode

The standard hydrogen electrode is inconvenient to operate and not readily portable because it requires a constant supply of hydrogen gas. Furthermore, after a short period of operation, the H_3O^+ concentration in the electrolyte will have changed sufficiently so that the electrode will no longer be at its standard potential. To avoid these difficulties, the ***calomel electrode*** is often used as a reference standard in the laboratory. This electrode consists of a platinum wire dipping into a reservoir of mercury metal. The mercury is in contact with a solution saturated with respect to both Hg_2Cl_2 (calomel) and KCl, each salt also being present in excess in the undissolved state. One form of calomel electrode is shown in Fig. 14.4. A KCl salt bridge is an integral part of its construction.

The half-cell reaction in the calomel electrode is

$$2\ Hg(l) + 2\ Cl^- \rightleftharpoons Hg_2Cl_2(s) + 2\ e^-$$

The activities of all species present remain unchanged when the electrode

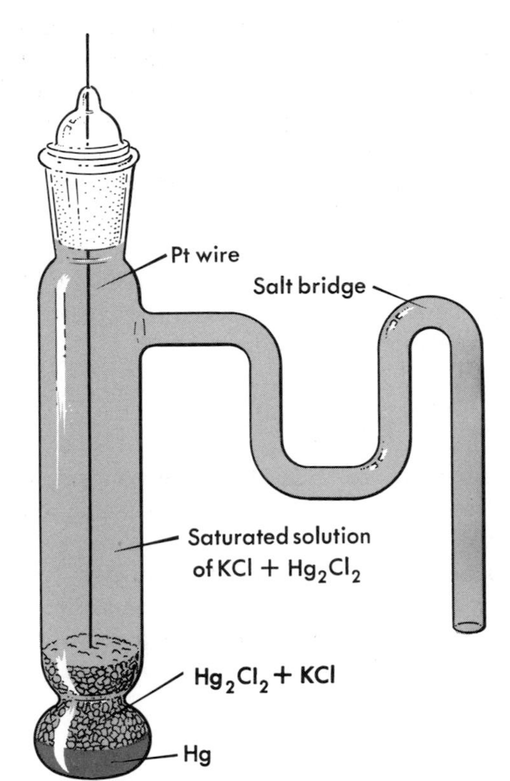

Fig. 14.4 Calomel electrode.

is in use. When it is operating as the negative electrode of a cell, any Cl^- consumed is replenished from the excess undissolved **KCl** with K^+ ions migrating out of the electrode compartment through the salt bridge, and the Hg_2Cl_2 precipitates as it is formed. When the half-cell is operating as the positive electrode, the Hg_2Cl_2 is replenished from the excess solid which is present, the **Hg** formed is added to the reservoir of metal and Cl^- precipitates as **KCl**, keeping the solution saturated and the concentration unchanged. The saturated calomel electrode has a potential of −0.26 volt at 25°C, relative to the standard hydrogen electrode.

Two other calomel electrodes find extensive use. The first uses 1.0 *M* **KCl** solution rather than a saturated solution and operates at a potential of −0.28 volt. The other employs 0.1 *M* **KCl** and has a potential of −0.33 volt. Besides the calomel electrodes, a large number of standardized reference electrodes of various designs and chemical compositions are commercially available for the chemist to choose from.

Effect of Concentration on Electrode Potentials 14.5

Le Chatelier's principle will lead us to conclude that the oxidation of zinc

$$Zn \rightleftharpoons Zn^{++} + 2\ e^-$$

will tend to be favored by a decrease in the concentration of Zn^{++}. This should be reflected (1) by a change in ΔG^0, which should become more negative as the oxidation becomes more spontaneous with increasing dilution, and (2) by an increase in the electrode potential. A difference in potential should therefore exist between two **Zn**, Zn^{++} half-cells which differ in their respective Zn^{++} ion concentrations. Two such half-cells may be coupled, forming a ***concentration cell.*** In a concentration cell, the current flow is from the more dilute half-cell toward the more concentrated one, which is therefore the positive electrode. The greater the difference in concentration, the greater the emf of the cell.

If we prepare a number of **Zn**, Zn^{++} concentration cells and measure their respective emf's, we will find that the cell potential in each case is proportional to the logarithm of the concentration ratio:

$$\mathcal{E} = k \log \frac{C_A}{C_B}$$

where C_A is the molar concentration* of Zn^{++} in the more concentrated half-cell, and C_B is the concentration of Zn^{++} in the more dilute one, and k has a value of approximately 0.030 volt.

Exactly the same relationship between concentration ratio and emf is found for any concentration cell where the half-cells consist of a metal in contact with a solution of its ions. The value of k depends in a very simple way upon the number of electrons transferred in the cell reaction. At 25°C,

$$k = 0.059/n$$

and

$$\mathcal{E}_{\text{cell}} = \frac{0.059}{n} \log \frac{C_A}{C_B}$$

If the more concentrated half-cell is a standard electrode, $C_A = 1$, and $C_B = C$. Then,

$$\mathcal{E}_{\text{cell}} = \frac{0.059}{n} \log \frac{1}{C}$$

and since the standard electrode is the more positive electrode of this particular cell:

$$\mathcal{E}_{\text{cell}} = \mathcal{E} - \mathcal{E}^0$$

Equating these two expressions for $\mathcal{E}_{\text{cell}}$, we obtain

$$\mathcal{E} - \mathcal{E}^0 = \frac{0.059}{n} \log \frac{1}{C}$$

and

$$\mathcal{E} = \mathcal{E}^0 - \frac{0.059}{n} \log C$$

This expression can be used to calculate the electrode potential of a half-cell when the electrolyte concentration is other than 1 M.

Example 14.4

Calculate the electrode potential of a **Zn**, Zn^{++} half-cell in which the concentration of Zn^{++} is 0.1 M; $n = 2$.

* More precisely, the *activity* (Sec. 14.3).

Solution: From Table 14.1, $\mathcal{E}^0 = 0.76$ volt.

$$\mathcal{E} = 0.76 - \frac{0.059}{2} \log 0.1$$
$$= 0.76 + 0.03$$
$$= 0.79 \text{ volt}$$

Instead of a metal in contact with a solution of its ions, a half-cell can also consist of an inert electrode in contact with a solution of the same substance in two different oxidation states. The $Pt \mid Fe^{++}, Fe^{+++}$ half-cell is an example:

$$Fe^{++} \rightleftharpoons Fe^{+++} + e^- \qquad \mathcal{E}^0 = -0.77 \text{ volt}$$

A change in the concentration of the reduced species (Fe^{++}) in this half-cell will have the opposite effect from a similar change in the concentration of the oxidized species (Fe^{+++}), and the expression relating concentration to potential becomes

$$\mathcal{E} = \mathcal{E}^0 - \frac{0.059}{n} \log Q$$

where $n = 1$ and $Q = [Fe^{+++}]/[Fe^{++}]$ in this particular case.

Example 14.5

What is the electrode potential of a Fe^{++}, Fe^{+++} half-cell when both ions are at a concentration of 0.1 mole/liter? If the half-cell is allowed to operate until the concentration of Fe^{+++} is 0.05 M, what will the electrode potential be at that time?

Solution: With both ions 0.1 M,

$$\mathcal{E} = \mathcal{E}^0 - \frac{0.059}{1} \log \frac{0.1}{0.1}$$
$$= -0.77 \text{ volt}$$

For every Fe^{+++} ion consumed during the operation of the half-cell, an Fe^{++} ion is formed; therefore when $[Fe^{+++}] = 0.05\ M$, $[Fe^{++}] = 0.15\ M$.

$$\mathcal{E} = -0.77 - \frac{0.059}{1} \log \frac{0.05}{0.15}$$
$$= -0.74 \text{ volt}$$

Now suppose that we construct a zinc-copper cell from two nonstandard half-cells in which the Zn^{++} and Cu^{++} concentrations are $[Zn^{++}]$ and $[Cu^{++}]$, respectively. The emf of this cell will then be

$$\mathcal{E}_{\text{cell}} = \mathcal{E}_{Zn,Zn^{++}} - \mathcal{E}_{Cu,Cu^{++}}$$
$$= \left(\mathcal{E}^0_{Zn,Zn^{++}} - \frac{0.059}{2} \log [Zn^{++}]\right) - \left(\mathcal{E}^0_{Cu,Cu^{++}} - \frac{0.059}{2} \log [Cu^{++}]\right)$$
$$= \mathcal{E}^0_{\text{cell}} - \frac{0.059}{2} \log \frac{[Zn^{++}]}{[Cu^{++}]}$$

Example 14.6

The Daniell cell employs saturated (1.3 *M*) $CuSO_4$ as the electrolyte in the cathode compartment and 0.1 *M* $ZnSO_4$ as the electrolyte in the anode compartment. Calculate the initial emf of the cell.

Solution:

$$\mathcal{E}_{cell} = 1.10 - \frac{0.059}{2} \log \frac{0.1}{1.3}$$

$$= 1.10 - (0.03)(-1.11)$$

$$= 1.13 \text{ volts}$$

The expression which relates the potential of a nonstandard cell to the standard cell potential and to the concentrations of the reacting species is known as the ***Nernst equation.*** For the general case, representing the cell reaction as follows:

$$a\text{A} + b\text{B} + \cdots \rightarrow c\text{C} + d\text{D} + \cdots$$

the Nernst equation has the form

$$\mathcal{E} = \mathcal{E}^0 - \frac{0.059}{n} \log \frac{[\text{C}]^c[\text{D}]^d[\cdots}{[\text{A}]^a[\text{B}]^b[\cdots}$$

14.6 Electrometric Determination of *p*H

One of the most practical applications of the Nernst equation is in the determination of the *p*H of aqueous solutions. If the solution whose *p*H is to be determined is made the electrolyte of a hydrogen electrode which is coupled with an electrode of known potential, the emf of the cell will depend upon the H_3O^+ concentration of the solution. A typical experimental setup, using a saturated calomel electrode as one half-cell, is shown in Fig. 14.5. From Table 14.1, the respective half-cell reactions and standard electrode potentials for this cell are

		$\mathcal{E}^0$
(1)	$H_2(g) + 2\,H_2O \rightleftharpoons 2\,H_3O^+ + 2\,e^-$	0.00 volt
(2)	$2\,Hg(l) + 2\,Cl^- \rightleftharpoons Hg_2Cl_2(s) + 2\,e^-$	−0.26 volt

The overall cell reaction, therefore, is

$$H_2(g) + 2\,H_2O + Hg_2Cl_2(s) \rightleftharpoons 2\,H_3O^+ + 2\,Hg(l) + 2\,Cl^-$$

and $\mathcal{E}^0_{cell} = 0.26$ volt. Then, applying the Nernst equation, we get

$$\mathcal{E}_{cell} = \mathcal{E}^0_{cell} - \frac{0.059}{2} \log \frac{[H_3O^+]^2[Hg]^2[Cl^-]^2}{[H_2][Hg_2Cl_2]}$$

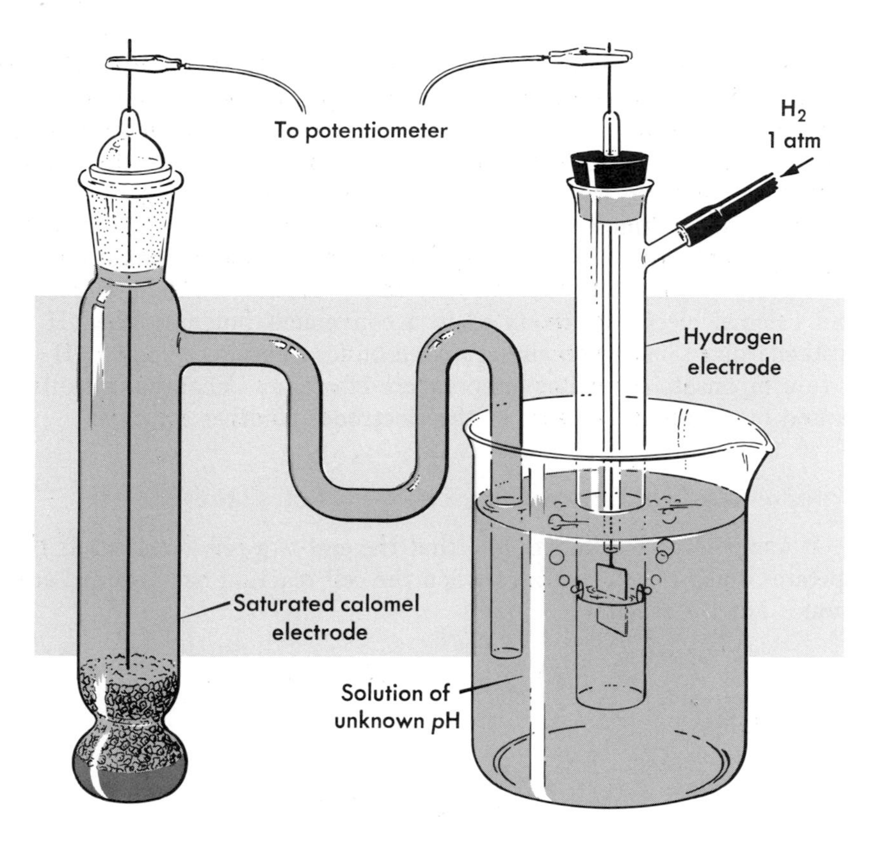

Fig. 14.5 Determination of pH.

In this particular case, all species except H_3O^+ are at unit activity, and the above expression reduces to

$$\mathcal{E}_{cell} = 0.26 - \frac{0.059}{2} \log [H_3O^+]^2$$

$$\mathcal{E}_{cell} = 0.26 - 0.059 \log [H_3O^+]$$

Since $pH = -\log [H_3O^+]$,

$$\mathcal{E}_{cell} = 0.26 + 0.059\, pH$$

and

$$pH = \frac{\mathcal{E}_{cell} - 0.26}{0.059}$$

The emf of this particular cell is seen to be a linear function of the pH of the solution.

Because a hydrogen electrode is inconvenient to use and the platinized platinum of the electrode is easily contaminated, a "glass electrode" is usually employed in the routine measurement of pH. This consists of a bulb of special conductive glass containing a silver wire coated with silver chloride and dipping into a 0.1 M solution of HCl. When this is coupled with a calomel reference electrode constructed of similar glass, and the two electrodes are dipped into the solution under test, the emf developed depends upon the H_3O^+ concentration, and hence the *p*H, of the solution, which is the only variable in the system. Because of the extremely high internal resistance of the glass electrode, which may be as much as 10^8 ohms, the emf cannot be measured with an ordinary potentiometer. Instead, a sensitive vacuum tube voltmeter, which draws virtually no current from the cell, must be employed. The ordinary laboratory *p*H meter consists of such a voltmeter, calibrated to read directly in *p*H units, with the necessary glass and calomel electrodes mounted in a convenient holder. The *p*H meter is standardized just before use against a buffer solution of known *p*H. This is to compensate for minor temperature effects and changes in calibration caused by previous exposure of the electrodes to other solutions.

14.7 Determining Equilibrium Constants from Cell Potentials

It was pointed out in Sec. 14.1 that the emf of a cell decreases as the cell operates, finally becoming zero when the cell reaction has attained equilibrium. For the reaction

$$a\mathrm{A} + b\mathrm{B} + \cdots \rightarrow c\mathrm{C} + d\mathrm{D} + \cdots$$

at equilibrium,

$$\frac{[\mathrm{C}]^c[\mathrm{D}]^d[\cdots}{[\mathrm{A}]^a[\mathrm{B}]^b[\cdots} = K_c$$

and

$$\mathcal{E} = 0$$

Introducing these values into the Nernst equation gives

$$0 = \mathcal{E}^0 - \frac{0.059}{n} \log K_c$$

$$\mathcal{E}^0 = \frac{0.059}{n} \log K_c$$

Example 14.7

The $\mathcal{E}^0$ for the **Zn-Cu** cell is 1.10 volts. Calculate K_c for the reaction

$$\mathrm{Zn} + \mathrm{Cu}^{++} \rightleftharpoons \mathrm{Zn}^{++} + \mathrm{Cu}$$

Solution:

$$1.10 = \frac{0.059}{2} \log K_c$$

$$\log K_c = 37$$

$$K_c = 10^{37}$$

The very large value of K_c for this reaction indicates that the oxidation of **Zn** by Cu^{++} proceeds essentially to completion.

Example 14.8

In the quantitative determination of iron by ceric sulfate oxidation,

$$Fe^{++} + Ce^{++++} \rightleftharpoons Fe^{+++} + Ce^{+++}$$

what fraction of the total Fe^{++} originally present remains unoxidized at the equivalence point?

Solution: From Table 14.1,

	$\mathcal{E}^0$
$Fe^{++} \rightleftharpoons Fe^{+++} + e^-$	-0.77 volt
$Ce^{+++} \rightleftharpoons Ce^{++++} + e^-$	-1.61 volts

$$\mathcal{E}^0_{cell} = (-0.77) - (-1.61) = 0.84 \text{ volt}$$

Assuming that the solution is in a state of equilibrium at the equivalence point, we have

$$0.84 = \frac{0.059}{1} \log K_c$$

$$K_c = 1.74 \times 10^{14} = \frac{[Fe^{+++}][Ce^{+++}]}{[Fe^{++}][Ce^{++++}]}$$

At the equivalence point, $[Fe^{+++}] = [Ce^{+++}]$, and $[Fe^{++}] = [Ce^{++++}]$. Therefore,

$$K_c = \frac{[Fe^{+++}]^2}{[Fe^{++}]^2} = 1.74 \times 10^{14}$$

$$\frac{[Fe^{+++}]}{[Fe^{++}]} = \sqrt{1.74 \times 10^{14}}$$

$$= 1.3 \times 10^7$$

This result shows that only about 1 out of every 10 million Fe^{++} ions remains unoxidized at the equivalence point. The suitability of this reaction for the quantitative determination of iron depends on the fact that it proceeds that far to completion.

The solubility of a sparingly soluble salt is usually very difficult to determine directly with any degree of accuracy, but the K_{sp} of the salt can often be calculated from standard electrode potentials. It is only necessary to choose the two half-cell reactions which, when combined, give the equation that represents the equilibrium existing between dissolved and undissolved salt. The equilibrium constant, which in this case is K_{sp}, can then be calculated from the standard cell potential as in the previous examples.

Example 14.9

Calculate the solubility product constant for AgCl.

$$K_{sp} = [Ag^+][Cl^-]$$

Solution: The appropriate half-cell reactions are found in Table 14.1. These are

	$\mathcal{E}^0$
$Cl^- + Ag(s) \rightleftharpoons AgCl(s) + e^-$	-0.22 volt
$Ag(s) \rightleftharpoons Ag^+ + e^-$	-0.80 volt

Combining these two half-reactions gives the cell reaction:

$$Ag^+ + Cl^- + Ag(s) \rightleftharpoons AgCl(s) + Ag(s)$$

Since $Ag(s)$ appears on both sides of this equation, it can be omitted, giving:

$$Ag^+ + Cl^- \rightleftharpoons AgCl(s)$$

$\mathcal{E}^0_{cell}$ for this reaction is $(-0.22) - (-0.80 \text{ volt}) = 0.58$ volt.

$$\mathcal{E}^0_{cell} = \frac{0.059}{n} \log K_c$$

$$0.58 = \frac{0.059}{1} \log \frac{[AgCl]}{[Ag^+][Cl^-]}$$

Since $AgCl$ is a solid, its activity is 1, and this becomes

$$\begin{aligned} 0.58 &= 0.059 \log (1/K_{sp}) \\ &= -0.059 \log K_{sp} \\ -9.8 &= \log K_{sp} \\ K_{sp} &= 1.6 \times 10^{-10} \end{aligned}$$

14.8 ΔG^0 and the Equilibrium Constant

The proportionality constant $0.059/n$ in the Nernst equation can be shown (by means of theoretical arguments beyond the scope of this text) to be equal to $2.3\,RT/n\mathfrak{F}$, where R is the gas constant, expressed in this case in joules/mole-°K,* T is the absolute temperature, and $\mathfrak{F}$ is the faraday, 96,500 coulombs/mole. From Sec. 14.2,

$$\begin{aligned} \Delta G^0 &= -n\mathfrak{F}\mathcal{E}^0 \\ &= -(n\mathfrak{F}) \frac{2.3RT}{n\mathfrak{F}} \log K_c \\ &= -2.3RT \log K_c \end{aligned}$$

This relationship between the standard free energy change and the equilib-

* $R = 0.082$ liter-atm/mole-°K

$$= \frac{82 \text{ cm}^3\text{-atm}}{\text{mole-°K}} \times \frac{1.01 \times 10^6 \text{ dynes}}{\text{cm}^2\text{-atm}} = \frac{8.3 \times 10^7 \text{ dyne-cm}}{\text{mole-°K}}$$

$= 8.3$ joule/mole-°K $= 8.3$ volt-coulomb/mole-°K

rium constant, derived here for an electrochemical system, is perfectly general and holds with equal validity for all chemical systems, even those which cannot be set up in the form of an electrochemical cell. The following examples illustrate how this equation can be applied.

Example 14.10

In Example 11.4, ΔG^0 for the reaction

$$C_2H_6(g) \rightleftharpoons C_2H_4(g) + H_2(g)$$

was found to be 24.13 kcal. Calculate K_c for this reaction at 298°K.

Solution: $R = \dfrac{8.3 \text{ joule/mole-°K}}{4.18 \text{ joules/cal}} = 2.0 \text{ cal/mole-°K}$

$$24{,}130 = (-2.3)(2.0)(298) \log K_c$$

$$-17.6 = \log K_c$$

$$K_c = 2.5 \times 10^{-18}$$

Example 14.11

One mole of acetic acid was mixed with 1 mole of ethyl alcohol and allowed to stand at 25°C until the reaction mixture came to equilibrium. When the equilibrium mixture was analyzed, it was found to contain $\frac{1}{3}$ mole of acetic acid. Calculate ΔG^0 for the reaction

$$HC_2H_3O_2 + C_2H_5OH \rightleftharpoons C_2H_3O_2C_2H_5 + H_2O$$

Solution: The first step in the solution is the calculation of K_c from the experimental data. If $\frac{1}{3}$ mole of acetic acid remains, $\frac{2}{3}$ mole of the acid must have reacted with $\frac{2}{3}$ mole of ethyl alcohol, leaving $\frac{1}{3}$ mole of alcohol remaining and forming $\frac{2}{3}$ mole each of ethyl acetate ($C_2H_3O_2C_2H_5$) and of water.

$$K_c = \frac{[C_2H_3O_2C_2H_5][H_2O]}{[HC_2H_3O_2][C_2H_5OH]}$$

Let V = volume of the solution; then,

$$K_c = \frac{\left(\frac{2}{3V}\right)\left(\frac{2}{3V}\right)}{\left(\frac{1}{3V}\right)\left(\frac{1}{3V}\right)} = 4$$

Once K_c is known at 25°C (298°K), ΔG^0 can be calculated as follows:

$$\Delta G^0 = -2.3RT \log 4$$

$$= -(2.3)(2.0)(298)(0.60)$$

$$= -820 \text{ cal}$$

Effect of Concentration on ΔG^0 14.9

If we multiply both sides of the Nernst equation by $-n\mathfrak{F}$, we obtain

$$-n\mathfrak{F}\mathcal{E} = -n\mathfrak{F}\mathcal{E}^0 + 2.3RT \log \frac{[C]^c[D]^d[\cdots}{[A]^a[B]^b[\cdots}$$

Since $-n\mathfrak{F}\mathcal{E} = \Delta G$,

$$\Delta G = \Delta G^0 + 2.3RT \log \frac{[C]^c[D]^d[\cdot\cdot\cdot}{[A]^a[B]^b[\cdot\cdot\cdot}$$

where $T = 298°K$. This equation can be used to calculate the free energy change for a reaction with the reactants not at unit concentration (activity), provided that the standard free energy change for the reaction is known. Inspection of the equation will show that any increase in the concentrations (activities) of the products of the reaction

$$aA + bB + \cdot\cdot\cdot \rightleftharpoons cC + dD + \cdot\cdot\cdot$$

will cause ΔG to become less negative (or more positive). As a result, the reverse reaction will become more spontaneous at the expense of the forward reaction, exactly as predicted by Le Chatelier's principle. At equilibrium, $\Delta G = 0$, and, as before,

$$\Delta G^0 = -2.3RT \log K_c$$

14.10 Some Practical Electrochemical Cells

(a) The Dry Cell. Perhaps the most familiar of all electrochemical cells is the ***dry cell.*** The anode of this cell is a zinc can. A lining of porous paper separates the zinc from the electrolyte, which is a thick paste of water, ammonium chloride, zinc chloride, and some porous inactive material such as sawdust. The cathode, in the center of the cell, consists of a graphite rod, around which is packed a layer of a mixture of manganese dioxide and graphite. The cell is sealed with pitch or wax in order to prevent evaporation of water. Most dry cells are enclosed in a second sealed container of steel to further minimize evaporation and leakage of the electrolyte. The cell is dry only in the sense that the electrolyte is a damp paste rather than a solution.

The reactions in the dry cell are complicated, and not everyone is in agreement on what they are. At the anode, the zinc is oxidized:

$$Zn \rightleftharpoons Zn^{++} + 2\,e^-$$

while NH_4^+ and MnO_2 are reduced at the cathode:

$$2\,NH_4^+ + 2\,MnO_2 + 2\,e^- \rightarrow Mn_2O_3 + 2\,NH_3 + H_2O$$

Part of the Zn^{++} formed at the anode probably reacts with NH_3 produced at the cathode to give the complex ion $Zn(NH_3)_4^{++}$; the rest appears to form solid $ZnMn_2O_4$ by reaction with MnO_2. In this way the accumulation of Zn^{++} is avoided, and the potential of the zinc electrode remains nearly constant during the life of the cell. These reactions are relatively slow, however, and if the current drain on the cell is large they cannot keep up with the rate of formation of Zn^{++}. The cell rapidly becomes *polarized,* and the voltage drops drastically from the initial value of about 1.5 volts. Unless the cell has been completely discharged, it will generally regenerate itself, at least partially, upon standing. The overall cell reaction may be summarized as follows:

$$2\ Zn + 4\ NH_4^+ + 6\ MnO_2 \rightarrow Zn(NH_3)_4^{++} + 2\ Mn_2O_3 + 2\ H_2O + ZnMn_2O_4$$

This reaction is not reversible in practice, and the dry cell therefore cannot be recharged.

(b) The Lead Storage Cell. A ***storage cell*** is one which, after having served as a source of electrical energy for a time, can be recharged to its original condition when a direct current of electricity from an outside source is caused to flow through the cell in the opposite direction from that in which the current is delivered by the cell. In the common lead storage cell both electrodes consist of lead plates in the form of grids, one filled with a paste of lead dioxide and the other with spongy lead. The electrolyte is dilute sulfuric acid, usually about 3.7 *M* when the cell is fully charged. Oxidation takes place at the spongy lead electrode, which is therefore the negative electrode of the cell:

$$Pb(s) + SO_4^{--} \rightarrow PbSO_4(s) + 2\ e^-$$

PbO_2 is reduced at the positive electrode:

$$PbO_2(s) + 4\ H_3O^+ + SO_4^{--} + 2\ e^- \rightarrow PbSO_4(s) + 6\ H_2O$$

Solid $PbSO_4$ is formed as a coating of crystals on both electrodes. Sulfuric acid is used up in both reactions, and the density of the electrolyte therefore decreases as the cell operates.

To charge the cell, the lead (−) electrode of the cell is connected to the negative terminal of an external source of direct current, and the PbO_2 (+) electrode to the positive terminal, so that current flows through the cell in the opposite direction from that in which it is delivered by the cell. The overall cell reactions for the charging and discharging processes are

$$Pb + PbO_2 + 4\ H_3O^+ + 2\ SO_4^{--} \underset{\text{charge}}{\overset{\text{discharge}}{\rightleftharpoons}} 2\ PbSO_4 + 6\ H_2O$$

The electrolyte in a fully charged lead storage cell has a specific gravity of from 1.25 to 1.30 (specific gravity of pure water = 1). When the specific gravity falls below 1.15 to 1.20, the cell needs to be recharged. With a full charge, the cell delivers about 2 volts. Most automobile storage batteries consist of three or six cells in series, giving an emf of 6 or 12 volts.

A storage battery can be recharged repeatedly, but its lifetime is not unlimited. Particularly if the battery is discharged rapidly, some of the $PbSO_4$ produced in the cell reaction will fall to the bottom of the cell instead of clinging to the electrodes, and the electrical capacity of the battery will be decreased accordingly. When most of the lead of the electrodes is in the form of $PbSO_4$ suspended in the electrolyte, the battery is said to be "sulfated," and it cannot be recharged. Rapid charging of the battery leads to irregular deposition of **Pb** and **PbO_2** and consequent warping of the plates. This may cause them to touch and short-circuit the cell.

(c) The Fuel Cell. The largest available source of controlled energy is in the oxidation of natural fuels such as coal, petroleum, and natural gas. The usual way of employing this energy is in the form of heat. The fuel is burned, and the heat produced can be used, for example, to make steam to drive a turbine. The conversion of heat to mechanical energy is notably inefficient. Much of the energy is lost in increasing the entropy of the system; some goes to heat up the surroundings; and mechanical losses account for still more. At best, only about 30% of the energy of the fuel is converted into useful work in a conventional heat engine. In contrast, in an electrochemical cell, in which the chemical energy is converted directly into electrical energy without the inherently wasteful intermediate conversion to heat, from 65 to 80% conversion can be achieved. For this reason much effort has been expended in recent years in the development of fuel cells so designed that the oxidation of the fuel takes place at an anode separated by an electrolyte from a cathode where the oxidant, usually oxygen (air), is reduced. Conventional fuels such as hydrogen, carbon monoxide, alcohol, coal, and gasoline are for the most part covalent substances, as is the oxygen used for their oxidation. They are generally nonpolar and insoluble in the electrolyte, and they do not readily gain or lose electrons to form ions. As a result, the activation energies for reactions in fuel cells are quite high, and catalysts are important to lower the activation energy and increase the reaction rate so that useful quantities of electricity can be obtained.

In the hydrogen-oxygen fuel cell the anode is porous carbon mixed with a finely divided catalyst of platinum or palladium. The cathode consists of porous carbon impregnated with silver, platinum, or oxides of cobalt. The electrolyte is a concentrated solution of sodium hydroxide. Hydrogen is supplied continuously to the anode and pure air to the cathode. The half-cell reactions are

At the anode: $$2\,H_2 + 4\,OH^- \rightarrow 4\,H_2O + 4\,e^-$$

At the cathode: $$4\,e^- + O_2 + 2\,H_2O \rightarrow 4\,OH^-$$

giving the overall cell reaction

$$2\,H_2 + O_2 \rightarrow 2\,H_2O$$

The operation of hydrogen fuel cells in conjunction with the production of electricity from nuclear energy has been suggested as offering economic advantages. The excess power produced by the nuclear plant during periods of low demand can be used for the electrolysis of water. The hydrogen and oxygen so produced can then be oxidized later in the fuel cells to supply additional electricity during peak demand periods.

(d) The Solar Cell. In Sec. 9.13 it was pointed out that the electrical conductivity of a metal results from the presence in the metal of a partially filled band (conduction band) of molecular orbitals. In a nonmetal, the occupied band of highest energy is completely filled and is separated by a wide energy gap from the next higher band, which is completely empty. If the energy gap between the bands is very great, the substance will be an insulator. If, on the other hand, the gap is relatively small, it may be possible for an electron to be excited thermally or photoelectrically across the gap to the empty band where it is free to circulate through the crystal and carry current. This gives rise to the property of ***semiconductance.*** Semiconductors have much lower conductivities than metals, but whereas the conductivity of a metal decreases with increasing temperature, that of a semiconductor increases as more electrons obtain the necessary energy to bridge the gap and enter the conducting band.

Insulators such as highly purified silicon and germanium can be converted to semiconductors by the introduction of certain impurities into the crystal lattice. Control of the semiconducting properties is effected by controlling the amount and type of impurity present. For example, silicon has four valence electrons while arsenic has five. If some of the silicon lattice points are occupied by arsenic atoms, there will be an excess electron over the normal complement at each such point. These electrons occupy orbitals lying between the filled and empty bands of the silicon. From there they can be raised comparatively easily to the empty band, and the crystal is therefore a semiconductor. Arsenic in this case is a ***donor impurity*** because it donates an extra electron to the lattice. A crystal which is a semiconductor because of the presence of a donor impurity is called an ***n-type semiconductor.***

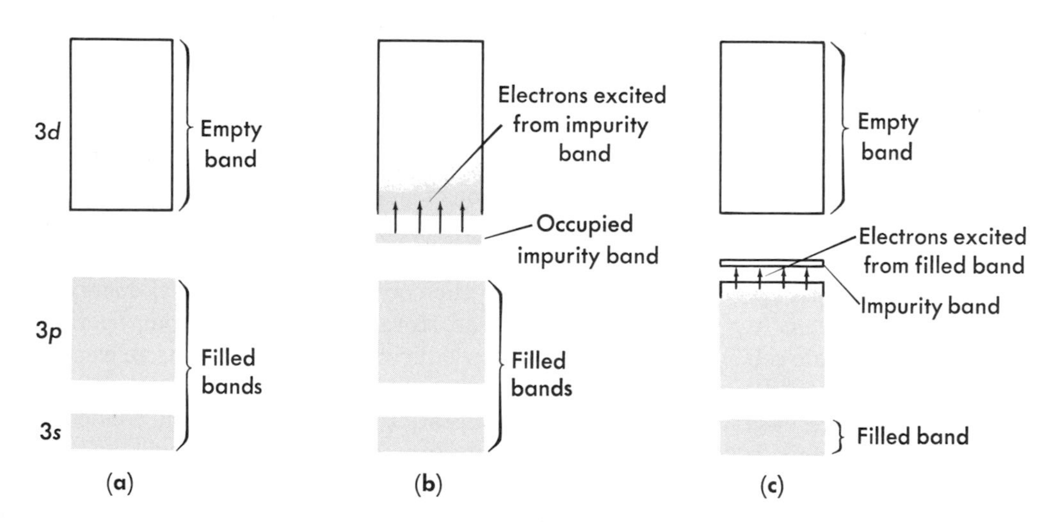

Fig. 14.6 Band models of (a) insulator, (b) n-type semiconductor, and (c) p-type semiconductor.

Semiconductor properties can also arise from the presence of electron-deficient impurity atoms. If boron atoms, for example, which possess only three valence electrons, occupy some of the lattice points in a silicon crystal, the crystal will contain orbital vacancies, or "holes," whose energies again lie between those of the filled and empty bands. Electrons can enter these holes from the lower (filled) band, making conducting orbitals available in that band. The boron is called an ***acceptor impurity***, and the crystal in this case is a ***p-type semiconductor***. Band diagrams of both types of semiconductors are shown in Fig. 14.6.

A ***solar cell*** consists of a wafer of *n*-type silicon semiconductor coated with a thin layer of *p*-type silicon. The interface between the two types of silicon is called a ***p-n junction***. Electrons flow across the junction from the *n*-type silicon which possesses excess lattice electrons to the electron-deficient *p*-type silicon. The resulting accumulation of positive charge on the *n*-type crystal inhibits further migration of electrons across the junction, and an equilibrium is soon established. Exposure to sunlight is accompanied by the absorption of radiant energy, which raises additional electrons to conducting levels. These migrate across the junction under the influence of the potential difference existing between the two types of semiconductor. An appreciable emf is built up, and if the cell is connected through an external circuit, a current will continue to flow as long as the cell is exposed to light.

A number of such cells connected in series and in parallel constitute a ***solar battery***. Solar batteries are capable of generating 90 watts of electrical energy per square yard of illuminated surface. They are reliable and operate indefinitely without loss of efficiency, but they are large, heavy, and very costly in relation to the amount of energy produced. So far, they have found their greatest use in powering artificial satellites and space vehicles, in which the advantages of continuous operation without recharging or attention of any kind far outweigh any disadvantage of cost.

14.11 Electrolytic Cells

All the cells discussed thus far are what are known as ***voltaic cells***. A voltaic cell is one in which a spontaneous reaction occurs, converting chemical energy to electrical energy. In an electrolytic cell, electrical energy supplied from an external source is used to bring about the reversal of the spontaneous process, and in this way the conversion of electrical energy to chemical energy is carried out. A lead storage cell, for example, operates as a voltaic cell while discharging and producing electricity and as an electrolytic cell while it is being recharged.

During electrolysis, positive ions migrate toward the electrode connected to the negative terminal of the external source of current and take up electrons, and negative ions migrate toward the positive electrode and lose electrons. If there are several ions that can undergo electrolysis, the positive ion that will be discharged is the one that has the greatest tendency to accept electrons. This will be the ion produced in the half-cell reaction which has the smallest electrode potential. The negative ion discharged at the positive electrode will be the one for which the half-cell reaction representing its oxidation has the largest electrode potential. It is therefore possible to predict the order in which the various ions in a mixture will be liberated during electrolysis.

Consider the electrolysis between inert platinum electrodes of a solution which is 1 M in Cu^{++}, Zn^{++}, and H_3O^+. The possible reactions taking place at the negative electrode are

	$\mathcal{E}^0$
$Zn \rightleftharpoons Zn^{++} + 2\ e^-$	0.76 volt
$H_2 + 2\ H_2O \rightleftharpoons 2\ H_3O^+ + 2\ e^-$	0.00 volt
$Cu \rightleftharpoons Cu^{++} + 2\ e^-$	−0.34 volt

The third of these reactions has the smallest electrode potential, and from this we may conclude that, of the three ions, Cu^{++} is the most easily reduced, and copper will therefore be deposited first in the electrolysis.

Now let us suppose that the negative ions present in this solution are Br^- and Cl^-. The possible reactions at the positive electrode, together with the standard electrode potentials, are

	$\mathcal{E}^0$
$2\ Br^- \rightleftharpoons Br_2 + 2\ e^-$	−1.07 volts
$6\ H_2O \rightleftharpoons O_2 + 4\ H_3O^+ + 4\ e^-$	−1.23 volts
$2\ Cl^- \rightleftharpoons Cl_2 + 2\ e^-$	−1.36 volts

Here the oxidation of bromide has the largest electrode potential, which means that Br^- is more easily oxidized than either H_2O or Cl^-. Bromine should therefore be discharged at the positive electrode.

From the example given it can be seen that selective electrolytic separation of the components of a solution is theoretically possible. Ideally, however, this can be achieved only when the applied emf is only slightly greater than the equilibrium potential. The equilibrium potential is the voltage which will just balance the emf of the voltaic cell that is formed as the result of the accumulation of the products of electrolysis at the electrodes. In practice, the equilibrium potential must not only be exceeded in order for a current to flow, but it must be exceeded by an amount known as the ***overvoltage,*** plus whatever emf is necessary to overcome the cell resistance. The magnitude of the overvoltage is influenced by a number of factors, including the electrode materials and the nature of their surfaces, the temperature, and the current density (the amount of current flow per unit area of electrode surface). The overvoltage for the deposition of a metal usually amounts to less than 0.1 volt. When gases are liberated, the overvoltage is considerably greater, amounting to several tenths of a volt. The resistance of the cell itself to current flow depends upon the ion concentration and the temperature. The more ions present in the solution, the more current can flow and the less will be the cell resistance. Cell resistance also becomes less as the temperature rises, because this increases the kinetic energy of the ions and causes them to diffuse more rapidly through the solution. The emf necessary to overcome the cell resistance is given by

$$E_r = I \times R$$

where I is the current flow in amperes and R is the resistance in ohms.

The sum of the equilibrium potential E_{ep}, overvoltage E_o, and E_r is the decomposition potential E_{dp}:

$$E_{dp} = E_{ep} + E_o + E_r$$

No current will flow in an electrolytic cell until the decomposition potential is reached. Beyond this point the current flow will increase linearly with further increase in applied voltage. During the course of any electrolytic process, the decomposition potential will increase as the ionic concentration of the solution decreases.

The effective separation of two metals by electrodeposition can be accomplished if the decomposition potentials of their ionic solutions lie relatively far apart, about 0.3 volt being the minimum difference. Under these conditions, the cation requiring the lower decomposition potential will be almost completely deposited at the negative electrode and the other will remain in solution, provided that the applied potential is maintained between the two decomposition potentials at all times during the course of the electrolysis. After the first metal is completely deposited, the deposition of the second can be accomplished by raising the potential above the decomposition potential of its solution.

14.12 Reading Suggestions

Chapters 5 and 6 of *Chemical Energy*, by L. E. Strong and W. J. Stratton (Selected Topics in Modern Chemistry Series, Reinhold Publishing Corp., New York, 1965), are a good general reference for this chapter. The relationship of electrode potentials to atomization energies, ionization energies, electron affinities, and hydration energies is discussed by R. T. Sanderson in *J. Chem. Ed.* **43,** 584 (1966). This is a companion paper to *The Activity Series of the Metals*, by W. F. Kieffer, *J. Chem. Ed.* **27,** 659 (1950), an excellent discussion of the factors which together determine the chemical activity of a metal.

An amusing thumbnail sketch of Walter Nernst appears as part of an article on *Physical Chemists in Berlin, 1919–1933*, by Paul Harteck, *J. Chem. Ed.* **37,** 462 (1960). Sketches of Fritz Haber, inventor of the process for the manufacture of ammonia from its elements, and of Max Bodenstein, who with his students carried out monumental work in gas kinetics and laid the foundations of that subject, also appear in this article.

Fuel cells are discussed in papers by G. J. Young and R. B. Rozelle, *J. Chem. Ed.* **36,** 68 (1959), and by Joseph Weissbart, *J. Chem. Ed.* **38,** 267 (1961). The main types of storage batteries and their characteristics are described by James E. Cassidy in *J. Chem. Ed.* **27,** 63 (1950). A good elementary summary of semiconductor theory by Robert A. Lefever appears in *J. Chem. Ed.* **30,** 554 (1953). More thorough, and also more mathematical, is the discussion of conduction and semiconduction by Norman J. Juster in *J. Chem. Ed.* **40,** 489 (1963).

Questions and Problems

14.1 What is a standard reference electrode? Cite examples. How are they used and for what reason?

14.2 What is a glass electrode? What advantages does it have over the hydrogen electrode?

14.3 Distinguish between voltaic cells and electrolytic cells.

14.4 Provide an explanation for the fact that hydrogen ion rather than sodium ion is reduced at the cathode during the electrolysis of aqueous sodium chloride solution.

14.5 Discuss the electrolysis between inert electrodes of aqueous solutions of (a) hydrogen iodide, (b) sodium sulfate. Consider the solutions to be about 1 molar. Write equations for the electrode reactions that occur.

14.6 In Section 14.11 the electrolysis of a solution that is 1 *M* each in $CuCl_2$, $ZnBr_2$, and H_3O^+ between platinum electrodes is discussed in some detail. If the same solution were electrolyzed between copper electrodes, what would be the electrode reactions at the lowest applied potential that would effect electrolysis?

14.7 In the lead storage battery: (a) What is oxidized at the anode and what is the product of oxidation? (b) What is reduced at the cathode and what is the reduction product? (c) Why does the specific gravity of the electrolyte serve as a measure of the amount of charge?

14.8 Given the cell

$$\text{Pt}, H_2 \text{ (1 atm)}, H_3O^+ \text{ (1 } M) \,||\, Ag^+ \text{ (1 } M), \text{Ag}$$

Calculate (a) $\mathcal{E}^0$, (b) ΔG^0 for the cell reaction. (c) In what direction does the reaction proceed spontaneously? (d) Which electrode is positive? Calculate (e) $\mathcal{E}$ and (f) ΔG at the time when the silver ion concentration of this cell has fallen to a value of 0.01 *M*. (g) What is the equilibrium constant for the reaction? (h) From a knowledge of the equilibrium constant, calculate ΔG^0.

14.9 (a) What is the potential for the cell

$$\text{Sn}, Sn^{++} \text{ (0.01 } M) \,||\, Ag^+ \text{ (0.50 } M), \text{Ag}$$

(b) What is the ΔG for the cell reaction?

14.10 (a) What potential should a zinc electrode dipping into a 0.001 *M* Zn^{++} ion solution at 25°C show relative to the standard hydrogen electrode? ($\mathcal{E}^0_{Zn,Zn^{++}} = +0.76$ volt). (b) If the zinc half-cell in (a) is coupled with a standard bromine half-cell

$$2\,Br^- \rightleftharpoons Br_2 + 2\,e^-;\ \mathcal{E}^0 = -1.07 \text{ volts}$$

what would be the voltage generated? (c) What kind of electrode would be required for the bromine half-cell? (d) Write the oxidation-reduction reaction in the direction in which it occurs while the battery (voltaic cell) is in operation. (e) Toward which of the two electrodes do the electrons flow? (f) What reaction occurs at the cathode? (g) What reaction occurs at the anode? (h) Calculate the equilibrium constant for the reaction in (d).

14.11 A solution containing Fe^{++}, Fe^{+++}, and I^- ions, each at a concentration of 0.1 *M* is saturated with I_2. Is Fe^{+++} reduced by I^- or Fe^{++} oxidized by I_2? (Calculate first the emf for the coupled pair of half-cells under the conditions given.)

14.12 A strip of pure iron is placed into a solution of ferrous and hydrogen ion at a concentration of 0.1 *M* each. What pressure of hydrogen gas must be applied to prevent the liberation of hydrogen by the action of iron on the acid?

14.13 The emf of the cell

$$\text{Pt, H}_2 \text{ (1 atm), HA (0.1 } M) \,\|\, \text{HCl (1 } M), \text{ H}_2 \text{ (1 atm), Pt}$$

is +0.17 volt. Calculate (a) the H_3O^+ ion concentration and (b) the ionization constant of HA. (c) Which pole of the cell is positive under the conditions given? (d) If the half-cell Pt, H_2 (1 atm), HA (0.1 M) is coupled against a saturated calomel electrode ($\mathcal{E}^0 = -0.26$ volt), what is the voltage generated by the coupled pair of half-cells?

14.14 A hydrogen electrode under pressure of hydrogen of 1 atm is immersed in pure water and coupled to a standard hydrogen electrode. The emf developed is +0.41 volt. Show how the K_w of water can be determined from this information. Note: Write the half-cell reaction for the hydrogen electrode in pure water as the first of the two concentration half-cells.

14.15 Compute the K_{sp} for AgI from:

$$\text{Ag} \rightleftharpoons \text{Ag}^+ + e^- \qquad \mathcal{E}^0 = -0.80 \text{ volt}$$

$$\text{I}^- + \text{Ag} \rightleftharpoons \text{AgI} + e^- \qquad \mathcal{E}^0 = +0.15 \text{ volt}$$

14.16 Calculate the K_{sp} for Hg_2Cl_2 from these data:

$$2\text{ Hg} \rightleftharpoons \text{Hg}_2^{++} + 2\,e^- \qquad \mathcal{E}^0 = -0.79 \text{ volt}$$

$$2\text{ Hg} + 2\text{ Cl}^- \text{ (1 } M) \rightleftharpoons \text{Hg}_2\text{Cl}_2 + 2\,e^- \qquad \mathcal{E}^0 = -0.28 \text{ volt}$$

14.17 A cell made of a hydrogen electrode with pressure of hydrogen at 1 atm and a saturated calomel electrode immersed in a solution of unknown hydrogen ion concentration has a potential of 0.65 volt at 25°C. Calculate the pH of the solution.

14.18 When the pH of a solution is determined by means of a hydrogen electrode against a saturated calomel electrode, the partial pressure of hydrogen may vary somewhat from 1 atm. (a) At 25°C, what change in the emf of a hydrogen electrode will accompany a rise in the partial pressure of hydrogen from 1.00 atm to 1.05 atm? (b) What error will this change in partial pressure of hydrogen introduce in the recorded pH of a solution measured by use of this hydrogen electrode and a saturated calomel electrode?

14.19 What is the potential at the equivalence point for the potentiometric titration of Cl^- by $AgNO_3$, using a saturated calomel electrode as reference electrode and a silver electrode as indicator electrode? Note that at the equivalence point $[Ag^+] = 1.3 \times 10^{-5}\ M$.

14.20 Use the given half-cell data to calculate the dissociation constant (instability constant, K_{inst}) for $[Ag(NH_3)_2]^+$ complex ion.

$$\text{Ag} \rightleftharpoons \text{Ag}^+ + e^- \qquad \mathcal{E}^0 = -0.80 \text{ volt}$$

$$2\text{ NH}_3\text{(aq)} + \text{Ag} \rightleftharpoons \text{Ag(NH}_3)_2^+ + e^- \qquad \mathcal{E}^0 = -0.37 \text{ volt}$$

Send me therefore
a skilful man that knoweth how
to work in gold, and in silver,
in brass, and in iron . . .

——II Chronicles 2:7

15 METALLURGY

About eighty percent of the elements are metals, and a major portion of inorganic chemistry is therefore the chemistry of the metallic elements. The isolation and purification of metals was already an ancient art when Solomon began his temple, and metallurgical processes underwent little change until comparatively recent times. Nothing was known of the chemical reactions that take place during the smelting of an ore or the refining of a metal. Improvements in the art were more the result of chance than design, and they were guarded by their discoverers as valuable trade secrets, which indeed they were.

The builders of Solomon's temple had eight metals and their alloys with which to work. These were gold, silver, copper, tin, zinc, lead, mercury, and iron, and among their alloys, bronze (copper and tin), brass (copper and zinc) and electrum (gold and silver). By 1700 only the semimetal antimony had been added to the list. The dawn of the eighteenth century saw a new spirit of scientific inquiry in the air, and among scientists there was a new understanding of the elemental nature of the metals. The discovery of cobalt and platinum in 1735 was followed by the isolation of eight other new metals before the end of the century. The discovery of the electric current led by 1808 to the isolation of many of the most active metals. Later, the discovery of the periodic law stimulated the active search for unknown elements, many of them metals, whose existence had been predicted by the periodic law. Today, not only are all of the naturally occurring metals known, but others (the transuranium metals, Sec. 20.4) have been prepared artificially which never before existed in nature.

The first scientific treatise on metallurgy, Réaumur's *Memoirs on Steel and Iron*, appeared in 1722. By the mid-nineteenth century, scientific knowledge had caught up with and passed the practical knowledge of metals that had slowly accumulated over thousands of years, changing the practice of metallurgy from the empirical art it had been into a modern technology based on sound scientific principles.

The isolation of a metal in usable form begins with the ***ore.*** This is usually a compound of the metal mixed with rock, sand, and other extraneous matter or ***gangue.*** Before any attempt is made to reduce the ore to the metal, it is usually desirable to remove as much of the gangue as possible by a process of concentration or ***beneficiation*** of the ore. The pretreatment of the ore may also include roasting to convert it to a form more suitable for reduction. With the exception of those few that are found in the native, or uncombined, state, all metals are in the oxidized form in their ores. Preparation of the metal therefore involves chemical or electrolytic reduction of the ore. The metal as first prepared is seldom pure enough for use, and must then be subjected to a final process of refining. The processes involved in converting the ore to the finished metal illustrate the application on an industrial scale of many of the most important chemical principles, and we will examine them briefly in this chapter.

15.1 Sources of Metals

(a) Native Metals and Alloys. Only the "noble metals," those that are least reactive—gold, silver, mercury, and the members of the platinum family (**Os**, **Ir**, **Pt**, **Ru**, **Rh**, and **Pd**)—occur in workable deposits in the native state. Small deposits of native copper are occasionally found, and iron and nickel occur in the free state in some meteorites, but few of these sources are of any commercial significance. Gold, and to a lesser extent silver, is often found intimately mixed with quartz, as flecks and nuggets of metal in the veins and interstices of the quartz crystals. Deposits in Alaska, California, Mexico, and the Southwest are largely of this type, which appears to be the result of ancient volcanic activity. Silica (quartz), gold, and silver are appreciably soluble in superheated water at the extremes of temperature and pressure existing in the interior of a volcano. They can thus be transported in solution toward the surface, where the water evaporates, leaving the quartz and metal to crystallize together. Erosion by an underground stream may carry particles of gold long distances underground. Eventually the stream reaches the surface, where the gold can be separated from the stream gravel. The classic prospector's dream, which sometimes has come true, has always been to follow such a stream to its source and the "mother lode."

A different type of gold ore, which requires more extensive chemical treatment, is found for example near Cripple Creek, Colorado. This town, in the vicinity of Pike's Peak, lies in a vast bowl formed by the crater of an extinct volcano. The granitic rock in the throat of the volcano contains a fraction of one percent of an alloy of gold with silver, tellurium, and selenium, in the form of shiny, microscopic specks. Treatment of this low-grade ore was made feasible by the introduction of the cyanide process (see below) about 1890. Beginning then, and for about 30 years thereafter, the Cripple Creek district enjoyed a boom during which it became one of the wealthiest communities in the world, with three railroads, mansions, theaters, and opera houses, and its population was nearly 55,000. Today, although some gold is still mined, most of it is in deposits too deep to be recovered profitably at the present price of the metal.

(b) Oxides. While many metals occur as oxides in the earth's crust, probably the most important oxide ores are those of iron, aluminum, and tin. The important iron-bearing minerals are ***hematite,*** Fe_2O_3, chemically identical with ordinary iron rust, and ***magnetite,*** Fe_3O_4 (magnetic iron oxide, or "lodestone"). The Mesabi range in northern Minnesota is a vast deposit of iron ore, much of it more than 70% pure Fe_2O_3. Extensive deposits of hematite ore are found in many parts of the world, but few of them approach the Mesabi in purity. Ever-increasing demands for iron have led to a greater interest in the lower-grade and less tractable ore ***taconite,*** a hard rock composed of fine black crystals of magnetite intermingled with silica.

Bauxite, a hydrated aluminum oxide distributed fairly widely over the earth, is the principal source of aluminum. Large deposits are found in Arkansas, eastern Canada, France (the ore is named after the town of Baux in southern France), Jamaica, and elsewhere. Besides silica, the principal impurity in bauxite is usually iron, which must be removed before the ore is reduced. Ruby and sapphire are crystalline Al_2O_3, colored by traces of other substances.

Tin is found as the oxide ***cassiterite,*** SnO_2. Important deposits of cassiterite are found in Malaysia and Bolivia, as well as in Cornwall, England, where the tin mines have been worked continuously since prehistoric times.

(c) Sulfides. Sulfide ores constitute major sources of copper (***chalcopyrite,*** $CuFeS_2$, and ***chalcocite,*** Cu_2S), zinc (***sphalerite,*** ZnS), mercury (***cinnabar,*** HgS), and lead (***galena,*** PbS). ***Iron pyrites,*** or ferrous persulfide, FeS_2, is widespread in nature, frequently occurring as large golden crystals ("fool's gold"). It is sometimes used as a source of SO_2 for sulfuric acid manufacture, but it is now of no value as iron ore. Iron produced from pyrites contains substantial amounts of sulfur which weaken it to the point of being completely useless. The use of pyrites as a source of iron will depend upon development of an economical way of removing all of this sulfur from the metal.

(d) Chlorides and Carbonates. The most important chloride ore is sodium chloride. This can be obtained by evaporating seawater, but most of it comes from large underground deposits of ***rock salt.*** These deposits are probably the remains of ancient inland seas that evaporated eons ago and became covered by overlying strata. The salt is mined either by conventional methods or by forcing water into the deposit and pumping the dissolved salt to the surface. Potassium is found as the chloride in ***sylvite,*** KCl, and ***carnallite,*** $KCl \cdot MgCl_2$. Magnesium occurs as the sulfate in ***epsom salts,*** $MgSO_4 \cdot 7\ H_2O$ (found near Epsom, England, famous as the site of Epsom Downs and the Derby), and also as the oxide (***periclase,*** MgO), hydroxide (***brucite,*** $Mg(OH)_2$), and the carbonate (***magnesite,*** $MgCO_3$, and ***dolomite,*** $MgCO_3 \cdot CaCO_3$). In this country, however, nearly all of the magnesium produced is obtained originally from seawater (Sec. 15.2d). Calcium is obtained by electrolysis of $CaCl_2$, prepared from ***limestone,*** $CaCO_3$.

(e) Silicates. Because of their intractable nature, silicate minerals are generally used as sources of metals only where there is no alternative. Examples of silicate ores are ***beryl,*** $Be_2Al_2Si_6O_{18}$, which is the major source of beryllium, and in the form of especially good crystals is the gemstone ***emerald,*** and ***spodumene,*** $LiAl(SiO_3)_2$, a lithium ore. Common clays are complex aluminosilicates (e.g., ***kaolinite,*** $Al_2(Si_2O_8)(OH)_4$) in which some of the silicon atoms in the silica lattice have been replaced by aluminum (Sec. 16.9). A method has recently been developed which promises to make the production of aluminum from clay a commercial reality.

15.2 Pretreatment of the Ore

Before being reduced to the metal, most ores must first be concentrated to remove as much sand, rock, and other extraneous material as possible. If there is more than one valuable component in the ore, these must be separated from one another. In some cases, the ore must be converted chemically to a form more suitable for reduction, and, especially if the reduction is to be done electrolytically, further purification may be necessary. A few specific examples will illustrate the pretreatment methods that can be used.

(a) Sulfide Ores. Many sulfides, such as those of copper, lead, and zinc, have a relatively high density, so that some concentration can be effected by blowing the crushed ore into a cyclone separator (Fig. 15.1).

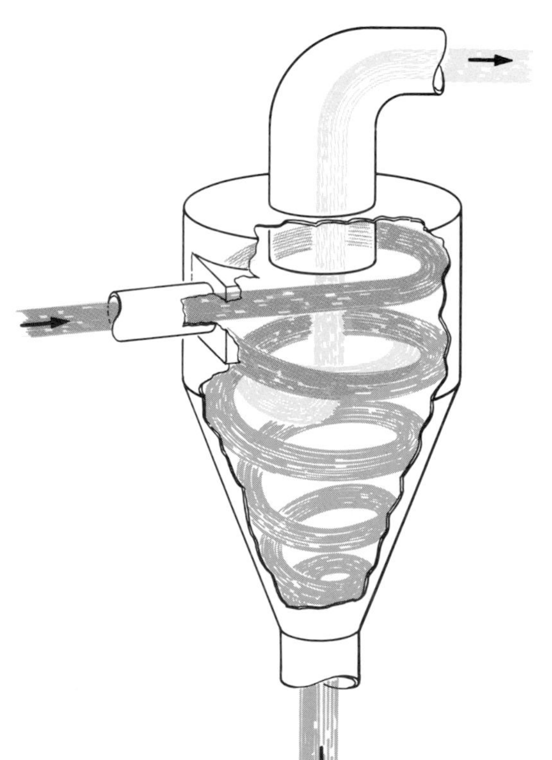

Fig. 15.1 Cyclone separator. The crushed ore is blown at high velocity along the inner wall of the separator. Centrifugal force carries the heavier ore particles out to the wall where they spiral down to the collecting bin. The lighter particles move toward the center and are carried out in the air stream.

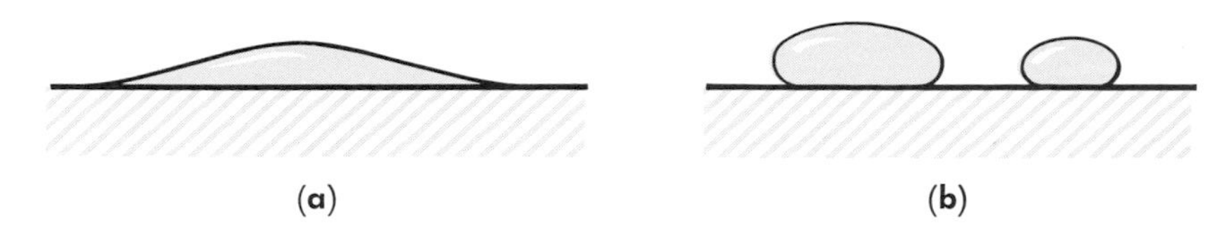

Fig. 15.2 Diagram showing the behavior of a liquid on a surface: (a) surface wet by the liquid; (b) surface not wet by the liquid.

More complete separation is accomplished by a flotation process which takes advantage of the peculiar wetting properties that are exhibited by most sulfide ores.

The majority of sulfide ores are wet by oil but not by water. This means that oil will spread out over the surface of the ore but that water will not. Instead, the water will either form nearly spherical droplets (Fig. 15.2) or else run off altogether, leaving the surface dry. On the other hand, water readily wets the rock and clay usually accompanying the ore. If the crushed ore is stirred vigorously with water and air blown through the mixture, air bubbles will stick preferentially to the less easily wet sulfide particles rather than to the rock. If the air bubbles are large enough, they can carry the sulfide particles to the surface along with themselves (Fig. 15.3).

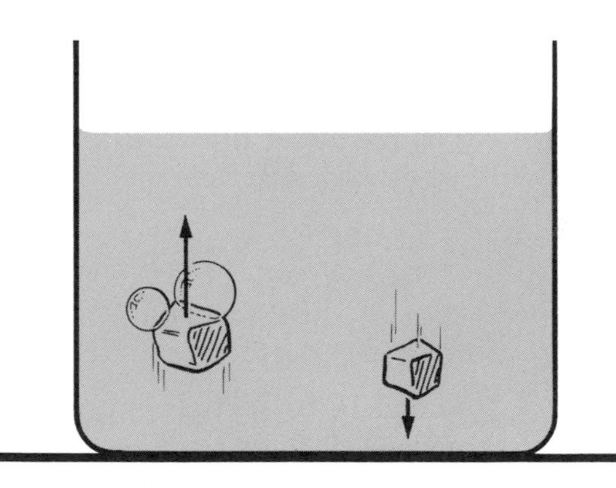

Fig. 15.3 Separation by flotation. Bubbles attach themselves to a sulfide particle, carrying it to the surface. The particle of gangue is wet by the water, and it sinks.

To keep the bubbles from breaking at the surface and letting the ore sink back to the bottom, a quantity of oil and a detergent are added to the mixture. This, together with the air bubbles and accompanying ore particles, forms at the surface a sudsy froth, which overflows and is collected (Fig. 15.4). By proper choice of the amount and kind of oil and detergent used, it is possible to control the wetting properties of the ore to such an extent that not only can the ore be separated from the gangue, but sulfides of different metals present in the ore can even be separated from one another.

The next step following concentration of a sulfide ore is usually an air-roasting process to convert the sulfide to the oxide. Sulfur is an especially undesirable impurity in most metals, and eliminating it before reduction of the ore is usually much easier and more economical than trying to remove

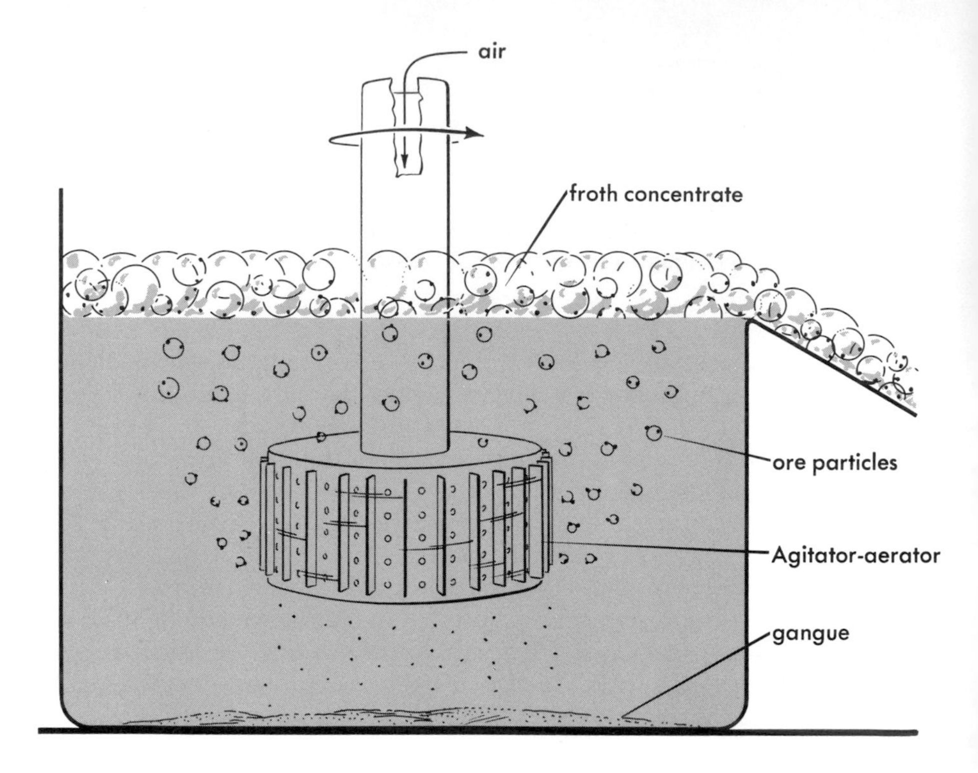

Fig. 15.4 Flotation apparatus.

it from the metal afterwards. The sulfur dioxide produced by roasting the ore is usually recovered and converted to sulfuric acid.

$$2\ ZnS + 3\ O_2 \rightarrow 2\ ZnO + 2\ SO_2\uparrow$$

$$2\ PbS + 3\ O_2 \rightarrow 2\ PbO + 2\ SO_2\uparrow$$

Complete or partial reduction to crude metal can in some cases be accomplished during the roasting process. Concentrated copper ore, for example, is mixed and roasted with limestone. The limestone acts to remove silica and iron as a fusible calcium and iron silicate slag, while partial oxidation of the charge produces metallic copper:

$$CaCO_3 \rightarrow CaO + CO_2\uparrow$$

$$2\ FeS + 3\ O_2 \rightarrow 2\ FeO + 2\ SO_2\uparrow$$

$$\left.\begin{array}{l} CaO + SiO_2 \rightarrow CaSiO_3 \\ FeO + SiO_2 \rightarrow FeSiO_3 \end{array}\right\}\text{slag}$$

$$Cu_2S + O_2 \rightarrow 2\ Cu + SO_2\uparrow$$

Lead sulfide ore can be partially roasted to the oxide or sulfate, which is then heated with more of the sulfide to yield the metal:

$$2\ PbS + 3\ O_2 \rightarrow 2\ PbO + 2\ SO_2\uparrow$$

$$PbS + 2\ O_2 \rightarrow PbSO_4$$

$$2\ PbO + PbS \rightarrow 2\ Pb + SO_2\uparrow$$

$$PbSO_4 + PbS \rightarrow 2\ Pb + 2\ SO_2\uparrow$$

Mercury is obtained from the sulfide in a similar manner. Here the volatility of the metal makes the process especially simple, since the metal can be distilled out of the mixture as fast as it is formed:

$$HgS + O_2 \rightarrow Hg\uparrow + SO_2\uparrow$$

(b) Gold and Silver. Panning for gold is one of the oldest ore-concentration methods. Gold-bearing gravel and water is scooped from the stream bed in a shallow pan. The mixture is stirred by hand, and the lighter sand and gravel are allowed to spill over the rim of the pan with the water. The dense particles of gold and larger pieces of gravel remain in the bottom of the pan to be separated by hand. This operation can be made more efficient by washing the crushed gravel through a ***cradle,*** a wooden box with strips nailed across the bottom, which is rocked by hand or mechanically, or across a ***shaking table,*** a mechanically vibrated, slanting table with a number of low metal barriers running across its width. The denser gold becomes lodged behind the cross strips of either device while the lighter sand and gravel is washed away. The shaking table is tipped slightly to one side so that the concentrated ore gradually works itself to the edge, where it drops off and is collected, making the process continuous. Further concentration is possible by passing the ore over a copper sheet covered with a thick layer of mercury. Gold and silver become ***amalgamated,*** or alloyed with the mercury, and can be recovered by distilling the mercury from the amalgam.

Gold and silver are recovered from low-grade ores by the ***cyanide process.*** In contrast to their usual behavior, gold and silver are readily oxidized in the presence of cyanide ions, forming complex ions. When air is passed through a mixture of the ore and a dilute cyanide solution, the metal is gradually oxidized and dissolves:

$$4\ Au + 8\ CN^- + O_2 + 2\ H_2O \rightarrow 4\ Au(CN)_2^- + 4\ OH^-$$

$$4\ Ag + 8\ CN^- + O_2 + 2\ H_2O \rightarrow 4\ Ag(CN)_2^- + 4\ OH^-$$

The metal is reprecipitated from the filtered solution by reduction with zinc or by electrolysis.

(c) Aluminum. Before electrolytic reduction of aluminum can be carried out, the crude bauxite must first be converted to pure alumina, Al_2O_3. Iron, an especially common and unwanted impurity that cannot be conveniently removed from the metal after reduction, must be eliminated beforehand. The remaining impurities are usually sand and other silicates. Here advantage is taken of the amphoteric nature of aluminum—the solubility of its oxide in base as well as acid:

$$Al_2O_3 + 6\ OH^- + 3\ H_2O \rightarrow 2\ Al(OH)_6^{---}$$

When the bauxite is digested with hot alkali, the alumina dissolves, but the iron oxide and silica are unaffected and are filtered off. Acidification of the solution precipitates the hydroxide, which is dried and heated, regenerating the oxide:

$$Al(OH)_6^{---} + 3\ H_3O^+ \rightarrow Al(OH)_3 + 6\ H_2O$$

$$2\ Al(OH)_3 \xrightarrow{\Delta} Al_2O_3 + 3\ H_2O\uparrow$$

(d) Magnesium. The "ore" in this case is generally seawater, which contains about 0.13% dissolved magnesium (the concentration of sodium ions in seawater, for comparison, is about 1.1%). Addition of lime precipitates the magnesium as the hydroxide, which is filtered, dried, and heated to form the oxide. The oxide is then converted to the chloride preparatory to electrolytic reduction:

$$Ca(OH)_2 + Mg^{++} \rightarrow Mg(OH)_2 + Ca^{++}$$

$$Mg(OH)_2 \rightarrow MgO + H_2O$$

$$MgO + C + Cl_2 \rightarrow MgCl_2 + CO\uparrow$$

The chlorine used in the last step is recovered in the subsequent electrolysis process.

(e) Lithium. The demand for lithium as a catalyst and as a reducing agent, especially in the form of lithium aluminum hydride $LiAlH_4$, has increased so much since World War II that the metal, which once was practically a laboratory curiosity, is now a major tonnage chemical. It is one of the very few metals prepared from a silicate ore. In the past the main source of lithium was the mineral ***lepidolite,*** $KLiAl(OH \cdot F)_2Al(SiO_3)_2$, which was crushed and digested at high temperatures with concentrated sulfuric acid to extract the lithium as the sulfate. A more economical process now involves heating the mineral ***spodumene,*** $LiAl(SiO_3)_2$, at 1100°C for a brief period, whereupon the tightly packed α-spodumene crystal lattice is converted to the more open β-spodumene. The lithium ions are loosely held in the cage-like aluminosilicate lattice (Sec. 16.9) and are readily leached out with sulfuric acid. The sulfate is converted to the chloride and reduced electrolytically.

(f) Lanthanides, or Rare Earths. The lanthanides are far more abundant in the earth's crust than the term "rare earths" would imply. Cerium and lanthanum are about as abundant as tin and lead, respectively, and even thulium, the rarest of the rare earths, is twice as abundant as silver. The rarity of these metals in the past has been due more to the difficulty in separating them from their ore and from one another than to any intrinsic scarcity.

The electronic configurations of the lanthanides differ only in the number of electrons in the $4f$ level, the outer levels remaining nearly unchanged throughout the series (Sec. 7.7). As a result, their chemical properties are very similar, and complete separation of a mixture of their salts by conventional methods involving successive precipitations and fractional crystallizations is extremely laborious, and in a few instances, nearly impossible. Indeed, for many years a mixture of neodymium and praseodymium was believed to be a single element.* Not until Moseley's determination of atomic numbers (Sec. 6.10) was the exact number of lanthanides known with certainty. The recent development of ion exchange methods has greatly simplified the separation of these metals and their salts in the pure state and greatly increased their availability.

A major source of the lanthanide elements is ***monazite sand,*** containing about 2% ***monazite,*** a mixture of the phosphates of the ***cerium subgroup,*** atomic numbers 57 to 62, with some thorium and traces of the other lanthanides, also as their phosphates. Treatment of the sand with hot, concentrated hydrochloric or sulfuric acid leaches out the elements in the form of their soluble chloride or sulfate salts. The solution is washed slowly through a long column of a cation exchange resin. This is an insoluble polymer of high molecular weight, possessing acidic functional groups. As the solution of ions passes through the resin, hydrogen ions are reversibly exchanged for those of the metals according to the equilibrium

$$3\,[\text{resin}]^- \,H^+ + M^{+++} \rightleftharpoons [\text{resin}]_3^- \,M^{+++} + 3\,H^+$$

No two of the metal ionic species have exactly the same affinity for the resin, although the differences may be very slight. Those that are most tightly bound to the resin, that is, those for which the above equilibrium lies most to the right, will be retained longer on the resin and will pass more slowly through the column. Each species will move through the column at its own rate in proportion to how tightly or loosely it is bound to the resin, and if the column is long enough, a complete separation can be effected. A single pass through the column then becomes the equivalent of hundreds of successive fractional precipitations and crystallizations.

Chemical Reduction 15.3

(a) Reduction with Carbon. Carbon in the form of coke is the cheapest chemical reducing agent, and it is the agent of choice whenever it can possibly be used. Typical of the reduction of a metal ore by carbon is the production of iron in a blast furnace. The blast furnace (Fig. 15.5), lined with silica brick and often standing as high as a ten-story building, is charged with a mixture of iron ore, coke, and limestone. The limestone serves to convert impurities in the ore to a slag, which melts and runs down to the bottom of the furnace, where it can be removed.

The proper temperature gradient is maintained in the furnace by controlling the hot air blast that enters through pipes, or tuyères (pronounced

* It was called didymium, from the Greek *didymos*, twin, because the oxide was very similar to—a twin of—that of lanthanum. The name proved unexpectedly prophetic.

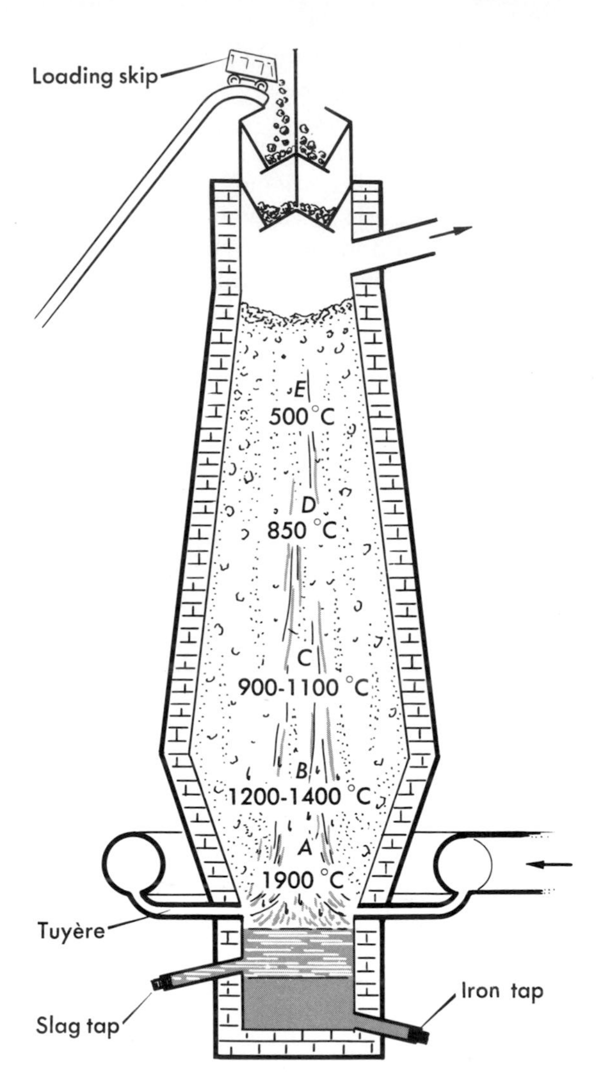

Fig. 15.5 Cross section of a blast furnace. The letters refer to the regions described in the text.

"tweers") spaced at intervals around the base of the furnace. At point A on the diagram the reaction is mostly oxidation of carbon, producing the heat necessary for the process:

$$C + O_2 \rightarrow CO_2 \qquad \Delta H_{298} = -94 \text{ kcal}$$

The temperature at this point may exceed 1900°C.

A short distance above (point B), the temperature falls rapidly to 1200–1400°C, while carbon monoxide, the actual reducing agent in the process, is formed by the endothermic reaction

$$CO_2 + C \rightarrow 2\,CO \qquad \Delta H_{298} = +44 \text{ kcal}$$

At point C, where average temperatures are in the range of 900 to 1100°C, SiO_2, Al_2O_3, MgO, and residual sulfur in the charge react with the limestone and with each other to form slag. The principal reactions can be summarized as follows:

$$CaCO_3 \rightarrow CaO + CO_2\uparrow$$

$$CaO + SiO_2 \rightarrow CaSiO_3$$

$$MgO + SiO_2 \rightarrow MgSiO_3$$

$$CaO + Al_2O_3 \rightarrow Ca(AlO_2)_2$$

$$CaO + FeS + C \rightarrow CaS + Fe + CO\uparrow$$

The alumina and silica in the slag come originally from the clay and rock present in the ore. Most of the sulfur is present as iron sulfide in the coke. The coke is prepared by heating bituminous coal to drive off volatile matter. Iron pyrites (FeS_2) present in the coal are converted to **FeS** in the process. Careful choice of low-sulfur coal is necessary to obtain the best quality iron. The amount of limestone added to the charge in the blast furnace is adjusted according to the relative amounts of silica, alumina, and other impurities in the ore, as determined by analysis, in order to obtain a slag which will be fluid at the operating temperature of the furnace. A typical slag might have an approximate analysis equivalent to 44% **CaO**, 35% SiO_2, 12% Al_2O_3, 4% **CaS**, and 3% **MgO**. Besides its function in removing impurities from the iron, the slag, which solidifies to a form of rock, finds use as road ballast and in cement manufacture.

The initial reduction in the blast furnace takes place near the top of the charge (point E) at a temperature of about 500°C. This first step is the conversion of hematite to magnetite:

$$3\ Fe_2O_3 + CO \rightarrow 2\ Fe_3O_4 + CO_2\uparrow$$

Somewhat farther down (point D), where the temperature is about 850°C, magnetite is further reduced to **FeO**:

$$Fe_3O_4 + CO \rightarrow 3\ FeO + CO_2\uparrow$$

Final reduction takes place at about 1000°C in region C:

$$FeO + CO \rightarrow Fe + CO_2\uparrow$$

The charge moves downward as the slag and molten iron are withdrawn periodically from the furnace, and fresh charge is added at the top, so that the entire process is continuous. The iron is either cast into ingots or, more commonly today, poured into heavily insulated tank cars and shipped directly to the steel plant in the molten state. When cooled and solidified, the ***pig iron**** is hard and brittle and contains substantial amounts of silicon, carbon, and other impurities, making further refining necessary.

* Many years ago it was the practice to draw off the molten iron into a trough joining a series of sand molds, thus:

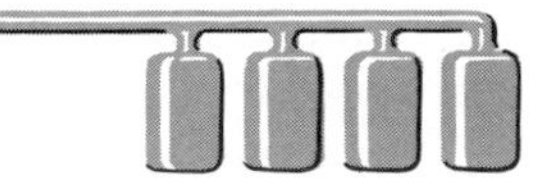

This shape reminded someone of a sow with her suckling pigs, and the term pig iron was born.

(b) Reduction with Hydrogen. Hydrogen finds some use as a chemical reducing agent, especially in small-scale reductions of rare or radioactive elements, when an especially pure metal is required, or when the presence of even a trace of carbon in the final product must be avoided. Even the slightest amount of carbon in tungsten, for example, renders the metal hard and brittle and makes drawing it into wires and filaments completely impossible. The use of hydrogen to reduce the oxide eliminates this problem:

$$WO_3 + 3\ H_2 \xrightarrow{1200^\circ} W + 3\ H_2O$$

(c) Reduction with a More Active Metal. Some metals are too reactive to be reduced by carbon or hydrogen but can be reduced by reaction with a still more active metal. Aluminum was first prepared by Wöhler in this manner (1827), with potassium as the reducing agent:

$$AlCl_3 + 3\ K \rightarrow Al + 3\ KCl$$

Rubidium is prepared by reduction of the chloride with calcium. Here, although rubidium is the more active metal of the two, its greater volatility allows it to be distilled from the mixture. This shifts the equilibrium to favor the production of rubidium:

$$Ca + 2\ RbCl \rightarrow CaCl_2 + 2\ Rb\uparrow$$

Titanium is prepared commercially by reduction of the tetrachloride vapor with molten magnesium in an inert atmosphere:

$$TiCl_4 + 2\ Mg \rightarrow 2\ MgCl_2 + Ti$$

The titanium metal is obtained in the form of a sponge, which is converted to a compact form by being melted in an electric arc under argon gas.

Many metal oxides can be reduced with aluminum in what is known as the ***Goldschmidt reaction.*** The aluminum is mixed intimately with the oxide to be reduced, and the mixture is ignited with a fuse. A mixture of Fe_2O_3 and coarsely powdered aluminum, known as ***thermite,*** is sometimes used in welding when a comparatively large amount of metal is needed, as to fill the joints between railroad rails. During the reaction

$$Fe_2O_3 + 2\ Al \rightarrow Al_2O_3 + 2\ Fe$$

the temperature approaches 3000°C. A mixture of thermite encased in a magnesium canister was used as an incendiary bomb during World War II. The burning bombs were almost impossible to extinguish, since they required no external source of oxygen, and any water sprayed on them decomposed at the high temperatures attained, producing H_2 and O_2 which then recombined, adding to the conflagration.

The Goldschmidt reaction has also been used to prepare chromium, titanium, and other metals whose oxides are difficult to reduce by other methods:

$$Cr_2O_3 + 2\ Al \rightarrow Al_2O_3 + 2\ Cr$$

$$3\ TiO_2 + 4\ Al \rightarrow 2\ Al_2O_3 + 3\ Ti$$

Electrolytic Reduction 15.4

Reduction by electrolysis is a very convenient method where a good supply of cheap electrical power is available, and it is an absolute necessity for the most reactive metals which cannot be reduced in any other way. It has the further advantage of generally giving a very pure product that often requires no further refining. Any metal can be prepared by an electrolytic process, and the alkali metals (except rubidium, Sec. 15.3c), calcium, and aluminum almost always are.

(a) Sodium. This metal is prepared by electrolysis of fused (molten) NaCl in an apparatus such as the Downs cell (Fig. 15.6). The graphite anode

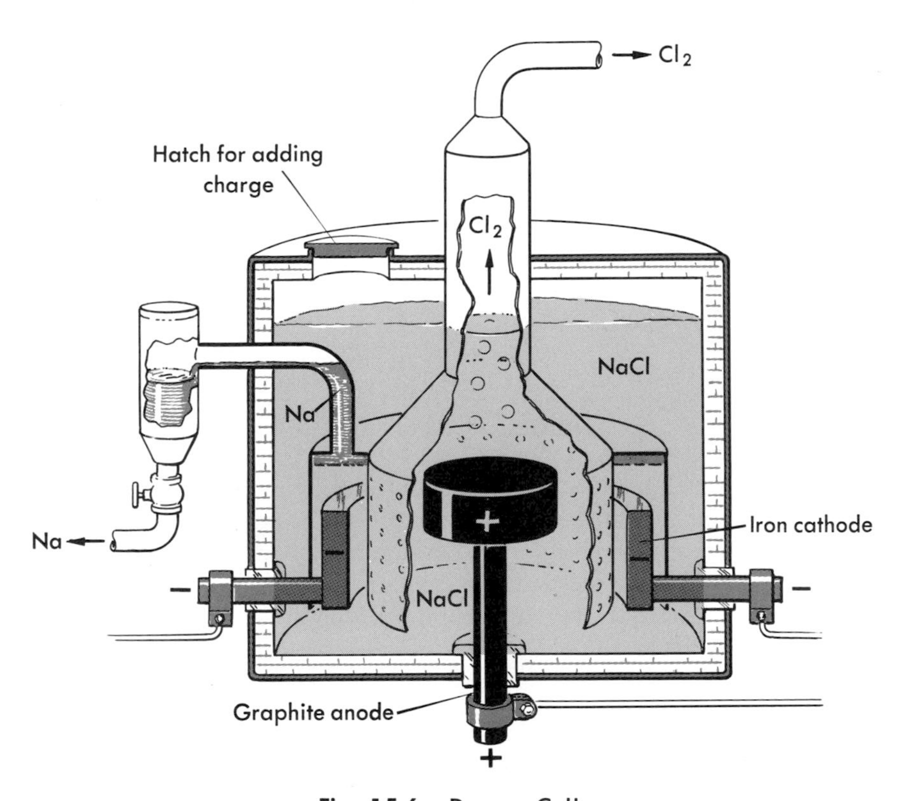

Fig. 15.6 Downs Cell.

of this cell is surrounded by the circular iron cathode, and the two are separated by a perforated barrier. This permits the flow of ions between the electrodes but keeps the products, chlorine and sodium, from coming in contact with one another and recombining. Sodium sulfate or carbonate is added to the electrolyte to lower its melting point from that of pure NaCl (801°C) to about 600°C. The heat generated by the electrical resistance of the cell is then sufficient to keep the electrolyte molten without the necessity of external heating. The cell is operated continuously. Pure sodium metal (m.p. 97.5°C) rises in the pipe over the cathode and is collected as a liquid. Chlorine, a valuable by-product of the process, is drawn off from the anode compartment. Additional electrolyte is added periodically through the hatch. Because sodium is so reactive, especially toward moisture, and will tarnish rapidly in air, the liquid metal is drawn off, cast into bricks, and shipped, all under an atmosphere of dry nitrogen. In the laboratory, the metal is usually kept under kerosene to protect it from air and moisture.

(b) Aluminum. Aluminum is a very reactive metal and its compounds are difficult to reduce chemically. Metallic aluminum rapidly becomes coated with a film of oxide upon exposure to air. This film, although thin enough to be transparent, nevertheless completely covers the surface of the aluminum and protects it from further oxidation. The extreme reactivity of aluminum can be made apparent by wiping the surface of the metal with a solution of mercury(II) chloride and then rinsing. This treatment disrupts the surface of the aluminum in some manner and prevents formation of the usual oxide film. Instead, the oxide grows rapidly in the form of long filaments, and after a few seconds the heat of reaction makes the metal too hot to touch.

Aluminum was first prepared by reduction of its chloride with potassium (Sec. 15.3c), and Bunsen prepared it in 1854 by electrolysis of aluminum chloride, but both processes were costly. In 1854 Sainte-Claire Deville heated aluminum oxide, sodium chloride, carbon, and chlorine together, producing the double chloride of sodium and aluminum, which could then be reduced with sodium:

$$2\ NaCl + Al_2O_3 + 3\ Cl_2 + 3\ C \rightarrow 2\ NaAlCl_4 + 3\ CO$$

$$NaAlCl_4 + 3\ Na \rightarrow Al + 4\ NaCl$$

This process made large pieces of aluminum available for the first time, and by 1886 improvements in the methods for production of sodium had brought the cost of a pound of aluminum down to about $4.00.* Really low-cost aluminum became available with the invention of the electrolytic reduction process (see below). Today, a pound of aluminum of 99.9+% purity costs less than 43 cents.

In 1886 Charles M. Hall, then 22 years of age and a recent college graduate, found that aluminum could be prepared by electrolyzing a solution of aluminum oxide in molten cryolite, Na_3AlF_6. By one of those remarkable coincidences which occur surprisingly often in chemistry, exactly the same process was discovered independently only three months later by a young Frenchman, Paul Héroult, who was also 22 years old and completely unaware of Hall's work. The industrial development of the process rapidly lowered

* The top of the Washington Monument, completed in 1884, is covered with a cap of aluminum prepared by this process. Chosen as a symbol of modern technology, it was the largest piece of aluminum ever fabricated up to that time.

the cost of aluminum to a few cents a pound, converting it from a laboratory curiosity to one of today's most important structural metals. It is one of the lightest of all metals (densities: Al = 2.7 g/cm³; Fe = 7.9 g/cm³), and its structural strength is relatively high, giving it the highest strength-to-weight ratio of any metal except magnesium.

The cell used for the Hall-Héroult process consists of a large iron box (Fig. 15.7) thickly lined with a mixture of pitch and coke, which becomes graphitized with use and serves as the negative electrode. Large carbon anodes are suspended from a bus bar overhead. These are gradually eroded

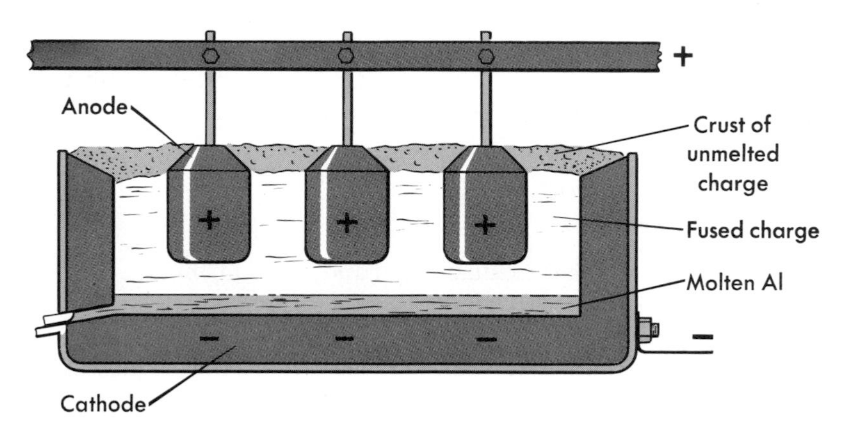

Fig. 15.7 Electrolytic cell for the production of aluminum.

away by reaction with the oxygen produced in the electrolysis, and must be replaced from time to time. The charge consists of purified alumina dissolved in a molten mixture of cryolite and calcium fluoride in the ratio $2\ Na_3AlF_6 : 3\ CaF_2$. The cryolite can be prepared simply by melting sodium and aluminum fluorides together. The calcium fluoride serves to lower the melting point of the charge. During the electrolysis, aluminum ions are reduced at the cathode (the cell lining):

$$2\ Al^{+++} + 6\ e^- \rightarrow 2\ Al$$

and oxygen is formed at the anode, with which it reacts to form CO_2:

$$3\ O^{--} + \tfrac{3}{2}\ C \rightarrow \tfrac{3}{2}\ CO_2\uparrow + 6\ e^-$$

Refining of Metals 15.5

The presence of small amounts of impurities, which lead to imperfections in the crystal structure, may have a large and usually detrimental effect on the strength and electrical properties of a metal. Traces of carbon in tungsten and sulfur in iron, for example, make those metals hard and brittle and cause almost complete loss of ductility. As little as 0.03% arsenic reduces the conductivity of copper by about 14%. Most metals, therefore, must undergo a further process of purification, or refining, subsequent to their reduction. The exceptions are those metals prepared by electrolytic methods, which usually require no additional treatment. Volatile metals, such as mercury, can often be purified by distillation. Zone refining (Sec. 16.12) is used to prepare exceptionally pure (99.999%) metals for special purposes. An especially interesting process is the recovery of small quantities of silver from lead by extraction with molten zinc. Molten zinc is nearly insoluble in lead at the melting point of zinc, but at that temperature silver is several thousand times more soluble in zinc than in lead. The silver therefore dissolves preferentially in the zinc, which is drawn off and separated from the silver by distillation. The Mond process for purifying nickel is another unique refining method, based upon the special affinity of nickel for carbon monoxide. Crude nickel is heated at 50–100°C in a stream of **CO**, which converts it to the volatile tetracarbonyl:

$$Ni + 4\ CO \rightarrow Ni(CO)_4\uparrow$$

The impurities in the nickel are unaffected and remain behind. Subsequent heating to 180°C decomposes the carbonyl, driving off **CO** and leaving 99.8% pure nickel behind.

With the exception of the above examples, the refining of most metals is done either electrolytically or by oxidizing the impurities and removing them either as gaseous oxides or in the form of slag. The electrolytic refining of copper and the manufacture of steel will serve to illustrate these two methods.

(a) Copper. The 99% pure copper as obtained from the smelter is cast into plates to serve as anodes in the electrolysis processes. These are alternated with cathodes consisting of thin sheets of refined copper and suspended in an electrolyte solution consisting of $CuSO_4$ and dilute H_2SO_4 (Fig. 15.8). The voltage is adjusted so as just to exceed the decomposition potential (Sec. 14.11) of Cu^{++} in the solution. Under these conditions, the

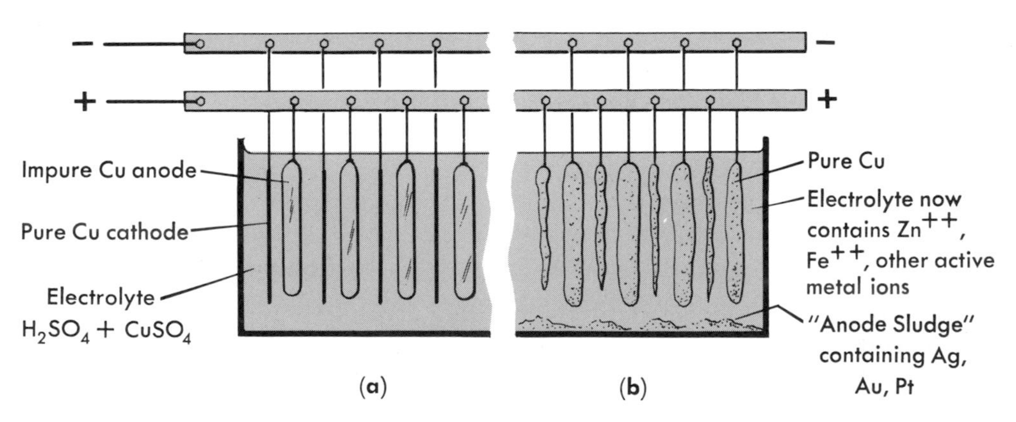

Fig. 15.8 Electrolytic cell for copper refining: (a) before electrolysis; (b) after electrolysis.

copper and more active metals in the anodes are oxidized and dissolve:

$$Cu \rightarrow Cu^{++} + 2\ e^-$$

$$Fe \rightarrow Fe^{++} + 2\ e^-$$

$$Zn \rightarrow Zn^{++} + 2\ e^-$$

Less active metals, such as silver, gold, and platinum are unaffected and drop to the bottom of the cell as the anodes disintegrate. At the cathode the Cu^{++}, but not the ions of the more active metals, is reduced and plates out 99.95+ % pure. Recovery of silver, gold, and platinum from the "anode sludge" generally pays the cost of refining the copper and may even produce a profit. The greater part of the gold produced in the United States is now obtained as a by-product of copper refining.

(b) Steel. Iron refining is a matter of removing silicon, manganese, sulfur, phosphorus, and other impurities from pig iron and of reducing the carbon content from 3–4% to 1.5% or less. The product, an alloy of pure iron and carbon, is ***steel.*** The properties and uses of steel are determined to a great extent by its carbon content. Up to a point, increasing the carbon content increases the tensile strength of the metal and makes it less ductile and malleable (Fig. 15.9).

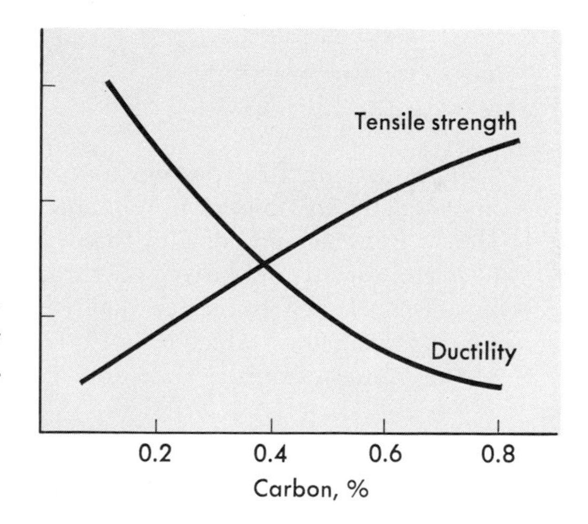

Fig. 15.9 Effect of carbon content on tensile strength and ductility of steel. Vertical scales arbitrary.

The amount of carbon in the product is adjusted to give the best combination of strength and workability, according to the use for which the steel is intended. ***Mild steels*** contain less than 0.2% carbon; they are malleable and ductile and can be drawn into wire. Steel cables, nails, spikes, chains, and horseshoes are usually made of mild steel. ***Medium steels*** have from 0.2 to 0.6% carbon and are tougher and less malleable than mild steels. Medium steels are used for girders, rails, and most structural purposes. ***High-carbon steels,*** with up to 1.5% carbon, are used for knives, razors, drills, and other cutting tools. ***Alloy steels*** contain considerable amounts of other metals added to give increased strength, hardness, or corrosion resistance to the steel. Ordinary stainless steel, for example, is an alloy of mild steel with about 18% chromium and 8% nickel.

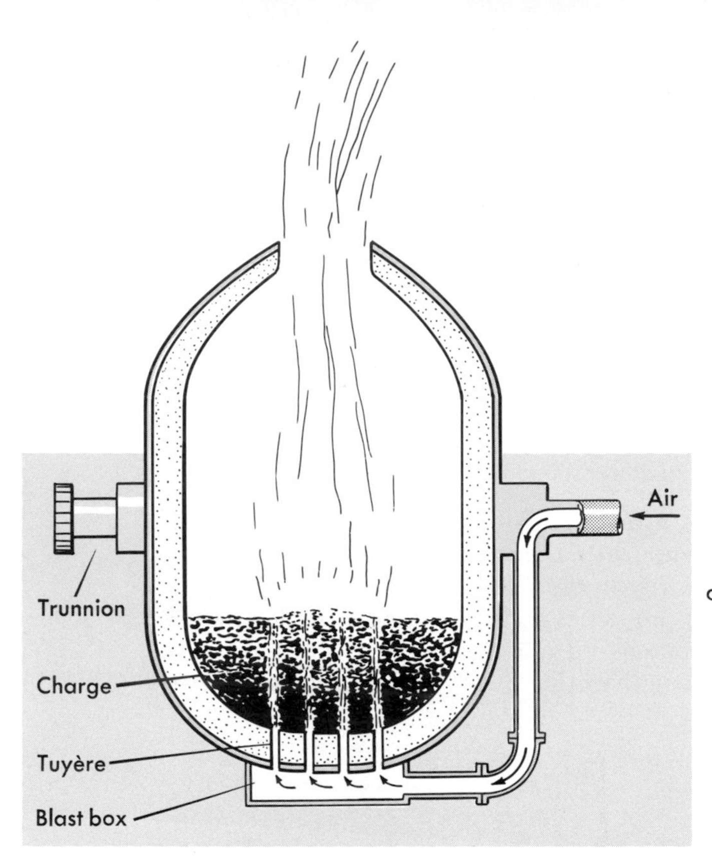

Fig. 15.10 Kelly-Bessemer converter.

The first practical process for producing steel in large quantities was invented by an American, William Kelly, in 1852, and independently by Henry Bessemer in England three years later. This process, now almost obsolete, consists of blasting air through 15–20 tons of molten iron contained in an egg-shaped converter that can be tipped for pouring (Fig. 15.10). During the "blow," which lasts 10–15 minutes, silicon, manganese, and some of the iron are oxidized and form a slag:

$$Si + O_2 \rightarrow SiO_2$$

$$2\ Mn + O_2 \rightarrow 2\ MnO$$

$$2\ Fe + O_2 \rightarrow 2\ FeO$$

$$\left.\begin{array}{r} MnO + SiO_2 \rightarrow MnSiO_3 \\ FeO + SiO_2 \rightarrow FeSiO_3 \end{array}\right\} \text{slag}$$

and the carbon is oxidized to **CO**:

$$2\ C + O_2 \rightarrow 2\ CO\uparrow$$

Small amounts of sulfur, phosphorus, and arsenic can also be burned away, but irons containing relatively large amounts of these impurities cannot be handled satisfactorily.

When the blue flame of burning CO dies down, signaling the end of the process, the converter is tipped on its side and the air is shut off. Since almost all of the carbon originally present has now been removed, the required amount of carbon is added to the charge, together with a small amount of manganese to reduce any iron oxide which has not combined with the slag:

$$FeO + Mn \rightarrow MnO + Fe$$

The MnO is removed with the slag when the charge is poured. It is easier to remove all the carbon and then add the proper amount at the end, rather than attempt to control the process so as to leave just the right amount of carbon behind in the metal.

The Kelly-Bessemer process has the advantage of speed, but for that very reason is difficult to control precisely, since there is no time to analyze the charge while the reaction is in progress. In the ***open-hearth process*** a charge of 200–300 tons of molten pig iron and steel scrap is heated in a shallow hearth by a gas-air or gas-oxygen flame playing on the surface (Fig. 15.11). Oxygen for combustion of C, S, P, and other impurities is furnished either by adding Fe_2O_3 to the charge, or by injecting it into the melt directly with a water-cooled lance. A basic hearth lining of CaO, MgO, or both, is used for iron containing phosphorus, sulfur, and other substances that form acidic oxides. If metallic impurities are present, an acid lining of silica brick (SiO_2) is used. The process takes 6–10 hours, allowing close control by periodic analysis of the melt. When the proper carbon content in the steel has been reached, any desired alloying materials are added, and the steel is poured. Although the open-hearth process takes much longer than the Kelly-Bessemer, the greater size of the charge more than compensates. Precise tailoring of the steel, such as by the addition of other metals to form alloy steels, is also more readily accomplished in the open hearth, where exact chemical analysis is possible throughout the entire process. Nevertheless the past importance of the Kelly-Bessemer process should not be undervalued. It furnished the steel for heavy rails and high-speed locomotives, making transcontinental railroads a practical reality and opening up the interior of the continent to settlement and commerce. Modern cities with their skyscrapers and mile-long bridges were made possible.

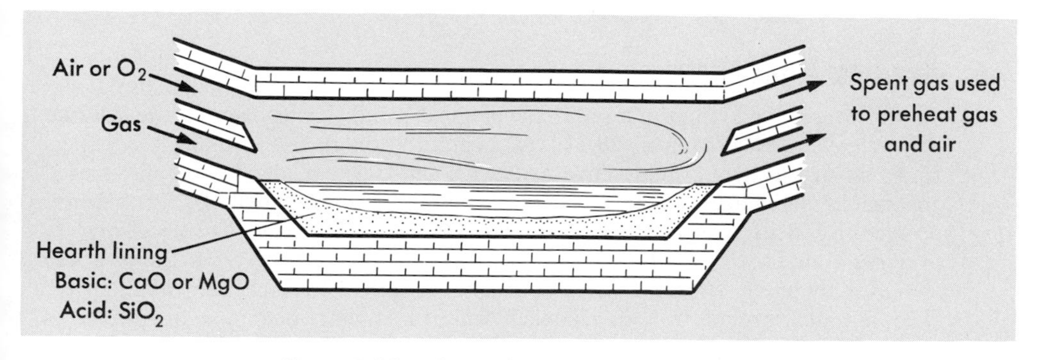

Fig. 15.11 Open-hearth furnace.

Nearly all of modern technology, in fact, dates from the invention of this first practical steelmaking process.

The availability today of pure oxygen at low cost is bringing many long-idle Kelly-Bessemer converters back into service. The ***basic oxygen process,*** or ***L-D process,*** developed in Germany in the 1950's, is rapidly becoming one of the most important steel-making methods. In this process pure oxygen from a water-cooled lance is played at high speed on the surface of molten iron contained in a basic-lined converter of the Kelly-Bessemer type. The process is as rapid as the Kelly-Bessemer, but it has the advantage of yielding a very pure product, free of sulfur and phosphorus and comparable to or better than open-hearth steel.

A revolutionary new chemical process is now being used to produce iron powder from scrap in a plant near Windsor, Ontario. In this process the iron-bearing raw material is first dissolved in hydrochloric acid to give a solution of iron(II) chloride:

$$Fe + 2\ HCl \rightarrow FeCl_2 + H_2$$

The hydrogen evolved is used later in the reduction step of the process. The solution is filtered to remove insoluble impurities and then concentrated to crystallize most of the iron salt. The crystals are filtered from the mother liquor, which contains any soluble impurities present in the ore, after which they are washed, dried, and compressed into briquets. The briquets are reduced at 800°C with hydrogen, which converts them into metallic iron:

$$FeCl_2 + H_2 \rightarrow Fe + 2\ HCl$$

Both the mother liquor from the crystallization and the hydrogen chloride evolved in the reduction step are recycled to an acid recovery plant and re-used. The iron produced is about 99.5% pure.

This process shows its greatest promise as an economical method for converting low-grade iron ores to a metal pure enough to be converted directly to steel. It is not necessary to concentrate the ore prior to treatment with acid, nor is there any need for a blast furnace to reduce the ore to pig iron. With sources of high-grade ores becoming more and more depleted, the importance of a process which allows ores of low iron content to be reduced economically cannot be overestimated.

15.6 Reading Suggestions

An interesting symposium on archaeological chemistry appears in the *Journal of Chemical Education*, vol. **28** (1951), beginning on p. 64. Among the papers included in this symposium, three deal with the types of metals and alloys used in ancient artifacts. These are: *The Corrosion Products of an Ancient Chinese Bronze*, by R. J. Gettens, *J. Chem. Ed.* **28,** 67 (1951); *Gold-Copper Alloys in Ancient America*, by W. C. Root, *ibid.*, p. 76; and *Ancient Syrian Coppers and Bronzes*, by R. J. Braidwood, J. E. Burke, and N. H. Nachtrieb, *ibid.*, p. 87. The manufacture of iron in colonial America is described in a biography of *Henry William Stiegel—Pioneer Iron and Glass Maker*, by R. D. Billinger, *J. Chem. Ed.* **30,** 356 (1953). The last charcoal-fired iron furnace of the type described in this article ceased operation about 1923. Its ruins are still visible at Centre Furnace, Pennsylvania. Nineteenth century metallurgy is described in an article by H. K. Work in *J. Chem. Ed.* **28,** 364 (1951). A general survey of steelmaking is presented by C. M. Parker, in *J. Chem. Ed.* **28,** 236 (1951), and by W. A. Dennis, *J. Chem. Ed.* **30,** 491 (1953).

The circumstances surrounding the discovery of the electrolytic process for aluminum production by Charles Martin Hall are described by A. B. Garrett in two articles in *J. Chem. Ed.* **39,** 415 (1962), and **41,** 479 (1964).

Questions and Problems

15.1 List the principal types of metallic ores (i.e., native metal, sulfide, oxide, etc.). Alongside each, write the symbols of those metals which are commonly prepared by smelting an ore of that type.

15.2 Describe the flotation process for the concentration of a sulfide ore. What is the purpose of adding oil and a detergent to the mixture of metal ore and water? How is it that, although the density of Cu_2S is more than twice that of sand (5.6 g/cm^3 vs 2.7 g/cm^3), in the concentration of copper ore by flotation it is the sulfide which rises to the top while the sand sinks to the bottom of the mixture?

15.3 Describe the Hall-Héroult process for the manufacture of aluminum. Include equations for the reactions involved in the purification of the bauxite ore and for the reactions at the electrodes, and draw a diagram of the electrolytic cell.

15.4 Describe the steps in the metallurgy of copper from the crude ore to the finished metal. Write balanced equations for all chemical reactions that occur. In the final refining step, what happens to the impurities Fe, Zn, Ag, Au, and Pt?

15.5 Besides iron ore, what two solids are added to a blast furnace? What is the purpose of each? Describe the preparation of iron in a blast furnace, giving chemical equations for the reactions taking place in various parts of the furnace, including those involved in slag formation.

15.6 Write a balanced equation for the reduction of $Au(CN)_2^-$ with zinc.

15.7 Describe, giving chemical equations where applicable, (a) the recovery of magnesium from seawater, (b) the cyanide process for the recovery of gold and silver from low grade ores, (c) the recovery of the lanthanide elements from monazite sand, (d) the preparation of chromium by the Goldschmidt reaction.

15.8 Iron ore is reduced with carbon, tungsten with hydrogen, sodium and aluminum are reduced electrolytically, rubidium is reduced with calcium, and titanium with magnesium or some other active metal. What dictates the choice of reducing agent in each case?

15.9 What is steel? How does steel differ from pig iron? How does the carbon content affect the tensile strength and ductility of steel?

15.10 Write balanced equations for the following: (a) Recovery of lead from galena (PbS). (b) Reduction of titanium(IV) chloride with magnesium. (c) Recovery of mercury from cinnabar (HgS). (d) Purification of nickel by the Mond process.

15.11 How do mild, medium, high-carbon, and alloy steels differ in their compositions and their properties? List some of the articles which are generally fabricated from each type of steel.

15.12 Cast iron contains substantial amounts of silicon and carbon which make the metal hard and brittle. How can these impurities be removed? Describe the Kelly-Bessemer process for steel manufacture, including equations for the principal reactions taking place during the "blow." How is the amount of carbon in the final product controlled?

15.13 Describe the open-hearth steelmaking process. What advantages does the open-hearth process have over the Kelly-Bessemer? What new development is bringing the old Kelly-Bessemer converters back into service?

15.14 The lining of a steel furnace is described as being either "basic" or "acidic." What do these terms mean? Which type of lining would probably be chosen if the principal impurity were manganese? What products will be formed by the reaction of the oxidized impurities with the furnace lining in each case? Give balanced equations for the reactions.

15.15 Carbon in steel is determined by burning the sample completely in an atmosphere of oxygen at 1000°C. The CO_2 produced is collected in an absorption tube containing ascarite (asbestos impregnated with $NaOH$). From the following data calculate the percentage of carbon in a sample of steel.

Weight of steel sample	2.3067 g
Weight of absorption tube before combustion	30.5433 g
Weight of absorption tube after combustion	30.8669 g

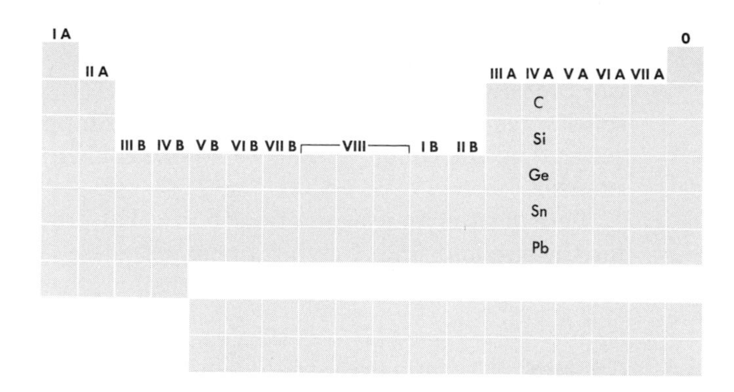

16 THE GROUP IVA ELEMENTS

Among the representative groups of elements group IVA occupies a unique position just midway between the most metallic and least metallic elements. The trend toward increasing metallic character with increasing atomic weight is especially pronounced in this group, which includes the nonmetals carbon and silicon, the metalloids germanium and tin, and the essentially metallic element lead.

Carbon, the first member of the group, is the basis of all living things and the only element to have an entire branch of chemistry—organic chemistry—devoted to it. Kingdoms have been risked and lives lost for carbon in the form of diamonds; as graphite and carbon black it is among the most versatile and useful of all of the elements. Silicon, in the forms of sand and the silicates, makes up most of the earth's crust. Germanium, once a laboratory curiosity, has the distinction of having been described by Mendeleev 15 years before Winkler's discovery of it (Sec. 4.2), and it is now found everywhere in the transistor. The discovery that tin would alloy with and harden copper introduced the Bronze Age, and the tin trade was instrumental in spreading the culture of Greece to Alexandria, to Rome, and westward to Britain, where tin mines have been worked since prehistoric times. The Romans used lead water pipes extensively, and our word plumbing comes from their word for lead: *plumbum*. Although not everyone agrees with the idea, one scholar has blamed the fall of the Roman Empire on chronic lead poisoning suffered by the ruling classes, who alone could afford lead pipes and cooking utensils.

Perhaps it is an exaggeration to say that group IVA has been responsible for the rise and fall of civilizations, yet these elements are interesting and important enough to warrant more than a passing glance.

16.1 Carbon

Carbon crystallizes in two allotropic modifications,* diamond and graphite. They could hardly differ more in their properties. Diamond is the hardest known natural substance and has long been a symbol of constancy and durability. The word diamond, in fact, is derived from the same root as adamant, meaning unflexible and unyielding. It is a nonconductor of electricity and is transparent when pure, with a refractive index almost twice that of glass. It is this latter property that gives properly cut and polished diamonds their fiery sparkle, and this, coupled with their durability and rarity, makes them among the most valuable of gemstones. Diamond powder and diamonds that are black or discolored with impurities are worthless as jewels but are used in drill bits, cutting tools, and abrasives, where advantage is taken of their extreme hardness.

At 1 atm, diamond is thermodynamically unstable with respect to graphite at all temperatures. ΔG^0 for the transition

$$C_{(diamond)} \rightarrow C_{(graphite)}$$

is -0.69 kcal/mole. The activation energy for this process is very large, however, and diamond shows no detectable inclination to revert to graphite at temperatures below 1200°C.

Graphite is almost the complete opposite of diamond in its physical properties. Its name, from the Greek for "I write," derives from its use in pencil "lead," where its softness and blackness make it ideal for the purpose. Its electrical conductivity, together with its relative chemical inertness and low cost, make it especially suitable for electrodes and other electrical components. In the absence of air, in which it burns slowly at red heat, graphite can withstand far higher temperatures than most metals and ceramics. Its vapor pressure is practically negligible up to about 3000°C and, most remarkable, its mechanical strength increases with temperature, so that at 2500°C it is nearly double what it is at room temperature. This makes it one of the strongest materials available for use at high temperatures. By comparison, iron melts at 1535°C and boils at 3000°; calcium oxide melts at 2850°, and silicon dioxide (silica brick and sand) melts at about 1600°C.

Graphite is easily shaped and machined to close tolerances, and it has been used for rocket nozzles and other parts of space vehicles and missiles which must be precisely shaped and yet withstand excessive heat. It has

* Allotropy, from the Greek for "other way," refers to the existence of more than one form of a substance in the same physical state. Both graphite and diamond are solids composed solely of carbon atoms, but their appearance and physical properties are quite different.

a remarkable ability to slow down, or "moderate," neutrons emitted during nuclear fission (Sec. 20.8), a property it shares with the far more costly heavy water (deuterium oxide). Slow neutrons are necessary if a steady, nonexplosive chain reaction is to be maintained, and large quantities of graphite bricks are used for this purpose in the construction of atomic piles and reactors.

The characteristic properties of both graphite and diamond derive from their crystal structures. In the diamond lattice, each carbon atom is covalently bound to four other atoms located at the corners of a tetrahedron (Fig. 16.1). The tetrahedral arrangement of the bonds suggests that they are formed by the overlap of sp^3 hybrid orbitals (Sec. 8.9). Since all of the valence electrons are involved in bonding, there are none available for electrical conduction, and the crystal is an insulator. All of the bonds in the crystal are the same length, 1.54 Å, and their dissociation energy is 85 kcal/mole. The characteristic hardness of diamond results from this strength and uniformity of bonding.

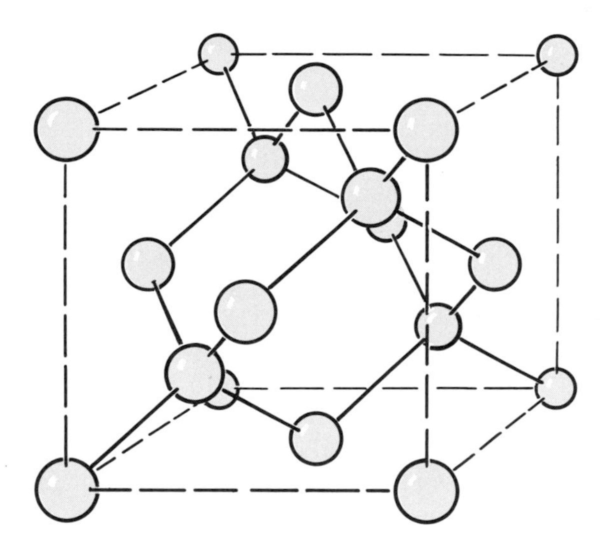

Fig. 16.1 The arrangement of atoms in the diamond lattice (cubic system).

The carbon atoms in graphite are hexagonally arranged in flat, parallel layers, with each atom covalently bonded to three neighbors. The bonds between the atoms form angles of 120°, typical of sp^2 hybridization. The carbon-carbon bond length in the layers is 1.42 Å; adjacent layers are 3.354 Å apart. This latter distance is too great for any covalent cross linking between the layers, which are instead held together by relatively weak van der Waals forces. Every second layer in the crystal is displaced so that a carbon atom in one lies directly above the center of each hexagon in the layer below. The atoms of every third layer lie directly above those of the first, the pattern repeating in a *ababab* sequence (Fig. 16.2). The crystal cleaves readily along the carbon layers, but cleavage perpendicular to the layers is much more difficult, since it involves the breaking of covalent bonds.

Vapor molecules such as H_2O, CO_2 and NH_3, which are below their critical temperatures, may diffuse into the space between the carbon layers where

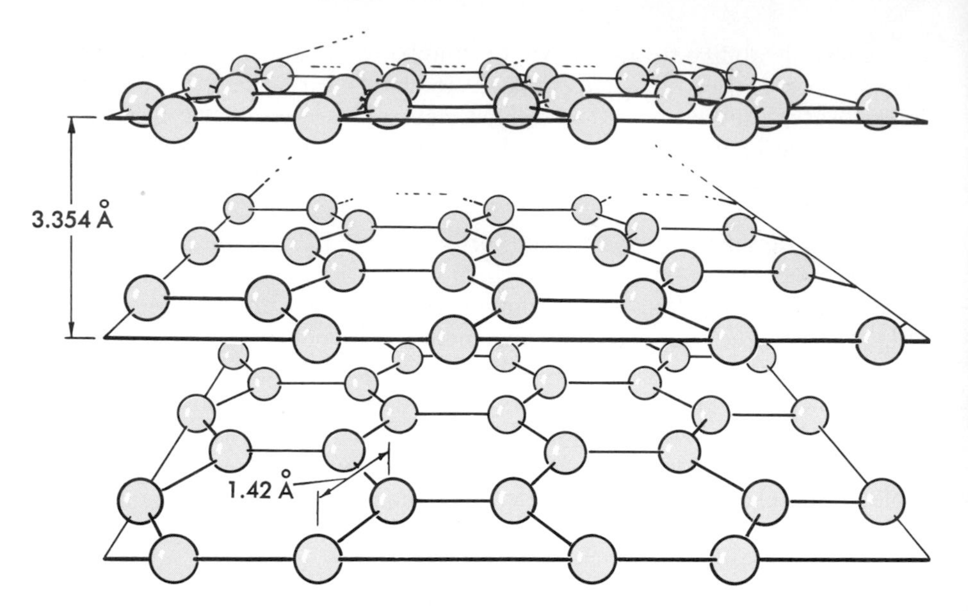

Fig. 16.2 Crystal structure of graphite (hexagonal system).

they condense and act like ball-bearings, letting the layers slide easily past one another. This gives graphite its lubricating property, a property it loses in a vacuum or in an atmosphere composed entirely of permanent gases.

Graphite exhibits metallic conductance along the carbon layers. After utilizing three sp^2 hybrid orbitals to form bonds with three other atoms, each carbon atom is left with a single p orbital containing one electron. This p orbital can overlap with the p orbitals of the adjacent carbon atoms, resulting in the formation of a π orbital system extending throughout the entire layer of carbon atoms (Fig. 16.3). Within this π orbital system the electrons are free to move from one atom to another, with electrical conductivity following as a natural consequence. There is no orbital overlap between layer planes, and graphite shows little conductivity perpendicular to the carbon layers.

The graphite crystal structure described above represents an ideal. Most carbons do not possess this ideal structure and are referred to as graphites, graphitic carbons, and nongraphitic carbons, according to the extent to which they deviate from ideality. Charcoal and carbon black possess

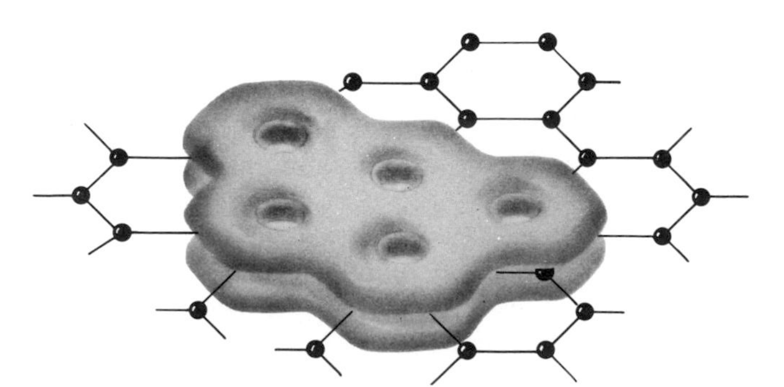

Fig. 16.3 Portion of a carbon layer in graphite showing a part of the extended π orbital system.

essentially no three-dimensional order and are commonly termed ***amorphous carbons.*** At one time, amorphous carbon was considered a distinct noncrystalline allotrope, but it is now known to be composed of groups of graphitic layers of limited size, stacked roughly parallel, but otherwise randomly arranged (Fig. 16.4).

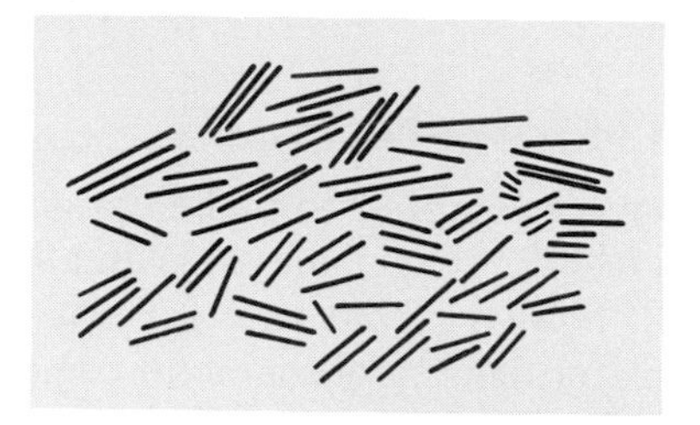

Fig. 16.4 Arrangement of graphitic layers in "amorphous" carbon (schematic).

Graphite Manufacture 16.2

Natural deposits of graphite exist in many parts of the world. The most perfect crystals are mined in Ceylon, and other important deposits are found in the United States, the Malagasay Republic, and in Siberia. These and other widely scattered deposits could not begin to supply the demand for this versatile substance. Natural graphite, furthermore, is generally in the form of a powder containing a certain amount of ash, and hence it is unsuitable for the manufacture of articles of any size.

In theory, any sample of carbon when recrystallized at moderate pressures should assume the most stable crystal structure and is, therefore, a potential source of graphite. The goal of producing graphite artificially on a practical scale was first achieved by E. G. Acheson in 1896, and his process is in essence that used today. In the Acheson process, the carbon to be graphitized is first ground, mixed with a binder of coal tar or pitch, extruded or molded to shape, and baked at 1000°–1800°C to remove volatile matter and carbonize the binder. The baked carbon is then converted to graphite in an electric furnace. The furnace (Fig. 16.5) consists of a brick foundation covered with a layer of fine carbon. The carbon to be graphitized is piled

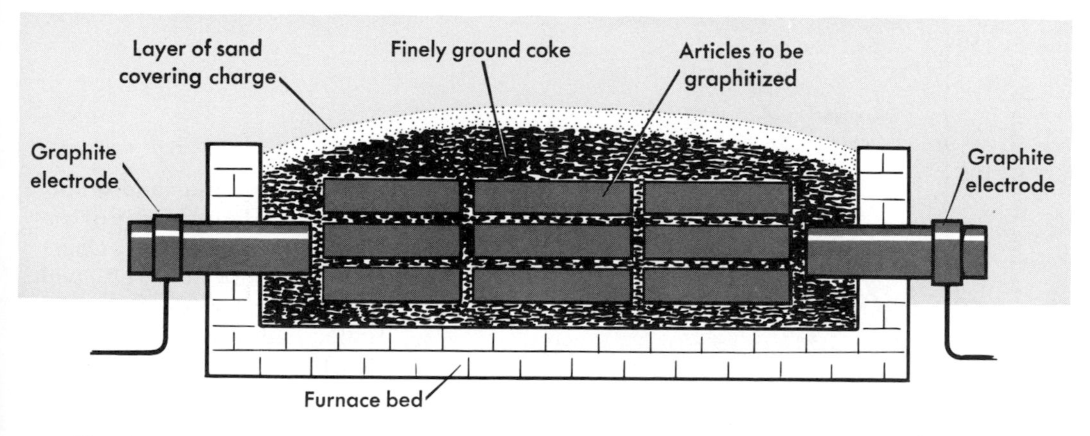

Fig. 16.5 Cross section of electric furnace for manufacture of graphite by the Acheson process.

on the furnace bed in uniform tiers separated by layers of coke. A heavy electric current is passed through the charge for several days. The resistance of the charge to the current causes the temperature to rise, reaching a maximum of about 4100°C. The resistance gradually decreases as the graphitization progresses, and the process is considered complete when the resistance attains a constant value.

16.3 Synthesis of Diamond

Men have attempted to make diamonds artificially ever since Lavoisier suggested in 1792 that diamond is an allotropic form of carbon. It was not until 1954, however, that the feat was actually accomplished.

The greater density of diamond compared with graphite (3.52 g/cm^3 vs. 2.25 g/cm^3 for graphite) suggests that its formation should be favored by high pressures, and most attempts at diamond synthesis, including those that were finally successful, have been concerned with the problem of attaining the necessary pressure. The most famous of the earlier attempts was that of Henri Moissan in 1892. Moissan dissolved graphite in molten iron which he then cooled suddenly. It was his hope that as the mass of iron cooled from the outside, part of the carbon would precipitate in the interior of the mass and be subjected to enormous pressures as the iron solidified. After he dissolved the iron in acid, Moissan found a few very hard, microscopic crystals, which appeared to be diamonds, in the residue. Whether they were in fact diamonds was debated for many years. Later calculations indicated that the pressure developed in the interior of the iron mass would not have been sufficient to effect the transformation. It has been suggested that the crystals obtained by Moissan were some type of chemically resistant spinel, or mixed metallic oxide, formed from impurities in the iron.

A portion of the diamond-graphite phase diagram is shown in Fig. 16.6.

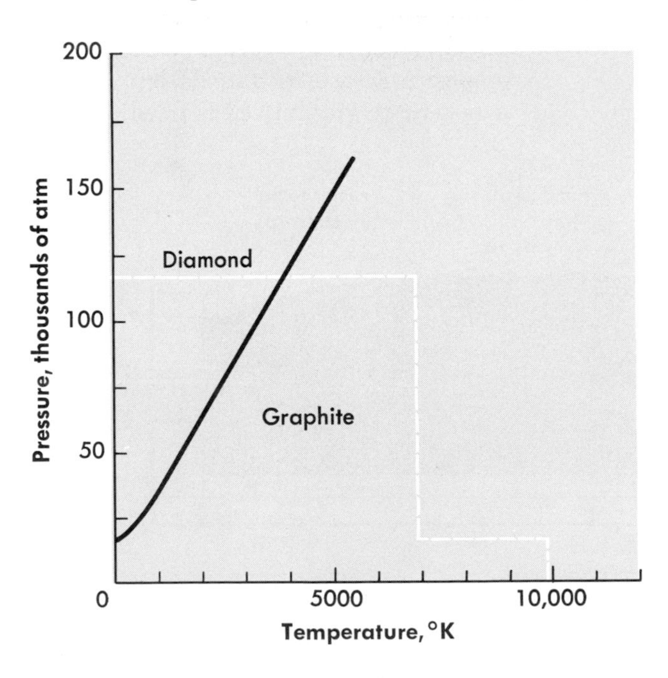

Fig. 16.6 Diamond-graphite equilibrium diagram. (From H. T. Hall, *J. Chem. Ed.*, **38,** 484 (1961), with corrections furnished by Dr. Hall. Redrawn with permission.)

From this diagram it would appear necessary merely to subject graphite to conditions of temperature and pressure lying in the region above the diamond-graphite equilibrium curve in order to bring about its conversion to diamond. Although graphite has been subjected in the laboratory at one time or another to those conditions within the shaded portion of the diagram, its direct transformation to diamond has never been observed. There is obviously more to the problem than merely attaining the conditions under which diamond is the stable allotrope—the activation energy barrier must be surmounted as well. From the phase diagram it is seen that raising the temperature in order to furnish the activation energy requires that the pressure be increased as well in order to stay within the diamond region. Furthermore, there is evidence that during the transition from graphite to diamond carbon must pass through an intermediate state having an expanded structure of low density. Thus high pressures, while leading to thermodynamically favorable conditions for diamond formation, at the same time hinder the formation of the necessary transition state, leading to an apparent impasse.

The key to the solution of this problem, as is so often the case, lay in finding a catalyst both to lower the activation energy and, if possible, to avoid the necessity of passing through the low-density transition state. The latter might be accomplished by the use of an appropriate solvent, which would dissolve the graphite as individual atoms. Under proper conditions these atoms might be expected to migrate through the solvent and precipitate in the form of diamond. A clue to the proper solvent is the fact that natural diamonds are frequently found imbedded in a matrix of ferro-magnesium silicates or in other ferrous minerals from which they have evidently crystallized.

The first successful diamond synthesis was accomplished at the General Electric Research Laboratories* in Schenectady, New York, in 1954. A small graphite cell containing ferrous sulfide was subjected to a temperature of about 1650°C and a pressure between 80,000 and 95,000 atm, and these conditions were maintained for about three minutes. Transparent diamond crystals formed in the vicinity of the graphite plugs at the ends of the cell (Fig. 16.7). Subsequent experiments showed that pure iron powder could

* Now a part of the General Electric Research and Development Center.

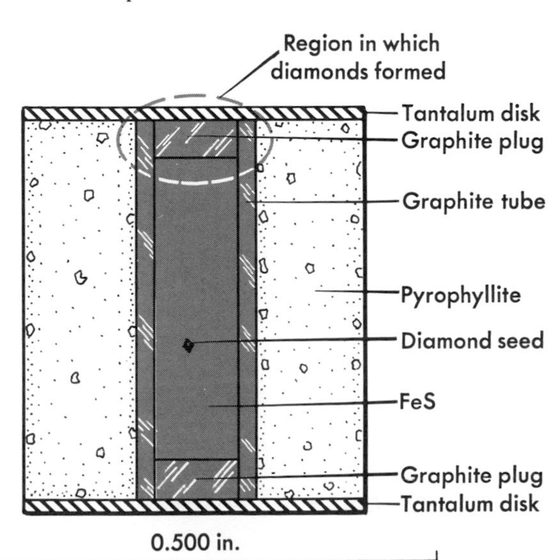

Fig. 16.7 Cross section of cell in which diamonds were first prepared artificially. (From H. T. Hall, *J. Chem. Ed.*, **38**, 484 (1961). Redrawn with permission.)

Fig. 16.8 Photomicrograph of Man-Made diamond crystals. The largest crystal in the photograph is 2.5–3 mm across. (Photograph courtesy General Electric Research and Development Center.)

be substituted for the **FeS**. These diamonds (Fig. 16.8) are not large enough to be classed as gems, but they are entirely suitable for industrial use and in some respects are superior to the natural product. Synthetic diamonds are grown under controlled conditions, and close control can be exercised over their properties. For example, the ideal crystal for many purposes is an octahedron of the correct size. As shown in Fig. 16.8, such octahedra are readily grown. Fine-mesh natural diamond on the other hand is usually produced by crushing larger stones, a process which does not necessarily yield crystals of the desired shape.

16.4 Carbon Dioxide

Carbon, and carbon products such as the hydrocarbons (Sec. 17.1), burn in air to give the dioxide.

$$C + O_2 \rightarrow CO_2$$

$$2\ C_8H_{18} + 25\ O_2 \rightarrow 16\ CO_2 + 18\ H_2O$$

These reactions are exothermic, leading to the use of carbon compounds and such carbonaceous materials as coal and coke as fuels.

Since oxygen is more electronegative than carbon, carbon-oxygen bonds are polar, with the carbon atom normally at the positive end of the dipole. Carbon dioxide nevertheless has no dipole moment. This is possible only if the CO_2 molecule is linear, allowing the two carbon-oxygen dipoles to cancel. For the dipoles to cancel they must be of the same magnitude, which means that the bonds to the two oxygens are equivalent. X-ray diffraction confirms the linearity of the molecule and shows that the bonds are all of the same length and somewhat shorter than expected for a carbon-oxygen double bond. To account for the bond length the suggestion has been made that while the molecule may be largely represented by (a), small and equal contributions to the structure are made by (b) and (c), in which a triple bond exists between the carbon and one of the oxygens:

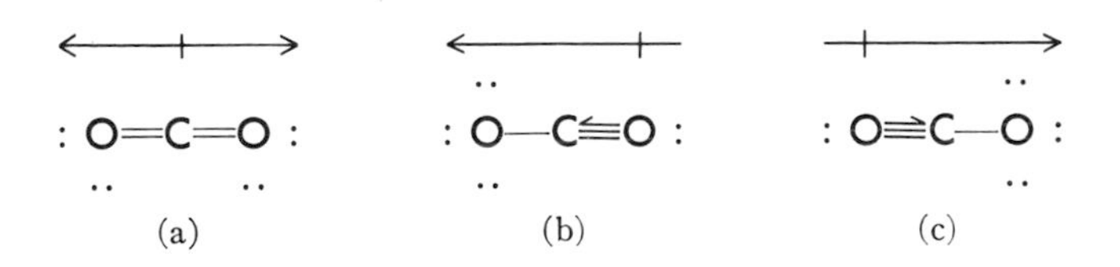

Carbon dioxide is a colorless, odorless gas with a density about 1.5 times that of air. It is a normal product of respiration, fermentation, and decay, and is not ordinarily considered toxic. Because of its density, it tends to collect in low sections of mines, caves, and sewers, where it displaces the air and may cause asphyxiation for lack of oxygen. Carbon dioxide is found underground in many parts of the world, particularly where there is, or has been, volcanic activity. It often dissolves under pressure in the ground waters of such regions, giving rise to effervescent "soda springs" such as those found at Vichy, France; Saratoga Springs, New York; Manitou Springs, Colorado, and elsewhere. In some places, the gas issues from fissures in the earth. This is the case in the famous Grotto del Cano, or Cave of the Dogs near Naples. This cave owes its name to the observation that dogs that enter the cave are immediately overcome by the CO_2 which collects near the floor, while humans are unaffected because their heads are above the level of the gas. In concentrations of the order of five parts per thousand in the air, CO_2 exhibits some toxicity. At this concentration the partial pressure of CO_2 in the lungs is high enough to prevent its elimination from the blood during respiration. The supposedly prophetic babblings of the ancient oracles have been attributed by some to intoxication resulting from inhalation of CO_2 issuing from the earth.

Carbon dioxide has a critical temperature of 31°C and a critical pressure of 73 atm, or about 1100 lb/in.^{2} At room temperature, therefore, pressure alone is sufficient to liquefy the gas, and a cylinder of CO_2, such as a fire extinguisher, contains both liquid and gas in equilibrium, at a pressure equal to the vapor pressure. The triple point at which liquid, solid, and gaseous CO_2 are in equilibrium occurs at -56.6°C and 5.1 atm, and the liquid therefore cannot be observed at ordinary atmospheric pressure. The vapor pressure of the solid reaches 1 atm at -78.5°C, at which temperature it sublimes directly to the gas. Solid CO_2, often sold under the trade-name Dry Ice, is used to keep ice cream frozen and for other purposes where a temperature of about -78°C is desired.

Carbonic Acid and the Carbonates 16.5

Carbon dioxide is moderately soluble in water. At 25°C, 1.45 g of the gas dissolves in a liter of water at 1 atm to give an approximately 0.033 M solution. Its solubility is greatly increased by pressure. Carbonated soft drinks, beer, and champagne all contain dissolved CO_2. Releasing the pressure lowers the solubility of the gas and causes the liquid to effervesce. Only about 0.4% of the dissolved gas reacts with the water to form carbonic acid:

$$CO_2 + H_2O \rightleftharpoons H_2CO_3$$

Carbonic acid can exist only in dilute aqueous solution. It is a fairly weak diprotic acid, ionizing as follows:

$$H_2CO_3 + H_2O \rightleftharpoons H_3O^+ + HCO_3^- \qquad K_1 = 4.3 \times 10^{-7} \text{ at } 25°C^*$$

$$HCO_3^- + H_2O \rightleftharpoons H_3O^+ + CO_3^{--} \qquad K_2 = 5.6 \times 10^{-11} \text{ at } 25°C^*$$

Carbon dioxide reacts readily with alkali metal hydroxides, either in solution or in the solid state, to form the alkali metal carbonates, which, unlike the carbonates of other metals, are soluble in water:

$$CO_2 + 2\ LiOH \rightarrow Li_2CO_3 + H_2O$$

$$CO_2 + 2\ NaOH \rightarrow Na_2CO_3 + H_2O$$

When CO_2 is bubbled through limewater (saturated calcium hydroxide solution) or barium hydroxide solution, the insoluble carbonate is precipitated, and formation of the precipitate can be used as a test for the presence of carbon dioxide:

$$CO_2 + Ca(OH)_2 \rightarrow CaCO_3\downarrow + H_2O$$

$$CO_2 + Ba(OH)_2 \rightarrow BaCO_3\downarrow + H_2O$$

The carbonates of most metals are insoluble, and treatment of solutions of their salts with a soluble carbonate will cause precipitation:

$$Mg^{++} + CO_3^{--} \rightarrow MgCO_3\downarrow$$

In some cases a stable carbonate is not formed, and the precipitate is the oxide:

$$2\ Fe^{+++} + 3\ CO_3^{--} \rightarrow 3\ CO_2 + Fe_2O_3\downarrow$$

Carbonates decompose upon heating to form the oxide and CO_2. Heavy metal carbonates tend to be the least stable. The most stable carbonates

* These values for the ionization constants are based on the assumption that the molarity of the acid is equal to the molarity of dissolved CO_2; that is, that all of the dissolved CO_2 reacts with water to form carbonic acid. When the ionization constants are calculated on the basis of the amount of carbonic acid actually present, the true value of K_1 is found to be about 5×10^{-4}, showing that carbonic acid itself actually ionizes to a much greater extent than does acetic acid. A somewhat similar situation exists with solutions of ammonia. Ammonium hydroxide is completely ionized and is a strong base. The weak basicity of ammonia solutions arises from the fact that ammonia, like CO_2, reacts with water to only a very small degree.

are those of the alkali and alkaline earth metals:

$$Ag_2CO_3 \xrightarrow{218°C} Ag_2O + CO_2$$

$$PbCO_3 \xrightarrow{315°C} PbO + CO_2$$

$$CaCO_3 \xrightarrow{825°C} CaO + CO_2$$

$$Li_2CO_3 \xrightarrow{1310°C} Li_2O + CO_2$$

Replacement of only one of the two hydrogens of carbonic acid gives rise to the acid salt, or ***bicarbonate,*** so named because it can be considered as resulting from the reaction of the oxide with twice as much carbonic acid as is required to form the normal salt:

$$\text{Carbonate:} \quad Na_2O + H_2CO_3 \rightarrow Na_2CO_3 + H_2O$$

$$\text{Bicarbonate:} \quad Na_2O + 2\ H_2CO_3 \rightarrow 2\ NaHCO_3 + H_2O$$

Many metal carbonates, although insoluble in pure water, will dissolve to some extent in water containing CO_2, to form the bicarbonates:

$$CaCO_3 + H_2CO_3 \rightarrow Ca^{++} + 2\ HCO_3^-$$

$$FeCO_3 + H_2CO_3 \rightarrow Fe^{++} + 2\ HCO_3^-$$

The reaction is reversible, and upon evaporation of the solution the carbonate is redeposited:

$$Ca^{++} + 2\ HCO_3^- \rightarrow CaCO_3\downarrow + H_2O + CO_2$$

$$Fe^{++} + 2\ HCO_3^- \rightarrow FeCO_3\downarrow + H_2O + CO_2$$

In this way, groundwater, which always contains some dissolved CO_2, seeping through a deposit of limestone ($CaCO_3$), slowly dissolves away the rock, leaving a limestone cave. As the calcium bicarbonate solution drops from the roof of the cave, part of it evaporates, redepositing $CaCO_3$ in the form of stalactites and stalagmites.

Solutions of ammonia and carbon dioxide react to yield a solution of ammonium bicarbonate:

$$NH_3 + CO_2 + H_2O \rightarrow NH_4^+ + HCO_3^-$$

If sodium and chloride ions are simultaneously present in the solution, at 0°C the least soluble combination of ions is $NaHCO_3$, and that salt therefore precipitates:

$$NH_4^+ + HCO_3^- + Na^+ + Cl^- \rightarrow NaHCO_3\downarrow + NH_4^+ + Cl^-$$

Heating the sodium bicarbonate causes its decomposition to the carbonate,

CO_2, and water:

$$2\ NaHCO_3 \xrightarrow{270°C} Na_2CO_3 + H_2O + CO_2\uparrow$$

This series of reactions forms the basis of the ***Solvay process*** for the manufacture of sodium carbonate, which was developed by Ernest Solvay about 1865. The commercial feasibility of the Solvay process depends upon the recovery of ammonia by lime treatment of the solution of ammonium chloride which remains after filtration of sodium bicarbonate:

$$CaO + H_2O \rightarrow Ca(OH)_2$$

$$2\ NH_4Cl + Ca(OH)_2 \rightarrow 2\ NH_3\uparrow + CaCl_2 + 2\ H_2O$$

The calcium oxide used in the recovery step is obtained by heating limestone, which also serves as the source of CO_2 for the process:

$$CaCO_3 \xrightarrow{900°C} CaO + CO_2\uparrow$$

The ammonia, since it is recovered at the end, is seen to be acting as a catalyst for the overall reaction, which is

$$CaCO_3 + 2\ NaCl \rightarrow CaCl_2 + Na_2CO_3$$

This reaction does not take place directly; normally the equilibrium overwhelmingly favors the formation of the insoluble compound, calcium carbonate.

Sodium carbonate, or "soda ash," is one of the principal ingredients of ordinary glass, and it is a major industrial heavy chemical used in the manufacture of other chemicals and finished products. It gives an alkaline reaction by hydrolysis:

$$2\ Na^+ + CO_3^{--} + H_2O \rightarrow 2\ Na^+ + HCO_3^- + OH^-$$

and is used therefore as a mild alkali and industrial detergent. Its decahydrate, "washing soda," $Na_2CO_3 \cdot 10\ H_2O$, is used as a water softener, effectively precipitating dissolved calcium, magnesium, and other ions present in hard water,

$$Ca^{++} + CO_3^{--} \rightarrow CaCO_3\downarrow$$

before they can precipitate as scale in pipes or boilers, or interfere with the action of soap by forming insoluble curds:

$$\underset{\text{sodium soap: soluble}}{2\ NaC_{18}H_{35}O_2} + CaSO_4 \rightarrow \underset{\text{calcium soap: insoluble}}{Ca(C_{18}H_{35}O_2)_2\downarrow} + Na_2SO_4$$

As salts of a weak acid, all carbonates and bicarbonates react with stronger acids to form carbonic acid, which decomposes spontaneously to

CO_2 and H_2O:

$$CaCO_3 + H_2SO_4 \rightarrow CaSO_4 + H_2O + CO_2\uparrow$$

$$NaHCO_3 + HCl \rightarrow NaCl + H_2O + CO_2\uparrow$$

$$FeCO_3 + 2\ HCl \rightarrow FeCl_2 + H_2O + CO_2\uparrow$$

or, in general,

$$CO_3^{--} + H_3O^+ \rightleftarrows HCO_3^- + H_2O$$

$$HCO_3^- + H_3O^+ \rightleftarrows H_2CO_3 + H_2O$$

$$H_2CO_3 \rightarrow H_2O + CO_2\uparrow$$

Carbonates and bicarbonates can be recognized by their reaction with acid to form a gas which forms a precipitate when it is bubbled through limewater.

Soluble carbonates undergo hydrolysis to give basic solutions:

$$CO_3^{--} + H_2O \rightleftharpoons HCO_3^- + OH^-$$

$$HCO_3^- + H_2O \rightleftharpoons H_2CO_3 + OH^-$$

In the case of the alkali metal bicarbonates, hydrolysis (1) and ionization (2) of the bicarbonate ion occur to about the same extent, and the solution as a result is very nearly neutral:

$$(1) \qquad HCO_3^- + H_2O \rightleftharpoons H_2CO_3 + OH^-$$

$$(2) \qquad HCO_3^- + H_2O \rightleftharpoons H_3O^+ + CO_3^{--}$$

The carbonate ion is planar and symmetrical. All of the bonds are equivalent, and the charge on the ion is distributed equally among the three oxygen atoms. No single representation using conventional symbols can be drawn for this ion, whose actual structure is best envisioned as a hybrid of three structures:

```
-O                  -O                  O
  \                   \                  \\
   C=O      ↔          C—O-      ↔        C—O-
  /                   //                 /
-O                   O                 -O
```

When a molecule cannot be adequately described in terms of a single conventional structure, but only as a hybrid of several such structures differing from one another only in the arrangement of bonds, it is said to exhibit ***resonance,*** symbolized by the double headed arrow ↔ shown above. The term resonance is an unfortunate one, since it implies that the various structures have an independent existence, something which is decidedly not so. A molecular orbital picture comes closest to representing the actual structure of a molecule exhibiting resonance, but in all but the simplest cases this representation

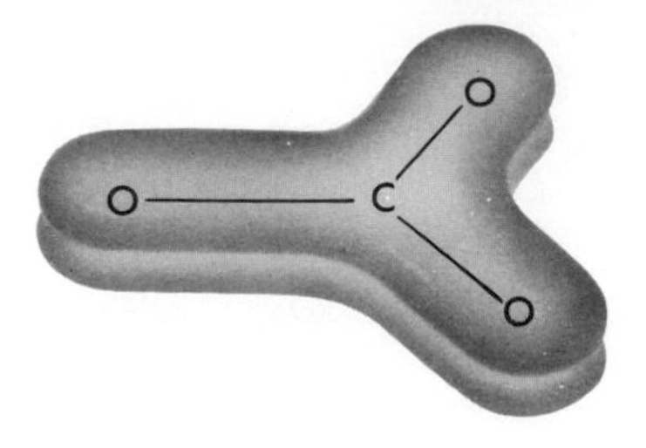

Fig. 16.9 Molecular orbital representation of the carbonate ion.

is too clumsy and difficult to draw, and the concept of a "resonance hybrid" is more convenient. A molecular orbital picture of the carbonate ion is shown in Fig. 16.9. The 2 p_y orbitals of the three oxygen atoms are seen to overlap with the 2 p_y orbital of the carbon to give a π orbital system occupied by four electrons and extending over the entire ion.

16.6 Carbon Monoxide

When carbon is burned in an insufficient supply of air, the carbon dioxide initially formed is reduced to the monoxide. The reaction

$$CO_2 + C \rightleftharpoons 2\ CO \qquad \Delta H^0 = +41.21 \text{ kcal}$$

is endothermic and reversible. At 500°C about 95% of the equilibrium mixture is the dioxide, while at 1000° the yield of the monoxide is nearly quantitative. The monoxide is also formed during the combustion of gasoline and other hydrocarbons and carbonaceous materials if the supply of oxygen is restricted:

$$2\ C_8H_{18} + 17\ O_2 \rightarrow 16\ CO + 18\ H_2O$$

In contrast to the dioxide, carbon monoxide is highly toxic. CO has a greater affinity for the hemoglobin of the blood than does oxygen. It is therefore rapidly absorbed by the blood and may cause death of the tissues for lack of oxygen. Carbon monoxide is odorless and gives no warning of its presence. Because only a small difference exists between a toxic dose, which causes symptoms of dizziness and nausea, and a lethal dose, many persons have been overcome before they realized that they were exposed to the gas. To prevent CO poisoning, care must be taken that furnaces and heaters are adequately supplied with air and properly vented. Automobiles and gasoline engines, which always produce CO, should be operated only outdoors or in well-ventilated areas.

Large amounts of CO are used as fuel, much of it in the form of ***water gas,*** a mixture of CO and H_2 which is produced by the reaction of steam with hot coke:

$$C(s) + H_2O(g) \rightarrow CO(g) + H_2(g) \qquad \Delta H_{298} = +89.2 \text{ kcal}$$

The reaction is endothermic, and the process must be periodically interrupted to pass air through the fuel bed in order to reheat it by burning some of the coke. Otherwise the fuel bed would soon cool down, and the process would stop. A large amount of heat is released when the water gas is burned:

$$CO(g) + \tfrac{1}{2}O_2(g) \rightarrow CO_2(g) \qquad \Delta H_{298} = -67.6 \text{ kcal}$$

$$H_2(g) + \tfrac{1}{2}O_2(g) \rightarrow H_2O(g) \qquad \Delta H_{298} = -57.8 \text{ kcal}$$

Carbon monoxide reacts with superheated steam, forming CO_2 and H_2:

$$CO(g) + H_2O(g) \rightarrow CO_2(g) + H_2(g) \qquad \Delta H_{298} = -9.8 \text{ kcal}$$

The CO_2 may be absorbed in water and recovered. If the hydrogen is then added to a water gas mixture, the resulting mixture of CO and H_2 can be used in the synthesis of methyl alcohol and other organic compounds:

$$CO + 2\,H_2 \xrightarrow[\text{heat, pressure}]{\text{catalyst}} \underset{\text{methyl alcohol}}{CH_3OH}$$

$$CO + 3\,H_2 \xrightarrow[250^\circ\text{C, 1 atm}]{\text{catalyst}} \underset{\text{methane}}{CH_4} + H_2O$$

Almost all of the methyl alcohol produced industrially today is prepared in this way, and the synthesis of hydrocarbons from CO-H_2 mixtures is becoming increasingly important.

Carbon monoxide is the anhydride of formic acid,* from which it may be prepared by treatment of the acid with a dehydrating agent such as concentrated sulfuric acid:

$$HCHO_2 + H_2SO_4 \rightarrow CO + H_2SO_4 \cdot H_2O$$

Unlike the dioxide, carbon monoxide is almost insoluble in water and does not react with it to any detectable extent. It will, however, react with alkalis to give formates:

$$CO + NaOH \xrightarrow[6\text{–}10\text{ atm}]{200^\circ\text{C}} \underset{\text{sodium formate}}{NaCHO_2}$$

The dipole moment of CO is surprisingly small, considering the difference in electronegativities of the atoms, and the C—O bond is shorter than would be expected for a double bond, although not as short as a triple bond. This is interpreted as indicating that the structure of the molecule is a resonance hybrid of (a) and (b):

$$:\text{C}{=}\ddot{\text{O}}: \;\leftrightarrow\; :\text{C}{\equiv}\text{O}:$$

$$\underset{(a)}{+\!\!\longrightarrow} \qquad \underset{(b)}{\longleftarrow\!\!+}$$

* The term formic acid, from the Latin *formica*, meaning ant, derives from the alchemists' preparation of this acid by the distillation of red ants. It is the principal irritant in the stings of ants, bees, and many other insects.

Carbon monoxide reacts with the halogens fluorine, chlorine, and bromine to give the ***carbonyl halides.*** The chloride ***phosgene*** was used as a poison gas in World War I, and this reactive compound is an important intermediate in organic synthesis:

$$CO + Cl_2 \rightarrow \underset{\text{phosgene}}{COCl_2}$$

Certain transition metals react with CO to give ***metal carbonyls.*** These are volatile compounds which are decomposed by heat. The formation, distillation, and decomposition of nickel carbonyl, $Ni(CO)_4$, is the basis of the Mond process for refining that metal (Sec. 15.5).

A third oxide, ***carbon suboxide,*** C_3O_2, is known but is of little importance. It is the anhydride of malonic acid, from which it is formed by distillation of the acid with P_4O_{10}:

$$\underset{\text{malonic acid}}{H_2C_3H_2O_4} + P_4O_{10} \rightarrow \underset{\text{carbon suboxide}}{O{=}C{=}C{=}C{=}O} + 4\ HPO_3$$

It is an evil-smelling gas (b.p. 7°C) which reacts with water to regenerate the acid:

$$C_3O_2 + 2\ H_2O \rightarrow H_2C_3H_2O_4$$

16.7 Silicon

Silicon makes up nearly 28% of the earth's crust, and is the second most abundant element on the surface of the earth, exceeded only by oxygen. It is not found free in nature but exists chiefly in the form of its dioxide (*silica*, SiO_2), and in the minerals known as ***silicates.*** Silicon is usually prepared by the reduction of silica (quartz sand) with carbon in an electric furnace:

$$SiO_2 + 2\ C \rightarrow Si + 2\ CO$$

The element is used as a deoxidant in steel making, as an ingredient in acid-resistant steel alloys, and to some extent as a reducing agent in certain special applications. Ultrapure silicon, obtained by reducing the tetrahalide with sodium:

$$SiBr_4 + 4\ Na \rightarrow 4\ NaBr + Si$$

finds some application as a semiconductor in transistors and solar batteries (Sec. 14.10d). Silicon crystallizes exclusively in the diamond lattice arrangement, and no allotropic modification of silicon corresponding to graphite exists. Crystalline silicon is dark gray, almost black, with a metallic luster. Its appearance superficially resembles graphite, but it is much harder, and a poor conductor of electricity.

Silicon dioxide, the product of the complete oxidation of silicon, has the empirical formula SiO_2. Unlike CO_2, which is monomeric, SiO_2 is a polymeric crystalline solid, the crystal lattice of which is held together by strong single bonds extending in three dimensions. Each silicon atom is surrounded by four oxygen atoms and singly bound to each in a tetrahedral arrangement (Fig. 16.10). This is in accord with a general rule that the elements of the third and subsequent periods show less tendency to form

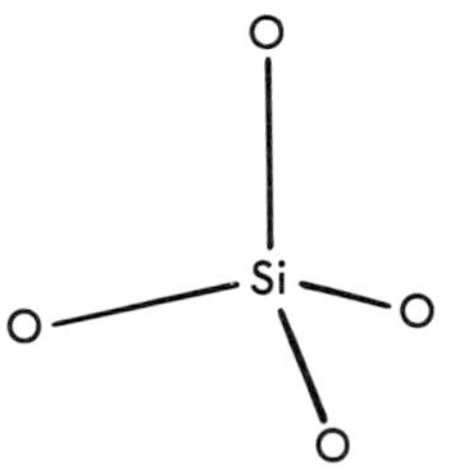

Fig. 16.10 A representation of the tetragonal SiO_4^- unit.

double bonds than do those of the second period. Perhaps the greater atomic size of the heavier elements causes the lateral overlap of *p* orbitals to be decreased. This would cause the π bond, if formed, to be weak, and a system of strong single bonds might be expected to be energetically favored over one containing double bonds. The tetrahedral units may be arranged in different ways, leading to three distinct crystalline forms of silica (Fig. 16.11).

Small fragments of quartz are familiar as sand. Large, clear crystals are known as ***rock crystal.*** They are rare, and if nearly perfect they may be quite valuable. A fortune-teller's crystal ball is usually a highly polished sphere of rock crystal. Certain semiprecious and precious stones, such as amethyst, agate, jasper, and opal, are crystals of quartz, tridymide, or

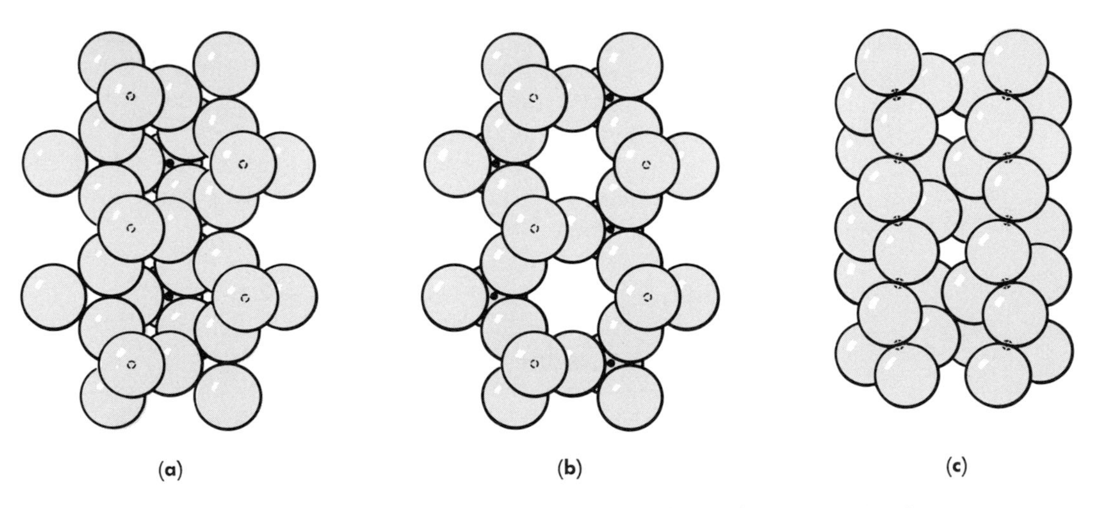

Fig. 16.11 Crystal structures of (a) cristobalite, (b) tridymite, and (c) quartz.

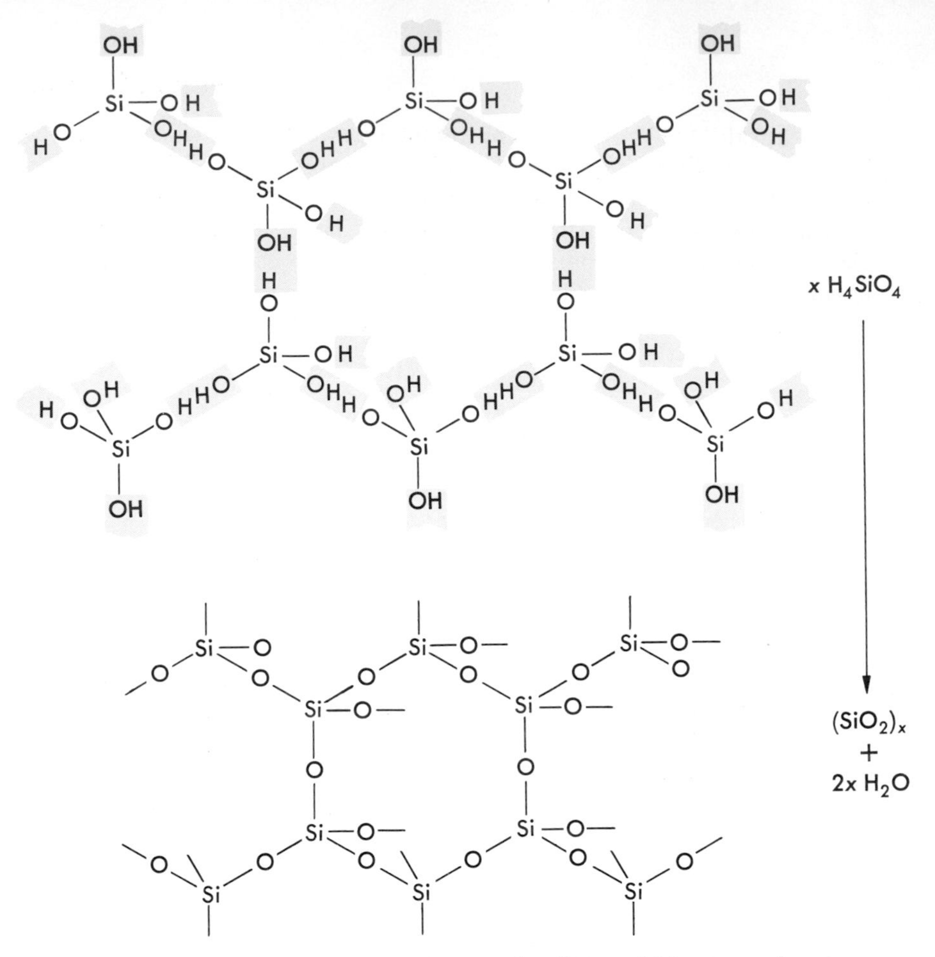

Fig. 16.12 Formation of silica from orthosilicic acid by loss of water.

cristobalite colored by small amounts of impurities. If crystalline silica is melted and allowed to cool rapidly, it forms an amorphous glass known as "fused silica," or "fused quartz." Because fused silica is unaffected by most chemicals and has a very low coefficient of expansion, it is used in fabricating beakers, crucibles, and other vessels which must withstand chemical attack or sudden temperature changes.

Silicon dioxide is the anhydride of silicic acid, which is stable only in the form of its salts, the ***silicates.*** Silica is slowly attacked by caustic alkalis, forming the soluble alkali metal silicates:

$$SiO_2 + 4\ NaOH \rightarrow \underset{\text{sodium orthosilicate}}{Na_4SiO_4} + 2\ H_2O$$

$$SiO_2 + 2\ NaOH \rightarrow \underset{\text{sodium metasilicate}}{Na_2SiO_3} + H_2O$$

$$2\ SiO_2 + 6\ NaOH \rightarrow \underset{\text{sodium pyrosilicate}}{Na_6Si_2O_7} + 3\ H_2O$$

The silicic acid which first precipitates upon acidifying a solution of a soluble silicate is unstable, and it rapidly loses water to form a series of partially hydrated silicas, and finally SiO_2 (Fig. 16.12). Silica precipitated in this manner, when dried to a water content of about 5%, gives a porous powder with a large surface area. This material, known as ***silica gel,*** has the property of adsorbing large amounts of water and certain vapors. It is widely used as a drying agent and dehumidifier. When saturated, it can be reactivated by heating and used again.

Heating SiO_2 to high temperatures with carbon or silicon yields silicon monoxide in the gaseous state:

$$SiO_2 + Si \rightarrow 2\ SiO$$

$$SiO_2 + C \rightarrow SiO + CO$$

When cooled, the gas appears to disproportionate to silicon and SiO_2:

$$2\ SiO \rightarrow Si + SiO_2$$

but there is some controversy over whether or not a solid polymeric oxide $(SiO)_x$ can exist under certain circumstances.

Silicates 16.9

Natural silicates form one of the major mineral classes of the materials of the earth's crust. At first, the compositions of the natural silicates may appear hopelessly varied. In fact, however, all may be classified into but a few groups, based upon the structure of the anion, which in turn is composed of one or more silicon-oxygen tetrahedra.

1. Simple Orthosilicates. These are known as the ***olivines*** and include such minerals as ***phenacite,*** Be_2SiO_4, and the magnesium and ferrous olivines Mg_2SiO_4 and Fe_2SiO_4. The transparent, semiprecious stone ***zircon,*** which is colorless when pure and has a high refractive index, is the olivine $ZrSiO_4$.

2. Pyrosilicates. The anion here is composed of two tetrahedra sharing an oxygen in common to give the group $Si_2O_7^{-6}$ (Fig. 16.13a). Included among the pyrosilicates are ***hardystonite,*** $Ca_2ZnSi_2O_7$, ***thortveitite,*** $Sc_2Si_2O_7$, and ***mellilite,*** $Ca_2MgSi_2O_7$.

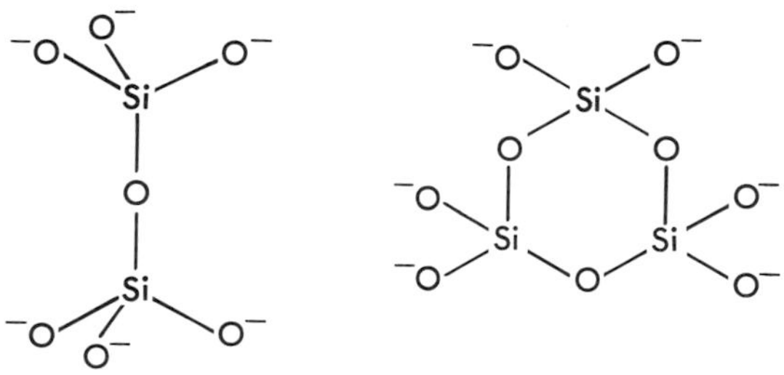

$Si_2O_7^{=}$

(a)

$Si_3O_9^{-6}$

(b)

Fig. 16.13 Pyrosilicate (a) and trisilicate (b) ions.

3. Trisilicates. These are based upon the anion $Si_3O_9^{-6}$, which consists of three tetrahedra joined in a ring (Fig. 16.13b). Representative trisilicates are ***wollestonite,*** $Ca_3Si_3O_9$, and ***benitoite,*** $BaTiSi_3O_9$.

4. Hexasilicates. ***Beryl,*** $Be_3Al_2Si_6O_{18}$, is the best known member of this class, in which the anion is composed of six tetrahedra hexagonally arranged (Fig. 16.14).

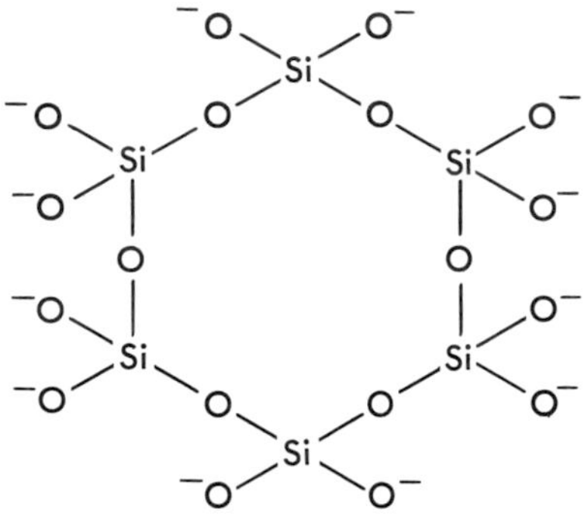

$Si_6O_{18}^{-12}$

Fig. 16.14 Hexasilicate ion.

5. Single and Double Chain Silicates. These contain the ions $(SiO_3)_x^{-2x}$ and $(Si_4O_{11})_x^{-6x}$, respectively. In these minerals, the tetrahedra are arranged in chains of indefinite length (Fig. 16.15). The single chain silicates are also known as ***metasilicates,*** or ***pyroxenes.*** ***Diopside,***

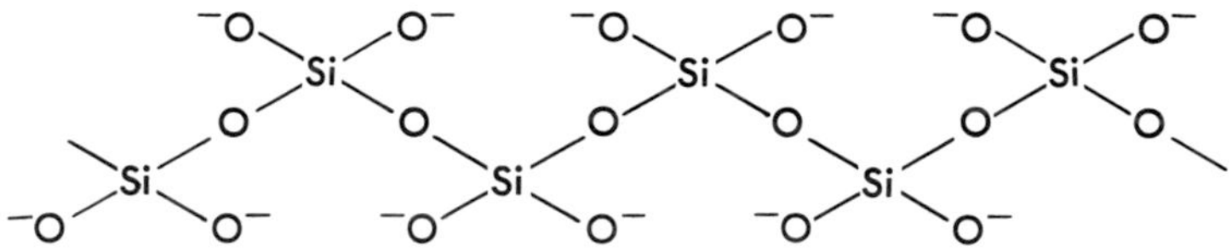

$(SiO_3)_x^{-2x}$

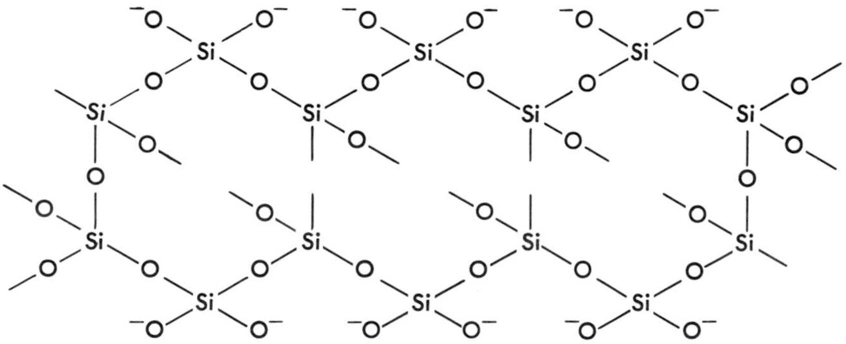

$(Si_4O)_x^{-6x}$

Fig. 16.15 Single and double silicate chains.

$[CaMg(SiO_3)_2]_n$, and ***asbestos***, $[Ca_2Mg_5(Si_4O_{11})_2(OH)_2]_n$, are representative of these two classes. As might be anticipated from their structure, many of these minerals form needle-like or fibrous crystals.

6. Sheet Silicates. ***Talc***, $[Mg_2Si_2O_5(OH)_2]_n$, is an example of this class of silicate in which the tetrahedra are arranged in two-dimensional sheets with the metal ions sandwiched between (Fig. 16.16). The characteristic flakiness of these minerals is a result of their crystal structure.

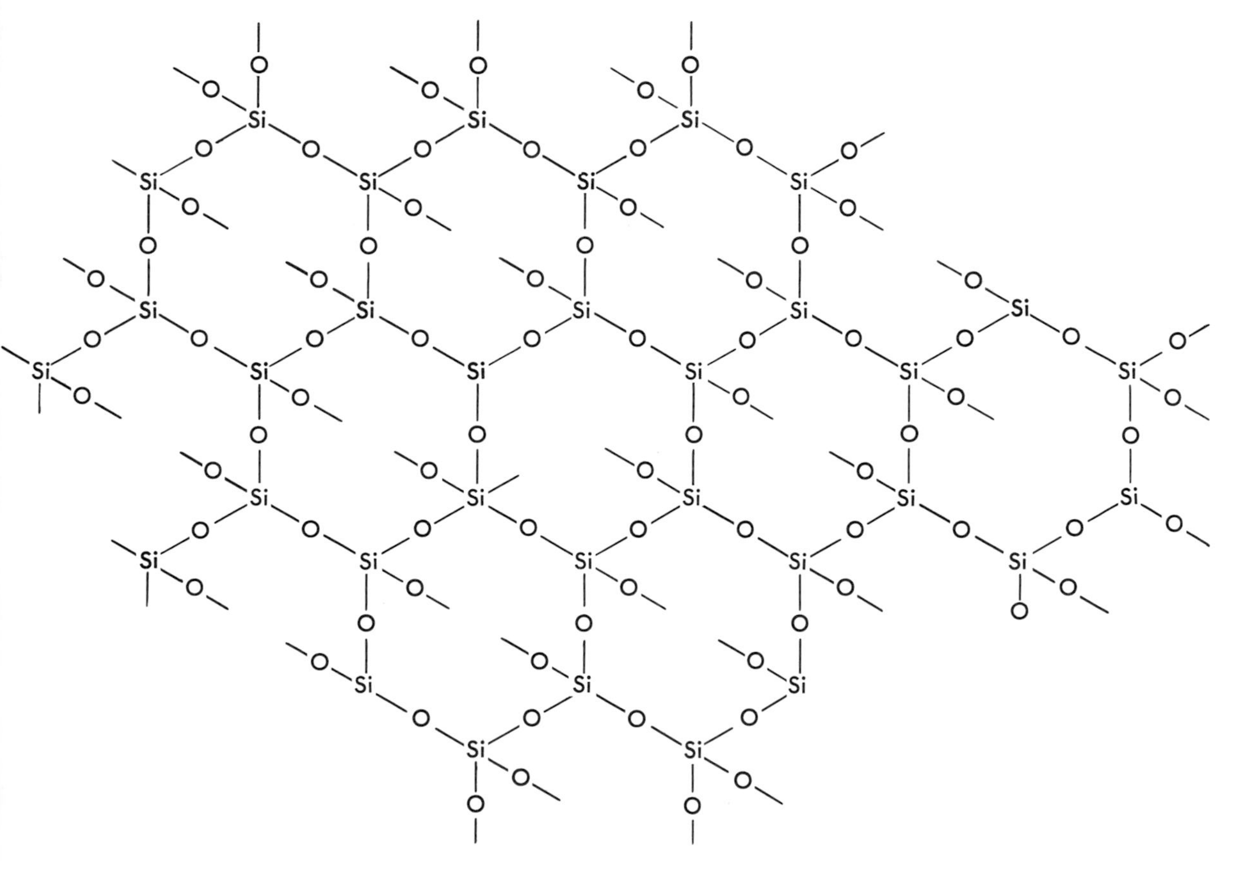

Fig. 16.16 Sheet silicate anion.

7. Aluminosilicates. In the aluminosilicates, some of the silicon atoms have been replaced by aluminum atoms, which are of very nearly the same size. While this has very little effect upon the crystal structure, it does make an important difference chemically. Aluminum has one less positive charge than silicon in its nucleus, hence substitution of **Al** for **Si** leaves the tetrahedral unit with an overall charge of -1. Electrical neutrality requires the presence of a cation, usually Na^+ or K^+. If the basic structure of the crystal before substitution of aluminum was that of silica, the general formula of the corresponding aluminosilicates is $[M_xAl_xSi_yO_{2(x+y)}]_n$, as exemplified in ***feldspar***, $(KAlSi_3O_8)_n$, and the ***zeolite clays***, $(Na_2Al_2Si_3O_{10} \cdot 2\ H_2O)_n$. ***Micas*** have a silicate sheet structure similar to talc, but with approximately 1 out of 4 of the Si atoms replaced by Al. The unit ion in these minerals therefore is $(AlSi_3O_{10})^{-5}$. Examples are ***muscovite,*** $[KAl_2(AlSi_3O_{10})(OH)_2]_n$, and ***phlogopite,*** $[KMg_3(AlSi_3O_{10})(OH)_2]_n$.

The sodium and potassium ions of the clays may be exchanged for other metallic ions. Water containing Ca^{++}, Mg^{++}, or other ions is softened by passing it through a bed of zeolite clay:

$$[Na_2Al_2Si_3O_{10} \cdot 2\ H_2O]_n + n\ Ca^{++} \rightleftharpoons [CaAl_2Si_3O_{10} \cdot 2\ H_2O]_n + 2n\ Na^+$$

Afterward, the zeolite can be regenerated by washing with a solution of NaCl. The "Permutit" water softener is a bed of zeolite clay in a cartridge or container arranged for installation in the water supply system. Hydrogen ions also can displace metal ions in these clays. This is often accompanied by a change in such physical properties of clay-water mixtures as stickiness and "slip," and these properties are therefore sensitive to changes in pH.

16.10 Other Compounds of Silicon

1. Hydrides. Carbon forms stable hydrides of infinite variety and complexity, but the hydrides of silicon, known as the ***silanes,*** all decompose above 300° and burn spontaneously in air.

$$SiH_4 + 2\ O_2 \rightarrow SiO_2 + 2\ H_2O$$

They are attacked by water and dilute alkalis, forming silica and hydrogen:

$$SiH_4 + 2\ H_2O \rightarrow SiO_2 + 4\ H_2$$

Their ease of hydrolysis is probably the result of two factors, first the availability of d orbitals, which allow the silicon to coordinate with water molecules, and secondly the strength of the Si—O bond, which has a dissociation energy of the order of 189 kcal/mole. Bonds between silicon atoms are weak, and while silanes have been prepared with chains of as many as 7 or 8 Si atoms, the stability of these compounds decreases rapidly as the chain length increases.

2. Silicones. The basic structure of a silicone is a silicon-oxygen chain to which are attached various substituents, frequently methyl (CH_3) and hydroxyl (OH) groups (Fig. 16.17). Depending upon the length of the chains and the degree of cross-linking between chains, the silicone may have oily, rubbery, or resinous properties. The oils remain fluid at very low temperatures and retain their viscosity at temperatures above the decomposition points of ordinary hydrocarbon oils. Silicone rubber is not attacked by ozone in the atmosphere, which causes ordinary rubber to harden. It remains elastic at very low temperatures, and is unaffected by oil, grease, and most solvents. Refrigerator door gaskets are usually made of silicone rubber.

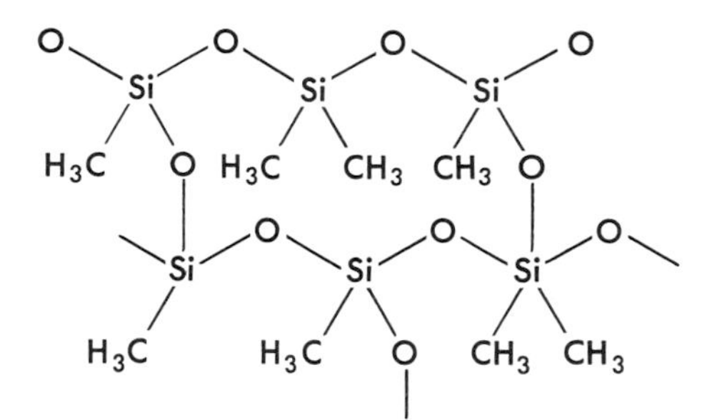

Fig. 16.17 Structure of a silicone polymer showing cross linking between chains.

3. Silicon Carbide. After diamond, silicon carbide is one of the hardest substances known. It is familiar as an abrasive under the trade name ***Carborundum.*** It is manufactured by heating coke and sand to about 3000°C in an electric furnace:

$$SiO_2 + 3\ C \rightarrow SiC + 2\ CO$$

4. Silicon Halides. Silica is attacked by hydrofluoric acid, forming gaseous silicon tetrafluoride:

$$SiO_2 + 4\ HF \rightarrow 2\ H_2O + SiF_4$$

The same reaction is involved when ordinary glass is etched by **HF**. SiF_4 is slowly hydrolyzed by water to SiO_2:

$$SiF_4 + 2\ H_2O \rightarrow SiO_2 + 4\ HF$$

In the presence of excess **HF**, it forms the strong fluosilicic acid, H_2SiF_6, which is stable only in solution or as the tetrahydrate:

$$SiF_4 + 2\ HF + 4\ H_2O \rightarrow H_2SiF_6 \cdot 4\ H_2O$$

The other tetrahalides can be prepared by heating sand and carbon to high temperatures in the presence of the halogen:

$$SiO_2 + C + 2\ X_2 \rightarrow SiX_4 + CO_2 \qquad (X = Cl, Br, \text{ or } I)$$

$SiCl_4$ and $SiBr_4$ are volatile liquids; SiI_4 is a solid melting at 121°C. All are readily hydrolyzed by water:

$$SiX_4 + 2\ H_2O \rightarrow SiO_2 + 4\ HX$$

It is interesting to note that while SiI_4 is a stable compound, I_4C is not, decomposing slowly at room temperature and rapidly at 171°C. Part of the reason for this may be that four bulky iodine atoms can approach the large silicon atom more closely than they can the smaller carbon atom. This would be expected to lead to more effective orbital overlap and stronger bonds.

16.11 Glass

Glass is not a true compound of silicon in the sense of having a fixed composition, nor is it a single substance. Commercial glasses are of several types, each having different properties of hardness, softening temperature, density, refractive index, and chemical and thermal stability. All are essentially fused mixtures of silica with various metal oxides, especially those of sodium, potassium, boron, and lead.

Lime glass is made by melting together a mixture of pure sand with up to 30% sodium and calcium carbonates. Carbon dioxide is evolved, and the final product can be considered a solid solution of sodium and calcium silicates in silica. Lime glass has a low softening temperature and a large coefficient of thermal expansion, making it unsuitable for any application where it might be exposed to high temperatures or sudden temperature changes. It is satisfactory for cheap glassware and bottles. Substitution of potassium for sodium in the glass yields a somewhat harder and stronger product.

Borosilicate glasses, of which ***Pyrex*** is the most familiar example, have all or part of the sodium and calcium replaced by boron, and a somewhat higher proportion of silica than lime glass. They have considerable mechanical strength, are chemically resistant, and have a small coefficient of expansion. Their softening point is relatively high, but they are easily worked in a gas-oxygen flame. Borosilicate glasses are especially suitable for laboratory apparatus and oven ware. The 200-in. mirror of the Hale telescope at Mount Palomar, California, is made of Pyrex, chosen for its strength and thermal stability. Any appreciable expansion and contraction of the mirror with changes in temperature would distort the image and seriously limit the resolving power of the telescope. Soft glass or metal therefore would not have been satisfactory materials for the mirror because of their large coefficients of expansion.

Flint, or ***lead glasses,*** are made from sand, K_2CO_3, and PbO. They are brilliant glasses with high refractive indices, which makes them especially

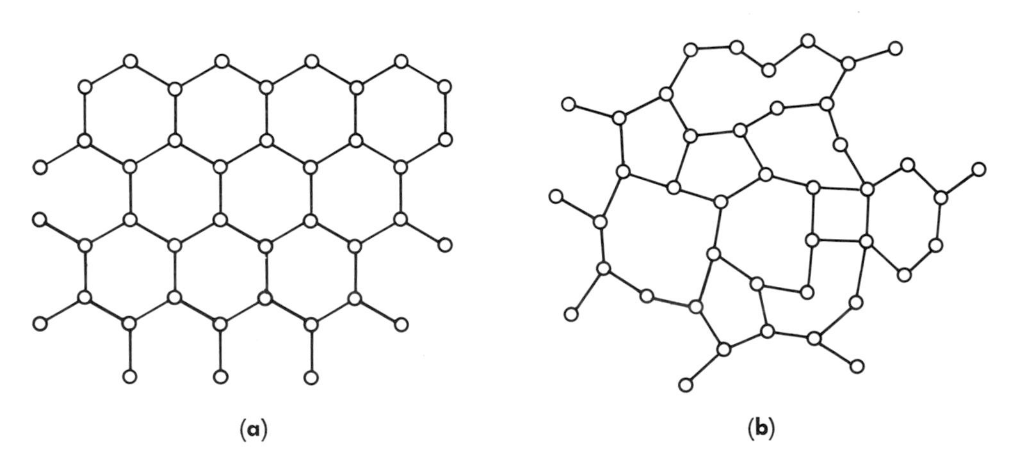

Fig. 16.18 Two-dimensional representations of (a) crystalline silicate and (b) glass structures. Circles represent silicate units.

suitable for decorative glassware and for lenses and prisms in optical instruments. A dense glass made with a high proportion of lead absorbs atomic radiation almost as effectively as the same mass of lead, but it is transparent and so can be used for viewing ports in laboratories where radiation is a hazard.

All glasses are characterized by a lack of crystallinity. When struck, they break to form curved, or "conchoidal," surfaces, whereas crystalline solids typically break along the cleavage planes. Glasses have no sharp melting points but soften gradually upon heating. They appear solid, but they give diffuse X-ray diffraction patterns and lack the internal regularity of true solids. The fundamental unit in these glasses is probably the same **Si-O** tetrahedron encountered in the silicate minerals, but the tetrahedra are arranged in the more random manner of liquids (Fig. 16.18). Glasses are therefore sometimes described as supercooled liquids, that is, as liquids whose viscosities are so high that their rate of flow is negligible.

Germanium 16.12

Most germanium is obtained as the oxide GeO_2 as a by-product of the smelting of lead and zinc. The element is prepared by reducing the oxide with carbon or hydrogen:

$$GeO_2 + 2\ H_2 \rightarrow Ge + 2\ H_2O$$

Its appearance is more metallic than carbon or silicon, but germanium is a poor electrical conductor and crystallizes exclusively in the diamond lattice. The semiconducting properties of germanium lead to its use in transistors and solar batteries (Sec. 14.10d). The highly purified germanium needed for this purpose is obtained by the process of ***zone refining***. This process, which is useful in the purification of other substances as well, takes advantage of the fact that impurities usually cannot fit into the lattice framework of a perfect crystal. The substance to be purified is placed in a tube equipped with a heating coil that can be moved slowly along the tube. As the heating coil travels along the tube, a small molten zone moves with it through the mass of material to be purified (Fig. 16.19). Crystals slowly

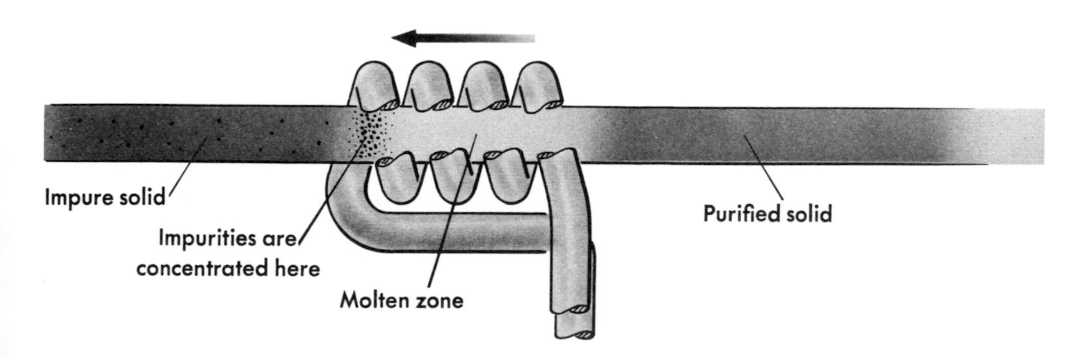

Fig. 16.19 Zone-melting apparatus.

form at the trailing edge of the molten zone, while the impurities remain in the melt and move along with it. If greater purification is desired than can be obtained by one pass of the heater along the tube, the process can be repeated one or more times.

Germanium forms both a monoxide and a dioxide. The dioxide, which is the normal product of the oxidation of germanium, is slightly soluble in water, giving a faintly acid solution. GeO_2 is also somewhat soluble in acid, which shows it to have some basic character as well, but the element nevertheless is chemically more of a nonmetal than a metal. The monoxide is formed by the hydrolysis of $GeCl_2$, or by reduction of the dioxide with hypophosphorous acid:

$$GeCl_2 + H_2O \rightarrow GeO + 2\ HCl$$

$$GeO_2 + H_3PO_2 \rightarrow GeO + H_3PO_3$$

Hydrides of germanium, the ***germanes,*** are known from GeH_4 through Ge_5H_{12}, but these compounds are even less stable than the corresponding silanes.

Germanium tetrafluoride, like SiF_4, is a gas which readily coordinates with fluoride ion to form the ion GeF_6^{--}. The hydrate $GeF_4 \cdot 3\ H_2O$ can be obtained by dissolving the dioxide in concentrated aqueous **HF** and evaporating the solution, but attempts to prepare the anhydrous tetrafluoride from the hydrate by heating result in partial hydrolysis and decomposition. Pure GeF_4 is best prepared by thermal decomposition of the salt $BaGeF_6$. $GeCl_4$ is a liquid; the tetrabromide melts close to room temperature (26°C); and the tetraiodide is a solid melting at 144°C. All are hydrolyzed by water:

$$GeCl_4 + 2\ H_2O \rightarrow GeO_2 + 4\ HCl$$

16.13 Tin

Tin is appreciably more metallic than germanium. It crystallizes in two principal allotropic modifications: ***white tin,*** or β-tin, which despite its rather poor electrical conductivity appears to possess a metallic lattice; and ***gray tin,*** or α-tin, a lower-density crystal with the diamond lattice. Gray tin is the stable form at low temperatures, the transition temperature between gray and white tin being 13.2°C. At low temperature, the transition is initially very slow, but it is autocatalytic, and once started, accelerates rapidly. This transition from white to gray tin is the cause of the so-called "tin disease," which in the past caused damage to many ancient artifacts in unheated museums before its nature was understood.

The principal tin ore is the dioxide ***cassiterite,*** SnO_2, still extracted commercially from the ancient mines in Cornwall, England, although Bolivia and Malaysia are the main sources of the ore today. The oxide is reduced to the metal with carbon:

$$SnO_2 + C \rightarrow Sn + CO_2$$

Metallic tin is highly resistant to corrosion, which leads to its use as a protective coating on steel, as in the familiar "tin can." Its standard electrode potential is lower than that of iron, however, which means that the steel is protected only so long as the tin coating is unbroken. Once any of the steel is exposed, an electrolytic cell is established in which the steel becomes the negative electrode and corrosion of the steel is accelerated.

Tin(II) oxide, SnO, can be obtained by heating tin in a limited supply of air or by heating the hydroxide precipitated upon addition of alkali to a tin(II) salt:

$$Sn^{++} + 2\ OH^- \rightarrow Sn(OH)_2$$

$$Sn(OH)_2 \rightarrow SnO + H_2O$$

Both the monoxide and the dioxide react with acids to give the corresponding Sn(II) and Sn(IV) salts:

$$SnO + 2\ HCl \rightarrow H_2O + SnCl_2$$

$$SnO_2 + 2\ H_2SO_4 \rightarrow 2\ H_2O + Sn(SO_4)_2$$

The oxides and hydroxides of tin are amphoteric and dissolve in excess alkali, forming ***stannites*** and ***stannates:***

$$SnO + NaOH \rightarrow NaHSnO_2$$

$$SnO_2 + 2\ NaOH \rightarrow H_2O + Na_2SnO_3$$

$SnCl_2$ is a water-soluble solid with a relatively low melting point (246°C), which suggests that the Sn—Cl bonds are probably not entirely ionic. It and the other tin(II) halides are obtained when tin is dissolved in the appropriate halogen acid:

$$Sn + 2\ HX \rightarrow SnX_2 + H_2$$

In acid solution $SnCl_2$ is readily oxidized, making it a strong reducing agent. If it is oxidized in the presence of HCl, the product is the very stable complex ion $SnCl_6^{--}$:

$$Sn^{++} + 6\ Cl^- \xrightarrow{-2\ e^-} SnCl_6^{--}$$

Tin(IV) chloride, $SnCl_4$, produced by direct reaction between the elements,

$$Sn + 2\ Cl_2 \rightarrow SnCl_4$$

is a volatile liquid (b.p. 114°C), indicating that the bonds in the molecule are essentially covalent. The compound fumes in moist air and is readily hydrolyzed by water:

$$SnCl_4 + 12\ H_2O \rightarrow Sn(OH)_6^{--} + 6\ H_3O^+ + 4\ Cl^-$$

A portion of the complex ion reacts to form colloidal SnO_2,

$$Sn(OH)_6^{--} + 2\ H_3O^+ \rightarrow SnO_2 + 6\ H_2O$$

and some combines with chloride ions released in the hydrolysis, forming $SnCl_6^{--}$ ions:

$$Sn(OH)_6^{--} + 6\ H_3O^+ + 6\ Cl^- \rightarrow SnCl_6^{--} + 12\ H_2O$$

Only one hydride of tin, stannane, SnH_4, is known. Stannane is a toxic gas which decomposes slowly at room temperature and immediately at 145°C.

16.14 Lead

Lead is the most metallic of the group IVA elements, and it crystallizes only in the metallic form. Its principal ore is the mineral ***galena,*** **PbS**. Part of the ore is roasted in air to convert the sulfide to the oxide and the sulfate:

$$2\ PbS + 3\ O_2 \rightarrow 2\ PbO + 2\ SO_2$$

$$PbS + 2\ O_2 \rightarrow PbSO_4$$

The roasted ore is then heated with untreated ore, coke, and some limestone to act as a flux and remove silica as a slag of calcium silica. A number of reactions take place, of which the following are representative:

$$PbO + C \rightarrow Pb + CO$$

$$PbO + CO \rightarrow Pb + CO_2$$

$$PbS + 2\ PbO \rightarrow 3\ Pb + SO_2$$

$$PbS + PbSO_4 \rightarrow 2\ Pb + 2\ SO_2$$

$$CaCO_3 + SiO_2 \rightarrow CaSiO_3 + CO_2$$

Among the group IVA elements, lead shows the greatest tendency to exist in the lower oxidation state. In fact, salts of Pb(IV) are relatively rare and are all strong oxidizing agents, as is the dioxide PbO_2. Heating lead in air produces the yellow monoxide ***litharge:***

$$2\ Pb + O_2 \rightarrow 2\ PbO$$

The brown dioxide is formed by electrolytic oxidation, or by the action of strong oxidizing agents:

$$PbO + OCl^- \rightarrow PbO_2 + Cl^-$$

PbO_2 is unstable to heat and decomposes above 300°C to the monoxide and oxygen:

$$2\ PbO_2 \rightarrow 2\ PbO + O_2$$

PbO is essentially a basic oxide, but it is sufficiently amphoteric to react with concentrated alkali to form the unstable salts known as ***plumbites:***

$$PbO + 2\ OH^- + H_2O \rightarrow Pb(OH)_4^{--}$$

The properties of the dioxide, on the other hand, are more acidic than basic. PbO_2 reacts with basic oxides or hydroxides to form ***plumbates:***

$$2\ CaO + PbO_2 \rightarrow Ca_2PbO_4 \qquad \text{(calcium orthoplumbate)}$$

$$2\ KOH + PbO_2 \rightarrow H_2O + K_2PbO_3 \qquad \text{(potassium metaplumbate)}$$

The compounds Pb_2O_3 (lead sesquioxide) and Pb_3O_4 (red lead) contain lead in both the +2 and +4 oxidation states. They are best described as the meta and orthoplumbates of lead(II), $PbPbO_3$ and Pb_2PbO_4, respectively, rather than as true oxides. Red lead is used as a pigment in antirust paints used to inhibit corrosion of iron and steel, and as the positive electrode in lead-acid storage batteries (Sec. 14.10b).

The only known hydride of lead is ***plumbane,*** PbH_4, a very unstable compound formed in trace amounts by the action of acid on certain lead alloys (e.g., Mg_2Pb), and during the electrolysis of dilute sulfuric acid between lead electrodes. Lead(II) acetate, $Pb(C_2H_3O_2)_2$, is one of the very few soluble lead salts. It is sometimes called ***sugar of lead*** because of its sweet taste, but it is extremely poisonous. Lead(IV) acetate, or lead tetraacetate, $Pb(C_2H_3O_2)_4$, prepared by dissolving red lead in a mixture of glacial acetic acid and acetic anhydride, is a powerful oxidizing agent used especially in organic chemistry. The bonds in the tetraacetate (m.p. 175°C) appear to be largely covalent. The compound is hydrolyzed by water, forming PbO_2 and acetic acid:

$$Pb(C_2H_3O_2)_4 + 2\ H_2O \rightarrow PbO_2 + 4\ HC_2H_3O_2$$

Basic lead carbonate, or ***white lead,*** $Pb_3(OH)_2(CO_3)_2$, is formed by exposing lead to the vapors of acetic acid, water, air, and CO_2. The lead is oxidized by the air, converted to the acetate, and then to the carbonate by the action of the CO_2. At one time white lead was the most important white pigment for paint, but it has been largely displaced in recent years by titanium dioxide and various nonmetallic pigments which are whiter and have the advantage of being nonpoisonous and less likely to discolor. Lead-based paints slowly darken on exposure to the atmosphere because of the reaction between the pigment and any H_2S fumes in the air, forming black PbS. Tetraethyl lead, probably the most important compound of $Pb(IV)$, is used in large amounts as an antiknock agent in gasoline. It is a covalent liquid (b.p. 202°C), prepared by the reaction of a sodium-lead alloy with ethyl chloride:

$$Na_4Pb + 4\ C_2H_5Cl \rightarrow Pb(C_2H_5)_4 + 4\ NaCl$$

16.15 Reading Suggestions

The physical and chemical character of graphite is discussed in a review by P. A. H. Tee and B. L. Tonge, appearing in *J. Chem. Ed.* **40,** 117 (1963). The factors responsible for the lubricating properties of this carbon allotrope are described by Vasilis Lavrakas in *J. Chem. Ed.* **34,** 240 (1957). Colloidal carbon, which includes lampblack and furnace black, is a remarkably versatile and valuable industrial chemical. Its manufacture and its use in a myriad of products—rubber shoes and rubber tires, inks and insecticides, crayons and candy, to mention just a few—is described by Carl W. Sweitzer in an article entitled *Colloidal Carbon—Valuable Soot*, in *J. Chem. Ed.* **29,** 493 (1952).

The history of the many attempts at diamond synthesis that have been made ever since Lavoisier showed that diamond is a form of carbon is reviewed by P. W. Bridgman in the November 1955 issue of *Scientific American*. *The Synthesis of Diamond—A Case History in Modern Science*, by C. G. Suits, is available as a booklet from the General Electric Research and Development Center, Schenectady, N.Y. This very interesting account of the efforts of a modern scientific research team also includes an extensive bibliography. A key member of that successful team, H. Tracy Hall, describes the reasoning behind the choice of reaction conditions for diamond synthesis in an article in *J. Chem. Ed.* **38,** 484 (1961). This article also includes a discussion of the crystal structure and properties of diamond.

Many other transition metals besides nickel form complex carbonyls with carbon monoxide. The preparation and properties of these interesting compounds are reviewed by Harold E. Podall in *J. Chem. Ed.* **38,** 187 (1961).

The manufacture of glass is one of the oldest chemical industries, its origin being lost in antiquity. A. J. Sofianopoulos tells about primordial glasses, including hard resins and gums as well as siliceous glass in *J. Chem. Ed.* **29,** 503 (1952). The history of glass and its importance in the development of science is reviewed by Alexander Silverman in *J. Chem. Ed.* **32,** 149 (1955). Also by the same author is *Glass Historical Notes, 1900 to 1950*, *ibid.*, **30,** 32 (1953). Some of the newer types of glass, including photosensitive glass and exceptionally strong glass, are described in an article by Robert H. Dalton, *J. Chem. Ed.* **40,** 99 (1963). Also described in this paper is a remarkably accurate method of dating ancient glass artifacts by counting corrosion layers in much the same way that the age of a tree is determined by counting its rings.

Questions and Problems

16.1 Write equations for the reactions involved in the Solvay process for the manufacture of sodium carbonate, including the steps involved in ammonia recovery.

16.2 When carbon dioxide is bubbled through a solution of calcium hydroxide, a white precipitate forms, but it slowly redissolves as the flow of gas continues. The white precipitate again forms when the final clear solution is heated. Explain what is taking place, and write balanced equations for all chemical reactions which occur.

16.3 Account for each of the following: (a) CO_2 is a gas at standard conditions, SiO_2 is a solid. (b) Diamond is hard, but graphite is soft. (c) $CaCO_3$ is less soluble in freshly boiled water than in water that has been exposed to the air for a long time. (d) Solutions of sodium carbonate are basic, but solutions of sodium bicarbonate are very nearly neutral.

16.4 How are stalactites and stalagmites formed?

16.5 Describe how hard water is softened by being passed through a zeolite clay. How is the zeolite regenerated after use? Give equations for any reactions described.

16.6 Account for the differences in the properties of asbestos, mica, and quartz in terms of their structures.

16.7 Account for the lubricating properties of graphite. Graphite would seem to be an ideal material from which to make self-lubricating bearings, but such bearings are worthless when exposed to the conditions of outer space. Why?

16.8 Show how the silicates and silicones are related to SiO_2.

16.9 How do the following properties change in going down group IVA: (a) metallic character, (b) ability to form long-chain hydrogen compounds, (c) ability to form +2 ions, (d) tendency to exhibit tetravalence, (e) type of crystal lattice?

16.10 As^{+5} has nearly the same size as Si^{+4}. What would be the effect of replacing some of the Si^{+4} units in the silica lattice with As^{+5}? Write the formula of a hypothetical "arsenosilicate" with an As to Si ratio of 1:4. Would you expect the properties of such an arsenosilicate to be affected by changes in pH? Assuming that the arsenosilicate is neutral to begin with, which should have the greater effect: an increase in pH or a decrease?

16.11 Write balanced equations for the following: (a) The reaction between carbon monoxide and hydrogen to form methyl alcohol. (b) Preparation of sodium formate from CO and NaOH. (c) The formation of ortho-, meta-, and pyrosilicates by reaction of caustic alkali with silica. (d) The reaction of SiH_4 with water. (e) The reaction between SiO_2 and excess hydrofluoric acid to form fluosilicic acid.

16.12 Account for the fact that graphite is an electrical conductor while diamond is an insulator. Why is there such a great difference in the electrical conductivity parallel and perpendicular to the cleavage plane of the graphite crystal?

16.13 Many years ago, in a church in northern Europe, some of the organ pipes, which were made of tin, suddenly developed holes and then disintegrated. On another occasion, tin ingots stored in a Russian custom house over the winter were found to have crumbled to powder. What had happened in each case?

16.14 What is meant by the term "resonance" applied to a molecule? How does a resonance hybrid differ from an equilibrium mixture? How does the resonance concept account for the fact that the bonds to the three oxygens of the carbonate ion are indistinguishable from one another?

16.15 Calculate the concentration of carbonate ion in pure water saturated with CO_2 at 25°C and 1 atm.

16.16 A 0.5482-g sample of a prehistoric bronze was treated with concentrated nitric acid which dissolved the copper and other metals and precipitated tin as metastannic acid:

$$3\,Sn + 4\,HNO_3 + H_2O \rightarrow 3\,H_2SnO_3\downarrow + 4\,NO$$

The precipitate was filtered, ignited to convert it to the oxide, and weighed:

$$H_2SnO_3 \xrightarrow{\Delta} SnO_2 + H_2O$$

The oxide weighed 0.1478 g. Calculate the percentage of tin in the bronze.

Organic chemistry appears to me like a primeval forest . . . full of the most remarkable things.

——Friedrich Wöhler in a letter to Jöns Jakob Berzelius, 1835

17 ORGANIC CHEMISTRY

Two classes of substances were recognized by the early chemists: ***organic compounds,*** such as sugar, alcohol, and uric acid, which were typically of plant or animal origin; and ***inorganic compounds,*** like nitric acid, caustic soda, and salt, which were produced from minerals. While occasionally one organic compound might be transformed into another in the laboratory, prior to the nineteenth century none had ever been prepared entirely from substances of nonliving origin. Most of them, in fact, seemed to defy laboratory preparation entirely, and the majority of chemists assumed that the formation of these compounds required the action of some unspecified "vital force" present only in living organisms.

The first synthesis of a typical organic compound from compounds of inorganic origin was accidental. In 1828 Friedrich Wöhler attempted to prepare ammonium cyanate by the reaction between silver cyanate and ammonium chloride, both of which were generally considered typical inorganic salts. To his surprise, when he boiled away the water from a solution of the two salts, what he obtained was not ammonium cyanate but urea, a product of nitrogen metabolism normally excreted in the urine:

$$NH_4Cl + AgCNO \rightarrow AgCl + \underset{\text{urea}}{CH_4N_2O}$$

This one chance synthesis did not bring about the immediate downfall of the vital force theory, but it did encourage other chemists to attempt the preparation of organic compounds. So many of these compounds were synthesized during the next twenty years that by about 1850 it was recognized that the division between organic and inorganic chemistry was an artificial one, and the concept of a vital force was gradually abandoned. By that time, too, it was clear that all the compounds called organic contained carbon, and the term ***organic chemistry*** came to mean *the chemistry of the compounds of carbon*, the meaning it has today.

Devoting an entire branch of chemistry to one element while lumping all of the others together under the heading ***inorganic chemistry*** may not seem fair to the other 102 elements, but it is justified simply because carbon forms so many compounds. Organic compounds far outnumber inorganic ones. There are probably no more than 150,000 compounds known which do not contain carbon, but easily 1,500,000 which do contain that element. Furthermore, given the necessary time and the incentive, there appears to be no limit to the number of organic compounds which the chemist could make. Two factors are responsible for this: the almost unique ability of carbon atoms to form strong bonds with one another, and the element's valence, which is normally 4. These permit carbon atoms to form stable chains and rings of unlimited size while still retaining enough unsaturated valences to form bonds with other elements. In contrast, one need only consider silicon and sulfur. Silicon, carbon's closest relative, also has a valence of 4 but cannot form strong enough bonds with itself to produce chains of any appreciable length (Sec. 16.10). Sulfur, on the other hand, forms stable chains and rings, but in doing so it uses up all or most of its valences:

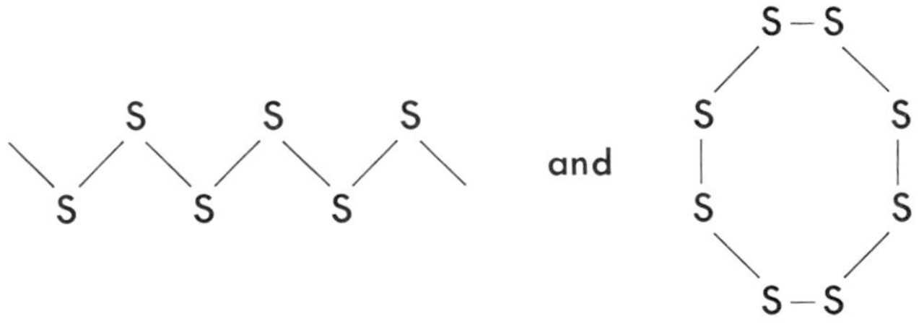

```
                                          S—S
                                         /   \
      S     S     S                     S     S
   \ / \ / \ / \ / \         and        |     |
    S     S     S                       S     S
                                         \   /
                                          S—S
```

17.1 Functional Groups

The basic framework of any organic compound is its ***carbon skeleton,*** which may be a single carbon atom or may contain hundreds or even thousands of carbon atoms. The nature of the compound is then determined by what atoms or groups of atoms are attached to the carbon skeleton. If these are all hydrogen atoms, the compound is called a ***hydrocarbon.*** Examples of hydrocarbons are *methane*, *ethane*, and *propane*,* compounds of the type known collectively as ***alkanes,*** which are present in natural gas and petroleum.

* A brief discussion of organic nomenclature will be found in Appendix C.

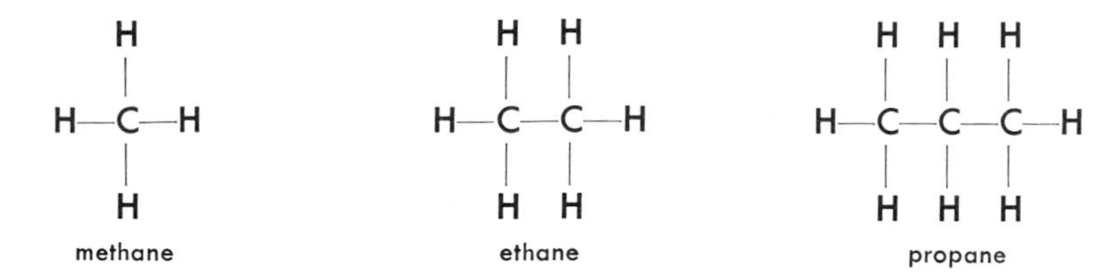

Single bonds between carbon atoms, or between carbon and hydrogen atoms, are relatively unreactive, and the alkanes therefore show little tendency to react with other substances. For this reason, the alkanes are sometimes called ***paraffins,*** from the Latin, ***parum affinis,*** meaning "little affinity."

One or more of the hydrogens may be replaced or *substituted* by some other atom or group of atoms. An atom or group of atoms other than hydrogen is called a ***functional group,*** because its presence results in a characteristic function, or behavior, on the part of the molecule. For example, substitution of —H by —OH makes the compound an ***alcohol:***

$$\begin{array}{c}\mathrm{H}\\ |\\ \mathrm{H{-}C{-}O{-}H}\\ |\\ \mathrm{H}\end{array}\qquad\qquad \begin{array}{c}\mathrm{H\ \ H}\\ |\ \ \ |\\ \mathrm{H{-}C{-}C{-}O{-}H}\\ |\ \ \ |\\ \mathrm{H\ \ H}\end{array}\qquad\qquad \begin{array}{c}\mathrm{H\ \ H\ \ H}\\ |\ \ \ |\ \ \ |\\ \mathrm{H{-}C{-}C{-}C{-}O{-}H}\\ |\ \ \ |\ \ \ |\\ \mathrm{H\ \ H\ \ H}\end{array}$$

methyl alcohol (methanol) — ethyl alcohol (ethanol) — propyl alcohol (1-propanol)

The various alcohols have different physical properties, but they all undergo similar chemical reactions. For instance, they all react with cold, concentrated sulfuric acid to form ***alkyl sulfates:***

$$\begin{array}{c}\mathrm{H}\\ |\\ \mathrm{H{-}C{-}O{-}H}\\ |\\ \mathrm{H}\end{array} + \begin{array}{c}\mathrm{O}\\ \|\\ \mathrm{H{-}O{-}S{-}O{-}H}\\ \|\\ \mathrm{O}\end{array} \rightarrow \begin{array}{c}\mathrm{H\ \ \ \ \ \ \ O}\\ |\ \ \ \ \ \ \ \|\\ \mathrm{H{-}C{-}O{-}S{-}O{-}H}\\ |\ \ \ \ \ \ \ \|\\ \mathrm{H\ \ \ \ \ \ \ O}\end{array} + \mathrm{H_2O}$$

methyl alcohol — sulfuric acid — methyl sulfate

$$\mathrm{CH_3{-}CH_2{-}OH + H_2SO_4 \rightarrow CH_3{-}CH_2{-}O{-}SO_2{-}OH + H_2O}$$

ethyl alcohol — ethyl sulfate

$$\mathrm{CH_3{-}CH_2{-}CH_2{-}OH + H_2SO_4 \rightarrow CH_3{-}CH_2{-}CH_2{-}O{-}SO_2{-}OH + H_2O}$$

propyl alcohol — propyl sulfate

and they can be oxidized to ***carboxylic acids:***

$$\mathrm{CH_3{-}OH} \xrightarrow{\mathrm{KMnO_4,\ \Delta}} \mathrm{H{-}C}\begin{array}{l}\mathrm{{/\!\!/}O}\\ \mathrm{\backslash OH}\end{array}$$

formic acid

$$CH_3—CH_2—OH \xrightarrow{KMnO_4,\ \Delta} CH_3—C\begin{matrix} \diagup O \\ \\ \diagdown OH \end{matrix} \quad \text{acetic acid}$$

$$CH_3—CH_2—CH_2—OH \xrightarrow{KMnO_4,\ \Delta} CH_3—CH_2—C\begin{matrix} \diagup O \\ \\ \diagdown OH \end{matrix} \quad \text{propionic acid}$$

All of the alkyl sulfates are seen to possess the functional group $—O—SO_2—OH$, while the presence of a ***carboxyl group*** (written either $—C\begin{matrix} \diagup O \\ \\ \diagdown OH \end{matrix}$ or $—COOH$) makes the compound a carboxylic acid. A few of the more important functional groups are shown in Table 17.1. Multiple bonds between carbon atoms are included among the functional groups because they impart a characteristic reactivity to the molecule. (See, for example, Sec. 17.4b.)

TABLE 17.1 Some Functional Groups

Structure of Group	Name of Group	Class of Compound	Example
$\begin{matrix} \diagdown & & \diagup \\ & C=C & \\ \diagup & & \diagdown \end{matrix}$	double bond	alkenes	$\begin{matrix} H & & H \\ & C=C & \\ H & & H \end{matrix}$
$—C\equiv C—$	triple bond	alkynes, or acetylenes	$H—C\equiv C—H$
$—F$, $—Cl$, $—Br$, $—I$	halide, or halo-	alkyl halides, or haloalkanes	$\begin{matrix} & H & H & \\ & \vert & \vert & \\ H— & C— & C— & Cl \\ & \vert & \vert & \\ & H & H & \end{matrix}$
$—O—H$	hydroxyl	alcohols	$\begin{matrix} & H & H & \\ & \vert & \vert & \\ H— & C— & C— & O—H \\ & \vert & \vert & \\ & H & H & \end{matrix}$

TABLE 17.1 Some Functional Groups (Continued)

Group	Name	Compound class	Example
$>C{=}O$	carbonyl	aldehydes	$H_3C{-}CHO$
		ketones	$H_3C{-}CO{-}CH_3$
$-C(=O)OH$	carboxyl	carboxylic acids	$H_3C{-}C(=O)OH$
$-NH_2$	amino	amines	$H_3C{-}CH_2{-}NH_2$
$-C(=O)NH_2$	amido	amides	$H_3C{-}C(=O)NH_2$

More than one functional group may be present in the same molecule, in which case the compound will undergo reactions typical of each of the functional groups. An example of this is the bifunctional compound ***glycine,***

$$H_2N{-}CH_2{-}C(=O)OH$$

Since it contains both an amino group and a carboxyl group, glycine is called an ***amino acid.*** It exhibits the properties of both an amine and a carboxylic acid.

17.2 Properties of Alcohols

It seems logical to start our survey of organic reactions with the alcohols, since ethyl alcohol was very likely the first organic compound to be deliberately manufactured.* Whatever man first discovered that a dilute alcohol solution resulted from the enzymatic fermentation of any substance containing sugar,

$$\underset{\substack{\text{glucose} \\ \text{(grape sugar)}}}{C_6H_{12}O_6} \xrightarrow{\text{enzyme}} 2\ \underset{\text{ethyl alcohol}}{C_2H_5OH} + 2\ CO_2$$

did not know what the chemical process was, nor did he care, but he soon found that a little of the product taken internally made his drafty cave seem a little cozier. Since then, man in his ingenuity has succeeded in preparing alcohol from an almost incredible variety of things: fruit, vegetables, potato peelings, flowers, roots, and at least once—by a chemist who had lost an election bet—a straw hat.

The word alcohol has an interesting origin. In the days of the pharaohs, fashionable Egyptian ladies painted their eyelids with a black powder—usually antimony sulfide, Sb_2S_3—known as *kohl.* The Arabs adopted the term to mean any finely divided powder, only in Arabic it came out *al kuhl*, with *al* being the Arabic for "the." Alchemy originated with the Arabs, and when the Europeans took it up in the later Middle Ages, they adopted many of the Arabic terms. One of these was *al kuhl*, which eventually came to be spelled *alcohol.* At first the term was applied to any finely divided substance, including vapors, or "spirits," which appeared to be about as finely divided as anything could possibly be. Gradually it came to refer particularly to the spirit of wine, which we now know to be ethyl alcohol, and then, by extension, to any organic compound possessing the characteristic hydroxyl functional group.

Physiologically, ethyl alcohol, or ***ethanol,*** C_2H_5OH, is a narcotic. In moderate amounts it causes dilation of the blood vessels, lowering of blood pressure, and a feeling of relaxation. Larger quantities cause intoxication, loss of coordination and motor control, stupor, and even death. Prolonged excessive use can permanently damage the liver, the organ which always gets the job of detoxifying poisonous substances in the blood.

Methyl alcohol, or ***methanol,*** CH_3OH, also known as ***wood alcohol,*** is a deadly poison. Taken in even small amounts it attacks the central nervous system. For some reason, it destroys the optic nerve first, causing blindness, then the motor system, leading to loss of muscular control and eventual death. Even excessive inhalation of the vapors can damage the optic nerve. The process is irreversible and incurable, so great care must be used in handling anything containing methanol.

The higher molecular weight alcohols with up to five or six carbons are less poisonous than methanol but cause headaches and nausea. Those with more than six carbons are nearly insoluble in water and have little or no physiological activity.

* Genesis 9: 20–21.

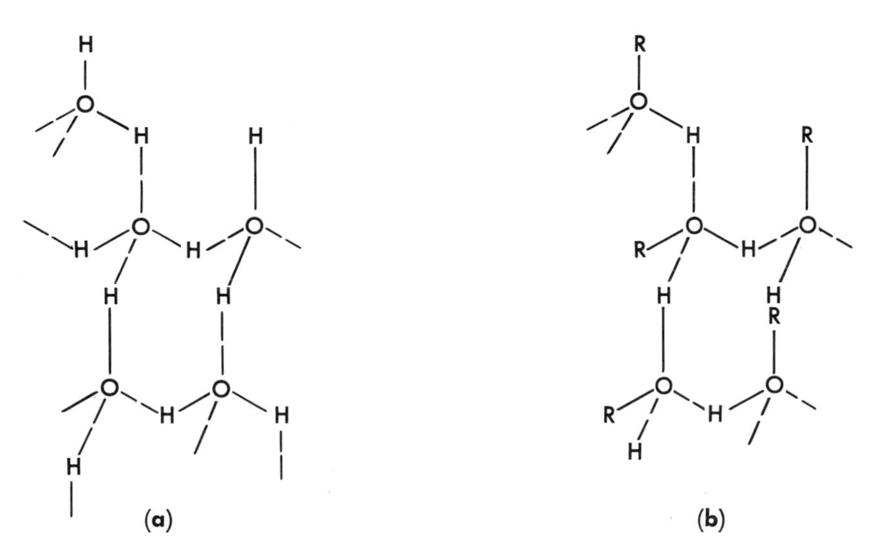

Fig. 17.1 Hydrogen bonding in (a) water and (b) alcohol. The symbol R represents the hydrocarbon portion of the alcohol molecule.

Like water, all of the alcohols are associated liquids because of the presence of hydrogen bonding between molecules (Sec. 9.14). Hydrogen bonding in alcohols is less extensive than in water because there is only one hydrogen atom available for such bonding in each alcohol molecule, compared with two in water (Fig. 17.1). Nevertheless, because of this association, alcohols have boiling points consistently higher than those of alkanes with about the same molecular weight (Fig. 17.2). Largely as a result of their

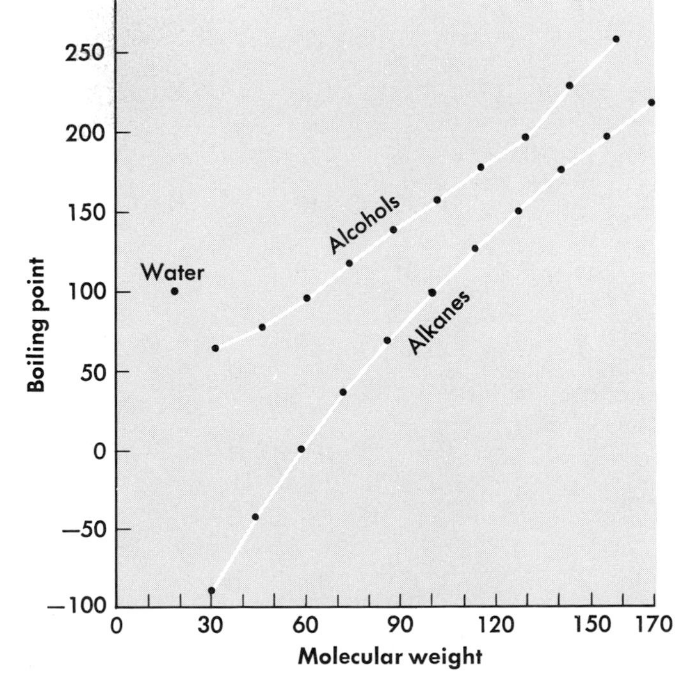

Fig. 17.2 Boiling points (1 atm) of normal chain alkanes and alcohols.

ability to form hydrogen bonds, the lower molecular weight alcohols are water soluble. The process of solution requires that intermolecular attractive forces be overcome in both the solvent and the solute (Sec. 10.3). Although this requires appreciable energy in the case of water and alcohols, where the intermolecular forces are hydrogen bonds, a substantial part of this energy is furnished by the formation of new hydrogen bonds between water and alcohol molecules. Methyl and ethyl alcohols are soluble in all proportions. The three- and four-carbon alcohols are all very soluble, but beyond four carbons, the solubility decreases very rapidly. Octyl alcohol, $C_8H_{17}OH$, is insoluble.

In order to accommodate the greater bulk of the hydrocarbon component of a high-molecular-weight alcohol, a larger number of water molecules must be pushed aside, and this means that more hydrogen bonds must be broken. Since only a small part of the energy that is necessary for the breaking of these bonds can be supplied by the formation of new hydrogen bonds between the alcohol and water molecules, the overall effect is a lower solubility for the higher-molecular-weight alcohols.

17.3 Reactions of Alcohols

(a) Oxidation. Depending upon whether an alcohol is primary, secondary, or tertiary, it will react differently toward oxidizing agents such as potassium dichromate ($K_2Cr_2O_7$), chromic anhydride (CrO_3), or potassium permanganate ($KMnO_4$). An alcohol is classified as *primary* (informally abbreviated 1°), *secondary* (2°), or *tertiary* (3°) according to whether the carbon bearing the functional group is attached to one (or none), two, or three other carbons:

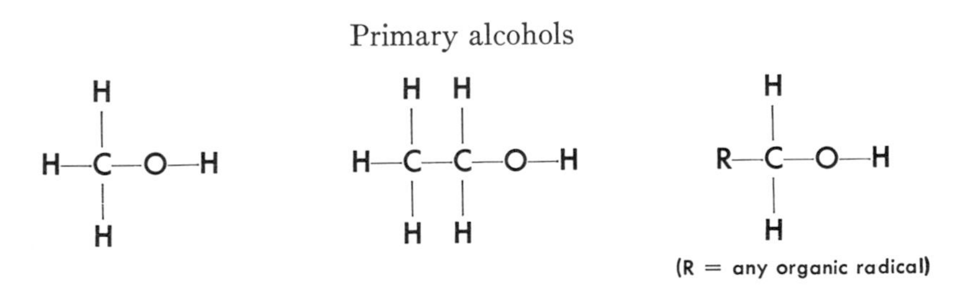

Secondary alcohols

```
    H  H  H                H
    |  |  |                |
 H—C—C—C—H            R—C—R'
    |  |  |                |
    H  O  H                O
       |                   |
       H                   H
```

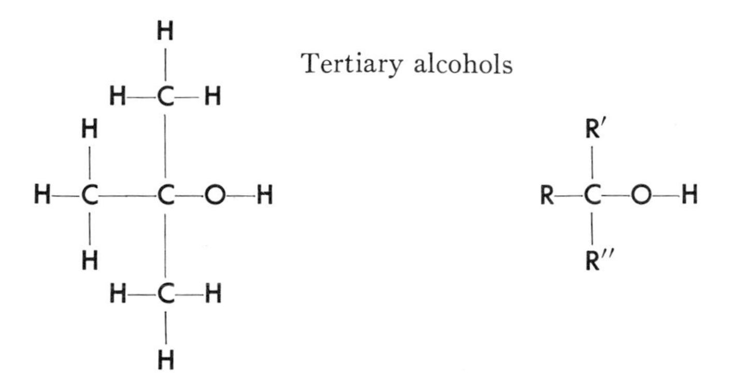

Tertiary alcohols

Primary alcohols are oxidized by $K_2Cr_2O_7$ in H_2SO_4, or by CrO_3 in acetic acid, to form compounds known as ***aldehydes.*** These are distinguished by the presence of the functional group $-C\begin{smallmatrix} \diagup H \\ \diagdown\!\!\diagdown O \end{smallmatrix}$ as in these two cases:

$$3\ CH_3{-}CH_2{-}OH + Cr_2O_7^{--} + 8\ H^+ \rightarrow 3\ CH_3{-}C\begin{smallmatrix} /\!\!/ O \\ \diagdown H \end{smallmatrix} + 2\ Cr^{+++} + 7\ H_2O$$

ethyl alcohol (ethanol) — acetaldehyde (ethanal)

$$CH_3{-}CH_2{-}CH_2{-}OH \xrightarrow[CH_3COOH]{CrO_3} CH_3{-}CH_2{-}CHO^*$$

n-propyl alcohol (1-propanol) — propionaldehyde (propanal)

The aldehyde must be distilled from the reaction mixture as fast as it is formed in order to avoid further oxidation to the acid (see below). Usually this is possible, because aldehyde molecules are unable to form hydrogen bonds with one another. The boiling point of an aldehyde is therefore invariably lower than that of the alcohol from which it is formed.

More complete oxidation of primary alcohols leads to the formation of ***carboxylic acids.*** The intermediate aldehyde is not isolated in this case:

$$3\ CH_3{-}CH_2{-}OH + 2\ Cr_2O_7^{--} + 16\ H^+ \rightarrow$$

ethyl alcohol (ethanol)

$$3\ CH_3{-}C\begin{smallmatrix} /\!\!/ O \\ \diagdown OH \end{smallmatrix} + 4\ Cr^{+++} + 11\ H_2O$$

acetic acid (ethanoic acid)

* It is common practice among organic chemists to balance equations only partially, writing inorganic reagents, reagents used in excess, solvents, and reaction conditions on the arrow as in this and subsequent examples.

Secondary alcohols give ***ketones*** upon oxidation:

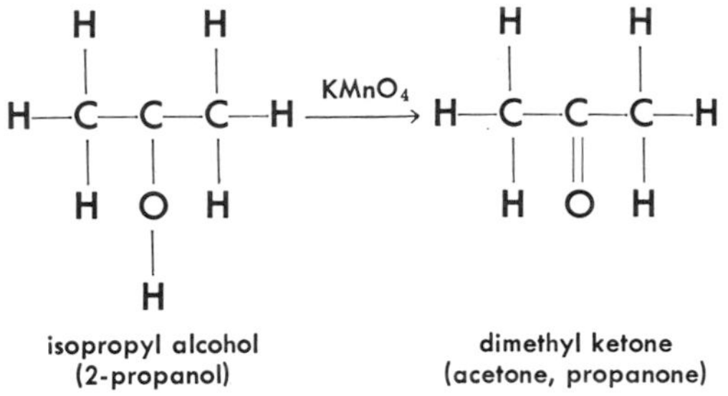

$$H-\underset{H}{\overset{H}{C}}-\underset{\underset{H}{O}}{C}-\underset{H}{\overset{H}{C}}-H \xrightarrow{KMnO_4} H-\underset{H}{\overset{H}{C}}-\underset{O}{\overset{}{\underset{\|}{C}}}-\underset{H}{\overset{H}{C}}-H$$

isopropyl alcohol (2-propanol) — dimethyl ketone (acetone, propanone)

Ketones are resistant to further oxidation. Only under very vigorous conditions will the molecule cleave, with the formation of mixtures of carboxylic acids:

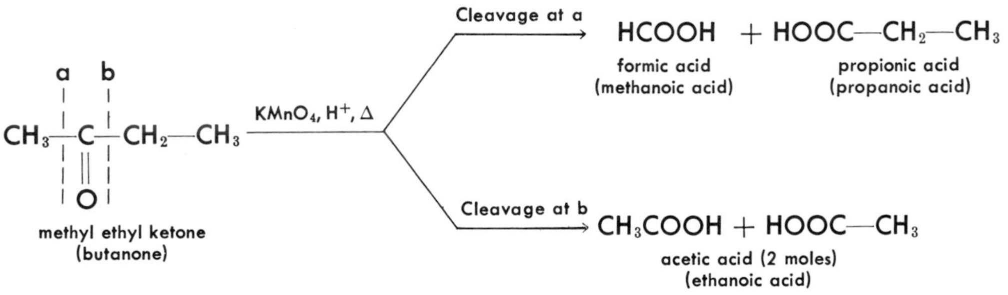

$$CH_3 \overset{a}{|} \underset{\underset{O}{\|}}{C} \overset{b}{|} CH_2-CH_3 \xrightarrow{KMnO_4,\ H^+,\ \Delta}$$

methyl ethyl ketone (butanone)

Cleavage at a: $HCOOH + HOOC-CH_2-CH_3$

formic acid (methanoic acid) — propionic acid (propanoic acid)

Cleavage at b: $CH_3COOH + HOOC-CH_3$

acetic acid (2 moles) (ethanoic acid)

Tertiary alcohols are unaffected by oxidizing agents except under the most severe conditions, whereupon they cleave to give mixtures of ketones, carboxylic acids, and carbon dioxide.

(b) Dehydration. Alcohols react with H_2SO_4 and certain other dehydrating agents to form ***alkenes.*** Thus, ethylene may be prepared by adding ethyl alcohol dropwise to hot, concentrated H_2SO_4:

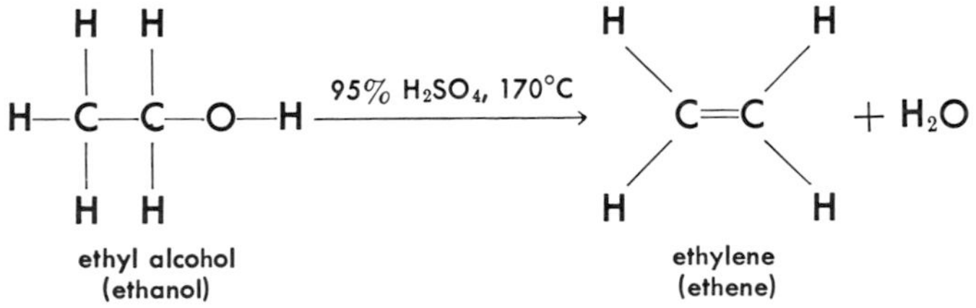

$$H-\underset{H}{\overset{H}{C}}-\underset{H}{\overset{H}{C}}-O-H \xrightarrow{95\%\ H_2SO_4,\ 170°C} \underset{H}{\overset{H}{}}\!\!>C=C<\!\!\underset{H}{\overset{H}{}} + H_2O$$

ethyl alcohol (ethanol) — ethylene (ethene)

The different classes of alcohols differ in their ease of dehydration: 3° alcohols are more easily dehydrated than 2°, and 2° in turn are more easily dehydrated than 1° alcohols:

$$1° \quad CH_3-CH_2-CH_2-CH_2-OH \xrightarrow{75\%\ H_2SO_4,\ 140°} CH_3-CH_2-CH=CH_2$$

n-butyl alcohol (1-butanol) — 1-butene

$$2^\circ \quad CH_3{-}CH_2{-}\underset{\displaystyle OH}{\underset{|}{CH}}{-}CH_3 \xrightarrow{60\%\ H_2SO_4,\ 100^\circ} CH_3{-}CH{=}CH{-}CH_3$$

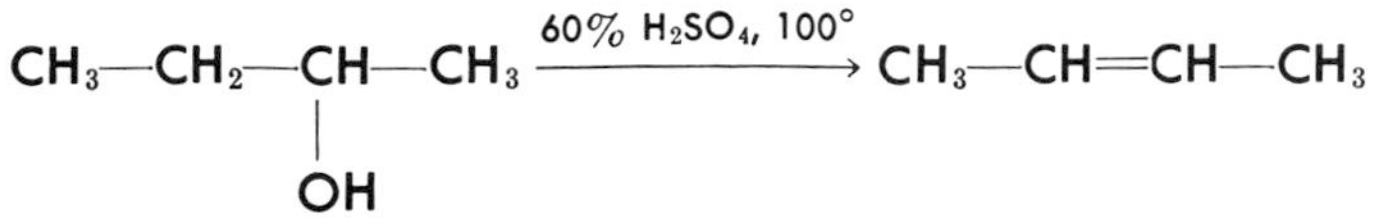

sec-butyl alcohol (2-butanol) — 2-butene

$$3^\circ \quad CH_3{-}\overset{\displaystyle CH_3}{\overset{|}{\underset{\displaystyle CH_3}{\underset{|}{C}}}}{-}OH \xrightarrow{20\%\ H_2SO_4,\ 85^\circ} CH_3{-}\overset{\displaystyle CH_3}{\overset{|}{C}}{=}CH_2$$

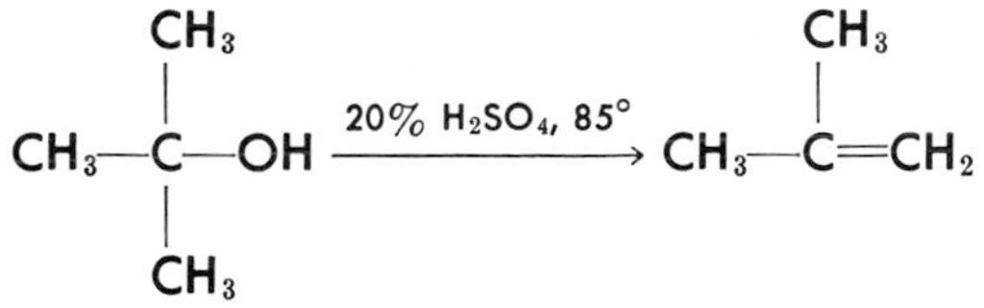

tert-butyl alcohol (2-methyl-2-propanol) — isobutylene (2-methylpropene)

Under milder conditions, particularly if the alcohol is always kept present in excess, for example by adding H_2SO_4 dropwise to the boiling alcohol rather than the reverse, intermolecular dehydration may occur, yielding an ***ether.*** Ordinary anesthetic ether is prepared in this way from ethyl alcohol:

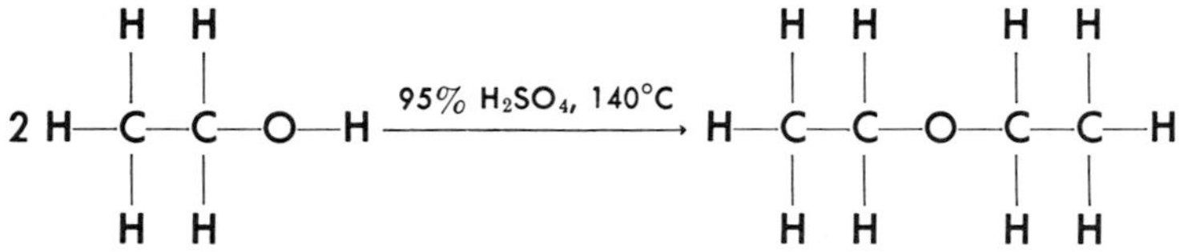

$$2\ H{-}\overset{\displaystyle H}{\overset{|}{\underset{\displaystyle H}{\underset{|}{C}}}}{-}\overset{\displaystyle H}{\overset{|}{\underset{\displaystyle H}{\underset{|}{C}}}}{-}O{-}H \xrightarrow{95\%\ H_2SO_4,\ 140^\circ C} H{-}\overset{\displaystyle H}{\overset{|}{\underset{\displaystyle H}{\underset{|}{C}}}}{-}\overset{\displaystyle H}{\overset{|}{\underset{\displaystyle H}{\underset{|}{C}}}}{-}O{-}\overset{\displaystyle H}{\overset{|}{\underset{\displaystyle H}{\underset{|}{C}}}}{-}\overset{\displaystyle H}{\overset{|}{\underset{\displaystyle H}{\underset{|}{C}}}}{-}H$$

ethyl alcohol (ethanol) — diethyl ether (a common anesthetic)

(c) Esterification. Alcohols react with both inorganic and organic acids to form compounds known as ***esters:***

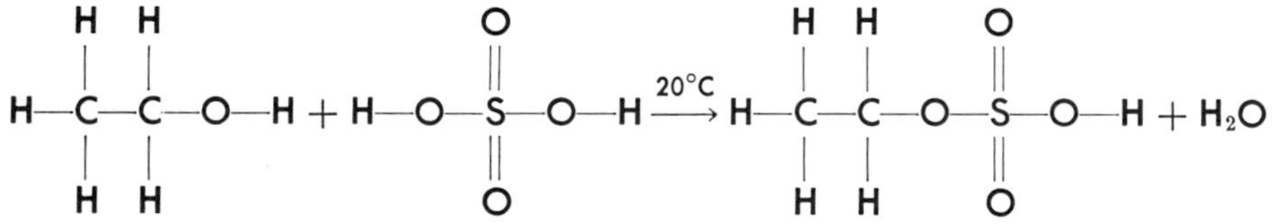

$$H{-}\overset{\displaystyle H}{\overset{|}{\underset{\displaystyle H}{\underset{|}{C}}}}{-}\overset{\displaystyle H}{\overset{|}{\underset{\displaystyle H}{\underset{|}{C}}}}{-}O{-}H + H{-}O{-}\overset{\displaystyle O}{\overset{\|}{\underset{\displaystyle O}{\underset{\|}{S}}}}{-}O{-}H \xrightarrow{20^\circ C} H{-}\overset{\displaystyle H}{\overset{|}{\underset{\displaystyle H}{\underset{|}{C}}}}{-}\overset{\displaystyle H}{\overset{|}{\underset{\displaystyle H}{\underset{|}{C}}}}{-}O{-}\overset{\displaystyle O}{\overset{\|}{\underset{\displaystyle O}{\underset{\|}{S}}}}{-}O{-}H + H_2O$$

ethyl alcohol (ethanol) — sulfuric acid — ethyl sulfate (an inorganic ester)

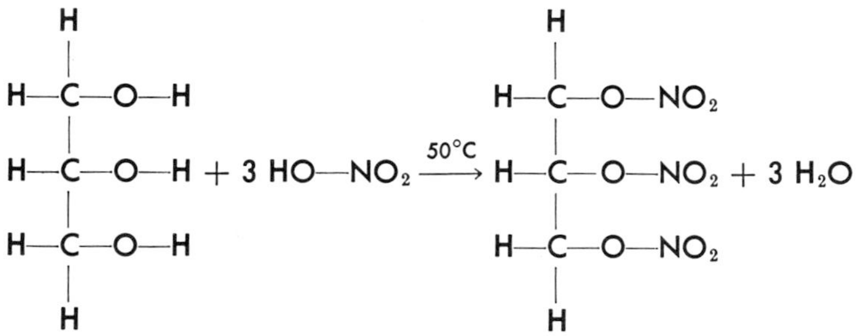

$$\begin{array}{c} H \\ | \\ H{-}C{-}O{-}H \\ | \\ H{-}C{-}O{-}H \\ | \\ H{-}C{-}O{-}H \\ | \\ H \end{array} + 3\ HO{-}NO_2 \xrightarrow{50^\circ C} \begin{array}{c} H \\ | \\ H{-}C{-}O{-}NO_2 \\ | \\ H{-}C{-}O{-}NO_2 \\ | \\ H{-}C{-}O{-}NO_2 \\ | \\ H \end{array} + 3\ H_2O$$

glycerol (1,2,3-propanetriol) — glyceryl trinitrate (nitroglycerin, a high explosive)

A small amount of concentrated H_2SO_4, anhydrous HCl, or other strong acid is usually used to catalyze the reaction between the weaker organic acids and alcohols:

```
      H                                                  H
      |                                                  |
    H—C—H                                              H—C—H
 H    |    H          O       H               H          |       H     O  H
 |    |    |           \\     |       H+      |          |       |     ‖  |
H—C———C————C—O—H  +      C—C—H    →    H—C———————C———————C—O—C—C—H
 |    |    |            /     |               |          |       |        |
 H    H    H        H—O       H               H          H       H        H
```

isobutyl alcohol acetic acid isobutyl acetate

The reaction of an alcohol with a halogen acid yields an ***alkyl halide.*** These compounds contain no oxygen, and are not usually considered to be esters:

```
   H  H  H  H                   H  H  H  H
   |  |  |  |                   |  |  |  |
H—C—C—C—C—H + HBr → H—C—C—C—C—H + H2O
   |  |  |  |                   |  |  |  |
   H  H  O  H                   H  H  Br H
         |
         H
```

sec-butyl alcohol (2-butanol) 2-bromobutane (an alkyl halide)

Many of the simple esters are found in fruits and essential oils of plants, and they are largely responsible for the pleasant aromas of these substances. Esters are widely used in the preparation of synthetic flavorings and perfumes. A few examples are given in Table 17.2.

17.4 Preparation of Alcohols

(a) By Hydrolysis of Esters. Esterification is a reversible reaction, and an ester may be readily hydrolyzed to a mixture of an alcohol and an acid. Either acid or base can be used to catalyze the hydrolysis. If an acid catalyst is used, maximum yields are obtained only if one of the products (usually the alcohol) can be distilled from the mixture as it is formed. Otherwise the system will soon attain equilibrium with both hydrolysis and re-esterification occurring at the same rate.

```
      H                                         H
      |                                         |
    H—C—H                                     H—C—H
 H    |    H      O  H                      H   |   H            O     H
 |    |    |      ‖  |             H+       |   |   |             \\   |
H—C———C————C—O—C—C—H + H2O ⇌ H—C———C———C—O—H  +       C—C—H
 |    |    |         |                      |   |   |              /   |
 H    H    H         H                      H   H   H            HO    H
```

isobutyl acetate isobutyl alcohol acetic acid

TABLE 17.2 Some Common Esters Used in Flavoring and Perfumery

Ester	Formula	Flavor or Aroma
Methyl butyrate	$CH_3{-}O{-}\overset{\overset{\displaystyle O}{\|}}{C}{-}CH_2{-}CH_2{-}CH_3$	pineapple
Ethyl butyrate	$CH_3{-}CH_2{-}O{-}\overset{\overset{\displaystyle O}{\|}}{C}{-}CH_2{-}CH_2{-}CH_3$	apricot
Isoamyl acetate	$CH_3{-}\overset{\overset{\displaystyle CH_3}{\vert}}{CH}{-}CH_2{-}CH_2{-}O{-}\overset{\overset{\displaystyle O}{\|}}{C}{-}CH_3$	banana
Ethyl heptoate	$CH_3{-}CH_2{-}O{-}\overset{\overset{\displaystyle O}{\|}}{C}{-}(CH_2)_5{-}CH_3$	cognac
Isoamyl isovalerate	$CH_3{-}\overset{\overset{\displaystyle CH_3}{\vert}}{CH}{-}CH_2{-}CH_2{-}O{-}\overset{\overset{\displaystyle O}{\|}}{C}{-}CH_2{-}\overset{\overset{\displaystyle CH_3}{\vert}}{CH}{-}CH_3$	apple
Octyl acetate	$CH_3{-}(CH_2)_7{-}O{-}\overset{\overset{\displaystyle O}{\|}}{C}{-}CH_3$	orange
Ethyl laurate	$CH_3{-}CH_2{-}O{-}\overset{\overset{\displaystyle O}{\|}}{C}{-}(CH_2)_{10}{-}CH_3$	tuberose
Methyl myristate	$CH_3{-}O{-}\overset{\overset{\displaystyle O}{\|}}{C}{-}(CH_2)_{12}{-}COOH$	orris root
Methyl salicylate	$\begin{array}{ccccccc} & & & H & H & & \\ & & & \vert & \vert & & \\ & O & & C & = C & & \\ & \| & / & & & \backslash & \\ CH_3{-}O{-} & C{-}C & & & & & C{-}H \\ & & \backslash\backslash & & & // & \\ & & & C & {-}C & & \\ & & & \vert & \vert & & \\ & & & O & H & & \\ & & & \vert & & & \\ & & & H & & & \end{array}$	wintergreen

The use of a base both catalyzes the reaction and forces it to completion, because as soon as the acid is formed it reacts with the base to form the salt. This effectively removes the acid from the scene and prevents the reverse reaction:

$$(CH_3)_2\text{—}CH\text{—}CH_2\text{—}O\text{—}\overset{\overset{\large O}{\|}}{C}\text{—}CH_3 + NaOH \rightarrow (CH_3)_2\text{—}CH\text{—}CH_2\text{—}OH + Na^+ \ {}^-O\text{—}\overset{\overset{\large O}{\|}}{C}\text{—}CH_3$$

isobutyl acetate — isobutyl alcohol — sodium acetate

If desired, the acid can later be recovered by treating the salt with a strong mineral acid:

$$CH_3\text{—}\overset{\overset{\large O}{\|}}{C}\text{—}O^- \ {}^+Na + H^+ \rightarrow CH_3\text{—}\overset{\overset{\large O}{\|}}{C}\text{—}OH + Na^+$$

The basic hydrolysis of an ester is known as ***saponification*** (from Latin *sapon*, soap) because the same reaction is involved in the preparation of soap from the natural fats, which are esters of glycerol with various long-chain ***fatty acids:***

$$\begin{array}{l} H_2C\text{—}O\text{—}\overset{\overset{\large O}{\|}}{C}\text{—}(CH_2)_{14}\text{—}CH_3 \\ \quad | \\ HC\text{—}O\text{—}\overset{\overset{\large O}{\|}}{C}\text{—}(CH_2)_{16}\text{—}CH_3 \\ \quad | \\ H_2C\text{—}O\text{—}\overset{\overset{\large O}{\|}}{C}\text{—}(CH_2)_7\text{—}CH{=}CH\text{—}(CH_2)_7\text{—}CH_3 \end{array}$$

typical fat molecule (mixed palmitate, stearate, oleate)

aqueous NaOH ↓

$$\begin{array}{c} H_2C\text{—}OH \\ | \\ HC\text{—}OH \\ | \\ H_2C\text{—}OH \\ \text{glycerol} \end{array} + \left\{ \begin{array}{l} Na^+ \ {}^-O\text{—}\overset{\overset{\large O}{\|}}{C}\text{—}(CH_2)_{14}\text{—}CH_3 \quad \text{sodium palmitate} \\ Na^+ \ {}^-O\text{—}\overset{\overset{\large O}{\|}}{C}\text{—}(CH_2)_{16}\text{—}CH_3 \quad \text{sodium stearate} \\ Na^+ \ {}^-O\text{—}\overset{\overset{\large O}{\|}}{C}\text{—}(CH_2)_7\text{—}CH{=}CH\text{—}(CH_2)_7\text{—}CH_3 \quad \text{sodium oleate} \end{array} \right\} \text{Soap}$$

The cleansing power of soap is the result of its ability to emulsify the grease and oils in the dirt. A soap molecule has a water-soluble ionic head as well as an oil-soluble hydrocarbon tail. In the presence of both oil and water, the hydrocarbon tail dissolves in the oil, leaving the head sticking out into the water (Fig. 17.3a). When the mixture is shaken, the oil is broken up into droplets. In the presence of soap, these droplets are unable to coalesce because of repulsion between the like-charged heads of the soap molecules at their surfaces (Fig. 17.3b). The oil droplets thus remain suspended, or emulsified, and can then be washed away along with the dirt.

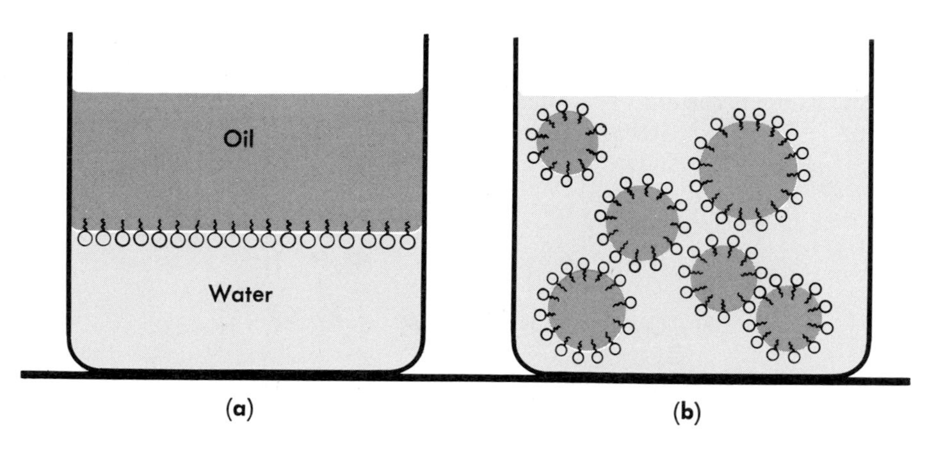

Fig. 17.3 Behavior of soap molecules at oil-water interface.

(b) By Hydration of Alkenes. In the presence of an acid catalyst, water will add across the double bond of an alkene to form an alcohol. Most of the industrial ethyl alcohol used in this country is made in this way from ethylene obtained as a by-product of petroleum refining. Hydration may be accomplished directly in the vapor phase at high temperature ($\approx 300°C$) and pressure (≈ 100–300 atm) using a large excess of water and a catalyst such as phosphoric acid on an inert support, or certain metallic oxides which can function as Lewis acids (Sec. 13.5):

$$\underset{\text{ethylene (ethene)}}{H_2C{=}CH_2} + H_2O \xrightarrow[\text{catalyst}]{300°,\ 100\text{–}300\ \text{atm}} \underset{\text{ethyl alcohol (ethanol)}}{H{-}CH_2{-}CH_2{-}O{-}H}$$

Alternatively, the alkene may first be dissolved in concentrated H_2SO_4, with which it will react at ordinary temperatures to give the sulfate ester:

$$H_2C{=}CH_2 + H_2SO_4 \rightarrow H{-}CH_2{-}CH_2{-}O{-}SO_2{-}OH$$

Hydrolysis of the ester is then effected by diluting it with water and distilling off the alcohol:

$$CH_3CH_2{-}O{-}SO_2{-}OH + H_2O \rightarrow CH_3CH_2{-}O{-}H + H_2SO_4$$

Ethyl alcohol is the only 1° alcohol which can be prepared by hydration of an alkene. All other alkenes besides ethylene yield 2° or 3° alcohols by hydration:

$$CH_3{-}CH{=}CH_2 \xrightarrow{H_2O,\ H^+} CH_3{-}CH(OH){-}CH_3$$

propene → isopropyl alcohol (2-propanol)

$$(CH_3)_2C{=}CH_2 \xrightarrow{H_2O,\ H^+} (CH_3)_3C{-}OH$$

isobutylene (2-methylpropene) → *tert*-butyl alcohol (2-methyl-2-propanol)

As a general rule (Markovnikov's rule), when an unsymmetrical reagent such as H_2O, H_2SO_4, or HCl adds across the double bond of an alkene, the hydrogen of the reagent becomes attached to the carbon which, in the alkene, already had the greater number of hydrogens, i.e., the rich get richer:

$$CH_3{-}CH{=}CH_2 + H_2SO_4 \rightarrow CH_3{-}CH(O{-}SO_2OH){-}CH_3$$

```
            H                                   H
            |                                   |
         H—C—H                               H—C—H
   H        |     H  H               H          |      H  H
   |        |     |  |               |          |      |  |
H—C————C═══C—C—H + HCl → H—C————C————C—C—H
   |              |                  |          |      |  |
   H              H                  H          Cl     H  H
```

(c) By Reduction of Carbonyl Compounds. Aldehydes and ketones may be reduced to 1° and 2° alcohols, respectively, by direct addition of hydrogen across the carbonyl double bond. The addition is carried out at moderate hydrogen pressures, using a nickel or platinum catalyst. Any carbon-carbon multiple bonds present in the molecule will also be hydrogenated at the same time:

```
   H  H     H                        H  H  H
   |  |    /                         |  |  |
H—C—C—C      H2, Ni, 3–5 atm     H—C—C—C—O—H
   |  |    \\   ————————————→        |  |  |
   H  H     O                        H  H  H
propionaldehyde                    n-propyl alcohol
                                     (1-propanol)
```

```
   H     H                            H  H  H
   |     |                            |  |  |
H—C—C—C—H    H2, Pt, 1–3 atm      H—C—C—C—H
   |  ‖  |    ————————————→           |  |  |
   H  O  H                            H  O  H
                                         |
                                         H
 acetone                          isopropyl alcohol
(propanone)                         (2-propanol)
```

```
   H  H  H     H                      H  H  H  H
   |  |  |    /                       |  |  |  |
H—C—C═C—C      H2, Ni, 3–5 atm    H—C—C—C—C—O—H
   |       \\   ————————————→         |  |  |  |
   H        O                         H  H  H  H
crotonaldehyde                      n-butyl alcohol
 (2-butanal)                          (1-butanol)
```

Certain metal hydrides can be used to reduce carbonyl groups. These reagents do not affect carbon-carbon multiple bonds and so can be used to prepare unsaturated alcohols from unsaturated aldehydes and ketones. Lithium aluminum hydride (**$LiAlH_4$**) in anhydrous ether solution reacts with aldehydes and ketones to give a metal-alcohol complex (***alkoxide***):

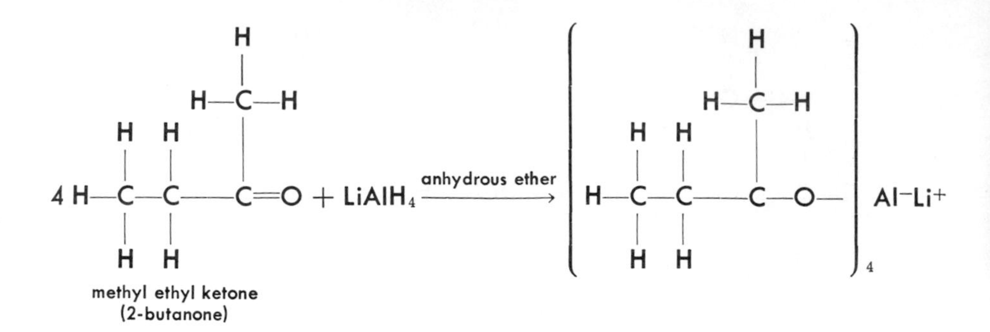

The solution of the alkoxide is added to water, which hydrolyzes it to the alcohol:

$$\left(\mathrm{H{-}CH_2{-}CH_2{-}C(H)(CH_3){-}O{-}}\right)_4\mathrm{Al^{-}Li^{+}} + 4\,\mathrm{H_2O} \rightarrow 4\,\mathrm{H{-}CH_2{-}CH_2{-}CH(OH){-}CH_2{-}H} + \mathrm{Al(OH)_3} + \mathrm{LiOH}$$

2-butanol

Reduction with sodium borohydride ($NaBH_4$) follows a similar course. In this case, however, the reaction can be carried out in water solution, in which $NaBH_4$ is soluble without decomposition. Reduction and hydrolysis occur simultaneously:

$$\mathrm{H{-}CH_2{-}CH{=}CH{-}C(H){=}O} \xrightarrow{\mathrm{NaBH_4\ (aqueous)}} \mathrm{H{-}CH_2{-}CH{=}CH{-}CH_2{-}O{-}H}$$

crotonaldehyde → 2-buten-1-ol

Lithium aluminum hydride (but not $NaBH_4$) can also be used to reduce acids and esters to 1° alcohols:

$$\mathrm{H{-}CH_2{-}CH_2{-}CH_2{-}C({=}O){-}OH} \xrightarrow{\mathrm{LiAlH_4}} \xrightarrow{\mathrm{H_2O}} \mathrm{H{-}CH_2{-}CH_2{-}CH_2{-}CH_2{-}O{-}H}$$

n-butyric acid (butanoic acid) → *n*-butyl alcohol (1-butanol)

$$\text{H—}\underset{\underset{\text{H}}{|}}{\overset{\overset{\text{H}}{|}}{\text{C}}}\text{—}\underset{\underset{\text{H}}{|}}{\overset{\overset{\text{H}}{|}}{\text{C}}}\text{—}\underset{\underset{\text{H}}{|}}{\overset{\overset{\text{H}}{|}}{\text{C}}}\text{—}\overset{\overset{\text{O}}{\|}}{\text{C}}\text{—O—}\underset{\underset{\text{H}}{|}}{\overset{\overset{\text{H}}{|}}{\text{C}}}\text{—H} \xrightarrow{LiAlH_4} \xrightarrow{H_2O} \text{H—}\underset{\underset{\text{H}}{|}}{\overset{\overset{\text{H}}{|}}{\text{C}}}\text{—}\underset{\underset{\text{H}}{|}}{\overset{\overset{\text{H}}{|}}{\text{C}}}\text{—}\underset{\underset{\text{H}}{|}}{\overset{\overset{\text{H}}{|}}{\text{C}}}\text{—}\underset{\underset{\text{H}}{|}}{\overset{\overset{\text{H}}{|}}{\text{C}}}\text{—O—H} + \text{H—}\underset{\underset{\text{H}}{|}}{\overset{\overset{\text{H}}{|}}{\text{C}}}\text{—O—H}$$

methyl butyrate   *n*-butyl alcohol   methyl alcohol

Isomerism 17.5

Several years after Wöhler first prepared urea, he and Justus Liebig, working together, succeeded in isolating ammonium cyanate. They found it to be stable, both as a solid and in solution, unless its solution were evaporated by heating, in which case it was converted to urea. Both compounds were shown to have the same elemental composition and molecular weight, and chemists were forced to conclude that the differences between them arose from a difference in the way in which their atoms were arranged. We now know that ammonium cyanate is an ionic compound composed of ammonium and cyanate ions:

$$NH_4^+CNO^-$$

ammonium cyanate

while urea is a covalent compound with the following structure:

$$\begin{array}{ccccc} H & & O & & H \\ & \diagdown & \| & \diagup & \\ & N & —C— & N & \\ & \diagup & & \diagdown & \\ H & & & & H \end{array}$$

Where two or more compounds have the same molecular formula but differ in the arrangement of their atoms, they are said to be ***isomers,*** *and the phenomenon is called* ***isomerism.*** Examples of isomerism abound in organic chemistry. Besides *structural* isomerism, such as that shown by urea and ammonium cyanate, two other types of isomerism, *geometric* and *optical*, are recognized. The latter arise not from any difference in the order in which the atoms are attached to one another, but rather from differences in the ways in which the atoms are arranged in three-dimensional space.

Structural Isomerism 17.6

The four hydrogens of methane are described as being *equivalent* to one another. This means that replacement of any one of the hydrogens by some other atom or group will give the same product. Thus, all four of the structures given below represent the same substance:

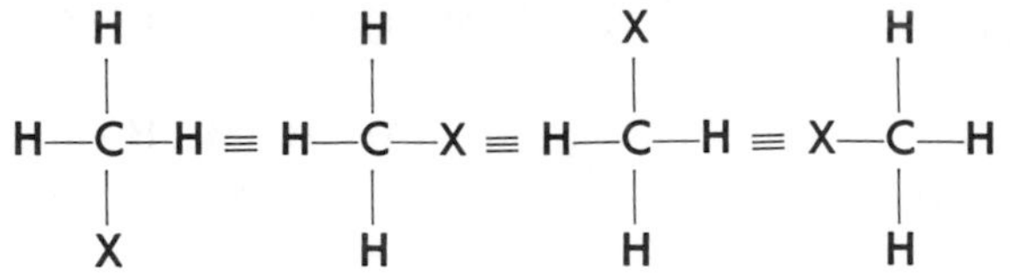

```
     H            H            X            H
     |            |            |            |
  H—C—H  ≡  H—C—X  ≡  H—C—H  ≡  X—C—H
     |            |            |            |
     X            H            H            H
```

(Here **X** is any atom or group of atoms other than **H**.) Similarly, the six hydrogens of ethane are also equivalent:

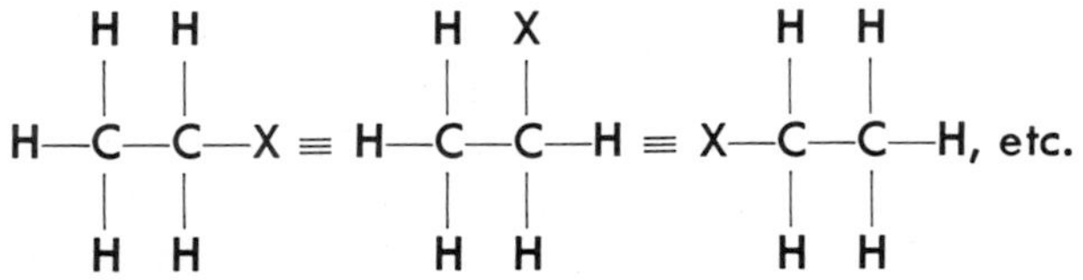

```
    H  H           H  X            H  H
    |  |           |  |            |  |
 H—C—C—X  ≡  H—C—C—H  ≡  X—C—C—H, etc.
    |  |           |  |            |  |
    H  H           H  H            H  H
```

The situation is different with propane. Here the two hydrogens on the middle carbon are different from the six on the ends. A fourth carbon or some functional group may be attached either to the end or to the middle of the chain, giving two possible products, e.g.,

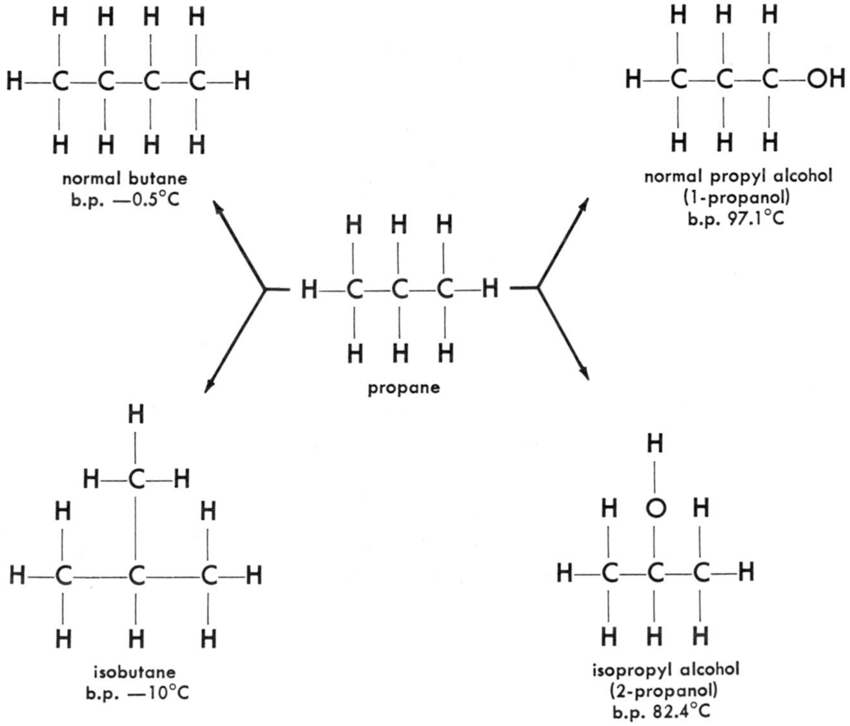

```
    H  H  H  H
    |  |  |  |
 H—C—C—C—C—H
    |  |  |  |
    H  H  H  H
```

normal butane
b.p. —0.5°C

```
    H  H  H
    |  |  |
 H—C—C—C—OH
    |  |  |
    H  H  H
```

normal propyl alcohol
(1-propanol)
b.p. 97.1°C

```
    H  H  H
    |  |  |
 H—C—C—C—H
    |  |  |
    H  H  H
```

propane

```
        H
        |
     H—C—H
  H     |     H
  |     |     |
H—C————C————C—H
  |     |     |
  H     H     H
```

isobutane
b.p. —10°C

```
       H
       |
    H  O  H
    |  |  |
 H—C—C—C—H
    |  |  |
    H  H  H
```

isopropyl alcohol
(2-propanol)
b.p. 82.4°C

The six hydrogens on the end carbons of propane are equivalent, and replacement of any one of them by a methyl group (—CH_3) gives *n*-butane.

Replacement of either hydrogen on the middle carbon leads to *iso*butane. Both of these compounds are known. They are different substances, and have different physical properties. Similarly, depending upon whether the hydroxyl group is attached to the first or second carbon of the chain (counting from either end), either 1- or 2-propanol is obtained. Both of the butanes have the molecular formula C_4H_{10}, and both propyl alcohols have the molecular formula C_3H_8O. The two butanes are ***structural isomers,*** as are the two propyl alcohols.

Calling one of the isomers *normal* in each case is not intended to imply that there is anything abnormal about the other. The term *normal* merely signifies that all of the carbons of the molecule are joined to one another in single file. Such an arrangement of carbon atoms is commonly called a ***straight chain,*** to distinguish it from a ***branched chain,*** e.g.,

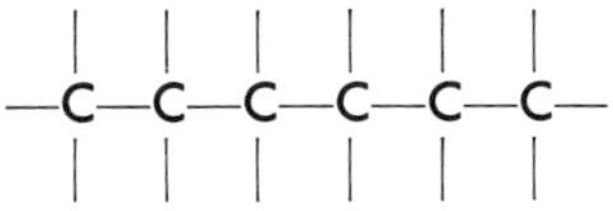

$$\text{—C—C—C—C—C—C—}$$

Straight chain

$$\text{—C—C(—C—)—C(—C—)—C—C—}$$

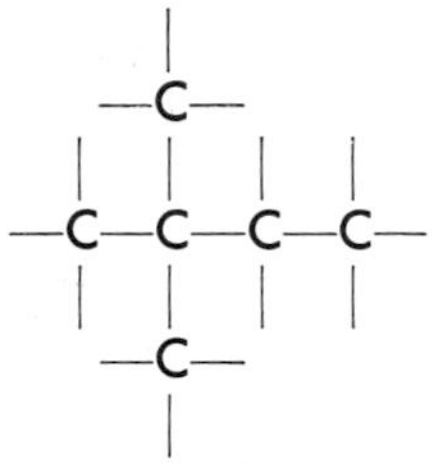

Branched chain

With greater numbers of carbon atoms, the number of isomers possible is increased. Thus while there are only two isomeric butanes, there are three *pentanes:*

$$CH_3\text{—}CH_2\text{—}CH_2\text{—}CH_2\text{—}CH_3$$

n-pentane

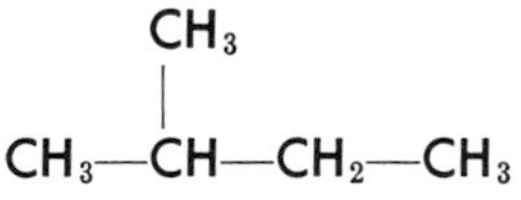

$$CH_3\text{—}CH(CH_3)\text{—}CH_2\text{—}CH_3$$

isopentane
(2-methylbutane)

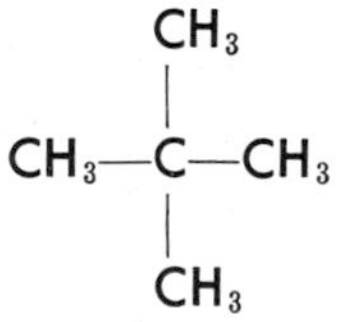

$$CH_3\text{—}C(CH_3)_2\text{—}CH_3$$

neopentane
(2,2-dimethylpropane)

and five *hexanes:*

$$CH_3\text{—}CH_2\text{—}CH_2\text{—}CH_2\text{—}CH_2\text{—}CH_3$$

n-hexane

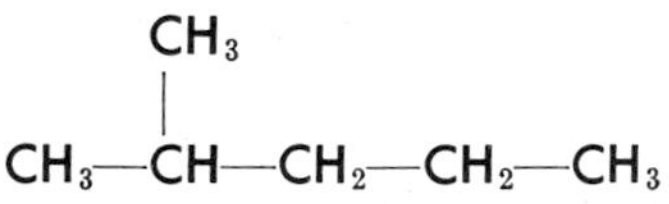

$$CH_3\text{—}CH(CH_3)\text{—}CH_2\text{—}CH_2\text{—}CH_3$$

isohexane
(2-methylpentane)

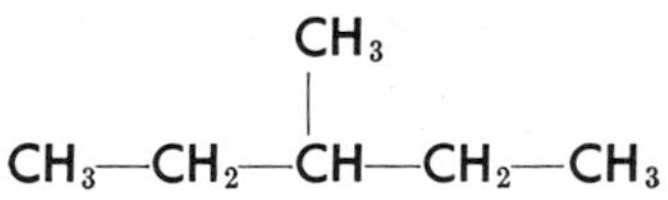

$$CH_3\text{—}CH_2\text{—}CH(CH_3)\text{—}CH_2\text{—}CH_3$$

3-methylpentane

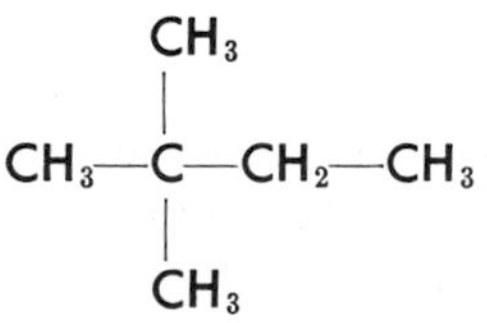

$$CH_3\text{—}C(CH_3)_2\text{—}CH_2\text{—}CH_3$$

2,2-dimethylbutane

$$CH_3\text{—}CH(CH_3)\text{—}CH(CH_3)\text{—}CH_3$$

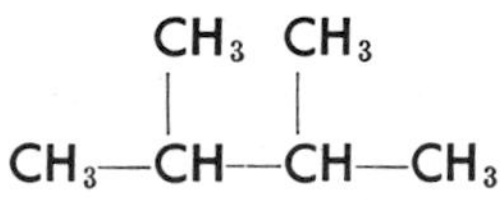

2,3-dimethylbutane

The number of isomers possible for a given molecular formula increases rapidly as the number of carbon atoms increases and soon reaches astronomical proportions. This is shown for the alkane hydrocarbons in Table 17.3. The possibilities of isomerism, great as they are among the alkanes, are multiplied by the presence of functional groups. Thus, while there are nine isomeric heptanes C_7H_{16}, there are 39 possible heptyl alcohols $C_7H_{15}OH$.

TABLE 17.3 Numbers of Possible Isomeric Alkanes

Molecular Formula	Number of Possible Isomers
C_7H_{16}	9
C_8H_{18}	18
C_9H_{20}	35
$C_{10}H_{22}$	75
$C_{20}H_{42}$	366, 319
$C_{30}H_{62}$	4, 111, 846, 763

The preparation of all of the isomeric alkanes is at least theoretically possible, but beyond $C_{10}H_{22}$, there are only a few compounds of each of the molecular formulas that have actually be prepared, since there has been no particularly good reason for anyone to spend the time necessary to make the others. Nevertheless, it is easy to see that the phenomenon of isomerism is among the factors responsible for the multiplicity of carbon compounds.

Not only is it important to recognize those isomers which have a given molecular formula, it is equally important to be able to recognize when two structural formulas which superficially may appear to be different actually represent a single compound. To avoid seeing isomers where none exist, it is well to remember that while a structural formula shows which atoms in the molecule are attached to which, it does not always adequately represent the molecule's actual shape. The structural formulas suffer from the limitation that they are two-dimensional representations. The molecules, on the other hand, are three-dimensional, with the bonds arranged tetrahedrally around the carbons (sp^3 hybridization, Sec. 8.9). The various parts of a molecule are also free to rotate with respect to one another so long as no bonds are broken in the process. At any particular moment, therefore, the molecule may exist in any one of a large number of possible ***conformations*** (Fig. 17.4). A structural formula may also be bent or turned around on the paper at will, and so long as the atoms remain attached in the same sequence, the formula will represent the same structural isomer. The following formulas, for example, all represent the same compound, because the sequence of atoms is the same in each, that is, a chain of five carbons with

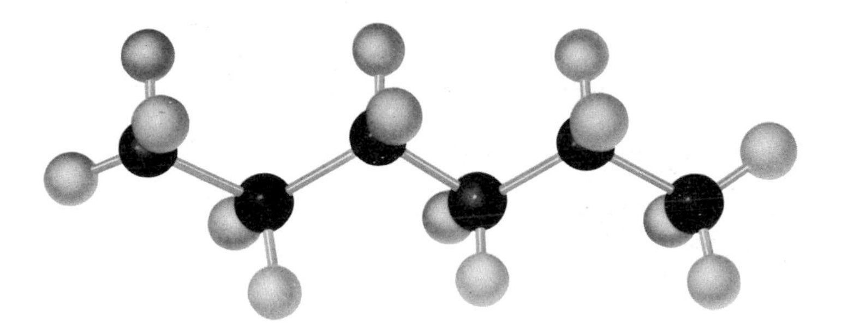

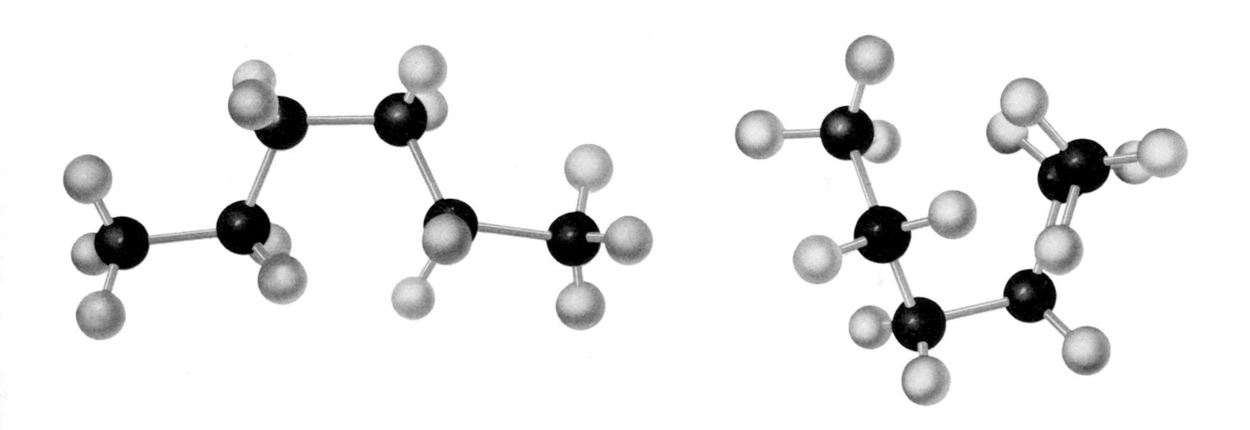

Fig. 17.4 Models of *n*-hexane in four of its possible conformations.

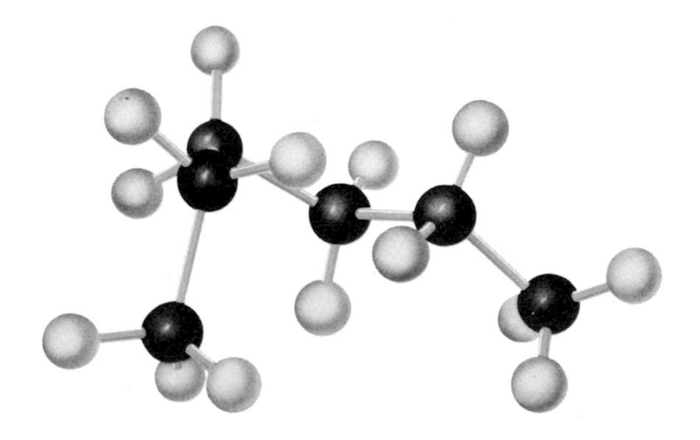

two other carbons attached to the second carbon of the chain:

```
         H                              H         H    H
         |                              |         |    |
   H  H—C—H  H  H  H              H  H—C—H  H—C————C—H
   |     |     |  |  |              |     |         |    |
H—C—————C—————C——C——C—H          H—C—————C—————————C—H  H
   |     |     |  |  |              |     |         |
   H  H—C—H  H  H  H              H  H—C—H         H
         |                                |
         H                                H
```

```
                                              H     H
                                              |     |
                                           H—C—————C—H
              H                               |     |
              |                            H—C—H   H
   H  H  H  H—C—H  H                    H     |     H
   |  |  |     |     |                  |     |     |
H—C——C——C—————C—————C—H              H—C—————C—————C—H
   |  |  |     |     |                  |     |     |
   H  H  H  H—C—H  H                    H  H—C—H   H
              |                               |
              H                               H
```

```
              H                                 H
              |                                 |
   H       H  H—C—H  H                    H  H—C—H  H
   |       |     |     |                  |     |     |
H—C———————C—————C—————C—H              H—C—————C—————C—H
   |       |     |     |                  |     |     |
H—C—H     H  H—C—H   H                  H     |     H
   |             |                              |  H  H
   H             H                              |  |  |
                                             H—C——C——C—H
                                                |  |  |
                                                H  H  H
```

17.7 Geometric Isomerism

Two dicarboxylic acids are known which have the same molecular formula: $C_4H_4O_4$. These are ***maleic acid*** (m.p. 130°C), and ***fumaric acid*** (m.p. 287°C). Both acids are unsaturated, that is, each contains a double bond, and catalytic hydrogenation of either one yields the same product, ***succinic acid:***

```
C4H4O4
maleic acid  \
              \      H2, Ni
               >————————————————> HOOC—CH2—CH2—COOH
              /                       succinic acid
C4H4O4       /
fumaric acid
```

This result shows that the sequence of atoms in both maleic and fumaric acids is the same, namely,

$$HOOC—CH{=}CH—COOH$$

yet the two compounds are clearly different. Their structures must, therefore, differ in some way. Jacobus van't Hoff suggested in 1874 that the presence of the double bond prevented free rotation of the two halves of the molecule with respect to each other, and as a result two different geometrical arrangements of the atoms were possible:

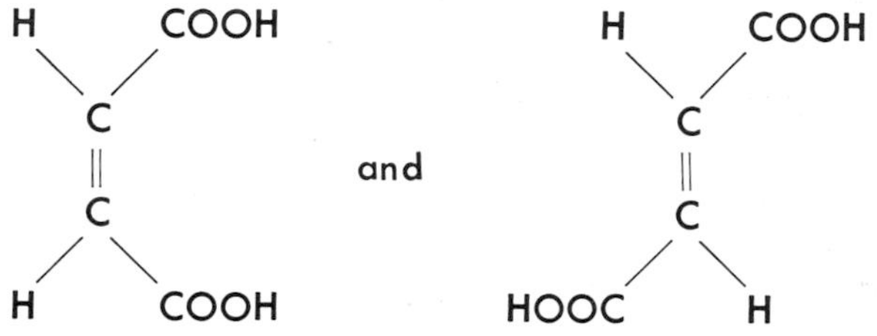

```
H     COOH            H     COOH
 \   /                 \   /
   C                     C
   ||        and         ||
   C                     C
 /   \                 /   \
H     COOH        HOOC      H
```

one of which was maleic acid, while the other was fumaric. Elimination of the double bond restored free rotation to the molecule, so that hydrogenation of either acid gave the same product (Fig. 17.5).

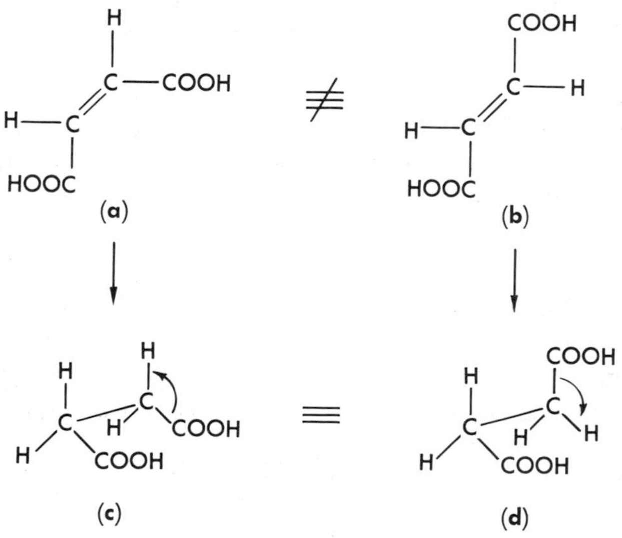

Fig. 17.5 Formation of succinic acid by hydrogenation of maleic and fumaric acids. (a) and (b) represent different compounds. (c) and (d) on the other hand are two conformations of the same compound. Each can be converted to the other by rotation about the central bond. Such rotation requires no breaking of bonds and is therefore described as unhindered, or free.

Maleic acid readily loses water when heated in a vacuum at 100°C, to give a product, maleic anhydride, with the molecular formula $C_4H_2O_3$. This compound reacts in turn with water, regenerating maleic acid. Fumaric acid, on the other hand, loses water only when heated to a much higher temperature, and the product once again is maleic anhydride. One might reasonably conclude that since maleic acid loses water more readily, it must have the two carboxyl groups on the same side of the molecule. Fumaric acid, which is the other geometrical isomer, forms the anhydride only at high temperatures, when energy is available to break the π bond, and allow the carboxyl groups to approach one another:

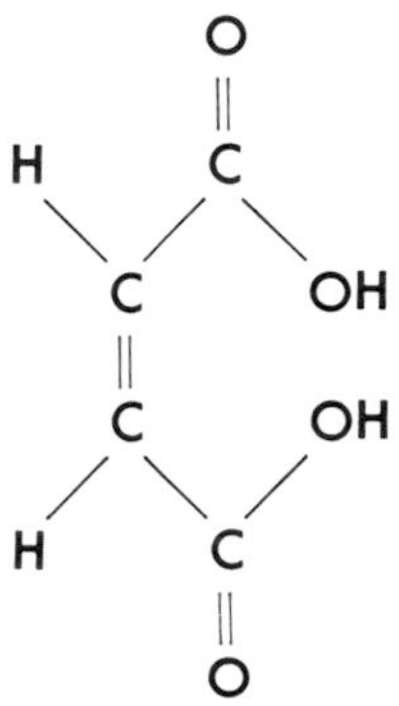

maleic acid 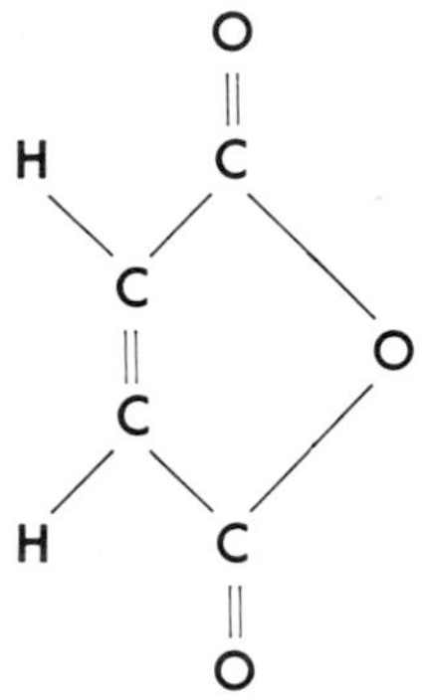   maleic anhydride 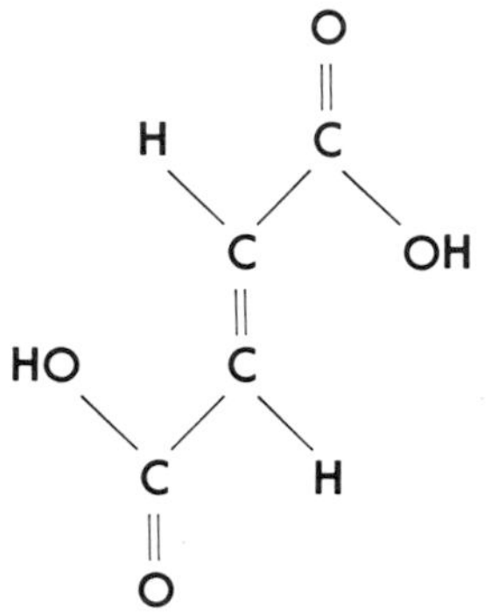   fumaric acid

The geometric isomerism exhibited by maleic and fumaric acids is a form of ***stereoisomerism.*** Whereas structural isomers differ in the sequence in which the atoms are joined in the molecule, in stereoisomers the sequence of atoms is the same, but the arrangement of these atoms in space is different. Geometric isomerism is also known as ***cis-*** and ***trans-isomerism*** (from Latin *cis*, on the same side; *trans*, across). The compound which has both functional groups, or both parts of the principal carbon chain on the same side of the molecule, is designated *cis*. Thus, maleic acid is the *cis* acid, and fumaric is the *trans* acid. Some other examples of *cis* and *trans* isomers are the following:

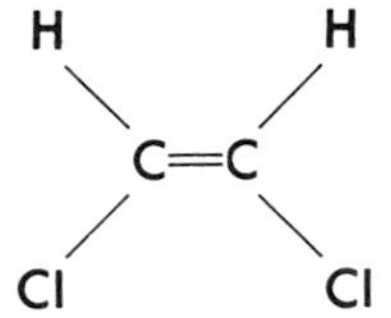

cis-1,2-dichloroethene 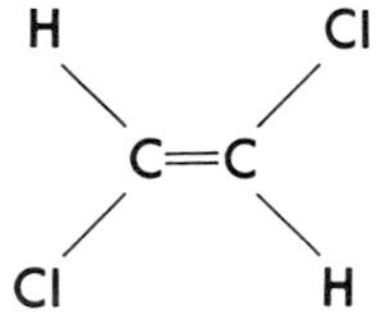   *trans*-1,2-dichloroethene

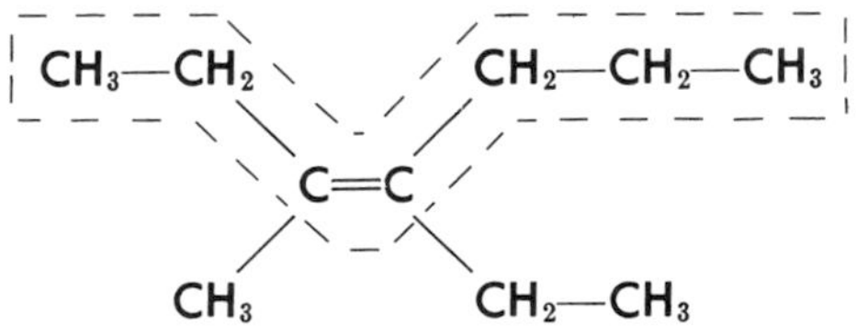

cis-3-methyl-4-ethyl-3-heptene 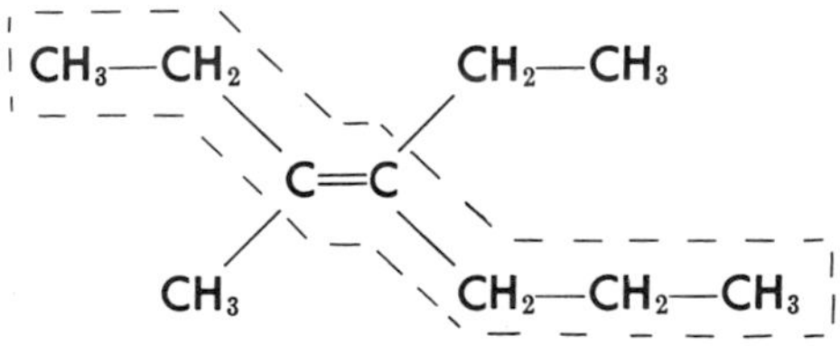   *trans*-3-methyl-4-ethyl-3-heptene

(the principal carbon chain is indicated by the dotted lines)

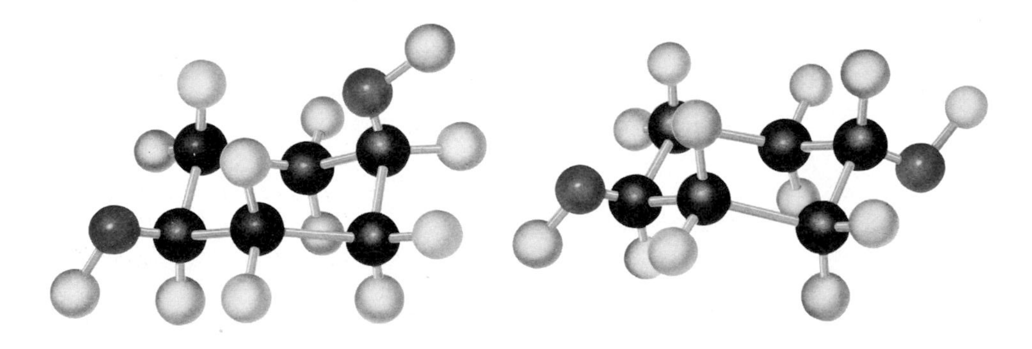

Fig. 17.6 Models of *cis*- (left) and *trans*-1,4-cyclohexanediol.

The presence of a ring can lead to *cis* and *trans* isomerism by preventing free rotation in the same manner as a double bond. This is illustrated by *cis*- and *trans*-cyclohexanediol (below, and Figure 17.6):

HO — OH

HO — OH

Optical Isomerism 17.8

A more subtle form of stereoisomerism is exhibited by most compounds whose molecules possess no ***plane of symmetry.*** An object or molecule is said to possess a plane of symmetry when it can be divided into two equal halves, each of which is the mirror image of the other. A football and a molecule of isopropyl alcohol have one thing in common in that a plane of symmetry may be drawn through each (Fig. 17.7).

An organic molecule is most likely to lack a plane of symmetry if it contains one or more ***asymmetric carbon atoms.*** An asymmetric carbon atom is one to which four different groups are attached. For example, in *sec*-butyl alcohol, the carbon bearing the hydroxyl group is an asymmetric carbon:

$$CH_3—\overset{\overset{H}{|}}{\underset{\underset{OH}{|}}{C^*}}—CH_2—CH_3$$

sec-butyl alcohol

* Asymmetric carbon atom

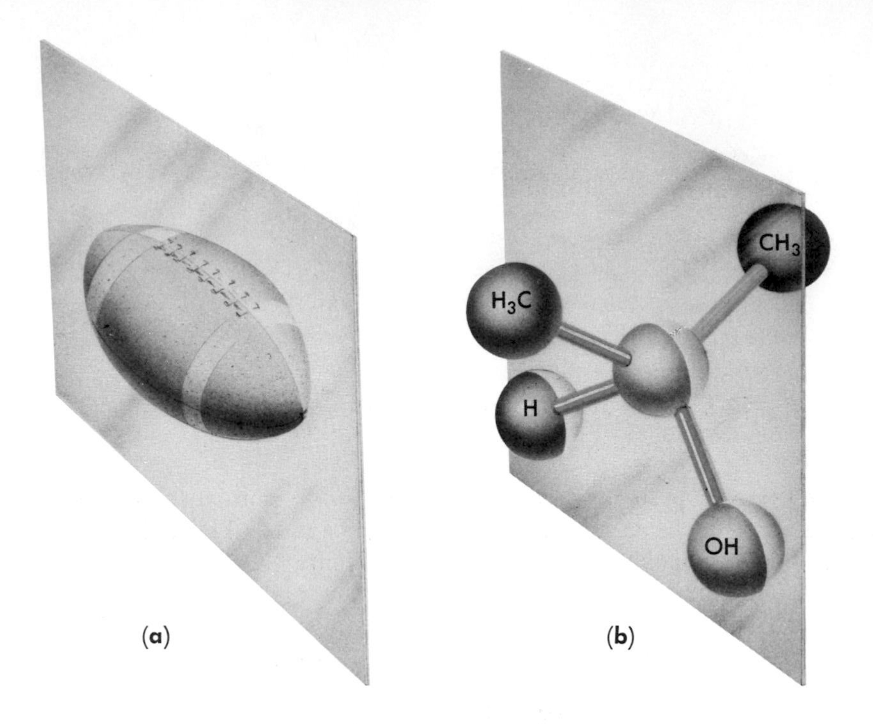

Fig. 17.7 Planes of symmetry. (a) a football, (b) isopropyl alcohol.

The four groups attached to this carbon are: **—OH**, **—H**, **—CH_3**, and **—C_2H_5**. These groups may be arranged about the carbon in either of two possible ways. Looking toward the hydroxyl group along the **C—O** bond, one sees that the other three groups may be arranged either clockwise or counterclockwise in the sequence **—H**, **—CH_3**, **—C_2H_5** (Fig. 17.8). The two arrangements are seen to bear a right- and left-hand, or ***nonsuperimposable mirror image*** relationship to one another. In much the same way, one's right hand is the mirror image of his left, but the two hands are not identical, that is, they cannot be superimposed on one another so that every point coincides.

Compounds whose molecules bear such a mirror image relationship to one another are known as **enantiomers.** Since all of the bond angles and interatomic distances in their molecules are the same, two compounds which are enantiomers will have the same melting point, boiling point, and other ordinary physical properties. For the same reason they will exhibit the same

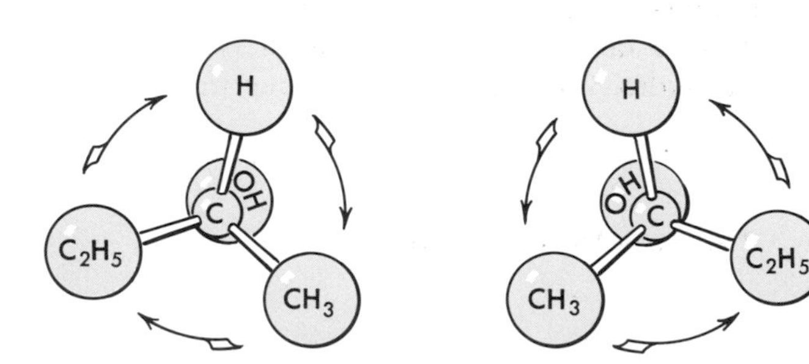

Fig. 17.8 Two ways of arranging 4 different groups about a carbon atom.

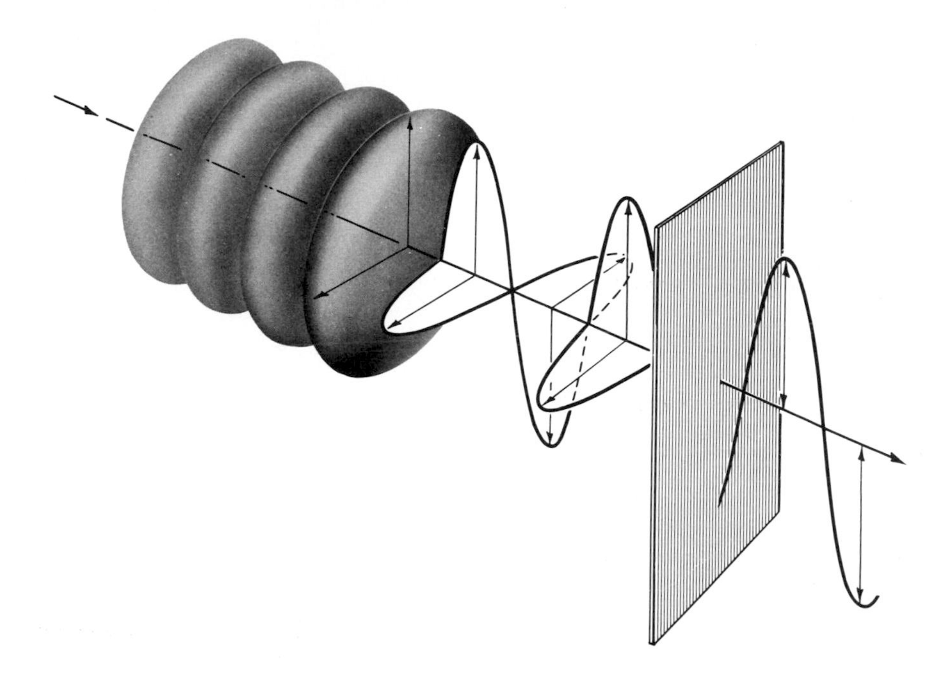

Fig. 17.9 Polarization of light. After it passes through the polarizer, the light is found to have its electrical field fluctuating in a single plane rather than in all directions, as was the case before the light was polarized. The effect on the magnetic field is the same, except that the plane of the magnetic field is at right angles to that of the electrical field.

chemical reactivity toward symmetrical reagents. They differ from one another, however, in two important respects: their ability to rotate the plane of polarized light, and their reactivity toward other compounds which are themselves asymmetric.

Polarized Light. Light is described as electromagnetic radiation. That is, the light photons are accompanied by an electric and a magnetic field, each of which fluctuates with a frequency corresponding to the frequency of the light. Normally, each of these fields fluctuates symmetrically in all directions perpendicular to the direction in which the light ray is traveling. Certain substances, such as crystals of calcite (Iceland spar, $CaCO_3$), have the property of *polarizing* the light, that is, after it passes through one of these crystals, the light is found to have its electrical and magnetic fields each fluctuating in a single plane, the two planes being at right angles to one another (Fig. 17.9). The light is said to be *plane polarized* and can be thought of as *vibrating in a single plane*, that of either the electrical or the magnetic field.

Compounds whose molecules lack a plane of symmetry have the property of *rotating the plane of polarized light*. This property is called ***optical activity***. Optical activity is measured by means of a ***polarimeter***. In essence, a polarimeter consists of a source of light, a rigidly mounted polarizing crystal, a container for the sample, which is usually examined in solution, and another polarizing crystal, the ***analyzer***, which is mounted so that

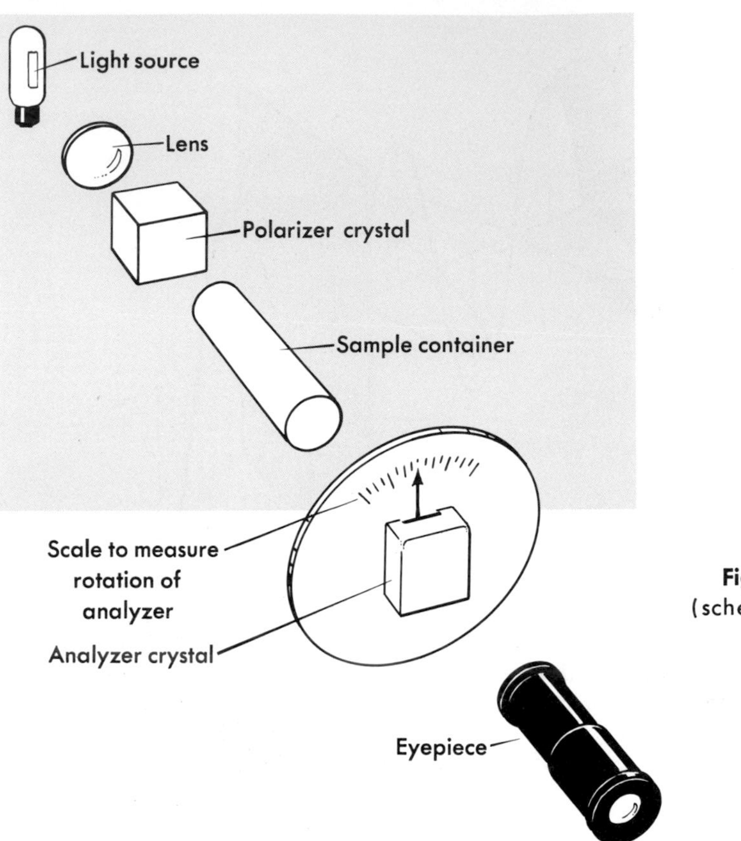

Fig. 17.10 Polarimeter (schematic).

it can be rotated about the axis of the polarimeter and its angle of rotation can be measured (Fig. 17.10). The light source must be monochromatic, since the optical rotatory power of a substance varies with the frequency of the light. A sodium vapor lamp, which emits almost perfectly monochromatic yellow light, is the usual source.

With no sample in the polarimeter, and the analyzer set to polarize the light in the same plane as the polarizing crystal, the brightness of the light seen through the eyepiece will be at a maximum. If, on the other hand, the polarizer and analyzer are *crossed*, that is, set so as to polarize the light at right angles, then little or no light will pass through the analyzer and the brightness will be at a minimum. This is shown diagrammatically in Figure 17.11. An optically active sample placed in the polarimeter will rotate the plane of the polarized light by some amount. To restore the maximum brilliance of the light, the analyzer must be rotated to the same degree (Fig. 17.12). The number of degrees through which the analyzer must be rotated is referred to as the ***optical rotation*** of the sample. Rotation to the right, or clockwise, is called ***dextrorotation*** (symbol: +); rotation to the left, or counterclockwise, is called ***levorotation*** (symbol: −). Since the observed rotation for a given substance will vary with the amount of substance placed in the light path, the ***specific rotation,*** $[\alpha]$, which is *the number*

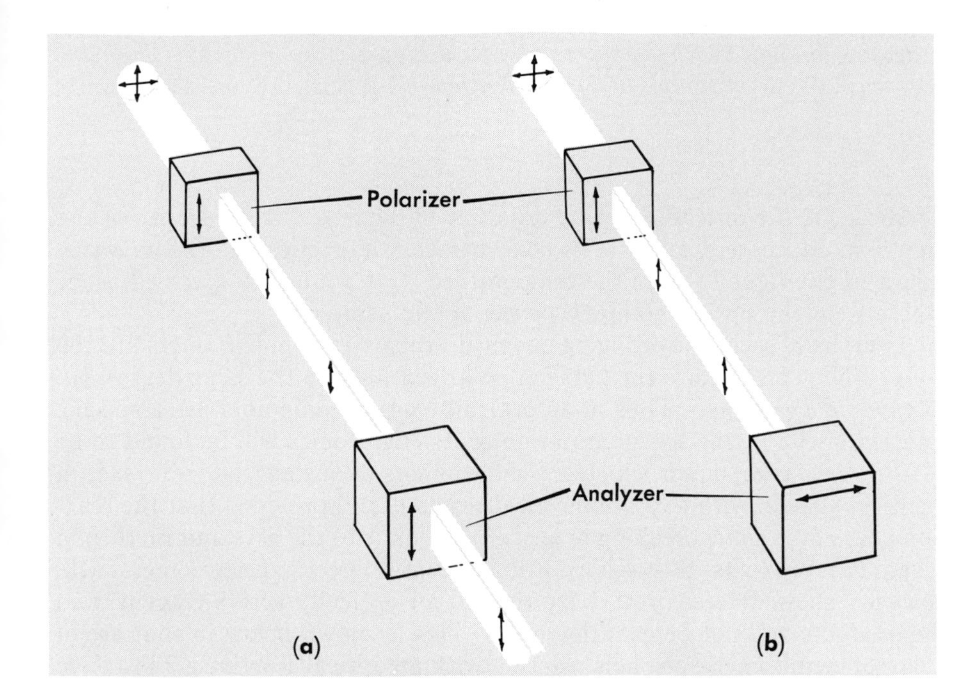

Fig. 17.11 Polarimeter. (a) With polarizer and analyzer parallel, light passes freely through both. (b) With polarizer and analyzer "crossed," no light passes through analyzer.

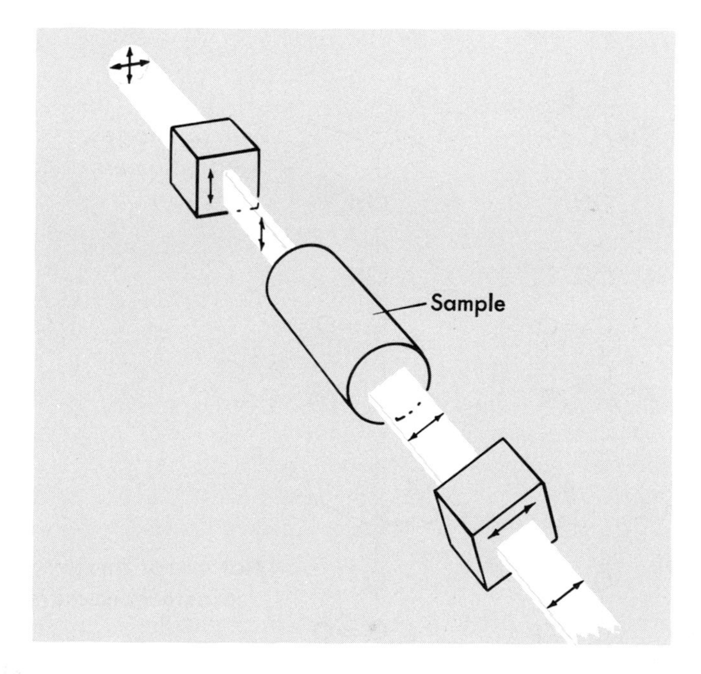

Fig. 17.12 Polarimeter. With an optically active sample in the light path, the analyzer crystal must be rotated if the maximum amount of light is to pass through.

of degrees through which the plane of the light is rotated upon passage through 1 decimeter (10 cm) *of sample at a concentration of* 1 g/cm³, is defined as follows:

$$[\alpha]_\lambda^t = \frac{\alpha_{obs}}{l \times c}$$

where α_{obs} is the observed optical rotation in degrees, l is the length of the sample in decimeters, and c is its concentration in g/cm³. Both the wavelength of the light (λ) and the temperature (t, °C) must be specified, since each affects the optical rotatory power of the sample.

As we have seen, the ordinary physical properties of enantiomers are the same. They also rotate the plane of polarized light to the same degree, *but in opposite directions*. Thus, if an optically active compound has a specific rotation of +50°, the specific rotation of its enantiomer will be found to be −50°. Two compounds which are enantiomers of one another will react in identical fashion with any symmetrical reagent, and provided that the reaction does not involve breaking of any of the bonds to the asymmetric carbon atom, the products themselves will be enantiomers. Enantiomers will, however, show different reactivity toward an optically active reagent, and the products will not be enantiomeric. This is shown below in the case of a pair of enantiomeric alcohols reacting with an optically active acid to form their respective esters. The products are seen to be asymmetric, and they are optically active as a result, *but they are not mirror images of one another*. Not only will their optical activity be different, but their ordinary physical and chemical properties will be different as well. Such isomers are called ***diastereoisomers,*** and they can exist whenever there is more than one asymmetric center in the molecule.

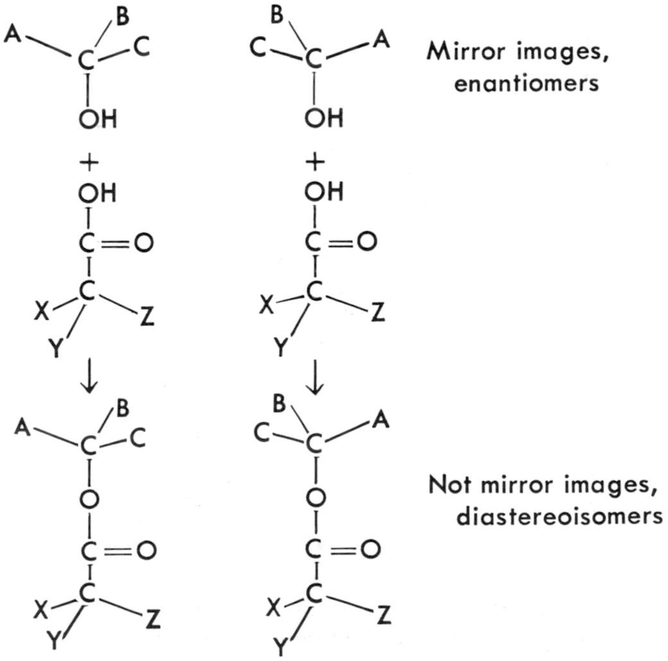

Mirror images, enantiomers

Not mirror images, diastereoisomers

With one asymmetric carbon in the molecule there can be two optical isomers. With two asymmetric carbons, there can be a total of four optical isomers consisting of two pairs of enantiomers. Designating each asymmetric carbon as either right-handed (R) or left-handed (L), these are:

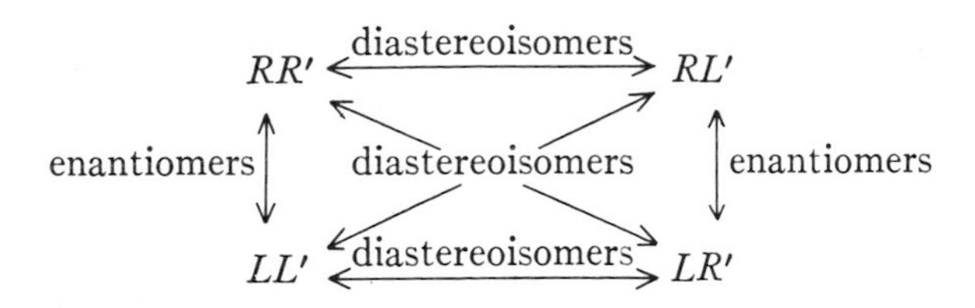

With three asymmetric carbons there will be eight isomers (four enantiomeric pairs). In general, *the maximum number of optical isomers is* 2^n, where n is equal to the number of asymmetric centers in the molecule .

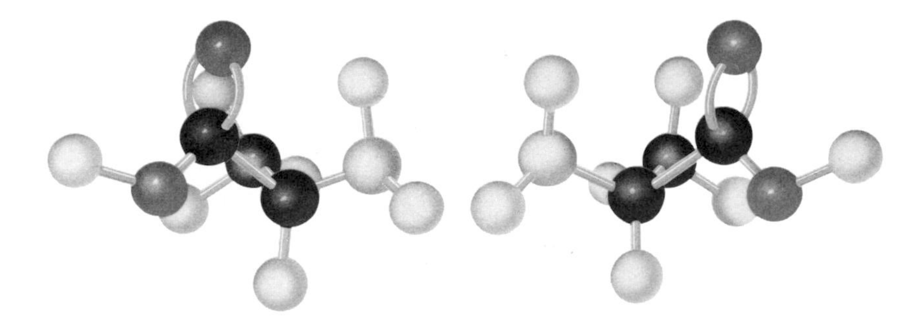

Fig. 17.13 Models of 2-aminopropionic acid (alanine), showing the configuration about the asymmetric carbon atom. The configurations of the naturally occurring protein amino acids correspond to that of the model on the left.

Almost all important natural products, that is, the sugars and other carbohydrates; amino acids and proteins; vitamins; enzymes; hormones; and alkaloids contain asymmetric carbons and are optically active. Because diastereoisomers may differ appreciably in their chemical and physical properties, reactions between such optically active substances are often highly ***stereospecific***. This means that in the reaction between asymmetric compounds to form products which are diastereoisomeric, the formation of one of the diastereoisomers may be overwhelmingly favored over the formation of the other. Thus, an optically active enzyme may be able to catalyze the metabolism of one form of an amino acid, but show little or no activity toward its enantiomer. The stereospecificity of reactions between asymmetric reagents is the underlying reason behind the fact that all amino acids obtained from natural proteins have the same configuration about the asymmetric carbon (Fig. 17.13). It is also the reason why, for example, a nutritional deficiency in the essential amino acid (−)-leucine cannot be corrected by furnishing (+)-leucine in the diet. The (+)

isomer does not fit into the protein structure and is nutritionally worthless.

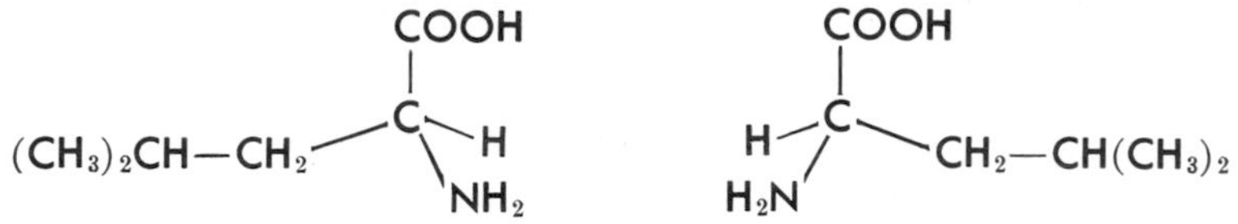

(—)-leucine (+)-leucine

A striking example of the relation between molecular asymmetry and physiological activity is afforded by the antimalarial drug ***quinine.*** This naturally occurring alkaloid, extracted from cinchona bark, has been used for centuries in the treatment of malaria. The molecule has four asymmetric centers (indicated below by asterisks).

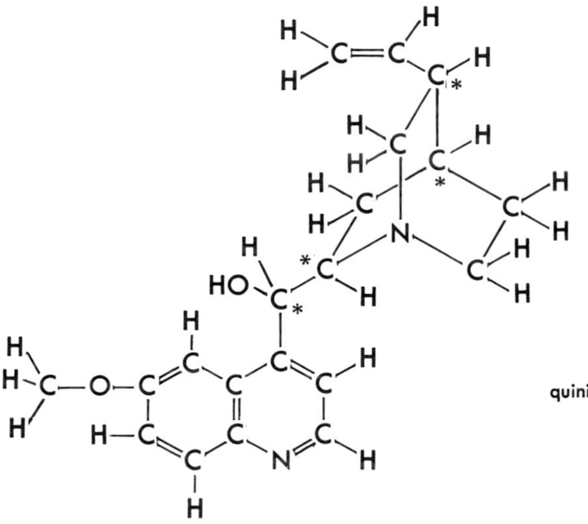

quinine

There are thus $2^4 = 16$ optical isomers, but only one of these shows any substantial antimalarial activity. The laboratory synthesis of quinine was accomplished in 1945 by R. B. Woodward and W. von E. Doering, who were the first to succeed in solving the problem of obtaining the correct configuration about each of the four asymmetric carbons.

17.9 Aromatic Compounds

As soon as suitable methods of analysis were available, it was found that certain organic compounds appear to be unsaturated on the basis of their carbon-hydrogen ratio and yet show little or no reactivity toward reagents which ordinarily add to alkenes. That is to say, their characteristic reactions involve substitution rather than addition. These were originally called ***aromatic compounds,*** because most of them possessed distinctive, often pleasant, aromas. The term aromatic has since come to refer instead to the type of chemical behavior typical of these compounds. These compounds are based on a unit of six carbons, which is retained throughout most reactions. Michael Faraday isolated the parent hydrocarbon ***benzene,*** C_6H_6, in 1825.

The structure of benzene presents a number of difficulties. In 1865 August Kekulé proposed a ring of six carbons with alternating single and double bonds:

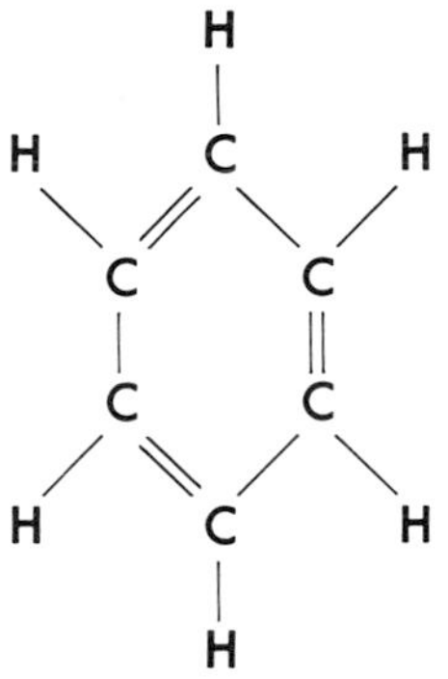

H C H C C C C H C H H H (Kekulé structure) symbolized by (hexagon)

Subsequent work, more recently including X-ray diffraction analysis, has confirmed the planar cyclic structure of benzene, but this leaves open the question of why benzene, with three double bonds, does not behave like a typical alkene. That benzene is indeed unsaturated is indicated by the fact that it will add hydrogen and chlorine and does undergo oxidative cleavage, but the conditions necessary for addition or oxidation to take place are in general much more drastic than in the case of the alkenes:

$$\underset{\text{1,3,5-hexatriene}}{CH_2{=}CH{-}CH{=}CH{-}CH{=}CH_2} \xrightarrow[25^\circ C,\ 2\text{–}3\ atm]{H_2,\ Ni} \underset{\text{hexane}}{CH_3{-}CH_2{-}CH_2{-}CH_2{-}CH_2{-}CH_3}$$

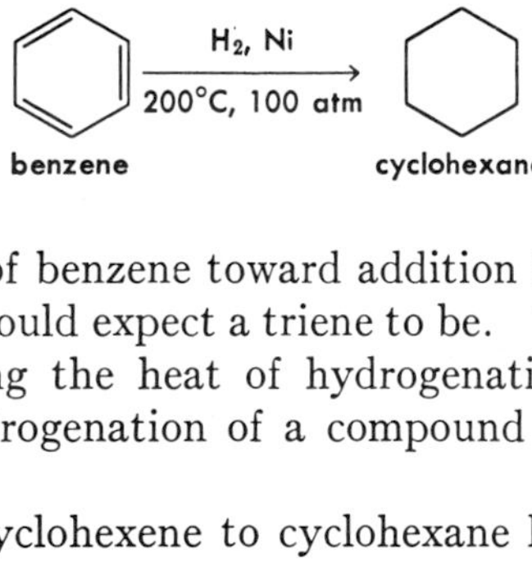

$$\text{benzene} \xrightarrow[200^\circ C,\ 100\ atm]{H_2,\ Ni} \text{cyclohexane}$$

The low reactivity of benzene toward addition indicates that benzene is more stable than one would expect a triene to be. This can be shown quantitatively by comparing the heat of hydrogenation of benzene with the calculated heat of hydrogenation of a compound containing three double bonds.

Hydrogenation of cyclohexene to cyclohexane liberates 28.6 kcal/mole:

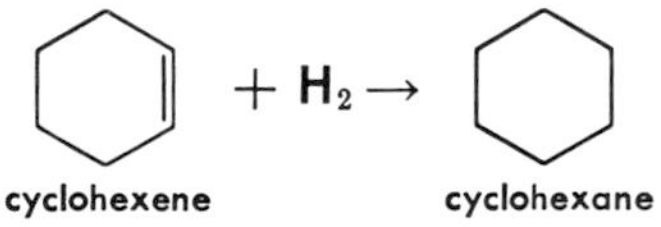

$$\text{cyclohexene} + H_2 \rightarrow \text{cyclohexane} \qquad \Delta H = -28.6\ \text{kcal}$$

Heats of hydrogenation are approximately additive for compounds having several double bonds, so we would anticipate ΔH for the hydrogenation of benzene to be $(-28.6 \times 3) = -85.8$ kcal/mole. The measured enthalpy change, however, is -49.8 kcal/mole:

$$\text{benzene} + 3\ H_2 \rightarrow \text{cyclohexane} \qquad \Delta H = -49.8 \text{ kcal}$$

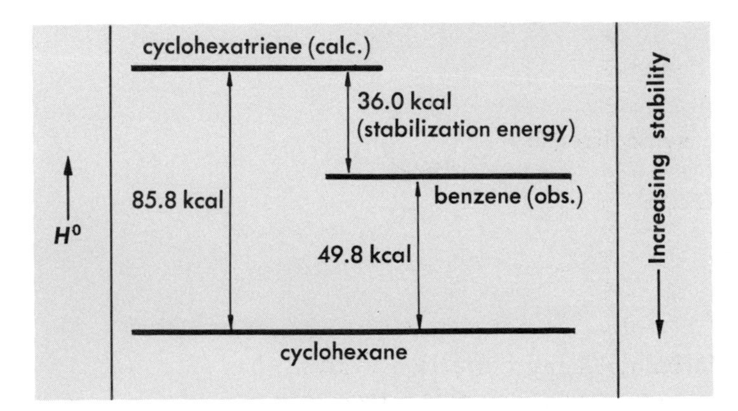

Fig. 17.14 Relative stabilities of benzene, cyclohexane, and the hypothetical cyclohexatriene.

It was pointed out in Sec. 11.2 that ΔH for a reaction is equal to the difference between the heats of formation of the reactants and products, and that the products of an exothermic reaction are more stable than the reactants inasmuch as more energy is required to bring about their complete dissociation. In the present case it is seen that although cyclohexane is more stable than benzene, the difference in stability is not as great as expected. Benzene, in other words, is more stable than the hypothetical cyclohexatriene to the extent of $(-85.8 + 49.8) = -36.0$ kcal/mole. This is shown diagrammatically in Fig. 17.14. The difference, -36.0 kcal, in the calculated and observed heats of hydrogenation is called the ***stabilization energy*** of benzene. The greater-than-calculated stability of benzene means an increase in the activation energy for addition reactions (Fig. 17.15) and can account in this way for the low reactivity of benzene toward addition.

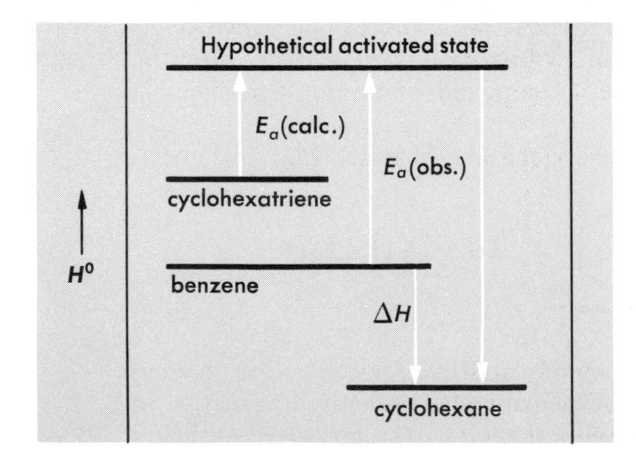

Fig. 17.15 Enthalpy diagram for the reaction $C_6H_6 + 3\ H_2 \rightarrow C_6H_{12}$.

By similar calculations based upon heats of hydrogenation, it can be shown that cyclohexadiene

1,3-cyclohexadiene

is about 6 kcal/mole *less stable* than benzene. Any reaction, then, which would lead to disruption of the characteristic system of three double bonds in benzene by saturation of one of them, would involve destabilization of the compound. It should therefore be less likely than a reaction which would permit retention of the double bond system of benzene. A comparison of the reactions of ethylene and of benzene with bromine will serve to illustrate this.

The initial step appears to be the same in each case. The π-electrons of the double bond repel the electrons of the approaching bromine molecule, polarizing the **Br—Br** bond. The more positive bromine atom then forms a bond with one of the carbons, leaving a positive charge on the other carbon, and a negative charge on the other bromine:

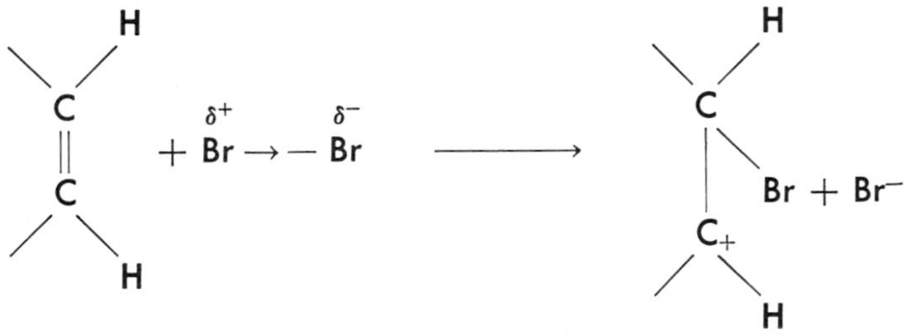

H
C
‖ + $\overset{\delta^+}{\text{Br}} \rightarrow \overset{\delta^-}{\text{— Br}}$ ⟶
C
H

H
C
| Br + Br⁻
C₊
H

The charges can now be neutralized either by addition of the remaining bromide ion, or by elimination of a proton:

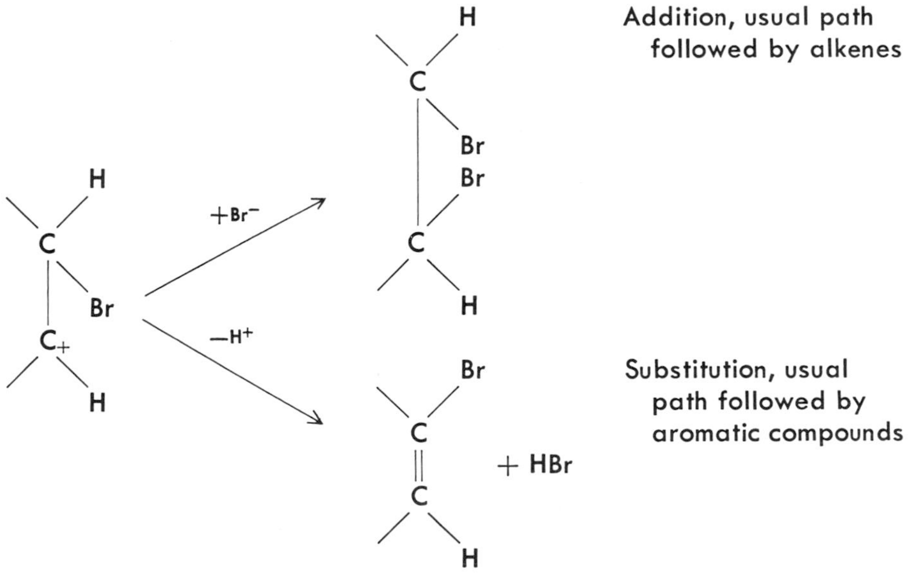

H
C
| Br
C₊
H

+Br⁻ ⟶

H
C
Br
Br
C
H

Addition, usual path followed by alkenes

−H⁺ ⟶

Br
C
‖ + HBr
C
H

Substitution, usual path followed by aromatic compounds

With ethylene, the path followed is addition; with benzene, elimination of hydrogen restores the more stable double bond system and is favored over addition. Because of the large activation energy involved in the attachment of the first halogen atom to the ring, halogenation of benzene usually requires the presence of a Lewis acid catalyst such as $FeCl_3$. The function of the catalyst, or "halogen carrier," appears to be to bring about partial or complete ionization of the halogen molecule:

$$Cl_2 + FeCl_3 \rightarrow Cl^+ + FeCl_4^-$$

$$C_6H_6 + Cl^+ \rightarrow C_6H_6Cl^+$$

$$C_6H_6Cl^+ + FeCl_4^- \rightarrow C_6H_5Cl + FeCl_3 + HCl$$

The reaction of concentrated H_2SO_4 with benzene is quite different from its reaction with alkenes. With ethylene, for example, the first step consists in protonation of the alkene, followed by addition of bisulfate ion to the "carbonium ion" formed initially:

$$H_2C{=}CH_2 + HOSO_3H \rightarrow H_3C{-}CH_2^+ + {}^-OSO_3H$$

ethylene | sulfuric acid | ethylcarbonium ion | bisulfate ion

$$H_3C{-}CH_2^+ + {}^-OSO_3H \rightarrow H_3C{-}CH_2OSO_3H$$

ethyl sulfate

The oxygen of the sulfuric acid becomes attached to the carbon of ethylene, and the product is an ester. In the case of benzene, the attacking agent is SO_3, present in the sulfuric acid as a result of the equilibrium:

$$2\,H_2SO_4 \rightleftarrows H_3O^+ + HSO_4^- + SO_3$$

The SO_3 reacts with benzene to form the ***sulfonic acid*** as follows:

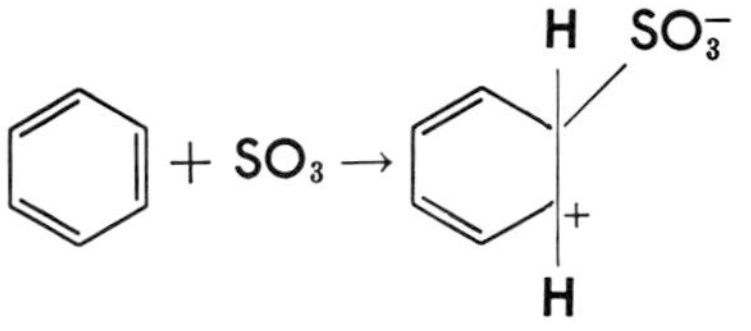

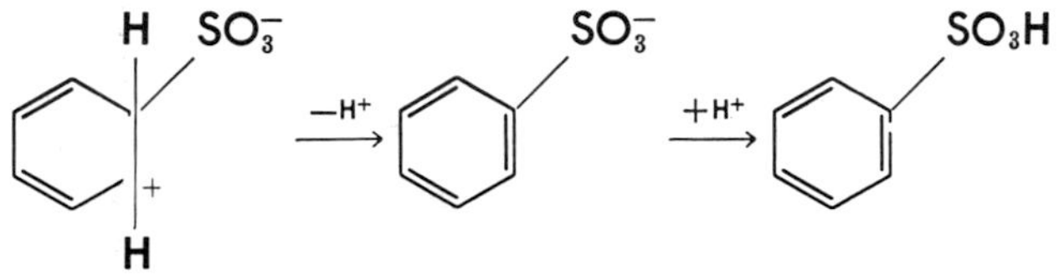

$$C_6H_6 + SO_3 \rightarrow C_6H_6(SO_3^-)^+ \text{ (ring C bearing H and } SO_3^-\text{)}$$

$$C_6H_6(SO_3^-)^+ \xrightarrow{-H^+} C_6H_5SO_3^- \xrightarrow{+H^+} C_6H_5SO_3H$$

benzenesulfonic acid

In the sulfonic acid, the sulfur is attached directly to the carbon atom of the ring.

Benzene and its derivatives react with concentrated HNO_3, usually in the presence of H_2SO_4, to form ***nitro compounds:***

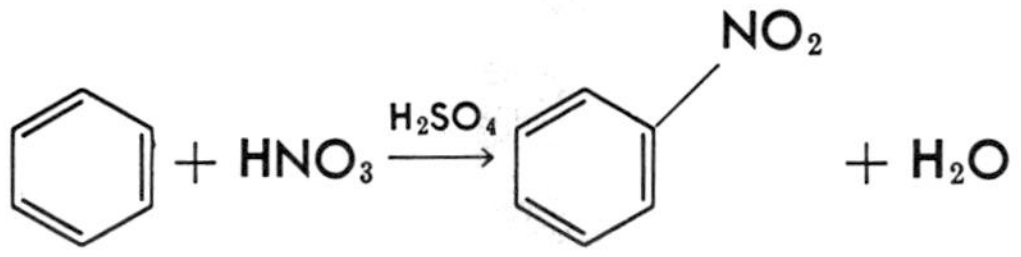

$$C_6H_6 + HNO_3 \xrightarrow{H_2SO_4} C_6H_5NO_2 + H_2O$$

nitrobenzene

The function of the H_2SO_4 is to generate the nitronium ion, NO_2^+, by the reaction:

$$HNO_3 + 2\,H_2SO_4 \rightleftarrows H_3O^+ + 2\,HSO_4^- + NO_2^+$$

The nitronium ion then reacts with the benzene ring as follows:

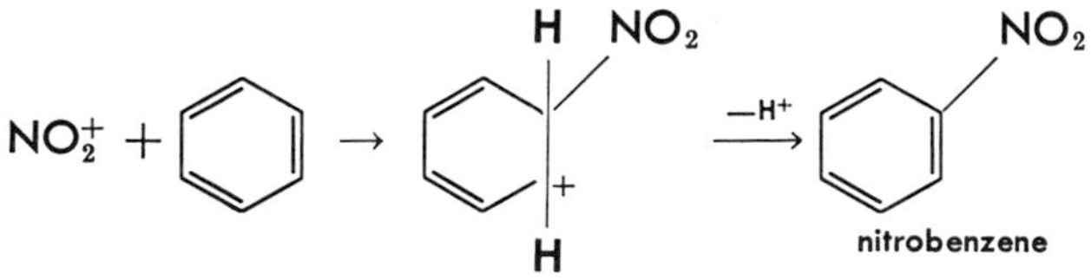

$$NO_2^+ + C_6H_6 \rightarrow C_6H_6(NO_2)^+ \text{ (ring C bearing H and } NO_2\text{)} \xrightarrow{-H^+} C_6H_5NO_2$$

nitrobenzene

Reduction of the nitro group affords the ***amine:***

$$\text{nitrobenzene } C_6H_5NO_2 \xrightarrow{Sn + HCl} \text{aniline (aminobenzene) } C_6H_5NH_2$$

Aromatic amines react with nitrous acid to form the unstable ***diazonium salts,*** which are not isolated, but which occupy a key position as intermediates in the synthesis of other aromatic compounds:

$$\text{aniline } C_6H_5NH_2 \xrightarrow{HNO_2\ (HCl + NaNO_2),\ 0°C} \text{benzenediazonium chloride } C_6H_5N_2^+Cl^-$$

$$C_6H_5N_2^+Cl^- \xrightarrow{H_2O,\ \Delta} C_6H_5OH \quad \text{phenol (carbolic acid)}$$

$$C_6H_5N_2^+Cl^- \xrightarrow{HX,\ CuX} C_6H_5X \quad \text{halobenzene } (X = Cl, Br, \text{ or } I)$$

$$C_6H_5N_2^+Cl^- \xrightarrow{HBF_4,\ \Delta} C_6H_5F \quad \text{fluorobenzene}$$

$$C_6H_5N_2^+Cl^- \xrightarrow{CuCN} C_6H_5CN \xrightarrow{H_2O,H^+} C_6H_5COOH \quad \text{benzoic acid}$$

$$C_6H_5N_2^+Cl^- \xrightarrow{C_6H_5\text{—}OH} C_6H_5\text{—}N\text{=}N\text{—}C_6H_4\text{—}OH \quad \text{p-hydroxyazobenzene (an azo dye)}$$

Phenol reacts with CO_2 in the presence of $NaOH$ to form the sodium salt of ***salicylic acid:***

$$\text{phenol } C_6H_5OH \xrightarrow[125°C,\ 4\text{–}7\ atm]{CO_2,\ NaOH} \text{sodium salicylate } C_6H_4(OH)COO^-Na^+$$

Reaction of salicylic acid with acetic anhydride yields acetylsalicylic acid, or ***aspirin:***

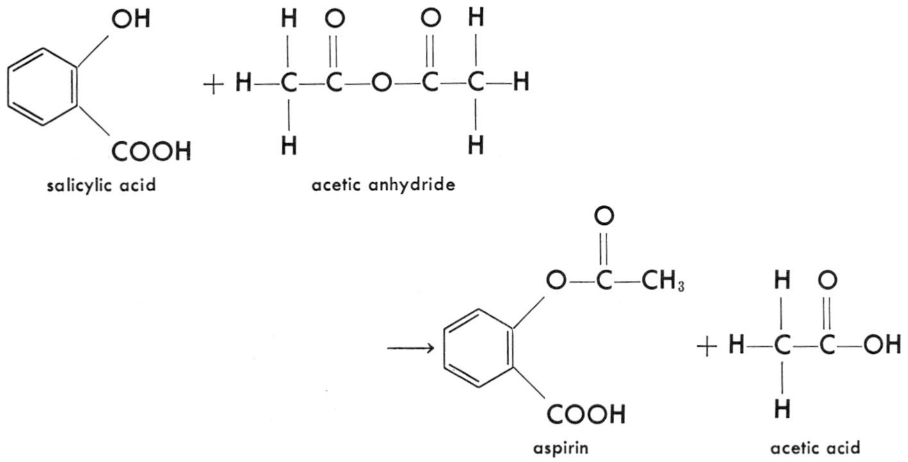

salicylic acid + acetic anhydride ($H_3C-CO-O-CO-CH_3$) $\longrightarrow$ aspirin (o-$CH_3COO-C_6H_4-COOH$) + acetic acid (CH_3-COOH)

Esterification of salicylic acid with methyl alcohol affords methyl salicylate, or ***oil of wintergreen:***

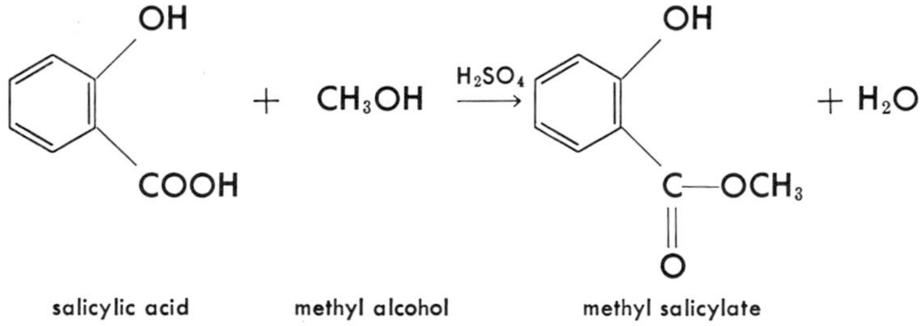

$$\text{salicylic acid} + CH_3OH \xrightarrow{H_2SO_4} \text{methyl salicylate } (o\text{-}HO-C_6H_4-C(=O)-OCH_3) + H_2O$$

salicylic acid methyl alcohol methyl salicylate

Sulfanilamide, the first of the sulfa drugs, is prepared from aniline as follows:

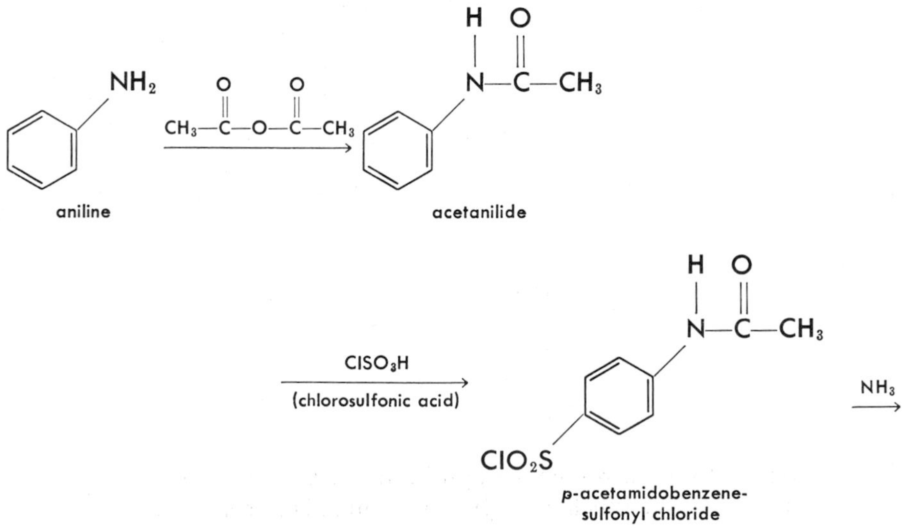

$$\text{aniline } (C_6H_5NH_2) \xrightarrow{CH_3-CO-O-CO-CH_3} \text{acetanilide } (C_6H_5-NH-CO-CH_3)$$

aniline acetanilide

$$\xrightarrow[\text{(chlorosulfonic acid)}]{ClSO_3H} p\text{-}ClO_2S-C_6H_4-NH-CO-CH_3 \xrightarrow{NH_3}$$

p-acetamidobenzene-sulfonyl chloride

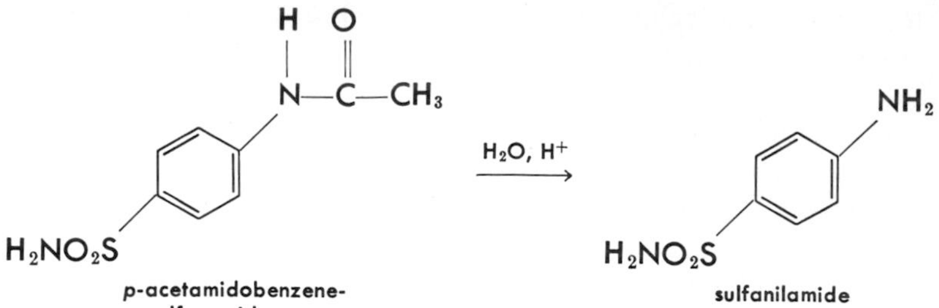

$$H_2NO_2S-C_6H_4-NH-CO-CH_3 \xrightarrow{H_2O,\ H^+} H_2NO_2S-C_6H_4-NH_2$$

p-acetamidobenzene-sulfonamide — sulfanilamide

17.10 The Structure of Benzene

The way in which we have been writing the structure of benzene would imply that the compounds shown below are isomeric:

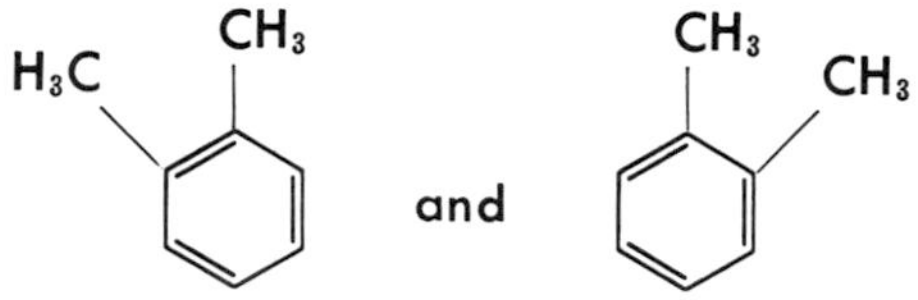

H_3C, CH_3 and CH_3, CH_3

In fact, only one compound corresponding to this formula, ***o-xylene,*** exists. To reconcile this fact with the structure for benzene which he had proposed, Kekulé supposed that the bonds in the benzene ring underwent rapid oscillation, making the two structures equivalent:

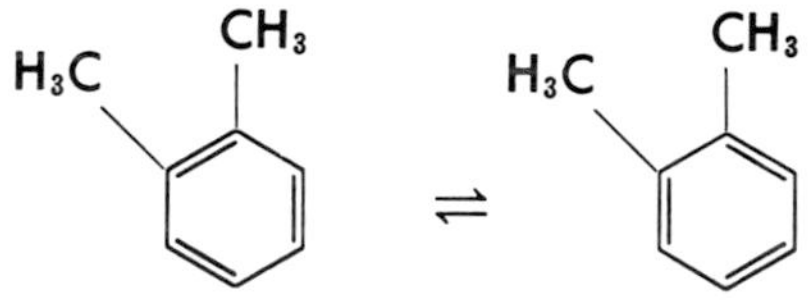

H_3C, CH_3 ⇌ H_3C, CH_3

Later work showed all six bonds in the benzene ring to be identical, and to be intermediate in length between a single and a double bond. It is impossible, therefore, to draw a single structure of the conventional type which fully describes the benzene ring. Benzene and its derivatives are said to be ***resonance hybrids*** (Sec. 16.5), whose actual structures are intermediate between those of the two Kekulé structures that can be written for them. Resonance among contributing structures is symbolized by a double-headed arrow to distinguish the resonance concept from an equilibrium between isomers.

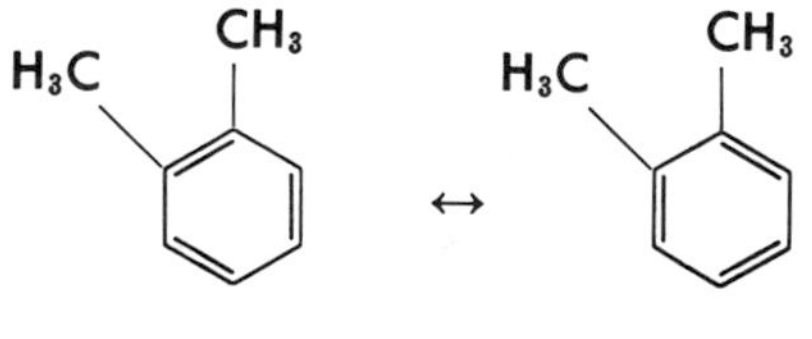

H_3C, CH_3 ↔ H_3C, CH_3

The analogy between a resonance hybrid and a biological hybrid was first pointed out by G. W. Wheland. Just as a mule is not a horse one minute and a donkey the next, but always a hybrid of both, so none of the structures contributing to a resonance hybrid has any independent existence. Resonance is merely a device which allows us to get around the fact that it is impossible to draw the actual structure of the compound using conventional formulas.

Benzene is by no means alone in being a resonance hybrid. There are many compounds and ions, both organic and inorganic, which cannot be fully described in terms of one structure of the conventional type. In general, whenever more than one structure can be written for a compound where these structures differ only in the arrangement of electrons, the true structure is not represented by any of those which can be written, but is rather a resonance hybrid of all of them. Most important, it has been found from experience that *compounds which exhibit resonance*, that is, those whose true structures are resonance hybrids, *show greater stability than would be calculated for any of the structures contributing to the hybrid.* In the case of benzene, this resonance stabilization was seen to be equivalent to −36 kcal/mole.

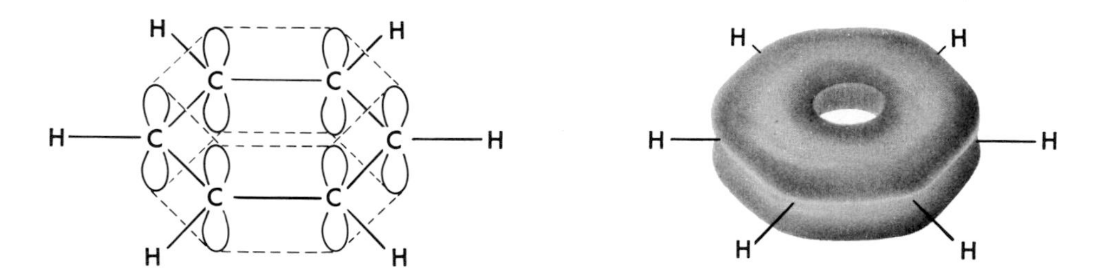

Fig. 17.16 Two representations of π overlap in benzene.

From a molecular orbital point of view, the resonance hybrid of benzene is seen to arise from mutual overlap of all six *p* orbitals—one on each carbon—to form a π orbital system extending over the entire ring. The resulting delocalization of the six π electrons lowers their energy, and results in stabilization of the system (Fig. 17.16).

Carbohydrates 17.11

The carbohydrates include the simple sugars, disaccharides, and polysaccharides. They are polyhydroxy compounds, most of whose formulas correspond to the general formula $C_x(H_2O)_y$, hence the name ***carbohydrate.***

The most important representative of the simple sugars is (+)-glucose, also known as ***dextrose,*** from the sign of its optical rotation, and as ***grape sugar,*** from its presence in that fruit. The molecular formula of (+)-glucose is $C_6H_{12}O_6$. It is a ***reducing sugar,*** that is, it reacts with Tollens' reagent (ammoniacal silver nitrate) and with Fehling's solution (Cu^{++} complexed with tartrate ion), reducing the former to silver and the latter to Cu_2O. Both of these reactions are characteristic of aldehydes, yet several of the other reactions expected of aldehydes are not exhibited by (+)-glucose. This has been interpreted as indicating that the molecules of (+)-glucose and other reducing sugars, all of which behave similarly toward aldehyde reagents, exist largely in the form of rings which are in equilibrium with small amounts of open chains, each bearing a free reducing carbonyl group:

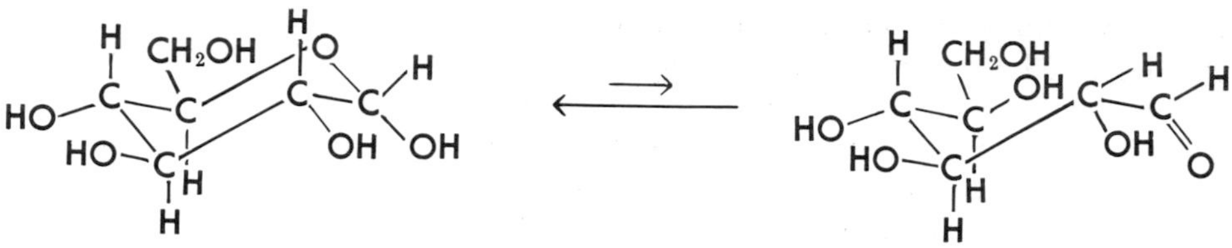

Ordinary table sugar, or ***sucrose,*** is a ***disaccharide,*** which means that hydrolysis of 1 mole of sucrose yields 2 moles of simple sugars, in this case (+)-glucose and (−)-fructose:

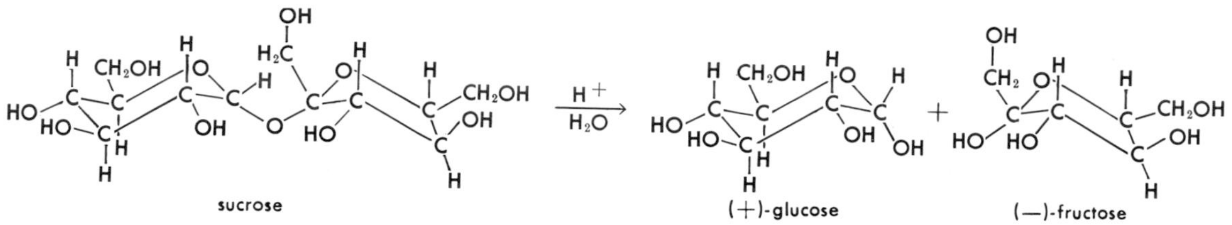

sucrose $\xrightarrow[H_2O]{H^+}$ (+)-glucose + (−)-fructose

Sucrose is dextrorotatory. The mixture of (+)-glucose and (−)-fructose produced by its hydrolysis is levorotatory. Since hydrolysis is accompanied by inversion of the sign of rotation, the product is called ***invert sugar.*** Invert sugar is sweeter than sucrose and does not crystallize. It is widely used in confectionery, especially in cream fillings and fondants. Sucrose is a nonreducing sugar, since the potential carbonyl groups are tied up in the linkage between the rings.

Maltose is a reducing disaccharide which yields only glucose upon hydrolysis.

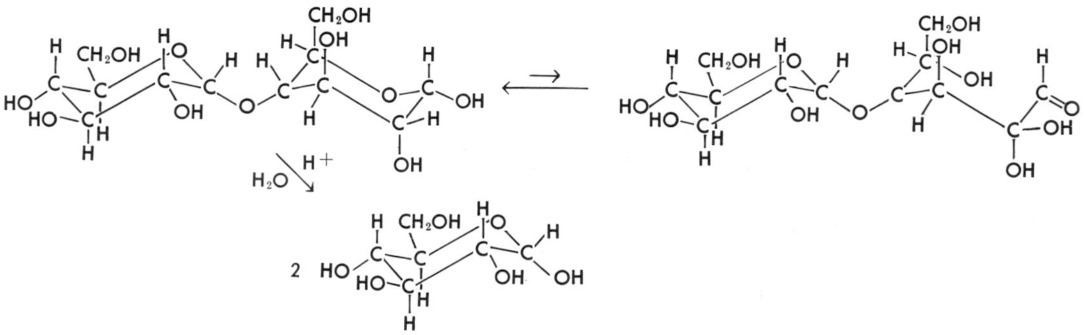

A new asymmetric center is created when the aldehyde form of a sugar is converted to the ring form. Ring closure can lead to either of two possible

configurations about the newly asymmetric carbon, and hence in solution a reducing sugar will exist as an equilibrium mixture of the open-chain structure together with the two epimeric* ring structures.

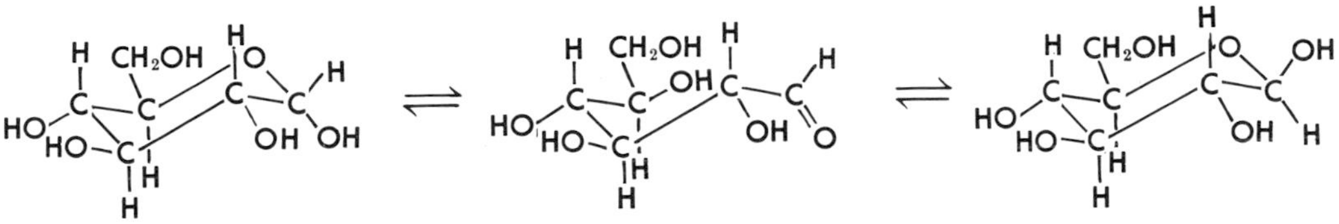

α-(+)-glucose
$[\alpha]_D^{20} = +113°$

β-(+)-glucose
$[\alpha]_D^{20} = +19°$

The two epimeric structures are known as the α and β forms, respectively. Being diastereoisomers, they have different specific rotations and different physical and chemical properties. Depending upon conditions, either the α or β form may be crystallized from solution. When either form is redissolved, the initial optical rotation as measured gradually changes as equilibrium is established, finally attaining an equilibrium value. Thus, when either α- or β-(+)-glucose is dissolved in water, the optical rotation changes from the initial value of +113° or +19° to a final value of +52.5°. *Such a change in the optical rotation of a solution, which results from the establishment of an equilibrium between epimeric structures is called* **mutarotation.**

Starch and ***cellulose*** are ***polysaccharides*** consisting of long chains of glucose units. The molecular weights of these substances are indefinite and range from about 30,000 for the amylose fraction of starch to upwards of 500,000 for glycogen (animal starch) and cellulose. Chemically, starch and cellulose differ from one another only in that all of the linkages between glucose units have the α configuration in starch, while in cellulose they are all β:

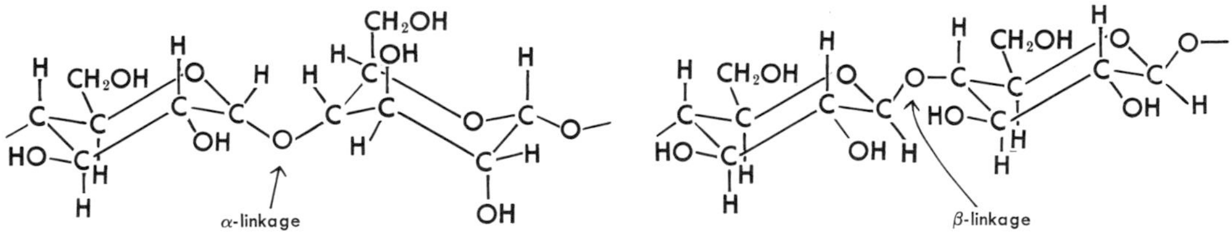

α-linkage

β-linkage

This seemingly minor difference between starch and cellulose has a profound effect on their physical and physiological properties. Because of this structural difference, the cellulose chain is straighter than that of starch, and this probably has a great deal to do with the greater crystallinity and rigidity of cellulose. Furthermore, the α-linkages of starch are readily hydrolyzed by enzymes normally present in the human digestive tract, but these enzymes have no effect on the β-linkages of cellulose. Starch, as a result, is digestible, and cellulose is not. The effect of the type of linkage

* Epimers are optical isomers differing in configuration about a single asymmetric center.

(α or β) on the shape of the chain can be seen in the projection formulas of starch and cellulose given below.

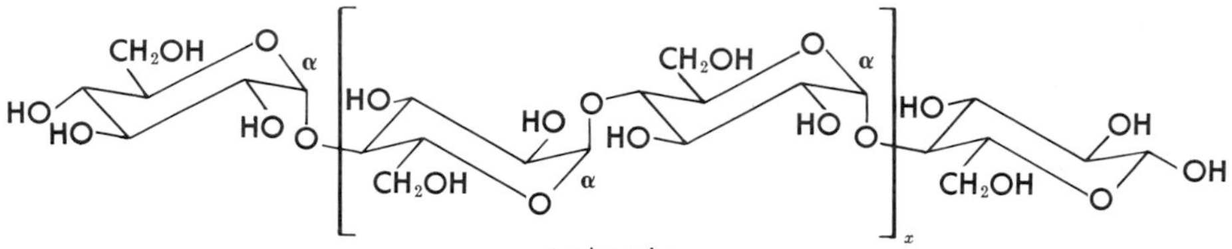

starch amylose

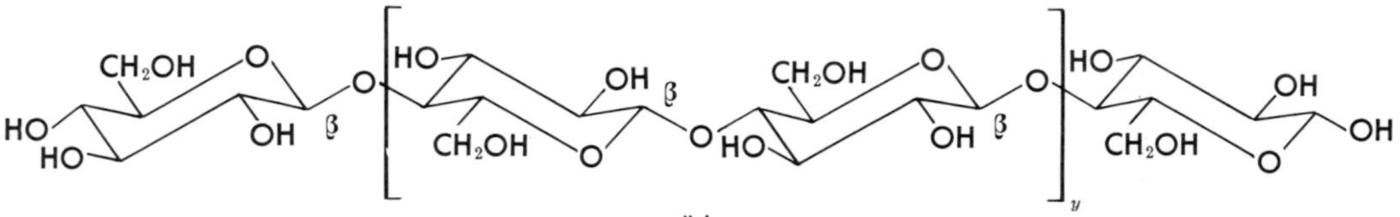

cellulose

Polymers are substances formed by joining large numbers of relatively simple molecules to one another, either by direct addition (***addition polymers***) or by condensation with the loss of a small molecule (***condensation polymers***).

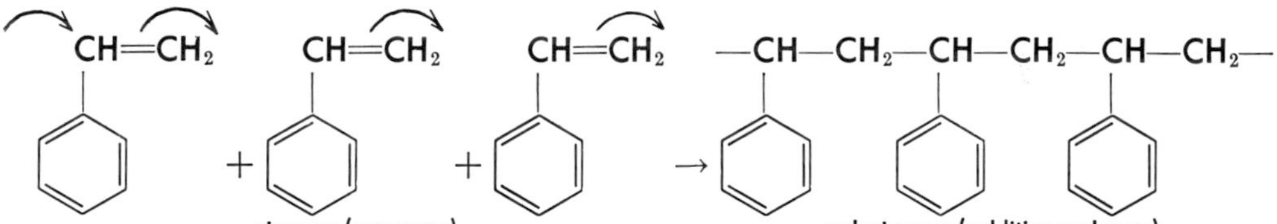

styrene (monomer)

polystyrene (addition polymer)

$$x\ H_2N—(CH_2)_6—NH_2 + x\ HOOC—(CH_2)_4—COOH$$

hexamethylenediamine adipic acid

$$\xrightarrow{-H_2O}$$

$$—NH—(CH_2)_6—NH\left[CO—(CH_2)_4—CO—NH—(CH_2)_6—NH\right]_{(x-1)}CO—(CH_2)_4—CO—$$

nylon 66 (condensation polymer)

By this definition, both cellulose and starch are polymers. Other important natural polymers are the proteins, nucleic acids, and rubber.

(a) Proteins. Proteins are polyamides formed by condensation polymerization of α-amino acids. The α-carbon is the one adjacent to the carboxyl group, and it is this carbon which bears the amine functional group in an α-amino acid:

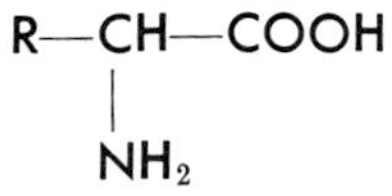

$$\underset{\substack{|\\ NH_2}}{R{-}CH{-}COOH}$$

α-amino acid

Loss of water between a carboxylic acid and ammonia or an amine leads to the formation of an ***amide:***

$$\underset{\text{acetic acid}}{CH_3COOH} + \underset{\text{ammonia}}{NH_3} \xrightarrow{\Delta} \underset{\text{acetamide}}{CH_3{-}CO{-}NH_2} + H_2O$$

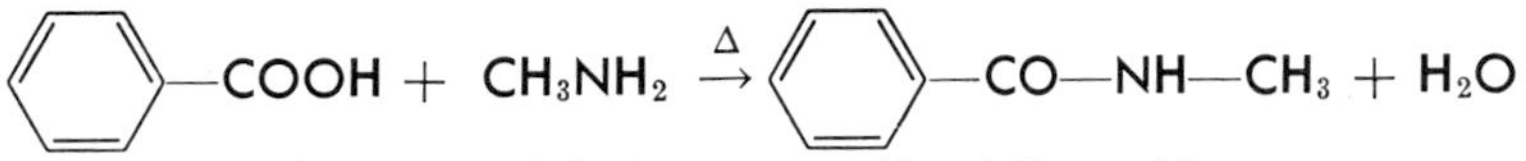

$$\underset{\text{benzoic acid}}{C_6H_5{-}COOH} + \underset{\text{methylamine}}{CH_3NH_2} \xrightarrow{\Delta} \underset{\textit{N}\text{-methylbenzamide}}{C_6H_5{-}CO{-}NH{-}CH_3} + H_2O$$

Since the amide molecule produced by condensation of two amino acids itself bears both the amino and carboxyl functional groups, it can continue to react with other amino acid molecules, and the product is a ***polyamide:***

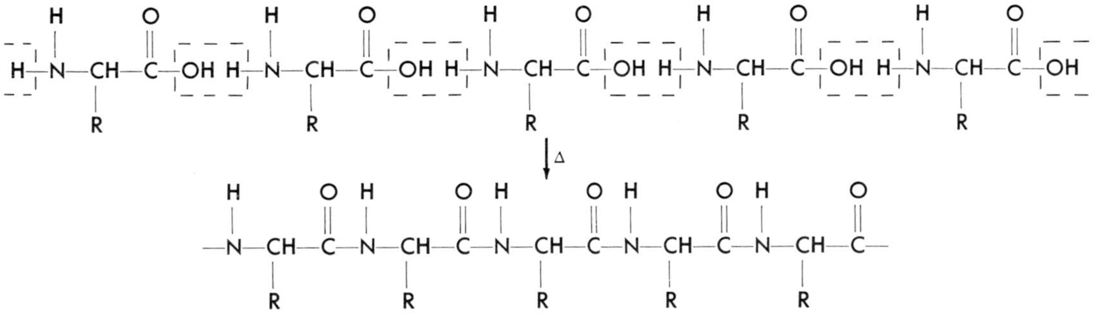

$$H{-}\overset{H}{\overset{|}{N}}{-}\underset{\underset{R}{|}}{CH}{-}\overset{O}{\overset{\|}{C}}{-}OH \;\; H{-}\overset{H}{\overset{|}{N}}{-}\underset{\underset{R}{|}}{CH}{-}\overset{O}{\overset{\|}{C}}{-}OH \;\; H{-}\overset{H}{\overset{|}{N}}{-}\underset{\underset{R}{|}}{CH}{-}\overset{O}{\overset{\|}{C}}{-}OH \;\; H{-}\overset{H}{\overset{|}{N}}{-}\underset{\underset{R}{|}}{CH}{-}\overset{O}{\overset{\|}{C}}{-}OH \;\; H{-}\overset{H}{\overset{|}{N}}{-}\underset{\underset{R}{|}}{CH}{-}\overset{O}{\overset{\|}{C}}{-}OH$$

$$\Big\downarrow \Delta$$

$$-\overset{H}{\overset{|}{N}}{-}\underset{\underset{R}{|}}{CH}{-}\overset{O}{\overset{\|}{C}}{-}\overset{H}{\overset{|}{N}}{-}\underset{\underset{R}{|}}{CH}{-}\overset{O}{\overset{\|}{C}}{-}\overset{H}{\overset{|}{N}}{-}\underset{\underset{R}{|}}{CH}{-}\overset{O}{\overset{\|}{C}}{-}\overset{H}{\overset{|}{N}}{-}\underset{\underset{R}{|}}{CH}{-}\overset{O}{\overset{\|}{C}}{-}\overset{H}{\overset{|}{N}}{-}\underset{\underset{R}{|}}{CH}{-}\overset{O}{\overset{\|}{C}}-$$

Proteins yield mixtures of their component amino acids upon hydrolysis with mineral acid. Some 26 amino acids have been isolated from natural protein hydrolysates, six of which are found in only a few proteins from special sources. The remaining 20 are found in nearly all protein material, whether from animal or plant tissue. There is, nevertheless, no end to the number of possible sequences in which this limited number of amino acids may be joined to form a protein molecule containing hundreds or thousands of amino acid units. The sequence of amino acid units in the nucleoproteins (associated with the nucleic acids in the nucleus of each cell) differs for each individual. So characteristic is this sequence that the presence of a foreign protein is usually not tolerated by the body, but triggers an allergic reaction, often followed by the production of antibodies. Much of the discomfort of virus diseases probably arises from the reaction of the body to the foreign protein of the virus.

(b) Nucleic Acids. The nucleic acids are natural polymers of high molecular weight (about 1,000,000) found associated with the nucleoprotein in the nuclei of cells. Their function is believed to be that of transmitting genetic information during reproduction and cell division. The basic monomer units in nucleic acids are ***nucleotides,*** each of which is composed of a molecule of a 5-carbon monosaccharide chemically combined with a molecule of a pyrimidine or purine derivative and one of phosphoric acid. In ribonucleic acids (RNA), the monosaccharide is ribose. The corresponding component of the deoxyribonucleic acids (DNA) is deoxyribose. DNA is the chief component of the chromosomes of cells. The pyrimidine and purine derivatives are adenine, guanine, cytosine, thymine, uracil, and 5-methylcytosine (Table 17.4). The nucleotide units of the nucleic acids are joined through phosphate ester linkages between carbon 3 and carbon 5

TABLE 17.4 Components of RNA and DNA

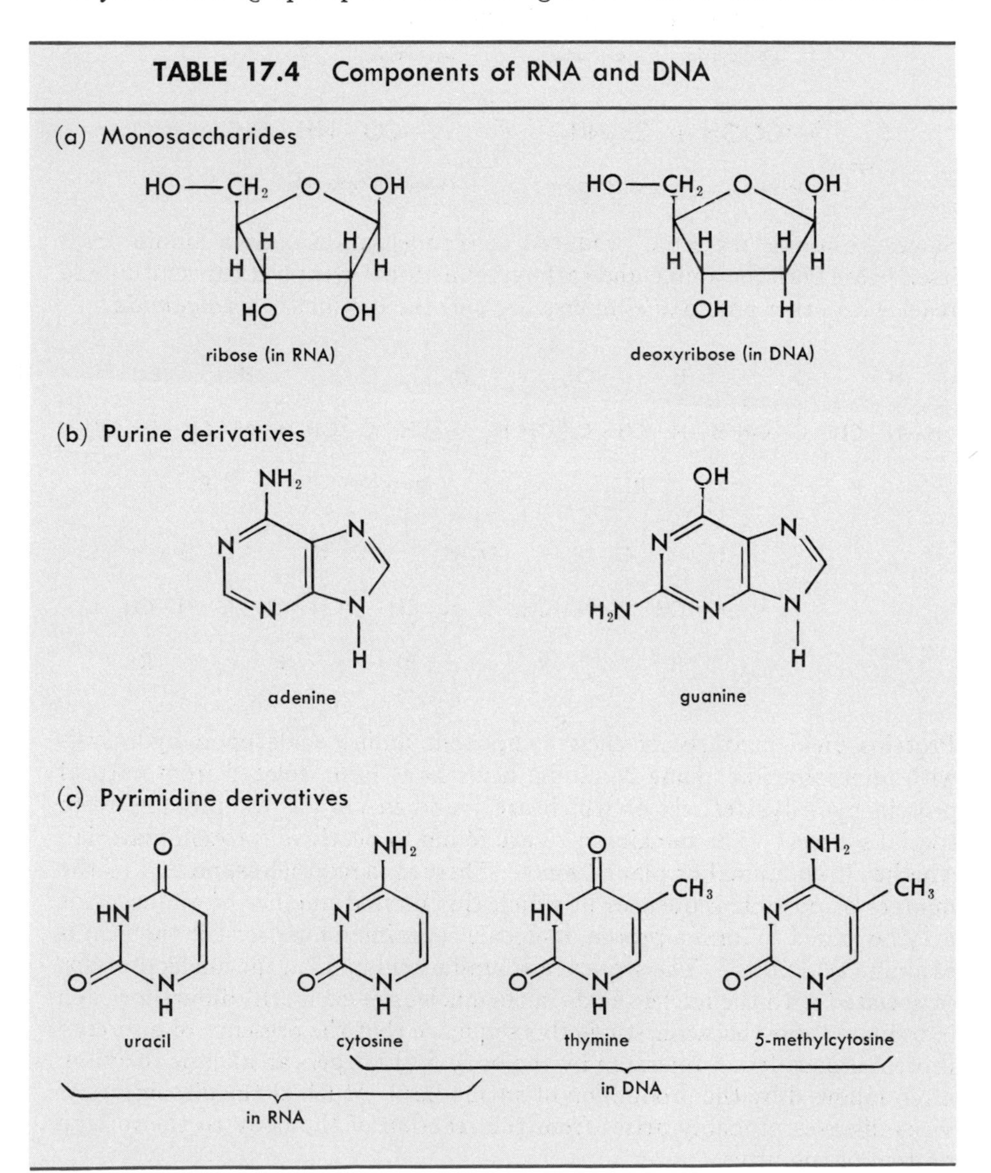

of the monosaccharide, while the purine or pyrimidine group (R) is attached to carbon 1:

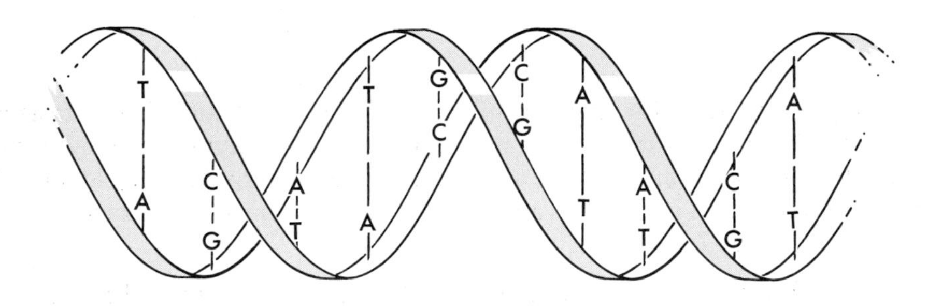

A = Adenine C = Cytosine T = Thymine G = Guanine

Fig. 17.17 DNA double helix. The ribbon-like strands represent the deoxyribose-phosphate chains.

DNA is ordinarily present in the chromosomes in the form of a right-handed double helix composed of two strands of the DNA coiled about one another with the head of one opposite the tail of the other (Fig. 17.17). The sequence of nucleotides in each DNA molecule is such that when the strands are coiled in this way each adenine group is opposite a thymine, and each guanine is opposite a cytosine. The helix is then held together by hydrogen bonding between these groups as shown:

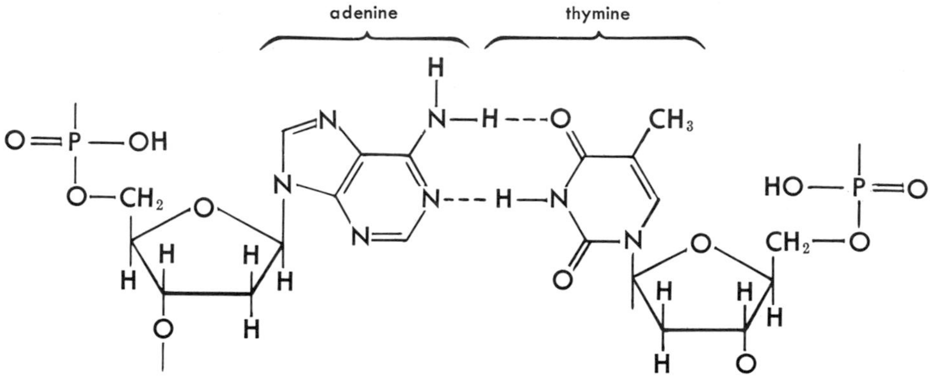

adenine — thymine

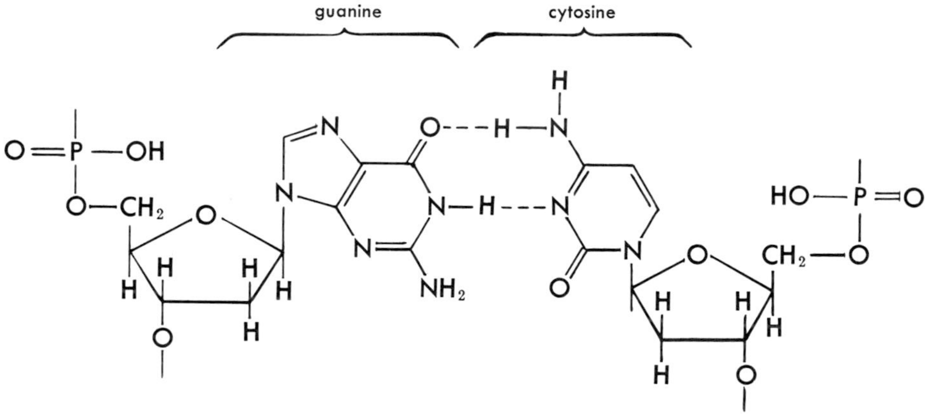

guanine — cytosine

During cell division, the helix uncoils and each DNA strand then acts as a template for the construction of a new DNA strand. Thymine and cytosine units take up positions opposite adenine and guanine units in the old strand and vice versa, and in this way a new strand is built which is an exact replica of the old (Fig. 17.18).

(c) Rubber. Natural rubber and gutta percha are both addition polymers of the compound ***isoprene,*** or 2-methyl-1,3-butadiene:

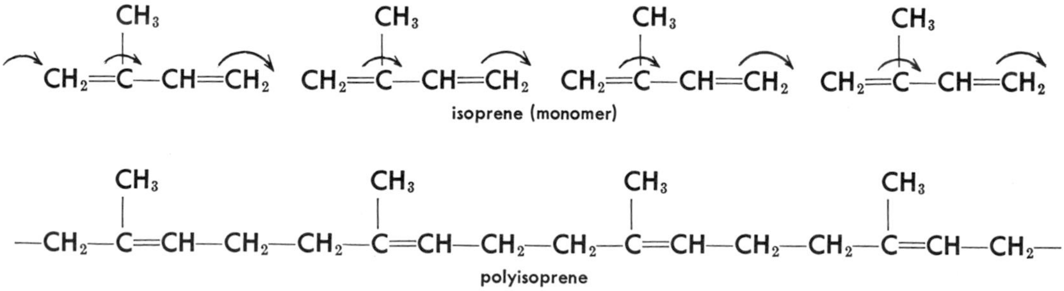

$$CH_2{=}C(CH_3){-}CH{=}CH_2 \quad CH_2{=}C(CH_3){-}CH{=}CH_2 \quad CH_2{=}C(CH_3){-}CH{=}CH_2 \quad CH_2{=}C(CH_3){-}CH{=}CH_2$$

isoprene (monomer)

$$-CH_2-C(CH_3){=}CH-CH_2-CH_2-C(CH_3){=}CH-CH_2-CH_2-C(CH_3){=}CH-CH_2-CH_2-C(CH_3){=}CH-CH_2-$$

polyisoprene

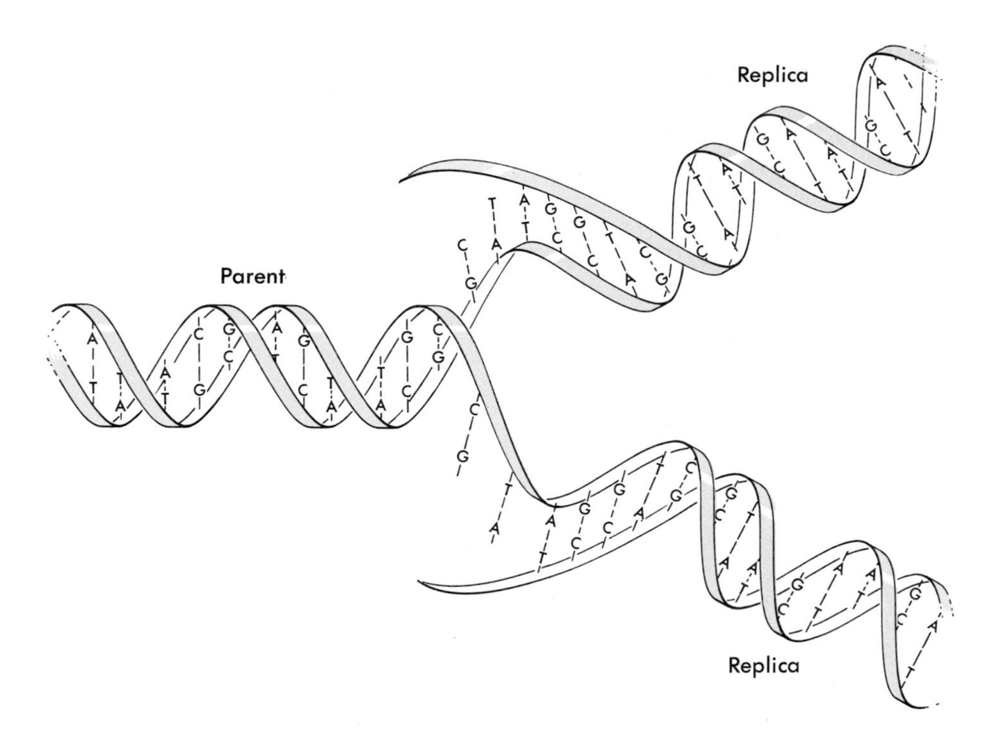

Fig. 17.18 Diagrammatic representation of DNA replication process.

At each double bond, the carbon chain may have either the *cis* or *trans* configuration. In natural rubber the chain is all *cis*:

H_3C H H_3C H
$C{=}C$ $C{=}C$
$—CH_2$ $CH_2—CH_2$ $CH_2—CH_2$ $CH_2—CH_2$ $CH_2—$
$C{=}C$ $C{=}C$
H_3C H H_3C H

natural rubber (*cis*-polyisoprene)

Evidently, the properties of natural rubber are to a large degree determined by this structural feature, since gutta percha (used in the past to cover golf balls), which differs from natural rubber only in having an all-*trans* configuration, is hard and horny, and it lacks the flexibility, tensile strength, and abrasion resistance of natural rubber.

H_3C H_3C H_3C
H_3C CH_2 C CH_2 C CH_2 C $CH_2—$
$C{=}C$ CH_2 C CH_2 C CH_2 C
$—CH_2$ H H H H

gutta percha (*trans*-polyisoprene)

Isoprene may be polymerized in the laboratory to give a product in which the chain is not uniformly *cis* or *trans*, but contains both types of linkages randomly arranged. Control over the chain geometry can be obtained by carrying out the polymerization in the presence of certain structurally asymmetric solid catalysts such as those developed by K. Ziegler in Germany, and G. Natta in Italy. Using such catalysts, all-*cis* polyisoprene identical with natural rubber was first prepared artificially in 1955.

17.13 Reading Suggestions

The significance of Wöhler's synthesis of urea in the decline of the vital force theory is discussed by Timothy O. Lipman in *J. Chem. Ed.* **41,** 452 (1964). Working independently, August Kekulé and Archibald Couper arrived at an understanding of the tetravalence of carbon and the ability of carbon atoms to link with one another. Thus, in 1858 the foundations of organic structural theory were laid, and the "age of confusion" in organic chemistry drew to a close. The early history of organic structural theory is reviewed by Herbert C. Brown in *J. Chem. Ed.* **36,** 104 (1959). Excerpts from an address given by Kekulé in 1890, in which he described how he arrived at his concept of molecular structure while dozing on a London bus, appear in this article, and the address appears in its entirety in *J. Chem. Ed.* **35,** 21 (1958).

The geometry of giant molecules as it relates to the physical properties of these substances is discussed by Charles C. Price in *J. Chem. Ed.* **36,** 160 (1959). The article, "New Horizons in Elastic Polymers," by Harry L. Fisher (*ibid.*, **37,** 369 (1960)), includes a very complete chart showing the various types of elastomers and the compounds from which they are prepared. Perhaps the most revolutionary development in polymer chemistry in recent years has been the discovery of catalysts which permit the stereochemistry of the polymerization process to be controlled. The function of the catalyst in stereospecific polymerization is described by Guilio Natta, one of the discoverers of the process, in an article in *Scientific American*, September 1957, p. 98 ff.

The chemical nature and biological function of nucleic acids, genes, and viruses are discussed by Hames L. Fairly in *J. Chem. Ed.* **36,** 544 (1959). The role of RNA in the transmission of the genetic code is clearly described by H. Fraenkel-Conrat in *J. Chem. Ed.* **40,** 216 (1963). Especially recommended for those who would like a more complete discussion of the subject are two books by Isaac Asimov: *The Genetic Code* (Orion Press, New York, 1962), and *Wellsprings of Life* (Abelard-Schuman, London and New York, 1960).

J. D. Watson, one of the architects of the double helix model of DNA, and corecipient, with F. H. C. Crick and M. H. F. Wilkins, of the 1962 Nobel Prize in Medicine and Physiology, has written a remarkable first-person account of the investigation which led to the unraveling of the DNA structure. Titled *The Double Helix* (Atheneum, New York, 1968), it reveals the scientists involved as living people, dedicated to their science, yet still subject to the same ambitions and desires, strengths and weaknesses common to all men.

A brief comparison of the organic chemistry of carbon and silicon is presented by I. J. Wilk in *J. Chem. Ed.* **34,** 463 (1957).

Questions

17.1 What is meant by a functional group?

17.2 Write structural formulas for an example of each of the following:

alkene	alkyne	amide
carboxylic acid	amine	amino acid
ketone	aldehyde	ester

17.3 Both ethyl alcohol and dimethyl ether are very soluble in water.

Ethyl alcohol is a liquid (b.p. 78.5°C) and dimethyl ether is a gas (b.p. −24°C). How can these observations be accounted for in terms of hydrogen bonding?

17.4 Draw structural formulas for a primary, a secondary, and a tertiary alcohol, each with four carbons. What organic products are obtained when each of these alcohols undergoes (a) mild oxidation? (b) vigorous oxidation?

17.5 In preparing an aldehyde from a primary alcohol, how is it possible to avoid further oxidation of the aldehyde to a carboxylic acid?

17.6 Compound A has the molecular formula C_3H_8O. Oxidation of A with $KMnO_4$ gives compound B, which has the molecular formula C_3H_6O, and is resistant to further oxidation. Write structural formulas for A and B.

17.7 A certain compound is identified as a ketone. Vigorous oxidation of the compound causes the molecule to cleave. Analysis of the cleavage products shows them to be acetic acid, propionic acid, and *n*-butyric acid (CH_3—CH_2—CH_2—$COOH$). Write the structural formula of the original ketone and show how the three acids are formed from it.

17.8 Write equations showing how 1-propanol can be converted to 2-propanol.

17.9 Write equations for the preparation of ethanol from (a) ethylene, (b) ethyl acetate, (c) acetaldehyde, (d) acetic acid.

17.10 In acid solution, ordinary soap loses its cleansing power, but octadecylamine ($CH_3(CH_2)_{17}NH_2$) acts as a detergent. Explain.

17.11 Write structural formulas for the nine isomeric heptanes (C_7H_{16}).

17.12 Write structural formulas for four compounds with the molecular formula $C_4H_{10}O$.

17.13 What is meant by geometric isomerism? How does geometric isomerism differ from structural isomerism?

17.14 There are three compounds, A, B, and C, each of which has the molecular formula $C_2H_2Cl_2$. When hydrogen is added to either A or B, the same product (D, $C_2H_4Cl_2$) is obtained. Addition of hydrogen to C yields E, a compound which is isomeric with D. Write structural formulas for A, B, C, D, and E.

17.15 What are optical isomers? How is optical activity measured?

17.16 What is meant by an asymmetric carbon atom?

17.17 Which of the following compounds would be expected to exhibit optical activity?

$H_3C{-}C(Cl)(H){-}CH_2Cl$ $\qquad$ $(H)(H)C{=}C(Cl)(Cl)$ $\qquad$ $H_3C{-}C(H)(OH){-}CH_3$ $\qquad$ $H_3C{-}C(CH_3)(OH){-}CH_2{-}CH_3$

$Cl{-}C(H)(F){-}Br$ $\qquad$ $H_3C{-}C(H)(OH){-}CH_2{-}CH_2{-}CH_3$ $\qquad$ $H_3C{-}CH_2{-}C(H)(OH){-}CH_2{-}CH_3$

$H_3C{-}CH_2{-}C(CH_3)(H){-}CH(CH_3)_2$ $\qquad$ $H_3C{-}C(H)(NH_2){-}COOH$ $\qquad$ $H_2N{-}C(H)(H){-}COOH$

17.18 A solution prepared by dissolving 12.35 g of D-glucose in 100.0 cm^3 of water shows an optical rotation of $+12.97°$ when measured at 25°C in a 20-cm polarimeter tube using sodium light. A solution of 16.97 g of L-glucose in 50.00 cm^3 of water at 25°C shows an optical rotation of $-26.73°$, measured in a 15-cm polarimeter tube using sodium light. Show that D- and L-glucose are enantiomers.

17.19 Show that when X, an optically active reagent, reacts with a pair of enantiomers the products are diastereoisomers.

17.20 Contrast the behavior of benzene and ethylene toward a halogen and toward concentrated sulfuric acid.

17.21 Outline a suitable synthesis of aspirin from benzene and any other necessary reagents.

17.22 Write the structure of the final product formed in each of the following reaction sequences:

(a) Benzene $\xrightarrow{HNO_3,\ H_2SO_4}$ A $\xrightarrow{Sn,\ HCl}$ B $\xrightarrow{HNO_2,\ 0°C}$ C $\xrightarrow{CuCN}$ D (C_7H_5N)

(b) Aniline $\xrightarrow[\text{anhydride}]{\text{acetic}}$ E $\xrightarrow{ClSO_3H}$ F $\xrightarrow{NH_3}$ G $\xrightarrow{H_2O,\ H^+}$ H $(C_6H_8N_2O_2S)$

(c) 1-propanol $\xrightarrow{H_2SO_4,\ 170°}$ J $\xrightarrow{H_2SO_4,\ 20°}$ K $\xrightarrow[\text{distilled}]{H_2O}$ L (C_3H_8O).

17.23 Benzene is described as a "resonance hybrid." What does this mean? What connection is there between the existence of resonance and the relative stability of a compound?

17.24 What is meant by each of the following terms? monosaccharide disaccharide polysaccharide reducing sugar mutarotation

17.25 What is a polymer? Distinguish between addition polymers and condensation polymers and give an example of each.

17.26 The solubility of an amino acid in water depends on the *p*H of the solution. Solubility is greatest at high or low *p*H. At some intermediate *p*H characteristic of the particular amino acid or protein (the "isoelectric point"), solubility is at a minimum. How can one account for this behavior?

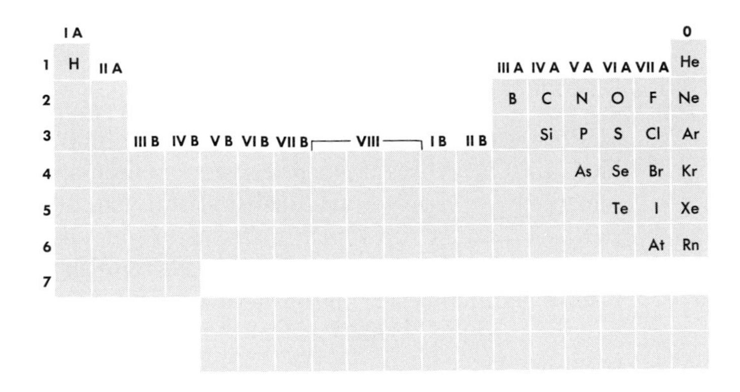

18

THE NONMETALS

With only 22 members, the nonmetals form a rather exclusive society of elements. Exactly half of them are gases at standard conditions. Of the remaining 11, bromine is a liquid, and the rest are solids. Bonding between the atoms, where it exists, is covalent, and the elements as a result form covalent or molecular crystals (Sec. 9.12). For the most part, these lack the luster, ductility, and electrical and thermal conductivity characteristic of metallic crystals. Chemically, the nonmetals are distinguished from the metals by their electronegativity. Their oxides are acidic, reacting with metallic oxides and with bases to form salts, and, where soluble, with water to form acids.

In our discussion of the chemistry of the nonmetals, we will consider the natural occurrence of these elements, their preparation, and their principal uses, as well as their important physical and chemical properties, some of which have been described briefly elsewhere, especially in Chapters 4 and 8. The chemistry of carbon and silicon has been examined in detail in Chapter 16, and will not be considered further in this chapter.

HYDROGEN

18.1 Discovery and Properties

Robert Boyle and other chemists of the 1600's were aware that a flammable "air" is evolved when certain metals are acted upon by acid. It remained for Henry Cavendish to establish, 100 years later, in 1766, that this "air" was a substance in its own right, distinct from such other combustible gases as methane. In 1783 Cavendish showed that water is formed when "flammable air" is burned. It was first called ***hydrogen*** (from the Greek, meaning water former) a few years later by de Morveau and by Lavoisier.

Hydrogen's position in the periodic table is unique. Except for the noble gas helium, hydrogen is the only member of the first period. It is difficult to assign hydrogen to any group. Because it exhibits oxidation states of +1 and −1 in its compounds, hydrogen is often included as a member of both groups IA and VIIA, but in no other respect does it closely resemble either the alkali metals or the halogens in its properties. It is intermediate in electronegativity between the most active metals and nonmetals (Fig. 8.17). Its oxide (water) is amphoteric, reacting with both acids and bases:

$$\text{With acid:} \qquad H^+ + H_2O \rightarrow H_3O^+$$

$$\text{With base:} \qquad NH_3 + H_2O \rightarrow NH_4^+ + OH^-$$

Hydrogen is a colorless, nontoxic gas, odorless when pure, and nearly insoluble in water and most other liquids. It is the lightest of all gases, with a density at standard conditions of 0.0894 g/liter. Its low density has led to its use in the past for filling lighter than air balloons and airships, but because of the hazards associated with its flammability, it has largely been supplanted by helium for this purpose. Its boiling point, −253°C, and its melting point, −259°C, are lower than those of any other element but helium. About one-sixth of the atoms in the earth's crust are hydrogen, yet because the element is so light, it constitutes less than 1% of the mass of the crust. Most of the hydrogen on the earth is combined with oxygen in the form of water. A substantial part of the remainder is found in the organic compounds present in the bodies of living creatures and in petroleum, natural gas, and coal. Other than as water of crystallization, very little hydrogen is present as a constituent of inorganic minerals, and only very minute amounts (about 1 part in 2×10^6) of the free element are found in the atmosphere. Despite its relative scarcity on the earth, hydrogen appears to be the most abundant element in the universe taken as a whole. It is the major constituent of the sun and stars, whose energy is produced in a fusion reaction for which hydrogen is the principal fuel (Sec. 20.9). Most of the matter in interstellar space is believed to be isolated hydrogen atoms. Although the atoms are so far apart that space is a more perfect vacuum than any that can be attained on earth, it has nevertheless been estimated that the total mass of hydrogen in the vast regions of space is greater than that of all of the stars and planets.

Preparation and Use 18.2

Large quantities of hydrogen are produced by electrolysis, especially as a by-product with chlorine in the manufacture of caustic soda (NaOH) by the electrolysis of brine (Sec. 5.3). The reaction of red-hot coke with superheated steam produces ***water gas,*** a mixture of hydrogen and carbon monoxide, useful as fuel:

$$C + H_2O \xrightarrow{1000°C} CO + H_2$$

If more steam is added to the hot gas, it reacts with the carbon monoxide to form carbon dioxide and more hydrogen:

$$H_2O + CO \xrightarrow{1000°C} H_2 + CO_2$$

The CO_2 can be removed from the mixture by taking advantage of its solubility in water under pressure. Hydrogen is also produced in the thermal decomposition of hydrocarbons:

$$CH_4 \xrightarrow{1000°C} C + 2\ H_2$$

$$H_3C{-}CH_3 \xrightarrow{500°C} H_2C{=}CH_2 + H_2$$

and appreciable amounts of the element are obtained in this way as a by-product of petroleum refining.

Active metals displace hydrogen from solutions of acids, and this forms the basis of the usual laboratory preparation of the element:

$$Zn + 2\ H_3O^+ \rightarrow Zn^{++} + 2\ H_2O + H_2$$

$$Fe + 2\ H_3O^+ \rightarrow Fe^{++} + 2\ H_2O + H_2$$

The alkali metals and calcium displace hydrogen from cold water:

$$2\ Na + 2\ H_2O \rightarrow 2\ Na^+ + 2\ OH^- + H_2$$

$$Ca + 2\ H_2O \rightarrow Ca(OH)_2\downarrow + H_2$$

Magnesium displaces hydrogen from water near its boiling point:

$$Mg + 2\ H_2O \rightarrow Mg(OH)_2\downarrow + H_2$$

while iron reacts with superheated steam to form hydrogen and the magnetic oxide Fe_3O_4, in which the iron is present in both the +2 and +3 oxidation states:

$$3\ Fe + 4\ H_2O \xrightarrow{600°C} Fe_3O_4 + 4\ H_2$$

The last reaction was in the past an important industrial source of the element.

Certain amphoteric metals, such as zinc and aluminum, displace hydrogen from bases as well as from acids:

$$Zn + 2\ H_2O + 2\ OH^- \rightarrow Zn(OH)_4^{--} + H_2$$

$$2\ Al + 6\ H_2O + 6\ OH^- \rightarrow 2\ Al(OH)_6^{---} + 3\ H_2$$

The alkali and alkaline earth metals react directly with hydrogen at elevated temperatures to form solid, salt-like hydrides in which the hydrogen is present as the ion H^-. The hydrides in turn react readily with water to yield hydrogen and the hydroxides of the metals:

$$CaH_2 + 2\ H_2O \rightarrow Ca(OH)_2\downarrow + 2\ H_2$$

$$LiH + H_2O \rightarrow Li^+ + OH^- + H_2$$

The principal use of hydrogen is as a fuel, either alone, or admixed with other fuel gases. The combustion of hydrogen is accompanied by the evolution of a large amount of heat,

$$H_2(g) + \tfrac{1}{2}\ O_2(g) \rightarrow H_2O(g) \qquad \Delta H = -58.6\ \text{kcal}$$

and a temperature of approximately 2500°C is reached in an oxy-hydrogen flame. Still higher temperatures—between 4000 and 5000°C—are attained in the flame of the atomic hydrogen torch. In this torch the hydrogen is first passed through an electric arc where it is dissociated into atoms before being mixed with oxygen and burned. The dissociation requires the absorption of a large amount of heat (the bond energy) by the gas:

$$H_2(g) \rightarrow 2\ H(g) \qquad \Delta H = +104\ \text{kcal}$$

This heat is then released as part of the heat of combustion when the atomized gas is burned:

$$2\ H(g) + \tfrac{1}{2}\ O_2(g) \rightarrow H_2O(g) \qquad \Delta H = -163\ \text{kcal}$$

Large amounts of hydrogen gas are used for the production of ammonia by direct combination with nitrogen over a catalyst (the Haber process, Sec. 12.12):

$$N_2 + 3\ H_2 \xrightarrow[\text{Fe catalyst}]{500°C,\ 200\ \text{atm}} 2\ NH_3$$

Other important uses for the element include the hydrogenation of unsaturated organic compounds (Sec. 17.4), and the reduction of certain metal oxides (Sec. 15.3).

Isotopes of Hydrogen 18.3

In addition to ordinary hydrogen, whose nucleus consists solely of a single proton, two isotopes of hydrogen are known. These are ***deuterium*** ^2_1H (or ^2_1D) and ***tritium,*** ^3_1H (or ^3_1T). Deuterium, present to the extent of about 1 part in 6000 in natural hydrogen, contains a neutron in addition to a proton in its nucleus. Tritium, with a nucleus consisting of two neutrons plus a proton, is radioactive.

$$^3_1T \rightarrow ^3_2He + ^0_{-1}\beta$$

Its ***half-life,*** that is, the time it takes for one-half of the tritium in a given sample to undergo radioactive disintegration (Sec. 20.5) is 12.26 years. The isotopes of hydrogen are noteworthy in that differences in their physical and chemical properties are more pronounced than is usually the case among isotopes of the same element. This is undoubtedly associated with the fact that the masses of deuterium and tritium are, respectively, two and three times that of ordinary hydrogen. The relative differences in mass are much less among the isotopes of any other element. The greater masses of deuterium and tritium mean, of course, that their densities, and those of their compounds, are correspondingly greater than those of ordinary hydrogen and its compounds. It also means that because of the greater inertia of atoms of the heavier isotopes, when one of them is bound to another atom in a compound, it takes more energy to set it oscillating violently enough to break the bond (Sec. 8.1). Thus, for example, the bond dissociation energy of D_2 is 1.8 kcal/mole greater than that of H_2. Similar energy differences exist among the bonds formed by the three isotopes with other elements. As a result, although hydrogen, deuterium, and tritium all undergo the same types of reactions, they do so at different rates. Advantage is taken of this in the preparation of deuterium oxide (***heavy water,*** D_2O) by the electrolysis of dilute sodium hydroxide solution. During electrolysis, ordinary hydrogen is preferentially liberated at the cathode, and the concentration of deuterium in the evolved gas is only about 15–20% of what it is in the water being electrolyzed. Prolonged electrolysis therefore results in the accumulation of heavy water in the residue. Some properties of hydrogen, deuterium, and their oxides are listed in Table 18.1 for purposes of comparison.

Tritium, which exists in only the most minute amounts in nature, may be prepared by bombarding deuterium with deuterons (D^+), or from deuterium by a slow neutron capture:

$$^2_1D + ^2_1D \rightarrow ^3_1T + ^1_1H$$

$$^2_1D + ^1_0n \rightarrow ^3_1T + \gamma$$

TABLE 18.1 Properties of Ordinary Hydrogen, Deuterium, and Their Oxides

	H_2	D_2	H_2O	D_2O
Density	0.089 g/liter (STP)	0.18 g/liter (STP)	1.00 g/cm³	1.11 g/cm³
Melting point	14.0°K	18.7°K	0.00°C	3.80°C
Boiling point (1 atm)	20.4°K	23.6°K	100.0°C	101.4°C
Heat of fusion (cal/mole)	28	47	1436	1520
Heat of vaporization (cal/mole)	—	—	9710	9969

The small amount of tritium which has been detected in the atmosphere is believed to be formed by the reaction of nitrogen atoms with neutrons generated by cosmic radiation:

$$^{14}_{7}N + ^{1}_{0}n \rightarrow ^{12}_{6}C + ^{3}_{1}T$$

Both tritium and deuterium are useful as tracer elements to follow the course of chemical reactions. Atoms of either isotope may be substituted for ordinary hydrogen in a compound taking part in a reaction, and the path of the reaction may then be followed either by measuring the radioactivity of intermediates and products where tritium is used, or by mass spectroscopy if the isotope is deuterium.

THE NOBLE GASES

18.4 Discovery

To Sir William Ramsay belongs the unique distinction of having discovered an entire group of elements, the noble gases. Between 1882 and 1892, Lord Rayleigh, then professor of physics at Cambridge, was engaged in determining the relative densities of a number of gases. In the course of this work he observed that nitrogen prepared by the decomposition of ammonia was decidedly less dense than the nitrogen left after removing oxygen, water vapor, carbon dioxide, and other known gases from atmospheric air. Believing that this might indicate the presence of an allotrope such as N_3, he encouraged Ramsay to make a chemical investigation of the problem.

More than a century before, Henry Cavendish had found that a solution of nitrates was formed when an electrical spark was passed through a mixture of air and oxygen confined over a solution of caustic potash (KOH). The gases gradually disappeared as sparking converted the nitrogen to NO_2 which then dissolved in the caustic. When no further reaction took place, Cavendish absorbed the remaining oxygen in a solution of potassium sulfide and found that a small bubble of gas remained, whose volume he estimated at no more than $\frac{1}{120}$ of the initial volume. It is a tribute to Cavendish's observational skill that, rather than ignoring this trifling residue, he carefully recorded it, commenting that ". . . if there is any part of the phlogisticated air (nitrogen) of our atmosphere which differs from the rest, and cannot be reduced to nitrous acid, we may safely conclude that it is not more than $\frac{1}{120}$ of the whole."

Ramsay was aware of Cavendish's observation, and with this as a clue, he passed a large sample of atmospheric nitrogen, carefully freed of water vapor and CO_2, over hot magnesium. The magnesium combined with the nitrogen to form the solid nitride. The residual gas, amounting to only $\frac{1}{80}$ of the original volume, had a density about 19 times that of hydrogen (nitrogen is 14 times as dense as hydrogen). Examination of its spectrum showed lines which corresponded to no known element. Rayleigh and Ramsay named the new element ***argon*** (Greek: inactive, lazy). Later it was shown to be monatomic, and to have an atomic weight of 39.9 amu. On the basis of its atomic weight, argon belonged between potassium (39.1) and calcium (40.1), but since there was obviously no place for it there, Ramsay suggested that a new group (group 0) be created for it between the halogens and the alkali metals.

Shortly after the discovery of argon, Ramsay learned that the American geochemist William Hillebrand had obtained an inert gas, which he assumed was nitrogen, upon heating the mineral uraninite with sulfuric acid. Suspecting that the gas might be argon, Ramsay heated the related mineral cleveite in similar manner. He obtained not argon, but a gas whose spectrum showed a bright yellow line coinciding with that attributed to helium in the spectrum of the sun (Sec. 7.2). With an atomic weight later shown to be 4.0, helium fit between hydrogen and lithium, occupying the new group 0 with argon. The discovery of helium confirmed Ramsay in his belief that other inert elements existed to complete the group, and he set out to look for them. He first sought them in minerals, but without success. Then he and his associate Morris Travers examined the last cubic centimeter of liquid air remaining after the rest of a liter of the liquid had boiled away. In addition to the argon lines, the spectrum of this material showed new yellow and green lines. These were attributed to a new element which they named ***krypton*** (Greek: hidden). Shortly afterwards, Ramsay and Travers succeeded in isolating ***neon*** (Greek: new) and ***xenon*** (Greek: stranger) by careful fractionation of liquified argon.

Meanwhile, Rutherford and others working with radioactive substances began to suspect the existence of a radioactive gas. In 1900 Rutherford showed that thorium compounds emit such a gas, which he named *emanation*. At the same time, F. E. Dorn isolated a similar gas from radium, and three years later Andre Debierne discovered a gaseous emanation in actinium preparations. Ramsay and R. W. Gray determined the density of the radium emanation and found it to be the heaviest known gas, occupying the last place in group 0. The emanation from radium, radon-222, is the longest-lived isotope of radon. Half of it disintegrates every 3.82 days, emitting an alpha particle in the process, to form polonium-218. Radon-220, the emanation from thorium, has a half-life of 51.5 sec, and is also an α-emitter. Radon-219, from actinium, is an α- and γ-emitter with a half-life of 4 sec.

18.5 Occurrence and Physical Properties

Although substantial amounts of helium are present in the sun and stars, where it is the major product of hydrogen fusion (Sec. 20.9), all the noble gases are relatively rare on the earth. The atmosphere contains nearly 1% argon but only minute amounts of the other gases (Table 18.2). The natural gas from certain wells contains as much as 7% helium, and this is the principal source of that gas. The other noble gases, except radon, are obtained by the fractional distillation of liquid air.

TABLE 18.2 Concentration of Noble Gases in the Atmosphere (parts per million)

He	Ne	Ar	Kr	Xe	Rn
5	15.4	9400	1	0.5	—

Some of the more important physical properties of the noble gases are listed in Table 18.3. They are all colorless, odorless, and tasteless. Only

TABLE 18.3 Physical Properties of the Noble Gases

	He	Ne	Ar	Kr	Xe	Rn
Melting point °C (1 atm)	−272.2[a]	−248.6	−189.3	−157	−112	−71
Boiling point °C (1 atm)	−268.9	−245.9	−185.6	−152.9	−107.1	−61.8
Density, g/liter (STP)	0.18	0.90	1.78	3.75	5.90	9.73
Solubility in water (cm³ of gas at STP/cm³ H_2O at 0°C)	0.0097	0.0114	0.053	0.111	0.242	0.51

[a] 26 atm.

xenon and radon show any physiological activity. Xenon has been found to have anesthetic properties. Radon, which is intensely radioactive, is used in radiotherapy to destroy cancerous tissues. The low melting and boiling points of the elements are in line with the nonpolarity of the monatomic molecules, and indicate that van der Waals forces among the molecules are weak. The temperature ranges over which these elements exist as liquids are very narrow, suggesting that the forces of attraction between atoms in the solid state are not markedly different from those operating in the liquid state. Both the melting and boiling points increase regularly as the atomic number, and hence the number of electrons per molecule, increases (Sec. 9.2). Helium has the lowest boiling point of any substance, even including hydrogen whose molecular weight is only half that of helium. The attractive forces between helium atoms are so small in fact that the element remains liquid at 1 atm even when cooled to the lowest temperature so far attainable (0.001°K). It can be solidified at that temperature only under a pressure of about 25 atm. When liquid helium is cooled to 2.18°K it becomes a ***superfluid.*** In this remarkable state, its viscosity is lower than that of any gas. It can flow through microscopic cracks virtually without friction, and it cannot be confined in an unsealed container but flows up the walls, over the top, and drips off the bottom. In the superfluid state, helium also exhibits superconductivity, conducting heat and electricity hundreds of times more readily than copper does at ordinary temperatures.

Of all the elements of group 0, helium finds the greatest use. Large quantities are used to fill observation balloons, particularly for meteorological studies. Its lifting power, which depends upon the difference between its density and that of air, is almost 93% that of hydrogen, despite the fact that its density is nearly twice as great:

Density of air, g/liter (STP)	1.29	1.29
Density of helium, g/liter (STP)	0.18	
Density of hydrogen, g/liter (STP)		0.09
Lifting power, g/liter (STP)	1.11	1.20
Relative lifting power, He/H_2: 1.11/1.20 = 0.925		

Nearly all of the world's supply of helium comes from the United States, where its production is regulated by the U.S. Bureau of Mines. In both World Wars the use of helium in barrage balloons, observation balloons, dirigibles, and blimps gave the Allies a distinct strategic advantage over their enemies, who were forced to use highly flammable hydrogen for the same purpose. A single hit by a tracer bullet will cause a hydrogen filled balloon to burst instantly into flame and be totally destroyed, but it will cause only a slow leak if the balloon is filled with helium. Because of its military importance, foreign sales of helium were severely restricted until the development of the helicopter rendered the slow-moving blimps and dirigibles obsolete.

The use of a helium-oxygen mixture rather than ordinary air enables deep sea divers to descend safely to greater depths by eliminating the danger of nitrogen narcosis. This dangerous intoxication, also known as "rapture of the deep," can cause a diver to lose all sense of caution and behave irrationally. When in this condition, divers have been known to forget that they are not fish and to descend beyond the limit of their equipment or even throw away their breathing apparatus, with tragic consequences. Oceanographers studying undersea life can live quite comfortably for long periods of time in an underwater observatory, breathing an atmosphere of helium and oxygen. Two curious, though minor problems arise, however. Fast-moving helium molecules carry heat away from the body more rapidly than heavier, slower nitrogen molecules, making it harder to keep warm in an atmosphere consisting mostly of helium. Furthermore, the low density of helium causes a change in voice pitch, so that the occupants of an underwater observatory all end up sounding like Donald Duck.

A helium-oxygen mixture is also used to relieve patients suffering from respiratory diseases. Because of its low density, the gas mixture flows more freely than ordinary air through restricted passages, and thus the patient receives more oxygen. Helium is also used in medicine to dilute gaseous anesthetics and reduce their flammability. The gas finds many industrial applications where an inert atmosphere is needed, for example, in welding easily oxidized metals such as aluminum. It has been used as a heat transfer medium in atomic reactors because it is not only chemically inert, but it does not become radioactive. Liquid helium is used in research to maintain extremely low temperatures.

Like helium, argon is used to furnish an inert atmosphere for arc welding and other metallurgical operations. Another major use of argon is for filling incandescent light bulbs. Its presence prolongs the life of the lamp by retarding the evaporation of the hot filament. The inertness and low heat conductivity of argon makes it preferable to nitrogen for this purpose. Neon finds its greatest use in electrical signs. At pressures of 10–20 torr, a small current from a high-voltage transformer is sufficient to cause the gas to glow with a characteristic orange-red light. The glow responds instantaneously to interruptions in the current, making flashing neon signs especially effective. This same fast response is shared by xenon. Because of this, and the excellent characteristics of its spectrum, xenon is used in high intensity flashlamps for high speed photography. Krypton is more efficient than argon in preserving the filament in incandescent lamps which must operate efficiently over long periods of time, and is used for this purpose in airport runway and approach lights.

Unstable solid hydrates of argon, krypton, xenon, and radon have been prepared at low temperatures and high gas pressures. These belong to the class of substances known as ***clathrates***. Clathrates are a type of interstitial solid solution. They appear to have definite compositions, e.g., $Ar_2(H_2O)_{11}$ and $Kr(H_2O)_5$, but chemical bonds in the usual sense do not exist between the noble gas "guest" atoms and the "host" water molecules. It appears that in these hydrates, as in other clathrates, the guest component is trapped in cage-like interstices between the molecules of the host. Linus Pauling has suggested that the anesthetic properties of xenon may result from a change in the fluid balance in the brain tissues as a result of hydrate formation. Clathrates of argon, krypton, and xenon with hydroquinone and phenol are also known, for example $Ar[C_6H_4(OH)_2]_3$ and $Ar(C_6H_5OH)_4$.

Prior to 1962, except for the clathrates and such transient ionic species as He_2^+ and HeH^+ produced by passing an electrical discharge through the gases, no compounds of the noble gases were known, and these elements were assumed to be chemically completely inert. In that year N. Bartlett, of the University of British Columbia, reported the preparation of a solid orange-yellow compound $XePtF_6$. Since that time, a number of compounds of xenon and krypton with fluorine and oxygen have been prepared. The chemistry of these compounds is discussed more fully in Sec. 8.7g.

THE HALOGENS

General Properties 18.6

There is a strong family resemblance among the halogens, and their properties vary in a regular fashion with increasing atomic number. At room temperature, fluorine and chlorine are gases, bromine is a liquid, and iodine a solid. The molecules of the elements are diatomic with the atoms joined by a single covalent bond. All of the halogens are active nonmetals,

TABLE 18.4 Some Properties of the Halogens

	F	Cl	Br	I
Physical state (25°C, 1 atm)	gas	gas	liquid	solid
Color	pale yellow	yellow-green	red-brown	violet-black (*s*) violet (*g*)
Melting point, °C	−218	−101	−73	114
Boiling point, °C, 1 atm	−188	−35	59	184
Atomic radius, Å	0.72	0.99	1.14	1.33
Ionic radius, Å	1.36	1.81	1.95	2.16
First ionization potential, eV	17.4	13.0	11.8	10.4
Electron affinity ($X + e^- \rightarrow X^-$), eV	3.6	3.8	3.5	3.2
Electronegativity (Pauling scale)	4.0	3.2	3.0	2.7
Heat of hydration of X^-, kcal/mole	−122	−89	−81	−72
X—X bond energy kcal/mole	37	58	46	36
Standard electrode potential, $2\,X^- \rightarrow X_2 + 2\,e^-$, eV	−2.87	−1.36	−1.07	−0.54
Solubility in water, M/liter, 20°C	reacts	0.09	0.21	0.0013

and they exhibit an oxidation state of -1 in most of their compounds. In addition, all of them except fluorine can exhibit positive oxidation states up to a maximum of $+7$ in compounds with oxygen and with each other. Because of their reactivity, none of the halogens occurs naturally in the uncombined state. Fluorine is the most reactive nonmetal, and perhaps the strongest chemical oxidizing agent known. Even oxygen itself is oxidized by fluorine, existing in the $+2$ state in the compound OF_2, which is formed when fluorine reacts with water. The oxidizing power of the remaining halogens decreases in regular fashion from chlorine through iodine. Little is known directly of the properties of astatine, which is a short-lived, radioactive element, but its probable chemical and physical properties can be predicted by extrapolation from the known properties of the other halogens, some of which are given in Table 18.4.

18.7 Preparation of the Halogens

Chlorine, which makes up about 0.3% of the earth's crust and is the most abundant of the halogens, was also the first to be isolated. It was first prepared in 1774 by Carl Wilhelm Scheele, by the action of muriatic acid (the old name for hydrochloric acid, derived from the Latin *muria*, brine) on pyrolusite (MnO_2). Scheele believed it to be a compound, and for many years it was thought to contain oxygen. Sir Humphry Davy demonstrated its elemental nature in 1810, and named it chlorine because of its color (Greek: *chloros*, green).

Chlorine is commonly prepared in the laboratory by heating a mixture of manganese dioxide, sodium chloride, and concentrated sulfuric acid:

$$MnO_2 + 2\ Cl^- + 4\ H^+ \rightarrow 2\ H_2O + Mn^{++} + Cl_2$$

Other oxidizing agents, such as permanganates and dichromates, may be used in place of MnO_2. For example, small amounts of chlorine may be prepared by allowing 6 M hydrochloric acid to fall drop by drop on $KMnO_4$ crystals:

$$MnO_4^- + 8\ H^+ + 6\ Cl^- \rightarrow Mn^{++} + 4\ H_2O + 3\ Cl_2$$

Chlorine for industry is produced in conjunction with the manufacture of caustic soda by electrolysis of brine, and of sodium metal by the electrolysis of fused sodium chloride (Sec. 15.4).

Bromine was first recognized to be an element by Antoine-Jerome Balard, who prepared it in 1826 by passing chlorine through the brackish solution remaining after removing most of the NaCl from concentrated sea water. The element had already been isolated earlier by Joss, who thought it was selenium, and by Liebig, who believed it to be a chloride of iodine. Its name, from the Greek *bromos*, meaning "stench," is most appropriate. The deep red-brown liquid has an appreciable vapor pressure (about 200 torr at 25°C), and the vapors are acrid-smelling and irritating in the extreme. Although bromine is not as powerful an oxidizing agent as chlorine, the high concentration of the liquid makes it dangerous to handle unless proper precautions are taken. It causes severe and painful burns, and the damaged tissues are slow to heal. The vapors, like those of the other halogens, are poisonous and cause irritation and damage to the mucosa.

Bromine may be prepared in the laboratory by oxidizing a bromide salt with MnO_2 in the presence of concentrated H_2SO_4. The mixture is heated, and bromine distills:

$$MnO_2 + 2\ Br^- + 4\ H^+ \rightarrow 2\ H_2O + Mn^{++} + Br_2$$

The reaction is perfectly analogous to that for the preparation of chlorine. Chlorine is a stronger oxidizing agent than bromine, and oxidizes Br^- to Br_2:

$$Cl_2 + 2\ Br^- \rightarrow 2\ Cl^- + Br_2$$

This reaction, which is the one Balard used to prepare the element, is the basis of a simple qualitative test for bromides. An aqueous solution of chlorine is added to a solution of the suspected bromide, and the mixture is then shaken with a small amount of carbon tetrachloride. Any free bromine formed dissolves in the carbon tetrachloride, which is insoluble in water and settles out upon standing. The presence of a bromide is indicated if the lower (CCl_4) layer is colored red-brown.

Bromine is obtained industrially from seawater and from certain salt-well brines, both of which contain small amounts of bromide salts in addition to sodium chloride. Seawater contains only about 65 parts of Br^- per million. Salt-well brines may contain Br^- in about 1300 ppm, but this is still very dilute. The seawater or brine is first acidified to a *p*H of 3 to 4, and then treated with chlorine to oxidize the bromides to bromine:

$$Cl_2 + 2\ Br^- \rightarrow 2\ Cl^- + Br_2$$

The reason for acidifying the solution is to prevent subsequent reaction of the bromine with hydroxide ions:

$$Br_2 + 2\ OH^- \rightarrow BrO^- + Br^- + H_2O$$

At this stage the concentration of bromine is so low that all of it remains in solution. Air is blown through the solution, carrying the bromine with it as vapor to a tower, where it is mixed with sulfur dioxide and then absorbed in water:

$$Br_2 + SO_2 + 2\ H_2O \rightarrow 2\ HBr + H_2SO_4$$

A fairly concentrated solution of HBr results. A mixture of chlorine and steam is blown through the solution, reoxidizing the bromide to bromine, which separates from the condensate as a liquid.

Alternatively, the diluted vapors of bromine from the initial chlorination of the brine may be absorbed in a hot solution of sodium carbonate. The result is a solution containing both bromide and bromate ions:

$$3\ CO_3^{--} + 3\ Br_2 \rightarrow 5\ Br^- + BrO_3^- + 3\ CO_2$$

from which bromine separates upon acidification:

$$5\ Br^- + BrO_3^- + 6\ H^+ \rightarrow 3\ Br_2 + 3\ H_2O$$

Iodine was discovered by Bernard Courtois in 1811. In France at that time, sodium and potassium salts were extracted from the ashes of seaweed collected along the coasts of Normandy and Brittany. Courtois observed that a violet vapor rose from the mother liquor remaining after extraction of the salts when it was acidified with sulfuric acid. These vapors, which had an irritating odor similar to chlorine, condensed on a cool surface as dark, lustrous crystals. Courtois suspected that he had discovered a new element, and his suspicions were confirmed shortly afterward by two of his friends, Charles-Bernard Desormes and Nicolas Clement, who were chemists. The name iodine, from the Greek *iodes*, violet, was given to the element because of the color of its vapor.

Iodine may be prepared from iodides in the same way that chlorine and bromine are obtained from their respective salts:

$$MnO_2 + 2\ I^- + 4\ H^+ \rightarrow 2\ H_2O + Mn^{++} + I_2$$

In the past, iodine was prepared commercially from seaweed in this way. The seaweed (kelp) was burned, and the ashes were boiled with water. The solution was concentrated by evaporation, causing the sodium and potassium chlorides, carbonates, and sulfates to crystallize, and the mother liquor was then heated with sulfuric acid and manganese dioxide. Today, most iodine is obtained from sodium iodate, which is present in small amounts in sodium nitrate mined from deposits in Chile (Chile saltpeter). The iodate is first reduced to iodide by bisulfite ion, the latter being produced either by passing sulfur dioxide through the solution or by adding $NaHSO_3$ to the solution:

$$IO_3^- + 3\ HSO_3^- \rightarrow I^- + 3\ HSO_4^-$$

An excess of iodate is added to the solution over and above that necessary to oxidize all of the bisulfite ions to bisulfate, whereupon the excess iodate oxidizes iodide to free iodine:

$$IO_3^- + 5\ I^- + 6\ H^+ \rightarrow 3\ I_2 + 3\ H_2O$$

This reaction cannot take place until all of the bisulfite has been oxidized, since iodine is rapidly reduced by HSO_3^-:

$$I_2 + HSO_3^- + H_2O \rightarrow HSO_4^- + 2\ H^+ + 2\ I^-$$

Iodides, like bromides, are oxidized to the free element by chlorine:

$$2\ I^- + Cl_2 \rightarrow 2\ Cl^- + I_2$$

If a solution of an iodide is treated with chlorine and then shaken with carbon tetrachloride, the liberated iodine dissolves in the organic (CCl_4) layer, imparting to it a beautiful violet color. The appearance of this color under these circumstances constitutes a qualitative test for iodides in solution. Interestingly, while solutions of iodine in non-polar solvents such as carbon tetrachloride are violet, the same color as iodine vapor, its solution in polar solvents such as water and alcohol are brown. Iodide ion is also oxidized to the element by bromine, showing that as an oxidizing agent, bromine is intermediate in strength between chlorine and iodine. A comparison of the standard electrode potentials of the halogens (Table 18.4) also shows this to be the case.

The existence of fluorine was suspected for many years before the element was actually isolated. In 1771 Scheele observed that the mineral ***fluorite*** (CaF_2, so called from the Latin *fluere*, to flow, because it melts at red heat) reacted with concentrated sulfuric acid, liberating an acid vapor which corroded glass. In 1810 Ampère suggested that this acid was analogous to hydrochloric acid, but that it contained an unknown halogen, fluorine, instead of chlorine. Many attempts were made to isolate the element, some of which ended tragically because of the extreme toxicity of fluorine and its salts. Henri Moissan finally succeeded in preparing fluorine in 1886 by electrolyzing a solution of potassium fluoride dissolved in anhydrous hydrofluoric acid. No chemical oxidizing agent is powerful enough to oxidize the fluoride ion, and therefore fluorine is always prepared by electrolysis. The electrolyte contains about 30% KF dissolved in anhydrous HF. The entire apparatus, except for the electrodes, is usually made of ***Monel metal,*** an alloy consisting of about 60% Ni, 35% Cu, and 5% Fe, which is one of the few materials which is not seriously attacked by fluorine. Pure copper may also be used. While it does react with fluorine, it rapidly becomes coated with a thin film of the fluoride, which protects it against further attack. Graphite is used for the anode, at which fluorine is liberated. Hydrogen is evolved at the cathode, which can be made of steel. A divider of Monel metal, solid above and perforated below the surface of the electrolyte, is used to separate the anode and cathode compartments and prevent the gases from mixing.

Fluorine is an unusually reactive element. It reacts directly, and often violently, with nearly all of the elements, and the only elements with which it fails to form compounds appear to be helium, neon, and argon. Glass, water, and asbestos burn freely in gaseous fluorine, as do clothing and flesh, making the gas extremely hazardous to handle. It is only comparatively recently that materials technology and handling methods have advanced sufficiently to make fluorine a large-scale industrial chemical. In contrast to the great reactivity of the element, and in fact because of it, the compounds of fluorine tend to be very stable. Bonds between carbon and fluorine are especially strong, and are broken only with great difficulty. The present availability of elementary fluorine has generated considerable interest in fluorocarbon research. One of the fruits of this research is polyperfluoroethylene, or ***Teflon*** $(CF_2—CF_2)_n$. This waxy-appearing plastic which is chemically almost totally inert, and which has the remarkable property of not being wet by any known liquid, finds hundreds of uses, from the fabrication of artificial heart valves to nonstick surfaces for frying pans.

The radioactive element ***astatine*** was first isolated in 1940 by D. R. Corson, K. R. MacKenzie, and E. Segre, at the University of California. They prepared the isotope $^{211}_{85}At$, which, with a half-life of 8.3 hours, is the longest-lived isotope of the element, by bombarding $^{209}_{83}Bi$ with α-particles. While other isotopes of astatine are known to be products of β-decay of $^{215}_{84}Po$, $^{216}_{84}Po$, and $^{218}_{84}Po$, the element has never been isolated from natural sources. This is understandable, for not only are astatine isotopes very short-lived, but polonium itself is very rare and usually undergoes α-decay rather than β-decay. The name astatine is derived from the Greek *astatos*, unstable.

18.8 Hydrogen Halides

Both hydrogen fluoride and hydrogen chloride can be prepared by the action of concentrated sulfuric acid on the corresponding halide salt:

$$CaF_2 + H_2SO_4 \rightarrow CaSO_4 + 2\ HF$$

$$NaCl + H_2SO_4 \rightarrow NaHSO_4 + HCl$$

Below 150°C, the temperature at which sulfuric acid begins to decompose into water and SO_3, the reaction with NaCl proceeds only as far as the formation of the acid salt $NaHSO_4$. By heating the acid salt to red heat with additional NaCl, the reaction may be forced to completion to give the normal salt and another mole of HCl:

$$NaCl + NaHSO_4 \xrightarrow{600\text{–}700°C} Na_2SO_4 + HCl$$

In the past, all of the commercial hydrochloric acid was prepared by this two-stage process. It is now being increasingly superseded by a process which involves the direct combination of the elements:

$$H_2 + Cl_2 \rightarrow 2\ HCl$$

The two gases are obtained as by-products of the production of caustic soda by electrolysis of brine. The explosive, light-catalyzed reaction between chlorine and hydrogen is controlled by mixing the gases in a device similar to an oversized laboratory burner set in the base of a water-cooled combustion chamber.

Hydrogen bromide and hydrogen iodide may be prepared by heating their salts with concentrated phosphoric acid:

$$NaBr + H_3PO_4 \rightarrow NaH_2PO_4 + HBr$$

$$NaI + H_3PO_4 \rightarrow NaH_2PO_4 + HI$$

Sulfuric acid is not suitable in this case because, although some hydrogen halide is formed, much of the halide is oxidized by the acid to the free halogen:

$$4\ H^+ + SO_4^{--} + 2\ Br^- \rightarrow SO_2\uparrow + 2\ H_2O + Br_2$$

$$10\ H^+ + SO_4^{--} + 8\ I^- \rightarrow H_2S\uparrow + 4\ H_2O + 4\ I_2$$

The greater reducing power of the iodide relative to the bromide is evidenced by the fact that whereas **HBr** reduces the sulfur of H_2SO_4 from the +6 to the +4 oxidation state, under the same conditions **HI** reduces it all the way to the −2 state.

In the laboratory, **HBr** and **HI** are generally prepared by hydrolysis of the phosphorus halides, which are in turn made by direct combination of the elements. When liquid bromine is added drop by drop to a paste of red phosphorus and water, the phosphorus tribromide initially formed is immediately hydrolyzed to **HBr** by the water:

$$3\ Br_2 + 2\ P \rightarrow 2\ PBr_3$$

$$PBr_3 + 3\ H_2O \rightarrow H_3PO_3 + 3\ HBr$$

Hydrogen iodide is prepared similarly by allowing water to fall drop by drop on a mixture of red phosphorus and iodine:

$$3\ I_2 + 2\ P \rightarrow 2\ PI_3$$

$$PI_3 + 3\ H_2O \rightarrow H_3PO_3 + 3\ HI$$

Hydrogen bromide is manufactured industrially by direct combination of the elements. The reaction is much less vigorous than the combination of chlorine with hydrogen, and the mixture of gases must therefore be passed over a platinum or charcoal catalyst at 200°C. Hydriodic acid is produced by a gas-phase reaction between hydrogen and iodine at 200°C in the presence of chromic acid and water. **HI** is the least stable of the hydrogen halides—it has, in fact, a positive heat of formation—and in the absence of water the reaction

$$H_2 + I_2 \rightleftharpoons 2\ HI$$

proceeds to equilibrium. The reaction is forced to completion by the presence of water, which dissolves the **HI** as fast as it is formed. Some properties of the hydrogen halides are listed in Table 18.5. With the exception of **HF**, all of the hydrogen halides are relatively low-boiling gases; their boiling points increasing in regular fashion with increasing molecular weight from **HCl** to **HI**. The anomalous behavior of **HF** suggests the existence of extensive hydrogen bonding among the molecules of that substance (Sec. 9.14).

TABLE 18.5 Properties of the Hydrogen Halides

	HF	HCl	HBr	HI
Boiling point, °C, 1 atm	19.5	−84.9	−66.8	−35.4
Solubility, g/100 g H_2O at 20°C, 1 atm	35.3	42.0	49.0	57.0
ΔH_f^0, kcal/mole	−64.2	−22.1	−8.7	+6.2
ΔG_f^0, kcal/mole	−64.7	−22.8	−12.7	+0.3
K_{diss}, 1000°C	negligible	2×10^{-10}	2.5×10^{-5}	2.4×10^{-1}

Vapor density measurements indicate that whereas the other hydrogen halides exist in the gaseous state as individual **HX** molecules, hydrogen fluoride is largely in the form of $(HF)_n$, where n ranges from 2 to about 6.

All of the hydrogen halides dissolve readily in water to give acid solutions. Hydrochloric, hydrobromic, and hydriodic acids dissociate completely according to the general equation

$$HX + H_2O \rightarrow H_3O^+ + X^-$$

and are therefore strong acids. Hydrofluoric acid, on the other hand, is relatively weak. Curiously, its acidity increases with increasing concentration, rather than the reverse. Rather than simply becoming hydrated, as they would in dilute solution, in more concentrated solutions the fluoride ions apparently unite with undissociated **HF** molecules to form bifluoride ions, HF_2^-:

Dilute solution: $$H_2O + HF \rightarrow H_3O^+ + F^-$$

Concentrated solution: $$H_2O + 2\,HF \rightarrow H_3O^+ + HF_2^-$$

Evidently the bifluoride ion is a more stable species (and a weaker base) than the hydrated fluoride ion, so that the equilibrium lies more to the right in the second of the reactions above. Thus, an increase in concentration, by favoring the second reaction over the first, is accompanied by an increase in the degree of dissociation of the acid. The existence of such well defined salts as potassium acid fluoride KHF_2, prepared by mixing equimolar amounts of **KF** and **HF**, is evidence for the remarkable stability of the HF_2^- ion.

The large negative values for the standard heat and free energy of formation of hydrogen fluoride show it to be the most stable of the hydrogen halides. The stabilities of the remaining halides decrease from **HCl** to **HI**. The small positive value of ΔG_f^0 for **HI** shows that this compound has a slight tendency to dissociate into its elements even at room temperature. At 1000°C it is 33% dissociated into hydrogen and gaseous iodine. In contrast, **HBr** and **HCl** are respectively 0.50% and 0.0014% dissociated at the same temperature. The free energies of formation of **HBr** and **HI** differ substantially from their respective heats of formation, reflecting the large increase in entropy which accompanies the conversion of liquid bromine or solid iodine to the gaseous hydride. With **HF** and **HCl** the entropy change is small, since the elements as well as their hydrides are gases in their standard states, and in each case ΔG_f^0 is very nearly equal to ΔH_f^0.

Oxides of the Halogens 18.9

(a) Oxides of Fluorine. Elementary fluorine reacts with dilute sodium hydroxide to give gaseous ***oxygen difluoride,*** OF_2, in small yield:

$$2\ F_2 + 2\ OH^- \rightarrow 2\ F^- + H_2O + OF_2$$

This compound is remarkable because in it the oxygen is in a positive oxidation state, +2. Oxygen difluoride is somewhat soluble in water (1 liter of water dissolves about 68 ml of the gas measured at 1 atm). Its aqueous solutions are neutral, but the compound is hydrolyzed by alkali to fluoride ions and elemental oxygen:

$$OF_2 + 2\ OH^- \rightarrow 2\ F^- + O_2 + H_2O$$

Both in the gaseous state and in solution, OF_2 is a powerful oxidizing agent. It reacts vigorously with metals and many nonmetals, and is capable, for example, of oxidizing chromium(III) to chromate in solution:

$$4\ Cr^{+++} + 3\ OF_2 + 39\ H_2O \rightarrow 4\ CrO_4^{--} + 26\ H_3O^+ + 6\ F^-$$

Oxygen monofluoride, O_2F_2, is obtained as a yellow-orange solid by passing an electrical discharge through a mixture of the elements at a pressure of 15–20 torr and a temperature below −160°C. The compound begins to decompose at about −100°C, and is completely dissociated into its elements at room temperature.

(b) Oxides of Chlorine. Chlorine forms four oxides, corresponding to oxidation states of +1, +4, +6, and +7. All of them are powerful oxidizing agents, very unstable, and explosive. ***Chlorine monoxide,*** Cl_2O, is prepared by passing chlorine gas over mercuric oxide at 0°C:

$$2\ Cl_2 + HgO \rightarrow HgCl_2 + Cl_2O$$

The yellowish-red gas decomposes above 20°C, often with explosive violence, and it condenses at 2°C to an even less stable red liquid. It is the anhydride of hypochlorous acid, which is formed when chlorine monoxide is dissolved in cold water:

$$Cl_2O + H_2O \rightarrow 2\ HClO$$

Chlorine dioxide is produced when concentrated sulfuric acid comes in contact with a chlorate. In the presence of acid the chlorate ion undergoes a redox reaction with itself to form the more stable perchlorate and chlorine dioxide:

$$3\ ClO_3^- + 2\ H^+ \rightarrow H_2O + ClO_4^- + 2\ ClO_2$$

Because of the unstable nature of the product, the reaction is dangerous and difficult to control. Chlorine dioxide may be prepared safely in solution by treating sodium chlorate with sulfuric acid and sulfur dioxide:

$$2\ ClO_3^- + SO_2 + H^+ \rightarrow 2\ ClO_2 + HSO_4^-$$

and considerable amounts of it are prepared in this way for use as a bleaching agent for paper pulp.

The electronic structure of ClO_2 is interesting. The molecule possesses an odd number of electrons, and no single entirely satisfactory structure can be written for it. It may be considered a resonance hybrid (Sec. 17.10) of such structures as the following, in which the odd electron is shared among the three atoms making up the molecule:

```
 ..   ..   ..          ..   ..   ..           ..   ..   ..
: O : Cl : O : ↔ : O : Cl : O . ↔ · O : Cl : O :
 ..   .    ..          ..   ..   ..           ..   ..   ..
```

Chlorine dioxide is very soluble in water. Although it is not, strictly speaking, an acid anhydride, it reacts slowly with water in the presence of light to give a mixture of chloric and hydrochloric acids:

$$6\ ClO_2 + 3\ H_2O \rightarrow 5\ HClO_3 + HCl$$

In alkaline solution it reacts more rapidly, forming the chlorite and the chlorate:

$$2\ ClO_2 + 2\ OH^- \rightarrow ClO_2^- + ClO_3^- + H_2O$$

Chlorine dioxide is oxidized by ozone to the ***trioxide,*** ClO_3:

$$ClO_2 + O_3 \rightarrow ClO_3 + O_2$$

Chlorine trioxide is the least volatile of the chlorine oxides, with a boiling point calculated to be about 203°C, and a melting point of 3.5°C. It also is an odd-electron compound for which several structures may be written, all of which contribute to the resonance hybrid:

```
       ..                  ..                  .                   ..
     : O :               : O :               : O :               : O :
 ..   ..   ..        ..   ..   ..        ..   ..   ..        ..   ..   ..
: O : Cl : O : ↔ · O : Cl : O : ↔ : O : Cl : O : ↔ : O : Cl : O ·
 ..   .    ..        ..   ..   ..        ..   ..   ..        ..   ..   ..
```

It exists as an equilibrium mixture of ClO_3 and the dimer Cl_2O_6 in both the liquid and solid states, but is apparently completely dissociated into the monomer in the vapor state:

$$
\begin{array}{ccccccccccc}
 & :\ddot{\mathrm{O}}: & & & :\ddot{\mathrm{O}}: & & & & :\ddot{\mathrm{O}}: & :\ddot{\mathrm{O}}: & \\
:\underset{..}{\ddot{\mathrm{O}}}: & \underset{..}{\ddot{\mathrm{Cl}}}\cdot & + & \cdot\underset{..}{\ddot{\mathrm{Cl}}} & : & \underset{..}{\ddot{\mathrm{O}}}: & \rightleftharpoons & :\underset{..}{\ddot{\mathrm{O}}}: & \underset{..}{\ddot{\mathrm{Cl}}}: & \underset{..}{\ddot{\mathrm{Cl}}}: & \underset{..}{\ddot{\mathrm{O}}}: \\
 & :\underset{..}{\mathrm{O}}: & & & :\underset{..}{\mathrm{O}}: & & & & :\underset{..}{\mathrm{O}}: & :\underset{..}{\mathrm{O}}: &
\end{array}
$$

Like the other oxides of chlorine, chlorine trioxide is violently explosive. It explodes when brought into contact with liquid water, decomposing into chlorine and oxygen, but when it is mixed with water vapor and then cooled, it reacts to give a mixture of chloric and perchloric acids:

$$2\ ClO_3 + H_2O \rightarrow HClO_3 + HClO_4$$

Chlorine heptoxide, the anhydride of perchloric acid, is formed by allowing perchloric acid to stand in contact with phosphorus(V) oxide, and then carefully distilling the mixture:

$$4\ HClO_4 + P_4O_{10} \rightarrow 4\ HPO_3 + 2\ Cl_2O_7$$

It is a colorless oil, boiling at 80°C. Even though it contains chlorine in its highest oxidation state, chlorine heptoxide is the most stable of the chlorine oxides, and it does not react at room temperature with sulfur, phosphorus, or organic substances such as paper—all substances which are set afire by the other oxides. It is, however, sensitive to sudden heating or mechanical shock, and it must be handled with great care.

(c) Oxides of Bromine. Three oxides of bromine are known, all of them extremely unstable. ***Bromine monoxide,*** an unstable brown liquid, is formed by reacting bromine vapor with mercury(II) oxide at 50–100°C, or by mixing the same substances in CCl_4 solution, in which bromine monoxide is soluble:

$$2\ Br_2 + HgO \rightarrow Br_2O + HgBr_2$$

Bromine monoxide is the anhydride of hypobromous acid, and it reacts with alkalis to give hypobromites. ***Bromine dioxide,*** a yellow solid stable only below −40°C, is formed by passing an electrical discharge through a mixture of bromine vapor and oxygen at low pressure and temperature. It decomposes in high vacuum to give the monoxide, and it reacts with strong alkali solutions to give the bromide and bromate. Little is known about the third oxide, which is formed as a white powder when bromine vapor reacts with excess ozone at about 0°C. It decomposes at temperatures above −80°C unless kept in contact with ozone. Whether the correct formula of this third oxide of bromine is Br_3O_8 or BrO_3 remains an open question.

(d) Oxides of Iodine. When heated carefully to about 170°C iodic acid decomposes to form its anhydride, ***iodine pentoxide,*** I_2O_5:

$$2\ HIO_3 \rightarrow I_2O_5 + H_2O$$

It is a white solid, very soluble in water, with which it reacts to give solutions of iodic acid. Compared with the other halogen oxides, iodine pentoxide is relatively stable, although it does begin to decompose into its elements above 300°C. It is a fairly powerful oxidizing agent; for example, it rapidly oxidizes carbon monoxide to the dioxide at temperatures above 65°C:

$$5\ CO + I_2O_5 \rightarrow I_2 + 5\ CO_2$$

Two other compounds of iodine and oxygen are known, but neither one is considered to be a true oxide. The first, ***iodine tetroxide*** is a yellow solid obtained by heating iodine with concentrated nitric or sulfuric acid and then adding water to the reaction mixture. The true structure of this compound is not known with certainty, but it is generally assumed to be the salt iodyl iodate, $(IO)IO_3$. When heated above 150°C, it decomposes into iodine and iodine pentoxide:

$$5\ I_2O_4 \rightarrow 4\ I_2O_5 + I_2$$

The light yellow solid I_4O_9 is obtained by treating iodine with ozone in chloroform solution at 0°C, or by heating iodic acid with phosphorus(V) oxide:

$$2\ I_2 + 3\ O_3 \rightarrow I_4O_9$$

$$12\ HIO_3 + P_4O_{10} \rightarrow 4\ H_3PO_4 + 6\ O_2 + 2\ I_2 + 2\ I_4O_9$$

The suggestion has been made that I_4O_9 is iodine(III) iodate, $I(IO_3)_3$.

18.10 Oxyacids of the Halogens

No oxyacids of fluorine are known. The remaining halogens form four series of acids corresponding to oxidation states of +1, +3, +5, and +7 for the halogen atom. All are strong oxidizing agents. Their strength as acids increases with increasing oxidation state of the halogen, and the thermal stability of the acids and their salts increases in the same direction. Thus, when a solution of a hypochlorite is heated, it first forms a mixture of a chloride and a chlorate, which then reacts further to give a chloride and a perchlorate:

$$3\ ClO^- \rightarrow 2\ Cl^- + ClO_3^-$$

$$4\ ClO_3^- \rightarrow Cl^- + 3\ ClO_4^-$$

(a) Oxidation State +1. Hypohalous Acids and Hypohalites. Chlorine, bromine, and iodine all react with water to give an equimolar mixture of hydrohalic acid and the weakly ionized hypohalous acid in solution as follows:

$$X_2 + 2\,H_2O \rightleftarrows H_3O^+ + X^- + HXO \qquad X = Cl, Br, \text{ or } I$$

The reaction proceeds only partially to completion with chlorine, and to a still lesser extent with bromine and iodine, the respective equilibrium constants being 4.8×10^{-4}, 5×10^{-9}, and 3×10^{-13} at 25°C. The equilibrium is displaced to the left by acid, and a solution of a hypochlorite, for example, liberates chlorine upon acidification. In the presence of base, on the other hand, the reaction is forced to completion and the hypohalite is formed rather than the free acid:

$$X_2 + 2\,OH^- \rightarrow X^- + XO^- + H_2O$$

A solution of sodium hypochlorite, commonly used as a laundry bleach (e.g., Clorox), is conveniently prepared by electrolyzing a well-stirred solution of sodium chloride, allowing the chlorine produced at the anode to react with the hydroxide ions formed at the cathode.

The hypohalous acids are all very weak, and their acid strength decreases in the order $HClO$ ($K_a = 10^{-8}$), $HBrO$ ($K_a = 10^{-9}$), HIO ($K_a = 10^{-13}$). They are quite unstable and can exist only in solution. Of their salts, only the hypochlorites and hypobromites of sodium and potassium, and calcium, strontium, and barium hypochlorites are stable enough to be prepared in the pure, solid state.

Most applications of hypohalous acids and their salts depend upon their strength as oxidizing agents. Sodium hypochlorite solution is used to bleach cotton and linen, and it is the main active ingredient of most laundry bleaches. A dilute solution (Dakin solution) is sometimes used as an antiseptic. It was extensively used in the days before the advent of antibiotics, and was credited with preventing hundreds of thousands of deaths from infected wounds during the first World War. Chloride of lime, or bleaching powder, is a mixture of $CaCl_2$, $CaCl(ClO)$, and $Ca(ClO)_2$ prepared by the reaction between chlorine and slaked lime ($Ca(OH)_2$). It is frequently used as a germicide and deodorizer around stables and barns. Hypohalite solutions find application in organic chemistry as specific oxidizing agents for methyl ketones and certain alcohols. Products of the oxidation are the trihalomethane (haloform) and the salt of a carboxylic acid:

$$R{-}\underset{\underset{O}{\|}}{C}{-}CH_3 \xrightarrow{OCl^-} R{-}\underset{\underset{O}{\|}}{C}{-}O^- + \underset{\text{chloroform}}{HCCl_3}$$

$$RCH(OH)CH_3 \xrightarrow{OBr^-} RCOO^- + \underset{\text{bromoform}}{HCBr_3}$$

The reaction between ethyl alcohol and sodium hypoiodite (I_2 in NaOH solution) produces ***iodoform,*** used as an antiseptic:

$$CH_3CH_2OH \xrightarrow{OI^-} HCOO^- + \underset{\text{iodoform}}{HCI_3}$$

(b) Oxidation State +3. Halous Acids and Halites. The only acid of this type known is ***chlorous acid,*** $HClO_2$. It is an appreciably stronger acid than hypochlorous acid, although still relatively weak ($K_a = 10^{-2}$). While it is more stable than hypochlorous acid, it nevertheless can exist only in solution. It undergoes self oxidation-reduction to give chlorine and chlorine dioxide as follows:

$$8\ HClO_2 \rightarrow 6\ ClO_2 + Cl_2 + 4\ H_2O$$

Sodium chlorite, $NaClO_2$, is fairly stable as a dry solid, and it is used as an ingredient in dry bleaches and chlorinated scouring powder. It is manufactured by passing chlorine dioxide into a solution of sodium and calcium hydroxides in which carbon black is suspended:

$$4\ NaOH + Ca(OH)_2 + 4\ ClO_2 + C \rightarrow CaCO_3 + 3\ H_2O + 4\ NaClO_2$$

The calcium carbonate precipitates and is filtered off, and the solution is concentrated to crystallize the sodium chlorite. Sodium chlorite is a weaker oxidizing agent than the hypochlorite and has some advantages over the latter as a bleach since it does not weaken the fibers of the cloth.

(c) Oxidation State +5. Halic Acids and Halates. Acids of the general formula HXO_3 are known for all of the halogens except fluorine, but only iodic acid is stable enough to be isolated in the pure state. It is a colorless solid which melts at 110°C with partial dehydration to the anhydride I_2O_5. Chloric and bromic acid are stable only in relatively dilute solution. Concentrated solutions, containing 50% or more of the acid, are prone to violent decomposition. Hypohalites are converted into the more stable halates and halides when heated, and halate salts may be prepared by the reaction of the free halogen with a solution of hot alkali, or by electrolysis of a stirred, hot solution of a halide salt:

$$2\ Cl^- + 2\ H_2O \xrightarrow{\text{electrolysis}} 2\ OH^- + Cl_2 + H_2$$

$$3\ Cl_2 + 6\ OH^- \longrightarrow ClO_3^- + 5\ Cl^- + 3\ H_2O$$

The halates decompose when heated to give the perhalates:

$$4\ KClO_3 \rightarrow 3\ KClO_4 + KCl$$

In the presence of certain catalysts, such as MnO_2 and Fe_2O_3, decomposition occurs at a lower temperature, yielding oxygen and the chloride:

$$2\ KClO_3 \rightarrow 2\ KCl + 3\ O_2$$

In line with the generally observed trend, the halates, despite their greater oxygen content, are weaker oxidizing agents than the corresponding halites and hypohalites. Mixtures of halate salts with combustible materials are very dangerous, however, and may explode violently on impact. Chlorates find some application in fireworks and other pyrotechnic compositions. The potassium salt, being less hygroscopic than the sodium salt, is generally preferred for that purpose.

(d) Oxidation State +7. Perhalic Acids and Perhalates. Both perchloric and periodic acids and their salts are known. Unlike the other oxygen acids of chlorine, perchloric acid, $HClO_4$, is stable in the pure state. It may be obtained by distilling a mixture of a perchlorate salt and concentrated sulfuric acid under reduced pressure:

$$KClO_4 + H_2SO_4 \rightarrow KHSO_4 + HClO_4$$

The normal boiling point of perchloric acid at 1 atm pressure is 92°C, at which temperature the acid begins to decompose. Decomposition may be violent above the boiling point, or even at room temperature in the presence of combustible matter.

The oxyacids of chlorine increase in acid strength from hypochlorous to perchloric acid, and perchloric acid is the strongest known proton donor acid. Even nitric acid behaves as a base towards perchloric acid in anhydrous acetic acid solution:

$$HNO_3 + HClO_4 \rightarrow H_2O + NO_2^+ + ClO_4^-$$

The salt, nitronium perchlorate, NO_2ClO_4, is a crystalline solid which reacts with water to give a mixture of nitric and perchloric acids. The monohydrate of perchloric acid, $HClO_4 \cdot H_2O$, is remarkable because it is a solid, m.p. 50°C. It is completely ionic, even in the solid state, and is, in fact, the salt ***hydronium perchlorate,*** $(H_3O)^+(ClO_4)^-$.

Most of the salts of perchloric acid are very soluble in water, and many of them are deliquescent. Potassium perchlorate is an exception. It is only slightly soluble in water (0.75 g/100 g H_2O at 0°C), and unlike most of the other perchlorates, it crystallizes from aqueous solution as the anhydrous salt rather than as a hydrate. It can be prepared by bubbling chlorine gas into a boiling solution of potassium hydroxide. The hypochlorite formed initially is converted first to the chlorate, and then to the perchlorate, which precipitates from the hot solution. Potassium perchlorate finds some application as an oxidant in the manufacture of matches, pyrotechnics, and blasting explosives. Ammonium perchlorate and polysulfide rubber can be mixed in regular rubber compounding equipment to make a solid rocket propellant. Sodium perchlorate is used as a weed killer.

Periodates are usually prepared by oxidizing iodates with chlorine in alkaline solution. Periodate salts are known which correspond to acids with the formulas HIO_4 (***metaperiodic acid***), H_3IO_5, $H_4I_2O_9$ (***dimesoperiodic acid***), and H_5IO_6 (***paraperiodic acid***). Paraperiodic acid is a weakly acidic, white solid, prepared by the action of sulfuric acid on a solution of barium periodate. The latter is made by heating barium iodate:

$$5\ Ba(IO_3)_2 \rightarrow Ba_5(IO_6)_2 + 4\ I_2 + 9\ O_2$$

$$Ba_5(IO_6)_2 + 5\ H_2SO_4 \rightarrow 5\ BaSO_4 + 2\ H_5IO_6$$

Paraperiodic acid loses water when kept in a vacuum desiccator below 100°C, forming first the dimeso acid, and finally metaperiodic acid:

$$2\ H_5IO_6 \rightarrow H_4I_2O_9 + 3\ H_2O$$

$$H_4I_2O_9 \rightarrow 2\ HIO_4 + H_2O$$

The existence of the paraperiodate and other complex periodate ions can be accounted for on the basis of the large size of the iodine atom compared with chlorine. While only four tetrahedrally arranged oxygen atoms can be accommodated around a chlorine, the larger iodine atom has room for six oxygens in an octahedral arrangement. Thus, while the only perchlorate ion is ClO_4^-, both the tetrahedral IO_4^- and the octahedral IO_6^{5-} can exist (Fig. 18.1). The dimesoperiodate ion, $I_2O_9^{4-}$, probably consists of an IO_4

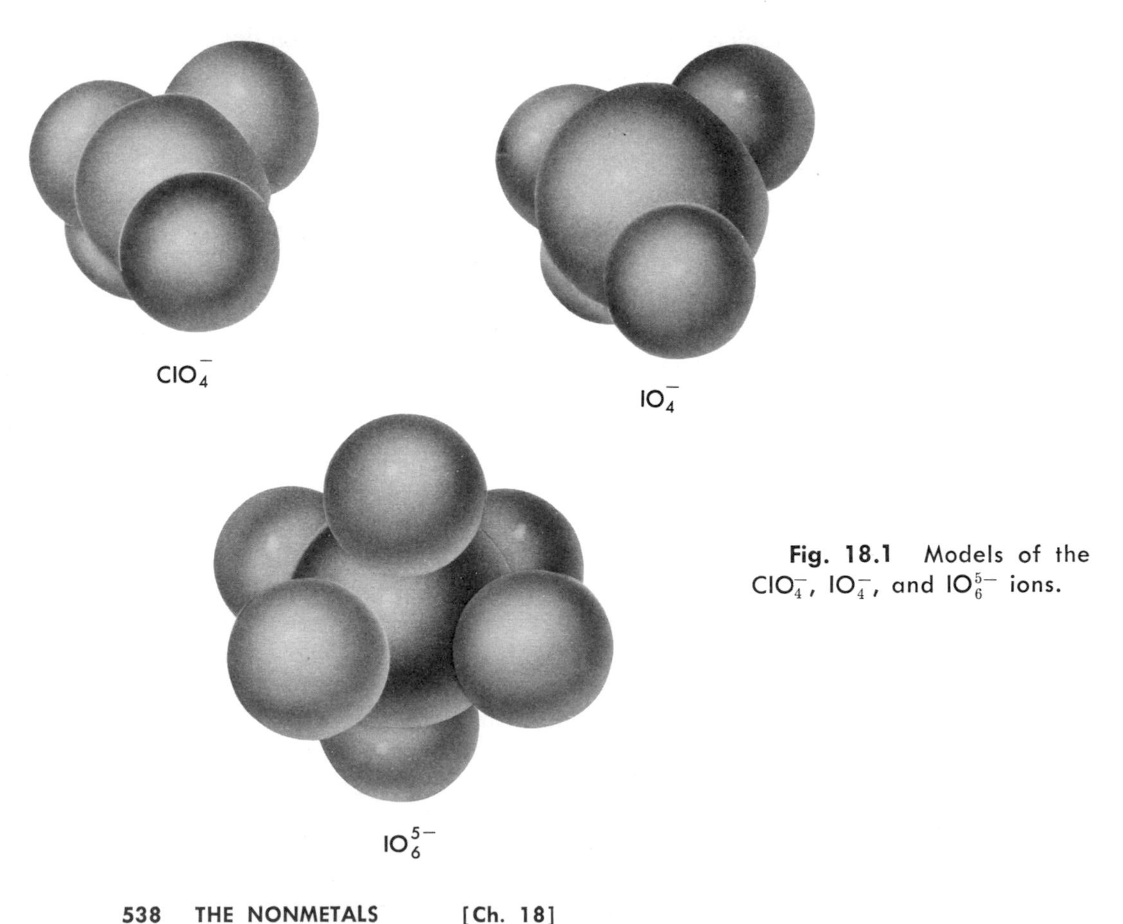

Fig. 18.1 Models of the ClO_4^-, IO_4^-, and IO_6^{5-} ions.

unit joined to an IO_6 through an oxygen bridge. Periodic acid and its salts are active oxidizing agents. They oxidize alcohols to aldehydes, ketones, and carboxylic acids, and both Mn^{++} and MnO_2 in acid solution to permanganate. Periodic acid is a useful reagent in organic chemistry for the specific cleavage of 1,2-diols:

$$R-\underset{OH}{\overset{H}{C}}-\underset{OH}{\overset{H}{C}}-R' + H_5IO_6 \rightarrow R-\underset{O}{\overset{\|}{C}}-OH + HO-\underset{O}{\overset{\|}{C}}-R' + HIO_3 + 3\,H_2O$$

OXYGEN

Occurrence and Preparation 18.11

Oxygen is the most abundant element on the surface of the earth. About 20% of the atmosphere by volume is elemental oxygen. The water in the oceans, rivers, lakes, and clouds is 89% oxygen by weight, and the outer crust of the earth contains about 47% oxygen in the form of silica and other oxides, sulfates, carbonates, hydrates, and other oxygen-containing minerals. Altogether, the earth's crust, the seas, and the air contain about 50% oxygen.

Many oxygen-containing compounds decompose to liberate the free element when they are heated. The oxides of certain of the less active metals such as mercury, silver, gold, and platinum lose all of their oxygen upon heating. Oxygen was prepared in this way in 1774 by Joseph Priestley, who heated mercury(II) oxide by focusing the sun's rays on it with a large magnifying glass:

$$2\,HgO \rightarrow 2\,Hg + O_2$$

In some cases, heating the higher oxide of a metal converts it to a lower oxide with liberation of oxygen:

$$2\,PbO_2 \rightarrow 2\,PbO + O_2$$

$$3\,MnO_2 \rightarrow Mn_3O_4 + O_2$$

Certain oxy-salts, notably the nitrates, chlorates, iodates, and permanganates, lose all or part of their oxygen upon heating:

$$2\,KNO_3 \rightarrow 2\,KNO_2 + O_2$$

$$2\,KMnO_4 \rightarrow K_2MnO_4 + MnO_2 + O_2$$

$$2\,KClO_3 \rightarrow 2\,KCl + 3\,O_2$$

Saltpeter (potassium nitrate, KNO_3) was used as a constituent of gunpowder and fireworks for centuries before its function as a source of oxygen for combustion of the powder was recognized. The decomposition of potassium chlorate represents the most common laboratory preparation of oxygen. In the absence of a catalyst, the first step in the reaction is the formation of the perchlorate, which then decomposes slowly at about 400°C. (Sec. 18.10c).

Peroxides decompose to form oxides and oxygen when they are heated:

$$2\ BaO_2 \rightarrow 2\ BaO + O_2$$

$$2\ Na_2O_2 \rightarrow 2\ Na_2O + O_2$$

$$2\ H_2O_2 \rightarrow 2\ H_2O + O_2$$

Sodium peroxide also reacts with water with liberation of oxygen:

$$2\ Na_2O_2 + 2\ H_2O \rightarrow 4\ NaOH + O_2$$

Most industrial oxygen is obtained by the fractional distillation of liquid air. Nitrogen (b.p. −196°C) and argon (b.p. −185.6°C) evaporate first, leaving nearly pure oxygen (b.p. −183°C) behind. Some oxygen is also prepared industrially by the electrolysis of water containing a little sulfuric acid (Sec. 5.1).

18.12 Bonding in Oxygen

Ordinary oxygen is composed of diatomic O_2 molecules. The observed dissociation energy of 118 kcal/mole indicates the presence of a double bond between the atoms:

$$:\ddot{O}::\ddot{O}:$$

Such a structure with all electrons paired does not, however, account for the fact that molecular oxygen is attracted by an external magnetic field. This behavior is characteristic of substances which possess unpaired electrons, and is known as ***paramagnetism.*** Any substance which has an unpaired electron, the spin moment of which is not canceled by that of another electron of opposite spin, possesses a permanent magnetic moment as a result. Because of this, it will be attracted by and drawn into an external magnetic field as its own magnetic moment aligns itself parallel to the external field. Since the magnetic moment is directly proportional to the number of unpaired electrons present, that number may be determined by measuring how strongly the substance is attracted into a magnetic field. In this way it can be shown that there are two unpaired electrons in a molecule of O_2.

Bonding and paramagnetism in O_2 are best accounted for in terms of a molecular orbital approach to its structure. In this approach the $1s$ electrons of each atom are assumed to be nonbonding and to remain in

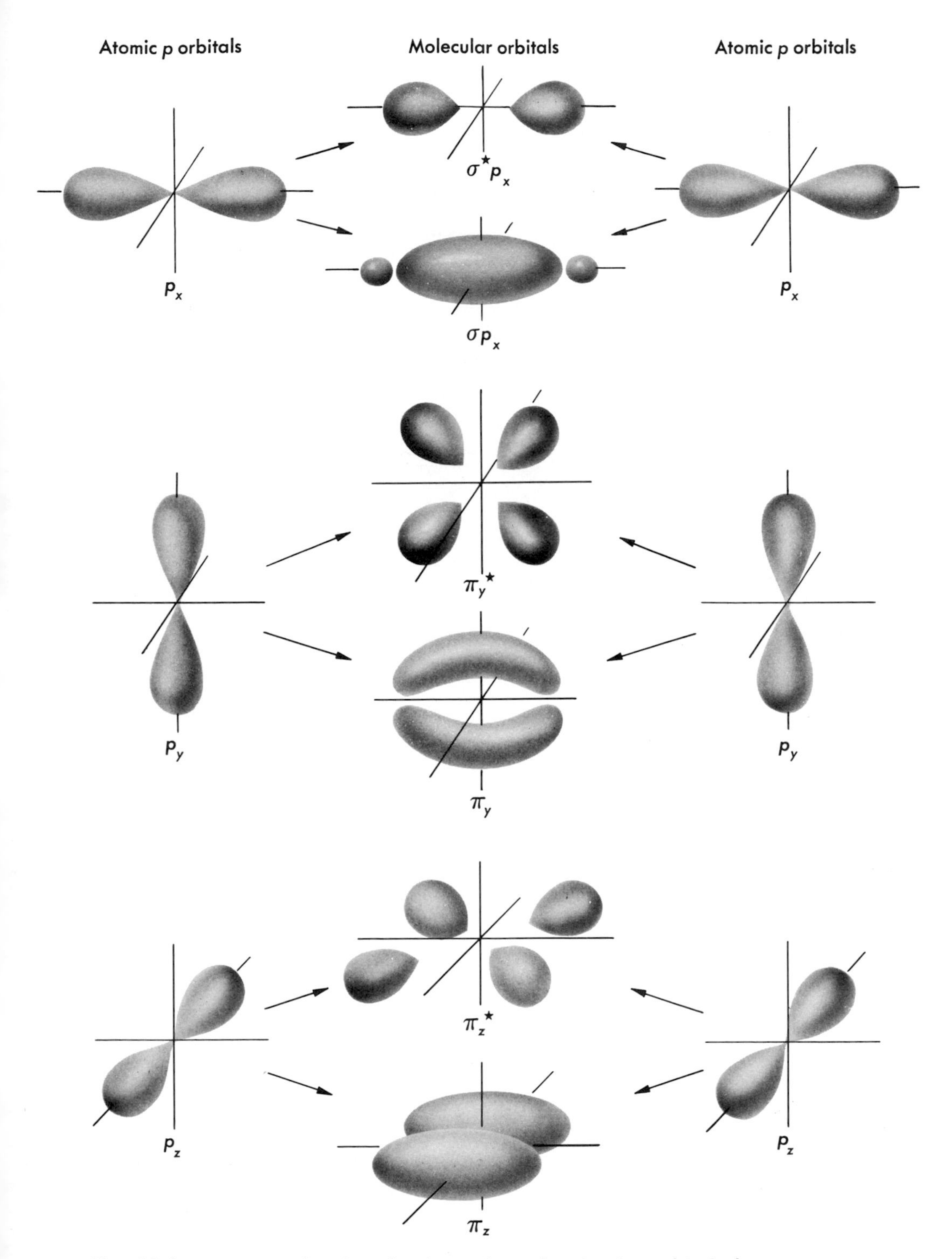

Fig. 18.2 Diagram showing the formation of molecular orbitals by combination of p_x, p_y, and p_z atomic orbitals.

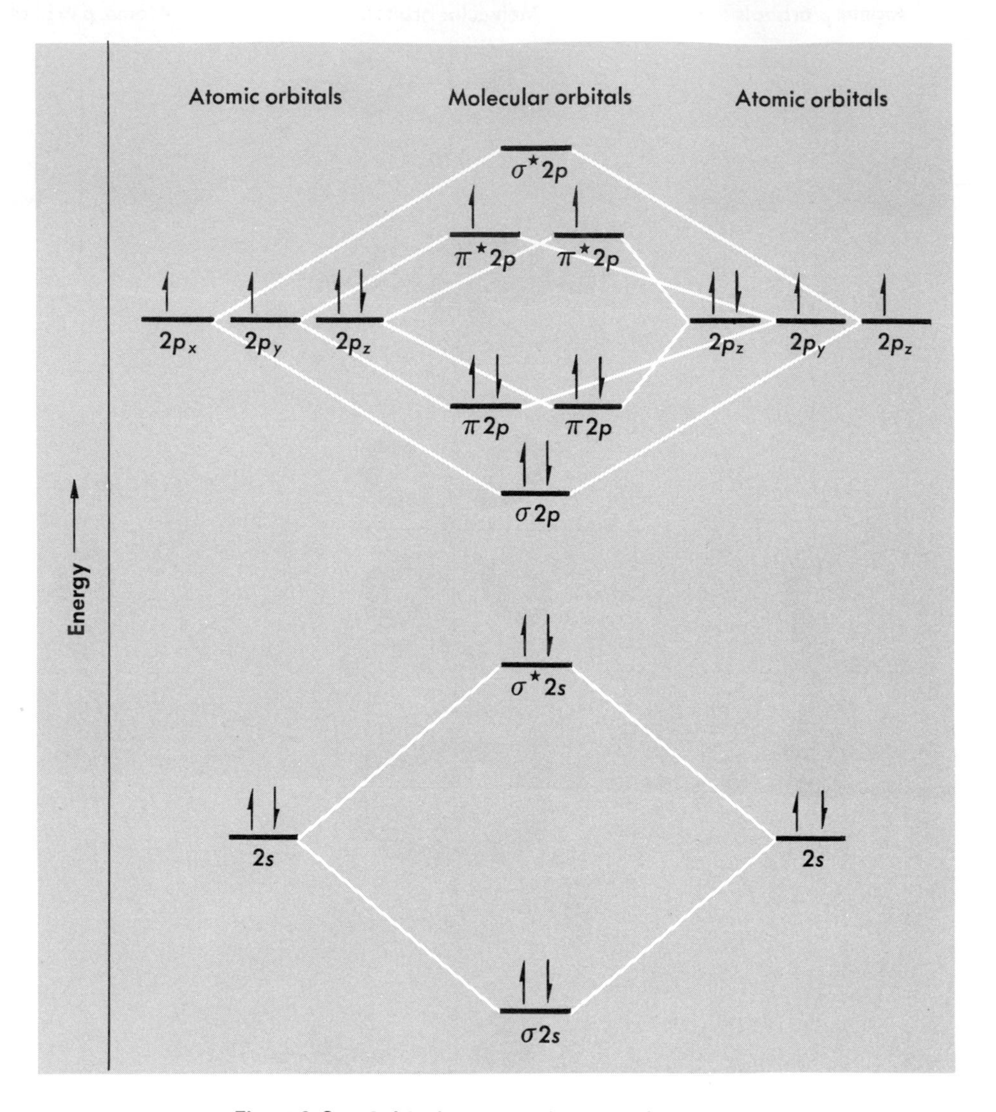

Fig. 18.3 Orbital energy diagram for oxygen.

atomic orbitals. The $2s$ and $2p$ electrons occupy molecular orbitals resulting from the combination of the respective atomic orbitals (Sec. 8.2). The $2s$ AO's combine to give a bonding $\sigma 2s$ MO and an antibonding $\sigma^\star 2s$ MO. The six $2p$ AO's (three from each atom) give rise to six MO's, of which three are bonding ($\sigma 2p, \pi 2p_y, \pi 2p_z$) and three antibonding ($\sigma^\star 2p, \pi^\star 2p_y, \pi^\star 2p_z$). The way in which these six AO's combine to give six MO's is illustrated in Fig. 18.2.

The relative energies of the eight oxygen MO's are shown in Fig. 18.3. The five MO's of lowest energy are occupied by five electron pairs. The next higher level consists of two antibonding orbitals of equal energy. In accord with Hund's rule (Sec. 7.7) the two remaining electrons do not pair, but occupy these orbitals singly and with their spins parallel. It is the presence of these two unpaired electrons which gives O_2 its paramagnetic properties. The number of bonds between the atoms equals one-half the difference between the number of electrons in bonding orbitals and the number in antibonding orbitals. For O_2 this is $\frac{1}{2}(8 - 4) = 2$ bonds.

Oxides 18.13

Oxygen combines directly or indirectly with all of the elements except the lighter noble gases to form oxides. Except in OF_2 (Sec. 18.9a), oxygen in these compounds is in the -2 oxidation state. Oxides of the active metals are ionic, and react with water to form strong hydroxide bases:

$$Na_2O + H_2O \rightarrow 2\,Na^+ + 2\,OH^-$$

Most other metallic oxides are insoluble in water, but react with acids to form salts:

$$CuO + H_2SO_4 \rightarrow CuSO_4 + H_2O$$

$$Fe_2O_3 + 6\,HCl \rightarrow 2\,FeCl_3 + 3\,H_2O$$

Oxides of the semimetals or metalloids are amphoteric, forming salts with both acids and bases (Sec. 4.4).

Bonding is covalent in the nonmetallic oxides. Those which are soluble in water generally react to give acid solutions:

$$CO_2 + 2\,H_2O \rightleftharpoons H_3O^+ + HCO_3^-$$

$$SO_3 + 2\,H_2O \rightarrow H_3O^+ + HSO_4^-$$

The preparation and properties of individual oxides are discussed in appropriate places throughout the text, and need not be considered again at this point.

Potassium, rubidium, and cesium form so-called "superoxides" when heated in oxygen at atmospheric pressure:

$$K + O_2 \rightarrow KO_2$$

The superoxides contain the O_2^- ion in which oxygen has an apparent oxidation number of $-\frac{1}{2}$. The ion is paramagnetic, with one unpaired electron. The electronic configuration of the ion is similar to that shown for O_2 in Fig. 18.3, except for the presence of an additional electron in one of the antibonding $\pi^\star 2p$ orbitals.

Sodium burns in air to form sodium peroxide, Na_2O_2:

$$2\,Na + O_2 \rightarrow Na_2O_2$$

while barium peroxide can be prepared by direct reaction of the metal with oxygen or by heating the monoxide in air under pressure:

$$2\ BaO + O_2 \rightarrow 2\ BaO_2$$

All of the electrons in the peroxide ion are paired, with both $\pi^\star 2p$ orbitals fully occupied:

$$:\ddot{\underset{..}{O}}:\ddot{\underset{..}{O}}:^{--}$$

If sodium or barium peroxide is treated with cold, dilute acid, a solution of hydrogen peroxide is obtained:

$$Na_2O_2 + 2\ H_3O^+ \rightarrow 2\ Na^+ + 2\ H_2O + H_2O_2$$

$$BaO_2 + 2\ H_3O^+ + SO_4^{--} \rightarrow BaSO_4\downarrow + 2\ H_2O + H_2O_2$$

If sulfuric acid is used with BaO_2, the insoluble $BaSO_4$ can be filtered off, leaving a relatively pure solution of H_2O_2.

Pure, anhydrous hydrogen peroxide is a covalent, viscous liquid, with a density at 20°C of 1.45 g/cm³, a melting point of −0.45°C, and a boiling point of 150.2°C at which it decomposes explosively. It is completely miscible with water, and like water is highly associated through hydrogen bonding. The two hydrogens of the molecule are in different planes, and the molecule has an appreciable dipole moment:

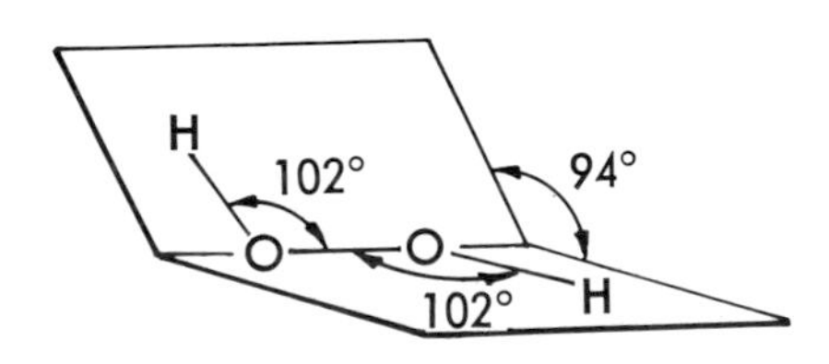

Hydrogen peroxide is prepared industrially by the electrolysis of cold, concentrated ammonium hydrogen sulfate solution or a 40% solution of sulfuric acid. The electrode reactions are:

At the anode: $2\ HSO_4^- \rightarrow S_2O_8^{--} + 2\ H^+ + 2\ e^-$

At the cathode: $2\ H^+ + 2\ e^- \rightarrow H_2$

The peroxydisulfate ion $S_2O_8^{--}$ is hydrolyzed as it is formed, producing hydrogen peroxide:

$$S_2O_8^{--} + 2\ H_2O \rightarrow 2\ HSO_4^- + H_2O_2$$

Concentrations as high as 90% H_2O_2 can be obtained by careful fractional distillation of the solution under reduced pressure. Pure H_2O_2 can be prepared by fractional crystallization of the 90% solution.

In the decomposition of hydrogen peroxide,

$$2\ H_2O_2 \rightarrow 2\ H_2O + O_2$$

the oxygen, originally in the −1 oxidation state, is both oxidized to the zero state, and reduced to the −2 state. Because the oxygen is in an intermediate oxidation state in H_2O_2, the compound can function as either a reducing or an oxidizing agent. It is a much stronger oxidizing than reducing agent, however, and acts as a reducing agent only toward such powerful oxidizing agents as the permanganate ion. The following equations show hydrogen peroxide functioning in both capacities:

As an oxidizing agent:

$$2\ HI + H_2O_2 \rightarrow I_2 + 2\ H_2O$$

$$SO_3^{--} + H_2O_2 \rightarrow SO_4^{--} + H_2O$$

As a reducing agent:

$$2\ MnO_4^- + 5\ H_2O_2 + 6\ H^+ \rightarrow 2\ Mn^{++} + 5\ O_2 + 8\ H_2O$$

Ozone 18.14

The passage of an electrical discharge through oxygen gas converts a portion of it to ***ozone,*** O_3. The name of this allotrope of oxygen comes from the Greek word for smell, and the peculiar pungent odor of the gas is often noticed around electrical machinery. Pure ozone is a pale blue gas $1\frac{1}{2}$ times as dense as O_2. It condenses to a deep blue liquid at −112°C. Chemically, ozone is unstable. Its formation from oxygen is highly endothermic:

$$3\ O_2 \rightarrow 2\ O_3 \qquad \Delta H = +68.4\ \text{kcal}$$

Its decomposition is therefore exothermic and may become explosive if the gas is concentrated. Ozone is a powerful oxidizing agent, and in that capacity finds some application especially in organic chemistry. Small concentrations of ozone are sometimes used to freshen and deodorize the atmosphere in a room and destroy microorganisms.

Ozone is formed when oxygen in the upper atmosphere absorbs ultraviolet radiation from the sun. In this way, the intensity of the harmful ultraviolet rays which reach the ground is reduced to a safe level. Most of the ozone formed in this way soon decomposes, but the small amount remaining seems to be at least partly responsible for the deterioration of rubber products and plastics left exposed to the atmosphere.

The ozone molecule is diamagnetic and has an angular structure. Both oxygen-oxygen bonds are identical in every respect and intermediate in length (1.26 Å) between that expected for a single bond (1.48 Å) and that for a double bond (1.10 Å). To account for this, the ozone molecule can be represented as a resonance hybrid:

$$:\ddot{O}{:}\ddot{O}{:}\ddot{O}: \longleftrightarrow :\ddot{O}{:}\ddot{O}{:}\ddot{O}:$$

SULFUR

18.15 Occurrence and Properties

Sulfur, the brimstone of the Bible, has been known since ancient times, and the fumes of burning sulfur were used for fumigation and for bleaching textiles in the time of Homer (about 900 B.C.) as they are today. In the past, nearly all of the world's supply of sulfur came from extensive deposits of volcanic origin located in Sicily. The sulfur-bearing rock was mined in the conventional way, and then heated in iron retorts to distill off the pure element. Today, although some sulfur is still mined in Sicily, it is a minor part of the total produced. During the exploration for oil in the Gulf states in the 1870's and 80's, the well borings often showed the presence of sulfur. The sulfur lay deep underground, sometimes in association with poisonous hydrogen sulfide, and frequently under a layer of quicksand, making conventional mining operations impractical. About 1890 Herman Frasch developed a process which made recovery of this sulfur possible. A set of three concentric pipes is inserted through a well casing extending to the sulfur deposit. Water, superheated under pressure to about 150°C, is forced down the outer pipe into the sulfur, melting it, and causing it to collect in a pool at the base of the well. Compressed air, pumped through the small inner pipe, converts the liquid sulfur to a froth and pushes it up through the middle pipe to the surface. Sulfur produced by the Frasch process is better than 99% pure, and is ready for use without further treatment. In addition to mined sulfur, substantial amounts of the element are recovered by burning hydrogen sulfide, extracted from natural and manufactured gas, in a limited supply of air:

$$2\ H_2S + O_2 \rightarrow 2\ S + 2\ H_2O$$

Sulfur exists in a number of allotropic modifications. Solid sulfur consists of molecular crystals in which the lattice points are occupied by S_8 units. The eight sulfur atoms in the molecule form a puckered ring in which the bond angles are 105°. The stable crystals at temperatures up to 95.6°C belong to the rhombic system. Between 95.6° and 119°C the stable form consists of monoclinic crystals. Conversion of one form to the other occurs slowly, so that rhombic sulfur may be rapidly heated to its melting point of 112.8°C without undergoing any appreciable transformation. If the liquid is cooled rapidly, it forms needle-like monoclinic crystals. At room temperature the monoclinic crystals take about a day to become converted to the rhombic form. Both forms of sulfur are readily soluble in carbon disulfide, the monoclinic crystals being somewhat more soluble than the rhombic.

At 120°C, sulfur is a pale yellow liquid of low viscosity, consisting largely of S_8 molecules. Above 160°C, the liquid turns brown and becomes increasingly sticky and viscous, until at 180°C it has the appearance of pitch, and cannot be poured. The increasing viscosity appears to be associated with opening of the S_8 rings and formation of long chains of sulfur which become entangled with one another. Above this temperature, the chains begin to break into smaller units, and the viscosity decreases until at the boiling point, 444.6°C, the liquid again pours easily. If this liquid is poured into cold water, it forms a rubbery mass of amorphous (Greek: formless), or noncrystalline sulfur, which is insoluble in carbon disulfide. Amorphous sulfur slowly changes to the rhombic form on standing.

Compounds of Sulfur 18.16

Sulfur forms compounds in which it exhibits oxidation states of −2, +4, and +6. In addition, sulfur forms a fluoride S_2F_{10} in which its oxidation state is +5.

(a) Oxidation State −2. Sulfur reacts directly with many metals to form sulfides, e.g.,

$$Hg + S \rightarrow HgS$$

$$2\ Al + 3\ S \rightarrow Al_2S_3$$

$$Zn + S \rightarrow ZnS$$

With such comparatively active metals as aluminum and zinc the reaction is highly exothermic and can become very violent. A mixture of zinc dust and powdered sulfur has been used as a propellant in amateur rocketry, but it is extremely dangerous to handle, besides being very inefficient in terms of the thrust it imparts to the rocket. Many metals occur as sulfides in their ores, and the treatment of sulfide ores is discussed in the chapter on metallurgy (Chapter 15).

Hydrogen sulfide is produced by the action of acid on a sulfide, for example,

$$FeS + 2\ HCl \rightarrow FeCl_2 + H_2S$$

Sulfides of some of the more active metals are hydrolyzed by water:

$$Al_2S_3 + 6\ H_2O \rightarrow 2\ Al(OH)_3 + 3\ H_2S$$

The compound thioacetamide is hydrolyzed to ammonium acetate and hydrogen sulfide in hot water, and it is often used to generate H_2S in solution for the precipitation of cations in qualitative analysis:

$$CH_3-\underset{\underset{S}{\|}}{C}-NH_2 + 2\ H_2O \rightarrow CH_3-\underset{\underset{O}{\|}}{C}-O^-NH_4^+ + H_2S$$

Hydrogen sulfide as usually prepared is a colorless gas with the characteristic foul odor of rotten eggs. Much of this odor is absent in really pure H_2S which has a curiously sweet smell. The gas is very poisonous, being in fact more toxic than hydrogen cyanide, and it should be handled with respect. It is somewhat soluble in water, and acts as a weak diprotic acid in solution (Secs. 13.8 and 13.9). The gas is unstable to heat, and at 500°C it is almost completely dissociated into hydrogen and sulfur.

Sulfur in H_2S is in its lowest oxidation state and is readily oxidized. Hydrogen sulfide as a result is a good reducing agent. It reacts with sulfuric acid, reducing it to sulfur dioxide, and being oxidized in turn to free sulfur:

$$H_2S + H_2SO_4 \rightarrow SO_2 + 2\ H_2O + S$$

It reduces concentrated nitric acid explosively, and is oxidized to sulfur by the halogens:

$$H_2S + 6\ HNO_3 \rightarrow 4\ H_2O + SO_2 + 6\ NO_2$$

$$H_2S + I_2 \rightarrow 2\ HI + S$$

Hydrogen sulfide is combustible and will burn freely in the air. Free sulfur is formed if the supply of air is limited; otherwise, the products are water and sulfur dioxide:

$$2\ H_2S + O_2 \rightarrow 2\ H_2O + 2S$$

$$2\ H_2S + 3\ O_2 \rightarrow 2\ H_2O + 2\ SO_2$$

Hydrogen sulfide reacts with the more active metals to form the sulfides, with displacement of hydrogen:

$$2\ Na + H_2S \rightarrow Na_2S + H_2$$

$$Pb + H_2S \rightarrow PbS + H_2$$

In the presence of moist air, the gas reacts even with such relatively inactive metals as copper and silver:

$$2\ Cu + 2\ H_2S + O_2 \rightarrow 2\ CuS + 2\ H_2O$$

$$4\ Ag + 2\ H_2S + O_2 \rightarrow 2\ Ag_2S + 2\ H_2O$$

The latter reaction is responsible for the tarnishing of silverware. Lead-based pigments in paint are converted to black PbS by H_2S in the air. The whiteness of the pigment can be restored by applying hydrogen peroxide solution, which oxidizes the sulfide to the sulfate:

$$PbS + 4\ H_2O_2 \rightarrow PbSO_4 + 4\ H_2O$$

A hot solution of an alkali metal sulfide will dissolve appreciable amounts of sulfur, forming ***polysulfides***:

$$Na_2S + (x - 1)S \rightarrow Na_2S_x$$

The polysulfide ions consist of chains of from two to five sulfur atoms joined by covalent bonds. The polysulfide acids, formed by acidifying the solution, are unstable and decompose to hydrogen sulfide and sulfur:

$$H_2S_x \rightarrow H_2S + (x - 1)S$$

Sodium polysulfide reacts with 1,2-dichloroethane to form a rubbery polymer (polysulfide rubber, Thiokol):

$$n\ Cl{-}CH_2{-}CH_2{-}Cl + n\ Na_2S_x \rightarrow$$
$$2n\ NaCl + (-CH_2{-}CH_2{-}S_x{-}CH_2{-}CH_2{-}S_x{-}CH_2{-}CH_2{-}S_x-)_{n/3}$$

(b) Oxidation State +4. Sulfur burns with a blue flame in the air to form sulfur dioxide together with a few percent of sulfur trioxide:

$$S + O_2 \rightarrow SO_2$$

Sulfur dioxide is also produced when sulfide ores are roasted in the air prior to smelting:

$$2\ ZnS + 3\ O_2 \rightarrow 2\ ZnO + 2\ SO_2$$
$$Cu_2S + 2\ O_2 \rightarrow 2\ CuO + SO_2$$

Iron pyrites, FeS_2, which is of no value as iron ore, is an important source of SO_2 for sulfuric acid manufacture, especially in Europe:

$$4\ FeS_2 + 11\ O_2 \rightarrow 2\ Fe_2O_3 + 8\ SO_2$$

Sulfur dioxide is a colorless gas with a peculiar choking odor. It liquefies at −10°C and 1 atm, and is readily condensed under pressure at room temperature. At 25°C, the vapor pressure of the liquid is less than 4 atm. The gas is appreciably soluble in water (about 3.5 moles of SO_2 dissolve in 1l of H_2O at 0°C and 1 atm) with which it reacts to form ***sulfurous acid,*** H_2SO_3. This is a weak diprotic acid which ionizes as follows:

$$SO_2 + H_2O \rightleftarrows H_2SO_3$$
$$H_2SO_3 + H_2O \rightleftarrows H_3O^+ + HSO_3^- \qquad K_a = 1.7 \times 10^{-2}$$
$$HSO_3^- + H_2O \rightleftarrows H_3O^+ + SO_3^{--} \qquad K_a = 5 \times 10^{-6}$$

Sulfur dioxide is much less soluble in hot water, and sulfurous acid is almost completely decomposed by boiling the solution.

Sulfur is in an intermediate oxidation state in sulfur dioxide, sulfurous acid, and the sulfites, and it can either be oxidized to the +6 state or reduced to the zero state:

$$SO_3^{--} + 3\ H_2O + Cl_2 \rightarrow SO_4^{--} + 2\ H_3O^+ + 2\ Cl^-$$

$$6\ H_3O^+ + SO_3^{--} + 2\ S^{--} \rightarrow 9\ H_2O + 3\ S$$

Many colored organic compounds are reduced to colorless substances by the action of SO_2, and the gas is sometimes used as a bleaching agent, especially for straw. Its action is milder than that of chlorine. Sulfur dioxide is also used as a preservative for certain foods, especially dried fruits and molasses. A solution of sulfurous acid and calcium hydrogen sulfite $Ca(HSO_3)_2$ is used to produce ***sulfite pulp*** from wood for paper manufacture. Wood chips are boiled in the solution which attacks and dissolves the lignin cementing the cellulose fibers together. Washing away the ***black liquor*** containing the dissolved lignin leaves a pulp which is almost pure cellulose.

(c) Oxidation State +6. Sulfur trioxide, SO_3, is the anhydride of sulfuric acid. Although its heat of formation is highly exothermic and the compound is very stable, very little SO_3 is formed when sulfur is burned. The equilibrium

$$2\ SO_2 + O_2 \rightleftharpoons 2\ SO_3$$

lies far to the right at low temperatures, but the activation energy for the forward reaction is so high that equilibrium is attained at a negligible rate. A catalyst is therefore necessary for effective conversion of SO_2 to SO_3. Finely divided platinum metal or vanadium pentoxide is used as a catalyst in the ***contact process*** for sulfuric acid manufacture. Vanadium pentoxide is not as effective as platinum, but has the advantage of being less expensive. Sulfur dioxide and excess oxygen is led over the catalyst bed at moderately high pressure (5–30 atm) and a temperature of about 425°C. From the equation for the equilibrium it can be seen that increased pressure favors the forward reaction. Reaction is too slow at temperatures lower than 425°, and at higher temperatures the equilibrium becomes less favorable. Under the given conditions, conversion of SO_2 to SO_3 is about 98% complete.

In the presence of even a trace of moisture, sulfur trioxide polymerizes to a fibrous form which is almost insoluble in water:

$$4x\ SO_3 + H_2O \rightarrow H\text{—}(\text{—}O\text{—}\underset{\underset{O}{\parallel}}{\overset{\overset{O}{\parallel}}{S}}\text{—}O\text{—}\underset{\underset{O}{\parallel}}{\overset{\overset{O}{\parallel}}{S}}\text{—}O\text{—}\underset{\underset{O}{\parallel}}{\overset{\overset{O}{\parallel}}{S}}\text{—}O\text{—}\underset{\underset{O}{\parallel}}{\overset{\overset{O}{\parallel}}{S}}\text{—})_x\text{—}OH$$

The SO_3 produced in the contact process therefore cannot be dissolved in water. Instead, it is absorbed in concentrated (98%) sulfuric acid, with which it reacts to form ***pyrosulfuric acid*** (***oleum, fuming sulfuric acid***), $H_2S_2O_7$:

$$SO_3 + HO{-}\overset{\overset{\displaystyle O}{\|}}{\underset{\underset{\displaystyle O}{\|}}{S}}{-}OH \rightarrow HO{-}\overset{\overset{\displaystyle O}{\|}}{\underset{\underset{\displaystyle O}{\|}}{S}}{-}O{-}\overset{\overset{\displaystyle O}{\|}}{\underset{\underset{\displaystyle O}{\|}}{S}}{-}OH$$

This is then mixed with the required amount of water to form 98–100% sulfuric acid:

$$H_2S_2O_7 + H_2O \rightarrow 2\ H_2SO_4$$

In the older ***lead chamber process,*** now largely supplanted by the contact process for sulfuric acid manufacture, the catalyst is a mixture of nitric oxide and nitrogen dioxide. The oxides of sulfur and nitrogen are mixed with air in a large, lead-lined room, or *chamber*, and subjected to a water spray. The reactions which take place are complex, but may be summarized as follows:

$$2\ SO_2 + NO + NO_2 + H_2O + O_2 \rightarrow \underset{\text{(nitrosylsulfuric acid)}}{2\ SO_2(OH)ONO}$$

$$2\ SO_2(OH)ONO + H_2O \rightarrow 2\ H_2SO_4 + NO + NO_2$$

The acid produced in the lead chamber process is about 70% H_2SO_4. If stronger acid is needed, it may be concentrated to about 94%, but this adds a great deal to its cost. Economical operation of a lead chamber plant depends upon efficient recovery and reuse of the nitrogen oxide catalyst.

Sulfuric acid is a strong dibasic acid. Ionization of the first proton is complete in aqueous solution, but ionization of the second is not:

$$HSO_4^- + H_2O \rightleftarrows H_3O^+ + SO_4^{--} \qquad K_a = 1.2 \times 10^{-2}$$

Since the sulfur is already in its highest oxidation state, sulfuric acid cannot be further oxidized, and is not a reducing agent. The concentrated acid is a moderately strong oxidizing agent and will, for example, oxidize bromides and iodides to the elements (Sec. 18.8), and copper to Cu^{++}:

$$2\ H_2SO_4 + 2\ NaBr \rightarrow Na_2SO_4 + SO_2\uparrow + 2\ H_2O + Br_2$$

$$Cu + 2\ H_2SO_4 \rightarrow CuSO_4 + 2\ H_2O + SO_2$$

NITROGEN

18.17 Occurrence and Properties

Nitrogen is a comparatively unreactive gas. It makes up about 80% of the atmosphere, where it serves a valuable function in diluting the oxygen to the point where it is safe to breathe and controlled combustion is possible. The relative inactivity of nitrogen is related to the great strength of the triple bond between the atoms of the N_2 molecule. Because 226 kcal/mole are required to dissociate N_2, nitrogen compounds often have positive heats of formation and are unstable. Many of them, especially those containing oxygen, are explosive, and nitrogen compounds make up the largest class of industrial and military explosives.

Nitrogen reacts directly with only a few other elements, and then usually only at high temperatures. In fact, one of the major uses of nitrogen in industry and in the laboratory is to furnish an inert atmosphere for welding easily oxidized metals and for carrying out reactions in the absence of oxygen. Lithium and the metals of group IIA react with nitrogen gas at elevated temperatures to give the ***nitrides:***

$$6\ Li + N_2 \xrightarrow{250^\circ C} 2\ Li_3N$$

$$3\ Mg + N_2 \xrightarrow{560^\circ C} Mg_3N_2$$

The direct reaction of nitrogen with hydrogen over a catalyst at high pressure and elevated temperature is the basis of the Haber process for the manufacture of ammonia (Sec. 12.12):

$$N_2 + 3\ H_2 \rightleftharpoons 2\ NH_3$$

A strong electrical discharge can bring about the combination of nitrogen with oxygen to form nitric oxide, NO:

$$N_2 + O_2 \rightarrow 2\ NO$$

This reaction occurs in the atmosphere to some extent during a thunderstorm. The nitric oxide is immediately oxidized to the dioxide, NO_2, which then reacts with the rainwater to form nitric acid. The nitric acid so produced is an important natural source of nitrates for fertilizing the soil.

Most industrial nitrogen is obtained by the fractional distillation of liquid air. Very pure nitrogen can be prepared in the laboratory by the decomposition of ammonium nitrite, NH_4NO_2. This very unstable and explosive salt need not be isolated. It is necessary only to warm a solution of sodium nitrite and ammonium chloride to obtain a steady stream of nitrogen gas:

$$NH_4^+ + NO_2^- \rightarrow N_2 + 2\ H_2O$$

Liquid nitrogen boils at −195.8°C at 1 atm and is often used as a cooling medium in low temperature baths.

Compounds of Nitrogen 18.18

(a) With the Halogens. Ammonia and fluorine react to form the compound nitrogen trifluoride, NF_3:

$$NH_3 + 3\ F_2 \rightarrow 3\ HF + NF_3$$

The product is a colorless gas, which liquefies at −129°C (1 atm). In contrast to the other nitrogen halides, it is a very stable compound, with a heat of formation equal to −26 kcal/mole.

Chlorination of ammonia in mildly acid solution produces nitrogen trichloride, NCl_3. This is a very unstable yellow oil (b.p. 71°C at 1 atm; $\Delta H_f = +55.4$ kcal/mole) which explodes violently upon impact, when exposed to light, when heated above its boiling point, when mixed with dust or other organic matter or, it seems, when looked at severely. The compound was first prepared in 1812 by P. L. Dulong, who lost three fingers and an eye in the process.

Nitrogen does not appear to form any true bromide or iodide. When a mixture of ammonia and bromine is cooled to −90°C, a purple solid with the composition $NBr_3 \cdot 6\ NH_3$ is formed, which explodes above −70°C. Brown crystals of ***nitrogen triiodide*** $NI_3 \cdot x\ NH_3$ form slowly when concentrated ammonia solution reacts with iodine. The solid can be handled safely when wet, but it is extremely sensitive when dry. The impact of a housefly's footstep on a crystal of nitrogen triiodide has been known to cause a violent explosion with devastating consequences to the fly.

(b) With Oxygen. Nitrogen forms a series of oxides corresponding to all oxidation states from +1 to +5. There is also some evidence that the unstable compounds NO_3 and N_2O_6 may also exist. ***Nitrous oxide,*** N_2O, is prepared by heating ammonium nitrate:

$$NH_4NO_3 \rightarrow 2\ H_2O + N_2O$$

Unless the heating is done very carefully, the reaction can get out of hand and become quite dangerous. At high temperatures, ammonium nitrate may detonate, especially if it has been allowed to absorb moisture and become caked, or if it is in contact with organic matter. Nitrous oxide is used as a mild general anesthetic, particularly for dental work. Inhalation of the gas causes intoxication and giddyness, which gives it its nickname, ***laughing gas.*** When heated above 500°C nitrous oxide decomposes into nitrogen and oxygen, and the gas will support combustion. A lighted splint thrust into a bottle of N_2O burns more brightly than in air. Oxygen makes up only one-fifth of the air, but it constitutes a third of the gas mixture produced by the decomposition of N_2O.

Nitric oxide, NO, can be prepared in the laboratory by the reaction between dilute nitric acid and copper:

$$3\ Cu + 8\ HNO_3 \rightarrow 3\ Cu(NO_3)_2 + 4\ H_2O + 2\ NO$$

The formation of nitric oxide by the oxidation of ammonia over a platinum catalyst is the first step in the industrial manufacture of nitric acid:

$$4\ NH_3 + 5\ O_2 \xrightarrow{\text{Pt catalyst}} 6\ H_2O + 4\ NO$$

The reaction is exothermic ($\Delta H_{298} = -216.6$ kcal), and the heat evolved during the reaction is sufficient to maintain a reaction temperature of about 1000°C. Nitric oxide is oxidized immediately to ***nitrogen dioxide*** upon exposure to the air:

$$2\ NO + O_2 \rightarrow 2\ NO_2$$

Nitrogen dioxide is in equilibrium with its dimer, ***nitrogen tetroxide,*** N_2O_4:

$$2\ NO_2 \rightleftharpoons N_2O_4$$

At room temperature the mixture contains a little more than 20% NO_2. Below −11.2°C, the melting point of the tetroxide, the equilibrium lies entirely to the right, while at 135°C the mixture is 99% NO_2. Nitrogen dioxide is a dark red-brown, and the tetroxide is almost colorless, so that upon heating, the color of the mixture darkens as more of the tetroxide dissociates. Nitrogen dioxide (or tetroxide) is not a true acid anhydride, but it dissolves in water to give a solution of nitric and nitrous acids:

$$2\ NO_2 + H_2O \rightarrow HNO_2 + HNO_3$$

Nitrogen sesquioxide, N_2O_3, is the anhydride of nitrous acid:

$$N_2O_3 + H_2O \rightarrow 2\ HNO_2$$

It is a blue liquid (b.p. 3.5°C, 1 atm) which solidifies at −103°C. The compound is prepared by cooling an equimolar mixture of NO and NO_2 to −20°C:

$$NO + NO_2 \rightleftarrows N_2O_3$$

The compound is unstable and dissociates readily. A mixture of NO and NO_2 in equimolar amounts contains about 10.5% of the sesquioxide at 25°C and 1 atm.

Nitrogen pentoxide, N_2O_5, the anhydride of nitric acid, can be prepared by dehydrating the 100% acid with phosphorus(V) oxide:

$$4\ HNO_3 + P_4O_{10} \rightarrow 2\ N_2O_5 + 4\ HPO_3$$

Alternatively, it can be made by treating NO_2 with ozone:

$$2\ NO_2 + O_3 \rightarrow N_2O_5 + O_2$$

It is a white solid melting at 30°C. The compound decomposes readily according to the equation

$$2\ N_2O_5 \rightarrow 4\ NO_2 + O_2$$

and cannot be stored for any length of time except at very low temperatures. It reacts vigorously with water to form nitric acid:

$$N_2O_5 + H_2O \rightarrow 2\ HNO_3$$

Nitrous acid, HNO_2, can exist only in dilute solution. It is a weak acid, with an acid dissociation constant of 6×10^{-4} at 30°C. It is usually prepared as needed by acidifying a solution of sodium nitrite. Sodium nitrite is formed by heating the nitrate to 255°C,

$$2\ NaNO_3 \rightarrow 2\ NaNO_2 + O_2$$

or at a lower temperature by mixing the nitrate with a reducing metal such as lead:

$$NaNO_3 + Pb \rightarrow PbO + NaNO_2$$

Nitrous acid slowly disproportionates into nitric oxide and nitric acid at room temperature:

$$3\ HNO_2 \rightarrow HNO_3 + H_2O + 2\ NO$$

The reaction is hastened by heating the solution. When a concentrated solution of a nitrite is acidified, the nitrous acid first formed dissociates rapidly into H_2O, NO, and NO_2:

$$2\ HNO_2 \rightarrow H_2O + NO + NO_2$$

Nitrous acid is an active oxidizing agent. Its presence in solution can be detected by placing a drop of the solution on a piece of filter paper which has been soaked in a solution of starch and potassium iodide and dried (***starch-iodide paper***). The nitrous acid oxidizes the iodide to iodine:

$$2\ HNO_2 + 2\ I^- + 2\ H_3O^+ \rightarrow 2\ NO + 4\ H_2O + I_2$$

The iodine then reacts with the starch in the paper to form a characteristic blue colored starch-iodine complex. Nitrous acid can also be oxidized, but only by strong oxidizing agents such as permanganate.

Nitric acid can be prepared by treating a nitrate salt with concentrated sulfuric acid and distilling it from the mixture:

$$NaNO_3 + H_2SO_4 \rightarrow NaHSO_4 + HNO_3$$

This reaction gives pure nitric acid, b.p. 83°C at 1 atm. The acid is colorless when pure, but turns yellow on standing because of partial decomposition:

$$4\ HNO_3 \rightarrow 2\ H_2O + 4\ NO_2 + O_2$$

The decomposition is slow at room temperature, but accelerates rapidly upon heating. A tightly stoppered bottle of concentrated HNO_3 may explode if left in the hot sunlight, and the pure acid has been known to detonate when heated rapidly.

The source of most commercial nitric acid today is ammonia, prepared by the Haber process. The ammonia is oxidized over a platinum catalyst,

$$4\ NH_3 + 5\ O_2 \rightarrow 6\ H_2O + 4\ NO$$

$$2\ NO + O_2 \rightarrow 2\ NO_2$$

and the nitrogen dioxide so produced is absorbed in hot water:

$$2\ NO_2 + H_2O \rightarrow HNO_2 + HNO_3$$

$$3\ HNO_2 \rightarrow HNO_3 + 2\ NO + H_2O$$

The NO formed in the second step is immediately oxidized to NO_2, and eventually all of it is converted to nitric acid.

Nitric acid is a strong acid which is completely ionized in aqueous solution. Its acid nature, however, is frequently overshadowed by its oxidizing properties. Thus, while active metals displace some hydrogen, the principal reaction frequently involves reduction of the acid. Aluminum, for example, reacts with fairly concentrated acid (25% +) to form the oxide:

$$2\ Al + 6\ HNO_3 \rightarrow 3\ H_2O + 6\ NO_2 + Al_2O_3$$

The oxide forms a thin, tough coating on the aluminum which prevents further reaction with the acid. Iron becomes "passive" in the same manner in contact with nitric acid, and iron and aluminum containers can safely be used to transport the concentrated acid.

Nitrogen exhibits all oxidation states from -3 to $+5$, and products representing all of these states are obtained when nitric acid is used as an oxidizing agent. As a general rule, the more dilute the acid, or the more active the reducing agent, the greater the change in oxidation state which the nitrogen undergoes. In this regard, it is interesting to compare the action of the three metals copper, lead, and zinc on concentrated and dilute nitric acid. Copper reduces concentrated (15 M) nitric acid to NO_2 with the nitrogen undergoing a change in oxidation state from +5 to +4:

$$Cu + 4\ HNO_3 \rightarrow Cu(NO_3)_2 + 2\ NO_2 + 2\ H_2O$$

The more active metal, lead, reacts with the concentrated acid, reducing the nitrogen from the +5 to the +3 state:

$$Pb + 3\ HNO_3 \rightarrow Pb(NO_3)_2 + HNO_2 + H_2O$$

Under the same conditions, the principal product obtained by the action of the still stronger reducing agent, zinc, is nitric oxide ($+5 \rightarrow +2$):

$$3\ Zn + 8\ HNO_3 \rightarrow 3\ Zn(NO_3)_2 + 2\ NO + 4\ H_2O$$

The same product, namely NO, is obtained when copper reacts with *dilute* (3 *M*) nitric acid:

$$3\ Cu + 8\ HNO_3 \rightarrow 3\ Cu(NO_3)_2 + 2\ NO + 4\ H_2O$$

Reduction of the dilute acid is more extensive with Pb and Zn, major products being N_2O in the first case ($+5 \rightarrow +1$) and N_2 in the second ($+5 \rightarrow 0$):

$$4\ Pb + 10\ HNO_3 \rightarrow 4\ Pb(NO_3)_2 + N_2O + 5\ H_2O$$

$$5\ Zn + 12\ HNO_3 \rightarrow 5\ Zn(NO_3)_2 + N_2 + 6\ H_2O$$

Zinc can reduce the nitrogen of very dilute nitric acid all the way to its lowest oxidation state ($+5 \rightarrow -3$):

$$4\ Zn + 10\ HNO_3 \rightarrow 4\ Zn(NO_3)_2 + NH_4NO_3 + 3\ H_2O$$

If a paste is made with very dilute nitric acid and a large excess of zinc dust, free ammonia is liberated, and can be detected by its odor:

$$4\ Zn + 9\ HNO_3 \rightarrow 4\ Zn(NO_3)_2 + NH_3 + 3\ H_2O$$

Hot nitric acid oxidizes sulfur to sulfuric acid. If the acid is concentrated, NO_2 is produced. With dilute acid the product is NO:

Concentrated: $S + 6\ HNO_3 \rightarrow H_2SO_4 + 2\ H_2O + 6\ NO_2$

Dilute: $S + 2\ HNO_3 \rightarrow H_2SO_4 + 2\ NO$

Dilute HNO_3 oxidizes sulfides to sulfur and sulfites to sulfates:

$$3\ S^{--} + 8\ H_3O^+ + 2\ NO_3^- \rightarrow 3\ S + 2\ NO + 12\ H_2O$$

$$3\ SO_3^{--} + 2\ H_3O^+ + 2\ NO_3^- \rightarrow 3\ SO_4^{--} + 2\ NO + 3\ H_2O$$

A mixture of concentrated nitric and hydrochloric acids is known as ***aqua regia*** (Latin: royal water). It has the ability to dissolve gold and platinum, metals that are unaffected by other acids. The **HCl** furnishes chloride ions which assist in the oxidation of the metal by forming stable complex ions:

$$Pt + 8\ H_3O^+ + 8\ Cl^- + 2\ NO_3^- \rightarrow PtCl_6^{--} + 2\ NOCl + 12\ H_2O$$

The product **NOCl** is known as ***nitrosyl chloride.*** Aqua regia cannot be stored for any length of time. It evolves chlorine gas on standing:

$$3\ HCl + HNO_3 \rightarrow NOCl + Cl_2 + 2\ H_2O$$

The reaction may become violent at elevated temperature, and heating aqua regia can be dangerous.

PHOSPHORUS

18.19 Preparation and Properties

The discovery of phosphorus is credited to the alchemist Hennig Brand, who prepared it in 1669 by heating a mixture of dried urine and sand. Brand was apparently quite a showman, and made himself a good living for a time demonstrating the remarkable properties of his new discovery in the courts of Europe. A bottle of dry phosphorus glows in the dark, because of combustion at the surface of the phosphorus, as long as there is any oxygen present. The element ignites spontaneously when exposed to an unlimited supply of air. The name phosphorus, from the Greek *phosphoros*, light-bearer, is descriptive of these properties.

The mixture from which Brand distilled phosphorus is essentially the same as that used today for the preparation of the element, namely phosphates, carbon, and sand. Present practice consists of heating a mixture of crushed phosphate rock, coke, and sand in an electric furnace:

$$2\ Ca_3(PO_4)_2 + 10\ C + 6\ SiO_2 \rightarrow 6\ CaSiO_3 + 10\ CO + P_4$$

The phosphorus distills and is condensed under water into sticks. The product obtained is called ***white phosphorus.*** This is a white or pale yellow waxy substance with a low melting point (44°C); it is volatile and readily soluble in carbon disulfide. It is spontaneously flammable in the air, and is therefore usually kept and handled under water. White phosphorus is extremely poisonous, as little as 0.1 g constituting a fatal dose. Continued exposure to low concentrations of the vapor causes chronic poisoning, characterized by softening and disintegration of the bones, especially that of the lower jaw. In the 1800's when white phosphorus was used in the manufacture of matches, this was a serious occupational disease among workers in match factories.

White phosphorus has a molecular weight corresponding to P_4 both in solution and in the vapor state below 1500°C. At higher temperatures it dissociates somewhat into P_2. In the P_4 molecule the phosphorus atoms occupy the apexes of a tetrahedron, with each atom joined to three others by covalent bonds (Fig. 18.4). The bond angles are all 60°, consider-

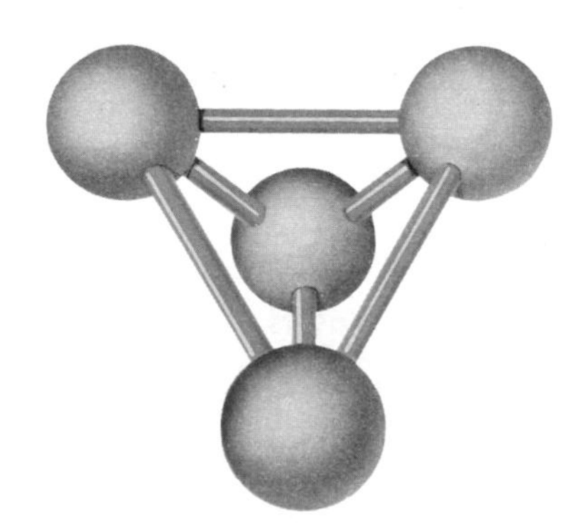

Fig. 18.4 Model of the P_4 molecule.

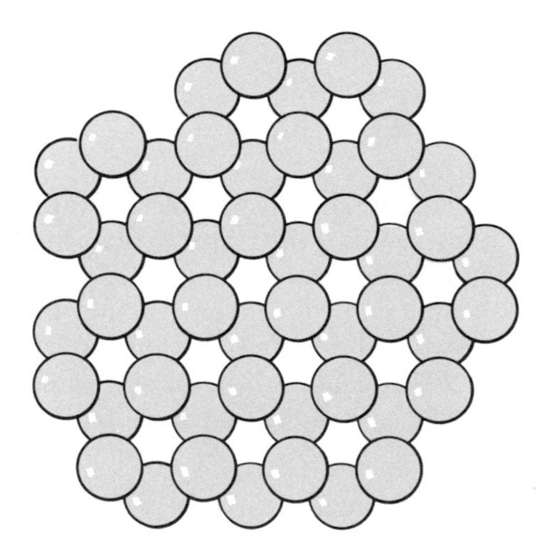

Fig. 18.5 Arrangement of atoms in a layer of black phosphorus.

ably less than the 90° angle corresponding to *p*-orbital overlap, and the resulting strain in the bonds may be partly responsible for the reactivity of the element. When white phosphorus is heated, especially in the presence of a trace of iodine which acts as a catalyst, it is transformed into a second allotropic modification, ***red phosphorus,*** which has very different properties from the white. Red phosphorus is very much less volatile than the white, and sublimes without melting. It is insoluble in carbon disulfide, not especially reactive, and must be heated above 240°C in order to ignite. It is relatively nonpoisonous and can be safely handled in air. The exact structure of this allotrope is not known, but it appears to be polymeric. A third form, ***black phosphorus,*** which exhibits appreciable electrical conductivity, is formed when white phosphorus is subjected to a pressure of 4000 atm at 200°C. The atoms in black phosphorus are arranged hexagonally in puckered sheets (Fig. 18.5).

18.20 Compounds of Phosphorus

(a) Phosphine. Phosphine, PH_3, unlike ammonia, cannot be prepared by the direct union of the elements. Phosphine is evolved when water acts on a metal phosphide. The reaction is analogous to that between water and a nitride to form ammonia:

$$Ca_3N_2 + 6\ H_2O \rightarrow 3\ Ca(OH)_2 + 2\ NH_3$$

$$Ca_3P_2 + 6\ H_2O \rightarrow 3\ Ca(OH)_2 + 2\ PH_3$$

Phosphine can also be prepared by boiling white phosphorus in sodium hydroxide solution:

$$P_4 + 3\ NaOH + 3\ H_2O \rightarrow 3\ NaH_2PO_2 + PH_3$$

Both methods of preparation also produce some diphosphine, P_2H_4, and the presence of this compound is believed to be responsible for the fact that the product ignites spontaneously in the air. If the gas is bubbled through water, as each bubble reaches the surface, it ignites and blows a smoke ring of phosphorus(V) oxide:

$$4\ PH_3 + 8\ O_2 \rightarrow 6\ H_2O + P_4O_{10}$$

In contrast to ammonia, phosphine is only slightly soluble in water, and its solution is not basic. A few phosphonium salts are known, but they are much less stable than the corresponding ammonium salts. Phosphonium iodide, PH_4I, is a crystalline compound formed by reaction between phosphine and gaseous HI. It is immediately decomposed by water, forming phosphine and hydriodic acid. Phosphonium bromide has properties similar to the iodide, but the chloride is unstable at room temperature except under pressure.

(b) Phosphorus Halides. Phosphorus reacts directly with all of the halogens to form trihalides with the general formula PX_3, and with fluorine, chlorine, and bromine to form pentahalides, PX_5. Unlike the nitrogen halides, phosphorus trihalides are all stable compounds. All of them (even the trifluoride, compare NF_3) are rapidly hydrolyzed by water and must be protected from moisture:

$$PX_3 + 3\ H_2O \rightarrow H_3PO_3 + 3\ HX$$

Phosphorus trichloride may be prepared by passing chlorine gas through melted white phosphorus contained in a flask equipped for distillation. A liquid, b.p. 74°C (1 atm), it reacts further, if left in contact with chlorine, forming the solid pentachloride PCl_5 (m.p. 167°C). Both the trichloride and the pentachloride are valuable reagents in organic synthesis. Both react with hydroxyl compounds such as alcohols and carboxylic acids, replacing —OH with —Cl:

$$3\ CH_3CH_2CH_2OH + PCl_3 \rightarrow 3\ CH_3CH_2CH_2Cl + H_3PO_3$$

1-propanol 1-chloropropane

$$2\ CH_3CH_2COOH + PCl_5 \rightarrow 2\ CH_3CH_2COCl + POCl_3 + H_2O$$

propionic acid propionyl chloride

Bromine and iodine may be introduced into organic compounds in similar fashion, using PBr_3 and PI_3.

The five valence electrons of phosphorus are in the third quantum level which has a maximum capacity of 18 electrons. Phosphorus can therefore readily accommodate 10 electrons to form five covalent bonds (Sec. 8.7c). Phosphorus pentafluoride is stable to heat, but the pentachloride is dissociated into chlorine and PCl_3 at 300°C, and the pentabromide is appreciably dissociated at 100°C. All three compounds are hydrolyzed by water, the reaction occurring in two steps:

$$PX_5 + H_2O \rightarrow POX_3 + 2\ HX$$

$$POX_3 + 3\ H_2O \rightarrow H_3PO_4 + 3\ HX$$

(c) Oxides of Phosphorus. Phosphorus forms two oxides, which are respectively the anhydrides of phosphorous and phosphoric acids. A third oxide, phosphorus tetraoxide, P_2O_4, is formed by heating phosphorus(III) oxide in a sealed tube, and is of minor importance. The simplest formula of phosphorus(III) oxide corresponds to P_2O_3, and the compound is commonly referred to as the trioxide. Similarly, phosphorus(V) oxide is often called the pentoxide because its simplest formula is P_2O_5. Molecular weight determinations, however, show that the correct molecular formulas of these compounds are P_4O_6 and P_4O_{10}, respectively. The structures of the two oxides are represented schematically in Fig. 18.6. The basic

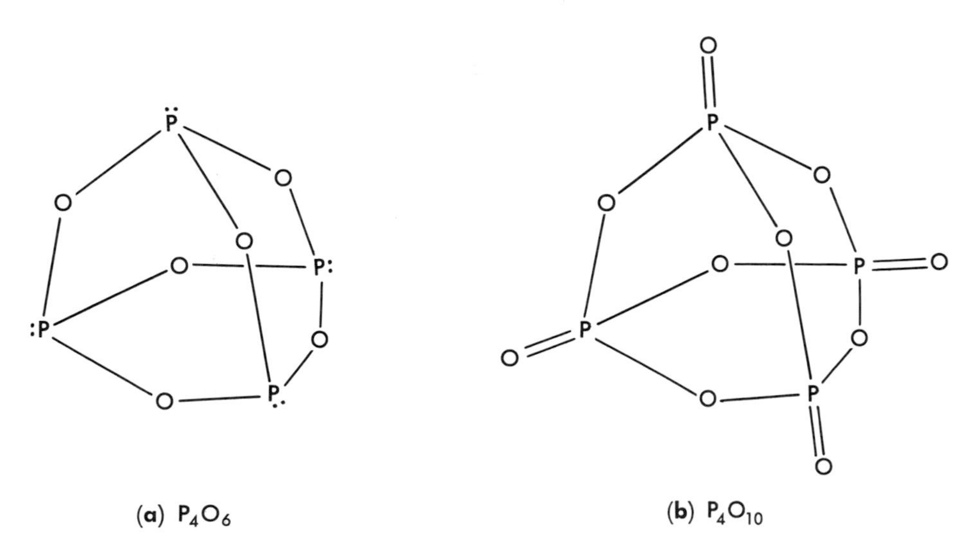

Fig. 18.6 Structures of (a) phosphorus(III) oxide; (b) phosphorus(V) oxide.

molecular skeleton is similar in both compounds, but the unshared pairs on the phosphorus atoms in P_4O_6 are used to form bonds with additional oxygen atoms in P_4O_{10}.

Both compounds are formed by direct reaction between phosphorus and oxygen. If the oxygen supply is limited, the product is P_4O_6, otherwise it is P_4O_{10}:

$$P_4 + 3\ O_2 \rightarrow P_4O_6$$

$$P_4 + 5\ O_2 \rightarrow P_4O_{10}$$

Each of the two oxides reacts vigorously with water to form the corresponding acid:

$$P_4O_6 + 6\ H_2O \rightarrow 4\ H_3PO_3$$

$$P_4O_{10} + 6\ H_2O \rightarrow 4\ H_3PO_4$$

The affinity of phosphorus(V) oxide for water is so great that it can even abstract it from nitric acid, which it converts to the anhydride:

$$P_4O_{10} + 4\ HNO_3 \rightarrow 2\ N_2O_5 + 4\ HPO_3$$

The acid produced in this case is metaphosphoric acid, HPO_3, which is also formed when P_4O_{10} reacts with a limited amount of water:

$$P_4O_{10} + 2\ H_2O \rightarrow 4\ HPO_3$$

Because it takes up water so readily, phosphorus(V) oxide is extensively used as a drying agent.

(d) Acids of Phosphorus. The most important of the phosphorus acids is ***orthophosphoric acid,*** H_3PO_4, formed by the reaction of phosphorus(V) oxide with water. It is a moderately strong triprotic acid, but only the first proton is appreciably ionized in water:

$$H_3PO_4 + H_2O \rightarrow H_3O^+ + H_2PO_4^- \qquad K_1 = 7.5 \times 10^{-3}$$

$$H_2PO_4^- + H_2O \rightarrow H_3O^+ + HPO_4^{--} \qquad K_2 = 6.2 \times 10^{-8}$$

$$HPO_4^{--} + H_2O \rightarrow H_3O^+ + PO_4^{---} \qquad K_3 = 4.8 \times 10^{-13}$$

Three series of salts derived by successive replacement of the three hydrogen atoms are known. As might be expected, the normal and monoacid salts are extensively hydrolyzed, and a solution of trisodium phosphate is strongly basic. The approximate pH values for 1 M solutions of H_3PO_4, NaH_2PO_4, Na_2HPO_4, and Na_3PO_4 are, respectively, 1, 3.7, 8, and 13.

When orthophosphoric acid is heated to 215°C, water is lost and the product is ***pyrophosphoric*** acid, $H_4P_2O_7$. The reaction can be represented as follows:

$$HO-\overset{\displaystyle O}{\overset{\|}{\underset{\displaystyle OH}{\underset{|}{P}}}}-OH + HO-\overset{\displaystyle O}{\overset{\|}{\underset{\displaystyle OH}{\underset{|}{P}}}}-OH \rightarrow HO-\overset{\displaystyle O}{\overset{\|}{\underset{\displaystyle OH}{\underset{|}{P}}}}-O-\overset{\displaystyle O}{\overset{\|}{\underset{\displaystyle OH}{\underset{|}{P}}}}-OH$$

orthophosphoric acid   pyrophosphoric acid

Pyrophosphoric acid is tetraprotic, and is appreciably stronger than the ortho- acid. The four acid dissociation constants are: $K_1 = 1.4 \times 10^{-1}$, $K_2 = 1.1 \times 10^{-2}$, $K_3 = 2.9 \times 10^{-7}$, and $K_4 = 3.6 \times 10^{-9}$. Only two series of salts—those corresponding to replacement of either 2 or 4 of the hydrogens—are known for this compound.

Stronger heating of ortho- or pyrophosphoric acid leads to the formation of ***metaphosphoric acid,*** a glassy polymer $(HPO_3)_n$:

$$H|O-\overset{\displaystyle O}{\overset{\|}{\underset{\displaystyle OH}{\underset{|}{P}}}}-|OH\quad H|O-\overset{\displaystyle O}{\overset{\|}{\underset{\displaystyle O}{\underset{\|}{P}}}}-|OH\quad H|O-\overset{\displaystyle O}{\overset{\|}{\underset{\displaystyle O}{\underset{\|}{P}}}}-|OH \xrightarrow{\Delta} -O-\overset{\displaystyle O}{\overset{\|}{\underset{\displaystyle OH}{\underset{|}{P}}}}-O-\overset{\displaystyle O}{\overset{\|}{\underset{\displaystyle OH}{\underset{|}{P}}}}-O-\overset{\displaystyle O}{\overset{\|}{\underset{\displaystyle OH}{\underset{|}{P}}}}-$$

Sodium trimetaphosphate, $(NaPO_3)_3$, can be prepared by heating either NaH_2PO_4 or $Na_2H_2P_2O_7$ (sodium dihydropyrophosphate):

$$3\ Na_2H_2P_2O_7 \rightarrow 3\ H_2O + 2\ (NaPO_3)_3$$

The anion in this compound is cyclic:

O   O⁻
P
⁻O O   O O
P   P
O   O   O⁻

Orthophosphorous acid, H_3PO_3, is formed by hydrolysis of the trihalide, or by the action of water on phosphorus(III) oxide. It is rather unstable, and in the free state, or in concentrated solutions, it decomposes to give phosphine and phosphoric acid:

$$4\ H_3PO_3 \rightarrow PH_3 + 3\ H_3PO_4$$

Despite its formula, orthophosphorous acid is diprotic ($K_1 = 2 \times 10^{-2}$, $K_2 = 2 \times 10^{-7}$). One of the three hydrogens is attached directly to phosphorus, and not to oxygen, and does not ionize:

$$\begin{array}{c} H \\ | \\ HO-P-OH \\ \| \\ O \end{array}$$

Its monosodium salt loses water at 160°C to give sodium pyrophosphite, corresponding to the acid $H_4P_2O_5$:

$$2\ NaH_2PO_3 \rightarrow Na_2H_2P_2O_5 + H_2O$$

Pyrophosphorous acid can be obtained by acidifying the solution, or by the action of PCl_3 on the ortho- acid. It is a low-melting solid (m.p. 38°C) which decomposes on heating. ***Metaphosphorous acid,*** HPO_2, is formed when phosphine burns in a limited supply of air:

$$2\ PH_3 + 3\ O_2 \rightarrow 2\ HPO_2 + 2\ H_2O$$

Both meta- and pyrophosphorous acids react with water to give the ortho- form. All of the phosphorous acids and their salts are readily oxidized to phosphoric acid and phosphates, and consequently they are strong reducing agents.

The barium salt of ***hypophosphorous acid,*** $Ba(H_2PO_2)_2$, is obtained by heating white phosphorus with aqueous barium hydroxide:

$$2\ P_4 + 3\ Ba(OH)_2 + 6\ H_2O \rightarrow 2\ PH_3 + 3\ Ba(H_2PO_2)_2$$

The free acid is obtained by acidifying the solution with H_2SO_4, precipitating the barium as $BaSO_4$. Again, its formula is misleading, because hypophosphorous acid possesses only one ionizable proton. The remaining two hydrogen atoms are directly joined to the phosphorus atom:

$$\begin{array}{c} O \\ \| \\ H-P-OH \\ | \\ H \end{array} \qquad K_a = 1 \times 10^{-2}$$

Hypophosphites are strong reducing agents in both acid and basic solution.

18.21 Reading Suggestions

There is a fascinating story behind the discovery of each of the elements, as you will find if you browse through *The Discovery of the Elements*, by Mary Elvira Weeks (Chemical Education Publishing Co., Easton, Pa., 6th edition, 1956). For more details on the chemical and physical properties of the group 0 elements, see *The Noble Gases*, by Howard H. Claasen (Topics in Modern Chemistry Series,

D. C. Heath and Co., Boston, 1966). Recommended as general references for this chapter are: *The Chemistry of the Non-Metals*, by William L. Jolly (Foundations of Modern Chemistry Series, Prentice-Hall, Inc., Englewood Cliffs, N.J., 1966); *Inorganic Chemistry*, by J. Kleinberg, W. J. Argersinger, Jr., and E. Griswold (D. C. Heath and Co., Boston, 1960); and the *Reference Book of Inorganic Chemistry*, by W. M. Latimer and J. H. Hildebrand (The Macmillan Co., New York, 3rd edition, 1951).

Clathrates are described in papers by Sr. Mary Martinette Hagan, B.V.M., *J. Chem. Ed.* **30,** 628 (1953) and **40,** 643 (1963), and by V. J. Bhatnagar, *ibid.*, **40,** 646 (1963). A method of preparing a simple clathrate of quinol and H_2S is described by Thomas F. Edwards, *ibid.*, **35,** A481 (1958).

Questions and Problems

18.1 On the basis of what properties is the distinction between nonmetals and metals usually made? Is the distinction between nonmetals and metals always well defined?

18.2 Hydrogen, nitrogen, oxygen, argon and carbon dioxide are colorless, odorless, and tasteless gases. How can they be distinguished from each other?

18.3 Discuss the abundance of hydrogen (a) on earth and (b) in the universe.

18.4 What is water gas? How is it prepared? Of what industrial importance is it? How can it be converted to almost pure hydrogen?

18.5 Provide an explanation for the higher temperature attainable in the flame of the atomic hydrogen torch than in the oxyhydrogen flame.

18.6 What metals are capable of forming metal hydrides? How are these hydrides formed? How can they serve as a source of hydrogen?

18.7 Give an account of the way in which the discovery of the noble gases and a knowledge of their properties has been of use in advancing our understanding of valence and the periodic system of elements.

18.8 Provide an explanation for the fact that though the density of helium is twice as great, its lifting power is 93% that of hydrogen.

18.9 The ionization potential of molecular oxygen is 12.2 volts, that of molecular fluorine is 17.8 volts. The compound OF_2 does exist though it is not formed directly by union of the elements. O_2F_2 is formed by passing an electric discharge through a mixture of oxygen and fluorine under reduced pressure and at liquid air temperature. In view of these facts, what might be predicted about the possibility of oxidation of (a) xenon (ionization potential 12.1 volts and (b) neon (ionization potential 21.6 volts)?

18.10 Write reactions for the laboratory preparation of (a) chlorine, (b) bromine, (c) iodine.

18.11 Describe, including reactions where needed, the preparation of (a) bromine from seawater or from salt-well brines and (b) iodine from the iodate content of Chile saltpeter.

18.12 Describe the industrial preparation of fluorine.

18.13 Account for the fact that fluorine is the strongest chemical oxidizing agent known.

18.14 With what elements does fluorine fail to form compounds? Suggest a reason.

18.15 Discuss the stability of fluorine compounds. Cite some commercially important examples.

18.16 Why cannot the action of concentrated sulfuric acid on the corresponding halide salt be used to prepare (a) hydrobromic acid and (b) hydroiodic acid?

18.17 Compare and contrast the industrial methods for the manufacture of HCl, HBr, and HI from the elements.

18.18 Provide an explanation for the fact that of the hydrohalic acids, hydrofluoric acid is the only one that is classified as a weak acid. Explain why the percentage ionization of hydrofluoric acid increases with increasing concentration while the percentage ionizations of other weak acids decrease with increasing concentration.

18.19 How does hydrofluoric acid etch glass?

18.20 Describe a qualitative test for the presence of (a) bromide ion, and (b) iodide ion in solution.

18.21 Write equations for the reaction that best describes what happens when each of the following is added to water:

(a) fluorine
(b) chlorine
(c) hydrogen chloride
(d) ammonia
(e) krypton under pressure
(f) chlorine monoxide
(g) chlorine dioxide
(h) chlorine trioxide
(i) iodine pentoxide
(j) nitronium perchlorate
(k) an oxide of a metal
(l) an oxide of a nonmetal
(m) phosphorus trichloride
(n) sodium peroxide
(o) calcium hydride
(p) calcium nitride
(q) calcium phosphide

18.22 Write equations for the reaction that occurs between aqueous sodium hydroxide and (a) F_2, (b) Cl_2, (c) I_2, (d) OF_2, (e) ClO_2.

18.23 What are the products of electrolysis of concentrated sodium chloride solution when (a) the solutions about the anode and the cathode of the electrolytic cell are kept separated by a barrier that is permeable to the electrolyte, (b) the barrier is removed and the solution in the electrolytic cell is stirred, (c) the solution in the electrolytic cell is mixed and kept hot?

18.24 The presence of the structural grouping $CH_3-\overset{|}{C}=O$ in an organic compound is frequently detected through its reaction with $NaOI$ ($I_2 + NaOH_{(aq)}$) to yield yellow crystalline iodoform, m.p. 119°. Since hypohalites oxidize alcohols, treatment of an alcohol with $NaOI$ with consequent formation of iodoform reveals the presence of what structural grouping in the alcohol? What alcohols possess this unit of structure?

18.25 Account for the paramagnetic property of oxygen.

18.26 On what grounds is the formula O_3 assigned to the molecule of ozone? Describe the structural features of the ozone molecule.

18.27 Provide a reasonable explanation for the fact that calcium oxide is a solid at room temperature while nitric oxide is a gas.

18.28 Write equations for the reactions by which the following oxides can be prepared: (a) OF_2, (b) Cl_2O, (c) Br_2O, (d) ClO_2, (e) Cl_2O_7, (f) I_2O_5.

18.29 Distinguish between oxides, peroxides, and superoxides, and cite for each class one method of preparation.

18.30 Provide an explanation for the fact that (a) the peroxide ion, O_2^{--}, is diamagnetic and (b) the superoxide ion, O_2^-, is paramagnetic.

18.31 Describe, using equations, the preparation of (a) dilute and (b) 30% or more concentrated solutions of hydrogen peroxide.

18.32 Provide an explanation for the fact that though hydrogen peroxide is a good oxidizing agent, it can also act as a reducing agent.

18.33 What is meant by the term "allotropic modification"? Cite several examples.

18.34 Give an account of the element sulfur, including a description of its main allotropic forms.

18.35 Rhombic and monoclinic sulfur behave similarly in chemical reactions, while oxygen and ozone, and red and white phosphorus behave quite differently. What suggestions can you make to explain these facts?

18.36 Describe the changes in the physical properties of sulfur as the temperature is raised from room temperature to above its boiling point. What changes in molecular structure are believed to be responsible for these physical changes?

18.37 Write equations for two convenient laboratory preparations of hydrogen sulfide.

18.38 Provide an explanation for the fact that H_2O (mol. wt. = 18) is a liquid boiling at 100°C while H_2S (mol. wt. = 34) is a gas that can be liquefied at −60.8°C.

18.39 How is the polysulfide rubber Thiokol made, and with what oxidizing agent is it made to react when used as a solid rocket propellant fuel?

18.40 Write equations for a suitable sequence of reaction steps including operating conditions for the industrial preparation of (a) sulfuric acid from sulfur by the contact process and the lead chamber process, (b) nitric acid from nitrogen.

18.41 Account for the chemical inertness of nitrogen in terms of structure.

18.42 What are nitrides? Cite several examples along with their methods of preparation.

18.43 Discuss the relationship of NO_2 to N_2O_4.

18.44 Discuss the action of nitric acid as an oxidizing agent including examples, giving equations and specifying reaction conditions, in which the oxidation number of nitrogen in nitric acid is reduced from +5 to (a) +4, (b) +3, (c) +2, (d) +1, (e) 0, (f) −3.

18.45 Give an account of the element phosphorus, including a description of its main allotropic forms, structure, solubility, reactivity, and physiological effects.

18.46 Starting with phosphate rock, coke, and sand, write equations for a suitable sequence of reaction steps by which each of the following acids can be prepared: (a) orthophosphoric, (b) pyrophosphoric, (c) metaphosphoric, (d) orthophosphorous, (e) pyrophosphorous, (f) metaphosphorous, (g) hypophosphorous.

18.47 Provide an explanation for the strongly basic property of 1 M solutions of sodium triphosphate.

18.48 Calculate the lifting power of the following quantities of helium at standard conditions: (a) 1 cubic foot (29.316 liters) (b) 1 gram atomic weight.

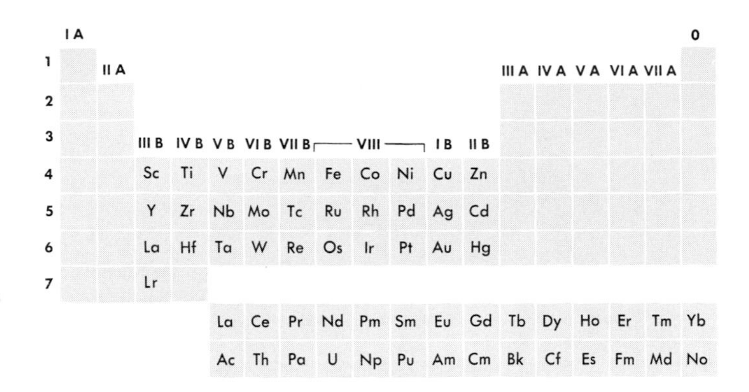

19 TRANSITION METALS AND COMPLEXES

Some 59 elements occupy the region between the representative groups IIA and IIIA of the periodic table. Of these, 28 are ***inner transition elements***—the lanthanides and actinides. The remainder form three ***short transition series,*** each of 10 elements, and the beginning of a fourth series. In this chapter we will be concerned mainly with the elements of the short transition series.

THE TRANSITION ELEMENTS

General Properties of Transition Elements 19.1

All of the transition elements are metals, and most are relatively hard, with high melting and boiling points. Zinc, cadmium, and mercury in

Period	IA	IIA	IIIB	IVB	VB	VIB	VIIB	VIII	VIII	VIII	IB	IIB	IIIA	IVA	VA
2	Li +1	Be +2													
3	Na +1	Mg +2											Al +3		
4	K +1	Ca +2	Sc +3	Ti (+2) +3 +4	V +2 +3 +4 +5	Cr +2 +3 (+4) +6	Mn +2 (+3) +4 (+6) +7	Fe +2 +3 (+4) (+6)	Co +2 +3 (+4)	Ni +2 (+3)	Cu +1 +2	Zn +2	Ga (+2) +3		
5	Rb +1	Sr +2	Y +3	Zr (+2) (+3) +4	Nb +3 +5	Mo +2 +3 +4 +6	Tc +4 (+6) +7	Ru +2 +3 +4 (+5) +6 +7 +8	Rh +3 +4 (+6)	Pd +2 (+3) +4	Ag +1 (+2) (+3)	Cd +2	In (+1) (+2) +3	Sn +2 +4	
6	Cs +1	Ba +2	Lu +3	Hf (+2) (+3) +4	Ta (+4) +5	W (+2) (+3) +4 +5 +6	Re (+3) +4 (+5) +6 +7	Os (+2) (+3) +4 +6 +8	Ir (+2) (+3) +4 (+6)	Pt +2 (+3) +4	Au +1 +3	Hg +1 +2	Tl +1 +3	Pb +2 +4	Bi +1 +2 +3 +4 +5
7	Fr +1	Ra +2	Lr +3												

Period														
6	La +3	Ce +3 +4	Pr +3 +4	Nd +3	Pm +3	Sm +2 +3	Eu +2 +3	Gd +3	Tb +3 +4	Dy +3	Ho +3	Er +3	Tm +3	Yb +2 +3
7	Ac +3	Th (+2) (+3) +4	Pa (+3) +4 +5	U +3 +4 +5 +6	Np (+2) +3 +4 +5 +6	Pu +3 +4 +5 +6	Am +3 (+4) +5 +6	Cm +3 (+4)	Bk +3 +4	Cf +3	Es +3	Fm +3	Md +3	No +3

Fig. 19.1 Oxidation states exhibited in their compounds by representative and transition metals. Comparatively rare or unstable states are shown in parentheses.

group IIB are notable exceptions in this regard, being comparatively low-melting and volatile. Most of the transition elements exhibit variable oxidation states in their compounds, in contrast to the representative metals, the majority of which exist in only a single such state (Fig. 19.1). There is a general, though irregular, decrease in electropositive character across any one series of transition metals (e.g., from **Sc** to **Zn**), but the trend is much less pronounced than it is among the representative elements. In other respects also, a greater horizontal similarity exists among the transition metals than between representative elements in adjacent groups of the same period. This similarity is especially striking among the inner transition elements.

Most of the transition elements, including all of the lanthanides, are active metals in the sense that the standard electrode potentials for their oxidation are positive. In general, the trend is toward decreasing activity across any series from group IIIB to group IB, and usually from top to bottom in a group. As a result, the ***noble metals***—those which have negative standard electrode potentials, and which do not displace hydrogen from dilute acids—are found among the heavier elements of groups IB, IIB, and

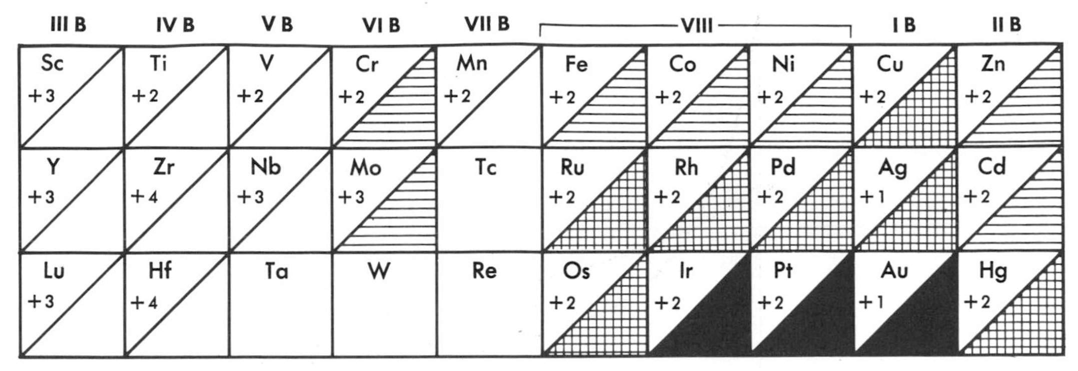

Fig. 19.2 Chart comparing activities of transition metals in terms of their standard electrode potentials: ◿, +1 volt or more; ◿, +0.1 to +0.99 volt; ◿, −0.1 to −0.99 volt; ◢, −1 volt or less. Number below symbol is the charge on the ion in electrode reaction: $M \rightarrow M^{+n} + ne^-$. If no number appears, standard potential is unavailable or in doubt.

VIII (Fig. 19.2). Among the lanthanides, standard electrode potentials for the reaction $M \rightarrow M^{+++} + 3\ e^-$ are nearly constant, decreasing in very regular manner by only 0.25 volt from lanthanum (+2.52 volts) to ytterbium (+2.27 volts). Despite being classed chemically as active metals, many of the transition elements, especially if in the form of large pieces, react at a negligible rate with acids and oxidizing agents under ordinary conditions. The corrosion resistance of chromium and nickel is typical. In finely divided form their activity becomes more evident, and in the powdered state a number of them, including nickel, are pyrophoric, igniting spontaneously in the air. The sparks generated by grinding a piece of iron are caused by the rapid oxidation of minute particles of the metal which in the massive state oxidizes (rusts) very slowly.

Especially characteristic of the members of the short transition series is their ability to combine with certain neutral molecules and negative ions without undergoing any change in oxidation state, forming stable ***coordination complexes*** of definite composition. These complexes may or may not be charged, and they are often colored. A well-known example is the deep blue complex formed when excess ammonia is added to a solution of a copper(II) salt. Ions of representative and inner transition metals are much less apt to form stable complexes of this sort.

Electronic Configuration of the Transition Elements 19.2

The arrangement of electrons in the atoms of the transition metals determines their properties and distinguishes them from the representative elements. You will recall from Chapter 7 that the appearance of the transition series of elements in the periodic table corresponds to the progressive filling of inner *d* and *f* orbitals with electrons. For the short transition series of the 4th, 5th, and 6th periods these are, respectively, the 3*d*, 4*d*, and 5*d* orbitals. In the inner transition series the 4*f* and 5*f* levels become occupied. Thus among the representative elements in their

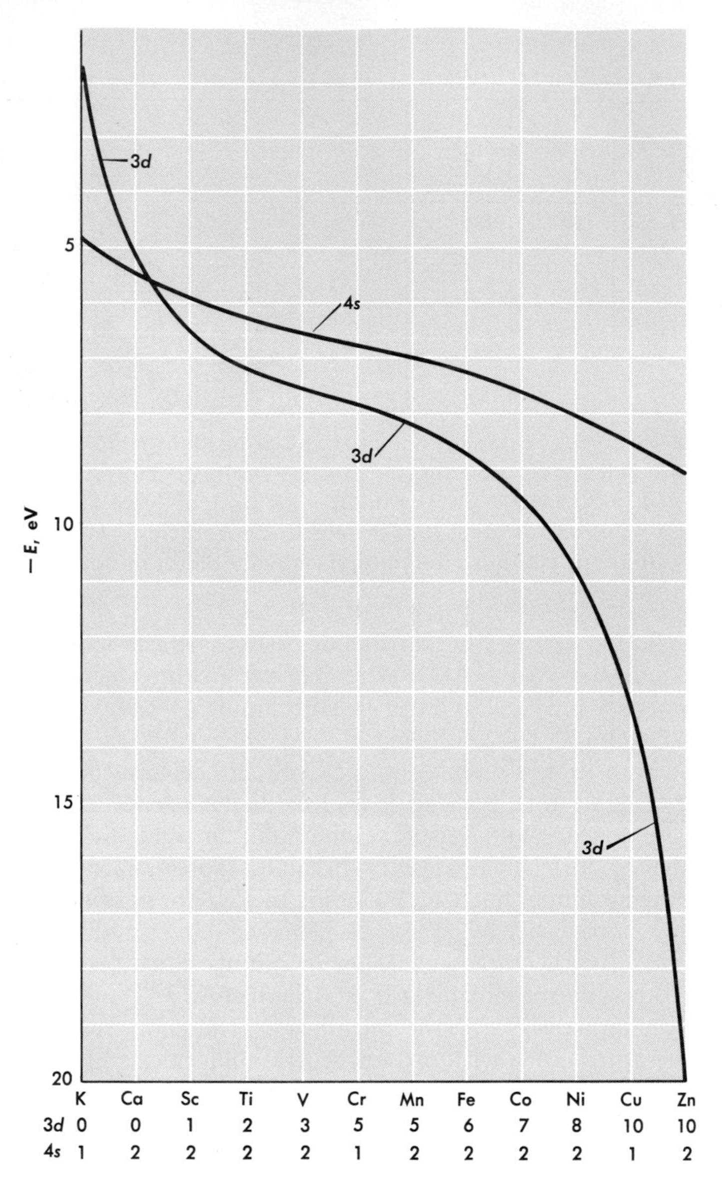

Fig. 19.3 Ground state energies of $3d$ and $4s$ levels from K ($3d^0 4s^1$) to Zn ($3d^{10} 4s^2$). On the diagram, $-E$ represents the energy (in electron volts) required to remove an electron from the atom. The larger the value of $-E$, that is, the harder it is to remove the electron, the smaller is its potential energy in the atom.

ground states all of these *d* and *f* electronic levels are either completely filled or completely empty, but among the transition metals one of these levels is usually partly occupied by electrons.

Figure 19.3 was constructed by drawing smooth curves through points representing the calculated potential energies of 3*d* and 4*s* levels in neutral atoms of the elements from **K** through **Zn**. Similar diagrams can be drawn for the corresponding elements of the 5th and 6th periods. Both curves show a decrease in potential energy across the period. This is to be expected because of the increasing positive charge on the nucleus, which results in a greater attraction for the electrons in a given level. This trend is not uniform, however. The vacant 3*d* orbitals of **K** and **Ca** are of higher energy than the 4*s*, thus accounting for the observed order of occupation (4*s* before 3*d*), but among the transition metals the situation is reversed. This means, for example, that the 4*s* electrons are apparently lost first when these elements ionize.

From the diagram one can see that, except for **Zn**, the energy difference between the 3*d* and 4*s* levels in the first short transition series is rather small, especially among the elements from **Sc** through **Fe**. It should not be surprising then to find that the electrons in both levels play an active part in determining the properties of these elements. In the 5th and 6th periods the situation is comparable. Between the fully occupied *d* and *s* levels of **Zn**, **Cd**, and **Hg**, on the other hand, the energy differences are so great that the *d* electrons are no longer available for reaction, and there is some justification for considering these three metals to be representative rather than transition elements.

Physical Nature of the Transition Elements 19.3

(a) Melting Points. The melting points of the transition metals are relatively high compared with those of the representative metals. This is evidence of stronger metallic bonding in the transition metals as a result of the participation of *d* orbitals. The trend, as shown in Fig. 19.4, is toward increasing melting points through group VIB, followed by a decrease thereafter. That there is a real correlation between the melting points of these elements and their electronic configurations can be seen by examining Table 19.1. Potassium has only a single electron available for metallic

TABLE 19.1 Ground-State Electronic Configurations and Melting Points of the Alkali, Alkaline Earth, and Transition Metals of the 4th Period

	3*d*					4*s*	Melting Point, °C
K	—	—	—	—	—	↑	63.2
Ca	—	—	—	—	—	↑↓	845
Sc	↑	—	—	—	—	↑↓	1200
Ti	↑	↑	—	—	—	↑↓	1690
V	↑	↑	↑	—	—	↑↓	1917
Cr	↑	↑	↑	↑	↑	↑	1890
Mn	↑	↑	↑	↑	↑	↑↓	1260
Fe	↑↓	↑	↑	↑	↑	↑↓	1535
Co	↑↓	↑↓	↑	↑	↑	↑↓	1495
Ni	↑↓	↑↓	↑↓	↑	↑	↑↓	1455
Cu	↑↓	↑↓	↑↓	↑↓	↑↓	↑	1083
Zn	↑↓	↑↓	↑↓	↑↓	↑↓	↑↓	419

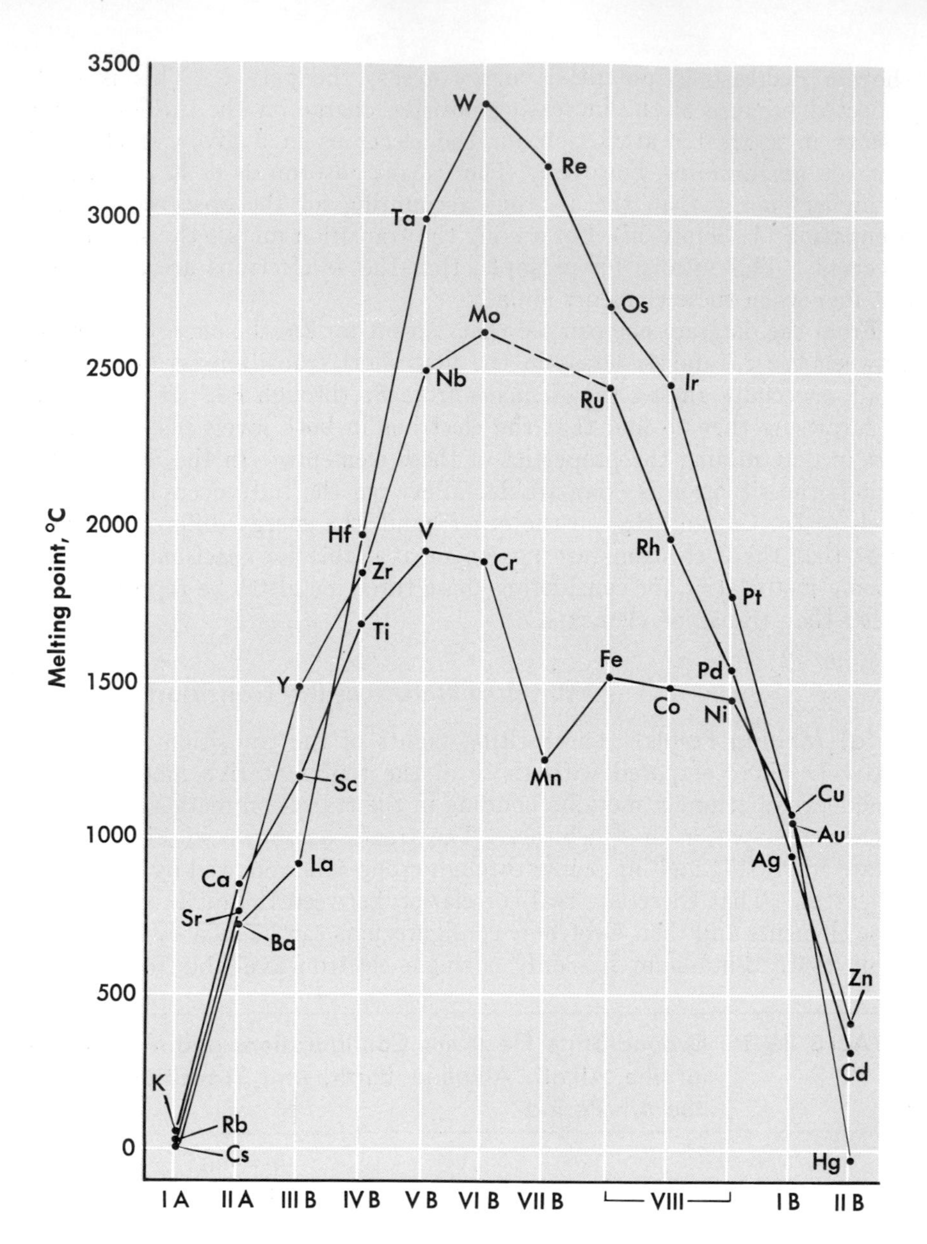

Fig. 19.4 Melting points of alkali, alkaline earth, and transition metals of the 4th, 5th, and 6th periods.

bonding. Bonding in the crystal therefore is weak, and this is reflected in its low melting point. In calcium, although the valence electrons are paired in the isolated atom, both can take part in metallic bonding because of the overlapping of the 4*s* and 4*p* bands in the crystal (Sec. 9.13). The result is stronger metallic bonding and a higher melting point.

From scandium through vanadium the melting points increase fairly regularly as the number of *d* electrons available for bonding increases from 1 to 3. The special stability associated with half-filled orbitals causes chromium to have the preferred configuration $3d^5\ 4s^1$ rather than $3d^4\ 4s^2$

(Sec. 7.7). Despite the presence of an additional electron, bonding in chromium appears to be weaker than in vanadium, and the melting point is slightly lower. This suggests that the element cannot make full use of orbitals in the half-filled 3*d* level in forming metallic bonds. In manganese, the 3*d* orbitals again are exactly half full, but in this case there are two 4*s* electrons. Judging from the low melting point alone, the result seems to be a still further decrease in the amount by which the *d* orbitals participate in bonding.

The melting points decrease across the iron triad (**Fe**, **Co**, and **Ni**) as the number of unpaired *d* electrons decreases from 4 to 2, but the decrease in melting point is small. A possible explanation for this lies in the fact that as the numbers of bonding electrons become less from **Fe** to **Ni**, the nuclear charges become greater. Thus, although **Ni**, for example, has fewer bonding electrons than **Fe**, they are more tightly held by the larger nucleus, and the total bond strength is nearly the same in both metals. The *d* electrons of **Cu** are all paired in the ground state, and judging from the melting point of the metal, they participate in bonding to only a limited degree. In **Zn**, the *d* electrons are no longer available, and its melting point is in line with those of the representative metals.

Across the 5th and 6th periods the melting points of the metals vary in a similar manner, the highest melting points being exhibited by **Mo** and **W**, both in group VIB. The exceptionally high melting point of tungsten helps make this metal especially suitable for use in lamp filaments. It is interesting to note that whereas the melting points of the representative metals tend to decrease from top to bottom in a group, the trend is in the opposite direction among the transition metals, with the exception of groups IB and IIB. Mercury, in group IIB, is remarkable in that it is a liquid at ordinary temperatures, and its melting point (−39°C) is the lowest of any metal.

(b) Atomic Radius. We might expect that as the charge on the nucleus becomes greater from left to right across a period, and its attraction for electrons increases accordingly, the atoms themselves should become smaller. On the other hand, atomic size should increase from top to bottom in a group because more electronic shells are being added. Examination of Table 19.2 and Fig. 19.5 will show that it is not quite as simple as all that, even though the general trends are more or less as expected. Starting with group IA and going across each period in turn, we see that although the atomic radii decrease rapidly at first, after group VB, mutual repulsion among the added *d* electrons tends to counteract the effect of the increased nuclear charge, and the atomic sizes remain nearly constant, even increasing slightly toward the end of each transition series.

Within the first three groups of each period, and between the first and second members of the remaining groups, we observe the expected increase in atomic radius with increasing atomic number. In groups IVB through IIB, however, the atoms of the second and third members of each group are of almost the same size. This is the result of the ***lanthanide contraction.*** In the 6th period, the 14 lanthanide elements plus lutetium intervene between **Ba** in group IIA and **Hf** in group IVB. By the time **Hf** is reached,

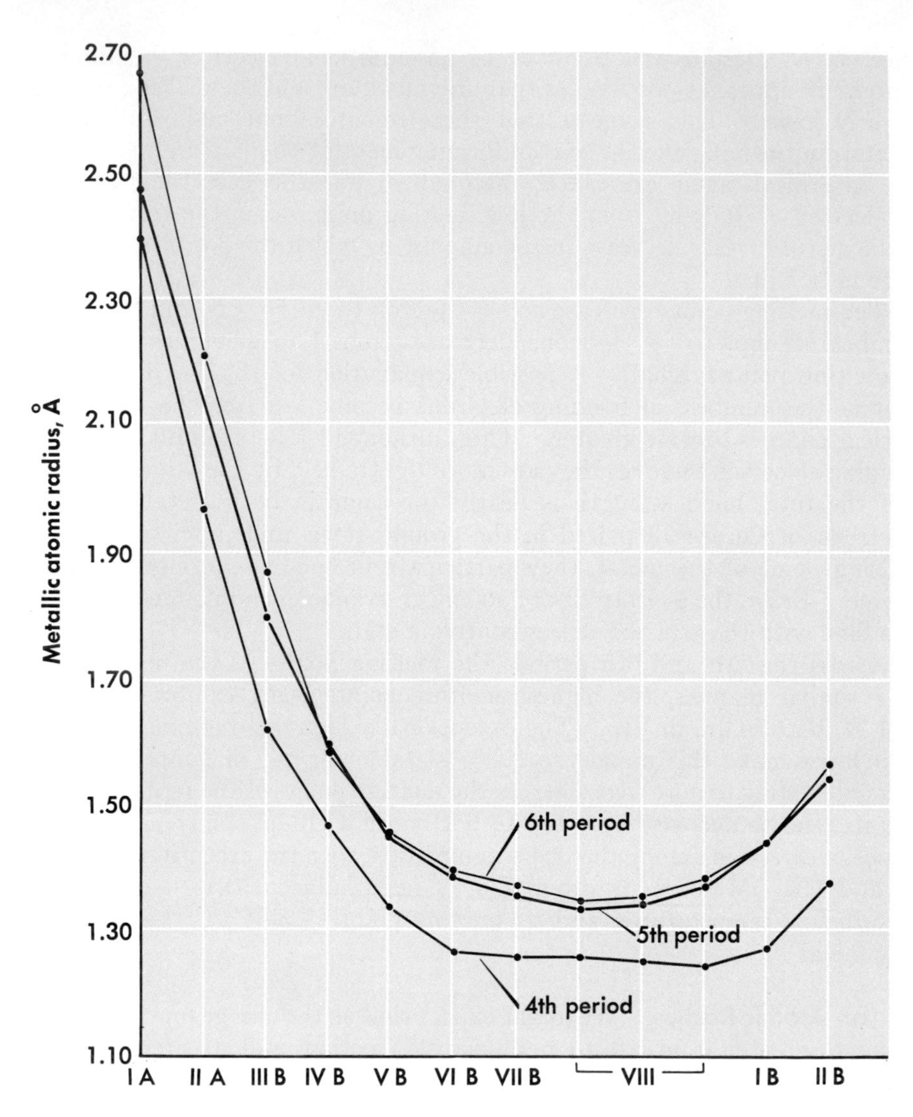

Fig. 19.5 Metallic atomic radii of alkali, alkaline-earth, and transition metals of the 4th, 5th, and 6th periods.

TABLE 19.2 Metallic Atomic Radii of the Alkali, Alkaline Earth, and Transition Metals of the 4th, 5th, and 6th Periods

Element	K	Ca	Sc	Ti	V	Cr	Mn	Fe	Co	Ni	Cu	Zn
Radius, Å	2.349	1.970	1.620	1.467	1.338	1.267	1.261	1.260	1.252	1.244	1.276	1.379
Element	Rb	Sr	Y	Zr	Nb	Mo	Tc	Ru	Rh	Pd	Ag	Cd
Radius, Å	2.48	2.148	1.797	1.597	1.456	1.386	1.358	1.336	1.342	1.373	1.442	1.543
Element	Cs	Ba	La	Hf	Ta	W	Re	Os	Ir	Pt	Au	Hg
Radius, Å	2.67	2.215	1.871	1.585	1.457	1.394	1.373	1.350	1.355	1.385	1.439	1.570

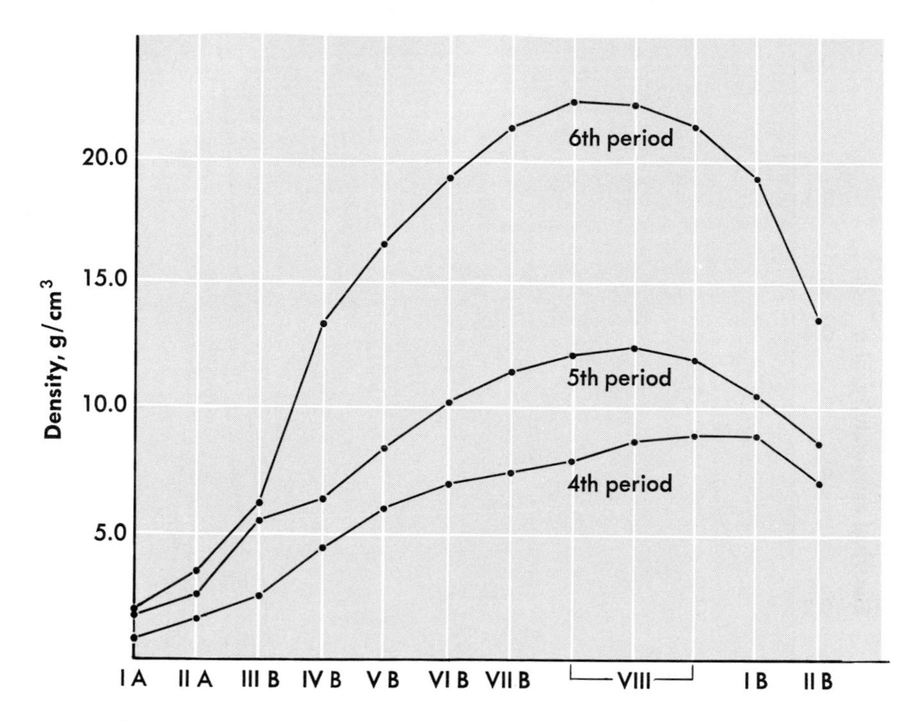

Fig. 19.6 Densities of the alkali, alkaline-earth, and transition metals of the 4th, 5th, and 6th periods.

the decrease in atomic size as a result of the addition of 15 positive charges to the nucleus is just enough to offset almost exactly the effect of the added shell of electrons. It should be expected, then, that as a result of the lanthanide contraction, a greater similarity often exists between the second and third elements in each of these groups than between the first and second.

(c) Density. A comparison of Figs. 19.5 and 19.6 shows a rough correlation between the densities of the transition metals and their metallic atomic radii. Worth noting are the especially high densities of the transition metals following **La** in the 6th period—a result of the lanthanide contraction.

(d) Electrical and Thermal Conductivity. The electrical conductivities of the transition metals vary irregularly, although the trend is toward greater conductivity as the number of *d* electrons increases. This is shown in Fig. 19.7 for the metals of the 4th period. Conductivities vary in a similar manner across the 5th and 6th periods, with maxima appearing at groups VIB and IB, and at **Rh** and **Ir** in group VIII, and pronounced minima at group VIIB. The metals of groups VIIB and IB are exceptional; the electrical conductivities of the VIIB metals are unusually low; those of the IB metals unusually high. Manganese, in group VIIB, is perhaps the poorest conductor of all the metals; silver, in group IB, is by far the best.*

* During World War II, when supplies of copper were restricted because of the great demand for that metal for the manufacture of brass shell casings and other ordnance material,

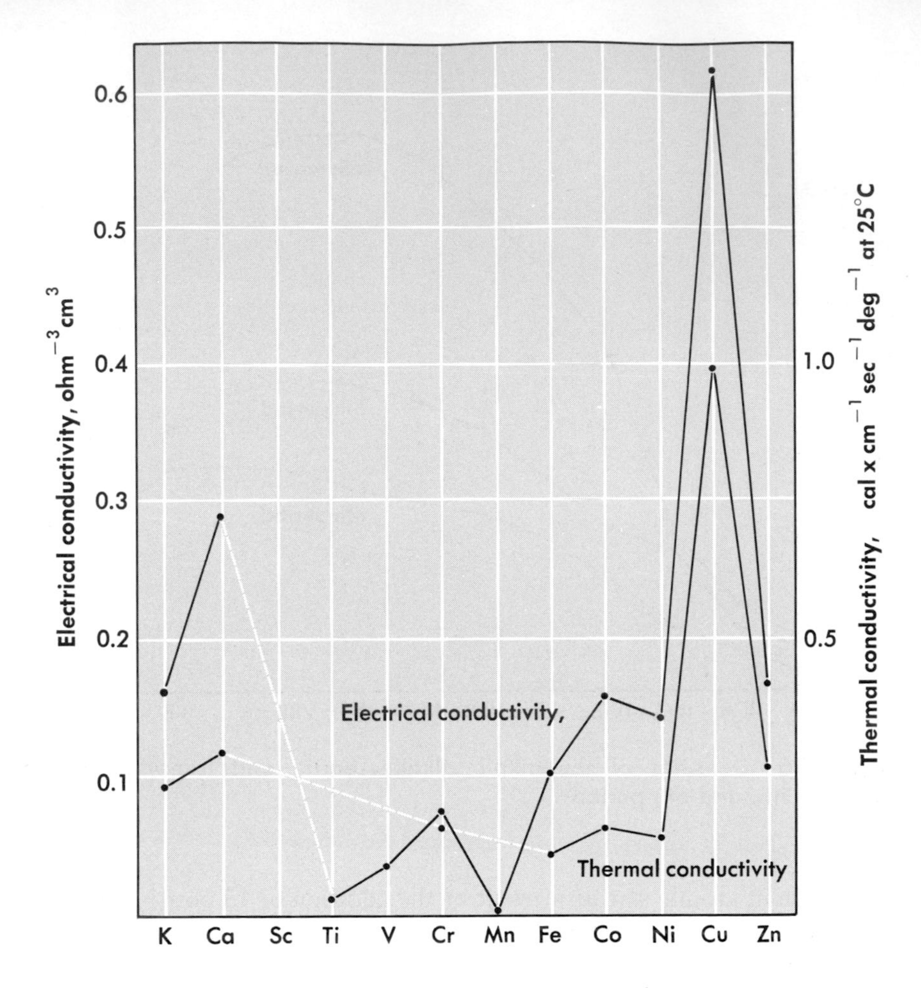

Fig. 19.7 Electrical and thermal conductivities of the alkali, alkaline earth, and transition metals of the 4th period.

All the transition metals are metallic conductors; that is, their electrical conductivities decrease as the temperature rises.

The thermal conductivities of these elements closely parallel their electrical conductivities (Fig. 19.7), indicating that the same electrons which carry the electrical current are also largely responsible for the conduction of heat through the metal.

19.4 Chemical Properties of the Transition Elements

(a) Oxidation States. We noted earlier that the exhibition of more than one oxidation state is the rule rather than the exception among the transition metals. In the short transition series the only exceptions to this

---

the bus-bars for the huge electrical installations at the Oak Ridge laboratories were fabricated from silver borrowed from the national depository at Fort Knox. The metal thus performed two jobs simultaneously: conducting electricity and serving as the backing for U.S. paper currency.

rule are found at the extremes of the series, in groups IIIB (**Sc**, **Y**, **Lu**, **Lw**) and IIB (**Zn**, **Cd**, **Hg**). The single *d* electron in **Sc**, and its relatives in group IIIB, has very nearly the same energy as the outer *s* electrons (Fig. 19.3), so that we might expect all three electrons to take part in any reactions involving these elements. In group IIB, on the other hand, the electrons in the filled *d* orbitals are so much lower in energy than the *s* electrons that there is little or no chance for them to participate in any reactions. Among the other transition elements any number of *d* electrons may be used to form bonds, from none at all to a maximum of seven, depending upon the circumstances. The oxidation number therefore can range from +2 (occasionally +1*), corresponding to use of only *s* electrons in bonding, up to a maximum of +8, and this only by **Os**, which has two *s* and six *d* electrons, and to a lesser degree by **Ru**, which has one *s* and seven *d* electrons.

Figure 19.1 shows that from group IIIB through group VIIB the maximum oxidation state exhibited increases regularly from +3 to +7 and is equal to the group number in every case. In group VIII, as we have already noted, only **Os** and **Ru** can exist in the +8 state. Thereafter the maximum oxidation state decreases until it reaches +2 for the members of group IIB. In general, a larger number of oxidation states is displayed by the elements in the middle groups of the transition series than by those of the groups at either end. Furthermore, in each group the highest state becomes more stable with increasing atomic number while the lower states become less stable. This trend is contrary to what is observed among the representative elements† and suggests that the *d* electrons become more available for reaction as one descends through a group. As might be expected, the bonds formed by the transition metals appear to become more covalent in character as the oxidation state increases. At the same time, for any given oxidation state, the bonds become less covalent and more nearly ionic, going down through a group. For example, Cr_2O_3 melts above 2400°C and is insoluble in both polar and nonpolar solvents, all properties indicative of the probable ionic nature of this compound. It is stable to oxidation under conditions which rapidly bring about the oxidation of Mo^{+++} and W^{+++} to the +6 state. In contrast, the covalent nature of CrO_3 is evidenced by its low melting point (196°C) and its solubility in ether. It is a powerful oxidizing agent, reacting explosively with many easily oxidizable substances (a drop of alcohol placed on a crystal of CrO_3 immediately bursts into flame). It decomposes with loss of oxygen at a temperature slightly above its melting point, forming Cr_2O_3. The trioxides of **Mo** and **W** are poor oxidizing agents, as are other compounds of these two elements in the +6 state. The relatively high melting points of MoO_3 (791°C) and WO_3 (1473°C) suggest that these compounds are more nearly ionic than

* The +1 oxidation state of **Cu**, **Ag**, and **Au** corresponds to loss of the single *s* electron of the ground-state atom, giving the ion the configuration $(n-1)d^{10}\ ns^0$. The +1 oxidation state of **Hg** is unusual in that the ion is not Hg^+, but rather Hg_2^{++}, in which one *s* electron has been lost by each atom; the remaining *s* electron of each pairing to form a covalent bond between the atoms.

† The relative stabilities of **Sn**(IV) and **Pb**(IV) and their strengths as oxidizing agents (Secs. 16.13 and 16.14) are a case in point.

CrO_3. Both oxides are stable at temperatures well above their melting points.

The lower oxides of the transition metals are, for the most part, typical metallic (basic) oxides. Higher oxides tend to be amphoteric or acidic. The oxides of the 4th period elements are generally more acidic (or less basic) than the corresponding oxides of the 5th and 6th periods. For example, although the dioxides of the group IVB metals (**Ti**, **Zr**, and **Hf**) are all amphoteric to some degree, TiO_2 readily forms titanates (e.g., Na_2TiO_3) when fused with alkali, and is almost unaffected by acid, while HfO_2 and ZrO_2 dissolve readily in acids, but exhibit less tendency to form hafniates and zirconates. Chromium trioxide, CrO_3, dissolves in water to form a solution of chromic acid:

$$CrO_3 + 3\ H_2O \rightarrow 2\ H_3O^+ + CrO_4^{--}$$

The solution is strongly acidic and a powerful oxidizing agent.* The less acidic oxide MoO_3 is only slightly soluble in water and in most acids but dissolves readily in ammonia and alkali solutions to form molybdates. Still less acidic is WO_3, which dissolves only in strong alkali, giving tungstates. Both the molybdates and tungstates are weak oxidizing agents compared to the chromates.

The heptoxides of **Mn**, **Tc**, and **Re** all dissolve readily in water to give strongly acid solutions:

$$Mn_2O_7 + 3\ H_2O \rightarrow 2\ H_3O^+ + 2\ MnO_4^-$$

Manganese heptoxide, Mn_2O_7, is an unstable liquid which begins to evolve oxygen at 0°C and decomposes explosively when warmed. The oxides Tc_2O_7 and Re_2O_7, on the other hand, are comparatively stable and can be sublimed without decomposition. Permanganic acid, $HMnO_4$, exists only in solution. It is more familiar in the form of its salts, the permanganates, which are fairly stable in the solid state. The perrhenates are much weaker oxidizing agents than the permanganates and are decidedly more stable to heat. Solid $KMnO_4$ begins to evolve oxygen at 200°C, but $KReO_4$ can be distilled without decomposition at 1370°C and 1 atm.

(b) Ionization Potentials. The first and second ionization potentials of nearly all of the transition elements measure the energy required to remove the two outermost *s* electrons from the atom. First and second ionization potentials for calcium and the members of the first transition series are given in Table 19.3. We find the expected trend toward higher ionization potentials as the nuclear charge increases from left to right across the series, but the differences from one element to the next, and between the transition metals and calcium, on the whole are not as great as the

* In solution, chromate and dichromate ions exist in equilibrium:

$$2\ CrO_4^{--} + 2\ H_3O^+ \rightleftarrows Cr_2O_7^{--} + 3\ H_2O$$

Both ions are strong oxidizing agents, and their relative concentrations are controlled by the acidity of the solution.

differences between successive representative elements (Sec. 8.6). This is not surprising, considering that the electrons are being removed from the 4*s* level in nearly every case. Chromium and copper are exceptions. Here the second electron is removed from a half-filled (**Cr**) or filled (**Cu**) 3*d* level, This is reflected in the second ionization potentials of these two elements, which are substantially higher than we would otherwise expect. In this connection it is interesting to note that to remove a third electron from the no longer filled 3*d* level of Cu^{++} requires far less energy (3rd ionization potential = 29.9 eV) than it does to remove an electron from the filled 3*d* level of Zn^{++} (3rd ionization potential = 39.3 eV).

TABLE 19.3 First and Second Ionization Potentials, in Electron Volts, of Calcium and the Elements of the First Transition Series

	Ca	Sc	Ti	V	Cr	Mn	Fe	Co	Ni	Cu	Zn
1st	6.11	6.56	6.83	6.74	6.76	7.43	7.90	7.86	7.63	7.72	9.39
2nd	11.87	12.89	13.63	14.2	16.49	15.64	16.18	17.05	18.15	20.29	17.96

TABLE 19.4 Standard Electrode Potentials ($M \rightarrow M^{++} + 2\,e^-$)

Element	Ti	V	Cr	Mn	Fe	Co	Ni	Cu	Zn
$\mathcal{E}^0$, volts	+1.63	+1.18	+0.91	+1.18	+0.44	+0.28	+0.25	−0.34	+0.76

(c) Standard Electrode Potentials. We might expect an inverse relationship to exist between the standard electrode potentials of the transition elements and their respective ionization potentials. A comparison of Tables 19.3 and 19.4 shows that a rough correlation does exist, at least among the members of the first transition series for which comparable data are available. Considering the ionization potentials alone, however, both **Mn** and **Zn** appear to have abnormally large electrode potentials, that is, they are more active metals than we might expect. The electrode potential of **Cu**, on the other hand, seems too low compared to those of the other members of the series.

The ionization potential is actually only one of several factors which determine how easily a metal can form ions in solution. The standard electrode potential is determined by the free energy change (Sec. 11.6) for the net reaction, which in the present case is

$$M(s) \rightarrow M^{++}(aq) + 2\ e^-$$

The total free energy change is the sum of the ΔG's for the processes:

(1)	$M(s) \rightarrow M(g)$	(vaporization)
(2)	$M(g) \rightarrow M^+(g) + e^-$	(first ionization)
(3)	$M^+(g) \rightarrow M^{++}(g) + e^-$	(second ionization)
(4)	$M^{++}(g) \rightarrow M^{++}(aq)$	(hydration)

which together make up the overall reaction.

$$\Delta G_{tot} = \Delta G_1 + \Delta G_2 + \Delta G_3 + \Delta G_4$$

ΔG_{tot} should have the smallest (i.e., least positive) value for the most active metal.

Although ΔG's for the separate processes are for the most part not available, we can usually determine the ΔH's. These are, in turn, the heat of vaporization of the metal (ΔH_1), the first and second ionization energies (ΔH_2 and ΔH_3), and the heat of hydration (ΔH_4). Ionization energies can be calculated from the ionization potentials; an ionization potential of 1 eV is equivalent to an ionization energy of 23.06 kcal/mole. Values for ΔH_1, ΔH_2, ΔH_3, ΔH_4, and ΔH_{tot} are given in Table 19.5.

TABLE 19.5 Enthalpy Changes (kcal/mole) in the Overall Reaction $M(s) \rightarrow M^{++}(aq) + 2\ e^-$

	Ti	V	Cr	Mn	Fe	Co	Ni	Cu	Zn
ΔH_1	112.6	122	94	68	99	105	101	81	31.2
ΔH_2	158	155	156	172	182	181	176	178	216
ΔH_3	314	328	380	360	373	393	418	468	414
ΔH_4	−446	−453	−460	−445	−468	−497	−507	−507	−491
ΔH_{tot}	138.6	152	170	155	186	182	188	220	170.2

On the reasonable assumption that the total entropy change should be approximately the same for each of these metals, we should expect the most active metals to be those with the smallest values of ΔH_{tot}. Furthermore, ΔH_{tot} for these metals should vary in the same manner as ΔG_{tot}. This is indeed the case. The striking correlation between ΔH_{tot} calculated as above, and the activities of the metals as given by their standard electrode potentials, is clearly shown in Fig. 19.8. Small deviations at V and Co probably represent entropy effects.

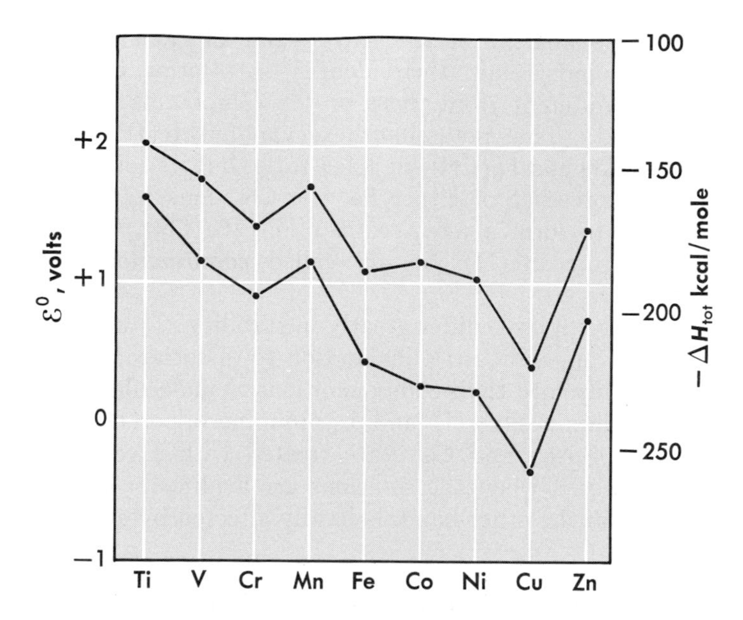

Fig. 19.8 Plots of $-\Delta H_{\text{tot}}$ (upper curve) and $\mathcal{E}^0$ (lower curve) for the reaction $M(s) \rightarrow M^{++}(aq) + 2e^-$ for metals of the first transition series.

The fact that **Mn** and **Zn** are such active metals compared with their immediate neighbors is now seen to be related to the comparatively low heats of vaporization of these metals. The low heats of vaporization, in turn, reflect the partial or total lack of participation in bonding between the atoms on the part of electrons in half-filled or completely filled *3d* levels (Sec. 19.3a). We also see that the low activity of **Cu** is largely the result of the metal's large second ionization energy. You will recall (Sec. 19.4b) that in **Cu** the second electron lost comes from a completely filled *3d* level.

COORDINATION COMPLEXES

The Nature of Coordination Complexes 19.5

There is a large class of substances which appear to be formed by the union, in definite proportions, of two or more compounds, each of which is itself capable of independent existence. Examples of such ***molecular compounds*** are the mineral carnallite, and the salt potassium hexacyanoferrate(II):

$KCl \cdot MgCl_2 \cdot 6\,H_2O$	$Fe(CN)_2 \cdot 4\,KCN$ or $K_4Fe(CN)_6$
carnallite	potassium hexacyanoferrate(II)

Carnallite is an example of a ***double salt.*** Double salts keep their identity only in the solid state, and behave in solution like simple mixtures of their component ions. A solution of carnallite, for example, shows the properties expected of a mixture of K^+, Mg^{++}, and Cl^- ions in water. Other molecular compounds retain their identity in solution and often exhibit properties very different from those of the compounds from which they have been formed. Thus potassium hexacyanoferrate(II) can be prepared by combining KCN and $Fe(CN)_2$ in a 4:1 ratio, but its solution shows little evidence of the presence of either Fe^{++} or CN^- ions. Instead they seem to be combined to form a new, *complex* ion, $[Fe(CN)_6]^{4-}$. Such entities as the hexacyanoferrate(II) ion are called ***coordination complexes,*** or ***Werner complexes.***

Coordination complexes differ greatly in stability. Some, like the hexacyanoferrate(II) ion, show little inclination to dissociate; others dissociate more or less readily into their component ions or molecules. For example, the familiar diamminesilver(I) and tetramminecopper(II) ions,* formed when solutions of Ag^+ and Cu^{++} are treated with excess ammonia, are completely destroyed when the solutions are acidified. The hexamminecobalt(III) ion, on the other hand, is hardly affected by acid:

$$Ag(NH_3)_2^+ + 2\ H_3O^+ \rightarrow Ag^+ + 2\ NH_4^+ + 2\ H_2O$$

$$Cu(NH_3)_4^{++} + 4\ H_3O^+ \rightarrow Cu^{++} + 4\ NH_4^+ + 4\ H_2O$$

$$Co(NH_3)^{+++} + H_3O^+ \rightarrow \text{No appreciable reaction}$$

The dissociation of a complex ion in solution leads to the establishment of an equilibrium between the complex and its components. In the case of the diamminesilver(I) ion, the equilibrium is

$$Ag(NH_3)_2^+ \rightleftharpoons Ag^+ + 2\ NH_3$$

for which we can write the equilibrium expression

$$\frac{[Ag^+][NH_3]^2}{[Ag(NH_3)_2^+]} = K_{\text{diss}}$$

Dissociation constants for a number of complex ions are given in Table 19.6. The relative stabilities of ions which dissociate into the same number of pieces (e.g., the complex ions of silver(I), copper(I), and gold(I) listed in the table) can be judged by comparing the sizes of their respective dissociation constants. Generally speaking, the smaller the value of K_{diss}, the more stable the complex.

The formation of a complex is often used to prevent the separation of a precipitate or to redissolve a precipitate already formed. The use of complex formation to prevent precipitation is illustrated in the following example.

* The naming of coordination complexes is discussed in Appendix B.

TABLE 19.6 Dissociation Constants of Complex Ions

Name of Ion	Formula	K_{diss}
Diamminesilver(I)	$Ag(NH_3)_2^+$	6×10^{-8}
Dicyanoargentate(I)	$Ag(CN)_2^-$	3.8×10^{-19}
Dichlorocuprate(I)	$CuCl_2^-$	2.9×10^{-6}
Diamminecopper(I)	$Cu(NH_3)_2^+$	1.3×10^{-11}
Dicyanocuprate(I)	$Cu(CN)_2^-$	10^{-16}
Dicyanoaurate(I)	$Au(CN)_2^-$	5×10^{-39}
Tetramminecopper(II)	$Cu(NH_3)_4^{++}$	4.6×10^{-14}
Tetrachloroaurate(III)	$AuCl_4^-$	5×10^{-22}
Hexamminecobalt(III)	$Co(NH_3)_6^{+++}$	2×10^{-34}
Hexacyanoferrate(II)	$Fe(CN)_6^{4-}$	10^{-27}
Hexacyanoferrate(III)	$Fe(CN)_6^{3-}$	10^{-44}

Example 19.1

What concentration of NH_3 must be present in a solution which is 0.10 M in both Ag^+ and Cl^- in order to prevent precipitation of $AgCl$?

Solution: If precipitation is to be avoided, the maximum concentration of free Ag^+ ions in solution must be no more than that amount which, when multiplied by the concentration of Cl^- (0.10 M), will give a product just equal to the solubility product constant for $AgCl$ ($K_{sp} = 1.8 \times 10^{-10}$):

$$[Ag^+](0.10) = 1.8 \times 10^{-10}$$

$$[Ag^+] = 1.8 \times 10^{-9}$$

The remainder of the silver ($0.10 - 1.8 \times 10^{-9}$ mole/liter) must be in the form of the complex ion $Ag(NH_3)_2^+$. Substituting these quantities in the expression for K_{diss} gives

$$\frac{[Ag^+][NH_3]^2}{[Ag(NH_3)_2^+]} = \frac{(1.8 \times 10^{-9})[NH_3]^2}{(0.10 - 1.8 \times 10^{-9})} = 6 \times 10^{-8}$$

Taking $(0.10 - 1.8 \times 10^{-9}) \approx 0.10$ gives

$$[NH_3]^2 = 3.3$$

$$[NH_3] = 1.8\ M$$

The solution must therefore contain an excess of 1.8 moles/liter of free NH_3 in addition to the 0.2 mole/liter which reacts to form the complex, for a total of at least 2.0 moles/liter altogether.

19.6 The Werner Coordination Theory

A mixture of three cobalt(III) ammine complexes is formed when a strongly ammoniacal solution of cobalt(II) chloride and ammonium chloride is oxidized with a current of air and then acidified with HCl. These are a bright yellow solid which can be formulated $CoCl_3 \cdot 6\ NH_3$; a purple solid, $CoCl_3 \cdot 5\ NH_3$; and a green compound, $CoCl_3 \cdot 4\ NH_3$. A fourth complex, prepared differently, has a composition that corresponds to the formula $CoCl_3 \cdot 3\ NH_3$. The ammonia in these compounds is not appreciably affected by acid. More remarkable still is the behavior of the chlorine atoms. While silver nitrate will precipitate all of the chlorine from a solution of the hexammine, it will precipitate only two-thirds of the chlorine from the pentammine, one-third from the tetrammine, and none at all from the triammine. Similar behavior is exhibited by the analogous series of iridium(III) complexes. Concentrated H_2SO_4, for example, liberates all of the chlorine as HCl from $IrCl_3 \cdot 6\ NH_3$, two-thirds of it from $IrCl_3 \cdot 5\ NH_3$, one-third from $IrCl_3 \cdot 4\ NH_3$, and none from $IrCl_3 \cdot 3\ NH_3$.

To account for the behavior of these and other complexes, Alfred Werner reasoned that in each, the metal ion is surrounded by a ***coordination sphere,*** consisting of a definite number of atoms or molecules which Werner called ***ligands*** (from the Latin *ligare*, to bind). The ligands, which can be either neutral molecules or ions, are in some manner directly bound to the metal ion to form a complex entity. The charge on this entity depends upon the charge on the central metal ion and the charges, if any, possessed by the ligands. The properties of the cobaltammines described above can thus be accounted for in terms of a coordination sphere containing six ligands. In the hexammine, the Co^{+++} ion is surrounded by six neutral molecules to give the complex ion $[Co(NH_3)_6]^{+++}$. To preserve electrical neutrality, the compound must also include three negative groups (e.g., Cl^- ions). These are outside the coordination sphere, hence keep their normal ionic character. In the pentammine, which we may now formulate $[Co(NH_3)_5Cl]Cl_2$, one of the chloride ions has entered the coordination sphere. This reduces the charge on the complex ion to +2, and leaves only two chloride ions to be precipitated by silver nitrate. Two of the three chloride ions of the tetrammine $[Co(NH_3)_4Cl_2]Cl$ are in the coordination sphere, while in the triammine $[Co(NH_3)_3Cl_3]$ they all are. With three negative chlorides in the coordination sphere to balance the +3 charge of the metal ion, the result is a neutral complex constituting the entire molecule.

The equivalent conductances and colligative properties of solutions of coordination complexes are consistent with Werner's theory of the constitution of these compounds. Table 19.7 lists the equivalent conductances of a number of complexes of Pt(IV) and Pt(II), together with the limiting value of the van't Hoff factor i, which is a measure of the number of particles present in solution per formula unit dissolved (Sec. 10.14). Also given are the numbers of chloride ions per unit which are precipitated by silver nitrate. We see that the experimental data are accounted for provided that the coordination spheres of Pt(IV) and Pt(II) accommodate six and four ligands, respectively. As the number of chlorides within the coordination sphere increases, both the positive charge on the complex and the equivalent con-

TABLE 19.7 Equivalent Conductances, van't Hoff Factors, and Numbers of Precipitable Chloride Ions for Some Pt(IV) and Pt(II) Complex Compounds

	Formula	Equivalent Conductance, 10^{-3} *N*, at 25°C; ohm^{-1}	Van't Hoff Factor, *i*	Precipitable Chloride Ions
Pt(IV)	$[Pt(NH_3)_6]Cl_4$	523	5	4
	$[Pt(NH_3)_5Cl]Cl_3$	404	4	3
	$[Pt(NH_3)_4Cl_2]Cl_2$	228	3	2
	$[Pt(NH_3)_3Cl_3]Cl$	97	2	1
	$[Pt(NH_3)_2Cl_4]$	0	1	0
	$K[Pt(NH_3)Cl_5]$	108	2	0
	$K_2[PtCl_6]$	256	3	0
Pt(II)	$[Pt(NH_3)_4]Cl_2$	260	3	2
	$[Pt(NH_3)_3Cl]Cl$	116	2	1
	$[Pt(NH_3)_2Cl_2]$	0	1	0
	$K[Pt(NH_3)Cl_3]$	107	2	0
	$K_2[PtCl_4]$	267	3	0

ductance of the compound decrease, both being zero when the number of ligand chlorides is equal to the charge on the platinum. The introduction of still more chlorides into the coordination sphere causes the complex to have a negative charge, and makes the presence of positive ions necessary to preserve electrical neutrality in the compound. The electrical conductivity increases as a result. Again we see that only those chloride ions which are outside the coordination sphere retain their ionic character and are precipitated by silver ions.

Coordination Number 19.7

From what we have seen so far it is apparent that each central atom has a definite number of positions within its coordination sphere which can be occupied by ligands, irrespective of whether the ligands are neutral or charged. This number is called the ***coordination number*** of the ion. Complexes are known of ions with coordination numbers from 2 to 9. Coordination numbers of 2, 4, and 6 are encountered most frequently, and 6 is especially common. Frequently, though not always, the coordination number is twice the charge on the central ion. Common examples are Fe(III), Co(III), Cr(III), Ir(III), and Al(III), all of which have a coordination number of 6; Cu(II), Zn(II), and Pt(II), coordination number 4; and Ag(I), and Au(I), coordination number 2. Exceptions are Fe(II), Co(II), and Pt(IV), coordination number 6; and Cu(I) with a coordination number of 4.

19.8 Typical Ligands

A number of the most common coordinating ligands are listed in Table 19.8. These fall into two main categories: neutral molecules and negative ions. All of them possess unshared electron pairs and are capable of functioning as electron donors, that is, as Lewis bases (Sec. 13.5). In fact, the possession of an unshared pair appears to be almost a necessity in order for a molecule or ion to serve as a ligand.* Thus ammonia, with its unshared pair, is a typical ligand group, while the ammonium ion, which lacks an unshared pair, is not. This has been taken to indicate that the metal ion and the members of its coordination sphere are joined by covalent bonds, both electrons of which are furnished by the coordinating ligand, that is, by coordinate covalent bonds (Sec. 8.2).

TABLE 19.8 Typical Coordinating Ligands

(a) Neutral Molecules		(b) Negative Ions	
Aquo	H_2O	Chloro	Cl^-
Ammine	NH_3	Fluoro	F^-
Carbonyl	CO	Cyano	CN^-
Nitrosyl	NO	Cyanato	CNO^-
		Hydroxo	OH^-
		Thio	S^{--}

Each of the molecules and ions in Table 19.8 possesses a single ***donor center*** (i.e., an atom bearing an unshared pair of electrons) and is capable of occupying a single position in the coordination sphere of a metal atom. Ligands of this kind are described as *unidentate* (Latin: one-toothed). It is entirely possible, however, for there to be two or more donor centers in the same ligand. Such a ligand, which can simultaneously occupy two or more positions in the coordination sphere, is said to be *multidentate*. A typical example is the bidentate ligand ethylenediamine ($H_2N—CH_2—CH_2—NH_2$, usually abbreviated en). Each nitrogen in this compound possesses an unshared pair, and the molecule is capable of forming complexes in which it is equivalent to two molecules of ammonia. Multidentate ligands such as ethylenediamine are commonly called ***chelating agents*** because of the way in which they seem to enclose the central atom in a pincerlike manner reminiscent of the action of a crab's claw (Greek: chele). The complexes which result are called ***chelates.***

* There are rare instances of species functioning as ligands which have only a single unshared electron rather than a pair. Certain other compounds that possess no unshared pairs but do contain multiple bonds can also sometimes act as ligands; the π electrons of the multiple bonds apparently in some way performing the function of the unshared pair of a typical ligand. Platinum(II), for example, forms a number of stable complexes with alkenes such as ethylene (Sec. 17.3b). One such complex is the compound $K[Pt(C_2H_4)Cl_3]$, known as "Zeise's salt."

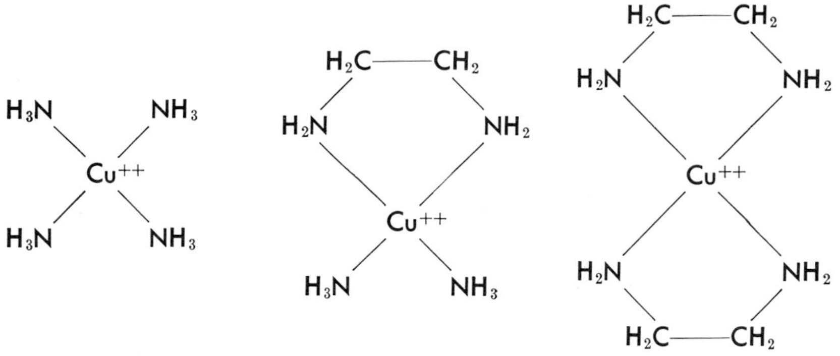

$[Cu(NH_3)_4]^{++}$ $[Cu(NH_3)_2en]^{++}$ $[Cu(en)_2]^{++}$

Chelate formation can often be put to practical use. The compound dimethylglyoxime, for example, which forms a very stable, insoluble, red complex with Ni^{++}, is used as a reagent for the detection and quantitative estimation of that ion:

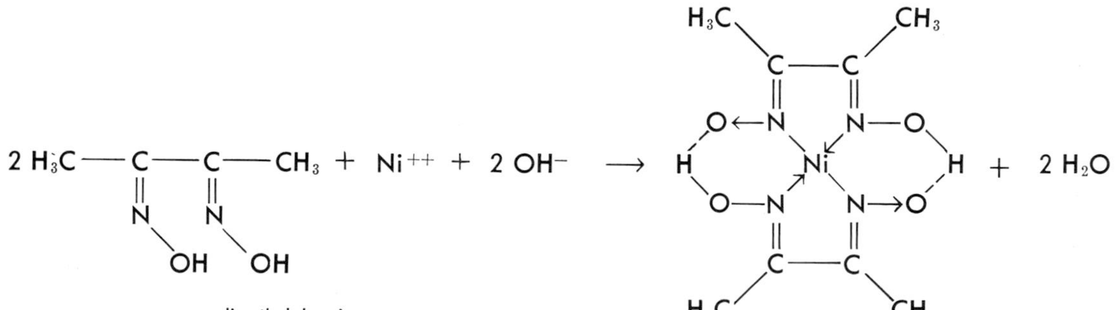

$$2\ H_3C{-}C({=}NOH){-}C({=}NOH){-}CH_3 + Ni^{++} + 2\ OH^- \longrightarrow \text{(nickel dimethylglyoxime)} + 2\ H_2O$$

dimethylglyoxime

The anion of ethylenediaminetetraacetic acid (EDTA, Versene, Sequestrene) is a very versatile chelating agent. It possesses six unshared electron pairs and might be expected to act as a sexidentate ligand, fully occupying the coordination sphere of any ion with a coordination number of 6. Probably for steric reasons, however, it normally occupies only five positions; the sixth is usually taken by a water molecule:

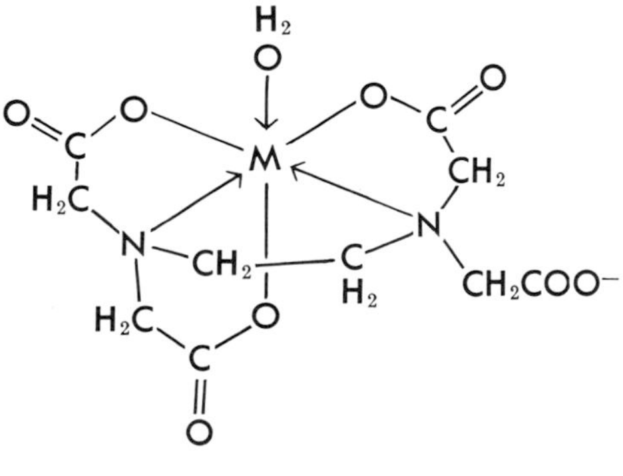

EDTA has the remarkable property of forming stable complexes with alkali and alkaline earth metal ions, something which few other ligands are capable of doing. Added to hard water, it binds, or *sequesters* calcium and other ions responsible for the hardness, preventing them from forming a precipitate with ordinary soaps. It is used in salad dressing and other foodstuffs to inhibit the development of off-flavors by complexing with traces of metal ions which otherwise would catalyze the oxidation of these products. EDTA has also been used in the treatment of heavy-metal poisoning. The toxicity of the metals is eliminated or greatly reduced when they are bound in stable complex form.

Two very important metal chelates found in nature are the green plant pigment ***chlorophyll,*** the function of which is to absorb light energy for photosynthesis, and ***heme,*** the oxygen-bearing prosthetic group of hemoglobin:

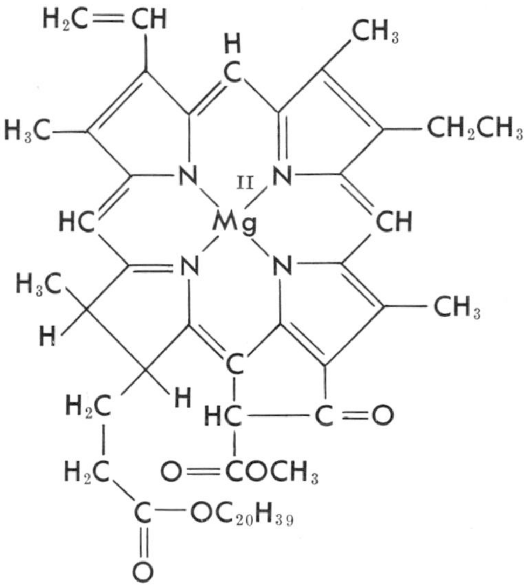

chlorophyll

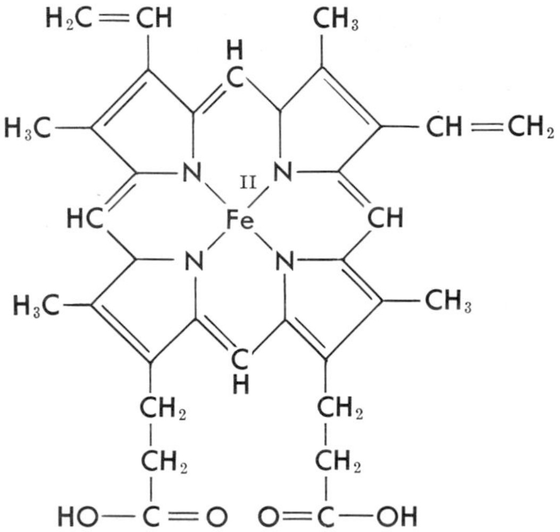

heme

19.9 Isomerism

Examples of isomerism abound among coordination complexes, and a triumph of the Werner theory is the way in which it can account for this isomerism. Both structural isomerism and stereoisomerism are observed. The former arises when two or more complexes have the same molecular formulas but differ in the order in which their atoms are joined (Sec. 17.6). The latter results when the same ligands may be arranged in space about the central atom in more than one way. It is analogous to the stereoisomerism observed with organic compounds. As it is with organic compounds, the stereoisomerism of coordination complexes is of two types: geometric and optical (Secs. 17.7 and 17.8).

(a) Structural Isomerism. There are several kinds of structural isomerism. The compounds $[Pt(NH_3)_4SO_4](OH)_2$ and $[Pt(NH_3)_4(OH)_2]SO_4$ are examples of ***ionization isomers.*** The first of these is strongly basic in solution and gives no precipitate of barium sulfate upon addition of barium chloride. From this it is clear that the sulfate is part of the coordination sphere in this compound whereas the hydroxide groups are ionic. The second compound forms a neutral solution which gives an immediate precipitate with barium chloride, showing that in this case the sulfate is ionic while the hydroxides are not. We see that ionization isomerism arises from the exchange of a ligand for one or more ions outside the coordination sphere.

Another interesting example of ionization isomerism is offered by the compounds $[Co(NH_3)_5NO_2]SO_4$ and $[Co(NH_3)_5SO_4]NO_2$. Here the exchange of SO_4^{--} for NO_2^- in the coordination sphere causes the complex cation to have a charge of +1 in the second compound compared to a charge of +2 in the first.

Hydrate isomerism is analogous to ionization isomerism. Three compounds with the composition $CrCl_3 \cdot 6\ H_2O$ can be prepared. Two of them are green; the third is violet. Treatment with silver nitrate shows that the violet form has three ionizable chlorides and that the green forms have two and one ionizable chlorides, respectively. The two green compounds lose water more or less readily, and the violet compound does not. From this evidence it appears that the three compounds must have the following structures:

$[Cr(H_2O)_6]Cl_3$	$[Cr(H_2O)_5Cl]Cl_2 \cdot H_2O$	$[Cr(H_2O)_4Cl_2]Cl \cdot 2\ H_2O$
violet	green	green

The differences among them arise from the exchange of chloride ions for water molecules in the coordination sphere. In the crystalline state the water of hydration is outside the coordination sphere and is probably present simply as lattice water molecules. These serve to fill the anion sites in in the crystal which were vacated when the chloride ions entered into coordination.

The presence of ligands which can coordinate to the central atom through different atoms in the ligand can give rise to ***linkage isomerism.*** Most examples of linkage isomerism involve the nitrite ion (NO_2^-), which can link through either the oxygen atom or the nitrogen atom, since both possess unshared electron pairs; for example,

$[Co(NH_3)_5ONO]Cl_2$	$[Co(NH_3)_5NO_2]Cl_2$
nitritopentamminecobalt(III) chloride (red)	nitropentamminecobalt(III) chloride (yellow)

The basis of the structural assignment in these compounds is the fact that treatment of the red form with acids yields nitrous acid (HONO), while treatment of the yellow form does not.

In spite of the apparent possibility of their existence, few authentic cases of linkage isomerism are known that involve other ligands, such as CN^-, SCN^-, and CO, which might conceivably coordinate through different atoms.

Coordination isomerism arises from the exchange of ligands between two coordination centers in the same compound. It can exist among salts in which both the cation and anion are complex. The following are a few examples of coordination isomers:

$$[Pt^{II}(NH_3)_4]^{++}[Pt^{II}Cl_4]^{--} \quad \text{and} \quad [Pt^{II}(NH_3)_3Cl]^{+}[Pt^{II}(NH_3)Cl_3]^{-}$$

$$[Pt^{II}(NH_3)_4]^{++}[Pt^{IV}Cl_6]^{--} \quad \text{and} \quad [Pt^{IV}(NH_3)_4Cl_2]^{++}[Pt^{II}Cl_4]^{--}$$

$$[Co^{III}(NH_3)_6]^{+++}[Co^{III}(NO_2)_6]^{---} \quad \text{and} \quad [Co^{III}(NH_3)_4(NO_2)_2]^{+}[Co^{III}(NH_3)_2(NO_2)_4]^{-}$$

$$[Co^{III}(en)_3]^{+++}[Cr^{III}(CN)_6]^{---} \quad \text{and} \quad [Cr^{III}(en)_3]^{+++}[Co^{III}(CN)_6]^{---}$$

(b) Stereoisomerism. The possibility of stereoisomerism exists among complexes in which the coordination number of the central atom is four or greater. It was from a study of stereoisomerism in coordination complexes that Alfred Werner was led in 1893 to assign either a square planar or a tetrahedral structure to 4-coordinate complexes, and an octahedral structure to those which were 6-coordinate.

The 4-coordinate platinum(II) ion forms a number of complexes in which two different kinds of ligands are present. Among those with the general formula $PtAB_3^{\pm n}$, only one form of each has ever been isolated. Those with the general formula $PtA_2B_2^{\pm n}$, such as $[Pt(NH_3)_2Cl_2]^0$, however, occur in two distinct forms which exhibit different physical and chemical properties. Werner pointed out that a square planar structure for Pt(II) complexes is consistent with the observed isomerism. He therefore assigned the structures shown in Figure 19.9 to the two isomeric forms of $[Pt(NH_3)_2Cl_2]$. In

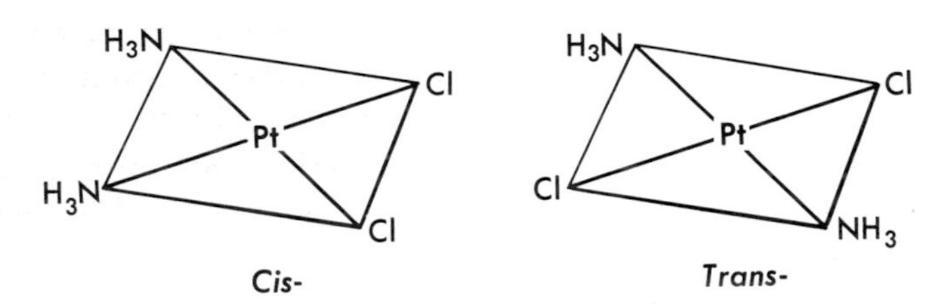

Fig. 19.9 Geometric (*cis-* and *trans-*) isomers of the planar complex dichlorodiammineplatinum(II).

the first of these the like ligands are situated on adjacent corners (along an edge) of an imaginary square drawn around the central Pt atom. In the second, the like ligands are located at opposite corners (along a diagonal) of the square. Although all four ligands are the same distance from the central atom, the distances between like ligands are different in the two structures, which therefore should represent different compounds. These compounds are ***geometric isomers.*** That in which the like ligands are on the same side of the central atom is called the *cis* isomer. Like ligands are on opposite sides of the central atom in the *trans* form. Among other ions which form square planar complexes that can exhibit *cis-trans* isomerism are those of Cu(II), Ag(II), Au(III), Co(II), Ni(II), and Pd(II).

In contrast to the above examples, complexes of the type MA_2B_2 of certain other metals have been found to exist in only one form. This has been interpreted as evidence for a tetrahedral geometry in these complexes. The four apexes of a symmetrical tetrahedron are equidistant from one another as well as from the center, and hence *cis-trans* isomerism is not possible.

If all four ligands in a tetrahedral complex are different, the complex will be asymmetric. Two forms of the complex should exist which are nonsuperimposable mirror images. These forms should be ***optical isomers*** of one another, each rotating the plane of polarized light to the same degree but in opposite directions (Sec. 17.8). Attempts to prepare tetrahedral complexes with four different unidentate ligands have been generally unsuccessful because the products have been too unstable to be isolated. Tetrahedral complexes of the type **M**(**A**—**B**)$_2$, where **A**—**B** is an unsymmetrical bidentate ligand, have been isolated and resolved into their enantiomeric forms. Such complexes, as shown in Fig. 19.10, have no center or plane

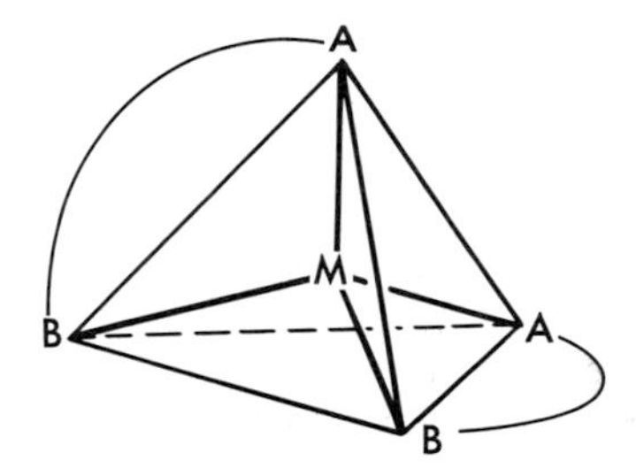

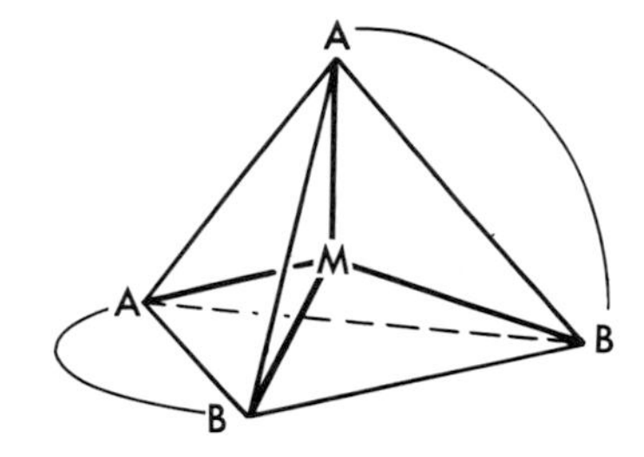

Fig. 19.10 Optical isomers (enantiomorphs) of the tetrahedral complex M(A—B)$_2$.

of symmetry, and are not superimposable on one another. They have been found, as expected, to have identical physical properties except for their opposite effect in rotating the plane of polarized light.

Tetrahedral geometry is more common among the complexes of representative metals than among transition metals. Among the transition elements, only the members of Group IIB, **Zn**(II), **Cd**(II), and **Hg**(II), commonly form tetrahedral complexes, and these same elements, as we have seen before, can equally well be considered representative (Sec. 19.2).

Werner demonstrated from chemical evidence that in 6-coordinate complexes the ligands are octahedrally arranged about the central atom. The regular octahedral structure of the coordination sphere is usually represented in either of the two ways shown in Fig. 19.11. The second of these

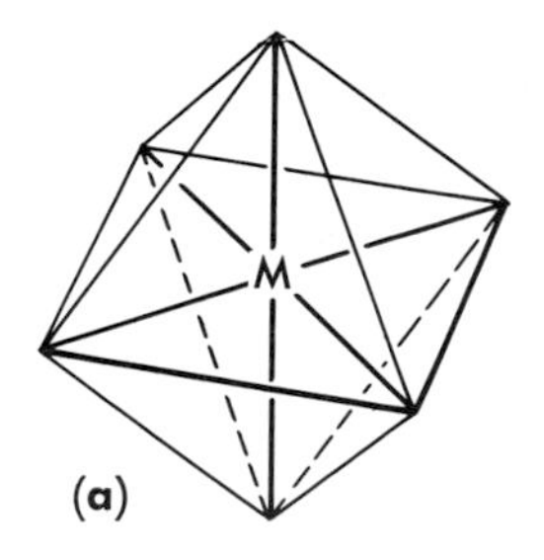

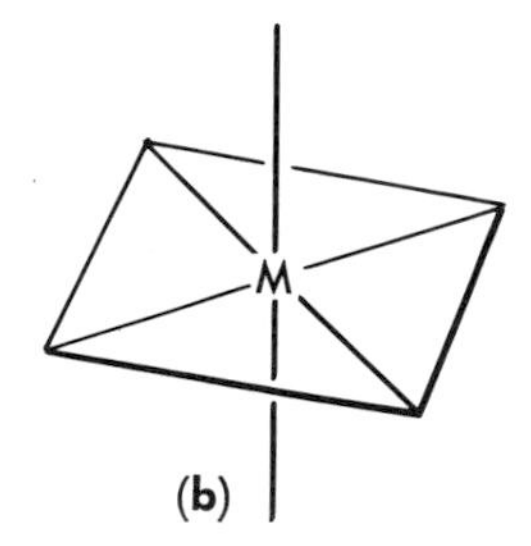

Fig. 19.11 Representation of octahedral complex geometry.

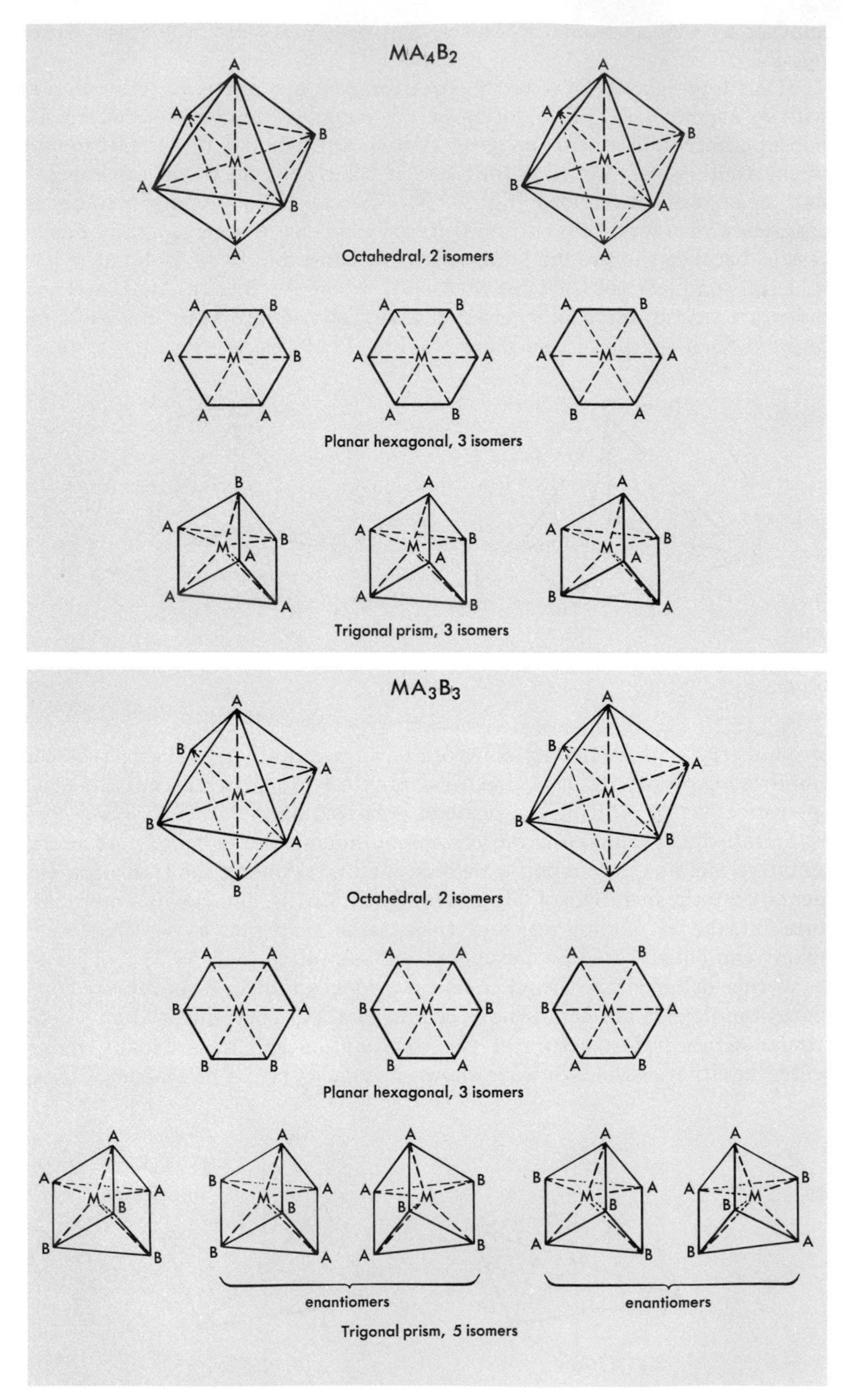

Fig. 19.12 Possible isomers of the complexes MA_4B_2 and MA_3B_3 in three different geometrical arrangements.

(Fig. 19.11b) is often used because it is easy to draw, but it may be misleading if one is not careful. The bonds along the vertical axis are not unique. Those along the other axes can equally well be placed in the vertical orientation simply by rotating the octahedron. In support of the octahedral geometry is the fact that although complexes of the types $\mathbf{MA_6}$ and $\mathbf{MA_5B}$ exist in only one form, complexes of the types $\mathbf{MA_4B_2}$ and $\mathbf{MA_3B_3}$ can be obtained in two, and only two, geometrically isomeric forms. These observations are not only consistent with octahedral geometry, but rule out the other possible symmetrical arrangements of six ligands (planar hexagonal and trigonal prism). A planar hexagonal arrangement would permit the existence of three isomers of $\mathbf{MA_4B_2}$ and three of $\mathbf{MA_3B_3}$. A trigonal prismatic arrangement would lead to three isomers of $\mathbf{MA_4B_2}$, and five, including two enantiomeric pairs, of formula $\mathbf{MA_3B_3}$ (Fig. 19.12).

The *cis* and *trans* isomers of $[\mathbf{Co(NH_3)_4Cl_2}]^+$ and the facial and peripheral isomers of $[\mathbf{Co(NH_3)_3Cl_3}]^0$ shown in Figs. 19.13 and 19.14 are examples of octahedral geometric isomers. Any two ligands are *cis*- if they are adjacent to one another along any single edge of the octahedron and *trans*- if they lie at opposite corners along any one of its axes. A ***facial isomer*** is one which has three like ligands on one triangular face and the other three like ligands on the opposite face. A peripheral isomer has three like ligands at points lying in a plane that bisects the octahedron and the other three ligands in a plane perpendicular to the first.

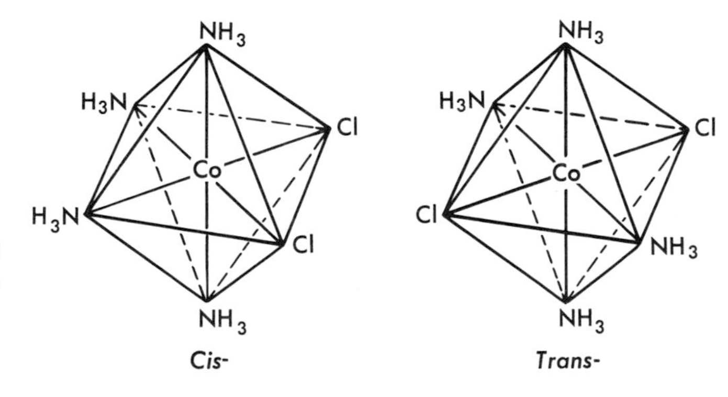

Fig. 19.13 *Cis*- and *trans*- isomers of dichlorotetramminecobalt(III) ion.

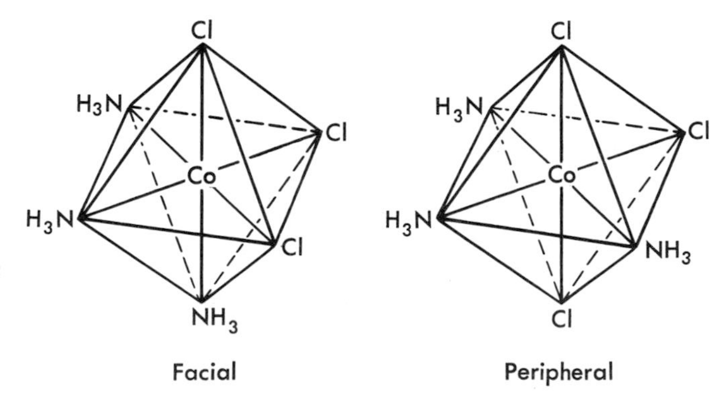

Fig. 19.14 Facial and peripheral isomers of trichlorotriamminecobalt(III).

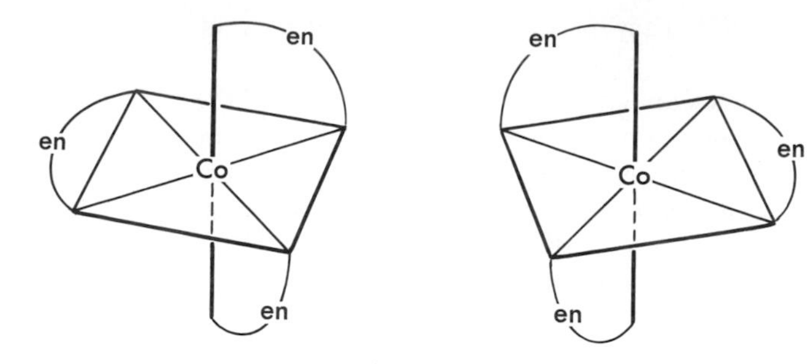

Fig. 19.15 Optical isomers of tris(ethylenediamine)-cobalt(III) ion.

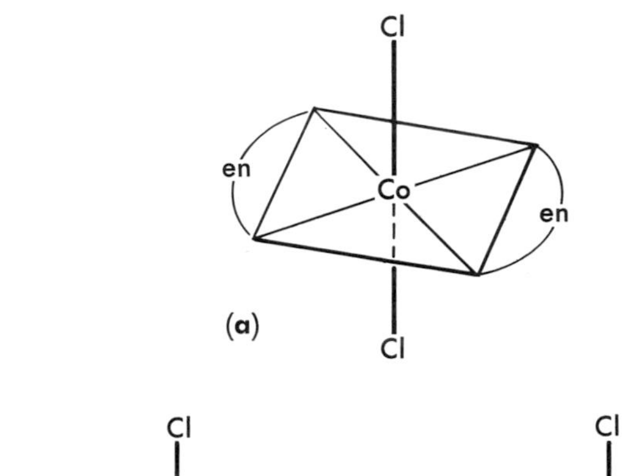

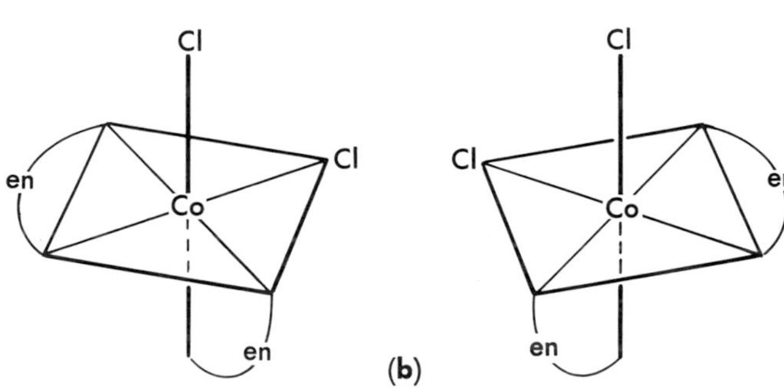

Fig. 19.16 Isomers of dichlorobis (ethylenediamine) cobalt(III) ion. (a) The *trans*- isomer has a plane of symmetry, and hence is identical with its mirror image. (b) The *cis*- form, with no plane of symmetry, exists in two enantiomeric forms.

A number of examples are known of optical isomers of octahedral compounds which contain two or three molecules of a bidentate ligand. Because of spatial requirements, most bidentate ligands are able to coordinate only to *cis* positions. As a result, the ion *tris* (ethylenediamine) cobalt(III), for example, is asymmetric. It can therefore exist in optically active nonsuperimposable forms (Fig. 19.15). The optical isomerism of this ion was predicted by Alfred Werner, who in 1911 succeeded in preparing it and resolving it into its enantiomers. He also prepared and separated the stereoisomers of the compound dichlorobis (ethylenediamine) cobalt(III) chloride. The ion in this case is especially interesting because it exists in both geometrically and optically stereoisomeric forms. Examination of the structure shown in Fig. 19.16 will show that there are two nonsuperimposable mirror-image configurations possible for the *cis*-dichloro isomer, but that there is only one structure for the *trans*- isomer. It is the *cis* compound, therefore, which is optically active. The *trans* compound is symmetrical and optically inactive.

In any attempt to describe the nature of bonding in coordination complexes one encounters a number of difficulties, not all of which have been entirely resolved. Among chemists there are three principal ways of interpreting bonding in these compounds. The first of these, ***valence bond theory,*** has the advantage of retaining the classical picture of the chemical bond and is perhaps the easiest to grasp. It is, however, less satisfactory than the other two in accounting for certain properties of complexes. It offers, for example, no adequate explanation for the pronounced color which is characteristic of so many coordination complexes. The other current interpretations, ***crystal field theory*** and ***ligand field theory*** offer greater promise and are gaining increasing acceptance. In the next few pages we will attempt to present a summary of the main features of each of these theories.

(a) Valence Bond Theory. In this interpretation bonding is considered to result from the use of unoccupied hybridized bonding orbitals of the metal for the formation of coordinate covalent bonds with the donor electron pairs of the ligands. The coordination number and configuration of the complex depends upon the number of available vacant orbitals, the size of the metal ion, and the magnitude of the charge effects between the metal ion and the ligands. Among the transition metals, unoccupied *d*-orbitals generally take part in the formation of hybrid orbitals for bonding. For any complex, the hybrid orbitals used must be those which result in equivalent bonds having the directional characteristics required for the geometry of the complex. According to this interpretation, the hybrid orbitals which should most often be encountered are those listed in Table 19.9.

TABLE 19.9 Hybrid Orbitals in Coordination Complexes

Type of Orbital	Coordination Number	Geometry	Example
sp	2	linear	$[Ag(NH_3)_2]^+$
sp^3	4	tetrahedral	$[Zn(NH_3)_4]^{++}$
dsp^2	4	square planar	$[Pt(NH_3)_4]^{++}$
d^2*sp*^{3}	6	octahedral	$[PtCl_6]^{--}$

Chromium, with the electronic configuration $3d^54s^1$, attains the configuration $3d^3$ in the Cr^{+++} ion. According to Hund's rule (Sec. 7.7) the three *d* electrons of the ion should be unpaired and singly occupy three *d* orbitals, so that the remaining two 3*d* orbitals along with the 4*s* and 4*p* orbitals are available for the formation of coordinate covalent bonds with six ligands. The octahedral geometry observed among the complexes of Cr(III) is consistent with the hybridization of the vacant orbitals of the metal ion to form six d^2sp^3 hybrid orbitals. This can be represented schematically as follows, using the hexamminechromium(III) complex as an example:

	3d					4s	4p		
Cr^{+++}	1	1	1	_	_	_	_	_	_
$[Cr(NH_3)_6]^{+++}$	1	1	1	1l	1l	1l	1l	1l	1l

(the last six orbitals of $[Cr(NH_3)_6]^{+++}$ boxed: d^2sp^3)

The ions Fe^{++} and Co^{+++} each have six $3d$ electrons, of which two would be expected to be paired, and the remaining four unpaired:

	3d					4s	4p		
Fe^{++}, Co^{+++}	1l	1	1	1	1	_	_	_	_

Both form stable octahedral complexes, which leads us to conclude that the formation of six bonds by coordination releases sufficient energy to overcome the resistance of the d electrons to pairing, thus making d^2sp^3 hybrid orbitals available for the electron pairs from the ligands:

	3d					4s	4p		
$[Fe(CN)_6]^{4-}$, $[Co(CN)_6]^{3-}$	1l	1l	1l	1l	1l	1l	1l	1l	1l

(the last six orbitals boxed: d^2sp^3)

That all of the electrons are indeed paired in these two complex ions is shown by the fact that they do not exhibit any paramagnetism (Sec. 18.12). The absence of any paramagnetism is evidence that all of the electrons in a substance are paired. Such a substance tends to move toward the weaker regions of an external magnetic field, and is described as *diamagnetic*. Diamagnetism is an induced effect which is a universal property of all matter, but since it is a weak effect, it can be observed only in the absence of paramagnetism.

Not only does our theory predict that the complexes of Fe(II) and Co(III) should be diamagnetic, in agreement with observation, it also predicts that $[Cr(NH_3)_6]^{+++}$ should have three unpaired electrons and be paramagnetic. Again, the prediction is borne out by experiment. Electronic configurations of a number of other transition metal ions and their complexes are shown schematically in Table 19.10, together with the shapes and magnetic properties of the complexes, as determined experimentally.

TABLE 19.10 Electronic Configurations of Transition Metal Ions and Complexes

	3d					4s	4p			Hybrid orbitals	
Mn^{+++}	↑	↑	↑	↑	—	—	—	—	—		
$[Mn(CN)_6]^{---}$	↑↓	↑	↑	↑↓	↑↓	↑↓	↑↓	↑↓	↑↓	d^2sp^3	octahedral, paramagnetic
Fe^{+++}	↑	↑	↑	↑	↑	—	—	—	—		
$[Fe(CN)_6]^{---}$	↑↓	↑↓	↑	↑↓	↑↓	↑↓	↑↓	↑↓	↑↓	d^2sp^3	octahedral, paramagnetic
Mn^{++}	↑	↑	↑	↑	↑	—	—	—	—		
$[MnBr_4]^{--}$	↑	↑	↑	↑	↑	↑↓	↑↓	↑↓	↑↓	sp^3	tetrahedral, paramagnetic
Ni^{++}	↑↓	↑↓	↑↓	↑	↑	—	—	—	—		
$[Ni(CN)_4]^{--}$	↑↓	↑↓	↑↓	↑↓	↑↓	↑↓	↑↓	↑↓	—	dsp^2	square planar, diamagnetic
$[NiCl_4]^{--}$	↑↓	↑↓	↑↓	↑	↑	↑↓	↑↓	↑↓	↑↓	sp^3	tetrahedral, paramagnetic
Cu^{+}	↑↓	↑↓	↑↓	↑↓	↑↓	—	—	—	—		
$[Cu(CN)_4]^{---}$	↑↓	↑↓	↑↓	↑↓	↑↓	↑↓	↑↓	↑↓	↑↓	sp^3	tetrahedral, diamagnetic
Cu^{++}	↑↓	↑↓	↑↓	↑↓	↑	—	—	—	—		
$[Cu(NH_3)_4]^{++}$	↑↓	↑↓	↑↓	↑↓	↑↓	↑↓	↑↓	↑↓	↑	dsp^2	square planar, paramagnetic
Zn^{++}	↑↓	↑↓	↑↓	↑↓	↑↓	—	—	—	—		
$[ZnCl_4]^{--}$	↑↓	↑↓	↑↓	↑↓	↑↓	↑↓	↑↓	↑↓	↑↓	sp^3	tetrahedral, diamagnetic

The experimentally determined geometry and observed magnetic properties of all of the complexes considered so far agree with the distribution of electrons and orbital hybridization predicted by the theory and shown on the diagrams. However, the promotion of an unpaired electron from the 3*d* to a 4*p* orbital, necessary in order to account for the square planar structure of $[Cu(NH_3)_4]^{++}$ and other complexes of Cu(II), is difficult to justify.

In a number of respects the apparently simple and straightforward valence bond approach is not altogether satisfactory. For example, unlike $[Fe(CN)_6]^{4-}$ and $[Co(CN)_6]^{3-}$, which as we have seen are diamagnetic, the ions $[Fe(NH_3)_6]^{++}$ and $[CoF_6]^{3-}$ are paramagnetic, and each has a magnetic moment of the same order of magnitude as do uncomplexed Fe^{++} and Co^{+++} ions. This indicates that within each of the paramagnetic complexes there must be four unpaired electrons, just as there are in the free metallic ions. It was at one time suggested that in these complexes the metal-ligand bonds might be predominantly electrostatic (ionic in $[CoF_6]^{3-}$ and ion-dipole attraction in $[Fe(NH_3)_6]^{++}$) rather than covalent, thus leaving the 3*d* electrons undisturbed. Bonding of this type would not necessarily result in any difference in the spatial arrangement of the ligands, since six ligands equally distant from each other and equally distant from the central ion to which they were electrostatically bound would still possess octahedral geometry. A different approach, which allows for the presence of four unpaired electrons while still retaining covalent bonding, is based on the assumption that the central ion can utilize empty 4*d* orbitals rather than the partly occupied 3*d*, to form sp^3d^2 hybrid orbitals. According to this view, the diamagnetic complexes of Fe(II) and Co(III) utilize *inner*, d^2sp^3 hybrid orbitals, and the paramagnetic complexes use *outer*, sp^3d^2 orbitals:

	3d					4s	4p			4d					
Fe^{++}, Co^{+++}	↑↓	↑	↑	↑	↑	_	_	_	_	_	_	_	_	_	
$[Fe(CN)_6]^{4-}$ $[Co(CN)_6]^{3-}$	↑↓	↑↓	↑↓	[↑↓	↑↓	↑↓	↑↓	↑↓	↑↓]	_	_	_	_	_	*diamagnetic*
				d^2sp^3											
$[Fe(NH_3)_6]^{++}$ $[CoF_6]^{3-}$	↑↓	↑	↑	↑	↑	[↑↓	↑↓	↑↓	↑↓	↑↓	↑↓]	_	_	_	*paramagnetic*
						sp^3d^2									

It is also possible to account for the existence of octahedral complexes of Ni(II) in terms of outer sp^3d^2 hybridization:

	3d					4s	4p			4d				
Ni^{++}	↑↓	↑↓	↑↓	↑	↑	_	_	_	_	_	_	_	_	_
$[Ni(NH_3)_6]^{++}$	↑↓	↑↓	↑↓	↑	↑	[↑↓	↑↓	↑↓	↑↓	↑↓	↑↓]	_	_	_
						sp^3d^2								

The only way to make two $3d$ orbitals available for bonding in this complex would be to promote the two unpaired $3d$ electrons to the $4d$ level. This would seem unlikely because of the amount of energy which would be required to bring it about.

To form the octahedral complex $[Co(NH_3)_6]^{++}$ from Co^{++} would appear to require the promotion of the seventh $3d$ electron to the higher energy $4d$ orbitals:

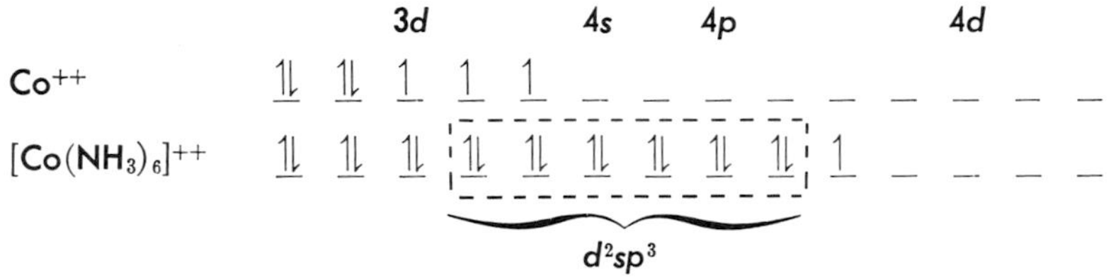

	3d					4s	4p			4d				
Co^{++}	↑↓	↑↓	↑	↑	↑	_	_	_	_	_	_	_	_	_
$[Co(NH_3)_6]^{++}$	↑↓	↑↓	↑↓	[↑↓	↑↓	↑↓	↑↓	↑↓	↑↓]	↑	_	_	_	_
				d^2sp^3										

It has been suggested that the single high-energy electron in the $4d$ orbital should be easily lost, and that this could account for the fact that complexes of Co(II) are much more easily oxidized than is the free Co^{++} ion. Extension of this argument to the square planar complexes of Cu(II), in which the ninth $3d$ electron is promoted to a $4p$ orbital, would lead us to expect that these also should be readily oxidized to form complexes of Cu(III). This prediction, however, is contrary to fact.

We have seen that the paramagnetic 4-coordinate complexes of Ni(II) are tetrahedral and that the diamagnetic complexes of this ion are square planar. The recent discovery of some square planar complexes of Ni(II) which are paramagnetic rather than diamagnetic exposes a serious defect in valence bond theory, since the theory can offer no reasonable explanation for the existence of these complexes. This and other defects of valence bond theory have been largely resolved by the development of crystal field theory.

(b) Crystal Field Theory. This theory abandons the idea of coordinate covalence altogether, and proposes instead that the bonding between the central ion and its ligands is electrostatic in nature and is the result of ion-ion or ion-dipole attraction. This theory is in general more successful than valence bond theory in accounting for both the magnetic properties and colors of coordination complexes.

The shapes of the d orbitals may be represented as shown in Fig. 19.17. Two of these orbitals, the d_{z^2} and the $d_{x^2-y^2}$, are oriented with their lobes lying along the x, y, and z axes. Each of the three remaining orbitals has its four lobes directed at 45° angles between a pair of axes. These orbitals are designated d_{xy}, d_{xz}, and d_{yz}, according to whether their four lobes lie in the xy, xz, or yz plane. All five d orbitals have the same energy in an isolated ion, and are said to be *degenerate*. When the ion is placed in an electrostatic field, however, such as that generated by the presence of ligands, this degeneracy is lost, and the energies of the d orbitals become differentiated, or *split*.

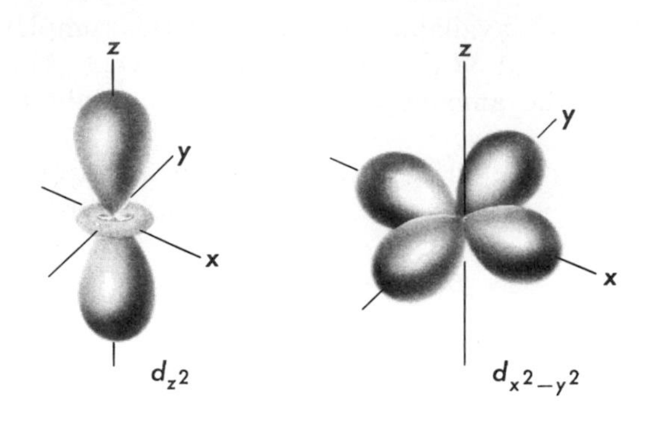

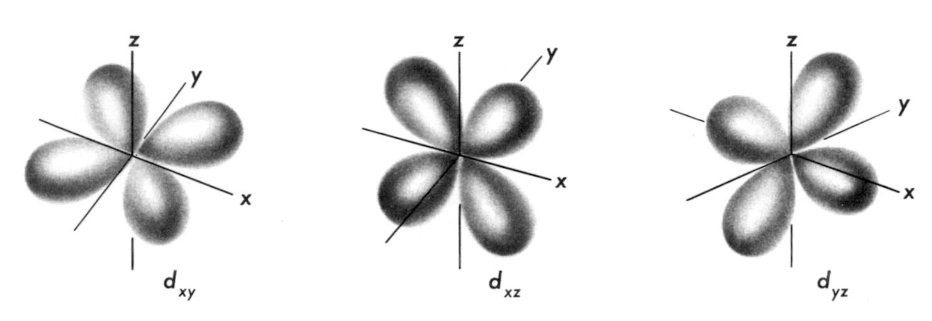

Fig. 19.17 The five d orbital boundary surfaces and their orientation in Cartesian coordinates.

Imagine a metal ion surrounded by six identical ligands arranged octahedrally. The electrons of the ligands, although attracted to the central ion, will nevertheless exert a certain repulsion toward an electron in any d orbital of the ion. As a result, in the presence of ligands, the entire d level has a higher energy than it does in the isolated ion. Not all of the d orbitals have their energies increased to the same degree. As shown in Fig. 19.18, the lobes of the d_{z^2} and $d_{x^2-y^2}$ orbitals lie along the major axes of the octahedron, pointing directly toward the surrounding ligands. An electron in either of these orbitals will therefore suffer a stronger repulsion than it would if it occupied one of the other three orbitals whose lobes point toward the regions between the ligands. Consequently, not only is the d level increased in energy overall, but it is further split into a higher-energy d_γ level consisting of the d_{z^2} and $d_{x^2-y^2}$ orbitals and a lower-energy d_ϵ level made up of the d_{xy}, d_{yz}, and d_{xz} orbitals. The effect of this crystal field splitting is shown diagrammatically in Fig. 19.19. The difference in energy between the low- and high-energy levels is given by Δ, with the d_γ level lying $\frac{3}{5}\Delta$ above, and the d_ϵ level $\frac{2}{5}\Delta$ below the mean value. The magnitude of Δ depends upon the strength of the field created by the ligands: the greater the field strength, the greater the value of Δ.

If the central ion of an octahedral complex possesses one, two, or three d electrons, we should expect these electrons preferentially to occupy the lower-energy d_ϵ orbitals. Because of crystal field splitting, the energy of each of these electrons is less than it would have been in the absence of splitting. This decrease in energy is called the ***crystal field stabilization energy*** (CFSE), and it amounts to $\frac{2}{5}\Delta$ for each electron in a d_ϵ orbital. Following Hund's rule, the electrons should remain unpaired and occupy

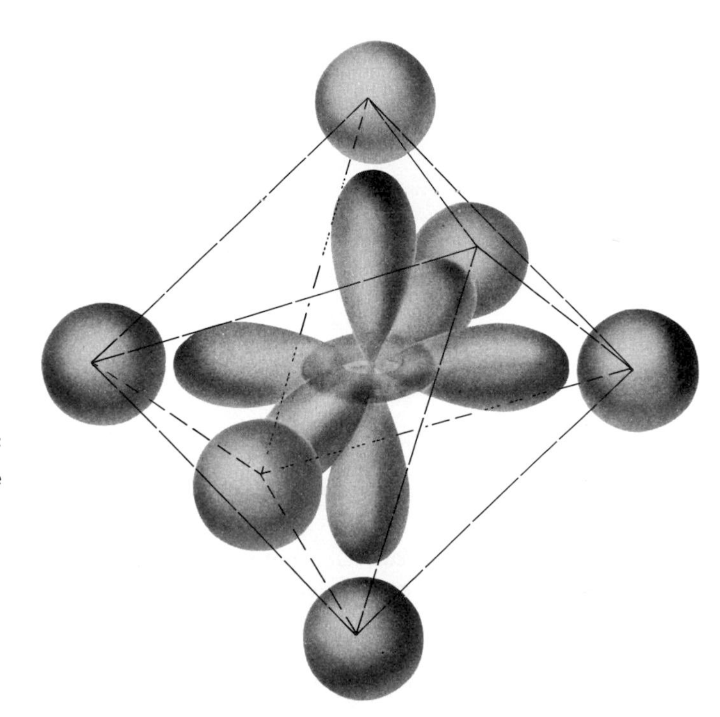

Fig. 19.18 Orientation of $d_{x^2-y^2}$ and d_{z^2} orbitals relative to the ligands in an octahedral complex.

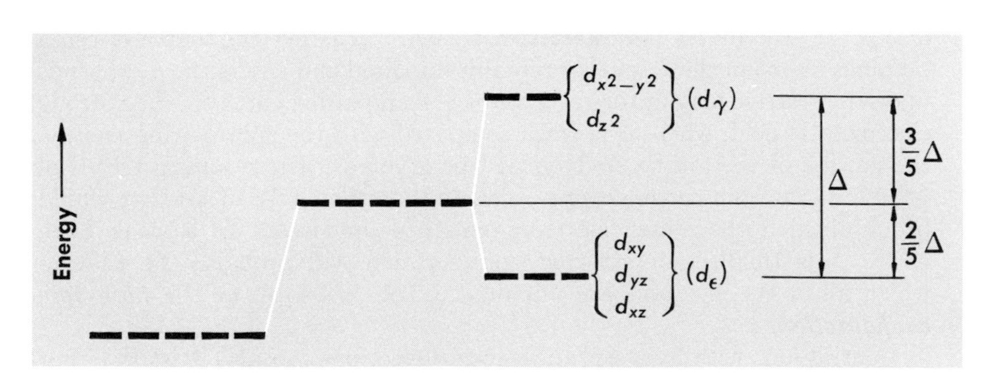

Fig. 19.19 Energy level diagram showing the splitting of the d orbitals in an octahedral field.

the orbitals singly, with their spins parallel. We therefore would predict, for example, that the octahedral complexes of Cr^{+++}, an ion which has three d electrons, should be paramagnetic, and have a magnetic moment corresponding to the presence of three unpaired electrons. This prediction is in agreement both with valence bond theory and with experimental observation.

There are two possible electronic configurations for an ion with four d electrons (Fig. 19.20). Three of the four electrons will preferentially occupy the lower d_ϵ level, and the fourth may either pair up with one of the d_ϵ electrons, or it may occupy one of the higher-energy d_γ orbitals, giving rise

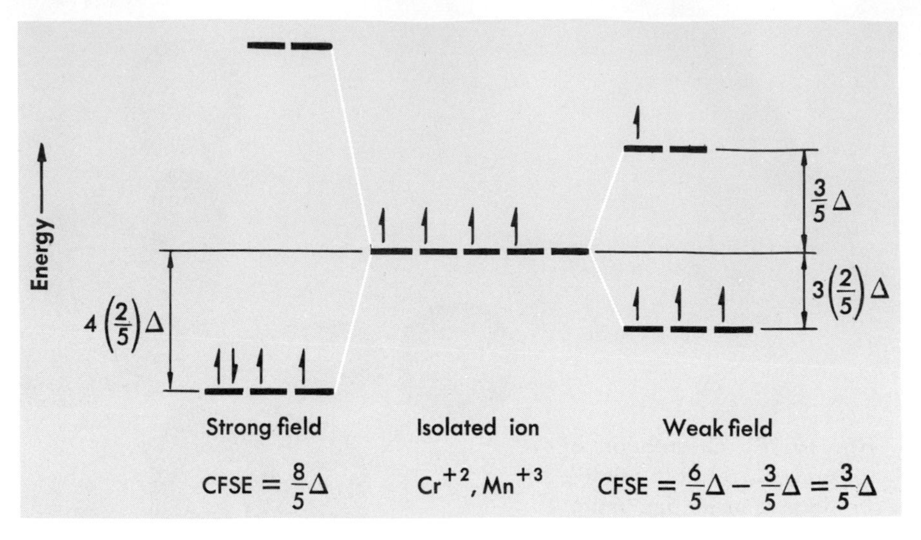

Fig. 19.20 Occupation of orbitals by four electrons in strong and weak octahedral crystal fields.

to a system with four unpaired electrons. In the first case, the CFSE will be $4 \times \frac{2}{5}\Delta$, or $\frac{8}{5}\Delta$, less whatever spin pairing energy must be expended to bring about the pairing of two electrons. In the second case, no spin pairing energy is lost, but while three electrons are stabilized to the extent of $3 \times \frac{2}{5}\Delta$, the fourth is destabilized by $\frac{3}{5}\Delta$. Whether the fourth electron becomes paired in the d_ϵ level or remains unpaired and enters the d_γ depends upon the relative magnitudes of Δ and the spin-pairing energy. In a strong electrostatic field, where Δ is large compared with the spin pairing energy, the pairing of the fourth electron will be favored if the resulting CFSE of $\frac{8}{5}\Delta$ minus the spin pairing energy is more than the CFSE of $\frac{3}{5}\Delta$ that would be obtained if the fourth electron remained unpaired. In a weak field, where Δ is small, the preferred configuration will probably be that in which all of the electrons are unpaired. This is known as the ***high-spin configuration.***

Central ions with five, six, and seven d electrons can also exist in either low- or high-spin configurations according to the strength of the crystal field. The ions Fe^{++} and Co^{+++}, each with six electrons in d orbitals, are

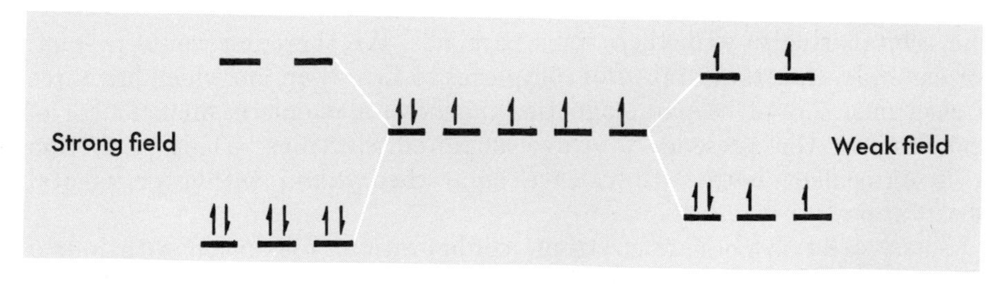

Fig. 19.21 Orbital occupancy for low- and high-spin configurations of Fe^{++} and Co^{+++}.

especially interesting in this regard. Here, in the low-spin configuration, all electrons are paired, whereas in the high-spin configuration four of them are unpaired (Fig. 19.21). Complexes of these ions with highly polar ligands such as CN^-, which should give rise to high field strength and large values for Δ, should be of the low-spin type, and diamagnetic. Complexes in which the field strength is relatively weak, ammines, for example, should be of the high-spin type, and paramagnetic. Thus we can account for the observed diamagnetism of $[Fe(CN_6)]^{4-}$ and $[Co(CN)_6]^{3-}$ and the paramagnetism of $[Fe(NH_3)_6]^{++}$ and $[CoF_6]^{3-}$ without the necessity of postulating either "inner" and "outer" orbital hybridization, or a difference in bond type.

The awkward "promotion" of electrons to vacant orbitals, required by valence bond theory in order to account for the formation and properties of certain complexes, is also not needed in crystal field theory. To allow for octahedral hybridization in the ion $[Co(NH_3)_6]^{++}$, for example, it was necessary to assume promotion of the seventh $3d$ electron to a $4d$ orbital. Crystal field theory, however, interprets this as a complex of the low-spin type, in which six of the d electrons are paired in lower-energy d_ϵ orbitals, with the seventh occupying a d_γ (Fig. 19.22).

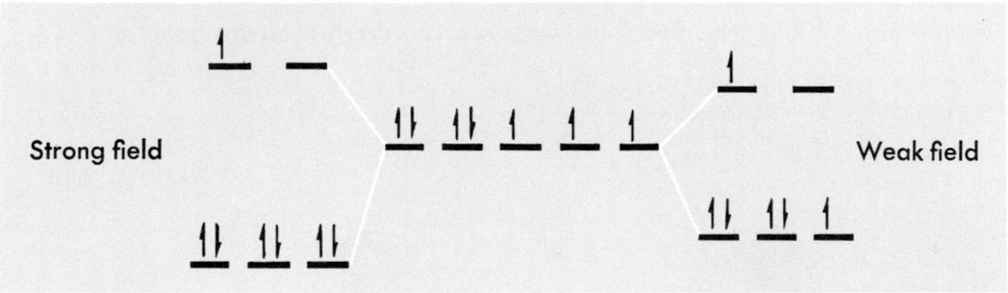

Strong field

Weak field

Fig. 19.22 Orbital occupancy for low- and high-spin configurations of Co^{++}.

The orientation of the five d orbitals in a tetrahedral field is shown in Fig. 19.23. In this case it is the d_{xy}, d_{yz}, and d_{xz} orbitals which point more nearly in the direction of the ligands. Therefore, electrons in these orbitals will be repelled more than those in the d_{z^2} and $d_{x^2-y^2}$ orbitals, and the orbital splitting is accordingly just the opposite of that which would be observed in an octahedral field.

Figure 19.24 shows the orientation of the d orbitals in a square planar field. Here the $d_{x^2-y^2}$ orbital, in the plane of and directed toward each of the ligands, is of highest energy, while the d_{z^2} orbital, perpendicular to the plane of the ligands, is lowest in energy. The relative crystal field splitting of the d orbitals in octahedral, tetrahedral, and square planar fields is shown diagrammatically in Fig. 19.25.

The characteristic colors of coordination complexes can be interpreted as arising from the absorption of light energy corresponding to the crystal field splitting Δ by an electron which is thereby raised to an unoccupied higher-energy orbital. For a given central ion, the magnitude of Δ, and

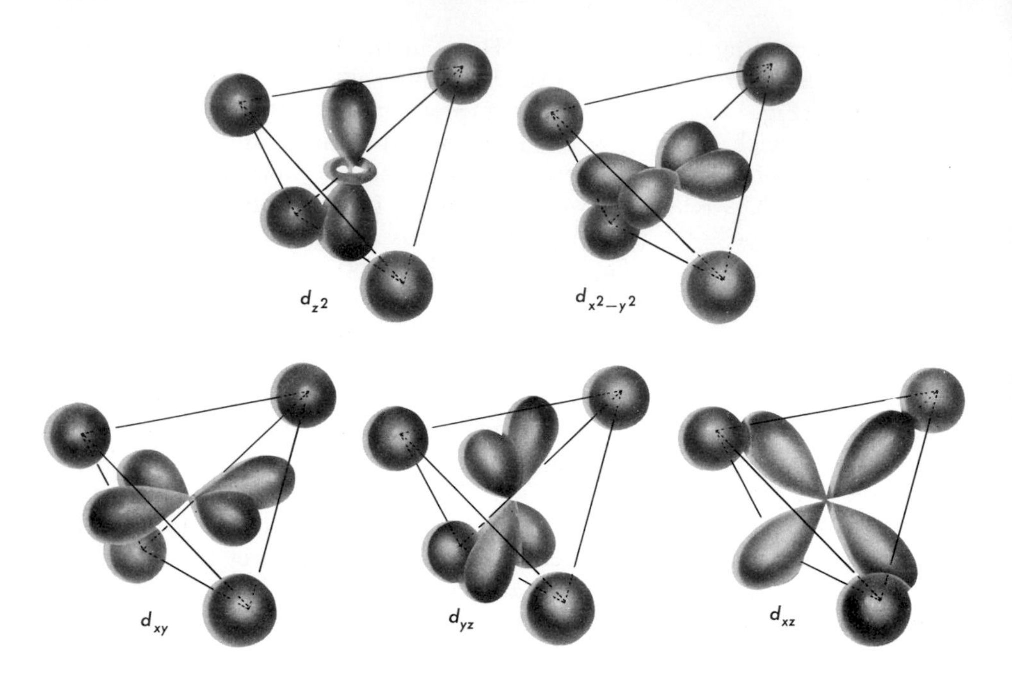

Fig. 19.23 The five d orbitals in a tetrahedral environment.

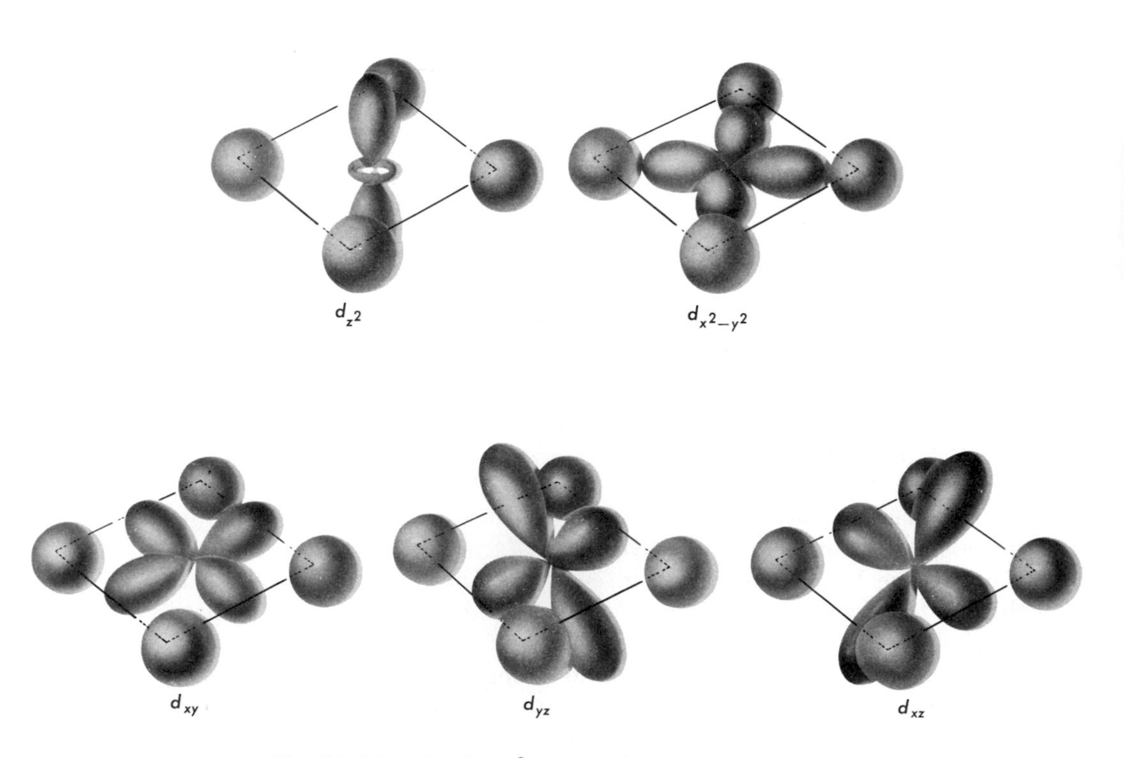

Fig. 19.24 The five d orbitals in a square planar environment.

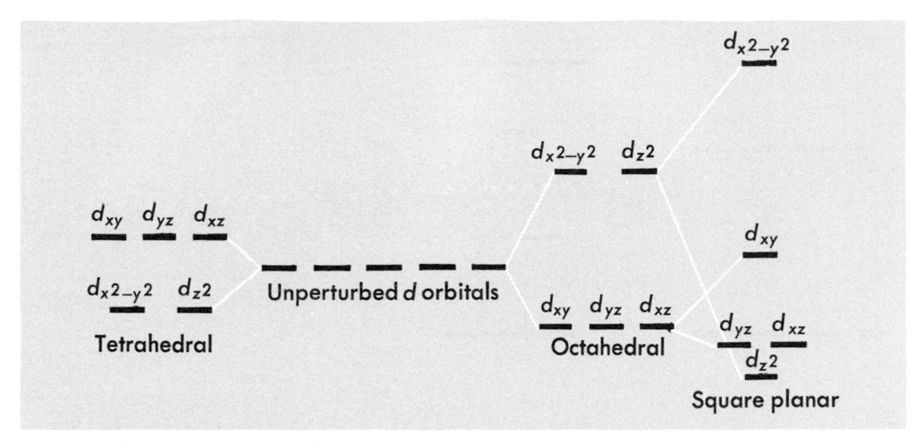

Fig. 19.25 Relative crystal field splitting in tetrahedral, octahedral, and square planar complexes.

hence the frequency of the light absorbed, will depend upon the strength of the electrostatic field produced by the ligands. We can thus account for the changes in color observed as the ligands of a complex are replaced by others. Aqueous solutions of copper(II) salts, for example, appear light blue, the color of the aquo complex $[Cu(H_2O)_4]^{++}$. When ammonia is added, converting the complex to $[Cu(NH_3)_4]^{++}$, the color becomes deep blue. Because of their greater polarity, the ammonia ligands produce a stronger field and cause a greater splitting of the d levels of the central ion. Light absorption occurs at shorter wavelength, corresponding to the larger value of Δ, and this is seen as a change in the color of the complex. The green color appearing when concentrated HCl is added to a solution of a copper salt arises from the replacement of some of the water molecules in the complex with chloride ions. The field splitting power of chloride ions is less than that of water molecules; hence Δ is smaller. Light absorption therefore occurs more toward the red (long wavelength) region of the spectrum in this case, and the solution appears green.

(c) Ligand Field Theory. The ligand field theory incorporates many features of both the crystal field and valence bond theories, but it differs from both in that it takes into account the covalent character of bonding in complexes, which crystal field theory does not, and unlike valence bond theory it treats covalency in terms of antibonding as well as bonding molecular orbitals. In this discussion, we will consider its application to octahedral complexes of the 4th period elements only.

The formation of an octahedral complex, according to this theory, involves the overlap of six ligand atomic orbitals (one from each ligand) with the $4s$, $4p_x$, $4p_y$, $4p_z$, $3d_{x^2-y^2}$, and $3d_{z^2}$ AO's of the metal, to form 12 molecular orbitals, six bonding and six antibonding (Sec. 8.2). The $3d_{xy}$, $3d_{yz}$, and $3d_{xz}$ AO's (the d_ϵ set) which are directed between the ligands, are assumed to be nonbonding.* A diagram of the resulting orbital energy

* It is recognized that these orbitals can sometimes take part in the formation of π bonds by sideways overlap with p orbitals of the ligands.

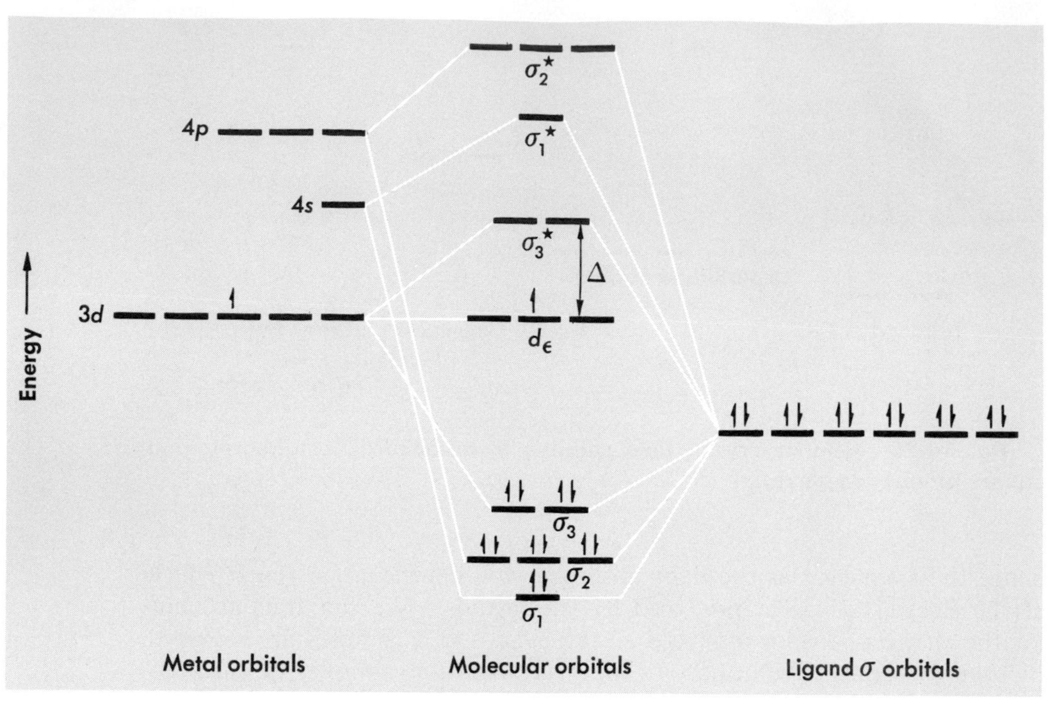

Fig. 19.26 Molecular orbital energy diagram for an octahedral complex of Ti(III).

levels in an octahedral complex of Ti(III) is given in Fig. 19.26. In the normal (ground state) of the complex, the six low-energy bonding MO's are occupied by six pairs of electrons. Any additional electrons are accommodated in the nonbonding d_ϵ AO's, and in the antibonding $\sigma_3^\star$ MO's of lowest energy. The remaining antibonding MO's of higher energy are not occupied in the ground state in any complex. The end result is the effective splitting of the d level of the metal into a triply degenerate lower level and a doubly degenerate upper level, separated by an energy gap Δ, exactly as in crystal field theory. Again, complexes of atoms or ions with 4, 5, 6, or 7 d electrons can exist in low-spin or high-spin configurations. Which configuration the metal will assume in a given complex is considered in this case to depend upon the degree of orbital overlap between the ligands and the metal. The greater the degree of overlap with the $d_{x^2-y^2}$ and d_{z^2} orbitals of the metal, the lower the energy of the σ_3 bonding MO's and the higher the energy of the antibonding $\sigma_3^\star$ MO's and hence the larger the value for Δ. A high degree of orbital overlap therefore should favor the low-spin configuration for the complex. On the other hand, if orbital overlap is small, Δ will have a smaller value and the high-spin configuration should be preferred.

The application of ligand field theory to square planar and tetrahedral complexes is similar in principle, but of considerably greater complexity. Nevertheless, the conclusions reached are generally in agreement with those of crystal field theory.

Chapter 6 of the book *Chemical Bonding*, by Audrey L. Companion (McGraw-Hill Book Company, New York, 1964), is a very clear discussion of the structure of transition metal complexes, with particular emphasis on metal complexes. n only 25 well-written pages, the author presents a readable account of the causes of color in transition metal compounds, their magnetic properties, and the fundamentals of crystal field and ligand field theory. In the same vein is Chapter 9 of *Electronic Structure and Chemical Bonding*, by Donald K. Sebera (Blaisdell Publishing Company, Waltham, Mass., 1964). This book also includes a discussion of the effect of the size of the central ion on the geometry of the complex. The general principles of coordination complex chemistry are discussed in Chapter 4 of *Chemical Periodicity*, by R. T. Sanderson (Reinhold Publishing Corporation, New York, 1960). The text is illustrated with photographs of models of linear, tetragonal, square planar, and octahedral complexes. The chapter includes a good discussion of isomerism in coordination complexes and gives summaries of the qualities inherent in typical ligands and in the atoms and ions with which they are likely to form complexes. Little mention is made, however, of the nature of bonding in complex compounds. Chapter 17 of the same book is a survey of coordination chemistry by periodic groups, including complexes of the representative elements. A survey of Werner's contributions to the theory of the structure of coordination complexes will be found beginning on page 379 of *The Development of Modern Chemistry*, by Aaron J. Ihde (Harper & Row, New York, 1964).

A number of articles on the subject of complex compounds have appeared in the *Journal of Chemical Education*. Particularly interesting is one by Arthur E. Martell, *J. Chem. Ed.* **29**, 270 (1952), in which the author discusses the effect of complex formation on such properties of the metal ion in aqueous solution as solubility, electrical conductance, color, and electrode potential, as well as some of the applications of complex formation to analytical chemistry. The electronic spectra of complexes are discussed by Richard L. Carlin, ibid., **40**, 135 (1963). The numbers and structures of isomers of 6-coordinate complexes are described by John C. Bailar, Jr., ibid., **34**, 334 (1957). A very complete presentation of valence bond theory will be found in a series of two articles by Daryle H. Busch, ibid., **33**, 376, 498 (1956). More recent developments in the theory of complex bonding are discussed in articles by Leslie E. Sutton, ibid., **37**, 498 (1960), Harry B. Gray, ibid., **41**, 2 (1964), and S. F. A. Kettle, ibid., **43**, 21 (1966). Ligand field theory is presented very clearly and thoroughly in a paper by F. Albert Cotton, ibid., **41**, 466 (1964). A selected annotated bibliography of ligand field theory is included in this paper.

Detailed presentations of the descriptive chemistry of the transition metals will be found in the *Reference Book of Inorganic Chemistry*, by W. M. Latimer and J. H. Hildebrand (Macmillan, New York, 3rd Edition, 1951), and in *Inorganic Chemistry*, by J. Kleinberg, W. J. Argersinger, Jr., and E. Griswold (D. C. Heath and Co., Boston, 1960).

Questions

19.1 What is the basis for the classification of metals as representative and transition?

19.2 What general statement can be made concerning the electron occupancy of *d* and *f* electronic levels of representative elements in their ground states? Why are zinc, cadmium and mercury not generally included amongst the representative elements?

19.3 Correlate such features of atomic structure as unpaired electrons, half-filled and otherwise partially filled *d* orbitals, and increasing nuclear charge with the melting point of metals within a given period as one proceeds from group IA to group IIB.

19.4 Provide an explanation in terms of metallic bonding theory for the fact that the melting points of the representative metals tend to decrease from top to bottom within a family group while the melting points within family groups of transition metals, except for group IIB, **Y** and **La**, and **Cu** and **Ag**, tend to increase from top to bottom.

19.5 Account for the changes in metallic atomic radii within the fourth, fifth, and sixth periods.

19.6 Account for the almost identical atomic radii of niobium and tantalum.

19.7 Account for the especially high densities of the sixth period transition metals that follow lanthanum.

19.8 In what group of the periodic table are the best metallic conductors of heat and electricity found? In what group of the periodic table are the poorest metallic conductors of heat and electricity found? Compare the ground state electronic configurations and electrical conductance of both zinc and manganese with that of copper, using Table 19.1 and Fig. 19.7.

19.9 Explain on the basis of the calculated potential energies of $3d$ and $4s$ orbitals, why the element **Sc** shows a single oxidation state of $+3$ in its compounds, and why **Zn** shows the single oxidation state of $+2$ in its compounds, while the remaining transition elements of the fourth period exhibit varying oxidation states in compound formation.

19.10 On the basis of electronic configuration, account for the fact that in its $+1$ oxidation state mercury exists as Hg_2^{++} ion.

19.11 What is the maximum oxidation state attainable by any of the elements, and what elements do attain that state?

19.12 Why do the stabilities of the lower oxidation state transition metal oxides of a given group increase with decreasing atomic number whereas for the higher oxidation states the oxide stabilities increase with increasing atomic number? Cite examples.

19.13 Cite examples illustrating the more acidic character of some oxides of fourth period transition metals over those of the corresponding elements of the fifth and sixth periods.

19.14 Provide an explanation for ground state electronic structures that give rise to a second ionization potential that is higher for chromium than for manganese and for copper than for zinc.

19.15 In terms of the differences in enthalpy changes involved in the oxidation

$$M(s) \rightarrow M^{++}(aq) + 2\,e^-$$

provide an explanation for the fact that manganese and zinc are considerably more active metals (have higher $\mathcal{E}^0$ values) than their fourth period neighbors. Relate the differences to the electronic configuration of the fourth period transition metals. In like manner account for the unexpected low activity of copper compared to nickel and zinc.

19.16 Provide an explanation for the solubility of **AgCl** in aqueous ammonia.

19.17 Write the formula for ethylenediaminetetraacetic acid (EDTA). By what other names is it known? Discuss some of its uses.

19.18 Distinguish between (a) ionization isomers, (b) hydrate isomers, (c) linkage isomers, (d) coordination isomers.

19.19 Name the following complex compounds:

$[Pt(NH_3)_6]Cl_4$	$K_3[Fe(CN)_6]$
$[Pt(NH_3)_2Cl_4]$	$K_4[Fe(CN)_6]$
$[Pt(NH_3)_4]Cl_2$	$Ag[Ag(CN)_2]$
$K_2[PtCl_4]$	$[Pt(NH_3)_4Cl_2][PtCl_6]$

19.20 What structural features are required to produce (a) geometric isomers and (b) optical isomers of complexes with coordination number of four?

19.21 What structural features are required to correctly account for (a) *cis* and *trans*, (b) facial and peripheral isomers of complexes with coordination number of six?

19.22 Why are the complex ions $[Cr(NH_3)_6]^{+++}$ and $[CoF_6]^{---}$ paramagnetic while $[Co(CN)_6]^{---}$ is diamagnetic?

19.23 Why is it that most compounds of the transition metals are colored?

Force and matter are two
different forms of one and the same thing.
The power to dissociate matter freely
would put at our disposal an
infinite source of energy . . . .

——Gustave Le Bon, 1907

20 NUCLEAR CHEMISTRY

So far, we haven't paid much attention to the nucleus of the atom, and this is perfectly reasonable, since an atom's chemical behavior is determined almost entirely by the arrangement of its extranuclear electrons. Nevertheless, when one stops to think about it, it is rather remarkable that the nucleus exists at all. We know now that, except for hydrogen, all atomic nuclei contain more than one proton, each of which bears a positive charge. Our experience has been that like charges repel, and very strongly at that, yet here we may have as many as 90 or 100 like positive charges all crammed into a volume of the order of 10^{-33} cm^3—about one billionth of the total volume of the atom. The neutron must evidently play a very important role in keeping the nucleus together, because no stable nucleus containing more than one proton is known which does not also contain at least an equal number of neutrons. Exactly how the neutron performs its function of stabilizing the nucleus, or for that matter, exactly what is the nature of the neutron and the proton, are still matters of conjecture and intensive research.

Stable Nuclei 20.1

Several interesting things show up when one draws a plot showing the number of neutrons versus the number of protons for all of the stable atomic

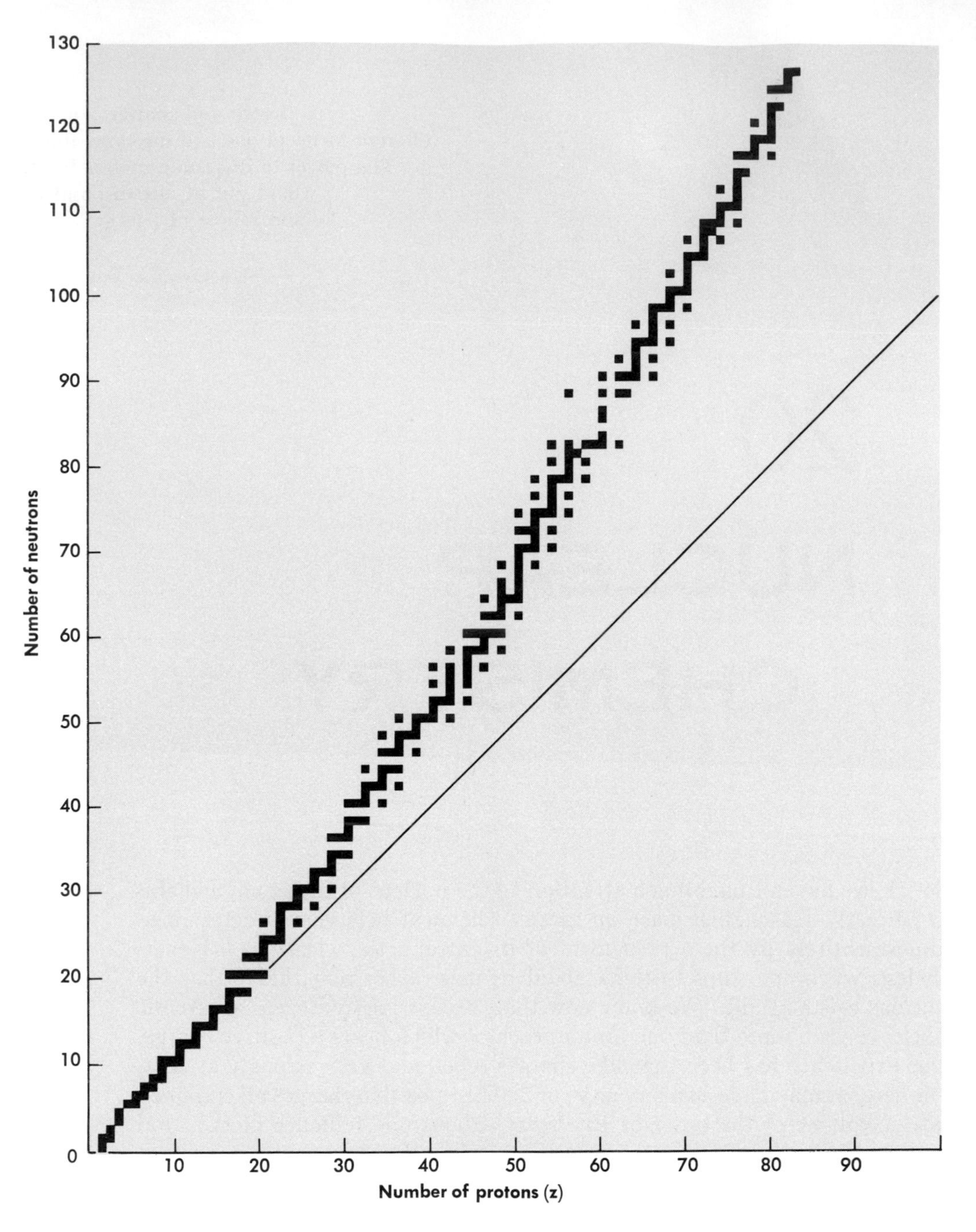

130
120
110
100
90
80
70
60
50
40
30
20
10
0
Number of neutrons
10
20
30
40
50
60
70
80
90
Number of protons (z)

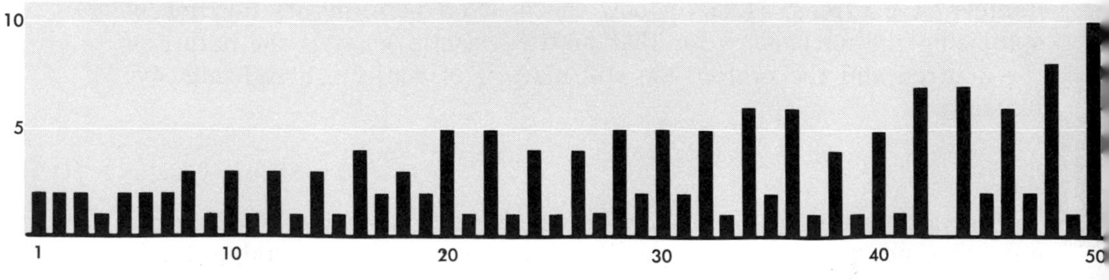

10
5
1
10
20
30
40
50

nuclei (Fig. 20.1). The stable nuclei, that is, those which exhibit no radioactivity, all fall within a narrow region along a curve. For the lighter elements, up to about $Z = 20$ (calcium), the number of neutrons required for stability is approximately equal to the number of protons, and the curve lies nearly along the straight line corresponding to equal numbers of both. With increasing atomic number, the curve rises more and more steeply. It seems that, for stability, the more protons there are in the nucleus, the more neutrons are needed per proton. While a 1:1 ratio of neutrons to protons is sufficient at first, for the heavier nuclei the ratio more nearly approaches 1.5:1. Beyond $Z = 83$, no number of neutrons is sufficient to impart stability to the nucleus, and all of the isotopes of the elements past bismuth are radioactive.

Closer inspection of Fig. 20.1 shows that the curve rises in a more or less stepwise fashion. This results from the fact that there are almost four times as many stable nuclei with even numbers of protons as there are with odd. This is shown strikingly in Fig. 20.2. The largest number (156) of stable nuclei have even numbers of both protons and neutrons. There are about as many with the numbers of protons even and neutrons odd (54) as there are with the numbers of protons odd and neutrons even (50). Rarest of all, there being only five examples, are stable nuclei with odd numbers of both neutrons and protons. This has been interpreted as an indication that, in combining to form atomic nuclei, protons and neutrons tend to pair up in a manner analogous to the pairing of electrons in molecules.

Isotopes whose nuclei contain 2, 8, 20, 28, 50, 82, or 126 neutrons or protons are found to be especially stable and abundant in nature. These "magic numbers" are reminiscent of those (2, 8, 18, 32, . . . , etc) which represent the numbers of electrons which can occupy successive quantum levels in the atom. This suggests an analogous "shell model" of the nucleus in which the magic numbers correspond to stable, closed shells of nuclear particles.

Fig. 20.1 (*left, top*) Chart of stable nuclei. The straight line on the chart corresponds to equal numbers of neutrons and protons.

Fig. 20.2 (*left, bottom, and below*) Chart showing the number of stable nuclei for every value of Z.

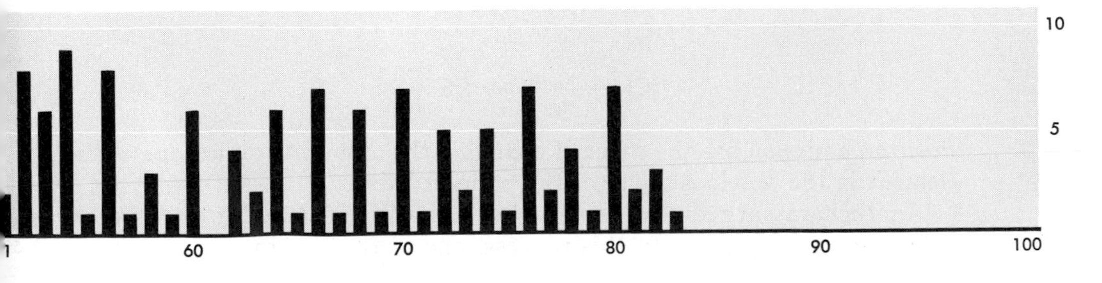

20.2 Radioactive Processes

The nuclei of isotopes lying outside of the narrow range of stability shown in Fig. 20.1 are unstable and exhibit radioactivity. In attempting to attain stability a nucleus may undergo any of a number of radioactive processes according to whether it lies above, below, or beyond the range of stability.

(a) Nuclei Above the Stable Region. The nuclei have too many neutrons for stability. The usual way in which a nucleus corrects this situation is to convert one of its neutrons into a proton plus an electron, emitting the electron as a beta (β) particle. This process, known as ***β emission,*** has the effect of increasing the atomic number by one unit, converting the atom into an isotope of the element in the next group following in the periodic table:

$${}^{14}_{6}C \xrightarrow{\beta \text{ emission}} {}^{14}_{7}N + {}^{0}_{-1}\beta$$

$${}^{56}_{25}Mn \xrightarrow{\beta \text{ emission}} {}^{56}_{26}Fe + {}^{0}_{-1}\beta$$

Since the relative mass of a β particle is negligible, the mass number of the product is the same as that of the parent atom. It is important to remember that in any balanced nuclear equation, the sum of the atomic numbers (subscripts) on the left of the equation must be equal to the sum of the atomic numbers on the right. Likewise, the sums of the atomic mass numbers (superscripts) must be equal on both sides of the equation.

On rare occasions, an atom may emit a neutron. The atomic number remains unchanged, but the mass number decreases by one unit. The following are among the very few examples of ***neutron emission*** processes:

$${}^{17}_{7}N \xrightarrow{\text{neutron emission}} {}^{16}_{7}N + {}^{1}_{0}n$$

$${}^{88}_{35}Br \longrightarrow {}^{87}_{35}Br + {}^{1}_{0}n$$

$${}^{137}_{53}I \longrightarrow {}^{136}_{53}I + {}^{1}_{0}n$$

(b) Nuclei Below the Stable Region. The problem here can be looked on as either too many protons or too few neutrons. Just as a neutron can be converted into a proton by emitting a negative β particle, or electron, a proton can eject a positive β particle, or ***positron,*** and become a neutron:

$${}^{11}_{6}C \xrightarrow{\text{positron emission}} {}^{11}_{5}B + {}^{0}_{+1}\beta$$

$${}^{12}_{7}N \longrightarrow {}^{12}_{6}C + {}^{0}_{+1}\beta$$

$${}^{32}_{17}Cl \longrightarrow {}^{32}_{16}S + {}^{0}_{+1}\beta$$

Positron emission has the effect of changing the atom into an isotope of the element in the previous group of the periodic table.

Another way of reducing the number of positive charges on the nucleus is by ***electron capture.*** In this process, one of the electrons of the innermost, or K level ($n = 1$) of the atom is drawn into the nucleus, converting a proton into a neutron. Because the electron was originally in the K level, the process is often called ***K*-capture.**

$$^{53}_{25}\text{Mn} + {}^{0}_{-1}\beta \xrightarrow{K\text{-capture}} {}^{53}_{24}\text{Cr}$$

$$^{73}_{33}\text{As} + {}^{0}_{-1}\beta \rightarrow {}^{73}_{32}\text{Ge}$$

The product obtained by K-capture is the same as that which would have been formed by positron emission. Often, in fact, the same isotope will react by both processes. For example:

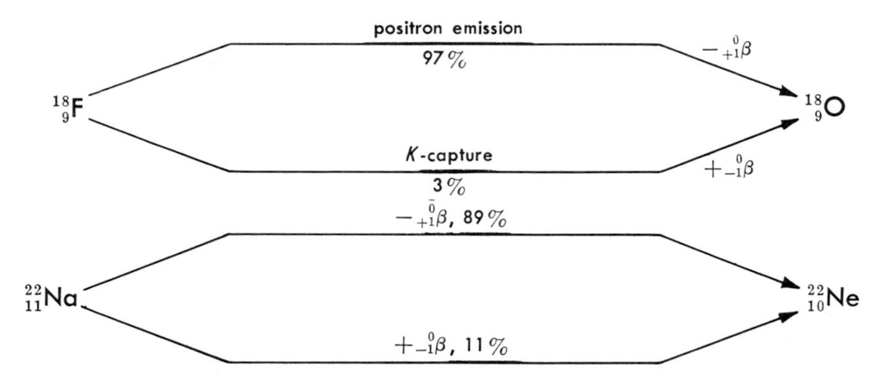

The question will probably arise at this point, "What about the mass of the electron or positron? True, their masses are so small that we usually neglect them, but they do weigh something. Does this mean that the $^{18}_{8}$O atoms formed by positron emission will weigh a little less than those formed by K-capture?" The answer to this question is no, their masses are exactly the same. Any excess mass will be emitted as energy in the form of γ-rays; any deficiency in mass is made up from the binding energy of the nucleus (Sec. 20.7).*

Isotopes of some of the heavier elements decay by emission of α particles (He^{++}), but this is relatively rare for elements with atomic numbers less than 83.

$$^{151}_{67}\text{Ho} \xrightarrow{\alpha\text{ emission}} {}^{147}_{65}\text{Tb} + {}^{4}_{2}\text{He}$$

$$^{204}_{82}\text{Pb} \longrightarrow {}^{200}_{80}\text{Hg} + {}^{4}_{2}\text{He}$$

A short-lived isotope of terbium is remarkable in that it decays by all three processes—electron capture, positron emission, and α emission:

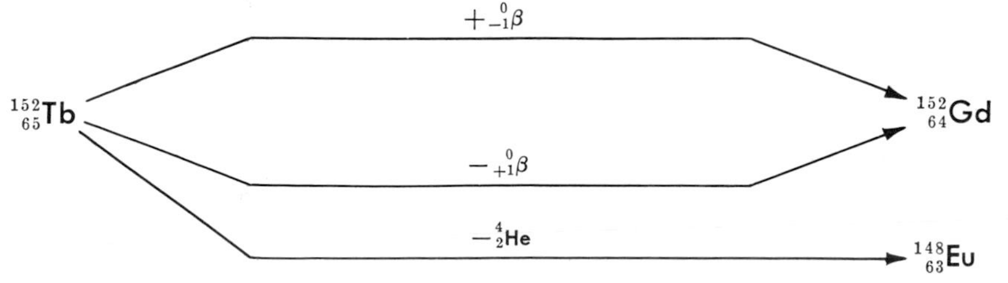

* Remember that mass and energy are interconvertible and equivalent, their equivalence being expressed in Einstein's well-known equation $E = mc^2$.

(c) Nuclei Beyond the Stable Region. All isotopes of the elements beyond $Z = 83$ are radioactive. Here, to attain stability, the numbers of protons and neutrons in most cases must both be reduced. This is accomplished most efficiently by α emission, which has the effect of shifting the element two places to the left in the periodic table and reducing the mass number by 4:

$$^{210}_{84}\text{Po} \rightarrow {}^{206}_{82}\text{Pb} + {}^{4}_{2}\text{He}$$

$$^{238}_{92}\text{U} \rightarrow {}^{234}_{90}\text{Th} + {}^{4}_{2}\text{He}$$

β emission, K-capture, and more rarely, positron emission can also occur with these elements.

Some isotopes of uranium and the transuranium elements undergo spontaneous ***fission*** into fragments with about half the mass of the parent element:

$$^{252}_{98}\text{Cf} \rightarrow {}^{142}_{56}\text{Ba} + {}^{106}_{42}\text{Mo} + 4\,{}^{1}_{0}n$$

Energy is released in all of these radioactive decay processes, some of it as kinetic energy of the products, the rest as electromagnetic radiation. The amounts of energy involved in nuclear transformations are very large, much greater than the amounts encountered in ordinary chemical reactions. The radiation is therefore at high frequencies, in the γ-ray region of the spectrum. The wavelengths of the γ-rays emitted during a radioactive process are characteristic of the particular parent isotope. In the dis-

$$^{226}_{88}\text{Ra} \rightarrow {}^{222}_{86}\text{Rn} + {}^{4}_{2}\text{He}$$

integration of radium by α emission, for example, γ radiation appears at wavelengths of 0.0663, 0.0477, 0.0296, and 0.019 Å, equivalent to energies of 0.187, 0.260, 0.420, and 0.64 million electron volts (MeV) respectively. These energies must correspond to differences between various permitted nuclear energy states in the daughter nuclei, clearly indicating that the energies of the particles in the nucleus are quantized in a manner analogous to the way in which the energies of the extranuclear electrons are quantized.

20.3 Radioactive Series

A single step is not always sufficient to bring an unstable nucleus within the region of stability. This is especially true among the heavier elements beyond bismuth. Here, a series of radioactive processes—perhaps a great many—may be necessary before a stable nucleus is finally achieved. Most of the naturally occurring radioactive isotopes are members of one of three well-defined radioactive series. These are known respectively as the uranium series, the actinium series, and the thorium series. Each of the series ends with the formation of a stable isotope of lead. The successive transformations which take place within the uranium and thorium series

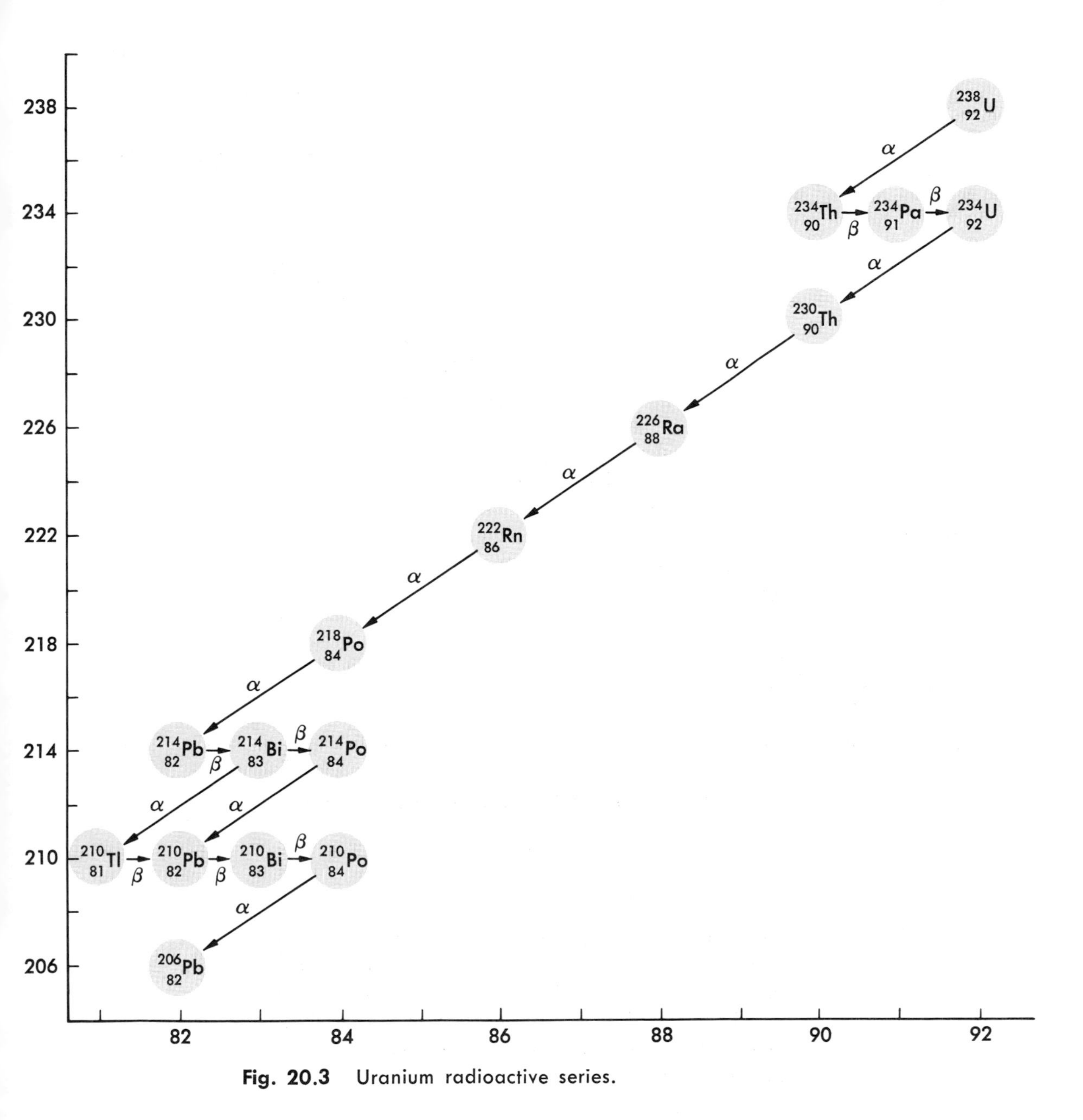

Fig. 20.3 Uranium radioactive series.

are summarized in Figs. 20.3 and 20.4. You will notice that there are several places in these series where the parent isotope can undergo β emission, followed by α emission on the part of the daughter, or the parent may emit an α particle while the daughter undergoes β emission. $^{214}_{83}$**Bi**, for example, may form either $^{214}_{84}$**Po** by β emission, or $^{210}_{81}$**Tl** by α emission. Whether the sequence is β followed by α, or α followed by β, the final result is the same—$^{210}_{82}$**Pb** in the example given.

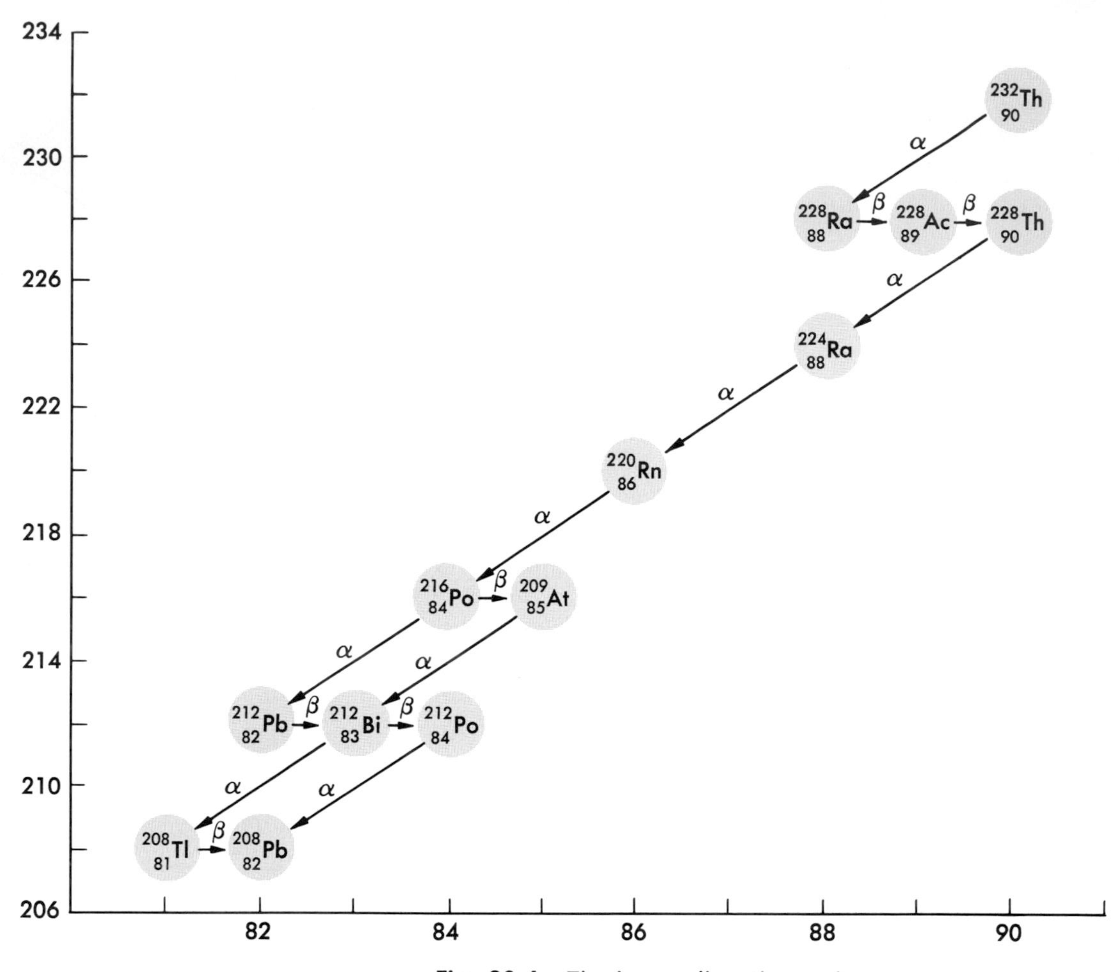

Fig. 20.4 Thorium radioactive series.

20.4 Nuclear Reactions and Transmutation

When the dream of artificially transmuting one element to another finally came true, an alchemist, had he been present, would probably have been disappointed, for the product was not gold, but oxygen. In 1919 Ernest Rutherford and James Chadwick obtained oxygen and hydrogen as products of the bombardment of nitrogen with α particles from a sample of radium. The reaction can be written,

$$^{14}_{7}\text{N} + ^{4}_{2}\text{He} \rightarrow ^{17}_{8}\text{O} + ^{1}_{1}\text{H}$$

Since then it has been found that many kinds of nuclei will react provided that they can be brought close enough to one another. The energy barrier to their close approach is the large coulombic repulsion that exists between like charges. This energy barrier, analogous to the activation energy in an ordinary chemical reaction, can be surmounted by imparting sufficient kinetic energy to one of the nuclei. In some cases, as in Rutherford's reaction, particles with the necessary energy are emitted by naturally radioactive elements. In most cases, though, the particle must be accelerated artificially. The cyclotron and the linear accelerator are two devices to accomplish this acceleration.

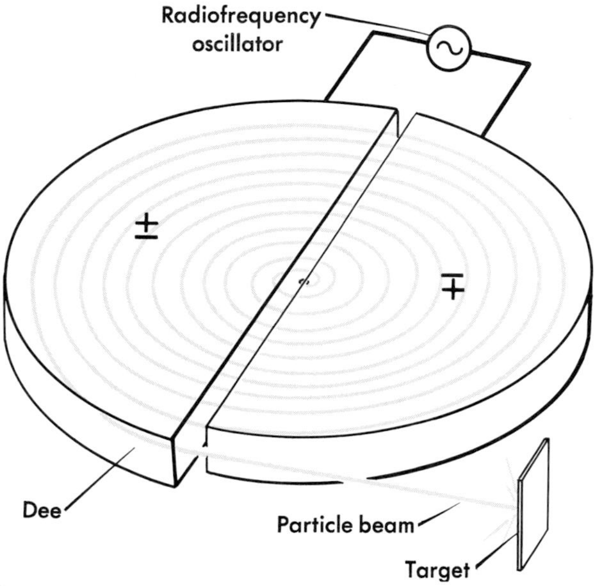

Fig. 20.5 Cyclotron. Only the dees are shown. For clarity, we have omitted the evacuated chamber surrounding the dees and the magnet poles above and below.

(a) The Cyclotron. This consists of two flat, hollow, semicircular containers, or ***dees*** (from their shape, like the letter D), supported alongside one another, with a small gap between their straight sides, in an evacuated chamber between the poles of a powerful electromagnet (Fig. 20.5). The dees are oppositely charged and are connected to a radiofrequency oscillator so that their polarity is constantly reversed. Charged nuclei (ions) are generated at the center of the gap between the dees. This can be done, for example, by using a positive-ray discharge tube in a manner similar to the production of ions in a mass spectrograph (Secs. 6.4 and 6.5). The ions will be pulled toward the oppositely charged dee. As the ions enter the dee, the magnetic field forces them into a curved path with a radius dependent upon the speed of the particles, their charge, and the magnetic field strength (Sec. 6.2). After executing a semicircle, they again approach the gap between the dees. At this moment, the polarities are reversed, the particles are accelerated across the gap, and the process is repeated. Each time the particles cross the gap, they are accelerated. As they move faster and faster, the radius of their path increases, until finally they reach the outer edge and leave the apparatus as a high-velocity beam. The target to be bombarded is placed in the path of the beam. Electrons can be accelerated in a cyclotron in the same manner.

(b) The Linear Accelerator. To obtain particles of very high velocity in a cyclotron, the particles must traverse the gap many times. This

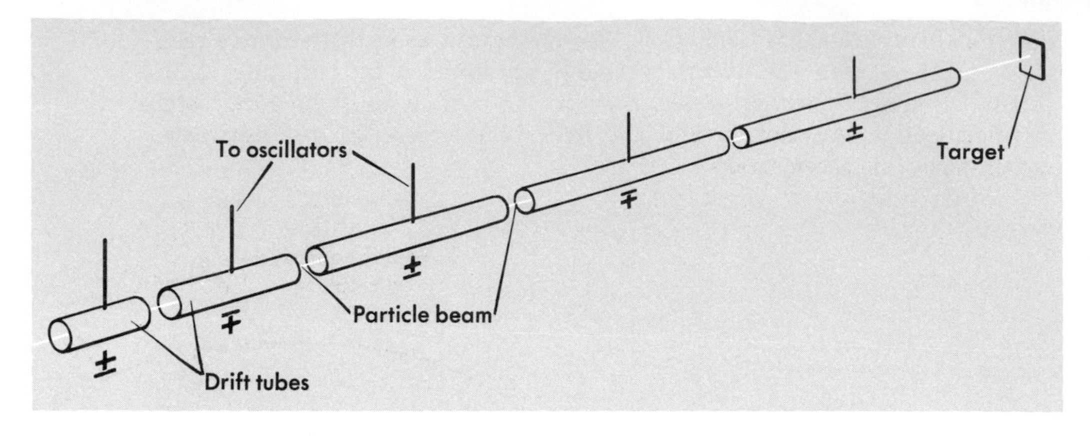

Fig. 20.6 Linear accelerator (schematic).

requires a very large apparatus and a correspondingly huge electromagnet to generate a field sufficiently strong to keep the fast-moving particles in a spiral path. The linear accelerator obviates the need for a magnet by accelerating the particles in a straight line. The principle of operation otherwise is similar.

In the linear accelerator the particle beam passes through a series of oppositely charged ***drift tubes*** suspended in an evacuated chamber (Fig. 20.6). Like the dees of a cyclotron, these tubes are connected to high-frequency oscillator tubes so that their polarity is constantly reversed. A particle will be drawn into the first drift tube if its charge and that of the tube are opposite. While it coasts through the tube, the polarities are reversed by the oscillators so that the particle is accelerated across the gap to the next tube, where the process is repeated. In this way, a beam of ions or electrons undergoes a series of successive accelerations as it passes through the line of tubes. The drift tubes must be made progressively longer, so that as the particles speed up they still take the same time to traverse each tube, in this way remaining in step with the oscillators. The main limitation to the energy which can be imparted to the particles is the length of the accelerator. The linear accelerator at Stanford University, designed to accelerate electrons to energies of 45 GeV (1 GeV = 1000 MeV), is two miles long.

Neutrons are especially effective in bringing about nuclear reactions. Since they have no charge, they are not repelled by the nucleus, and the activation energy for neutron-induced transformations is accordingly much lower than if the projectiles are electrons or positive ions. Neutrons are generated in a number of ways, for example, by bombardment of beryllium with α particles:

$$^{9}_{4}\text{Be} + ^{4}_{2}\text{He} \rightarrow ^{12}_{6}\text{C} + ^{1}_{0}n$$

An isotope of plutonium, which disintegrates by α emission, can be used as the source of α particles for this reaction. Most neutron reactions are carried out, however, by exposing the sample to the neutron flux of a nuclear reactor (Sec. 20.8).

Since Rutherford's first success, many other transmutations have been accomplished. Unfortunately, perhaps, it remains impractical, though theoretically possible, to convert base metals to gold, but it is possible to produce gold by bombarding the still more valuable metal, platinum, with deuterons (deuterium nuclei):

$$^{196}_{78}Pt + {}^{2}_{1}H \rightarrow {}^{197}_{78}Pt + {}^{1}_{1}H$$

$$^{197}_{78}Pt \rightarrow {}^{197}_{79}Au + {}^{0}_{-1}\beta$$

Among the most interesting transmutations have been those resulting in the creation of entirely new elements which never existed before in nature, at least in any detectable amounts. The synthesis of four of these, technetium (**Tc**, element 43), promethium (**Pm**, element 61), astatine (**At**, element 85), and francium (**Fr**, element 87), between 1937 and 1941, filled the last remaining gaps in the periodic table between hydrogen and the heaviest naturally occurring element, uranium:

$$^{96}_{42}Mo + {}^{2}_{1}H \rightarrow {}^{97}_{43}Tc + {}^{1}_{0}n$$

$$^{142}_{60}Nd + {}^{1}_{0}n \rightarrow {}^{143}_{61}Pm + {}^{0}_{-1}\beta$$

$$^{209}_{83}Bi + {}^{4}_{2}He \rightarrow {}^{210}_{85}At + 3\,{}^{1}_{0}n$$

$$^{230}_{90}Th + {}^{1}_{1}H \rightarrow {}^{223}_{87}Fr + 2\,{}^{4}_{2}He$$

The first transuranium element, neptunium (**Np**, element 93), was discovered in 1940 by E. M. McMillan among the products of neutron bombardment of uranium-238:

$$^{238}_{92}U + {}^{1}_{0}n \rightarrow {}^{239}_{92}U + {}^{0}_{0}\gamma$$

$$^{239}_{92}U \rightarrow {}^{239}_{93}Np + {}^{0}_{-1}\beta$$

Since then 11 additional transuranium elements, atomic numbers 94 through 104, have been synthesized. Two of these, einsteinium (**Es**, element 99) and fermium (**Fm**, element 100), were first isolated from radioactive debris from a thermonuclear explosion. The others have been prepared by nuclear bombardment reactions such as the following:

plutonium

$$\begin{cases} ^{238}_{92}U + {}^{1}_{0}n \rightarrow {}^{239}_{92}U + {}^{0}_{0}\gamma \\ ^{239}_{92}U \rightarrow {}^{0}_{-1}\beta + {}^{239}_{93}Np \\ ^{239}_{93}Np \rightarrow {}^{0}_{-1}\beta + {}^{239}_{94}Pu \end{cases}$$

americium

$$\begin{cases} ^{239}_{94}Pu + {}^{1}_{0}n \rightarrow {}^{240}_{94}Pu + {}^{0}_{0}\gamma \\ ^{240}_{94}Pu + {}^{1}_{0}n \rightarrow {}^{241}_{94}Pu + {}^{0}_{0}\gamma \\ ^{241}_{94}Pu \rightarrow {}^{0}_{-1}\beta + {}^{241}_{95}Am \end{cases}$$

curium $\quad ^{239}_{94}Pu + {}^{4}_{2}He \rightarrow {}^{1}_{0}n + {}^{242}_{96}Cm$

berkelium $\quad ^{241}_{95}Am + {}^{4}_{2}He \rightarrow 2\,{}^{1}_{0}n + {}^{243}_{97}Bk$

californium $\quad ^{242}_{96}Cm + {}^{4}_{2}He \rightarrow {}^{1}_{0}n + {}^{245}_{98}Cf$

mendelevium $^{253}_{99}Es + ^{4}_{2}He \rightarrow ^{1}_{0}n + ^{256}_{101}Md$

nobelium $^{246}_{96}Cm + ^{12}_{6}C \rightarrow 4\ ^{1}_{0}n + ^{254}_{102}No$

lawrencium $^{252}_{98}Cf + ^{11}_{5}B \rightarrow 6\ ^{1}_{0}n + ^{257}_{103}Lw$

The transuranium elements are of special theoretical interest, because together with actinium, thorium, protactinium, and uranium they form a second series of inner-transition elements, the ***actinides,*** which correspond to successive filling of the 5*f* electronic level in the same way in which the lanthanides correspond to filling of the 4*f* level. Efforts are underway to prepare elements 104 and 105 by such reactions as

$$^{242}_{94}Pu + ^{22}_{10}Ne \rightarrow ^{260}_{104}? + 4\ ^{1}_{0}n$$

$$^{252}_{98}Cf + ^{15}_{7}N \rightarrow ^{263}_{105}? + 4\ ^{1}_{0}n$$

Elements 104 and 105 should be transition elements with properties relating them to the naturally occurring IVB and VB elements hafnium and tantalum.

20.5 Half-life

No two radioactive isotopes decay at the same rate. Some are very unstable and are completely transformed in a few seconds, or even fractions of a second. Others decay more slowly and may take weeks, months, or centuries to undergo any appreciable change. It is impossible to say when a particular atom will decay, but a large number of atoms will be found to

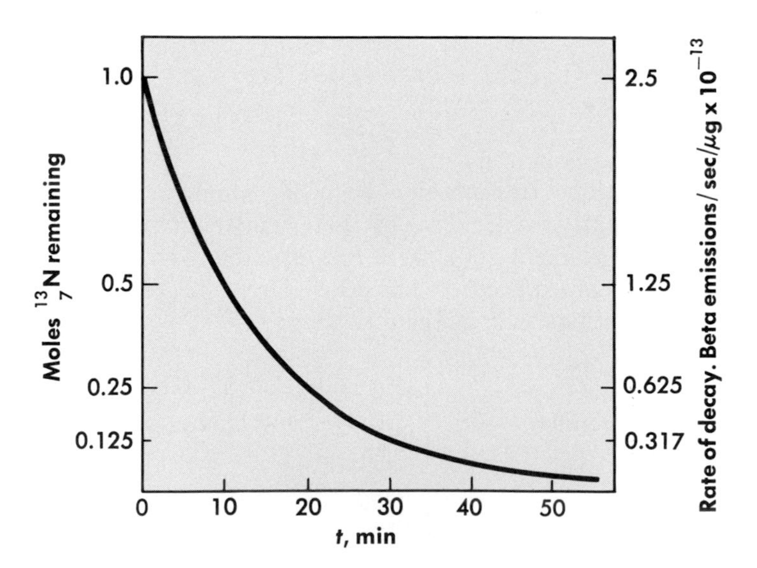

Fig. 20.7 Plot of the amount of $^{13}_{7}N$ remaining as a function of time, $t_{1/2}$ = 10 min. The rate of decay, measured as a function of the number of disintegration processes (β emissions in this case), is directly proportional to the amount of $^{13}_{7}N$ remaining in the sample, and follows the same logarithmic curve.

exhibit a constant decay rate which is unaffected by changes in temperature or pressure. Knowing this rate, it is possible to predict with certainty what fraction of the atoms will have decayed after a certain period of time. The decay rate of a radioactive isotope is expressed in terms of its ***half-life,*** which is the time it takes for one-half of the atoms in a given sample of the isotope to undergo radioactive change. Thus $^{13}_{7}N$ decays by positron emission with a half-life of 10 minutes. This means that if, for example, we started with 1 mole of $^{13}_{7}N$, after 10 minutes we would have only $\frac{1}{2}$ mole left—the rest would have disintegrated. After another 10 minutes, there would be only $\frac{1}{2} \times \frac{1}{2} = \frac{1}{4}$ mole left. After n half-lives, the amount of $^{13}_{7}N$ remaining would be $(\frac{1}{2})^n$ moles, the amount decreasing logarithmically with time (Fig. 20.7).

The rate of decay of a radioactive isotope is equal to the number of disintegration processes which occur in a given length of time. This in turn is proportional to the number of isotope nuclei N present in the sample:

$$\text{rate of decay} = \lambda N$$

The decay constant λ is related to the half-life by the expression:*

$$t_{1/2} = \frac{0.693}{\lambda}$$

Combining these equations yields the expression:

$$t_{1/2} = \frac{0.693\ N}{\text{rate of decay}}$$

If the rate of decay is plotted logarithmically as a function of time, the result is a straight line, from which the half-life may often be determined. Such a plot is shown in Fig. 20.8 for the decay of a sample of $^{80}_{35}Br$ by β emission. The half-life, which is the length of time required for the disintegration rate to fall to one-half its previous value, is seen to be 18 min for this isotope.

* For those who have had a little calculus, the derivation is as follows. The rate of decay is given by the expression

$$-\frac{dN}{dt} = \lambda N$$

where N is the number of nuclei remaining in the sample. If the number of nuclei initially present was N_0, then the number remaining after time t is obtained by integrating the previous equation between the limits 0 and t:

$$-\int_{N_0}^{N} \frac{dN}{N} = \lambda \int_0^t dt$$

$$\log_e \frac{N}{N_0} = -\lambda t$$

at $t_{1/2}$, $N/N_0 = \frac{1}{2}$, and

$$\lambda t_{1/2} = -\log_e \tfrac{1}{2} = \log_e 2$$

$$t_{1/2} = \frac{0.693}{\lambda}$$

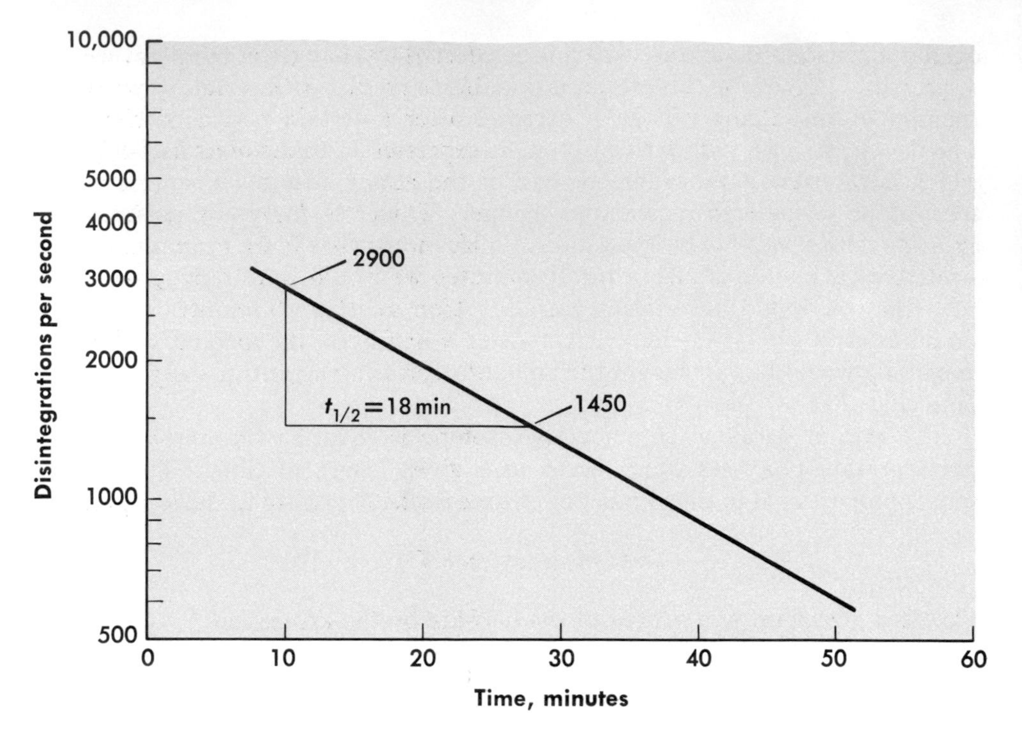

Fig. 20.8 Radioactive decay curve for $^{80}_{35}Br$.

This method of determining half-life is practical only if the rate of decay undergoes an appreciable change in a reasonably short length of time. In the case of a relatively long-lived isotope it is better to calculate $t_{1/2}$ from the rate of decay of a sample containing a known number of nuclei. The following example will illustrate how this might be done.

Example 20.1

A 1.0-μg sample of $^{226}_{88}RaCl_2$ undergoes radioactive decay at a rate of 2.8×10^4 disintegrations per second. From this information, calculate $t_{1/2}$ for $^{226}_{88}Ra$.

Solution: The number of atoms of $^{226}_{88}Ra$ in 1.0 μg (10^{-6} g) of $RaCl_2$ (mol wt 297) is

$$\frac{1.0 \times 10^{-6}}{297} \times 6.02 \times 10^{23} = 2.0 \times 10^{15} \text{ atoms}$$

$$t_{1/2} = \frac{(0.693)(2.0 \times 10^{15})}{(2.8 \times 10^4)} = 5.0 \times 10^{10} \text{ sec}$$

$$\frac{5.0 \times 10^{10} \text{ sec}}{3.15 \times 10^7 \text{ sec/yr}} = 1.6 \times 10^3 \text{ yr}$$

The intensity of radiation emanating from a sample depends upon both the concentration and the half-life of the isotope present. The greater the concentration, or the shorter the half-life, the more atoms will disintegrate in a given length of time, and as a result, the greater will be the intensity of the radiation. The radiation intensity is usually expressed as counts per minute (cpm). The unit of radiation intensity is the ***curie,*** which is *the amount of any radioactive material which will undergo* 3.70×10^{10} *disintegrations per second.* This is very near the disintegration rate of 1 g of radium. The energy of radiation is measured in terms of its ability to ionize dry air and is measured in ***roentgens,*** one roentgen being *the amount of radiation which when absorbed by* 1 cm^3 *of air at standard conditions will produce ions of either sign having a total charge of* 3.3×10^{-10} *coulombs.* This is equivalent to the total charge on 2.1×10^9 electrons.

Isotopic Dating 20.6

The age of a radioactive sample can be determined from the radiation intensity, provided that the half-life and initial decay rate are known or can be determined. This provides a way for example of calculating the age of archeological relics.

Nitrogen in the upper atmosphere is bombarded by cosmic ray neutrons and some of it is converted to $^{14}_{6}C$:

$$^{14}_{7}N + ^{1}_{0}n \rightarrow ^{14}_{6}C + ^{1}_{1}H$$

The rate of formation of $^{14}_{6}C$ is balanced by its rate of radioactive decay, so that its concentration in the atmosphere remains constant:

$$^{14}_{6}C \rightarrow ^{0}_{-1}\beta + ^{14}_{7}N \qquad t_{1/2} = 5760 \text{ years}$$

The $^{14}_{6}C$, as it is formed, is oxidized to $^{14}_{6}CO_2$ and taken up by plants along with ordinary $^{12}_{6}CO_2$ during photosynthesis. Animals obtain their carbon by eating the plants, and the ultimate result is that all living organisms contain carbon-12 and carbon-14 in the same, constant relative proportions. When a living thing, plant or animal, dies, it no longer exchanges carbon with the atmosphere. The carbon-14 is no longer replenished, and the level of carbon-14 radioactivity in the lifeless organism steadily decreases from the constant value of 15.3 ± 0.1 disintegrations per minute per gram of carbon which it has in all living things (Fig. 20.9). After one half-life,

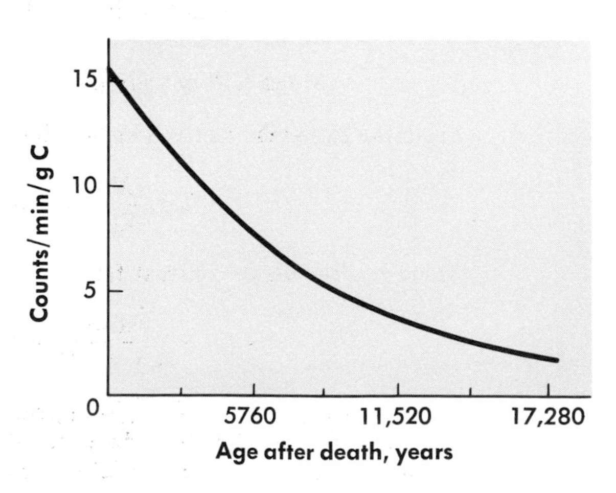

Fig. 20.9 Plot of $^{14}_{6}C$ radioactivity of organic remains as a function of age after death.

5760 years, the radioactivity will have fallen to 7.65 cpm/g **C**; after two half-lives, to 3.83 cpm/g **C**. Measurement of the carbon-14 disintegration of a once-living specimen thus gives its age since death within a few decades.

Example 20.2

Carbon from the door lintel of a Mayan temple showed a disintegration rate of 13 cpm/g, and a sample from an Indian sandal found in Oregon shows a rate of 4.9 cpm/g. What are the respective ages of the two specimens?

Solution: From the plot of disintegration rate vs. age given in Fig. 20.9, the age of the door lintel is seen to be about 1650 years and that of the sandal to be about 9230 years.

Practical difficulties encountered in attempting to measure very low disintegration rates limit carbon-14 dating to objects between 1500 and 15,000 years old. Fortunately, the period between A.D. 500 and 13,000 B.C. which this represents is of the greatest interest to archeologists, since it coincides with the development of civilization.

The ages of still older objects, and inorganic matter such as rocks, can sometimes be determined by similar dating methods using other isotopes with longer half-lives. Rocks, for example, have been dated by measuring the relative amounts of radioisotopes and disintegration products, as shown in the following example.

Example 20.3

Analysis of a sample of uraniferous rock shows that for every 1.000 g of $^{238}_{92}U$ present, the rock also contains 0.228 g of $^{206}_{82}Pb$. From this information, and the half-life of $^{238}_{92}U$, which is 4.5×10^9 years, calculate the age of the rock.

Solution: Let N_0 equal the moles of $^{238}_{92}U$ initially present when the rock was formed, and N equal the moles of $^{238}_{92}U$ now remaining. If it is assumed that all of the $^{206}_{82}Pb$ in the rock was produced by radioactive disintegration of $^{238}_{92}U$ originally present, then

$$\text{Moles } ^{206}_{82}\text{Pb in sample} = \frac{0.228}{206} = 1.11 \times 10^{-3}$$

$$\text{Moles } ^{238}_{92}\text{U in sample } (N) = \frac{1.000}{238} = 4.20 \times 10^{-3}$$

$$\text{Moles } ^{238}_{92}\text{U initially present } (N_0) = 5.31 \times 10^{-3}$$

From the expression derived earlier (footnote, p. 625):

$$\log_e \frac{N}{N_0} = 2.303 \log_{10} \frac{N}{N_0} = -\lambda t$$

where λ is the decay constant for $^{238}_{92}U$:

$$\lambda = \frac{0.693}{4.5 \times 10^9} = 1.54 \times 10^{-10} \text{ year}^{-1}$$

Only the decay constant for $^{238}_{92}U$ appears in the expression, because even though the conversion of $^{238}_{92}U$ to $^{206}_{82}Pb$ proceeds through a large number of steps, the half-lives of all of the intermediate species are very much shorter than that of the uranium. On a geological time scale, therefore, once the initial disintegration of $^{238}_{92}U$ occurs, the remaining steps leading to $^{206}_{82}Pb$ take place in a negligible length of time, so that we may assume that the rate of formation of the lead is the same as the rate of disintegration of the uranium.

Substituting the appropriate values for N, N_0, and λ:

$$2.303 \log \frac{4.20 \times 10^{-3}}{5.31 \times 10^{-3}} = -1.54 \times 10^{-10}\, t$$

$$t = 1.53 \times 10^{9} \text{ years}$$

The rock is therefore about 1.53 billion years old.

The uranium-lead method described in Example 20.3 is of limited applicability because of the rarity of uranium-bearing minerals. Perhaps the method most frequently used today for the absolute dating of geological specimens is based upon the natural radioactivity of potassium. Despite the fact that the radioactive isotope $^{40}_{19}K$ is present only to the extent of 0.012% in the natural isotopic mixture, potassium is such a common element in minerals and rocks that the disintegration of this isotope accounts for a large part of the background radiation detectable at the surface of the earth. Disintegration of $^{40}_{19}K$ can proceed either by β emission or by K-capture:

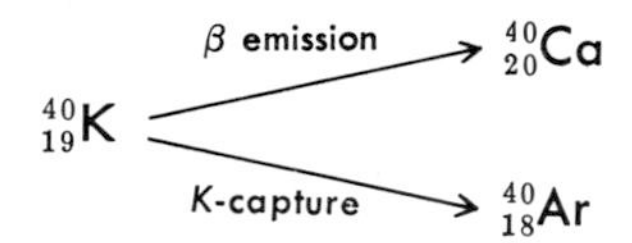

The half-life for the overall process is 1.3×10^9 years. Only one out of every 10 disintegrations leads to the formation of argon, yet it is that element rather than calcium which is usually measured, because it is difficult to distinguish the calcium formed as a disintegration product from that otherwise present in the mineral. The amount of $^{40}_{18}Ar$ is determined by fusing the sample in a vacuum and analyzing the evolved gas in a mass spectrometer. Potassium can also be measured by use of a mass spectrometer, or it can be determined chemically.

The accuracy of the potassium-argon dating method depends upon the complete retention in the mineral of all of the argon generated by disintegration of $^{40}_{19}K$. Since argon is a gas and can easily escape from the mineral, it is important that the specimen chosen be fresh, unweathered, and unfractured, and that it not have undergone heating such as that which has occurred in metamorphic rock. The original age of a rock that has undergone metamorphosis can be determined by measuring the relative proportions of $^{87}_{37}Rb$ and its daughter $^{87}_{38}Sr$ in the specimen. The process

$$^{87}_{37}Rb \rightarrow {}^{87}_{38}Sr + {}^{0}_{-1}\beta$$

proceeds with a half-life of 5×10^{10} years. The main drawback of this method lies in the relative scarcity of rubidium in most minerals.

20.7 Nuclear Binding Energy

The masses of atoms have been found by careful measurement always to be somewhat less than the sum of the masses of their component electrons, protons, and neutrons. For example, $^{84}_{36}Kr$ is composed of 36 protons, 36 electrons, and 48 neutrons. Since the mass of a proton is 1.00728 amu, that of an electron is 0.000548 amu, and that of a neutron is 1.00867 amu (Sec. 6.11), a krypton atom should have a mass of

$$36(1.00728) + 36(0.000548) + 48(1.00867) = 84.6980 \text{ amu}$$

Actually, the experimental value is 83.9115 amu. The difference represents the binding energy of the krypton nucleus. That is to say, in forming the nucleus from protons and neutrons, that much mass was converted to energy. Furthermore, the equivalent amount of energy would be required to dissociate the nucleus back into protons and neutrons. The nuclear binding energy is similar in this respect to the heat of formation of a chemical compound (Sec. 11.2), except that the nuclear energies are enormously greater.

The equivalence of mass and energy is expressed in Einstein's equation

$$E = mc^2$$

For $^{84}_{36}Kr$, the ***mass defect*** corresponding to the binding energy is (84.6980) − (83.9115) = 0.7865 amu, or 0.7865 g/mole. The equivalent amount of energy is therefore

$$\begin{aligned} E &= (0.7865 \text{ g/mole})(2.998 \times 10^{10} \text{ cm/sec})^2 \\ &= 7.053 \times 10^{20} \text{ ergs/mole} \\ &= 1.686 \times 10^{10} \text{ kcal/mole} \\ &= 731.1 \text{ MeV/mole} \end{aligned}$$

An idea of the magnitude of this nuclear binding energy can be gained by comparing it with typical heats of formation of compounds which are usually of the order of a few hundred kcal/mole.

Dividing the nuclear binding energy by the number of protons and neutrons in the nucleus gives the binding energy per nuclear particle, or ***nucleon.*** The binding energy per nucleon varies with the mass number of the element, reaching a maximum at a mass number of about 60 (Fig. 20.10). The nuclei of atoms which are heavier or lighter than this are not as strongly held together, that is, the heaviest and lightest atoms are less stable than those with intermediate masses. The ***fission*** of a heavy atom into lighter ones with masses around 60 amu, or the ***fusion*** of two or more light atoms into a heavier one, should result in the liberation of energy.

20.8 Nuclear Fission

Beginning in 1934 Enrico Fermi and his associates at the University of Rome studied the effect of neutron bombardment on various elements, using a mixture of radon and beryllium as a source of neutrons (Sec. 20.4).

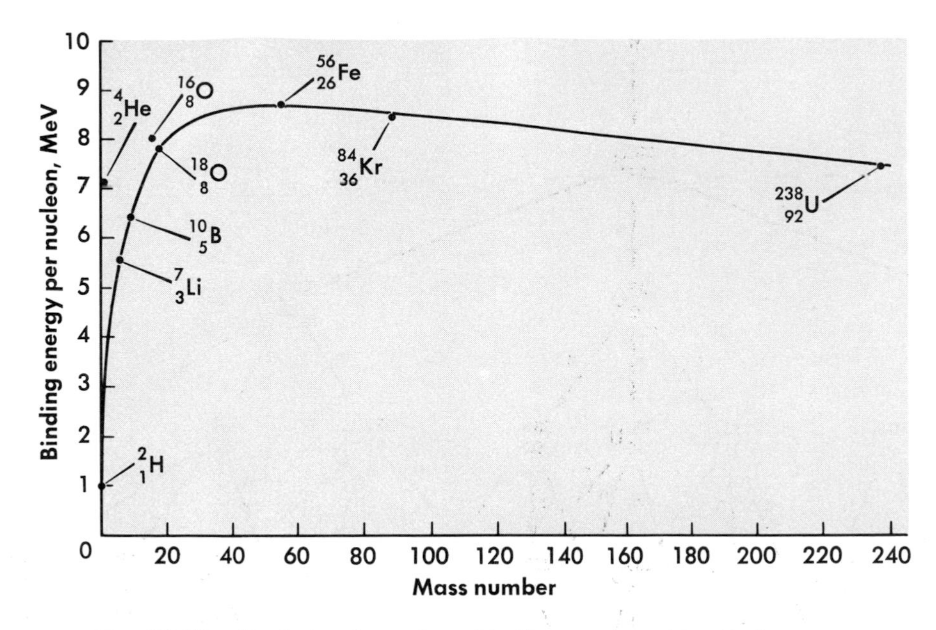

Fig. 20.10 Variation in nuclear binding energy with atomic mass.

With the lighter elements the usual result of neutron bombardment was formation of an isotope of the next higher element by a process of β decay, for example,

$$^{23}_{11}\text{Na} + ^{1}_{0}n \rightarrow ^{24}_{11}\text{Na} + ^{0}_{0}\gamma$$

$$^{24}_{11}\text{Na} \rightarrow ^{24}_{12}\text{Mg} + ^{0}_{-1}\beta$$

Neutron bombardment of uranium resulted in radioactivity which suggested that several elements with different half-lives had been produced. At first these were believed to be the previously unknown transuranium elements 93 and 94. In 1939 Otto Hahn and Fritz Strassmann, working at the Kaiser Wilhelm Institute in Berlin, reported the presence of barium, lanthanum, and cerium (elements 56, 57, and 58) among the products of the reaction. Somewhat later, elements 36, 37, and 38 (**Kr**, **Rb**, and **Sr**) were also identified.

The obvious conclusion to be drawn from Hahn and Strassmann's work was that the uranium had undergone fission or fragmentation into lighter elements. Later it was shown that of the several isotopes of uranium known to be present, the one which mainly underwent fission was ^{235}U. A possible fission reaction might be the following:

$$^{235}_{92}\text{U} + ^{1}_{0}n \rightarrow ^{142}_{56}\text{Ba} + ^{91}_{36}\text{Kr} + 3\ ^{1}_{0}n$$

An important feature of the fission process is the fact that for every neutron that induces a fission, two, three, or more neutrons are produced. If these neutrons collide with other ^{235}U nuclei, they will cause their fission as well.

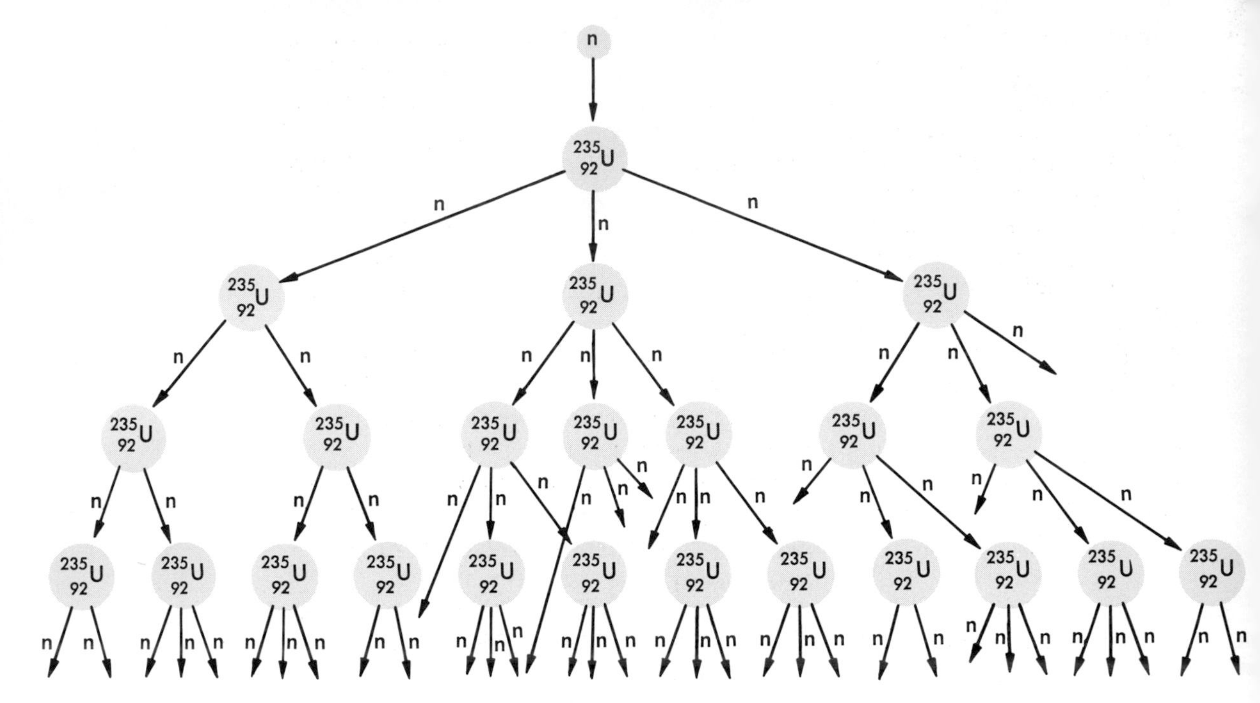

Fig. 20.11 Self-propagating nuclear chain reaction. A stray neutron induces a single fission, liberating three more neutrons. Each of these induces another fission, each of which is accompanied by release of two or three neutrons. The chain continues to branch in this way, finally resulting in an explosive rate of fission.

It is easy to see the possibility of establishing a self-propagating chain of nuclear fission reactions (Fig. 20.11).

A chain reaction of this sort cannot occur in ordinary uranium, which contains 99.28% ^{238}U and only about 0.71% ^{235}U. Most of the neutrons released by fissioning ^{235}U nuclei in this case will collide with nuclei of ^{238}U, either losing energy without bringing about any nuclear reaction, or else being absorbed, ultimately forming plutonium (Sec. 20.4).

Pure $^{235}_{92}U$ can be separated from its isomers by mass spectroscopy or by gaseous diffusion, taking advantage of the fact that gaseous $^{235}UF_6$, because of its smaller molecular weight, will effuse through a porous plug at a slightly faster rate than will $^{238}UF_6$, permitting partial separation of the two gases (Graham's Law, Sec. 3.10). To achieve a chain reaction in a sample of $^{235}_{92}U$, it is only necessary to exceed a certain critical sample size. If the sample is smaller than the critical size, most of the neutrons generated will escape from the sample before colliding with another nucleus. At the critical size, the number of neutrons escaping from the mass exactly balances the number causing fission, so that a steady state is established. Above the critical size, most of the neutrons cause fission, and the chain is propagated at an increasingly rapid, and ultimately explosive, rate.

As implied previously, the amount of energy liberated in nuclear fission reactions is enormous. The destruction that can be wrought by a chain reaction involving a larger than critical mass is legendary and has been amply demonstrated. The atomic bomb dropped over Hiroshima in 1945 contained only a few pounds of ^{235}U, but the energy it released was sufficient to flatten a large part of the city.

The energy produced by nuclear fission can be recovered nondestructively in a nuclear reactor. One form of nuclear reactor contains a large number of rods of uranium enriched with a greater than natural percentage of fissionable ^{235}U. These rods are inserted into holes in graphite blocks or are suspended in water. The graphite or water serves to *moderate*, or slow down, the neutrons from the fuel rods, slow neutrons having been found more effective in inducing nuclear reactions. Control rods of cadmium or other material effective in absorbing neutrons are interspersed among the fuel rods in such a way that they can be inserted or withdrawn at will. With the control rods inserted, most of the neutrons are absorbed, effectively shutting down the reactor. As the control roads are withdrawn, the neutron flux, and hence the rate of fission in the reactor, increases. The heat generated by the nuclear processes going on within the reactor can be converted to mechanical or electrical power by conventional means.

A reactor fueled with a mixture of ^{238}U and ^{235}U has the remarkable ability of generating its own fuel. As the reactor operates, the ^{238}U is gradually converted to $^{239}_{94}Pu$ (Sec. 20.4), which, unlike ^{238}U, is fissionable. In this way the ^{238}U itself becomes a source of power. A reactor operating on this principle is called a ***breeder reactor.***

Nuclear Fusion 20.9

Still greater amounts of energy than are released during fission can be obtained by fusion of small nuclei. The reaction

$$2\ ^{2}_{1}H \rightarrow ^{3}_{2}He + ^{1}_{0}n$$

for example, releases 3.3 MeV. The activation energy for fusion reactions, however, is very much greater than that for fission, and these reactions occur at appreciable rates only at temperatures of the order of millions of degrees. These temperatures are available in the interior of the sun, where the following fusion cycles are believed to furnish much of the sun's energy:

Hydrogen Cycle	Carbon Cycle
$2\ ^{1}_{1}H \rightarrow ^{2}_{1}H + ^{0}_{+1}\beta$	$^{12}_{6}C + ^{1}_{1}H \rightarrow ^{13}_{7}N$
$^{1}_{1}H + ^{2}_{1}H \rightarrow ^{3}_{2}He$	$^{13}_{7}N \rightarrow ^{13}_{6}C + ^{0}_{+1}\beta$
$2\ ^{3}_{2}He \rightarrow ^{4}_{2}He + 2\ ^{1}_{1}H$	$^{13}_{6}C + ^{1}_{1}H \rightarrow ^{14}_{7}N$
	$^{14}_{7}N + ^{1}_{1}H \rightarrow ^{15}_{8}O$
	$^{15}_{8}O \rightarrow ^{15}_{7}N + ^{0}_{+1}\beta$
	$^{15}_{7}N + ^{1}_{1}H \rightarrow ^{12}_{6}C + ^{4}_{2}He$

Temperatures of the necessary magnitude are difficult to obtain on the surface of the earth. It is possible to fuse tritium and deuterium,

$$^{3}_{1}H + ^{2}_{1}H \rightarrow ^{4}_{2}He + ^{1}_{0}n$$

by using an atomic fission bomb as the triggering device to obtain the necessary high temperature. This is the principle of the hydrogen bomb. Obtaining energy from this or other fusion reactions in a controlled and nondestructive manner is another story. Some progress has been made in overcoming the technical problems, but the goal of sustained, controlled nuclear fusion still seems a long way off.

20.10 Other Subatomic Particles

Besides the familiar protons, neutrons, and electrons, a large number of short-lived subatomic particles have been detected as transitory products of nuclear reactions. We are already familiar with the positive electron, or positron. Collision of a high-energy proton with an atom of ^{63}Cu results in creation of a positively charged particle known as a π^+ ***meson:***

$$^{63}_{29}Cu + ^{1}_{1}H \rightarrow ^{63}_{28}Ni + ^{1}_{1}H + \pi^+$$

The π^+ meson has a mass about 273 times that of an electron. Its half-life is of the order of 10^{-8} sec, whereupon it decomposes into a μ^+ meson, or ***muon,*** with a mass about 207 times that of an electron, and a stable particle, the ***neutrino,*** which has no charge and negligible mass. The muon, in turn, decomposes with a half-life of about 10^{-6} sec into a positron and one or more neutrinos. The mass that disappears in each of these decompositions is converted into energy. There is a particle of ***antimatter,*** with the same mass but opposite charge, corresponding to each charged subatomic particle. Thus we have electrons and positrons, protons and antiprotons, π^+ and π^- mesons, μ^+ and μ^- mesons. Even among neutral particles there are neutrons and antineutrons; neutrinos and antineutrinos. Collision between a particle of matter and one of antimatter results in annihilation of both with liberation of an equivalent amount of energy.

With the availability of more powerful accelerators producing higher and higher energy particles with which to bombard atomic nuclei, subatomic particles of all sorts have been and are being discovered in ever-increasing numbers. Where five or six years ago about 30 such particles were known, now about 100 have been identified, leaving the physicist suffering from an embarrassment of riches. With more and more particles being discovered, the problem of trying to fit them into a reasonable theory of the atom becomes ever more acute. Which of these particles, if any, actually exist within the atom and how they are produced in nuclear reactions are questions still needing answers.

The situation today reminds one of that time 70 or 80 years ago when it was first realized that Dalton's billiard ball atom was not quite the fundamental particle it was thought to be. There is evidence now to suggest that, just as the nucleus is composed of protons and neutrons, so are these particles made up of still smaller ones. As Jonathan Swift expressed it over 200 years ago:

> "*. . . So naturalists observe, a flea*
> *Hath smaller fleas that on him prey.*
> *And these have smaller still to bite 'em,*
> *And so proceed* ad infinitum."

Reading Suggestions 20.11

It is impossible even to begin to do justice to the fascinating subject of nuclear chemistry in a chapter necessarily as brief as this one. A truly superb introduction to the subject is the book *Nuclear Chemistry*, by Bernard G. Harvey, one volume in the excellent Prentice-Hall *Foundations of Modern Chemistry* series (Prentice-Hall, Inc., Englewood Cliffs, N.J., 1965). Also in this series is Glenn T. Seaborg's *Man-Made Transuranium Elements* (Prentice-Hall, 1963), which is the story of the discovery, theoretical significance, and application of elements 93–103. Dr. Seaborg's intimate association with the research described, together with his fine writing style, brings both the subject and those concerned in its investigation to life on the pages of this book.

A profusely illustrated popular account of the applications of atomic energy, *You and the Obedient Atom*, by Allan C. Fisher, Jr., appeared in the *National Geographic Magazine* (**114**, 303 (September 1958)). The radioactive dating of archaeological specimens is described by Lyman J. Briggs and Kenneth F. Weaver in an article entitled *How Old Is It?* which appeared in the same magazine (**114**, 234 (August 1958)). The determination of absolute geologic time by the measurement of isotopic abundances is described in Chapter 4 of the book, *How Old is the Earth?* by Patrick M. Hurley (Anchor Books Science Study Series, Doubleday & Co., Inc., Garden City, N.Y., 1959).

Questions and Problems

20.1 What effect does each of the following radioactive processes have on the atomic number and mass number of an atom?

β-emission	K-capture	γ-emission
α-emission	positron emission	neutron emission

20.2 Why is α-emission most likely to occur among elements with atomic numbers greater than 83 and rarely among elements with smaller atomic numbers?

20.3 Predict the radioactive disintegration process which each of the following unstable isotopes will probably undergo. Write the nuclear equation for the process in each case:

$^{74}_{35}Br$	$^{197}_{84}Po$	$^{3}_{1}H$	$^{244}_{96}Cm$
$^{84}_{35}Br$	$^{8}_{3}Li$	$^{33}_{17}Cl$	$^{63}_{28}Ni$

20.4 Radioactive isotopes below the stable region usually undergo either positron emission or K-capture. Suggest a reason why it is found that the greater the atomic number of the isotope the more likely it is to undergo K-capture.

20.5 Complete each of the following equations:

(a) $^{5}_{2}He \rightarrow ^{1}_{0}n +$

(b) $^{234}_{90}Th \rightarrow ^{234}_{91}Pa +$

(c) $^{30}_{15}P \rightarrow ^{0}_{+1}\beta +$

(d) $^{37}_{18}Ar \xrightarrow{K\text{-capture}}$

(e) $^{238}_{92}U \rightarrow \alpha +$

20.6 Describe how a particle undergoes acceleration in a cyclotron and in a linear accelerator. Can neutrons be accelerated in either device? Explain.

20.7 Complete each of the following equations:

(a) $^{240}_{94}Pu + ^{1}_{0}n \rightarrow ?$

(b) $? + 15\ ^{1}_{0}n \rightarrow ^{253}_{99}Es + 7\ ^{0}_{-1}\beta$

(c) $^{250}_{98}Cf + ^{11}_{5}B \rightarrow ^{257}_{103}Lw + ?$

(d) $^{235}_{92}U + ^{1}_{0}n \rightarrow ^{144}_{56}Ba + 2\ ^{1}_{0}n + ?$

20.8 Suggest a reaction which might be used to prepare an isotope of element 106.

20.9 Of what group in the periodic table would element 106 be a member? From the properties of the other members of the group, predict the following properties of element 106: melting point, boiling point, density, valence(s).

20.10 What is meant by the half-life of a radioactive element?

20.11 The half-life of the radioactive isotope $^{212}_{83}Bi$ is 1 hr. Starting with 2 mg of $^{212}_{83}Bi$, how much will remain undecayed after 12 hr?

20.12 The half-life of $^{14}_{6}C$ is 5760 yr. Calculate the decay constant in min^{-1} (1 yr $= 5.26 \times 10^5$ min).

20.13 Contemporary carbon obtained from a living plant exhibits a disintegration rate of 15.3 counts per minute per gram of carbon. Using the decay constant calculated in Problem 20.12, calculate the number of $^{14}_{6}C$ atoms present in 1 g of contemporary carbon.

20.14 Carbon from the ashes of a prehistoric Indian campfire was burned completely to CO_2, which was then absorbed in limewater, precipitated as $CaCO_3$, and dried. A sample of 4.38 g of the $CaCO_3$ so prepared showed a measured disintegration rate of 3.2 cpm. Assuming the radioactivity of the sample to be caused entirely by $^{14}_{6}C$, calculate the age of the sample.

20.15 The isotope $^{12}_{6}C$ has a mass of 12.00000 amu. Calculate the mass defect and the binding energy in kcal/mole.

20.16 The isotope $^{57}_{28}Ni$ decays both by *K*-capture and by positron emission. What product is formed in each process? Which process releases more energy? How much more?

20.17 A solution of uranyl nitrate was allowed to flow through a column containing a cation exchange resin. The column was then washed with water and 0.3*M* H_2SO_4 to remove uranyl ions, and the short-lived isotope $^{234}_{91}Pa$ was then eluted from the column with 5% HCl. The solution of $^{234}_{91}Pa$ was placed in a counting chamber and the rate of decay was determined at 20 second intervals. The following data were obtained.

Time, seconds	Counts per second (corrected for background)
20	408
40	338
60	294
80	242
100	187
120	158
140	141
160	118
180	87
200	71
220	60
240	49

Plot these data as in Figure 20.8, and determine the half-life of $^{234}_{91}Pa$ from the slope of the line obtained. (Reference: J. Braunstein and R. H. Young, *J. Chem. Ed.* 38, 31 (1961)).

APPENDIXES

A

HANDLING NUMBERS

Exponential Numbers A.1

A chemist finds himself constantly working with very large and very small numbers. Not only is it a nuisance for him to write such numbers in the conventional way, but the chance of making an error is very great. Just imagine keeping track of the zeros if you always had to write Avogadro's number as 602,300,000,000,000,000,000,000, or Planck's constant as 0.0000000000000000000000000066256! This situation is avoided by writing the number in exponential form. Take the number 100, for example. This is equal to 10×10, or 10^2. Similarly, 1000 is $10 \times 10 \times 10$, or 10^3, and 10,000 is $10 \times 10 \times 10 \times 10$, or 10^4. In each case the exponent of ten is equal to the number of zeros following the first digit of the number:

$$1 = 10^0$$
$$10 = 10^1$$
$$100 = 10^2$$
$$1{,}000 = 10^3$$
$$10{,}000 = 10^4$$
$$100{,}000 = 10^5$$
$$1{,}000{,}000 = 10^6$$
$$1{,}000{,}000{,}000 = 10^9$$
$$100{,}000{,}000{,}000{,}000{,}000{,}000{,}000 = 10^{23}$$

Now suppose that we have the number 6023. This is the same as $6.023 \times 1{,}000$, and since $1000 = 10^3$, the number can be written 6.023×10^3. In the same way, Avogadro's number can be written

$$6.023 \times 100{,}000{,}000{,}000{,}000{,}000{,}000{,}000$$

or, in exponential form, 6.023×10^{23}.

Very small numbers are also handled most conveniently in exponential form. The number 0.01, for example, is equal to 1/100 or $1/10^2$. Dividing by 10^2 is the same as multiplying by 10^{-2}, and therefore $0.01 = 10^{-2}$. Thus

$$0.1 = 10^{-1}$$

$$0.01 = 10^{-2}$$

$$0.001 = 10^{-3}$$

$$0.0001 = 10^{-4}$$

$$0.00001 = 10^{-5}$$

$$0.0000000001 = 10^{-10}$$

$$0.000000000000000000000000001 = 10^{-27}$$

We see here that if there are no zeros between the decimal point and the first digit of the number the exponent is -1; if there is one zero between the decimal and the first digit the exponent is -2; if two zeros the exponent is -3; if three zeros, -4; and so on. Planck's constant has 26 zeros between the decimal point and the first digit and therefore can be written exponentially as 6.6256×10^{-27}.

When numbers which are expressed exponentially are multiplied, the exponents are added, thus:

$$(6 \times 10^6)(6 \times 10^4) = 36 \times 10^{10}$$

$$(6 \times 10^{23})(1.6 \times 10^{-19}) = 9.6 \times 10^4$$

When exponential numbers are divided, the exponents are subtracted:

$$\frac{6.02 \times 10^{23}}{3.0 \times 10^3} = 2.0 \times 10^{20} \qquad \frac{5.2 \times 10^4}{1.8 \times 10^6} = 2.9 \times 10^{-2}$$

$$\frac{3.0 \times 10^{-5}}{6.0 \times 10^{-7}} = 0.50 \times 10^2 = 5.0 \times 10^1$$

It is customary to write exponential numbers so that the part of the number to be multiplied by some power of 10 is a number between 1 and 10. Therefore, rather than write 36×10^{10}, for example, we generally write 3.6×10^{11} $(= 3.6 \times 10^1 \times 10^{10})$, and instead of writing 0.085×10^{-6}, we write 8.5×10^{-8} $(= 8.5 \times 10^{-2} \times 10^{-6})$.

When an exponential number is itself raised to some power, the exponent is multiplied by the power to which the number is being raised:

$$(1.8 \times 10^{-5})^2 = (1.8)^2(10^{-5})^2 = 3.2 \times 10^{-10}$$

$$(5.0 \times 10^4)^3 = 125 \times 10^{12} = 1.25 \times 10^{14}$$

$$(9.0 \times 10^6)^{\frac{1}{2}} = 3 \times 10^3$$

Raising a number to the $\frac{1}{2}$ power, as in the last example above, is equivalent to taking the square root of the number. If the square root of an exponential number is to be taken, it is best to express the number in such a way that the exponent is divisible by 2:

$$\sqrt[2]{9.0 \times 10^3} = \sqrt[2]{90 \times 10^2} = 9.5 \times 10^1 = 95$$

Likewise, if the cube root is to be taken, the exponent should be divisible by 3, and so on:

$$\sqrt[3]{6.4 \times 10^8} = \sqrt[3]{0.64 \times 10^9} = 0.86 \times 10^3 = 8.6 \times 10^2$$

Precision and Accuracy A.2

Precision and accuracy mean quite different things. The precision of a series of measurements is determined by how closely they agree with one another; their accuracy is determined by how closely they agree with the known or accepted value. A scientist strives for both precision and accuracy, but it is quite possible for his work to be precise without being accurate, or accurate without being precise. To see how this can be, let us suppose that two students are asked to analyze a sample of soda ash which we know to contain 42.63% Na_2CO_3. Each student is to report the average of three separate analyses. The first student, working very carefully, but with a miscalibrated buret, obtains the following results:

Analysis No.	% Na_2CO_3
1	43.87
2	43.91
3	43.89
	43.89 ± 0.01

The precision of these results is very high, as shown by the close agreement among the three analyses, but they are not particularly accurate, being in error by (43.89 − 42.63) = 1.26 parts in 42.63, or nearly 30 parts in 1000.

The second student is more careless in his technique and obtains the following:

Analysis No.	% Na_2CO_3
1	44.12
2	41.39
3	42.30
	42.60 ± 1.01

In this case, the precision leaves a great deal to be desired. By a fortunate accident, however, the average of the three analyses differs from the correct value by less than 1 part in 1000, and in that sense the result is very accurate.

The moral to be drawn from this is not that careless work leads to accurate results. On the contrary, careful work is far more likely to be accurate as well as precise. Precision alone, however, is no guarantee of accuracy if there is some defect present in the apparatus or in the design of the experiment.

A.3 Significant Figures

Suppose that we have a rectangular block of metal whose density we wish to determine. Using a ruler graduated in millimeters (1 mm = 0.1 cm) we find the dimensions of the block to be: length 5.3 cm, width 2.6 cm, height 1.2 cm. In recording the dimensions in this way, we imply that we know each of them to the nearest 0.1 cm. In other words, when we say that the length is 5.3 cm, we mean that it is no less than 5.25 cm, and no more than 5.35 cm. The second figure in each measurement is therefore significant, although somewhat uncertain. By multiplying length $\times$ width $\times$ height, we calculate the volume to be 16.536 cm^3. But to record the volume in this way would imply that we know it to the nearest 0.001 cm^3, or to better than 1 part in 16,000. This is clearly ridiculous, since the height of the block, for example, is known only to the nearest 1 part in 12. We therefore round off the volume to 17 cm^3, a number with two significant figures, the same as the number of significant figures in our other measurements.

Now that we have the volume, our next task is to weigh the block. Using an analytical balance, we find that the block weighs 44.8963 g. Dividing this by the volume gives us the density:

$$\frac{44.8963 \text{ g}}{17 \text{ cm}^3} = 2.6409 \text{ g/cm}^3$$

Once again our answer implies greater precision than is actually the case. Although the mass of the block is known to six significant figures, its volume is known only to two. The result of a calculation cannot be more precise than the least precise item of data used in the calculation. Therefore, the density should be rounded off to 2.6 g/cm^3—two significant figures—the same as the volume, which is the less precise number in this case. There was actually no need for us to weigh the block of metal on an analytical balance. Knowing that our answer would be good to only two significant figures in any event, we could just as well have used a rough balance weighing to the nearest gram. On such a balance the block would weigh 45 g, and 45 $g/17\ cm^3$ = 2.6 g/cm^3, the same answer we obtained before.

Zeros in a number may or may not be significant figures. In a fraction less than 1, expressed in decimal form, the zeros preceding the first digit merely indicate the order of magnitude of the number and are not significant. Thus, the number 0.00026, for example, contains two significant figures. However, zeros following the digits to the right of the decimal point are significant. The numbers 12.00, 0.02600, and 50.00 all contain four significant figures. Numbers such as 186,000 and 3,000,000 are ambiguous. The zeros are necessary to indicate the order of magnitude of the numbers, but there is no way to tell whether or not they are significant. Expressing these numbers in exponential form, e.g. 1.86×10^5 and 3.0×10^6 leaves no doubt about the number of significant figures in each: three in the first case, and two in the second.

B

NAMING INORGANIC COMPOUNDS

B.1 Binary Compounds

Binary compounds are those that consist of only two different elements. In naming binary compounds the name of the more metallic element is given first, followed by the name of the other element with its final syllable changed to *-ide;* thus:

$NaCl$	sodium chloride
KI	potassium iodide
Al_2O_3	aluminum oxide
Mg_3N_2	magnesium nitride
CaC_2	calcium carbide

The Greek prefixes *mono-* (1), *di-* (2), *tri-* (3), *tetra-* (4), etc. are often used to indicate the number of atoms of an element where there might otherwise be some doubt:

CO	carbon monoxide
CO_2	carbon dioxide
UF_6	uranium hexafluoride
N_2O_5	dinitrogen pentoxide
IF_7	iodine heptafluoride

The oxidation state of an element which can exhibit more than one such state is indicated by a Roman numeral following its name as in the following examples.*

Cu_2O	copper(I) oxide	CuO	copper(II) oxide
$FeCl_2$	iron(II) chloride	$FeCl_3$	iron(III) chloride
$SnCl_2$	tin(II) chloride	$SnCl_4$	tin(IV) chloride
N_2O	nitrogen(I) oxide	NO	nitrogen(II) oxide
NO_2	nitrogen(IV) oxide	N_2O_5	nitrogen(V) oxide

When the element is known to exhibit only one such state in all its compounds, the Roman numeral is generally omitted from the name.

Bases B.2

Most inorganic bases consist of a metal combined with one or more **OH** (hydroxide) radicals. They are named in the same manner as binary compounds:

$NaOH$	sodium hydroxide
$Ba(OH)_2$	barium hydroxide
$Fe(OH)_2$	iron(II) hydroxide
NH_4OH	ammonium hydroxide
$Al(OH)_3$	aluminum hydroxide

Acids B.3

Most acids belong to either of two categories: binary acids and oxyacids. ***Binary acids*** consist of a single nonmetallic element and hydrogen. Binary

* The older type of name, in which the ending *-ous* or *-ic* is appended to the Latin name of the element to indicate the lower or higher oxidation state respectively, is still used to some extent. Some examples are

Cu_2O	cuprous oxide	CuO	cupric oxide
$FeCl_2$	ferrous chloride	$FeCl_3$	ferric chloride
$SnCl_2$	stannous chloride	$SnCl_4$	stannic chloride
N_2O	nitrous oxide	NO	nitric oxide

These names allow for only two oxidation states, whereas many elements exhibit three or more, and they presuppose that one is familiar with the respective lower and higher oxidation states in every case. Because these names are so unsatisfactory, their use is discouraged.

acids are named by prefixing *hydro-* to the name of the nonmetal, followed by the ending *-ic acid*, thus:

HF	hydrofluoric acid
HCl	hydrochloric acid
H_2S	hydrosulfuric acid
HCN	hydrocyanic acid
HN_3	hydrazoic acid

The compound **HCN**, though not actually binary, is nevertheless named as a binary acid. The name hydrazoic acid is derived from the French term *azote* (Greek: lifeless) for nitrogen.

Oxyacids, as the term implies, contain oxygen in addition to hydrogen and another nonmetal, which in an oxyacid is always in a positive oxidation state. The oxyacid of an element in its higher oxidation state is named by adding the ending *-ic acid* to the name of the element:

HNO_3	nitric acid
H_2SO_4	sulfuric acid
H_3PO_4	phosphoric acid
H_3AsO_4	arsenic acid

The ending *-ous acid* is used for the acid in which the element is in its lower oxidation state:

HNO_2	nitrous acid
H_2SO_3	sulfurous acid
H_3PO_3	phosphorous acid
H_3AsO_3	arsenious acid

If the element forms more than two oxyacids, the prefixes *hypo-* and *per-* are used to indicate respectively an oxidation state lower than that in the *-ous* acid and an oxidation state higher than that in the *-ic* acid. This is illustrated by the names of the various acids of chlorine:

HCl	hydrochloric acid
HClO	hypochlorous acid
$HClO_2$	chlorous acid
$HClO_3$	chloric acid
$HClO_4$	perchloric acid

An oxygen atom in an oxyacid may sometimes be replaced by a sulfur atom. This is indicated by adding the prefix *thio-* to the name of the acid:

H_2SO_4	sulfuric acid
$H_2S_2O_3$	thiosulfuric acid

Salts B.4

Salts of binary acids are generally binary compounds and are named as such:

Na_2S	sodium sulfide
$CoCl_2$	cobalt(II) chloride
NH_4Br	ammonium bromide

Salts of -ic acids are given the ending *-ate;* salts of per. . .ic acids are called *per. . .ates:*

$NaNO_3$	sodium nitrate
$CuSO_4$	copper(II) sulfate
$Na_2S_2O_3$	sodium thiosulfate
$Ca_3(PO_4)_2$	calcium phosphate
NH_4ClO_4	ammonium perchlorate

Salts of -ous acids end in *-ite;* salts of hypo. . .ous acids are *hypo. . .ites:*

$NaNO_2$	sodium nitrite
Cu_2SO_3	copper(I) sulfite
$KClO$	potassium hypochlorite
$NaIO$	sodium hypoiodite

If only part of the ionizable hydrogen of a polyprotic acid is replaced by a metal, the product is an ***acid salt.*** The presence of replaceable hydrogen in acid salts is indicated by inserting *hydrogen* or *acid* into the name of the salt:

$NaHCO_3$	sodium hydrogen carbonate (or sodium acid carbonate)
$Ca(HSO_3)_2$	calcium hydrogen sulfite (or calcium acid sulfite)
NaH_2PO_4	sodium dihydrogen phosphate (or sodium diacid phosphate)
Na_2HPO_4	disodium hydrogen phosphate (or disodium acid phosphate)

B.5 Coordination Complexes

In naming a coordination complex, the names of the ligands are given first, using the prefixes di-, tri-, tetra-, etc., to indicate the number of identical ligands present in the complex. If the name of the ligand is complex, the prefixes bis-, tris-, tetrakis-, etc., are used, followed by the name of the ligand enclosed in parentheses. Names of anionic ligands end in *-o*, while the name of the molecule is used for neutral ligands. Exceptions to this rule are the names of the neutral ligands H_2O (aquo), NH_3 (ammine), NO (nitrosyl), and CO (carbonyl). The name of the central atom is given next, with its oxidation state indicated by a Roman numeral in parentheses. If the complex is a cation or a neutral molecule, the name of the central atom is left unchanged. If the complex is a negative ion, the name of the central atom ends in *-ate*. The Latin form of the name is often used in this case. Some examples illustrating the application of these rules are given below:

$[Co(NH_3)_5Cl]Cl_2$	chloropentamminecobalt(III) chloride
$[Co(en)_3]Br_3$	tris(ethylenediamine)cobalt(III) bromide
$[Ni(CO)_4]$	tetracarbonylnickel(0)
$K_4[Fe(CN)_6]$	potassium hexacyanoferrate(II)
$K_3[Fe(CN)_6]$	potassium hexacyanoferrate(III)
$Na[Co(NH_3)_2(NO_2)_4]$	sodium tetranitrodiamminecobaltate(III)
$K_4[Ni(CN)_4]$	potassium tetracyanonickelate(0)

Complete, official rules for naming inorganic compounds will be found in the 1957 Report of the Commission on the Nomenclature of Inorganic Chemistry, International Union of Pure and Applied Chemistry (London, Butterworths Scientific Publications, 1959); and, with notes pertaining to American usage, in the *Journal of the American Chemical Society*, **82,** 5523 (1960).

C

NAMING ORGANIC COMPOUNDS

Ideally, an organic compound should be uniquely described by its name, and from the name alone it should be possible for one to draw the exact structure of the compound. With this in mind, the International Union of Pure and Applied Chemistry (IUPAC) has established rules for the naming of organic compounds. Because of the great number and variety of organic compounds, these rules are very extensive and detailed. Only a few of the basic rules will be discussed here, but these will be sufficient to handle the nomenclature of most of the organic compounds encountered in this book.

Aliphatic Compounds C.1

For purposes of nomenclature, all open-chain aliphatic compounds are considered to be derived from the simple straight-chain hydrocarbons by a process of substitution. The first four aliphatic hydrocarbons are in order: methane, ethane, propane, and butane. Following butane, the hydrocarbons are named according to the numbers of carbon atoms which they contain, using the Greek numerical prefixes. Thus:

CH_4	methane
$CH_3—CH_3$	ethane
$CH_3—CH_2—CH_3$	propane
$CH_3—CH_2—CH_2—CH_3$	butane

$CH_3—CH_2—CH_2—CH_2—CH_3$ pentane

$CH_3—CH_2—CH_2—CH_2—CH_2—CH_3$ hexane

etc. etc.

Removal of a hydrogen from an alkane converts it to an ***alkyl group.*** Names of alkyl groups are derived from those of the corresponding alkanes by replacing the ending *-ane* with *-yl:*

$CH_3—$ methyl

$CH_3—CH_2—$ ethyl

$CH_3—CH_2—CH_2—$ propyl

The first step in naming a branched-chain hydrocarbon is to pick out the longest continuous chain of carbon atoms in the compound. The compound is considered to be a derivative of that hydrocarbon which has the same number of carbon atoms as are present in the longest chain of the compound. Thus, the compound

```
        CH3      CH2—CH3
        |        |
CH3—C—CH2—CH—CH2—CH2—CH3
        |
        CH3
```

has a longest continuous chain of seven carbons and is therefore a heptane derivative. Next, the alkyl groups attached to the chain are identified. In the example above these are two methyl groups and an ethyl group. The prefixes *di-*, *tri-*, *tetra-*, etc., are used where several identical groups are present. The locations of the substituents on the chain are indicated by numbering the carbons of the chain in order, beginning at either end, so as to give the lowest possible numbers to the substituent positions. The compound is then named by listing the names of the substituents, each preceded by the number of its position on the chain, followed by the name of the hydrocarbon from which the compound is derived. If several identical groups are present, the position of each one must be given; if two identical groups are present on the same carbon of the chain, the number of that carbon must be written twice. Following this procedure, the compound above is named

2,2-dimethyl-4-ethylheptane

```
Methyl group↘                  ↙Ethyl group
             CH3       CH2—CH3
 ①        ② | ③    ④ |    ⑤      ⑥      ⑦
 CH3—C—CH2—CH—CH2—CH2—CH3
             |                ↖
             CH3                 \
Methyl group↗                   Heptane chain
```

If a double bond is present in the compound, the name of the compound ends in *-ene* instead of *-ane*. Again, if more than one double bond is present, the prefixes *di-*, *tri-*, etc., are used. Where geometric isomerism exists, the prefixes *cis-* and *trans-* are used to designate the geometry of the carbon chain from which the compound derives its name. The chain is numbered so that the carbons joined by the double bond are given the lowest possible numbers. Of those two numbers, the smaller one is used in the name to indicate the position of the double bond. The following examples will show the application of these rules:

$CH_3—CH═CH_2$ propene

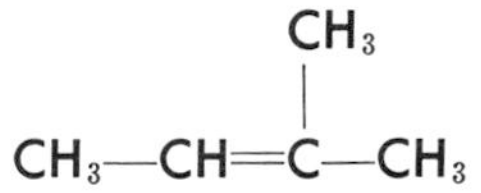

$CH_3—CH═C(CH_3)—CH_3$ 2-methyl-2-butene

$CH_2═CH—CH(CH_3)—CH_3$ 3-methyl-1-butene

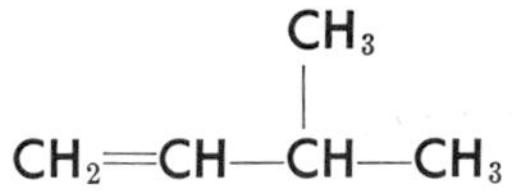

$CH_2═CH—CH═CH_2$ 1,3-butadiene

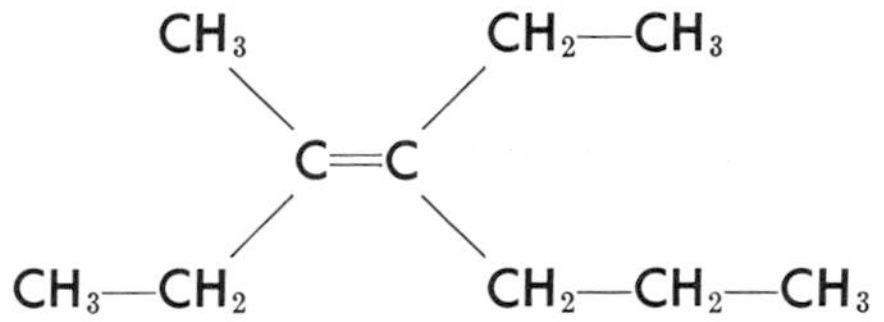

$(CH_3)(CH_3—CH_2)C═C(CH_2—CH_3)(CH_2—CH_2—CH_3)$, with CH_3 and $CH_2—CH_3$ on the same side: *cis*-3-methyl-4-ethyl-3-heptene

$(CH_3)(CH_3—CH_2)C═C(CH_2—CH_2—CH_3)(CH_2—CH_3)$, with CH_3 and $CH_2—CH_2—CH_3$ on the same side: *trans*-3-methyl-4-ethyl-3-heptene

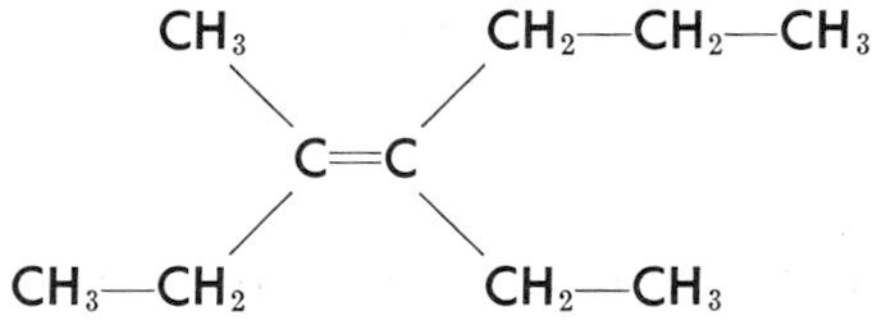

Triple bonds are handled in similar manner. The name ending for a triple bond is *-yne:*

$CH_3—C≡C—CH_3$ 2-butyne

$CH_3—CH═CH—C≡CH$ pent-3-ene-1-yne

The presence of certain functional groups is indicated by the use of characteristic name endings. Examples are:

Functional Group	Ending
—OH	-ol
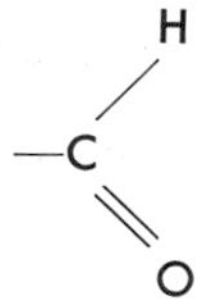 —C(H)═O	-al
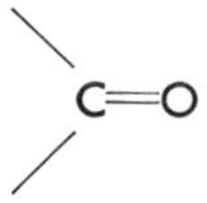 >C═O	-one

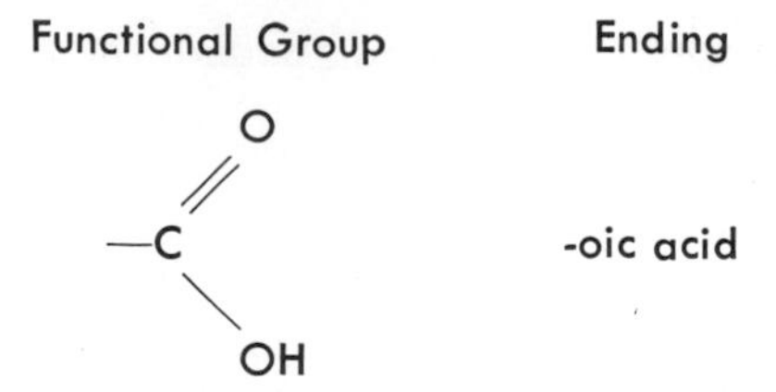

In naming compounds bearing these functional groups, the chain is numbered so as to give the lowest possible number to the carbon bearing the group. Some examples follow:

Structure	Name
$CH_3—CH(OH)—CH_2—CH_3$	2-butanol
$CH_3—CH_2—CH(CH_3)—CHO$	2-methylbutanal
$CH_3—CO—CH_2—CH_3$	2-butanone
$CH_3—CH_2—COOH$	propanoic acid

Note that if the functional group contains carbon, this carbon is included as part of the principal chain.

Ethers are named by giving the names of the two groups attached to the oxygen atom, followed by the name *ether*. Amines are also named by giving the names of the group or groups attached to the nitrogen atom, followed by the name *amine*. Primary amines may also be named as amino-substituted hydrocarbons:

Structure	Name
$CH_3—O—CH_2—CH_3$	methyl ethyl ether
$CH_3—CH_2—NH_2$	ethylamine
$CH_3—NH—CH_2—CH_3$	methylethylamine
$(CH_3)_2N—CH_2—CH_3$	dimethylethylamine
$CH_3—CH_2—CH(NH_2)—CH_2—CH_3$	3-aminopentane

The prefixes *fluoro-*, *chloro-*, *bromo-*, and *iodo-* are used for halogen substituents:

$CH_3—CCl_2—CH_3$ 2,2-dichloropropane

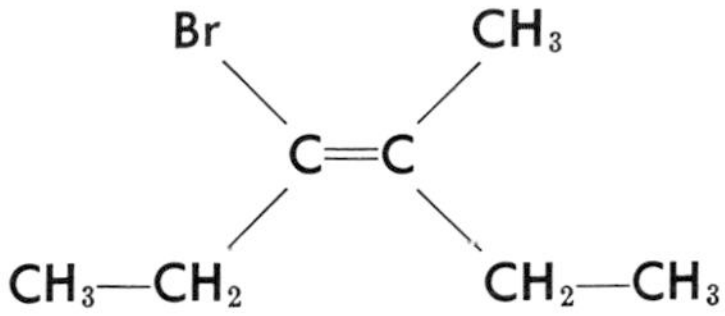

Br, CH_3 / C=C / $CH_3—CH_2$, $CH_2—CH_3$ *cis*-3-bromo-4-methyl-3-hexene

Aromatic Compounds C.2

Many aromatic compounds are named as substituted benzenes:

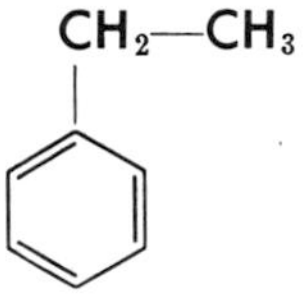

$CH_2—CH_3$
ethylbenzene

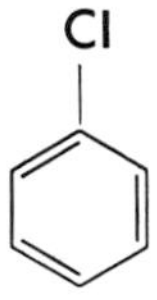

Cl
chlorobenzene

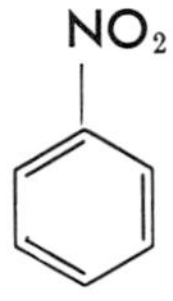

NO_2
nitrobenzene

If two substituents are present in the ring, their relative positions are indicated by use of the prefixes *ortho-* (*o-*), *meta-* (*m-*), and *para-* (*p-*):

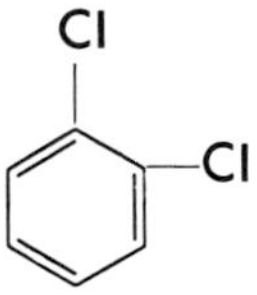

Cl, Cl
o-dichlorobenzene

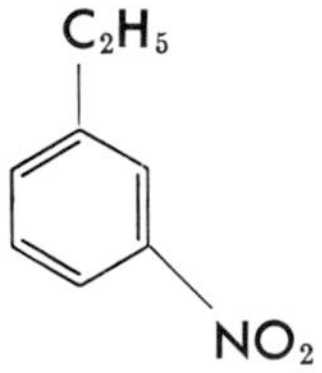

C_2H_5, NO_2
m-nitroethylbenzene

NO_2, Cl
p-chloronitrobenzene

When more than two substituents are present, the carbon atoms of the ring are numbered consecutively so as to give the lowest possible numbers to the substituents wherever possible:

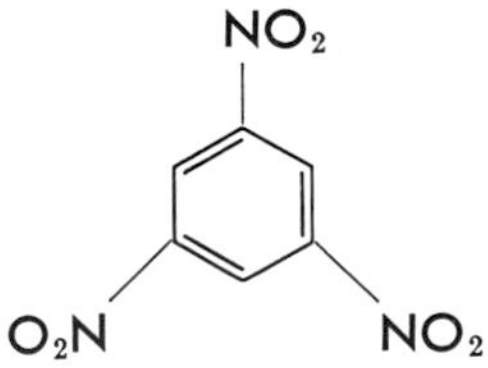

NO_2, O_2N, NO_2
1,3,5-trinitrobenzene

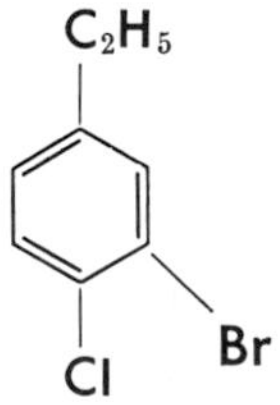

C_2H_5, Br, Cl
3-bromo-4-chloroethylbenzene

A number of benzene derivatives have their own characteristic names:

toluene ($C_6H_5CH_3$), *p*-xylene ($CH_3C_6H_4CH_3$), phenol (C_6H_5OH), benzaldehyde (C_6H_5CHO)

benzoic acid (C_6H_5COOH), styrene ($C_6H_5CH{=}CH_2$), aniline ($C_6H_5NH_2$), benzenesulfonic acid ($C_6H_5SO_3H$)

If other substituents are introduced into the compounds above, the products are named as derivatives of the parent compounds:

2,4,6-trinitrotoluene, *p*-chlorophenol, *o*-nitroaniline

For a more complete presentation of the IUPAC rules for organic nomenclature see, for example, the *Handbook of Chemistry and Physics* (The Chemical Rubber Co., Cleveland, Ohio).

In addition to the systematic names for organic compounds, many so-called "trivial" names remain in common use. This is especially true in the case of more complicated compounds for which the systematic names are often very cumbersome. Both the systematic (IUPAC) and trivial names are given in Chapter 17 for most of the compounds discussed therein.

D

VAPOR PRESSURE OF WATER AT VARIOUS TEMPERATURES

Temp., °C	Pressure, torr	Temp., °C	Pressure, torr
0	4.6	30	31.8
5	6.5	35	42.2
10	9.1	40	55.3
15	12.8	45	71.9
16	13.6	50	92.5
17	14.5	55	118.0
18	15.5	60	149.4
19	16.5	65	187.5
20	17.5	70	233.7
21	18.7	75	289.1
22	19.8	80	355.1
23	21.2	85	433.6
24	22.4	90	525.8
25	23.8	95	633.9
26	25.2	96	657.6
27	26.7	97	682.1
28	28.4	98	707.3
29	30.0	99	733.2
		100	760.0

E

COMMON LOGARITHMS

n	0	1	2	3	4	5	6	7	8	9	*n*
10	0000	0043	0086	0128	0170	0212	0253	0294	0334	0374	**10**
11	0414	0453	0492	0531	0569	0607	0645	0682	0719	0755	**11**
12	0792	0828	0864	0899	0934	0969	1004	1038	1072	1106	**12**
13	1139	1173	1206	1239	1271	1303	1335	1367	1399	1430	**13**
14	1461	1492	1523	1553	1584	1614	1644	1673	1703	1732	**14**
15	1761	1790	1818	1847	1875	1903	1931	1959	1987	2014	**15**
16	2041	2068	2095	2122	2148	2175	2201	2227	2253	2279	**16**
17	2304	2330	2355	2380	2405	2430	2455	2480	2504	2529	**17**
18	2553	2577	2601	2625	2648	2672	2695	2718	2742	2765	**18**
19	2788	2810	2833	2856	2878	2900	2923	2945	2967	2989	**19**
20	3010	3032	3054	3075	3096	3118	3139	3160	3181	3201	**20**
21	3222	3243	3263	3284	3304	3324	3345	3365	3385	3404	**21**
22	3424	3444	3464	3483	3502	3522	3541	3560	3579	3598	**22**
23	3617	3636	3655	3674	3692	3711	3729	3747	3766	3784	**23**
24	3802	3820	3838	3856	3874	3892	3909	3927	3945	3962	**24**
25	3979	3997	4014	4031	4048	4065	4082	4099	4116	4133	**25**
26	4150	4166	4183	4200	4216	4232	4249	4265	4281	4298	**26**
27	4314	4330	4346	4362	4378	4393	4409	4425	4440	4456	**27**
28	4472	4487	4502	4518	4533	4548	4564	4579	4594	4609	**28**
29	4624	4639	4654	4669	4683	4698	4713	4728	4742	4757	**29**
30	4771	4786	4800	4814	4829	4843	4857	4871	4886	4900	**30**
31	4914	4928	4942	4955	4969	4983	4997	5011	5024	5038	**31**
32	5051	5065	5079	5092	5105	5119	5132	5145	5159	5172	**32**
33	5185	5198	5211	5224	5237	5250	5263	5276	5289	5302	**33**
34	5315	5328	5340	5353	5366	5378	5391	5403	5416	5428	**34**
35	5441	5453	5465	5478	5490	5502	5514	5527	5539	5551	**35**
36	5563	5575	5587	5599	5611	5623	5635	5647	5658	5670	**36**
37	5682	5694	5705	5717	5729	5740	5752	5763	5775	5786	**37**
38	5798	5809	5821	5832	5843	5855	5866	5877	5888	5899	**38**
39	5911	5922	5933	5944	5955	5966	5977	5988	5999	6010	**39**
40	6021	6031	6042	6053	6064	6075	6085	6096	6107	6117	**40**
41	6128	6138	6149	6160	6170	6180	6191	6201	6212	6222	**41**
42	6232	6243	6253	6263	6274	6284	6294	6304	6314	6325	**42**
43	6335	6345	6355	6365	6375	6385	6395	6405	6415	6425	**43**
44	6435	6444	6454	6464	6474	6484	6493	6503	6513	6522	**44**

n	0	1	2	3	4	5	6	7	8	9	n
45	6532	6542	6551	6561	6571	6580	6590	6599	6609	6618	**45**
46	6628	6637	6646	6656	6665	6675	6684	6693	6702	6712	**46**
47	6721	6730	6739	6749	6758	6767	6776	6785	6794	6803	**47**
48	6812	6821	6830	6839	6848	6857	6866	6875	6884	6893	**48**
49	6902	6911	6920	6928	6937	6946	6955	6964	6972	6981	**49**
50	6990	6998	7007	7016	7024	7033	7042	7050	7059	7067	**50**
51	7076	7084	7093	7101	7110	7118	7126	7135	7143	7152	**51**
52	7160	7168	7177	7185	7193	7202	7210	7218	7226	7235	**52**
53	7243	7251	7259	7267	7275	7284	7292	7300	7308	7316	**53**
54	7324	7332	7340	7348	7356	7364	7372	7380	7388	7396	**54**
55	7404	7412	7419	7427	7435	7443	7451	7459	7466	7474	**55**
56	7482	7490	7497	7505	7513	7520	7528	7536	7543	7551	**56**
57	7559	7566	7574	7582	7589	7597	7604	7612	7619	7627	**57**
58	7634	7642	7649	7657	7664	7672	7679	7686	7694	7701	**58**
59	7709	7716	7723	7731	7738	7745	7752	7760	7767	7774	**59**
60	7782	7789	7796	7803	7810	7818	7825	7832	7839	7846	**60**
61	7853	7860	7868	7875	7882	7889	7896	7903	7910	7917	**61**
62	7924	7931	7938	7945	7952	7959	7966	7973	7980	7987	**62**
63	7993	8000	8007	8014	8021	8028	8035	8041	8048	8055	**63**
64	8062	8069	8075	8082	8089	8096	8102	8109	8116	8122	**64**
65	8129	8136	8142	8149	8156	8162	8169	8176	8182	8189	**65**
66	8195	8202	8209	8215	8222	8228	8235	8241	8248	8254	**66**
67	8261	8267	8274	8280	8287	8293	8299	8306	8312	8319	**67**
68	8325	8331	8338	8344	8351	8357	8363	8370	8376	8382	**68**
69	8388	8395	8401	8407	8414	8420	8426	8432	8439	8445	**69**
70	8451	8457	8463	8470	8476	8482	8488	8494	8500	8506	**70**
71	8513	8519	8525	8531	8537	8543	8549	8555	8561	8567	**71**
72	8573	8579	8585	8591	8597	8603	8609	8615	8621	8627	**72**
73	8633	8639	8645	8651	8657	8663	8669	8675	8681	8686	**73**
74	8692	8698	8704	8710	8716	8722	8727	8733	8739	8745	**74**
75	8751	8756	8762	8768	8774	8779	8785	8791	8797	8802	**75**
76	8808	8814	8820	8825	8831	8837	8842	8848	8854	8859	**76**
77	8865	8871	8876	8882	8887	8893	8899	8904	8910	8915	**77**
78	8921	8927	8932	8938	8943	8949	8954	8960	8965	8971	**78**
79	8976	8982	8987	8993	8998	9004	9009	9015	9020	9025	**79**
80	9031	9036	9042	9047	9053	9058	9063	9069	9074	9079	**80**
81	9085	9090	9096	9101	9106	9112	9117	9122	9128	9133	**81**
82	9138	9143	9149	9154	9159	9165	9170	9175	9180	9186	**82**
83	9191	9196	9201	9206	9212	9217	9222	9227	9232	9238	**83**
84	9243	9248	9253	9258	9263	9269	9274	9279	9284	9289	**84**
85	9294	9299	9304	9309	9315	9320	9325	9330	9335	9340	**85**
86	9345	9350	9355	9360	9365	9370	9375	9380	9385	9390	**86**
87	9395	9400	9405	9410	9415	9420	9425	9430	9435	9440	**87**
88	9445	9450	9455	9460	9465	9469	9474	9479	9484	9489	**88**
89	9494	9499	9504	9509	9513	9518	9523	9528	9533	9538	**89**
90	9542	9547	9552	9557	9562	9566	9571	9576	9581	9586	**90**
91	9590	9595	9600	9605	9609	9614	9619	9624	9628	9633	**91**
92	9638	9643	9647	9652	9657	9661	9666	9671	9675	9680	**92**
93	9685	9689	9694	9699	9703	9708	9713	9717	9722	9727	**93**
94	9731	9736	9741	9745	9750	9754	9759	9763	9768	9773	**94**
95	9777	9782	9786	9791	9795	9800	9805	9809	9814	9818	**95**
96	9823	9827	9832	9836	9841	9845	9850	9854	9859	9863	**96**
97	9868	9872	9877	9881	9886	9890	9894	9899	9903	9908	**97**
98	9912	9917	9921	9926	9930	9934	9939	9943	9948	9952	**98**
99	9956	9961	9965	9969	9974	9978	9983	9987	9991	9996	**99**

F

IMPORTANT PHYSICAL CONSTANTS

Acceleration of gravity, standard, G	980.7 cm sec^{-2}
Ångstrom, Å	10^{-8} cm
Atmosphere, standard, atm	760.0 torr
	1.01×10^{6} dynes cm^{-2}
Avogadro's number, N	6.023×10^{23} $mole^{-1}$
Calorie, cal	4.18×10^{7} ergs
Charge on the electron, **e**	1.602×10^{-19} coulomb
Electron volt, eV	1.602×10^{-12} erg $molecule^{-1}$
	23,061 cal $mole^{-1}$
Erg, dyne cm	2.389×10^{-8} cal
Faraday, $\mathfrak{F}$	96,489 coulombs $equivalent^{-1}$
Gas constant, R	0.082 liter atm $mole^{-1}$ deg^{-1}
	1.987 cal $mole^{-1}$ deg^{-1}
Planck's constant, h	6.6256×10^{-27} erg sec
Speed of light in vacuum, c	2.998×10^{10} cm sec^{-1}
Volume of ideal gas, standard conditions, V	22.4136 liters $mole^{-1}$

ANSWERS TO ODD-NUMBERED PROBLEMS

Chapter 1

1.5 10.9 ml
1.7 453 g/lb
1.9 Their kinetic energies are nearly the same.
1.11 −40°
1.13 Slightly less than 31°C
1.15 37.0°C
1.17 2.7 g/ml
1.19 2.1×10^{13} cal
1.21 39.37 in./m

Chapter 2

2.7 12.16 g
2.9 55.8 amu, valence = 3
2.11 116.8 g
2.13 $NaClO_2$
2.15 51.14%
2.17 FeO, Fe_2O_3, Fe_3O_4
2.19 Cu_2S
2.21 (a) 98.08 amu
(b) 249.19 amu
(c) 252.07 amu
(d) 1550.57 amu
(e) 267.46 amu
2.23 42.2 g $AgCl$
2.25 108 tons
2.27 (a) 114 amu
(b) valence = 1; exact atomic weight = 108 amu
2.29 47.42% C; 2.54% H
2.31 WO_3

Chapter 3

3.5 (a) 2.13×10^3 torr
(b) 2.81×10^3 torr
(c) 2.74 torr
(d) 25.2 torr
(e) 62.0 torr
3.7 (a) 455 ml, (b) 509 ml, (c) 1002 ml
3.9 166°C
3.11 544 ft^3
3.13 1085 atm

3.15 477 ml

3.17 Partial pressures: Xe = 0.20 atm
F_2 = 0.80 atm
N_2 = 1.0 atm
Volume of container, 0.29 liter

3.19 3.5 liters

3.21 2.5 sec

3.23 12.7 cm^3

3.25 Vapor pressure, 78 torr
Approximately 0.072 g of benzene evaporated.

3.27 $C_4H_{10}Zm$

3.31 (a) 0.008% (b) about 32 Å (c) 4.1% (d) about 2.4 Å

Chapter 5

5.15 0.0373 g H_2, 0.2984 g O_2

5.17 7 min, 36 sec

5.19 63.58

5.21

Question 5.12
(a) NO_3^-, 61.00; Cu, 31.77
(d) NO_3^-, 20.67; S, 17.03
(f) I_2, 126.90; $S_2O_3^{--}$, 112.13
(i) MnO_4^-, 23.79; H_2O_2, 17.01

Question 5.13
(a) $Cr_2O_7^{--}$, 36.00; Fe^{++}, 55.85
(d) MnO_4^-, 23.79; As_4O_6, 49.46
(e) IO_3^-, 34.98; I^-, 126.90

Question 5.14
(b) MnO_4^-, 39.65; ClO_2^-, 16.86

Chapter 7

7.9 0.40 eV

7.11 3770 Å

7.13 2.63×10^{-32} cm

Chapter 9

9.19 $d = 3.36$ Å
Second-order reflection at 29°36′

Chapter 10

10.15 (a) 0.05 *M*
(b) 0.025 *M*
(c) 8.7 *M*
(d) 0.1 *M*

10.17 15.8 *M*

10.19 (a) 1.07 *M*, (b) 1.13 *m*

10.21 359.3 ml

10.23 (a) 17.03 g
(b) 32

10.25 18.86%

10.27 190

10.29 (a) 172 g, (b) 334 g

10.31 (a) 17,000, (b) 1.2×10^{-3}, (c) 0.002°C

10.33 Mole fraction benzene in liquid = 0.253
Mole fraction benzene in vapor = 0.451

Chapter 11

11.11 (a) −142.75 kcal
(b) −6.39 kcal
(c) +1.13 kcal
(d) −118.36 kcal
(e) −67.42 kcal

11.13 −531.2 kcal/mole

11.17 at approximately 468°K (195°C)
11.19 above 1110°K
11.21 1461.3 cal/°C
11.23 $\Delta S_{\text{fusion}} = 2.42$ cal/deg
$\Delta S_{\text{vaporization}} = 20.7$ cal/deg

Chapter 12

12.7 0.288 k
12.9 16 times faster
12.11 p.p. H_2 = p.p. I_2 = 0.1114 atm, p.p. HI = 0.7772 atm.
12.13 (a) Rate = k[A][C]
(c) 2×10^{-2}
(d) $\frac{1}{4}$
(e) 0.3 mole, 0.9 mole
(f) Exp. 1, none; Exp. 2, [A] = 0.2, [B] = 0.1; Exp. 3, [B] = 0.2; Exp. 4, [B] = 0.1
12.15 0.5
12.17 (a) 15,000 cal/mole, (b) 10,000 cal/mole,
(c) and (d) 150 times faster
(e) yes

Chapter 13

13.19 (a) 4.17×10^{-4}, (b) 3.38, (c) 4.17%
13.21 (a) 6×10^{-9}, (b) 6×10^{-15}, (c) 6×10^{-17}, (d) 6×10^{-19},
(e) 6×10^{-21}, (f) 6×10^{-23}
13.23 (a) 4.76, (b) 0.05 pH units
13.25 (a) 14.8 g, (b) pH 4.92, (c) pH 2
13.27 (a) pH 9.96, (b) red
13.29 (a) 5.3, (b) 8, (c) 9, (d) 10
13.31 1.8×10^{-7} M
13.33 $K_{sp} = 5 \times 10^{-9}$, $[CO_3^{--}] = 5 \times 10^{-7}$ M
13.35 (a) 6.7×10^{-22} M, (b) yes, (c) no
13.37 (a) 8.6×10^{-50}, (b) 8.7×10^{-34}, (c) 8.4×10^{-26},
(d) 1.8×10^{-19}, (e) 5.1×10^{-13}, (f) MnS,
(g) 1.8×10^{-2}, (h) 710, an impossible condition
13.39 (a) 3.6×10^{-5}, (b) 1.8×10^{-9},
(c) AgCl, (d) 0.005%

Chapter 14

14.9 (a) 0.98 volt, (b) $G = -45.2$ kcal/mole of Sn oxidized
14.11 Fe^{+++} reduced by I^-.
14.13 (a) $[H^+] = 1.32 \times 10^{-3}$ M, (b) $K_a = 1.74 \times 10^{-5}$,
(c) The Pt electrode in 1 M HCl, (d) +0.43 volt
14.15 8×10^{-17} **14.17** 6.6 **14.19** 0.25 volt

Chapter 15

15.15 3.82%

Chapter 16

16.15 2.7×10^{-6} M

Chapter 20

20.11 4.9×10^{-4} mg
20.13 6.7×10^{10} atoms
20.15 2.76×10^{9} kcal/mole
20.17 72 sec

INDEX

TABLE OF ATOMIC WEIGHTS

ELEMENT	SYMBOL	ATOMIC NUMBER	ATOMIC WEIGHT*
Actinium	Ac	89	[227]
Aluminum	Al	13	26.9815
Americium	Am	95	[243]
Antimony	Sb	51	121.75
Argon	Ar	18	39.948
Arsenic	As	33	74.9216
Astatine	At	85	[210]
Barium	Ba	56	137.34
Berkelium	Bk	97	[247]
Beryllium	Be	4	9.0122
Bismuth	Bi	83	208.980
Boron	B	5	10.811
Bromine	Br	35	79.909
Cadmium	Cd	48	112.40
Calcium	Ca	20	40.08
Californium	Cf	98	[251]
Carbon	C	6	12.01115
Cerium	Ce	58	140.12
Cesium	Cs	55	132.905
Chlorine	Cl	17	35.453
Chromium	Cr	24	51.996
Cobalt	Co	27	58.9332
Copper	Cu	29	63.54
Curium	Cm	96	[247]
Dysprosium	Dy	66	162.50
Einsteinium	Es	99	[254]
Erbium	Er	68	167.26
Europium	Eu	63	151.96
Fermium	Fm	100	[257]
Fluorine	F	9	18.9984
Francium	Fr	87	[223]
Gadolinium	Gd	64	157.25
Gallium	Ga	31	69.72
Germanium	Ge	32	72.59
Gold	Au	79	196.967
Hafnium	Hf	72	178.49
Helium	He	2	4.0026
Holmium	Ho	67	164.930
Hydrogen	H	1	1.00797
Indium	In	49	114.82
Iodine	I	53	126.9044
Iridium	Ir	77	192.2
Iron	Fe	26	55.847
Kurchatovium†		104	[260]
Krypton	Kr	36	83.80
Lanthanum	La	57	138.91
Lawrencium	Lr	103	[256]
Lead	Pb	82	207.19
Lithium	Li	3	6.939
Lutetium	Lu	71	174.97
Magnesium	Mg	12	24.312
Manganese	Mn	25	54.9380